Scott Foresman - Addison Wesley
MIDDLE SCHOOL MATH
Course 3

Randall I. Charles   John A. Dossey   Steven J. Leinwand
Cathy L. Seeley   Charles B. Vonder Embse

L. Carey Bolster • Janet H. Caldwell • Dwight A. Cooley • Warren D. Crown
Linda Proudfit • Alma B. Ramírez • Jeanne F. Ramos • Freddie Lee Renfro
David F. Robitaille • Jane Swafford

Teacher's Edition
Volume 2
Chapters 7–12

Scott Foresman
Addison Wesley

Editorial Offices: Menlo Park, California • Glenview, Illinois
Sales Offices: Reading, Massachusetts • Atlanta, Georgia • Glenview, Illinois
Carrollton, Texas • Menlo Park, California

http://www.sf.aw.com

Math

that Makes Sense...

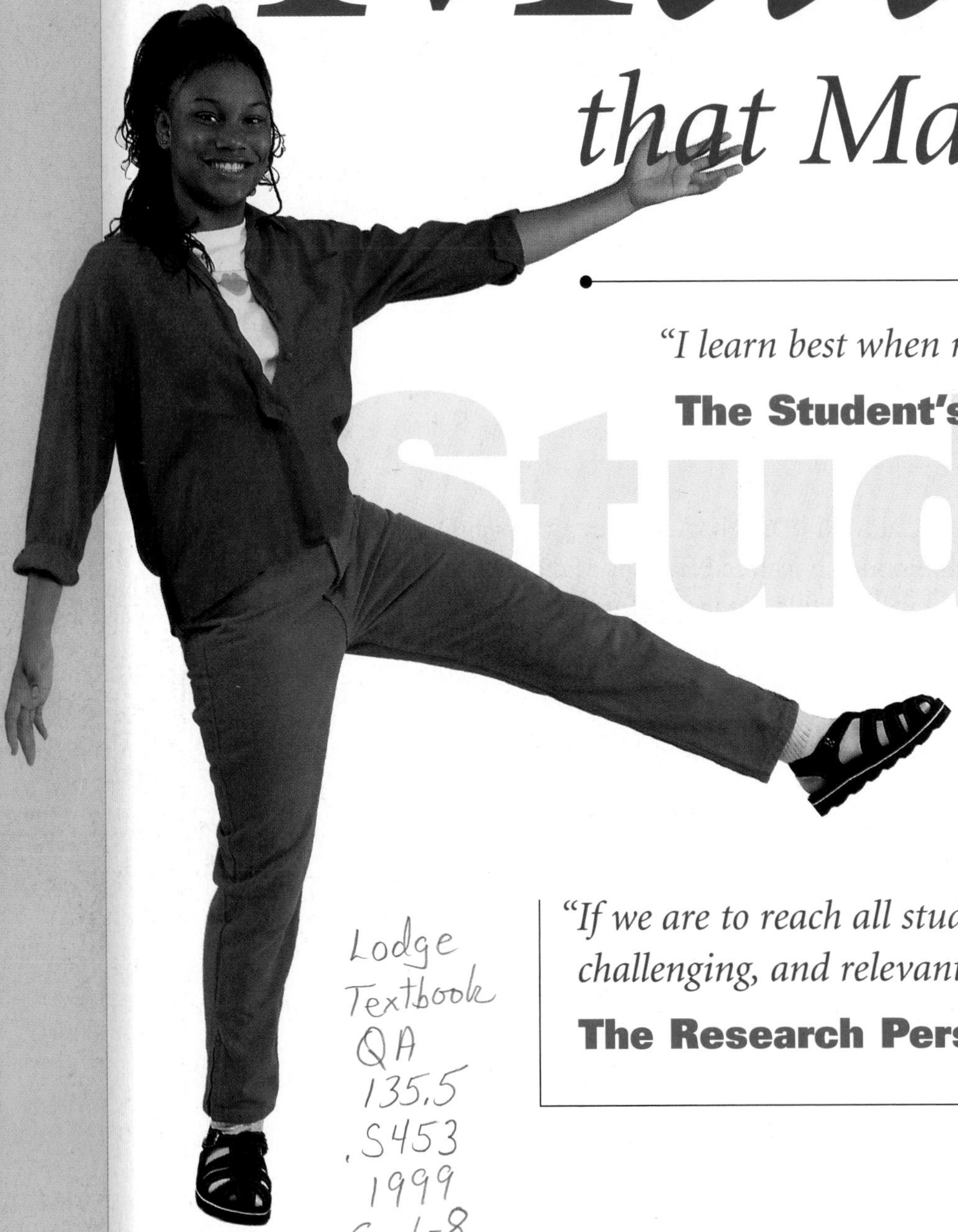

"I learn best when math is interesting to me."

The Student's Perspective

Student

"If we are to reach all students, we must strive for meaningful, challenging, and relevant learning in the classroom."

The Research Perspective

Re

ISBN 0-201-36438-7

2 3 4 5 6 7 8 9 10–DOW–02 01 00 99 98

Teacher

*"My primary concern in teaching is to help **all** my students succeed."*

from **EVERY** *Perspective*

What kind of a math program are you looking for? What about your students? And how about mathematics education research? Can one program really satisfy *all* points of view? Through its content, features, and format, *Scott Foresman - Addison Wesley Middle School MATH* recognizes the real-life needs and concerns specific to middle school—supported by research but grounded in real classroom experience.

Welcome to a math program that excels from every perspective—especially yours!

Math that Connects to the Student's World

Middle school students have a perspective all their own. We've tapped into their world with experiences and information that grab their attention and don't let go.

Relevance

"I want to know when I'll use this."

Real, age-appropriate data
Data based on what middle school students buy, eat, study in school, and enjoy permeate every lesson.

Cool themes like *Spiders, Disasters, Food,* and *Whales*
Student-friendly topics blend learning with what kids love.

MathSURF Internet Site
MathSURF's up and so is student interest! Kids can go online to explore text content of every chapter in safe and exciting destinations around the world.

Interactive CD-ROM
Interactive lessons for every chapter provide an exciting environment for learning.

Math that Promotes High School Success

Teachers in today's middle schools need a program that prepares their students for high school math. That means rigorous content, including preparation for algebra and geometry, NTCM content and process standards—PLUS practical strategies for taking tests and problem solving.

*"My students need to be prepared for high school math. And let's face it, how they perform is a reflection of how **I** perform!"*

Performance

The building blocks of algebra

Prepare students for success in high school math with instruction in mathematical reasoning.

Course 1—focuses on *numerical reasoning*.

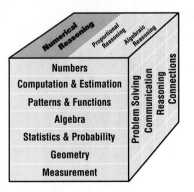

Course 2—focuses on *proportional reasoning*.

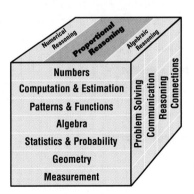

Course 3—focuses on *algebraic reasoning*.

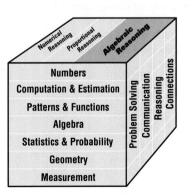

Test prep strategies

The next step in strategies! Helping students be smart about how they take standardized tests builds confidence and leads to success.

Problem solving that's no problem

Sharpen students' problem-solving skills with numerous opportunities to analyze and use the problem-solving process.

A Program that Supports Teaching Success

Teachers in today's middle schools face unique challenges—from improving student performance to adapting to each student's unique learning needs. This program is designed to help you meet those challenges. You'll find help for every teaching need—including *block scheduling* and *interdisciplinary team teaching,* PLUS *outstanding technology,* and more!

Student Edition

Colorful lessons, filled with student-oriented data, have a unique "middle school" look.

Teacher's Edition

(with Teacher's Resource Planner CD-ROM)

Two hardbound volumes, packaged with a CD-ROM Planner, provide complete lesson plans plus practical help to meet your every challenge—block scheduling, team teaching, and more.

Teacher's Resource Package

Practice Masters

Exercises reinforce content of every lesson. Also available as a workbook.

Alternative Lessons (Reteaching Masters)

Masters for every lesson offer another look at skills and concepts.

Extend Your Thinking (Enrichment Masters)

Masters enhance thinking skills and creativity in every lesson.

Problem-Solving Masters (for Guided Problem Solving)

Masters guide students step-by-step through one problem from every Student Edition exercise set. Also available as a workbook.

Assessment Sourcebook

Options to help profile students as learners. Includes multiple-choice, short-response, performance, and mixed-format chapter tests, as well as section quizzes and record forms.

Home and Community Connections

Make math a family affair! Booklet with letters in English and Spanish, also provides classroom tips, community projects, and more.

Teacher's Toolkit

Saves time with a variety of Management Resources, plus Teaching Tool Transparencies.

Technology Masters

Computer and calculator activities energize lessons with the power of technology.

Chapter Project Masters

Masters support the on-going project in each Student Edition chapter.

Interdisciplinary Team Teaching

Math across the curriculum! Masters provide an engaging 2-page interdisciplinary lesson for each section.

Resources to Customize Instruction

Print Resources

Block Scheduling Handbook
Practical suggestions let you tailor the program to various block scheduling formats.

Overhead Transparency Package
Daily Transparencies (for Problem of the Day, Review, and Quick Quiz) and Lesson Enhancement Transparencies help enliven class presentations.

Multilingual Handbook
Enhanced math glossary with examples in multiple languages provides a valuable resource for teaching. Especially useful with ESL students.

Mathematics Dictionary
Handy reference tool of middle school math terms.

Solutions Manual
Manual includes convenient solutions to Student Edition exercises.

Technology

Teacher's Resource Planner CD-ROM
The entire Teacher's Resource Package on CD-ROM! Includes an electronic planning guide which allows you to set criteria when planning lessons, customize worksheets, correlate your curriculum to specific objectives, and more!

Interactive CD-ROM
Interactive, multimedia lessons with built-in math tools help students explore concepts in enjoyable and involving ways.

MathSURF Internet Site (for Students)
Math on the Web! Provides links to other sites, project ideas, interactive surveys and more.

MathSURF Internet Site (for Teachers)
Offers exciting opportunities for in-service ideas and sharing.

MathSURF Internet Site (for Parents)
This Web site offers a variety of practical tips to parents.

TestWorks: Test and Practice CD-ROM
CD-ROM saves hours of test-prep time by generating and customizing tests and worksheets.

Manipulative Kits

Student Manipulative Kit
Quantities of angle rulers, Power Polygons, and other items help students grasp mathematics concepts on a concrete level.

Teacher's Overhead Manipulative Kit
Kit makes demonstrating concepts from an overhead projector easy and convenient.

Authors with Middle School Expertise!

Math that makes sense from every perspective—it's a commitment we've kept in all aspects of this program, including our outstanding team of authors. Their expertise in mathematics education brings to the program extensive knowledge of how middle school students learn math and how best to teach them.

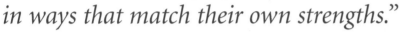

Expertise

"Students learn and perform better when they are taught in ways that match their own strengths."

Charles B. Vonder Embse

Professor of Mathematics Education and Mathematics

Central Michigan University
Mt. Pleasant, Michigan

Member of NCTM Instructional Issues Advisory Committee

Member of the Advisory Board of Teachers Teaching with Technology (T³)

Jane Swafford

Professor of Mathematics

Illinois State University
Normal, Illinois

Randall I. Charles

Professor, Department of Mathematics and Computer Science

San Jose State University
San Jose, California

Past Vice-President, National Council of Supervisors of Mathematics

Co-author of two NCTM publications on teaching and evaluating progress in problem solving

Dwight A. Cooley

Assistant Principal

Mary Louise Phillips
Elementary School
Fort Worth, Texas

*Member, NCTM Board
of Directors*

John A. Dossey

Distinguished University
Professor of Mathematics

Illinois State University
Normal, Illinois

Past President, NCTM

*Guided development
of NCTM Standards*

*Recipient, NCTM Lifetime
Achievement Award*

*Chairman, Conference Board
of the Mathematical Sciences*

*"A program that asks real-life questions
provides rich possibilities for students."*

Steven J. Leinwand

Mathematics Consultant

Connecticut Department
of Education
Hartford, Connecticut

*Member, NCTM Board
of Directors*

*Past President, National
Council of Supervisors
of Mathematics*

Cathy L. Seeley

Director of Policy and Professional
Development for Texas SSI

University of Texas
Austin, Texas

Texas State Mathematics Supervisor

Writer, Curriculum and
Evaluation Standards for School
Mathematics

Member, NCTM Board of Directors

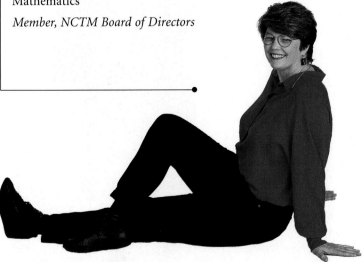

Turn the page, for more authors!

More Authors with Middle School Expertise!

Freddie Lee Renfro

Coordinator of Mathematics

Fort Bend Independent
School District
Sugarland, Texas

L. Carey Bolster

Director, K–12 Math Projects

Public Broadcasting Service
MATHLINE
Alexandria, Virginia

"Students construct new learning from a basis of prior knowledge and experience."

Linda Proudfit

University Professor of
Mathematics and Computer
Education

Governors State University
University Park, Illinois

Janet H. Caldwell

Professor of Mathematics

Rowan University
Glassboro, New Jersey

David F. Robitaille

Professor of Mathematics Education

University of British Columbia
Vancouver, British Columbia,
Canada

Alma Ramírez

Bilingual Mathematics and
Science Teacher

Oakland Charter Academy
Oakland, California

"To be successful in high school, students need a solid foundation in mathematical reasoning."

Jeanne F. Ramos

Assistant Principal

Nobel Middle School
Los Angeles, California

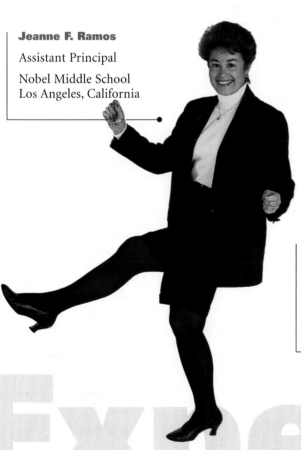

Warren D. Crown

Professor of Mathematics Education

Rutgers, The State University
of New Jersey
New Brunswick, New Jersey

Expertise

Contributors from Across the Country!

A Nationwide Perspective

Educators from across the country helped shape this program with valuable input about local needs and concerns.

Contributing Writers

Phillip E. Duren
California State University
Hayward, CA

Kathy A. Ross
Loyola University (LaSIP)
New Orleans, LA

Sheryl M. Yamada
Beverly Hills High School
Beverly Hills, CA

Content Reviewers

Ann Boltz
Coldwater, MI

John David Bridges
Greenville, SC

Glenn Bruckhart
Fort Collins, CO

Sharon Bourgeois Butler
Spring, TX

Carol Cameron
Seattle, WA

Steven T. Cottrell
Farmington, UT

Patricia Creel
Lawrenceville, GA

Wendi M. Cyford
New Market, MD

Scott Firkins
Owensboro, KY

Madelaine Gallin
New York, NY

Roy E. Griggs
Boise, ID

Lucy Hahn
Boise, ID

Allison Harris
Seattle, WA

Clay Hutson
Kingsport, TN

Beryl W. Jackson
Alexandria, VA

Janet Jomp
Wilson, NC

Ann P. Lawrence
Marietta, GA

Cheryl McCormack
Indianapolis, IN

Gary McCracken
Tuscaloosa, AL

Allison McNaughton
Marstons Mills, MA

Sandra A. Nagy
Mesa, AZ

Kent Novak
Greene, RI

Jeff C. Nusbaum
Rock Island, IL

Vince O'Connor
Milwaukee, WI

Mary Lynn Raith
Pittsburgh, PA

Kathleen Rieke
Zionsville, IN

Ellen G. Robertson
Norwich, NY

Nancy Rolsen
Worthington, OH

Edith Roos
Helena, MT

Lynn A. Sandro
Cedar Springs, MI

Carol Sims
Arcadia, CA

Paul E. Smith
Newburgh, IN

Donald M. Smyton
Kenmore, NY

Stella M. Turner
Indianapolis, IN

Tommie Walsh
Lubbock, TX

Terri Weaver
Houston, TX

Jacqueline Weilmuenster
Colleyville, TX

Multicultural Reviewers

Mary Margaret Capraro
Hialeah, FL

Robert Capraro
Miami, FL

Bettye Forte
Fort Worth, TX

Hector Hirigoyen
Miami, FL

James E. Hopkins
Auburn, WA

Patricia Locke
Mobridge, SD

Jimmie Rios
Fort Worth, TX

Linda Skinner
Edmond, OK

ESL Reviewers

Anna Uhl Chamot
Washington, DC

Jimmie Rios
Fort Worth, TX

Inclusion Reviewers

Lucy Blood
Amesbury, MA

Janett Borg
Monroe, UT

John David Bridges
Greenville, SC

Edith Roos
Helena, MT

Cross-Curricular Reviewers

Janett Borg
Monroe, UT

Kurt Brorson
Bethesda, MD

Geoffrey Chester
Washington, DC

Trudi Hammel Garland
Orinda, CA

M. Frank Watt Ireton
Washington, DC

Donna Krasnow
Carmel, CA

Chelcie Liu
San Francisco, CA

Edith Roos
Helena, MT

Technology Reviewers

Kurt Brorson
Bethesda, MD

Beverly W. Nichols
Overland Park, KS

Susan Rhodes
Springfield, IL

David L. Stout
Pensacola, FL

TABLE OF CONTENTS

Teacher's Edition

FROM THE AUTHORS

FROM THE AUTHORS

Dear Student,

We have designed a unique mathematics program that answers the question students your age have been asking for years about their math lessons: "When am I ever going to use this?"

In *Scott Foresman - Addison Wesley Middle School Math,* you'll learn about math in your own world and develop problem-solving techniques that will work for you in everyday life. The chapters have two or three sections, each with a useful math topic and an interesting theme. For example, you'll relate ratios to special effects, linear equations to pets, and rational numbers to water.

Each section begins with an opportunity to explore new topics and make your own conjectures. Lessons are presented clearly with examples and chances to try the math yourself. Then, real kids like you and your friends say what they think about each concept and show how they understand it. And every section contains links to the World Wide Web, making your math book a dynamic link to an ever-expanding universe of knowledge.

You will soon realize how mathematics is not only useful, but also connected to you and your life as you continue to experience the real world. We trust that each of you will gain the knowledge necessary to be successful and to be everything you want to be.

Randall I. Charles   *John A. Dossey*   *Steven J. Leinwand*
Cathy L. Seeley   *Charles B. Vonder Embse*

L. Carey Bolster   *Janet H. Caldwell*   *Dwight A. Cooley*   *Warren D. Crown*   *Linda Proudfit*
Alma B. Ramirez   *Jeanne F. Ramos*   *Freddie Lee Renfro*   *David Robitaille*   *Jane Swafford*

CHAPTER 1

Data Analysis

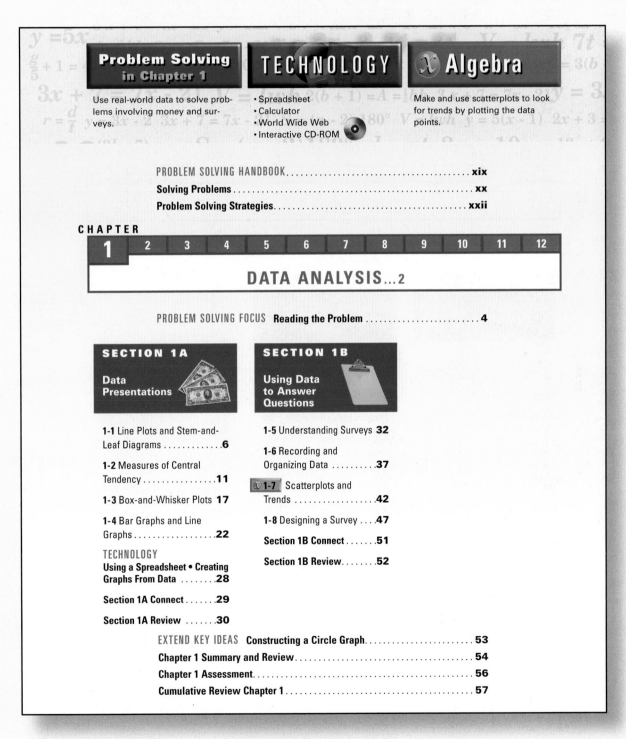

CHAPTER 2

Integers

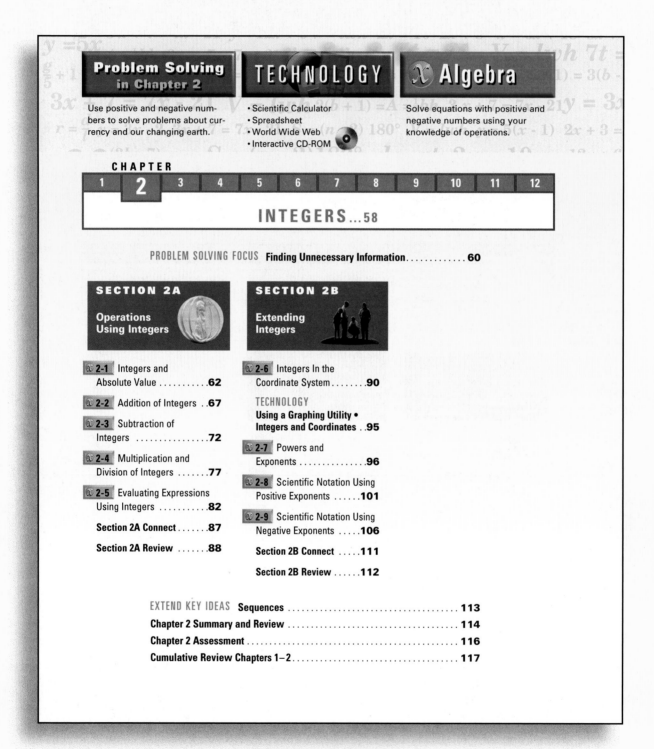

Problem Solving in Chapter 2

Use positive and negative numbers to solve problems about currency and our changing earth.

TECHNOLOGY

• Scientific Calculator
• Spreadsheet
• World Wide Web
• Interactive CD-ROM

Algebra

Solve equations with positive and negative numbers using your knowledge of operations.

CHAPTER

1	2	3	4	5	6	7	8	9	10	11	12

INTEGERS...58

CHAPTER 3

The Language of Algebra: Variables, Expressions, and Equations

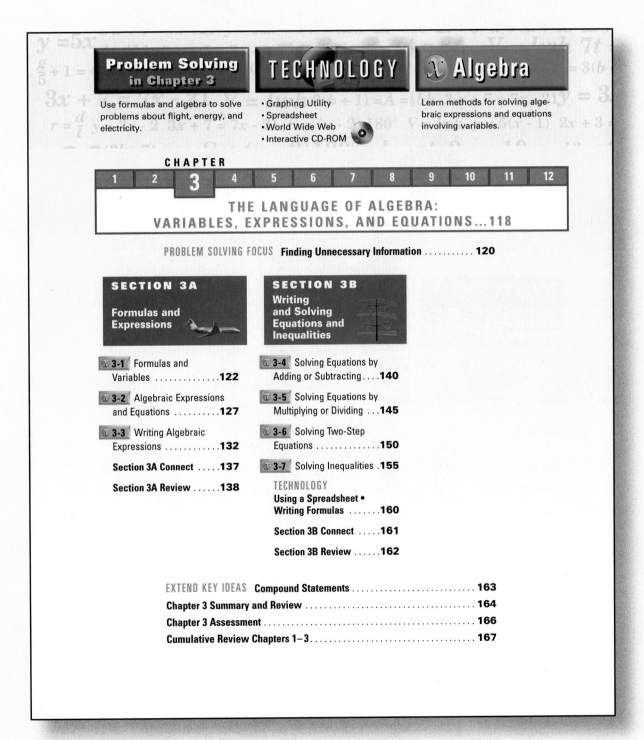

Problem Solving in Chapter 3

Use formulas and algebra to solve problems about flight, energy, and electricity.

TECHNOLOGY

• Graphing Utility
• Spreadsheet
• World Wide Web
• Interactive CD-ROM

Algebra

Learn methods for solving algebraic expressions and equations involving variables.

CHAPTER

| 1 | 2 | 3 | 4 | 5 | 6 | 7 | 8 | 9 | 10 | 11 | 12 |

CHAPTER 4

Algebra: Linear Equations and Inequalities

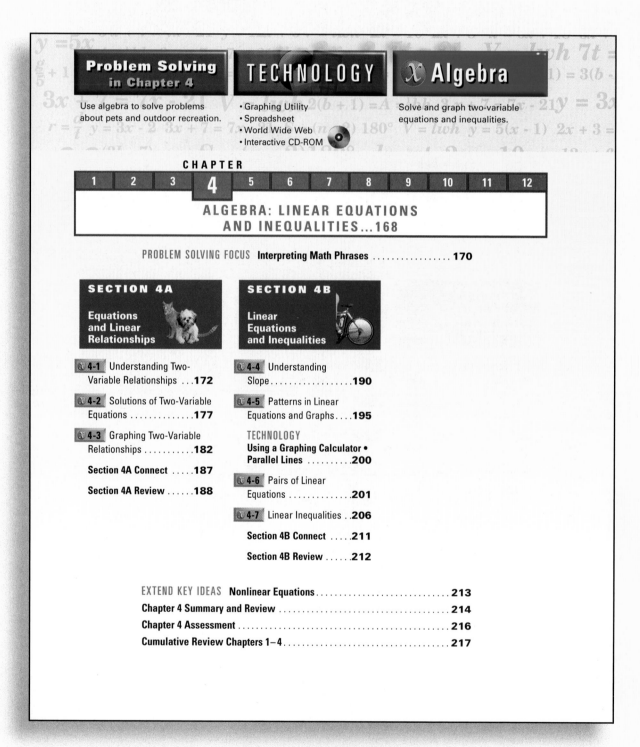

Problem Solving in Chapter 4
Use algebra to solve problems about pets and outdoor recreation.

TECHNOLOGY
• Graphing Utility
• Spreadsheet
• World Wide Web
• Interactive CD-ROM

Algebra
Solve and graph two-variable equations and inequalities.

CHAPTER

| 1 | 2 | 3 | **4** | 5 | 6 | 7 | 8 | 9 | 10 | 11 | 12 |

CHAPTER 5

Ratio and Proportion

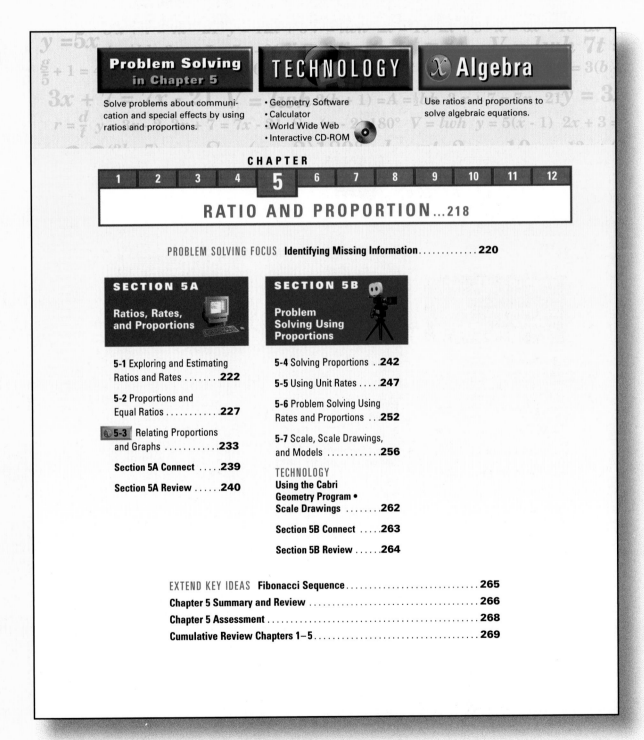

Problem Solving in Chapter 5

Solve problems about communication and special effects by using ratios and proportions.

TECHNOLOGY

• Geometry Software
• Calculator
• World Wide Web
• Interactive CD-ROM

Algebra

Use ratios and proportions to solve algebraic equations.

CHAPTER

| 1 | 2 | 3 | 4 | **5** | 6 | 7 | 8 | 9 | 10 | 11 | 12 |

CHAPTER 6

Percent

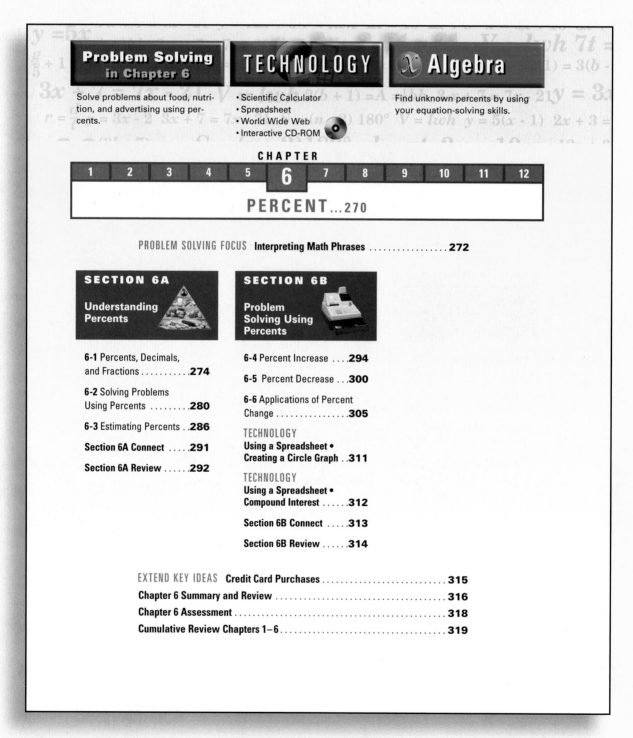

Problem Solving in Chapter 6

Solve problems about food, nutrition, and advertising using percents.

TECHNOLOGY

• Scientific Calculator
• Spreadsheet
• World Wide Web
• Interactive CD-ROM

Algebra

Find unknown percents by using your equation-solving skills.

CHAPTER

| 1 | 2 | 3 | 4 | 5 | **6** | 7 | 8 | 9 | 10 | 11 | 12 |

PERCENT...270

CHAPTER 7

Number Sense, Rational Numbers, and Irrational Numbers

Problem Solving in Chapter 7

Solve problems about codes, water, and houses by performing operations involving rational and irrational numbers.

TECHNOLOGY

• Spreadsheet
• Calculator
• World Wide Web
• Interactive CD-ROM

𝓧 Algebra

Solve equations involving rational and irrational numbers, square roots, and the Pythagorean Theorem.

CHAPTER

| 1 | 2 | 3 | 4 | 5 | 6 | **7** | 8 | 9 | 10 | 11 | 12 |

NUMBER SENSE, RATIONAL NUMBERS, AND IRRATIONAL NUMBERS...320

CHAPTER 8

Geometry and Measurement

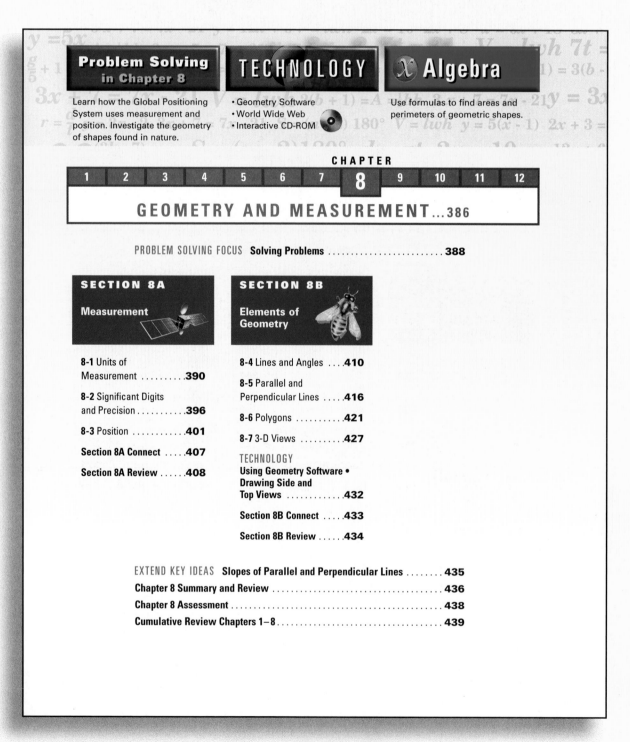

Problem Solving in Chapter 8

Learn how the Global Positioning System uses measurement and position. Investigate the geometry of shapes found in nature.

TECHNOLOGY

• Geometry Software
• World Wide Web
• Interactive CD-ROM

Algebra

Use formulas to find areas and perimeters of geometric shapes.

CHAPTER

| 1 | 2 | 3 | 4 | 5 | 6 | 7 | **8** | 9 | 10 | 11 | 12 |

GEOMETRY AND MEASUREMENT...386

CHAPTER 9

Area and Volume

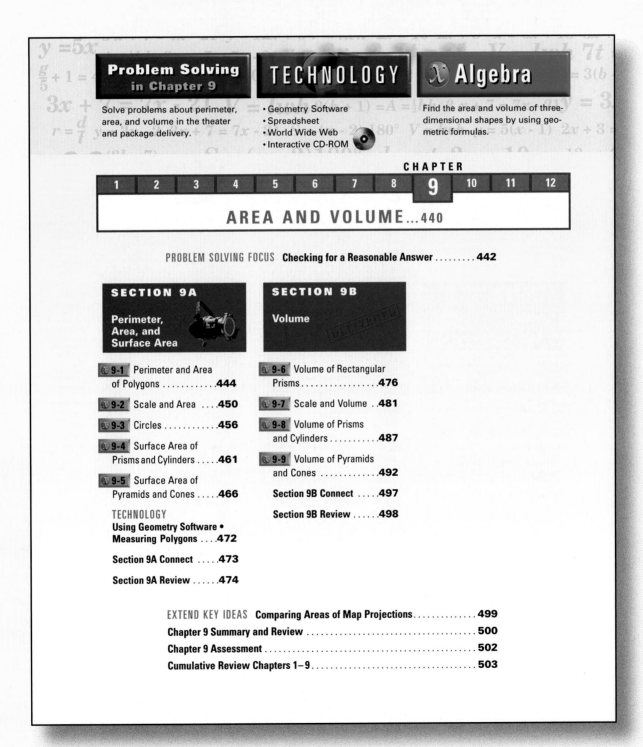

Problem Solving in Chapter 9

Solve problems about perimeter, area, and volume in the theater and package delivery.

TECHNOLOGY

• Geometry Software
• Spreadsheet
• World Wide Web
• Interactive CD-ROM

Algebra

Find the area and volume of three-dimensional shapes by using geometric formulas.

CHAPTER

| 1 | 2 | 3 | 4 | 5 | 6 | 7 | 8 | 9 | 10 | 11 | 12 |

AREA AND VOLUME...440

CHAPTER 10

Algebra: Functions and Relationships

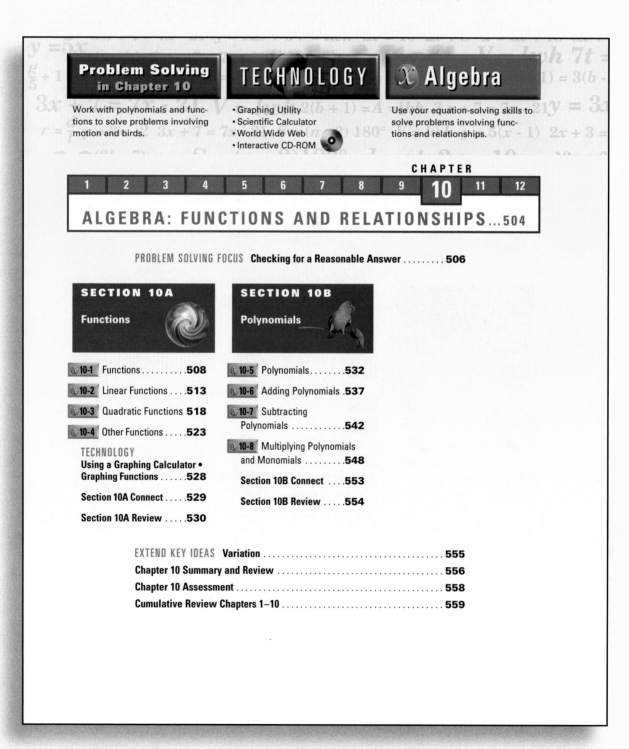

Problem Solving in Chapter 10

Work with polynomials and functions to solve problems involving motion and birds.

TECHNOLOGY

• Graphing Utility
• Scientific Calculator
• World Wide Web
• Interactive CD-ROM

ⅹ Algebra

Use your equation-solving skills to solve problems involving functions and relationships.

| 1 | 2 | 3 | 4 | 5 | 6 | 7 | 8 | 9 | **CHAPTER 10** | 11 | 12 |

ALGEBRA: FUNCTIONS AND RELATIONSHIPS...504

CHAPTER 11

Similarity, Congruence, and Transformations

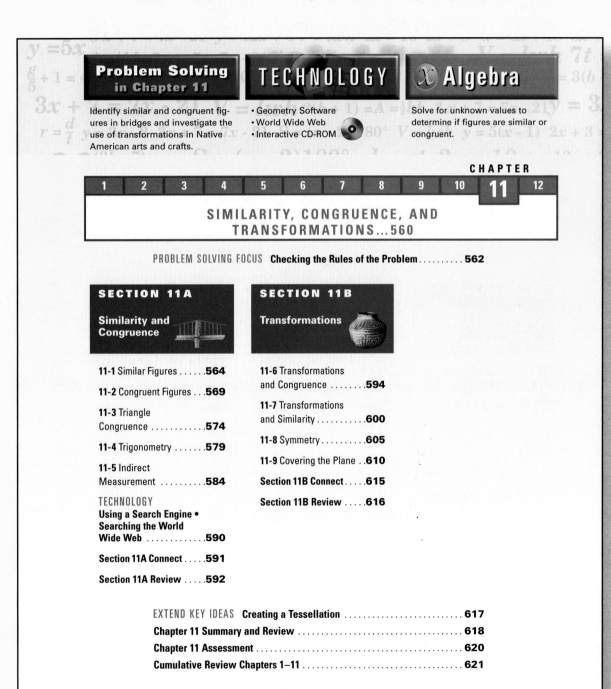

Problem Solving in Chapter 11

Identify similar and congruent figures in bridges and investigate the use of transformations in Native American arts and crafts.

TECHNOLOGY

• Geometry Software
• World Wide Web
• Interactive CD-ROM

Algebra

Solve for unknown values to determine if figures are similar or congruent.

CHAPTER

| 1 | 2 | 3 | 4 | 5 | 6 | 7 | 8 | 9 | 10 | **11** | 12 |

CHAPTER 12

Counting and Probability

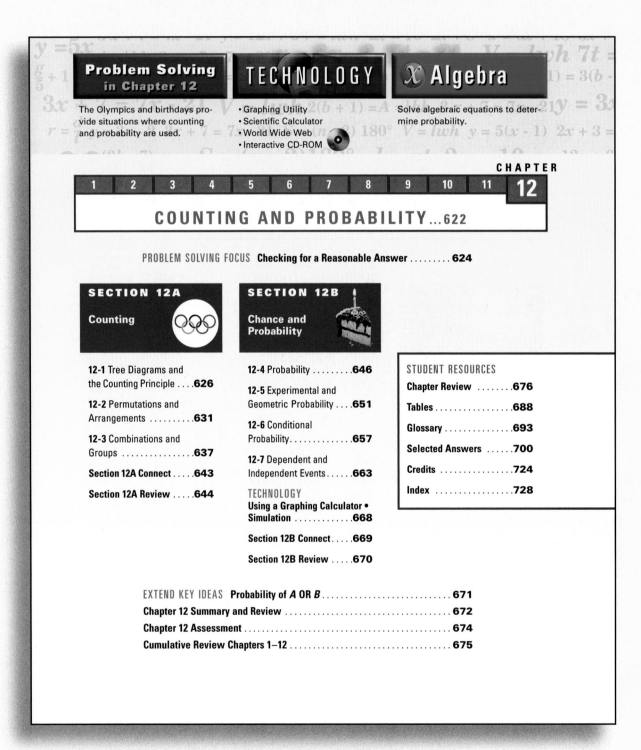

Problem Solving in Chapter 12

The Olympics and birthdays provide situations where counting and probability are used.

TECHNOLOGY

• Graphing Utility
• Scientific Calculator
• World Wide Web
• Interactive CD-ROM

Algebra

Solve algebraic equations to determine probability.

CHAPTER **12**

| 1 | 2 | 3 | 4 | 5 | 6 | 7 | 8 | 9 | 10 | 11 |

COUNTING AND PROBABILITY...622

Pacing Guide

The pacing suggested in the chart at the right assumes one day for most lessons, one day for end-of-section Connect and Review, and two days for end-of-chapter Summary, Review, and Assessment. The same number of days per chapter is used for the block scheduling options. For example, see page 2D.

You may need to adjust pacing to meet the needs of your students and your district curriculum.

CHAPTER		PAGES	NUMBER OF DAYS
1	Data Analysis	2–57	14
2	Integers	58–117	14
3	The Language of Algebra: Variables, Expressions, and Equations	118–167	13
4	Algebra: Linear Equations and Inequalities	168–217	13
5	Ratio and Proportion	218–269	13
6	Percent	270–319	13
7	Number Sense, Rational Numbers, and Irrational Numbers	320–385	16
8	Geometry and Measurement	386–439	16
9	Area and Volume	440–503	16
10	Algebra: Functions and Relationships	504–559	14
11	Similarity, Congruence, and Transformations	560–621	14
12	Counting and Probability	622–675	14
	Total Days		**170**

Materials List

CHAPTERS	1	2	3	4	5	6	7	8	9	10	11	12
2-Color Counters	■■				■■					■■		■■
Algebra Tiles		■■	■■						■■			■■
Blank Number Cubes with Stickers	■			■				■				■
Centimeter Cubes									■	■		
Safe-T Protractor™												
Geoboard								■■	■■		■■	
Power Polygons											■■	
Cuisenaire Angle Ruler											■	
Rulers	■	■		■	■	■	■	■	■		■	
Protractor								■			■	
Tangram											■	

■ **Student Manipulative Kit**   ■ **Teacher's Overhead Manipulative Kit**   ■ **Transparencies in Teacher's Toolkit**

Chapter 7

Number Sense, Rational Numbers, *and* Irrational Numbers

▶ **OVERVIEW**

Section 7A

Number Theory: Students use patterns and rules to determine multiples and divisibility. They apply these skills as they learn to find the greatest common factor and the least common multiple of two or more numbers.

7-1 Divisibility Patterns and Prime Factorization

7-2 Greatest Common Factors (GCF)

7-3 Least Common Multiples (LCM)

Section 7B

Rational Numbers: Students apply LCM and GCF to their work with rational numbers. They learn to add, subtract, multiply, and divide rational numbers.

7-4 Defining Rational Numbers

7-5 Add and Subtract Rational Numbers

7-6 Multiply and Divide Rational Numbers

Section 7C

Irrational Numbers: Students learn about perfect squares and square roots. The concept of square roots is then expanded to introduce irrational numbers. All of these ideas are tied together as students learn about the Pythagorean theorem.

7-7 Perfect Squares and Square Roots

7-8 Square Roots and Irrational Numbers

7-9 The Pythagorean Theorem

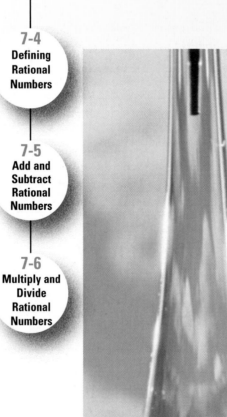

▶ Curriculum Standards

S T A N D A R D

			pages
1	**Problem Solving**	Skills and Strategies	322, 332, *334*, 339, 349, 352, 360, 368, 371, 378
		Applications	328–329, 333–334, 338–339, 348–349, 353–354, 359–360, 367–368, 372–373, 377–378
		Exploration	321, 324, 330, 335, 344, 350, 364, 369, 374
2	**Communication**	Oral	323, 327, *331*, 334, 337, 343, *345*, 349, 352, *356*, 358, 360, 363, 368, *370*, 373, *375*, 378
		Written	324, 327, 329, 334, 337, 340, 344, 347, 350, 352, 354, 358, 361, 366, 368, 371, 374, 376
		Cooperative Learning	324, 330, 335, 344, 350, 355, 364, 369, 374
3	**Reasoning**	Critical Thinking	334, 339, 360, *368*, 373
4	**Connections**	Mathematical	See Standards 5–9, 12, 13 below.
		Interdisciplinary	Consumer *343*, *363*; Geography 333, *343*, 353, *357*, 359, *363*, 372; Health *346*, 354; History *323*, *326*, 329, 349, *371*, 372; Industry 328, *337*, 338, *378*; Science 320, 328, 329, 334, 338, 348, 349, 351, *352*, 353, 359, 368, 372, 377; Social Science 320, 323, *332*, 353, *363*, 367, 377; Fine Arts *376*
		Technology	320, 321, 323, 340, 343, 349, 358, 360, 363, 365, 366, 370, 371, 372, 379
		Cultural	320, 337, *352*, *357*, 363, *366*, *371*, 375, *376*
5	**Number and Number Relationships**		320–384
6	**Number Systems and Number Theory**		320–384
7	**Computation and Estimation**		336, 350–360, 364–378
8	**Patterns and Functions**		323–339, 367, *373*, 378
9	**Algebra**		328, 329, 333, 338, 339, 349, 354, 359, 360, 367, 368, 371, 373, 374–378
10	**Statistics**		340–341, 353, 360–361
12	**Geometry**		339, 372, 374–378
13	**Measurement**		368, 374–378

Italic type indicates Teacher Edition reference.

▶ Teaching Standards

Focus on Pacing

No two classrooms have exactly the same make-up of students. Every teacher must choose how much time to spend on various activities. Teachers should

- make adequate plans, but be willing to adapt them.

▶ Assessment Standards

Focus on Mathematics

Ongoing The Mathematics Standard suggests that activities which present a new mathematical concept may be one means of measuring their ability to reason and communicate mathematically. Ongoing assessments in Chapter 7 probe students'

- understanding of **Explore** activities.

- ability to express a repeating decimal as a fraction.

TECHNOLOGY

▶ For the Teacher

- **Teacher Resource Planner CD-ROM**
  Use the teacher planning CD-ROM to view resources available for Chapter 7. You can prepare custom lesson plans or use the default lesson plans provided.

- **World Wide Web**
  Visit **www.teacher.mathsurf.com** for links to lesson plans from teachers and other professionals, NCTM information, and other sites.

- **TestWorks**
  TestWorks provides ready-made tests and can create custom tests and practice worksheets.

▶ For the Parent

- **World Wide Web**
  Parents can use the Web site at **www.parent.mathsurf.com**.

▶ For the Student

- **Interactive CD-ROM**
  Lesson 7-6 has an *Interactive CD-ROM Lesson.* The *Interactive CD-ROM Journal* and *Interactive CD-ROM Spreadsheet/Grapher Tool* are also used in Chapter 7.

- **Wide World of Mathematics**
  Lesson 7-1 Algebra: Breaking the German Code
  Lesson 7-9 Middle School: Youthbuild

- **World Wide Web**
  Use with Chapter and Section Openers; Students can go online to the Scott Foresman-Addison Wesley Web site at **www.mathsurf.com/8/ch7** to collect information about chapter themes.

SECTION 7A

LESSON	OBJECTIVE	ITBS Form M	CTBS 4th Ed.	CAT 5th Ed.	SAT 9th Ed.	MAT 7th Ed.	Your Form
7-1	• Use rules for determining whether a number is divisible by another number.	✗	✗	✗			
7-2	• Find the greatest common factor of two or more numbers.		✗		✗	✗	
7-3	• Find the least common multiple of two or more numbers.	✗	✗	✗			

SECTION 7B

LESSON	OBJECTIVE	ITBS Form M	CTBS 4th Ed.	CAT 5th Ed.	SAT 9th Ed.	MAT 7th Ed.	Your Form
7-4	• Compare and order rational numbers.	✗	✗	✗	✗	✗	
7-5	• Add and subtract rational numbers.	✗	✗	✗	✗	✗	
7-6	• Multiply and divide rational numbers.	✗	✗	✗	✗	✗	

SECTION 7C

LESSON	OBJECTIVE	ITBS Form M	CTBS 4th Ed.	CAT 5th Ed.	SAT 9th Ed.	MAT 7th Ed.	Your Form
7-7	• Compute square roots and identify perfect squares.		✗		✗	✗	
7-8	• Identify square roots that are irrational numbers.						
7-9	• Use the Pythagorean theorem with right triangles.		✗			✗	

Key: ITBS - Iowa Test of Basic Skills; CTBS - Comprehensive Test of Basic Skills; CAT - California Achievement Test; SAT - Stanford Achievement Test; MAT - Metropolitan Achievement Test

ASSESSMENT PROGRAM

▶ **Traditional Assessment**

QUICK QUIZZES	SECTION REVIEW	CHAPTER REVIEW	CHAPTER ASSESSMENT FREE RESPONSE	CHAPTER ASSESSMENT MULTIPLE CHOICE	CUMULATIVE REVIEW
TE: pp. 329, 334, 339, 349, 354, 360, 368, 373, 378	SE: pp. 342, 362, 380 *Quiz 7A, 7B, 7C	SE: pp. 382-383	SE: p. 384 *Ch. 7 Tests Forms A, B, E	*Ch. 7 Tests Forms C, E	SE: p. 385 *Ch. 7 Test Form F

▶ **Alternate Assessment**

INTERVIEW	JOURNAL	ONGOING	PERFORMANCE	PORTFOLIO	PROJECT	SELF
TE: p. 334	SE: pp. 329, 342, 349, 354, 362, 368 TE: pp. 322, 349, 354	TE: pp. 324, 330, 335, 341, 344, 350, 356, 361, 364, 368, 369, 374, 379	SE: pp. 384, 385 TE: pp. 329, 373 *Ch. 7 Tests Forms D, E	TE: p. 360	SE: pp. 321, 334, 349, 378 TE: pp. 321, 378	TE: p. 339

*Tests and quizzes are in *Assessment Sourcebook.* Test Form E is a mixed response test. Forms for Alternate Assessment are also available in *Assessment Sourcebook.*

 TestWorks: Test and Practice Software

▶ **REGULAR PACING**

Day	5 classes per week
1	Chapter 7 Opener; Problem Solving Focus
2	Section **7A** Opener; Lesson **7-1**
3	Lesson **7-2**
4	Lesson **7-3**
5	Technology
6	**7A** Connect; **7A** Review
7	Section **7B** Opener; Lesson **7-4**
8	Lesson **7-5**
9	Lesson **7-6**
10	**7B** Connect; **7B** Review
11	Section **7C** Opener; Lesson **7-7**
12	Lesson **7-8**
13	Lesson **7-9**
14	**7C** Connect; **7C** Review; Extending Key Ideas
15	Chapter 7 Summary and Review
16	Chapter 7 Assessment Cumulative Review, Chapters 1–7

▶ **BLOCK SCHEDULING OPTIONS**

Block Scheduling for Complete Course

Chapter 7 may be presented in

- eleven 90-minute blocks
- thirteen 75-minute blocks

Each block consists of a combination of

- Chapter and Section Openers
- Explores
- Lesson Development
- Problem Solving Focus
- Technology
- Extend Key Ideas
- Connect
- Review
- Assessment

For details, see *Block Scheduling Handbook.*

Block Scheduling for Lab-Based Course

In each block, 30–40 minutes is devoted to lab activities including

- Explores in the Student Edition
- Connect pages in the Student Edition
- Technology options in the Student Edition
- Reteaching Activities in the Teacher Edition

For details, see *Block Scheduling Handbook.*

Block Scheduling for Interdisciplinary Course

Each block integrates math with another subject area.

In Chapter 7, interdisciplinary topics include

- Codes
- Water
- Houses

Themes for Interdisciplinary Team Teaching 7A, 7B, and 7C are

- Prime Messages
- The Great Lakes
- The Great Pyramid

For details, see *Block Scheduling Handbook.*

Block Scheduling for Course with *Connected Mathematics*

In each block, investigations from **Connected Mathematics** replace or enhance the lessons in Chapter 7.

Connected Mathematics topics for Chapter 7 can be found in

- *Growing, Growing, Growing*
- *Looking for Pythagoras*

For details, see *Block Scheduling Handbook.*

INTERDISCIPLINARY BULLETIN BOARD

Set Up

Prepare a bulletin board with a display of the three problems shown. Or, you may choose to use one of your own favorite problems which requires the application of the Pythagorean theorem. Allow room under each problem for students to tack up their solutions.

Procedure

Organize students into small groups. Each group should solve each of the problems shown on the bulletin board and then post the solution under the problem. Have each group select its favorite problem and prepare a presentation of their solution for the class.

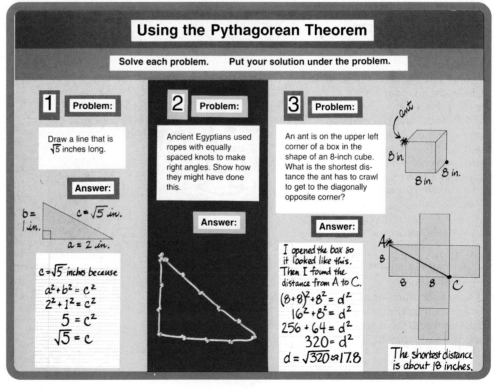

Using the Pythagorean Theorem

Solve each problem.   Put your solution under the problem.

1 Problem:

Draw a line that is $\sqrt{5}$ inches long.

Answer:

$c = \sqrt{5}$ inches because
$a^2 + b^2 = c^2$
$2^2 + 1^2 = c^2$
$5 = c^2$
$\sqrt{5} = c$

2 Problem:

Ancient Egyptians used ropes with equally spaced knots to make right angles. Show how they might have done this.

Answer:

3 Problem:

An ant is on the upper left corner of a box in the shape of an 8-inch cube. What is the shortest distance the ant has to crawl to get to the diagonally opposite corner?

Answer:

I opened the box so it looked like this. Then I found the distance from A to C.
$(8+8)^2 + 8^2 = d^2$
$16^2 + 8^2 = d^2$
$256 + 64 = d^2$
$320 = d^2$
$d = \sqrt{320} \approx 17.8$

The shortest distance is about 18 inches.

The information on these pages shows how number sense, rational numbers, and irrational numbers are used in real-life situations.

World Wide Web

If your class has access to the World Wide Web, you might want to use the information found at the Web site addresses given.

Extensions

The following activities do not require access to the World Wide Web.

People of the World
Rhythm patterns based on 12 pulses are very important in African music, since they can be combined using units of 2, 3, 4, or 6. Interested students may wish to listen for 12-pulse rhythm patterns in African music.

Arts & Literature
You might share with students the translation of the Japanese Haiku given in the students' book:
This road
No one walks along it
Dusk in the autumn

Entertainment
Review the meaning of ratios (see Chapter 5). Ask students why these ratios are described as *small*. Possible answer: There is a small difference between the numbers.

Social Studies
Morse code, once commonly used in communication, uses dots, dashes, and spaces to represent letters, numerals, and punctuation. Have students research the International Morse Code to write the words *Number Sense*. They should use ### between letters when they write the code.
— • ### • • — ### — — ###— • • •
• ### • — • ###• • • ### • ###—
• ###• • • ###•

Science
Review the first few numbers in the Fibonacci sequence (1, 1, 2, 3, 5, 8), where each number after the first two is the sum of the two previous numbers. Have students compute the sequence to 89. 13, 21, 34, 55, 89

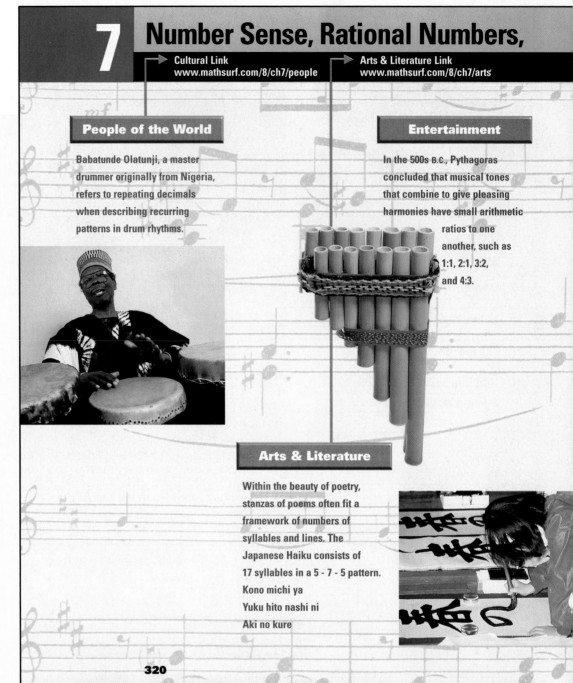

7 Number Sense, Rational Numbers,

→ Cultural Link
www.mathsurf.com/8/ch7/people

→ Arts & Literature Link
www.mathsurf.com/8/ch7/arts

People of the World

Babatunde Olatunji, a master drummer originally from Nigeria, refers to repeating decimals when describing recurring patterns in drum rhythms.

Entertainment

In the 500s B.C., Pythagoras concluded that musical tones that combine to give pleasing harmonies have small arithmetic ratios to one another, such as 1:1, 2:1, 3:2, and 4:3.

Arts & Literature

Within the beauty of poetry, stanzas of poems often fit a framework of numbers of syllables and lines. The Japanese Haiku consists of 17 syllables in a 5 - 7 - 5 pattern.
Kono michi ya
Yuku hito nashi ni
Aki no kure

320

TEACHER TALK

Meet Ruth T. Brinzo

West Hernando Middle School
Brooksville, Florida

I find that relay races can make teaching number theory fun and interesting. Students are first grouped into teams and then I pose a problem such as, "Write 172 as a product of prime factors." Each team is assigned a section of the board, and one member of each team goes to the board to begin the relay. Each team member can erase as much as he or she wants, but is allowed to write only one digit or operation symbol, after which he or she must pass the chalk to another team member. Team members are not allowed to confer. They learn that they must concentrate on the work being done because individual team members may not approach the problem in the same way.

and Irrational Numbers

Social Studies Link
www.mathsurf.com/8/ch7/social

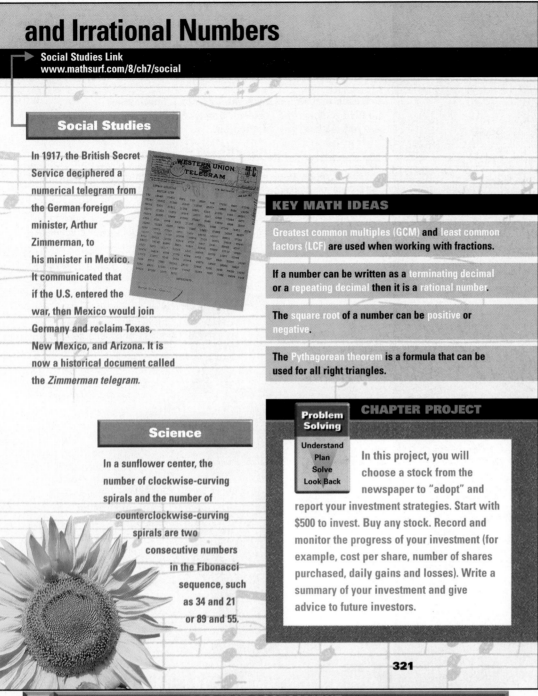

Social Studies

In 1917, the British Secret Service deciphered a numerical telegram from the German foreign minister, Arthur Zimmerman, to his minister in Mexico. It communicated that if the U.S. entered the war, then Mexico would join Germany and reclaim Texas, New Mexico, and Arizona. It is now a historical document called the *Zimmerman telegram*.

Science

In a sunflower center, the number of clockwise-curving spirals and the number of counterclockwise-curving spirals are two consecutive numbers in the Fibonacci sequence, such as 34 and 21 or 89 and 55.

KEY MATH IDEAS

Greatest common multiples (GCM) and least common factors (LCF) are used when working with fractions.

If a number can be written as a terminating decimal or a repeating decimal then it is a rational number.

The square root of a number can be positive or negative.

The Pythagorean theorem is a formula that can be used for all right triangles.

CHAPTER PROJECT

Problem Solving
Understand
Plan
Solve
Look Back

In this project, you will choose a stock from the newspaper to "adopt" and report your investment strategies. Start with $500 to invest. Buy any stock. Record and monitor the progress of your investment (for example, cost per share, number of shares purchased, daily gains and losses). Write a summary of your investment and give advice to future investors.

321

Chapter Project

Using problem solving strategies, students choose stocks, record, monitor, and summarize the progress of their investments, and prepare to give advice to future investors.

Materials
Newspapers

Resources
Chapter 7 Project Master

Introduce the Project
• Have students bring in newspaper stock market reports. Discuss how to read the reports and give examples of different ways to invest $500.

• Ask students to share ideas of how they would invest their $500.

Project Progress
Section A, page 334 Students consider how factors, multiples, and divisibility influence decisions when buying shares of stocks.

Section B, page 349 Students use negative numbers to help record their stocks' changes in value. They decide the most efficient way to write numbers in their records.

Section C, page 378 Students look for applications of irrational numbers or square roots in the stock market.

Community Project

A community project for Chapter 7 is available in *Home and Community Connections*.

Cooperative Learning

You may want to use Teaching Tool Transparency 1: Cooperative Learning Checklist with **Explore** and other group activities in this chapter.

PROJECT ASSESSMENT

You may choose to use this project as a performance assessment for the chapter.

Performance Assessment Key

Level 4 Full Accomplishment

Level 3 Substantial Accomplishment

Level 2 Partial Accomplishment

Level 1 Little Accomplishment

Suggested Scoring Rubric

4
• Stock choices and records indicate good number sense and a complete understanding of rational numbers.
• Summary and advice is accurate and logical.

3
• Stock choices and records indicate some number sense and an adequate understanding of rational numbers.
• Summary and advice is mostly accurate and logical.

2
• Stock choices and records indicate limited number sense and understanding of rational numbers.
• Summary and advice is inaccurate and not always logical.

1
• Stock choices and records indicate no number sense and a remote understanding of rational numbers.

Identifying Missing Information

The Point
Students focus on identifying additional information needed to solve problems.

Resources
Teaching Tool Transparency 17: Problem-Solving Guidelines

 Interactive CD-ROM Journal

About the Page

Using the Problem–Solving Process
A critical element in successful problem solving is the ability to identify missing information. Discuss these suggestions for identifying missing information:

- Determine what the problem is asking.
- Organize the given information.
- Try to solve the problem.
- Identify missing information.

Ask ...
- **How do you know when there is not enough information to solve a problem?** Possible answer: You try to solve the problem but find that you are missing information.

- **How might rewriting the problem as an equation or inequality, with numerals and variables, help you determine whether you need additional information?** Possible answer: If there are too many variables, you need additional information.

Answers for Problems
1. No information is missing.
2. No information is missing.
3. The percent of college seniors who go on to play professional football.
4. The number of players who play longer than three to four years. The total number of professional basketball players.

Journal

Ask students to describe a problem they have tried to solve and then discovered they did not have enough information. Have them explain what they did, if anything, to get the required information.

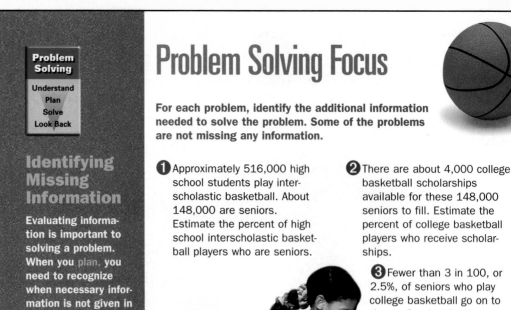

Problem Solving

Understand
Plan
Solve
Look Back

Identifying Missing Information

Evaluating information is important to solving a problem. When you plan, you need to recognize when necessary information is not given in the problem.

Problem Solving Focus

For each problem, identify the additional information needed to solve the problem. Some of the problems are not missing any information.

1 Approximately 516,000 high school students play interscholastic basketball. About 148,000 are seniors. Estimate the percent of high school interscholastic basketball players who are seniors.

2 There are about 4,000 college basketball scholarships available for these 148,000 seniors to fill. Estimate the percent of college basketball players who receive scholarships.

3 Fewer than 3 in 100, or 2.5%, of seniors who play college basketball go on to play professionally. How does that figure compare with the percent of college seniors who go on to play professional football?

4 The average professional basketball player has a career span of three to four years. However, many superstars like Michael Jordan play for many more years than the average player. What percent of professional basketball players play more than the average number of years?

322

Additional Problem

Identify the additional information that is needed to solve each problem.

1. Approximately 1600 students at Wilson High School plan to go to college. About 500 seniors plan to go to college. Estimate the percent of seniors at Wilson High School that plan to go to college. The number of seniors in Wilson High School.

2. There are about 150 scholarships available for seniors that can qualify for them. Estimate the percent of seniors who receive scholarships. The number of seniors who actually get scholarships.

3. Fewer than 3 in 20, or 15%, of these seniors plan on going to graduate school after earning their bachelors degree. How does that compare with the percent of seniors from Taylor High School that go to graduate school? The percent of seniors at Taylor who plan to go to graduate school.

4. The average college student goes to school for 4 years to earn a bachelors degree. However, students that go to graduate school attend school for more than 4 years. What percent of college students go to school for more than 4 years? The number of students who go on to college and the number of students in graduate school.

Section 7A

Divisibility and Patterns

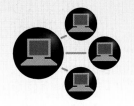

Visit **www.teacher.mathsurf.com** for links to lesson plans from teachers and other professionals, NCTM information, and other sites.

LESSON PLANNING GUIDE

▶ **Student Edition**

▶ **Ancillaries***

LESSON		MATERIALS	VOCABULARY	DAILY	OTHER
	Chapter 7 Opener				Ch. 7 Project Master Ch. 7 Community Project Teaching Tool Trans. 1
	Problem Solving Focus				Teaching Tool Trans. 17 *Interactive CD-ROM Journal*
	Section 7A Opener				
7-1	Divisibility Patterns and Prime Factorization	hundred chart	prime number, composite number, divisible, multiple, factor, prime factor, Fundamental Theorem of Arithmetic, prime factorization	7-1	Teaching Tool Trans. 12 Technology Master 26 *WW Math*—Algebra
7-2	Greatest Common Factors (GCF)		common factor, greatest common factor (GCF)	7-2	Teaching Tool Trans. 2, 3 Ch. 7 Project Master
7-3	Least Common Multiples (LCM)		common multiple, least common multiple (LCM)	7-3	Teaching Tool Trans. 2, 3
	Technology	computer, spreadsheet software			*Interactive CD-ROM Spreadsheet/Grapher Tool*
	Connect				Lesson Enhancement Trans. 27 Interdisc. Team Teaching 7A
	Review				Practice 7A; Quiz 7A; *TestWorks*

* Daily Ancillaries include Practice, Reteaching, Problem Solving, Enrichment, and Daily Transparency. Teaching Tool Transparencies are in *Teacher's Toolkits*. Lesson Enhancement Transparencies are in *Overhead Transparency Package*.

SKILLS TRACE

LESSON	SKILL	FIRST INTRODUCED			DEVELOP	PRACTICE/ APPLY	REVIEW
		GR. 6	GR. 7	GR. 8			
7-1	Finding prime factorization.	✗			pp. 324–327	pp. 328–329	pp. 395, 547, 568, 675
7-2	Finding GCF.	✗			pp. 330–332	pp. 333–334	pp. 382, 395, 552, 573
7-3	Finding LCM.	✗			pp. 335–337	pp. 338–339	pp. 382, 400, 439, 578

CONNECTED MATHEMATICS

The unit *Growing, Growing, Growing (Exponential Relationships)*, from the **Connected Mathematics** series, can be used with Section 7A.

Math and Science/Technology

(Worksheet pages 25–26: Teacher pages T25–T26)

In this lesson, students use prime numbers to create a cipher.

Name _____

Math and Science/Technology

Prime Messages

Use prime numbers to create a cipher.

Prime numbers have fascinated mathematicians for thousands of years. One of the first means of identifying them was worked out more than 2,000 years ago by Eratosthenes of Cyrene, a Greek mathematician and geographer. He used the grid below, called the Sieve of Eratosthenes, to identify every prime number between 1 and 100.

The Sieve of Eratosthenes

1	2	3	4	5	6	7	8	9	10
11	12	13	14	15	16	17	18	19	20
21	22	23	24	25	26	27	28	29	30
31	32	33	34	35	36	37	38	39	40
41	42	43	44	45	46	47	48	49	50
51	52	53	54	55	56	57	58	59	60
61	62	63	64	65	66	67	68	69	70
71	72	73	74	75	76	77	78	79	80
81	82	83	84	85	86	87	88	89	90
91	92	93	94	95	96	97	98	99	100

Today prime numbers play an important role in cryptography, the science of using codes and ciphers to disguise written messages and data. A code consists of text or data concealed by substituting whole words. A cipher consists of text or data concealed by substituting individual letters. In order to protect sensitive information stored in computer databases, data used by many banks, government agencies, and private companies are stored in computers as a cipher based on a prime number. For example, the data might be enciphered (put into a cipher) using a key number (N)

that is the product of two large prime numbers. Deciphering the system and reading the data requires knowledge of the two prime factors. Because N is likely to be more than 100 digits long, finding the primes and cracking the cipher is extremely difficult.

Computers can now determine very large prime numbers that are useful to cryptographers. The largest prime number found so far has more than 200,000 digits. Because such huge prime numbers are so difficult to find and use, using them as a "key" to data greatly improves database security.

No supercomputer is available to help you create a cipher or cipher key using enormous prime numbers. But the Sieve of Eratosthenes can be used to find prime numbers that can form a simple cipher you can use to conceal your own secrets.

1. Identify some types of computer information that might be protected by ciphers and codes.

Responses might include bank accounts, tax records, credit card information, or government documents.

2. What might be some limitations of the Sieve of Eratosthenes in constructing a code?

The grid is small, so the numbers available are limited.

Name _____

Math and Science/Technology

3. **a.** Use the following steps to determine the prime numbers in the Sieve of Eratosthenes: Cross out 1, which is not prime. Use a calculator to find the square root of the highest number in the grid. What is it?

$\sqrt{100} = 10$

b. Identify all of the prime numbers less than or equal to that square root by factoring. Cross out all multiples of the primes, not the primes themselves. Circle the numbers that are left, which are the prime numbers of the sieve. How many are there? What are they?

See below.

4. A substitution cipher is one in which each letter of the alphabet is replaced by a different letter or a number. Is it possible to create a substitution cipher for the alphabet using the prime numbers in the sieve? What problem would you need to solve?

See below.

5. Create a substitution cipher using the prime numbers in the sieve. Each number in the cipher should have two digits (2 would be 02). Be sure that the cipher takes into account the problem identified in question 4 above. Use the grid at the bottom of the page to record the key to your cipher.

6. Write this message using your cipher: A PRIME NUMBER IS AN INTEGER LARGER THAN ONE AND DIVISIBLE ONLY BY ITSELF AND ONE.

See below.

7. On a separate sheet of paper create a similar sieve for the prime numbers between 101 and 200. Is the number of primes the same? Is there a pattern?

See below.

8. Using knowledge gained above, explain why finding large prime numbers without the uses of computers would present a problem for cryptographers.

See below.

Key for cipher based on prime numbers found in the Sieve of Eratosthenes.

A	B	C	D	E	F	G	H	I	J	K	L	M
02	03	05	07	11	13	17	19	23	29	31	37	41

N	O	P	Q	R	S	T	U	V	W	X	Y	Z
43	47	53	59	61	67	71	73	79	83	89	97	?

Answers

3. b. The prime numbers less than 10 are 2, 3, 5, and 7. By crossing out the multiples of these numbers there are 25 prime numbers: 2, 3, 5, 7, 11, 13, 17, 19, 23, 29, 31, 37, 41, 43, 47, 53, 59, 61, 67, 71, 73, 79, 83, 89, 97.

4. Yes. There are 26 letters of the alphabet while there are just 25 prime numbers between 1 and 100. One would need an extra symbol for the 26th letter.

6. Responses will vary depending on the cipher chosen. If students place the prime numbers in ascending order from the beginning to the end of the alphabet, substituting some other symbol for Z, such as "?," the message would look this way: 02/53 61 23 41 11/43 73 41 03 11 61/23 67/02 43/23 43 71 11 17 11 61/37 02 61 17 11 61/71 19 02 43/47 43 11/02 43 07/07 23 79 23 67 23 03 37 11/47 43 37 97/03 97/23 71 67 11 37 13/02 43 07/47 43 11.

7. No. The number of primes is not the same (21 instead of 25). There is no easily recognizable pattern.

101	102	103	104	105	106	107	108	109	110
111	112	113	114	115	116	117	118	119	120
121	122	123	124	125	126	127	128	129	130
131	132	133	134	35	136	137	138	139	140
141	142	143	144	145	146	147	148	149	150
151	152	153	154	155	156	157	158	159	160
161	162	163	164	165	166	167	168	169	170
171	172	173	174	175	176	177	178	179	180
181	182	183	184	185	186	187	188	189	190
191	192	193	194	195	196	197	198	199	200

8. As numbers become larger, it becomes more difficult to find their factors and determine if they are prime. In addition, if prime numbers do not occur in an easily recognizable pattern, there are no easy clues to predict where they will occur.

BIBLIOGRAPHY

► FOR TEACHERS

Ascher, Marcia. *Ethnomathematics: A Multicultural View of Mathematical Ideas.* Pacific Grove, CA: Brooks/Cole Publishing Co., 1991.

Miller, William and Linda Wagner. "Pythagorean Dissection Puzzles." *Mathematics Teacher* (April 1993): pp. 302–314.

► FOR STUDENTS

Avi, J. *Nothing But the Truth: A Documentary Novel.* New York, NY: Orchard Books, 1991.

Beutelspacher, Albrecht. *Cryptology.* Washington, D.C.: The Mathematical Association of America, 1994.

SECTION 7A

Number Theory

► History Link   ► Science Link   ► www.mathsurf.com/8/ch7/codes

Smoke signals, Morse code, Braille, binary code, area codes, zip codes, bar codes— codes can be found everywhere. They've been used throughout history for various purposes.

A *Vigenère tableau* was based on shifted alphabets and could be compared to reading a coordinate grid. Using the key *LAMP* the message "code" is deciphered:

Encoded Message: NOPP
                Key: LAMP
Decoded Message: CODE

In 1835, Morse code was developed by ex-painter Samuel Morse and Alfred Vail. The first telegraph message, using short electric pulses called dots and dashes, followed a few years later.

During World War II, the Germans used a code generated by a machine called "Enigma" to communicate the strategic positions of their U-boats (submarines). Without the Germans' knowledge, the Allies broke Enigma's code and escaped the destruction once caused by the German U-boats.

Curing the Common CODE

1 How could "497" mean DIG?

2 How do you think mathematics is used in making and breaking codes?

3 How would you go about creating a code for secret communication?

323

Theme: Codes

World Wide Web

If your class has access to the World Wide Web, you might want to use the information found at the Web site address given. The interdisciplinary links relate to topics discussed in this section.

About the Page

This page introduces the theme of the section, codes, and discusses how different codes have been used throughout history.

Ask ...
• Have you ever used a secret code?

• How did you use your code?

• How is this similar to the way codes have been used throughout history?

Extensions

The following activities do not require access to the World Wide Web.

History
Encourage a discussion about how codes have been used throughout history. Have students investigate codes, other than those mentioned on this page, and report their historical significance. Suggest that they write a coded message on the board for the class to decode.

Science
DNA is an abbreviation for deoxyribonucleic acid, a substance of all living cells that carries the genetic code. Have students research DNA and report on the genetic code and heredity.

Connect

On page 341, students will use prime and composite numbers to make a code based on a bar graph.

Where are we now?

In Chapter 2, students used patterns to explore integers and to solve problems.

They learned how to

• use patterns to order and compare numbers.

• use patterns to extend a list of numbers.

Where are we going?

In Section 7A, students will

• use patterns and rules to determine multiples and divisibility.

• find the greatest common factors of numbers.

• find the least common multiple of numbers.

Answers for Questions
1. Possible answer: Each number is the position in the alphabet of the encoded word.

2. Possible answer: Use a number for each letter, add 1, and convert back to a letter.

3. Answers may vary.

Objective

- **Use rules for determining whether a number is divisible by another number.**

Vocabulary

- **Prime number, composite number, divisible, multiple, factor, prime factor, Fundamental Theorem of Arithmetic, prime factorization**

Materials

- **Explore: Hundred chart**

NCTM Standards

- **1, 2, 4, 5, 6, 8, 9**

▶ **Review**

1. Can the number be evenly divided by 2?
   a. 24 yes   b. 175 no

2. Can the number be evenly divided by 3?
   a. 284 no   b. 111 yes

3. Can the number be evenly divided by 5?
   a. 105 yes   b. 380 yes

Available on Daily Transparency 7-1

▶ **Lesson Link**

Discuss with students how following a pattern may help save time.

1 Introduce

Explore

You may wish to use Teaching Tool Transparency 12: Hundred Chart with **Explore**.

The Point
Students use a hundred chart to determine whether numbers are prime or composite.

Ongoing Assessment
Check that students understand the term *multiples*, and that they are crossing out the appropriate numbers.

7-1 Divisibility Patterns and Prime Factorization

You'll Learn ...

■ to use rules for determining whether a number is divisible by another number

... How It's Used

Egyptologists use divisibility to decipher patterns used in hieroglyphics.

Vocabulary

prime number

composite number

divisible

multiple

factor

prime factor

Fundamental Theorem of Arithmetic

prime factorization

▶ **Lesson Link** You have used patterns to solve problems. Now you will use patterns to determine whether a number divides without a remainder. ◀

A **prime number** is an integer larger than 1 that is only divisible by itself and 1.

Prime numbers: 2, 3, 5, 7, 11, ...

A **composite number** is a positive integer that is not prime. It has factors other than 1 and itself.

Composite numbers: 4, 6, 8, 9, 10, ...

Explore   Primes and Composites

The Chart Is Smart

Materials: Hundred chart

1. Circle 2 and cross out all the other multiples of 2.

2. Circle the next number that has not been crossed out and cross out all of its multiples.

3. Continue this process until all numbers except 1 are either circled or crossed out.

4. Did you use any shortcuts in this process? Describe.

5. Are the circled numbers prime numbers or composite numbers? How do you know?

1	2	3	4	5	6	7	8	9	10
11	12	13	14	15	16	17	18	19	20
21	22	23	24	25	26	27	28	29	30
31	32	33	34	35	36	37	38	39	40
41	42	43	44	45	46	47	48	49	50
51	52	53	54	55	56	57	58	59	60
61	62	63	64	65	66	67	68	69	70
71	72	73	74	75	76	77	78	79	80
81	82	83	84	85	86	87	88	89	90
91	92	93	94	95	96	97	98	99	100

Learn   Divisibility Patterns and Prime Factorization

We say that 15 is **divisible** by 5 because 15 divided by 5 has no remainder.

We say that 15 is a **multiple** of 5 because 15 is divisible by 5.

We say that 5 is a **factor** of 15 because 15 is divisible by 5.

$200 \div 4 = 50$ 4 and 50 are *factors* of 200.

$4 \times 50 = 200$ 200 is a *multiple* of 4 and 50.

▷ MEETING INDIVIDUAL NEEDS

Resources

7-1 Practice

7-1 Reteaching

7-1 Problem Solving

7-1 Enrichment

7-1 Daily Transparency
  Problem of the Day
  Review
  Quick Quiz

Teaching Tool Transparency 12

Technology Master 26

Wide World of Mathematics
Algebra: Breaking the German Code

Learning Modalities

Verbal Ask students to explain to the class how they determine the divisibility of a number such as 8820.

Logical Have students make a flow chart showing how to use factorization to determine that a number is prime.

Social In **Explore**, students may work in pairs to compare their work on the hundreds chart and to answer the questions.

Inclusion

Provide templates for visually impaired students to use when drawing circles and lines for factor trees, or provide them with partially completed factor trees. Also, you may wish to work with students to construct a "divisibility rule" chart for quick reference. Include examples on how to use the chart when making factor trees. Remind students to include new vocabulary in their notebook.

Divisibility rules can tell if a given number is divisible by another number.

	Divisibility Rule
2	The ones digit is a *2, 4, 6, 8,* or *0.*
3	The sum of the number's digits is divisible by *3.*
4	As a number, the last two digits are divisible by *4.*
5	The number ends in *5* or *0.*
6	The number is divisible by *2* and *3.*
8	As a number, the last three digits are divisible by *8.*
9	The sum of the number's digits is divisible by *9.*
10	The ones digit is *0.*

Example 1

Enemy X always end their secret messages with a number divisible by 3 and 5, and not 8. A suspicious message ending with 5385 was found. State the divisibility rules that satisfy 5385 to find out if it's from Enemy X.

Under the bridge when The crow caws.

Yours truly,
5385

▶ **Career Link**

A cryptanalyst's job is to encipher and decipher codes.

Divisible by 2, 4, 6, 8, or 10?   5385 is odd so it's not divisible by an even number.

No, because it is not even.   Eliminate the even numbers.

By 5? Yes, because it ends with 5.   Test for divisibility by an odd number.

By 3? Yes, because 5 + 3 + 8 + 5 = 21 is divisible by 3.

By 9? No, because 5 + 3 + 8 + 5 = 21 is not divisible by 9.

5385 is divisible by 3 and 5, and not 8, so the message is from Enemy X.

Try It

Is each number divisible by 2, 3, 4, 5, 6, 8, 9, or 10?

a. 38 **b.** 240 **c.** 236 **d.** 345 **3, 5**   **b. 2, 3, 4, 5, 6, 8, 10**
2 only   **2, 4**

A **prime factor** of a number is a factor that is a prime number. For example:

List all factors of 36 and identify the primes.   1, 2, 3, 4, 6, 9, 12, 18, 36

2 and 3 are the prime factors of 36.

FUNDAMENTAL THEOREM OF ARITHMETIC

All integers greater than 1 are prime or can be written as a unique product of prime numbers.

MATH EVERY DAY

▶ **Problem of the Day**

Some pet stores ordered a case of Yummy Bars for Pets. Store A put 4 bars in a package. Store B put 3 bars in a package. Store C put 2 bars in a package. Store D put 5 bars in a package and had 1 bar left over. Stores A, B, and C had no bars left over. What is the least number of bars that could have been in a case of Yummy Bars for Pets? 36 bars

Available on Daily Transparency 7-1

An Extension is provided in the transparency package.

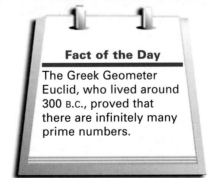

Fact of the Day

The Greek Geometer Euclid, who lived around 300 B.C., proved that there are infinitely many prime numbers.

Mental Math

Do these mentally.

1. How many $5 bills equal $100? 20

2. How many $10 bills equal $1000? 100

3. How many dimes equal $300? 3000

---

2 Teach

Learn

Remind students that a multiple of a number is greater than (or equal to) the number, but a factor of a number is less than (or equal to) the number. Also, in the Fundamental Theorem of Arithmetic, the order of the factors does not matter with respect to uniqueness.

Alternate Examples

1. The coach of the soccer team likes to keep the players on their toes by calling a coded number message on the intercom. A number divisible by 8 means that team A will practice. A number divisible by 9 is a signal that team B will practice. If any other number is called, then practice has been called off. Just before dismissal, the message on the intercom was 1053. Which team, if any, has practice today?

   According to the divisibility rules, 1053 is not divisible by 8, since the number formed by the last three digits, 053, is not divisible by 8. So team A will not practice. The number 1053 is divisible by 9 because the sum of its digits is divisible by 9. So team B will practice. There's no chance that practice will be called off.

Alternate Examples

2. Use a factor tree to find the prime factorization of 126. Circle all prime factors.

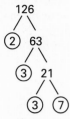

Write 126 as a product of the prime numbers: $126 = 2 \times 3^2 \times 7$, which is in standard form.

3. The prime factors of 210 written in descending order is the address of Ruth's house on Elm Street. What is her address?

Draw a factor tree and circle the prime factors:

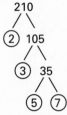

Write the prime factors in descending order to find that the address is 7532 Elm Street.

Remember

$2^3 = 2 \times 2 \times 2 = 8$

[Page 97]

Prime factorization is the result of writing a number as a product of prime numbers. The prime factorization of a number can be found using a factor tree.

Prime factorization is written in standard form using exponents, with factors in increasing order.

$24 = 2 \times 2 \times 2 \times 3 = 2^3 \times 3$

$2^3 \times 3$ is the prime factorization of 24.

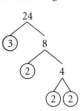

Example 2

Use a factor tree to find the prime factorization of 140.

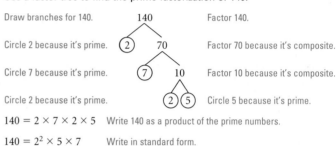

| Draw branches for 140. | | Factor 140. |

Circle 2 because it's prime. — Factor 70 because it's composite.

Circle 7 because it's prime. — Factor 10 because it's composite.

Circle 2 because it's prime. — Circle 5 because it's prime.

$140 = 2 \times 7 \times 2 \times 5$ Write 140 as a product of the prime numbers.

$140 = 2^2 \times 5 \times 7$ Write in standard form.

$2^2 \times 5 \times 7$ is the prime factorization of 140.

HINT

You can use your calculator to check for divisibility. For example, to check 138 for divisibility by 8, enter 138 ÷ 8 = into your calculator. 138 is not divisible by 8 because the result is not an integer.

Example 3

The message to the right provides the address for a secret party. You were informed to find the prime factorization for the address.

Secret Party

When? **3:30 p.m.**
Where? **Oak St.**
(you know what to do with the time)

Draw a factor tree for 330.

Write the prime factorization in standard form.

$330 = 2 \times 3 \times 5 \times 11$

The address could be 23511 Oak Street.

a. 2×3^3

b. $2^2 \times 3 \times 11$

c. $2^2 \times 59$

d. $2 \times 3 \times 59$

Try It

Use a factor tree to find the prime factorization of each number.

a. 54   **b.** 132   **c.** 236   **d.** 354

> ## MEETING MIDDLE SCHOOL CLASSROOM NEEDS

Tips from Middle School Teachers

I challenge my students by posting problems on the bulletin board. For example: Find all the two-digit prime numbers that result in prime numbers when the digits are interchanged (11, 13, 17, 31, 37, 71, 73, 79, and 97). I accept all answers that are reasonable and that show some thought. I keep a class list for prospective Math Hall of Famers and asterisk their names if they have a correct answer and check their names if they had a reasonable answer.

History Connection

Prime numbers have been studied since at least 300 B.C. The Greek mathematicians Euclid and Eratosthenes discovered many properties of prime numbers. The method used in **Explore** is called the Sieve of Eratosthenes.

Cultural Connection

Christian Goldbach (1690–1764), a Russian mathematician, proposed two interesting problems regarding prime numbers. These problems are called Goldbach's conjectures.

1. Every even number greater than two is equal to the sum of two prime numbers. For example, $4 = 2 + 2$, $6 = 3 + 3$, $8 = 5 + 3$, $10 = 7 + 3$ or $5 + 5$.

2. Every whole number greater than five is equal to the sum of three prime numbers. For example, $6 = 2 + 2 + 2$, $7 = 3 + 2 + 2$, $8 = 3 + 3 + 2$, $9 = 3 + 3 + 3$, $10 = 5 + 3 + 2$.

What is the prime factorization of 138?

Steve thinks ...

138 is obviously even because it ends with 8.

69 is divisible by 3 because 6 + 9 = 15 is divisible by 3.

Hmm. ... The divisibility tests don't work for 23, so 23 is prime.

I'm done because 2, 3, and 23 are all prime.

The prime factorization for 138 is 2 × 3 × 23.

Tanisha thinks ...

I can use a factor tree to find the prime factorization.

I've circled all the prime numbers.

The ends of all the branches are circled, so I'm done.

Well, 2 × 3 × 23 is the prime factorization for 138.

What do you think?

1. What is the difference between Steve's and Tanisha's methods?

2. Why did both Steve and Tanisha stop when they found out 2, 3, and 23 are all prime?

3. How would you find the prime factorization for a number?

Check | **Your Understanding**

1. Which divisibility rules are similar? Explain.

2. How many prime numbers are there? Explain.

3. Describe how factor trees are related to the Fundamental Theorem of Arithmetic.

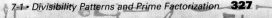

Point out that the prime factorization of a number is unique.

Answers for What Do You Think?

1. Steve uses divisibility rules and Tanisha uses a factor tree.

2. Prime factorization is writing a number as a product of primes.

3. Possible answer: Use a factor tree.

3 Practice and Assess

Check

Discuss using the divisibility rules to determine whether a large number, like 101, is prime:

- Have students use the divisibility rules to show that the first three primes, 2, 3, and 5, are not factors of 101. Then have them use a calculator to check that the next prime, 7, is also not a factor.

- Point out that the next possible prime factor would be 11. But since none of the prime numbers 2, 3, 5, and 7 are factors of 101, if 11 were a prime factor, there would have to be another prime factor equal to or greater than 11. This is not possible because their product would be greater than 101. So 101 must be prime.

- This line of reasoning suggests that to check if a number n is prime, it is necessary to test it for divisibility only by all primes less than or equal to $\sqrt{n}$.

As another example, consider 221:

- Since $\sqrt{221} = 14.87$, we need to test 221 for divisibility by 2, 3, 5, 7, 11, and 13.

- We would find that 2, 3, 5, 7, and 11 are not factors of 221, but 13 is a factor. So, 221 is not prime.

Answers for Check Your Understanding

1. Possible answers: 3 and 9; Use the sum of the digits. 2, 5, and 10; Check the ones digit.

2. Infinitely many; Possible answer: The number system is infinite.

3. Possible answer: A factor tree shows the prime factorization of a number.

Lesson 7-1 327

Assignment Guide

- **Basic**
  1–25, 31–34, 40, 42, 43, 45, 46, 50

- **Average**
  1–20, 24–26, 31–34, 39–41, 43, 45, 48–50

- **Enriched**
  1–20, 27–31, 35–41, 44, 45, 47, 50

Exercise Notes

■ **Exercises 29**

Error Prevention Watch for students who find it difficult to determine if 101 is a prime number.

■ **Exercises 33–35**

Error Prevention Some students may use exponents as factors. For example, they may evaluate 3^4 as 3×4. Have them write 3^4 as $3 \times 3 \times 3 \times 3$.

Exercise Answers

16–20. Prime factors are underlined.

16. 1, **2**, **5**, **7**, 10, 14, 35, 70

17. 1, **2**, 4, 8, **11**, 22, 44, 88

18. 1, **2**, **3**, 4, 6, 8, 12, 16, 24, 32, 48, 96

19. 1, **2**, 4, **5**, 10, 20, 25, 50, 100

20. 1, **2**, **3**, 6, **23**, 46, 69, 138

Reteaching

Activity

- Cut out 12 identical squares.

- How many different rectangles can you make with 12 squares? What are the dimensions of the rectangles? 3; 12×1, 6×2, 3×4

- How many different rectangles can you make with 7 squares? What are the dimensions of the rectangle? 1; 7×1

- Explain why you were able to make more rectangles with 12 squares than with 7 squares. Possible answer: 12 has 6 factors that can be paired to make three rectangles. Seven has only two factors, so only one rectangle can be made.

7-1 Exercises and Applications

Practice and Apply

Getting Started State whether each number is prime or composite.

1. 17 **P**   **2.** 28 **C**   **3.** 49 **C**   **4.** 42 **C**   **5.** 31 **P**

Determine whether each given number is divisible by 2, 3, 4, 5, 6, 8, 9, or 10.

6. 45 **3, 5, 9**   **7.** 63 **3, 9**   **8.** 79 **None**   **9.** 86 **2**   **10.** 102 **2, 3, 6**

11. 261 **3, 9**   **12.** 636 **2, 3, 4, 6**   **13.** 5354 **2**   **14.** 8004 **2, 3, 4, 6**   **15.** 4672 **2, 4, 8**

List all of the factors for each number and identify the prime factors.

16. 70   **17.** 88   **18.** 96   **19.** 100   **20.** 138

Use a factor tree to determine the prime factorization of each number. Express your answer using exponents.

21. 54 2×3^3 **22.** 80 $2^4 \times 5$ **23.** 128 2^7 **24.** 156 $2^2 \times 3 \times 13$ **25.** 220 $2^2 \times 5 \times 11$

26. 333 $3^2 \times 37$ **27.** 375 3×5^3 **28.** 480 $2^5 \times 3 \times 5$ **29.** 505 5×101 **30.** 1238 2×619

31. **Test Prep** Which of the following is the prime factorization of 42? **D**

Ⓐ 6×7 Ⓑ 2×21 Ⓒ 23×7 Ⓓ $2 \times 3 \times 7$

32. **Industry** A software company identifies its CD-ROMs with serial numbers. They use a six-digit code where the first five digits are divisible by the last digit. Are the following serial numbers from an imitation CD-ROM?

a. 34569-3 **No**   **b.** 88888-6 **Yes**

Algebra The equations below involve prime factorization. Solve for the variable in each equation.

33. $n = 3^4$
$n = 81$

34. $k = 2^3 \times 7$
$k = 56$

35. $w = 2 \times 5^4$
$w = 1250$

36. $g = 3 \times 5 \times 17$
$g = 255$

37. **Science** The Kamchatka Brown Bear lives in Russia. The male weighs up to 360 kilograms. Use a factor tree to find the prime factorization of 360. Express your answer using exponents. $2^3 \times 3^2 \times 5$

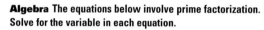

PRACTICE

Name _____

Practice 7-1

Divisibility Patterns and Prime Factorization

Determine whether each given number is divisible by 2, 3, 4, 5, 6, 8, 9, or 10.

1. 290 — 2, 5, 10
2. 420 — 2, 3, 4, 5, 6, 7, 10
3. 156 — 2, 3, 4, 6
4. 4547 — None
5. 3576 — 2, 3, 4, 6, 8
6. 8379 — 3, 9

List all of the factors for each number and identify the prime factors.

7. 110

Factors $\pm 1, \pm 2, \pm 5, \pm 10, \pm 11, \pm 22, \pm 55, \pm 110$

Prime factors: 2, 5, 11

8. 72

Factors $\pm 1, \pm 2, \pm 3, \pm 4, \pm 6, \pm 8, \pm 9, \pm 12, \pm 18, \pm 24, \pm 36, \pm 72$

Prime factors: 2, 3

Use a factor tree to determine the prime factorization of each number. Express your answer using exponents.

Possible factor trees:

9. 182 $2 \times 7 \times 13$ 10. 735 $3 \times 5 \times 7^2$ 11. 198 $2 \times 3^2 \times 11$

The equations below involve prime factorization. Solve for the variable in each equation.

12. $y = 2^5$ 13. $c = 11 \times 5^3$ 14. $k = 2^2 \times 5$ 15. $m = 2^4 \times 7$

$y = 32$ $c = 1375$ $k = 20$ $m = 112$

16. A *perfect number* is a whole number that is equal to the sum of its positive factors (excluding itself). For example, 6 is a perfect number because $6 = 1 + 2 + 3$. Find a perfect number between 20 and 30. ___28___

RETEACHING

Name _____

Alternative Lesson 7-1

Divisibility Patterns and Prime Factorization

A **prime number** is an integer greater than 1 that is only divisible by itself and 1. A **composite number** is a positive integer that is not prime. **Prime factorization** is the result of writing a number as a product of prime numbers. Divisibility rules can help to find prime factors.

A number is divisible by:

2 if the ones digit is 0, 2, 4, 6, or 8.
3 if the sum of its digits is divisible by 3.
4 if the last two digits form a number that is divisible by 4.
5 if the ones digit is 0 or 5.
6 if it is divisible by 2 and 3.
8 if the last three digits form a number that is divisible by 8.
9 if the sum of its digits is divisible by 9.
10 if the ones digit is 0.

— Example 1 —

Determine whether 945 is divisible by 2, 3, 4, 5, 6, 8, 9, or 10.

Review the divisibility rules.
945 is not divisible by 2, 4, 6, 8, or 10 because it is odd.
$9 + 4 + 5 = 18$, so 945 is divisible by 3 and by 9.
945 is divisible by 5 because the ones digit is 5.

945 is divisible by 3, 5, and 9.

Try It Determine whether each number is divisible by 2, 3, 4, 5, 6, 8, 9, or 10.

a. 504 2, 3, 4, 6, 8, 9   **b.** 930 2, 3, 5, 6, 10

— Example 2 —

Use a factor tree to find the prime factorization of 150.

Step 1: Draw branches for 150. Then factor 150.

Step 2: Circle all prime numbers. Circle 2. Then factor all composite numbers. Factor 75.

Step 3: Repeat step 2 until all factors are prime.

Step 4: Write 150 as a product of the prime numbers. $150 = 2 \times 5 \times 3 \times 5$

Step 5: Write in standard form. $150 = 2 \times 3 \times 5^2$

So, $2 \times 3 \times 5^2$ is the prime factorization of 150.

Try It Use a factor tree to find the prime factorization of 156.

c. 156 $2^2 \times 3 \times 13$

38. Science Every 17 years, cicadas emerge from dormancy in the Northeast and Midwest. This happened in Maryland in 1996. In what years will the next three outbreaks occur? **2013, 2030, 2047**

39. An eighth-grade class took care of 102 guppies and 136 mollies in the classroom aquarium. Each student took home an equal number of guppies and mollies. What is the greatest number of students there can be in the class? **34**

40. Logic Solve this puzzle: "The number is greater than 500 and less than 550. The number is odd and is a multiple of 9 and the ones digit is 1. What is the number?" **531**

41. History Marin Mersenne (1588–1648), a French mathematician, invented the Mersenne number $2^n - 1$. You can find Mersenne numbers by substituting integers for n. Prime numbers found using this formula are called Mersenne primes. Find two Mersenne primes.
Possible answers: $3 = 2^2 - 1$; $7 = 2^3 - 1$; $31 = 2^5 - 1$

Problem Solving and Reasoning

42. Communicate If you scramble the digits in a number that is divisible by 3, the number is still divisible by three. Does this work for numbers divisible by 2? By 4? By 5? By 8? By 9? Explain.

43. Math Reasoning A number is divisible by 12 if it is divisible by both 3 and 4. Find three multiples of 12 and explain why those numbers are divisible by 12 according to this rule.

44. Journal Devise a divisibility rule for 25. Show examples and explain why your rule works.

45. Test Prep The divisibility rule for 11 is this: Calculate the sum of every other digit. Calculate the sum of the other digits. Take the difference of the two sums. If the result is a multiple of 11, then the original number is a multiple of 11. Which of the following is a multiple of 11?

Ⓐ 3577   Ⓑ 4818   Ⓒ 7575   Ⓓ 111 **B**

Mixed Review

Find the slope of each line, given the coordinates A (0, 0), B (6, 3), C (−4, 5), D (−1, −2). *[Lesson 4-4]*

46. Line through A and B

47. Line through A and C

48. Line through C and D

49. Line through B and D

50. It takes a video editor 10 hours to edit 8 minutes of video. At this rate, how long would it take to edit 30 minutes of video? *[Lesson 5-6]*

42. Will only work for 9 since the divisibility rule for 3 and 9 use the sum of the digits. The other rules are dependent on the last digit(s).

43. Possible answers: 24, 36, 48, 600; The sum of the digits is divisible by 3 and the last two digits are divisible by 4.

44. Possible answer: The last two digits must be divisible by 25. Examples: 100, 275, 450. This works because 25, 50, 75, 100 are divisible by 25.

46. slope $= \frac{1}{2}$

47. slope $= -\frac{5}{4}$

48. slope $= -\frac{7}{3}$

49. slope $= \frac{5}{7}$

50. 37.5 hr or 37 hr and 30 min

Alternate Assessment

Performance Have students work in groups of three to write answers to these questions.

1. Explain how you use the divisibility rules to determine whether a number is divisible by 2, 3, 4, 5, 6, 7, 8, 9, or 10. When do you find these rules most helpful?

2. What is a factor tree? What are some guidelines that you use in making a factor tree?

3. Make up a secret message that requires the use of prime factorization in order to decode it.

▶ Quick Quiz

1. Which of these numbers is divisible by 4?
   a. 428   b. 892
   c. 1218   d. 5694 (a, b)

2. Which of these numbers are divisible by 3?
   a. 2115   b. 5112
   c. 5482   d. 255 (a, b, d)

3. For each number, find the prime factorization in standard form.
   a. 279 $3^2 \times 31$
   b. 1000 $2^3 \times 5^3$

Available on Daily Transparency 7-1

Name _____

Guided Problem Solving
7-1

GPS **PROBLEM 40, STUDENT PAGE 329**

Solve this puzzle: "The number is greater than 500 and less than 550. The number is odd and is a multiple of 9 and the ones digit is 1. What is the number?"

— Understand —
1. What numbers will the mystery number fall between? **500 and 550**
2. The mystery number is a multiple of which number? **9**
3. What is the ones digit in the mystery number? **1**

— Plan —
4. Let $x =$ the mystery number. Write an inequality that shows which numbers the mystery number falls between.
$500 < x < 550$
5. How can you use divisibility rules to determine if a number is a multiple of 9? **The sum of the digits is a number that can be divided by 9.**

— Solve —
6. List the numbers with a 1 in the ones place that would solve the inequality you wrote in Item 4.
501, 511, 521, 531, 541
7. Use divisibility rules to find which of the numbers in Item 6 is divisible by 9. **531**

— Look Back —
8. Why could you ignore the clue that the mystery number is odd? **Possible answer: Since the ones digit is 1, it is given that the mystery number is odd.**

SOLVE ANOTHER PROBLEM

Solve this puzzle: "The number is less than 475 but greater than 425. The number is a multiple of 3, 6, and 9 and the ones digit is 2. What is the number?" **432**

Name _____

Extend Your Thinking
7-1

Decision Making

Theresa schedules part-time employees at the library. Each person can work a four-hour shift, 3 or 4 times a week. The same number of part-time employees work each shift.

Four employees, Donna, Katrina, Elona, and Yuko, are only available on weekday evenings and Saturday afternoons. The remaining employees can work any shift.

Weekend shifts are Saturday from 9:00 A.M. to 1:00 P.M. and 1:00 P.M. to 5:00 P.M., and Sunday from 1:00 P.M. to 5:00 P.M.

Weekday shifts are Monday through Thursday from 1:00 P.M. to 5:00 P.M. and 5:00 P.M. to 9:00 P.M.

There are no part-time employees needed on Friday.

Complete a possible schedule for the part-time employees. Then find the number of hours worked by each employee.

Possible answer:

	Sun	Mon		Tue		Wed		Thur		Sat		Total
Name	1-5	1-5	5-9	1-5	5-9	1-5	5-9	1-5	5-9	9-1	1-5	hours worked
Donna		X		X		X						12
Katrina		X		X				X				12
Elona		X				X		X				12
Yuko				X		X		X		X		16
Aaron	X	X		X						X		16
Cary	X	X		X						X		16
Cody	X	X				X					X	16
Paco	X					X		X		X		16
Sam				X		X		X		X		16

Objective

- Find the GCF of two or more numbers.

Vocabulary

- Common factor, greatest common factor (GCF)

NCTM Standards

- 1–6, 8, 9

► Review

Write all the possible factors of each number.

1. 6   1, 2, 3, 6

2. 20   1, 2, 4, 5, 10, 20

Write the prime factorization of each number.

3. 52 $2^2 \times 13$

4. 324 $2^2 \times 3^4$

Available on Daily Transparency 7-2

► Lesson Link

Emphasize that the divisibility rules may be applied when trying to identify all the factors of a given number.

1 Introduce

Explore

The Point

Students gain an understanding of *common factor* and use prime factorization to find a common factor of two or more numbers.

Ongoing Assessment

Check that students select only the common factors in Step 3 and that they do not confuse products and factors as they work through each step.

7-2 Greatest Common Factors (GCF)

You'll Learn ...

■ to find the GCF of two or more numbers

... How It's Used

When carpenters and other craftspeople use fractions, they need the GCF.

Vocabulary

common factor

greatest common factor (GCF)

► **Lesson Link**   You have used divisibility rules to find prime factors of numbers. Now you will use these skills to find common factors between numbers. ◄

When two numbers have matching factors, they are called **common factors**.

Factors of 12 are 1, 2, 3, 4, 6, 12.   Factors of 16 are 1, 2, 4, 8, 16.

Common factors of 12 and 16 are 1, 2, and 4.

Explore   Greatest Common Factor

Birthday Connections

1. Write the month and the date of your birthday. Use a number for the month: January = 1, February = 2, and so on. Find the product of the month and date.

2. Find the prime factorization for this number.

3. List the factors that are common to every group member.

4. Multiply the common factors together.

5. Divide each of your group member's original products by this product. What happens?

Learn   Greatest Common Factors (GCF)

The **greatest common factor (GCF)** is the largest number of two or more numbers that is a common factor.

You can make a list of the common factors to find the GCF.

Factors of 12 are 1, 2, 3, 4, 6, 12.   Factors of 16 are 1, 2, 4, 8, 16.

The common factors are 1, 2, 4.

The greatest common factor of 12 and 16 is 4.

MEETING INDIVIDUAL NEEDS

Resources

7-2 Practice

7-2 Reteaching

7-2 Problem Solving

7-2 Enrichment

7-2 Daily Transparency

    Problem of the Day

    Review

    Quick Quiz

Teaching Tool Transparencies 2, 3

Chapter 7 Project Master

Learning Modalities

Verbal   Have students write a lesson on how to find the GCF of a number pair and present it to the class.

Kinesthetic   Have students list the factors of numbers as follows and circle common factors to find the GCF.

36: 1 2 3 4 6 9 12 18 36
54: 1 2 3 6 9 18 27 54

English Language Development

When discussing common factors, distinguish between the meaning of *common* as it is used in this section and its use as *ordinary*. Tell students that in this section *common* means that the factors are the same.

The *Multilingual Handbook*, with its glossary of math terms, illustrations, and worked-out examples, can help you with students who have limited English language skills. The glossary is provided in multiple languages.

Example 1

Find the GCF of 36 and 48.

1, 2, 3, 4, 6, 9, 12, 18, 36   List all the factors of 36.

1, 2, 3, 4, 6, 8, 12, 16, 24, 48   List all the factors of 48.

1, 2, 3, 4, 6, 12   List the common factors.

The GCF of 36 and 48 is 12.

Making a list to find the GCF for larger numbers can be impractical.

The GCF can also be found using prime factorization.

The GCF is found by multiplying together the smallest power of each common prime factor.

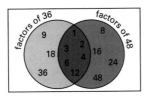

Example 2

Use prime factorization to find the GCF of 378 and 180.

Draw a factor tree for each number.

Write each prime factorization.

$378 = 3 \times 3 \times 2 \times 3 \times 7 = 2 \times 3^3 \times 7$

$180 = 2 \times 3 \times 3 \times 2 \times 5 = 2^2 \times 3^2 \times 5$

Identify the common prime factors.

2 and 3^2 are the smallest power of each common prime factor.

$2 \times 3^2 = 18$ Multiply the smallest power of each prime factor.

The GCF of 378 and 180 is 18.

Try It

Use prime factorization to find the GCF of each pair of numbers.

a. 72 and 138 **6**   **b.** 49 and 21 **7**   **c.** 276 and 136 **4**

You would use the same procedure of multiplying the smallest power of each common prime factor to find the GCF of more than two numbers.

Jarod's birthday is February 18 and Keisha's is April 27. What are the common prime factors of the products of their birth months and birthdays? $2^2 \times 3^2$

Follow Up
Have students share and explain any connections they find.

Answers for Explore
1–4. Answers may vary.

5. Possible answer: Every group members' product is divisible by the product of common factors.

2 Teach

Learn

Make sure students understand that two numbers may have several common factors but have only one greatest common factor.

Alternate Examples

1. Find the GCF of 24 and 40.

   The factors of 24 are 1, 2, 3, 4, 6, 8, 12, and 24. The factors of 40 are 1, 2, 4, 5, 8, 10, 20, and 40. The common factors are 1, 2, 4, and 8. The greatest common factor (GCF) is 8.

2. Use prime factorization to find the GCF of 120 and 216.

   Draw a factor tree for each number.

   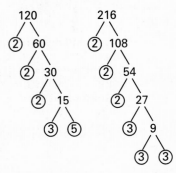

   The prime factorization of 120 is $2^3 \times 3 \times 5$. The prime factorization of 216 is $2^3 \times 3^3$. The common factors are $2^3 \times 3$. Multiply the common factors to find the GCF: $8 \times 3 = 24$.

MATH EVERY DAY

▶ Problem of the Day

Draw the next figure in this sequence.

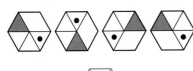

Available on Daily Transparency 7-2

An Extension is provided in the transparency package.

Fact of the Day

Perfect squares have an odd number of factors. For example, the factors of 36 are 1, 2, 3, 4, 6, 9, 12, 18, 36. All other whole numbers have an even number of factors.

Mental Math

Find each quotient mentally.

1. $72 \div 3$ 24

2. $52 \div 4$ 13

3. $87 \div 3$ 29

3. A bakery wants to package granola bars in boxes of three different quantities—24, 32, and 40 bars. The granola bars will also be packaged in plastic bags inside each box. In order to use the same size bags in each box and as few bags as possible, how many granola bars should there be per bag?

Find the GCF of 24, 32, and 40. Find the prime factorization for each number.

$24 = 2^3 \times 3$

$32 = 2^5$

$40 = 2^3 \times 5$

The common prime factor is 2^3.

The GCF is 2^3, or 8. So there should be 8 granola bars per bag.

4. Write $\frac{70}{84}$ in lowest terms.

$70 = 2 \times 5 \times 7$ and $84 = 2^2 \times 3 \times 7$

$2 \times 7 = 14$ is the GCF of 70 and 84.

$\frac{70 \div 14}{84 \div 14} = \frac{5}{6}$ is written in lowest terms.

3 Practice and Assess

Check

Be sure students understand that if the numerator and denominator of a fraction are both divided by their GCF, the resulting fraction is in lowest terms. You may also wish to discuss why the two fractions are equal.

Answers for Check Your Understanding

1. Possible answer: Find the prime factorization of each and multiply the smallest power of each common prime factor.

2. Both the numerator and the denominator are divided by their GCF.

Example 3

A juice company has a contest with twist-off caps. Each winner must provide the nine-digit code on the bottle. The winner is legitimate if the GCF of the code numbers is 28. Is 140-308-420 a winner?

Problem Solving TIP

If you're used to working with only two numbers and you're asked to work with three, the same technique will be effective.

Find the GCF of 140, 308, and 420.   Find the prime factorization for each number.

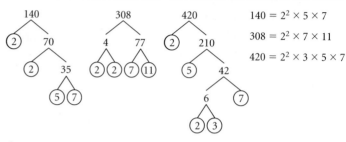

$140 = 2^2 \times 5 \times 7$

$308 = 2^2 \times 7 \times 11$

$420 = 2^2 \times 3 \times 5 \times 7$

$2^2 \times 7 = 28$ It's a winner because the GCF is 28.

The GCF is used when writing a fraction in lowest terms.

Example 4

Write $\frac{36}{42}$ in lowest terms.

$36 = 2^2 \times 3^2$ and $42 = 2 \times 3 \times 7$

$2 \times 3 = 6$ is the GCF of 36 and 42.

$\frac{36 \div 6}{42 \div 6} = \frac{6}{7}$ is written in lowest terms.

Try It

a. Find the GCF of 455, 230, and 160. **5**   b. Write $\frac{9}{12}$ in lowest terms. $\frac{3}{4}$

Check   Your Understanding

1. Explain how you would find the GCF of three numbers.

2. Explain how the GCF is used when writing a fraction in lowest terms.

MEETING MIDDLE SCHOOL CLASSROOM NEEDS

Team Teaching

Have the other teachers on your team suggest how the GCF may be used in their subject areas. For example, a music teacher might explain the role the GCF plays in producing closer harmony: The greater the GCF of the frequency of two musical notes, the closer the harmony. A, C, and C sharp have frequencies of 220, 264, and 275. Which pair of these notes has the closest harmony? A and C sharp

Cooperative Learning

For Exercises 39–42 on page 334, students might work in groups of two or three. Try to include students with different learning modalities in each group.

Social Science Connection

Have students solve the following problem: Brazil has the largest population in South America, about 150,000,000 people. The United States has the largest population in North America, about 260,000,000 people. What fraction of the United States population is Brazil's population? Write this fraction in lowest terms. $\frac{15}{26}$

7-2 Exercises and Applications

Practice and Apply

1. **Getting Started** Use the following steps to find the GCF of 27 and 45:
   a. List all the factors of 27. **1, 3, 9, 27**
   b. List all the factors of 45. **1, 3, 5, 9, 15, 45**
   c. List the common factors. **1, 3, 9**
   d. Identify the greatest common factor. **9**

Find the GCF of each group of numbers.

2. 12, 40 **4**   3. 8, 12 **4**   4. 9, 15 **3**   5. 28, 35 **7**   6. 6, 8, 14 **2**

7. 27, 63 **9**   8. 15, 90 **15**   9. 30, 60 **30**   10. 75, 100 **25**   11. 32, 56, 72 **8**

Use prime factorization to find the GCF of each group of numbers.

12. 75, 135 **15**   13. 56, 132 **4**   14. 33, 110 **11**   15. 70, 14 **14**   16. 34, 102 **34**

17. 20, 25, 50 **5**   18. 17, 31, 37 **1**   19. 24, 48, 60 **12**   20. 35, 45, 63 **1**   21. 18, 26, 72 **2**

Write each fraction in lowest terms.

22. $\frac{6}{8}$ **$\frac{3}{4}$**   23. $\frac{10}{25}$ **$\frac{2}{5}$**   24. $\frac{4}{12}$ **$\frac{1}{3}$**   25. $\frac{9}{36}$ **$\frac{1}{4}$**   26. $\frac{30}{40}$ **$\frac{3}{4}$**

27. $\frac{45}{50}$ **$\frac{9}{10}$**   28. $\frac{24}{36}$ **$\frac{2}{3}$**   29. $\frac{34}{51}$ **$\frac{2}{3}$**   30. $\frac{250}{300}$ **$\frac{5}{6}$**   31. $\frac{66}{121}$ **$\frac{6}{11}$**

32. Find a pair of numbers that has a GCF of 42. **42 and any of its multiples: 84, 126, 168...**

33. **Geography** An airline is having a contest: If your three-digit area code and 20 have a GCF ≥ 4, you can enter the drawing for round-trip tickets to anywhere in the United States. Which area codes in Texas qualify? **210, 512, 915, 972**

34. The following message is based on a code that uses ordered pairs. If the GCF = 1 the pair stands for A. If the GCF = 2 the pair stands for B. The pattern continues until the GCF = 26 = Z. Decipher this message: (9, 6) (16, 24) (15, 10) (6, 39) (22, 121)! **CHECK!**

35. **Algebra** Two numbers have a greatest common factor of $x(x^2 + 2x + 1)$. Substitute $x = 2$ to find the greatest common factor. Write the greatest common factor using prime factorization. **$18 = 2 \times 3^2$**

Assignment Guide

■ **Basic**
1–10, 12–18, 22–31, 34, 36–38, 40, 45–48

■ **Average**
3–21, 26–31, 34–38, 41, 45–48

■ **Enriched**
3–21, 26–33, 35–38, 46–48

Exercise Notes

■ **Exercise 32**

Error Prevention Watch for students who multiply 42 by any two numbers, not realizing that the two numbers cannot have common factors.

■ **Exercise 35**

Extension Another way to write $x(x^2 + 2x + 1)$ is $x(x+1)^2$. So, if $x = 2$, then $x(x + 1)^2 = 2 \cdot 3^2$.

Reteaching

Activity

Materials: $2\frac{1}{2}$" × 3" note cards or 3" × 5" index cards cut in half, 2 colored pencils (for example, red and blue)

• Work in pairs to make a GCF challenge for your classmates.

• Pick two numbers between 100 and 200 to factor into their prime factors. Make a factor tree for each number. Write each number in the tree on a card. Use one color for the first tree and the other color for the second tree.

• Use the prime numbers to find the GCF for your two original numbers. Circle the primes written on the cards that make the GCF *for each* original number. Collect all of your cards and shuffle them.

• Exchange cards with another group. See if you can recreate the factor trees and find the GCF.

PRACTICE

Practice 7-2

Greatest Common Factors (GCF)

Find the GCF of each group of numbers.

1. 16, 40 _**8**_   2. 9, 12 _**3**_   3. 40, 112 _**8**_

4. 42, 48 _**6**_   5. 154, 147 _**7**_   6. 35, 54 _**1**_

7. 49, 91, 168 _**7**_   8. 90, 50, 10 _**10**_   9. 16, 72, 104 _**8**_

Use prime factorization to find the GCF of each group of numbers.

10. $125 = $ _**5^3**_
    $440 = $ _**$2^3 \times 5 \times 11$**_
    GCF = _**5**_

11. $24 = $ _**$2^3 \times 3$**_
    $60 = $ _**$2^2 \times 3 \times 5$**_
    GCF = _**12**_

12. $120 = $ _**$2^3 \times 3 \times 5$**_
    $165 = $ _**$3 \times 5 \times 11$**_
    GCF = _**15**_

13. $156 = $ _**$2^2 \times 3 \times 13$**_
    $54 = $ _**2×3^3**_
    GCF = _**6**_

14. $100 = $ _**$2^2 \times 5^2$**_
    $84 = $ _**$2^2 \times 3 \times 7$**_
    GCF = _**4**_

15. $90 = $ _**$2 \times 3^2 \times 5$**_
    $72 = $ _**$2^3 \times 3^2$**_
    GCF = _**18**_

16. $216 = $ _**$2^3 \times 3^3$**_
    $144 = $ _**$2^4 \times 3^2$**_
    $180 = $ _**$2^2 \times 3^2 \times 5$**_
    GCF = _**36**_

17. $132 = $ _**$2^2 \times 3 \times 11$**_
    $60 = $ _**$2^2 \times 3 \times 5$**_
    $252 = $ _**$2^2 \times 3^2 \times 7$**_
    GCF = _**12**_

18. $96 = $ _**$2^5 \times 3$**_
    $90 = $ _**$2 \times 3^2 \times 5$**_
    $175 = $ _**$5^2 \times 7$**_
    GCF = _**1**_

Write each fraction in lowest terms.

19. $\frac{19}{38}$ _**$\frac{1}{2}$**_   20. $\frac{58}{64}$ _**$\frac{29}{32}$**_   21. $\frac{68}{114}$ _**$\frac{34}{57}$**_   22. $\frac{10}{120}$ _**$\frac{1}{12}$**_

23. $\frac{14}{18}$ _**$\frac{7}{9}$**_   24. $\frac{85}{90}$ _**$\frac{17}{18}$**_   25. $\frac{20}{196}$ _**$\frac{5}{49}$**_   26. $\frac{112}{175}$ _**$\frac{16}{25}$**_

27. $\frac{28}{62}$ _**$\frac{14}{31}$**_   28. $\frac{42}{61}$ _**$\frac{42}{61}$**_   29. $\frac{76}{236}$ _**$\frac{19}{59}$**_   30. $\frac{56}{100}$ _**$\frac{14}{25}$**_

31. The number of students in Mrs. Folsom's art classes are 28, 36, and 32. She wants to divide each class into groups for a class project. If all of the groups are to be the same size, what is the largest group size that will work? _**4**_

RETEACHING

Alternative Lesson 7-2

Greatest Common Factors (GCF)

The **greatest common factor (GCF)** is the largest number of two or more numbers that is a common factor. When you write a fraction in lowest terms, you find the GCF of the numerator and the denominator.

— Example 1 —

Use prime factorization to find the GCF of 63 and 84.

Step 1: Draw a factor tree for each number.

Step 2: Write each prime factorization.
$63 = 3 \times 3 \times 7 = 3^2 \times 7$
$84 = 2 \times 2 \times 3 \times 7 = 2^2 \times 3 \times 7$

Step 3: Identify the common prime numbers. Use the *smallest* power of each common prime factor. **3 and 7**

Step 4: Multiply the common factors. **$3 \times 7 = 21$**

The GCF of 63 and 84 is 21.

Try It Use prime factorization to find the GCF of 124 and 56.
a. Make a factor tree for each number. **124   56**
b. What is the smallest power of each of the common factors? **2^2**
c. Simplify. What is the GCF? **2^2 or 4**

— Example 2 —

Write $\frac{24}{42}$ in lowest terms.

Step 1: Find the prime factorization.
$24 = 2 \times 2 \times 2 \times 3 = 2^3 \times 3$
$42 = 2 \times 3 \times 7 = 2 \times 3 \times 7$

Step 2: Identify the common prime numbers. Use the *smallest* power of each common prime factor.

Step 3: Multiply the common factors to find the GCF. **$2 \times 3 = 6$**

Step 4: Divide the numerator and denominator by the GCF. **$\frac{24 \div 6}{42 \div 6} = \frac{4}{7}$**

In lowest terms, $\frac{24}{42} = \frac{4}{7}$.

Try It Write each fraction in lowest terms by finding the GCF.

d. $\frac{28}{63}$ GCF _**7**_ Fraction _**$\frac{4}{9}$**_   e. $\frac{40}{64}$ GCF _**8**_ Fraction _**$\frac{5}{8}$**_

■ Exercise 39

Error Prevention Watch for students who think relatively prime numbers must be prime numbers. Point out that neither 12 nor 35 is a prime number, but they are relatively prime because their GCF is 1.

■ Exercise 40

Problem-Solving Tip You may wish to use Teaching Tool Transparencies 2 and 3: Guided Problem Solving, pages 1–2.

A good strategy for this problem would be to work backwards. When the number is paired with 25, not the number, but 25 is the GCF. So the number must be a multiple of 25. The only multiples of 25 between 25 and 100 are 50 and 75. But 75 and 99 are not relatively prime. When 50 is paired with 100, 50 is the GCF. So 50 is the solution.

Project Progress

You may want to have students use Chapter 7 Project Master.

Exercise Answers

39. Possible answers: 4 and 7; 15 and 16; 9 and 20.

41. 1; Yes; The GCF is 1 for any pair of prime numbers.

42. Possible answer: A 5-by-15 rectangle.

43–47. See page C1.

48. 1.5 cm

Alternate Assessment

Interview You may wish to meet with small groups of students and audio or video record their answers to these questions.

- How would you find the GCF of two or more numbers?

- Can the GCF be used to solve any problems? Give an example.

▶ Quick Quiz

1. Find the GCF of each group of numbers.
   a. 48, 84 12
   b. 28, 56, 70 14

2. Write each fraction in lowest terms.

   a. $\dfrac{30}{42}$ $\dfrac{5}{7}$ b. $\dfrac{45}{75}$ $\dfrac{3}{5}$

Available on Daily Transparency 7-2

---

334 Chapter 7

---

36. **Science** Dr. Pascal studies the effects of light sources on house plants. The number of plants in each class are 24, 30, 36, and 42. He wants to subdivide the classes into groups of the same size for the research project. What is the largest group size that will work in all four classes? **Groups of 6**

37. **Test Prep** Which pair of numbers does not have 4 as a common factor? **A**

    Ⓐ 12, 14   Ⓑ 24, 36   Ⓒ 40, 60   Ⓓ 36, 44

38. The first two numbers in Lucia's lock combination are 12 and 16 and the last number in her combination is the GCF of 12 and 16. What is Lucia's combination? **12-16-4**

Problem Solving and Reasoning

39. **Critical Thinking** Two numbers that have a GCF of 1 are said to be *relatively prime*. The numbers may be prime or composite. Find three pairs of relative primes.

40. **Choose a Strategy** I am a number less than 100. I am relatively prime with 99. If I am paired with 100, I am our GCF. If I am paired with 25, 25 is the GCF and not me. What number am I? **50**

41. **Communicate** Select two prime numbers. What is their GCF? Will any pair of prime numbers have the same GCF? Explain.

42. **Geometry** Draw a rectangle that has sides with lengths that have a GCF of 5, and that has a perimeter that is a multiple of 4.

Problem Solving

STRATEGIES

- Look for a Pattern
- Make an Organized List
- Make a Table
- Guess and Check
- Work Backward
- Use Logical Reasoning
- Draw a Diagram
- Solve a Simpler Problem

Mixed Review

Graph each equation. Find the slope, the *x*-intercept, and the *y*-intercept for each of the following. *[Lesson 4-5]*

43. $y = 2x - 4$ 44. $y = x - 9$ 45. $y = -3x + 8$ 46. $y = \frac{1}{3}x + 6$ 47. $y = -7x$

48. An eye in a photograph is 13.5 cm long and is labeled "enlarged 9 times." What is the actual length of the eye? *[Lesson 5-7]*

Project Progress

Think about how you use your knowledge of factors, multiples, and divisibility to decide how many shares of a stock to buy.

Problem Solving

Understand
Plan
Solve
Look Back

---

334 *Chapter 7 • Number Sense, Rational Numbers, and Irrational Numbers*

▷ PROBLEM SOLVING

Name _____

Guided Problem Solving 7-2

GPS PROBLEM 36, STUDENT PAGE 334

Dr. Pascal studies the effects of light sources on house plants. The number of plants in each class are 24, 30, 36, and 42. He wants to subdivide the classes into groups of the same size for the research project. What is the largest group size that will work in all four classes?

— Understand —

1. Circle the number of plants in each of the four classes.

2. Are the groups to be the same size or different sizes? **Same size.**

— Plan —

3. How can finding the GCF of the class sizes help you find the group size? **Possible answer: It gives the greatest number that can be evenly divided into all the class sizes.**

4. Make a factor tree for the number of plants in each class. **Possible answer:**

— Solve —

5. What are the common factors for all four numbers? **2 and 3**

6. What is the largest group size for the four classes? **6 plants.**

— Look Back —

7. What is another way to find the GCF of a group of numbers? **Possible answer: Make a list of the multiples of each class size.**

SOLVE ANOTHER PROBLEM

In another study, the number of plants in each class are 32, 40, 48, and 64. Dr. Pascal wants to subdivide the classes into groups of the same size. What is the largest group size that will work in all four classes? **8 plants.**

▷ ENRICHMENT

Name _____

Extend Your Thinking 7-2

Critical Thinking

The set of factors for an integer is all the numbers that can be evenly divided into the integer. The **proper factors** of an integer include all these numbers *except* the integer itself.

For example, the set of factors for 12 are 1, 2, 3, 4, 6, and 12. The proper factors are 1, 2, 3, 4, and 6.

A positive integer is *perfect* if the sum of its proper factors is equal to the integer itself. It is *abundant* if the sum is greater than the integer and *deficient* if the sum is less than the integer.

To see if 12 is a perfect, abundant, or deficient number, add its proper factors: 1 + 2 + 3 + 4 + 6 = 16. Then compare the sum and the integer. Since 16 is greater than 12, 12 is an abundant number.

Complete the table to identify perfect, abundant, and deficient integers. **Possible answers: Items 10, 11, 12**

	Integer	Proper Factors	Sum	Type of Integer
1.	6	1, 2, 3	6	Perfect
2.	15	1, 3, 5,	9	Deficient
3.	16	1, 2, 4, 8	15	Deficient
4.	17	1	1	Deficient
5.	18	1, 2, 3, 6, 9	21	Abundant
6.	19	1	1	Deficient
7.	20	1, 2, 4, 5, 10	22	Abundant
8.	21	1, 3, 7	11	Deficient
9.	22	1, 2, 11	14	Deficient

10. Write a perfect number greater than 22. **28 = 1 + 2 + 4 + 7 + 14**

11. Write an abundant number greater than 22. **24**

12. Write a deficient number greater than 22. **23**

13. Write 24 as the sum of two abundant numbers. **12 + 12**

14. There are exactly two ways to write 36 as the sum of two abundant numbers. Write both ways. **12 + 24; 18 + 18**

Least Common Multiples (LCM)

▶ Lesson Link You applied your knowledge of factors to finding the greatest common factor. Now you will apply your knowledge of multiples to find the least common multiple. ◀

When two numbers have some multiples that are the same, these multiples are called **common multiples** .

Multiples of 3 are 3, 6, 9, 12, 15, 18, 21, 24, …

Multiples of 4 are 4, 8, 12, 16, 20, 24, 28, …

Common multiples of 3 and 4 are 12, 24, …

You'll Learn …
- to find the LCM of two or more numbers

… How It's Used

Architects and others who use rational numbers need the LCM when performing operations such as addition and subtraction.

Vocabulary

common multiple

least common multiple (LCM)

Explore | Common Multiples

Numbers Zip Something in Common

Everyone must remember numbers: phone numbers, zip codes, area codes, birthdates, ages, addresses, and so on.

1. What numbers do your group members have in common?

2. Find the first four multiples of your street address. Compare your results with your group. Are there any common multiples?

3. Does your zip code pass a divisibility rule? Which one(s)? If your zip code is prime, then explain why you think so and go to Step 5.

4. Name a number that is a factor of your zip code. Find a number that is a multiple of that factor and that is closest to your zip code, but is not your zip code.

5. Find two multiples of your zip code. Discuss how you did it.

Learn | Least Common Multiples (LCM)

The **least common multiple (LCM)** is the smallest non-zero common multiple.

You can make a list of the common multiples to find the LCM.

▷ MEETING INDIVIDUAL NEEDS

Resources

7-3 Practice

7-3 Reteaching

7-3 Problem Solving

7-3 Enrichment

7-3 Daily Transparency
    Problem of the Day
    Review
    Quick Quiz

Teaching Tool Transparencies 2, 3

Learning Modalities

Kinesthetic Have students write the first twelve multiples of 3 and 5 on index cards, arrange the cards in two adjacent rows, from the least to greatest, and identify the LCM of the two numbers.

Social Have students work in pairs to write and solve real-life problems where it is necessary to add fractions. For example, they might write: If $\frac{1}{5}$ of the class wears glasses and $\frac{1}{8}$ of the class wears contact lenses, what fraction of the class uses corrective eyewear?

Challenge

Challenge students to solve the following problem. A car manufacturer has two factories. At one factory there are 8 assembly lines and at the other there are only 6. If each factory must produce the same number of cars in a day, what would be the least number of cars produced at each factory in a day? 24

Objective

- **Find the LCM of two or more numbers.**

Vocabulary

- **Common multiple, least common multiple (LCM)**

NCTM Standards

- **1–6, 8, 9, 12**

➤ Review

Beginning with the number itself write the first five multiples of each number.

1. **6** 6, 12, 18, 24, 30

2. **8** 8, 16, 24, 32, 40

Write the prime factorization of each number.

3. **44** $2^2 \times 11$

4. **350** $2 \times 5^2 \times 7$

Available on Daily Transparency 7-3

▶ Lesson Link

Remind students that they used the GCF when writing fractions in lowest terms. In this lesson, students will use the LCM to add fractions that have different denominators.

1 Introduce

Explore

The Point
Students gain an understanding of *multiple* and learn how it is different from a factor.

Ongoing Assessment
Check that students are able to find the common multiples in Step 2.

Explain why two numbers cannot have a greatest common multiple. Possible answer: The multiples of the LCM go on forever, and each of these numbers is a common multiple of the original two numbers.

Follow Up

Have students suppose they tested the divisibility of their zip code using all of the rules of divisibility, but their zip code was not divisible by any of these numbers. Ask them how they can be sure that the number is prime. Test all prime numbers less than or equal to the square root of the zip code number.

Answers for Explore

1–5. Answers may vary.

2 Teach

Learn

To stress the meanings of *common* and *multiple*, write the first seven multiples of 6 and 8 on the chalkboard. Ask students to explain how the two sets of multiples were produced and to identify the common multiples. What is the least common multiple?

Alternate Examples

1. Lorraine earns $4 for every ceramic coaster set she makes and $5 for every ceramic vase she makes. Find the least common multiple of 4 and 5.

   List several multiples of 4 and several multiples of 5.

   4, 8, 12, 16, 20, 24, 28, 32, 36, 40

   5, 10, 15, 20, 25, 30, 35, 40, 45

   The common multiples are 20 and 40. The LCM is 20.

2. Use prime factorization to find the LCM of 42 and 63.

   Draw a factor tree for each number and circle all prime factors.

   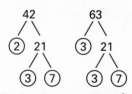

   $42 = 2 \times 3 \times 7$ $63 = 3^2 \times 7$

   The prime factors are 2, 3, and 7. The highest power of each is 2, 3^2, and 7.

   $2 \times 3^2 \times 7 = 2 \times 9 \times 7 = 126$

   The LCM of 42 and 63 is 126.

Example 1

Paul will water his yard every 3 days and mow the lawn every 7 days. When is the first day he will do both?

Find the least common multiple of 3 and 7.

3, 6, 9, 12, 15, 18, 21, 24, 27, 30, 33, 36, 39, 42, 45, … List multiples of 3.

7, 14, 21, 28, 35, 42, 49, 56, 63, 70, 77, 84, 91, 98, 105, … List multiples of 7.

21, 42, … List the common multiples.

The first day he will do both is the 21st.

Making a list to find the LCM for larger numbers can be impractical.

The LCM can also be found using prime factorization. The LCM is found by multiplying the highest power of each prime factor.

Example 2

Use prime factorization to find the LCM of 30 and 45.

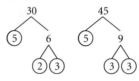

Draw a factor tree for each number.

Circle all of the prime factors.

$30 = 2 \times 3 \times 5$ Find the prime factorization for each number.

$45 = 3^2 \times 5$

2, 3^2, and 5   Identify the highest power of each prime factor.

$2 \times 3^2 \times 5 = 2 \times 9 \times 5 = 90$ Multiply.

The LCM of 30 and 45 is 90.

Try It

Use prime factorization to find the LCM of the following pairs of numbers.

a. 6 and 5 **30** **b.** 49 and 21 **147** **c.** 276 and 136 **9384**

You would use the same procedure to find the LCM of more than two numbers.

336   Chapter 7 • Number Sense, Rational Numbers, and Irrational Numbers

---

MATH EVERY DAY

▶ Problem of the Day

Your bank is changing its service fees. It used to cost $0.15 for each check written and a monthly service fee of $4. The new fees are $0.10 for each check written and a monthly service fee of $6. The bank says that if you write a lot of checks, the new fees will save you money. How many checks must you write each month before you save money? More than 40 checks

Available on Daily Transparency 7-3

An Extension is provided in the transparency package.

Fact of the Day

Between 1979 and 1999, Neptune was the most distant planet from the sun. But from 1999 until 2227 Pluto will regain that position because its orbit is highly elliptical.

Estimation

Estimate the percent of each number.

1. 11% of 39 4

2. 5% of 210 10

3. 15% of 300 45

Example 3

Cara bought an answering machine with a feature to check messages when she's not at home, but Cara needs a code. For the code, she wants to use the LCM of the numbers in her birthday 6/24/86. What's Cara's code?

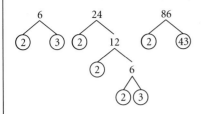

Find the prime factorization.

$6 = 2 \times 3$

$24 = 2^3 \times 3$

$86 = 2 \times 43$

$2^3 \times 3 \times 43 = 1032$ Multiply.

Cara's answering machine code is 1032.

The least common denominator (LCD) is a least common multiple (LCM).

Example 4

Write $\frac{1}{6}$ and $\frac{5}{8}$ using their LCD.

You need to find the LCM of 6 and 8.

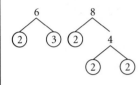

Determine the prime factorization.

$6 = 2 \times 3$

$8 = 2^3$

$2^3 \times 3 = 8 \times 3 = 24$ Multiply.

$\frac{1 \times 4}{6 \times 4} = \frac{4}{24}$ $\frac{5 \times 3}{8 \times 3} = \frac{15}{24}$

$\frac{1}{6} = \frac{4}{24}$ and $\frac{5}{8} = \frac{15}{24}$

Try It

Write each pair of fractions using its LCD.

a. $\frac{2}{7}$ and $\frac{2}{3}$ **b.** $\frac{7}{12}$ and $\frac{5}{16}$ a. $\frac{6}{21}$ and $\frac{14}{21}$ b. $\frac{28}{48}$ and $\frac{15}{48}$

Check **Your Understanding**

1. Explain how you would find the LCM of three numbers.

2. Explain how the LCM is used to find the LCD.

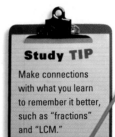

Study TIP

Make connections with what you learn to remember it better, such as "fractions" and "LCM."

Alternate Examples

3. Steve needs a PIN (personal identification number) to call home when he's at camp. The PIN is the LCM of the numbers in his birthday 8/18/87. What is Steve's PIN?

Find the prime factorizations of 8, 18, and 87.

$8 = 2^3$ $18 = 2 \times 3^2$
$87 = 3 \times 29$

Multiply the highest power of each factor.

$2^3 \times 3^2 \times 29 = 2088$

Steve's pin number for calling home is 2088.

4. Write $\frac{1}{12}$ and $\frac{2}{15}$ using their least common denominator.

First find the LCM of 12 and 15. Determine the prime factorization of each number.

$12 = 2^2 \times 3$ $15 = 3 \times 5$

Identify the highest power of each prime factor. Multiply the highest powers.

$2^2 \times 3 \times 5 = 4 \times 3 \times 5 = 60$

60 is the LCD.

$\frac{1 \times 5}{12 \times 5} = \frac{5}{60}$ $\frac{2 \times 4}{15 \times 4} = \frac{8}{60}$

$\frac{1}{12} = \frac{5}{60}$ and $\frac{2}{15} = \frac{8}{60}$

3 Practice and Assess

Check

Be sure students understand the relationship between the LCM and the LCD. The LCD of two or more fractions is the LCM of the denominators of those fractions. Finding the LCD is one of the uses of the LCM.

Answers for Check Your Understanding

1. Find the prime factorization of each and multiply the highest power of each common prime factor.

2. The least common denominator is the LCM of the denominators.

MEETING MIDDLE SCHOOL CLASSROOM NEEDS

Tips from Middle School Teachers

I provide my students with groups of fractions (for example, $\frac{5}{8}, \frac{2}{5}, \frac{3}{4}$) that I want them to write in lowest terms. I head this list with the following instructions: Write each group of fractions in order, from the least to the greatest. In order to do this, they have to find the least common denominator (LCD).

Industry Connection

The LCM is used to solve problems in many industries. For example, finding the number of revolutions of interlocking gears involves finding the LCM. Scheduling production and personnel can also involve using the LCM.

Cultural Connection

A positive integer can be classified according to the sum of its factors. For an *abundant* number this sum is greater than the number, for a *deficient* number, this sum is less than the number, and for a *perfect* number this sum is equal to the number. A nun named Hrotsvitha, who lived in Saxony in the 10th century, was a noted playwright, and many of her plays exhibited her interest in mathematics. For example, in one play a woman is asked the ages of her three daughters. The woman replies that their ages are a defective (deficient) even number, a defective odd number, and an abundant number.

Assignment Guide

■ **Basic**
1–16, 20–34 evens, 35, 40, 41, 44–52 evens

■ **Average**
6–14, 17–19, 22, 23–35 odds, 36–58 evens

■ **Enriched**
7–14, 20–22, 23–31 odds, 33–39, 42, 43, 45–57 odds

Exercise Notes

■ **Exercise 22**

Error Prevention Watch for students who have difficulty finding the prime factors of 365 and 687. These two numbers are relatively prime. $365 = 5 \times 73$ and $687 = 3 \times 229$, where 73 and 229 are prime numbers.

Exercise Answers

1. a. 8, 16, 24, 32, 40, 48, 56, 64, 72, 80
   b. 12, 24, 36, 48, 60, 72, 84, 96, 108, 120

33. Every 90 days.

7-3 Exercises and Applications

PRACTICE 7-3

Practice and Apply

1. **Getting Started** Use the following steps to find the LCM of 8 and 12.
   a. List the first ten multiples of 8.
   b. List the first ten multiples of 12.
   c. List the common multiples. **24, 48, 72**
   d. Identify the least common multiple. **24**

Find the LCM for each pair of numbers.

2. 12, 20 **60**   3. 8, 20 **40**   4. 4, 25 **100**   5. 15, 20 **60**   6. 25, 50 **50**

7. 36, 48 **144**   8. 10, 80 **80**   9. 60, 30 **60**   10. 42, 12 **84**   11. 7, 12 **84**

Use prime factorization to find the LCM for each group of numbers.

12. 14, 52 **364**   13. 22, 8 **88**   14. 13, 11 **143**   15. 24, 62 **744**   16. 47, 32 **1504**

17. 3, 4, 15 **60**   18. 6, 8, 36 **72**   19. 14, 56, 125 **7000**   20. 12, 20, 42 **420** 21. 24, 13, 11 **3432**

22. **Science** Suppose Earth and Mars were aligned with the sun. Earth completes its orbit in 365 days and Mars completes its orbit in 687 days (orbits rounded to the nearest Earth day). When do both planets return to these same positions in their orbits? **250,755 days or 687 years**

Rewrite each group of fractions with the LCD.

23. $\frac{2}{3}$ and $\frac{1}{6}$ **$\frac{4}{6}, \frac{1}{6}$**   24. $\frac{3}{5}$ and $\frac{2}{15}$ 25. $\frac{3}{8}$ and $\frac{3}{4}$ **$\frac{3}{8}, \frac{6}{8}$**

26. $\frac{1}{2}$ and $\frac{1}{8}$ **$\frac{4}{8}, \frac{1}{8}$**   27. $\frac{5}{9}$ and $\frac{5}{12}$ 28. $\frac{8}{15}$ and $\frac{7}{30}$ **$\frac{16}{30}, \frac{7}{30}$**

29. $\frac{3}{4}, \frac{2}{3}$, and $\frac{7}{10}$ 30. $\frac{1}{8}, \frac{4}{7}$, and $\frac{7}{12}$ 31. $\frac{1}{9}, \frac{4}{14}$, and $\frac{5}{12}$ 32. $\frac{4}{11}, \frac{5}{7}$, and $\frac{7}{12}$

24. $\frac{9}{15}, \frac{2}{15}$

27. $\frac{20}{36}, \frac{15}{36}$

29. $\frac{45}{60}, \frac{40}{60}, \frac{42}{60}$

30. $\frac{21}{168}, \frac{96}{168}, \frac{9}{...}$

31. $\frac{28}{252}, \frac{72}{252}, \frac{1...}{2...}$

32. $\frac{336}{924}, \frac{660}{924}, \frac{5...}{9...}$

33. **Industry** A city recycling program picks up different plastics on different days. Use the codes for plastic containers shown at the right to determine when it picks up all plastics on one day.

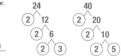

RECYCLING PICK UP
- PETE: Every 5 days
- HDPE: Every 9 days
- V: Every 6 days

34. **Algebra** Two numbers have a least common multiple of $k^3 + 4k$. Substitute $k = 2$ to find the least common multiple. Write the least common multiple using prime factorization. **$16 = 2^4$**

Reteaching

Activity

Materials: Yardstick, chalk

- Work in groups of three. Solve the following problem by marking off appropriate measurements on a wall.

- Boxes 24 inches tall are being stacked next to boxes 36 inches tall. What is the shortest height at which the two stacks will be the same height? **72 inches**

- What is the LCM of 24 and 36? **72**

PRACTICE

Name _____

Practice 7-3

Least Common Multiples (LCM)

Find the LCM for each pair of numbers.

1. 16, 12 **48**   2. 12, 8 **24**   3. 8, 3 **24**   4. 20, 45 **180**

5. 27, 15 **135**   6. 34, 18 **306**   7. 12, 15 **60**   8. 6, 75 **150**

9. 64, 20 **320**   10. 12, 6 **12**   11. 28, 8 **56**   12. 36, 24 **72**

Use prime factorization to find the LCM for each group of numbers.

13. 45 = **$3^2 \times 5$**   14. 22 = **2×11**   15. 39 = **3×13**
    50 = **2×5^2**   26 = **2×13**   36 = **$2^2 \times 3^2$**
    LCM = **450**   LCM = **286**   LCM = **468**

16. 24 = **$2^3 \times 3$**   17. 30 = **$2 \times 3 \times 5$**   18. 80 = **$2^4 \times 5$**
    20 = **$2^2 \times 5$**   18 = **2×3^2**   105 = **$3 \times 5 \times 7$**
    LCM = **120**   LCM = **90**   LCM = **1680**

19. 20 = **$2^2 \times 5$**   20. 33 = **3×11**   21. 60 = **$2^2 \times 3 \times 5$**
    15 = **3×5**   18 = **2×3^2**   56 = **$2^3 \times 7$**
    35 = **5×7**   12 = **$2^2 \times 3$**   35 = **5×7**
    LCM = **420**   LCM = **396**   LCM = **840**

Rewrite each group of fractions with the LCD.

22. $\frac{1}{3}$ and $\frac{7}{12}$ **$\frac{4}{12}, \frac{7}{12}$**   23. $\frac{7}{10}$ and $\frac{2}{15}$ **$\frac{21}{30}, \frac{4}{30}$**

24. $\frac{2}{3}, \frac{3}{5}$, and $\frac{5}{7}$ **$\frac{70}{105}, \frac{63}{105}, \frac{75}{105}$**   25. $\frac{5}{12}, \frac{5}{9}$, and $\frac{1}{16}$ **$\frac{60}{144}, \frac{64}{144}, \frac{45}{144}$**

26. A carousel has two rows of plastic ponies going at different speeds. Ralph is riding a pony that goes around every 135 seconds, and Lucy is riding a pony that goes around every 150 seconds. If Ralph and Lucy start on the east side of the carousel at the same time, how soon will they again meet on the east side of the carousel?
After 1350 seconds (22.5 minutes)

RETEACHING

Name _____

Alternative Lesson 7-3

Least Common Multiples (LCM)

When two numbers have multiples that are the same, these multiples are called **common multiples**. The **least common multiple (LCM)** is the smallest number that is a common multiple. You can find the LCM of a pair of numbers by finding the prime factorization of each number. You can find the LCM of the denominators to help you write two or more fractions using the least common denominator (LCD).

— Example 1 —

Find the LCM of 12 and 56.

Step 1: Make a factor tree for each number.
Step 2: Circle all the prime factors.
Step 3: Write each prime factorization.
   $12 = 2 \times 2 \times 3 = 2^2 \times 3$
   $56 = 2 \times 2 \times 2 \times 7 = 2^3 \times 7$
Step 4: Identify the *highest* power of each prime factor. 2^3, 3, and 7
Step 5: Multiply. $2^3 \times 3 \times 7 = 2 \times 2 \times 2 \times 3 \times 7 = 168$
The LCM of 12 and 56 is 168.

Try It Use prime factorization to find the LCM of 24 and 40. **Possible answer:**
a. Make a factor tree for each number.
b. What is the highest power of each prime factor? **2^3, 3, and 5**
c. Multiply. What is the LCM? **120**

— Example 2 —

Write $\frac{1}{18}$ and $\frac{7}{20}$ with the LCD.

Step 1: Find the LCM of the denominators. Use prime factorization. The LCM is 180, so the LCD is also 180.

Step 2: Rewrite each fraction with the LCD. $\frac{1}{18} = \frac{10}{180}$ and $\frac{7}{20} = \frac{63}{180}$

Try It Write each pair of fractions with the LCD.
d. $\frac{5}{12}$ and $\frac{7}{30}$ **$\frac{5}{12} = \frac{25}{60}, \frac{7}{30} = \frac{14}{60}$**   e. $\frac{9}{16}$ and $\frac{5}{36}$ **$\frac{9}{16} = \frac{81}{144}, \frac{5}{36} = \frac{20}{144}$**

35. **Test Prep** Mia sees a movie every 4 weeks, takes piano lessons every week, visits her cousins every 9 weeks, and meets with her book club every 3 weeks. When will Mia do all four of these things in the same week? **A**

Ⓐ Every 36 weeks Ⓑ Every 12 weeks

Ⓒ Every 27 weeks Ⓓ None of the above

Problem Solving TIP

When events occur at regular intervals, use the LCM to find out when they all occur at once.

Problem Solving and Reasoning

36. **Choose a Strategy** In order to break a code, you need to identify all the pairs of numbers that have an LCM of 40. Find two of these pairs of numbers. **Possible answers: 8 and 5; 20 and 8; 8 and 10**

37. **Critical Thinking** Instead of using prime factorization, how would you determine the LCM of two numbers that do not have any factors in common? **Multiply the two numbers; their product is the LCM.**

38. **Geometry** Determine the measurements and draw a rectangle such that the width and length are divisible by 2 and have an LCM of 30.

39. **Communicate** Since the year 1401, homophonic substitutions have been found in codes. These codes use several numbers to represent one letter. For example, A = 1, 8, 15; B = 2, 9, 16; and so on. Decode this message and describe how you could use multiples to develop a code similar to this one. **Help now.**

8,15,22; 5,12,19; 12,19,26;
16,23,30

14,21,28; 15,22,29; 23,30,37

Problem Solving STRATEGIES

• Look for a Pattern
• Make an Organized List
• Make a Table
• Guess and Check
• Work Backward
• Use Logical Reasoning
• Draw a Diagram
• Solve a Simpler Problem

Mixed Review

Solve each system of equations by graphing. *[Lesson 4-6]*

40. $y = 5x - 3$ **41.** $y = -x + 5$ **42.** $y = \frac{3}{4}x + 2$ **43.** $y = -\frac{1}{4}x$

$y = -3x$ $y = -2x + 2$ $y = -x - 5$ $y = -\frac{1}{2}x + 1$

$\left(\frac{3}{8}, -1\frac{1}{8}\right)$ $(-3, 8)$ $(-4, -1)$ $(4, -1)$

Express each number as a percent. *[Lesson 6-1]*

44. 3.7   **45.** 1.76   **46.** 2.02   **47.** 0.005   **48.** 2.004
    370%   176%   202%   0.5%   200.4%

49. 3.2   **50.** 2.064   **51.** 0.003   **52.** $1\frac{1}{2}$ **53.** $6\frac{2}{5}$
    320%   206.4%   0.3%   150%   640%

54. $\frac{1}{320}$ **55.** $2\frac{3}{4}$ **56.** $6\frac{1}{3}$ **57.** $\frac{1}{500}$ **58.** $4\frac{4}{6}$
    0.3125%   275%   633.3%   0.2%   466.6%

Name _____

Guided Problem Solving 7-3

GPS PROBLEM 22, STUDENT PAGE 338

Suppose Earth and Mars were aligned with the sun. Earth completes its orbit in 365 days and Mars completes its orbit in 687 days (orbits rounded to the nearest Earth day). When do both planets return to these same positions in their orbits?

— Understand —

1. How many days does it take the Earth to complete an orbit? **365 days.**

2. How many days does it take Mars to complete an orbit? **687 days.**

— Plan —

3. How can finding the LCM of the days it takes each planet to make one orbit around the sun help you find the number of days until the planets are aligned again? **Possible answer: It gives the smallest number of complete orbits for each planet to return to the original positions.**

4. Make a factor tree for each number.   365   687

— Solve —

5. What are the prime factors of 365 and 687? **3, 5, 73, and 229**

6. What is the highest power of each prime factor? **3, 5, 73, and 229**

7. When will the planets return to these same positions in their orbits? **250,755 days = 687 years.**

— Look Back —

8. Why should you express your answer in years? **Possible answer: Because it is easier to understand.**

SOLVE ANOTHER PROBLEM

Suppose Earth and Venus were aligned with the sun. Earth completes its orbit in 365 days and Venus its in 225 days (orbits rounded to the nearest Earth day). How many days until the planets are aligned again? **16,425 days = 45 years.**

Name _____

Extend Your Thinking 7-3

Critical Thinking

For some of the following problems, you need to find the GCF and for the other problems you need to find the LCM. Tell which you used and write an equation for each problem to show how you found your answer.

1. Andy decided to divide a book of sports cards into smaller books. Unfortunately, he found that there was always one card left over if he divided the cards 5 ways, 6 ways, 8 ways, or 12 ways. What is the smallest number of cards that the book could have contained? **LCM: $(2^3 \times 3 \times 5) + 1 = 121$; 121 cards**

2. The integers 3, 4, 5, 6, 7, 8, and 9 are all factors of this number. What is the smallest number possible? **LCM: $2^3 \times 3^2 \times 5 \times 7 = 2520$**

3. Find two integers whose product is 10 million. Neither integer contains any zeros. **LCM: $2^7 \times 5^7 = 10,000,000$ or $128 \times 78,125 = 10,000,000$**

4. A rectangular piece of fabric has a length of 350 in. and a width of 294 in. To make a quilted wall hanging, congruent square patches will be sewn to cover the entire rectangle. What is the largest square patch that could be made to make the wall hanging? **GCF: $2 \times 7 = 14$; 14-inch squares**

5. Some classes listen for a single bell to change class periods. Other classes listen for a double bell to change class periods. The single bell rings every 35 minutes and the double bell rings every 63 minutes. If both bells first ring at 8:30 A.M., at what time will they ring at the same time again? **LCM: $5 \times 7 \times 9 = 315$; $315 \div 60 = 5.25$; 1:45 P.M.**

6. Three runners run the same direction around a track. They all begin at the same time. One runner takes 25 seconds to run one lap, another takes 35 seconds, and the third takes 45 seconds. How many minutes will it take for them to all be side-by-side? **LCM: $5^2 \times 7 \times 9 = 1575$; $1575 \div 60 = 26.25$; 26.25 minutes**

Exercise Notes

■ Exercise 35

Test Prep Students who chose D may not realize that the wording of the problem requires us to assume that all four activities started in the same week.

■ Exercise 36

Problem-Solving Tip You may wish to use Teaching Tool Transparencies 2 and 3: Guided Problem Solving, pages 1–2.

A good strategy for solving this problem is to first solve a simpler related problem. For example, first solve for 6, instead of 40.

Exercise Answers

38. Possible answer: A 10-by-6 rectangle.

Alternate Assessment

Self Assessment Have students write a paragraph about how well they understand finding the least common multiple of two or three numbers. Suggest that they point out any steps that are confusing.

► **Quick Quiz**

Find the LCM for each group of numbers.

1. 15, 25 75

2. 12, 15, 20 60

Find the LCD for each group of fractions.

3. $\frac{1}{4}, \frac{3}{8}$ 8

4. $\frac{1}{2}, \frac{5}{6}, \frac{4}{15}$ 30

Available on Daily Transparency 7–3

Technology

Using a Spreadsheet • GCF and LCM

The Point
Students use spreadsheets to find the relationship between the product of the GCF and the LCM of a set of numbers.

Materials
Spreadsheet software

Resources

*Interactive CD-ROM
Spreadsheet/Grapher Tool*

About the Page

If students have not used spreadsheets before:

- Point out the columns, rows, and cells.

- Identify cell locations by column letter and row number.

- Discuss formulas and how they are typed into cells.

Ask …
- What does the formula in cell E2 represent? The product of A2 and B2 or 12 × 18.

- What does this formula do? Puts the product of 12 and 18 in cell E2.

- What does the formula in cell F2 represent? The product of C2 and D2, or 6 × 36.

- What does this formula do? Puts the product of 6 and 36 in cell F2.

Try It
Have student experiment further by repeating the process with two prime numbers. Does the rule hold? Have students discuss what they notice. Yes, the rule holds. In the case of using two prime numbers, the GCF is always 1 and the LCM is always the product of the two numbers.

Answers for Try It
a. 20,496

b. 864

On Your Own
Remind students that spreadsheets are used as a tool in mathematics, but do not replace the necessity of understanding the mathematics involved in the activity.

340

TECHNOLOGY

Using a Spreadsheet • GCF and LCM

Problem: What is the product of GCF (12, 18) and LCM (12, 18)?

A spreadsheet can help answer this question.

1 Label your spreadsheet columns as shown.

3 Enter their GCF and LCM in columns C and D, respectively.

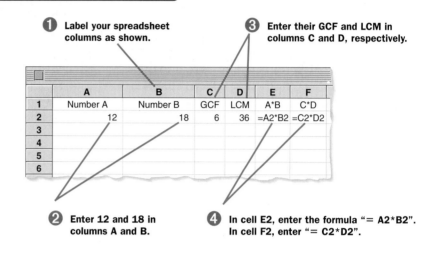

	A	B	C	D	E	F
1	Number A	Number B	GCF	LCM	A*B	C*D
2	12	18	6	36	=A2*B2	=C2*D2
3						
4						
5						
6						

2 Enter 12 and 18 in columns A and B.

4 In cell E2, enter the formula "= A2*B2". In cell F2, enter "= C2*D2".

Solution: GCF (12, 18) × LCM (12, 18) = 12 × 18 = 216.

TRY IT

a. Find the GCF and the LCM of 84 and 244. What is the product of the GCF and the LCM?

b. Repeat the process for 24 and 36.

ON YOUR OWN

▶ How does a spreadsheet help compute LCM × GCF?

▶ Describe how a spreadsheet can show $\frac{12 \times 18}{\text{LCM (12, 18)}} =$ GCF (12, 18).

▶ Describe how a spreadsheet can show a relationship between the LCM and the GCF of three numbers.

340

Answers for On Your Own
- Possible answer: It multiplies the numbers for you.

- Possible answer: Enter = E1/D1 in column G and then compare entries in G1 and C1.

- Possible answer: Add another column for the third number and change the formulas to include it.

Section 7A Connect

You've used prime and composite numbers to find the LCM and GCF. Now use primes and composites to make a code based on the bar graph below.

Curing the Common Code

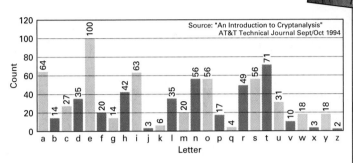

Source: "An Introduction to Cryptanalysis"
AT&T Technical Journal Sept/Oct 1994

By looking at the bar graph, you can determine the letters that occur most and least often in English.

Use the bar graph and the directions below to create a code.

It will work best when you use a number only once.

1. Identify all letters with a frequency less than or equal to 20 ($F \leq 20$). Represent each of them with a prime number.

2. Identify all letters with a frequency greater than 20 and less than or equal to 50 ($20 < F \leq 50$). Represent each of them with a number divisible by 6.

3. Identify all letters with a frequency greater than 50 ($F > 50$). Invent a method to represent each of these letters.

4. Create a way to determine the end of a message.

5. Write a message with your code. (This is called encoding.)

6. Exchange messages with a group member and decode them.

7. Discuss how you could make another code.

341

Curing the Common Code

The Point
In *Curing the Common Code* on page 323, students learned how codes have been used throughout history for various purposes. Now they will use prime and composite numbers to formulate a code.

Resources
Lesson Enhancement
Transparency 27

About the Page

- Point out that it is best to use a number only once.

- You may want to review how to read the bar graph.

- When students exchange their messages with a group member, have each student make suggestions for possible improvements to the code they are decoding. Then have each student review their own code and make any necessary changes.

- Discuss students' answers to Question 7. Be sure to discuss the similarities and differences among students' ideas for codes.

Ongoing Assessment
Check that students have followed the directions and have created a workable code.

Extension

Have students research and report on additional codes that use mathematical or logical concepts. One such example is the Rivest-Shamir-Adleman (RSA) cryptoalgorithm, which is based on a pair of very large prime numbers and depends on the fact that it is virtually impossible to factor extremely large integers.

Answers for Connect
1–7. Answers may vary.

Review Correlation

Item(s)	Lesson(s)
1–10	7-1
11–14	7-2, 7-3
15–19	7-2
20–24	7-3
25	7-1
26	7-2
27	7-3

Test Prep

Test-Taking Tip

Tell students that on multiple-choice tests they should examine the questions carefully to find unnecessary information. Only the useful information should be used to determine the correct choice.

Answers for Review

25. No. Possible answer: Use the divisibility rule for the last digit.

26. Possible answer: No, because an odd number is not divisible by an even number.

Section 7A Review

REVIEW 7A

Use divisibility rules. State whether the given number is divisible by 2, 3, 4, 5, 6, 8, 9, or 10. Indicate when the number is prime.

1. 342
2, 3, 6, 9

2. 622 2

3. 1280
2, 4, 5, 8, 10

4. 618
2, 3, 6

5. 93,509,188 2, 4

Find the prime factorization of each number.

6. 48
$2^4 \times 3$

7. 475
$5^2 \times 19$

8. 120
$2^3 \times 3 \times 5$

9. 144
$2^4 \times 3^2$

10. 3750 $2 \times 3 \times 5^4$

Find the GCF and the LCM of each group of numbers.

11. 4, 9

12. 12, 15

13. 15, 24

14. 24, 60, 120

11. GCF, 1; LCM, 36

12. GCF, 3; LCM, 60

13. GCF, 3; LCM, 120

14. GCF, 12; LCM, 120

Write each fraction in lowest terms.

15. $\frac{9}{15}$ $\frac{3}{5}$ **16.** $\frac{21}{56}$ $\frac{3}{8}$ **17.** $\frac{15}{35}$ $\frac{3}{7}$ **18.** $\frac{64}{80}$ $\frac{4}{5}$ **19.** $\frac{24}{36}$ $\frac{2}{3}$

Find the LCD for each group of fractions.

20. $\frac{4}{5}$ and $\frac{2}{3}$ 15 **21.** $\frac{1}{4}$ and $\frac{5}{12}$ 12 **22.** $\frac{1}{3}$ and $\frac{7}{9}$ 9 **23.** $\frac{5}{8}$ and $\frac{11}{12}$ 24 **24.** $\frac{2}{5}$, $\frac{9}{10}$, and $\frac{3}{4}$ 20

25. **Journal** If the first part of this credit card number is not divisible by the last digit, the credit card is a fake. Is the credit card number fake? Describe how to determine this.

26. Communicate Do you think the GCF of an odd and an even number can ever be even? Explain your answer.

ACME STORE CARD 3711G085236-6

Test Prep

Some multiple-choice questions include unnecessary information. You need to read them carefully to determine the useful information.

27. Suppose Cara stayed at school every Monday until 4:30 P.M. for the spirit squad, every other Wednesday until 5:00 P.M. to meet with the math club, and every third Thursday until 4:45 P.M. to study. How often would she stay late at school for three days in the same week ? **A**

Ⓐ Every sixth week　　Ⓑ Every week

Ⓒ Every second week　　Ⓓ Every fourth week

Resources

Practice Masters
　Section 7A Review

Assessment Sourcebook
　Quiz 7A

　TestWorks
　Test and Practice Software

PRACTICE

Name _____

Practice

Section 7A Review

Use divisibility rules. State whether the given number is divisible by 2, 3, 4, 5, 6, 8, 9, or 10. Indicate when the number is prime.

1. 1792 ___2, 4, 8___ 2. 2748 ___2, 3, 4, 6___ 3. 1492 ___2, 4___

4. 1947 ___3___ 5. 331 ___Prime___ 6. 4494 ___2, 3, 6___

Find the prime factorization of each number.

7. 150 $2 \times 3 \times 5^2$ 8. 360 $2^3 \times 3^2 \times 5$ 9. 96 ___$2^5 \times 3$___

10. 168 $2^3 \times 3 \times 7$ 11. 555 $3 \times 5 \times 37$ 12. 378 $2 \times 3^3 \times 7$

Find the GCF and the LCM of each group of numbers.

13. 20, 6　　14. 15, 2　　15. 28, 36　　16. 15, 25, 40

GCF: ___2___　GCF: ___1___　GCF: ___4___　GCF: ___5___

LCM: ___60___　LCM: ___30___　LCM: ___252___　LCM: ___600___

Write each fraction in lowest terms.

17. $\frac{28}{140}$ ___$\frac{1}{5}$___ 18. $\frac{25}{45}$ ___$\frac{5}{9}$___ 19. $\frac{320}{380}$ ___$\frac{16}{19}$___ 20. $\frac{54}{126}$ ___$\frac{3}{7}$___

Find the LCD for each group of fractions.

21. $\frac{5}{6}$ and $\frac{17}{18}$ ___18___ 22. $\frac{9}{10}$ and $\frac{4}{25}$ ___50___ 23. $\frac{3}{16}$, $\frac{7}{20}$, and $\frac{11}{24}$ ___240___

24. Do you think the LCM of an odd and even number is always even? Explain your answer.

___Possible answer: Yes, because the multiples of an even___

___number are always even.___

25. The Thrifty Copy Shop charges $0.10 per copy, plus a service charge of $0.50 for the entire order. Use *x* for the number of copies made, and graph the price paid. *[Lesson 4-3]*

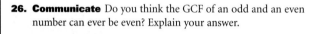

26. The population of Glendale, Arizona, increased from about 97,000 in 1980 to 148,000 in 1990. Find the percent increase. *[Lesson 6-4]*　___About 52.6%___

Section 7B

Rational Numbers

Visit **www.teacher.mathsurf.com** for links to lesson plans from teachers and other professionals, NCTM information, and other sites.

LESSON PLANNING GUIDE

▶ **Student Edition**　　　　　　　　　　　　　　　　　　　　　　▶ **Ancillaries***

LESSON		MATERIALS	VOCABULARY	DAILY	OTHER
	Section 7B Opener				Teaching Tool Trans. 20
7-4	Defining Rational Numbers	2 sheets of paper per student	rational numbers, terminating decimal, repeating decimal	7-4	Technology Master 27 Ch. 7 Project Master
7-5	Add and Subtract Rational Numbers			7-5	Lesson Enhancement Trans. 28 Technology Master 28
7-6	Multiply and Divide Rational Numbers	calculator	reciprocal	7-6	Teaching Tool Trans. 2, 3 Technology Master 29 *Interactive CD-ROM Lesson*
	Connect	calculator			Teaching Tool Trans. 24 Interdisc. Team Teaching 7B
	Review				Practice 7B; Quiz 7B; *TestWorks*

* Daily Ancillaries include Practice, Reteaching, Problem Solving, Enrichment, and Daily Transparency. Teaching Tool Transparencies are in *Teacher's Toolkits*. Lesson Enhancement Transparencies are in *Overhead Transparency Package*.

SKILLS TRACE

LESSON	SKILL	FIRST INTRODUCED			DEVELOP	PRACTICE/ APPLY	REVIEW
		GR. 6	GR. 7	GR. 8			
7-4	Comparing/ordering rational numbers.	✗			pp. 344–347	pp. 348–349	pp. 362, 383, 400, 583
7-5	Adding/subtracting rational numbers.	✗			pp. 350–352	pp. 353–354	pp. 406, 415, 439, 589
7-6	Multiplying/dividing rational numbers.	✗			pp. 355–358	pp. 359–360	pp. 383, 420, 559, 599

CONNECTED MATHEMATICS

The unit *Looking for Pythagoras (The Pythagorean Theorem),* from the **Connected Mathematics** series, can be used with Section 7B.

Math and Social Studies
(Worksheet pages 27–28: Teacher pages T27–T28)

In this lesson, students use fractions, decimals, and percent to compare the Great Lakes.

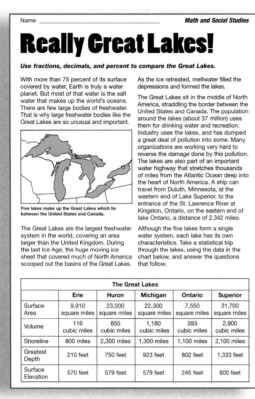

Name _____   *Math and Social Studies*

Really Great Lakes!

Use fractions, decimals, and percent to compare the Great Lakes.

With more than 75 percent of its surface covered by water, Earth is truly a water planet. But most of that water is the salt water that makes up the world's oceans. There are few large bodies of freshwater. That is why large freshwater bodies like the Great Lakes are so unusual and important.

Five lakes make up the Great Lakes which lie between the United States and Canada.

The Great Lakes are the largest freshwater system in the world, covering an area larger than the United Kingdom. During the last Ice Age, the huge moving ice sheet that covered much of North America scooped out the basins of the Great Lakes.

As the ice retreated, meltwater filled the depressions and formed the lakes.

The Great Lakes sit in the middle of North America, straddling the border between the United States and Canada. The population around the lakes (about 37 million) uses them for drinking water and recreation. Industry uses the lakes, and has dumped a great deal of pollution into some. Many organizations are working very hard to reverse the damage done by this pollution. The lakes are also part of an important water highway that stretches thousands of miles from the Atlantic Ocean deep into the heart of North America. A ship can travel from Duluth, Minnesota, at the western end of Lake Superior, to the entrance of the St. Lawrence River at Kingston, Ontario, on the eastern end of lake Ontario, a distance of 2,342 miles.

Although the five lakes form a single water system, each lake has its own characteristics. Take a statistical trip through the lakes, using the data in the chart below, and answer the questions that follow.

The Great Lakes					
	Erie	**Huron**	**Michigan**	**Ontario**	**Superior**
Surface Area	9,910 square miles	23,000 square miles	22,300 square miles	7,550 square miles	31,700 square miles
Volume	116 cubic miles	850 cubic miles	1,180 cubic miles	393 cubic miles	2,900 cubic miles
Shoreline	800 miles	2,300 miles	1,300 miles	1,100 miles	2,100 miles
Greatest Depth	210 feet	750 feet	923 feet	802 feet	1,333 feet
Surface Elevation	570 feet	579 feet	579 feet	245 feet	600 feet

Name _____   *Math and Social Studies*

1. The world has about 27,000 cubic miles of standing freshwater. Write a fraction that expresses the portion of the world's freshwater contained in the Great Lakes (rounded to the nearest hundred). Write the fraction in lowest terms. Then express that number as a percent.

$$\frac{5,400}{27,000} = \frac{1}{5} = 20\%$$

2. Why would the information you discovered in item 1 qualify the Great Lakes as an important resource?

See below.

3. Which lake is the largest? Set up a fraction that expresses the percentage of the total surface area of the Great Lakes covered by this largest lake. Use your calculator to express this number as a decimal (rounded to the nearest hundredth). Then express this decimal as a percent.

Lake Superior. The fraction would be: $\frac{31,700}{94,460} = .3355917...$
$\approx .34 = 34\%$.

4. Gravity makes water flow downhill. The water in the Great Lakes flows downhill from one lake to the next according to the elevations of the lake surfaces. Based only on "Surface Elevation" in the chart, predict where the flow of water through the Great Lakes begins and where it ends before moving into the river that carries the water to the sea.

See below.

5. Where is the greatest change in elevation from one lake surface to the next? What might the landscape in this area look like?

See below.

6. There are at least 4,500 known hazardous waste sites around the Great Lakes. If the sites are proportionally distributed around the shores of the lakes according to the fraction of the total shoreline each lake has, how many sites would be on Lake Ontario? Show how you arrived at your answer.

Add the length of shoreline for all of the lakes, which is 7,600 miles. Lake Ontario's portion of the total shoreline is expressed by this fraction and decimal:

$$\frac{1,100}{7,600} = .1447368... \approx .14$$
$$.14 \times 4,500 = 630 \text{ sites}$$

7. What danger might these sites represent for nearby populations?

Responses could include contamination of drinking water and fish species living in the lakes.

Answers

2. Standing freshwater is rare, but it has many uses, including drinking water. Such a large concentration of freshwater is an important resource deserving protection.

4. The flow starts in Lake Superior, which has the highest surface elevation. It ends in Lake Ontario, which has the lowest surface elevation.

5. Between Erie and Ontario, where there is a drop of 325 feet. The drop in elevation (over a relatively short area according to the map) indicates there would be rapids or a waterfall. In fact, the rapids of the Niagara River and Niagara Falls are located between Erie and Ontario.

BIBLIOGRAPHY

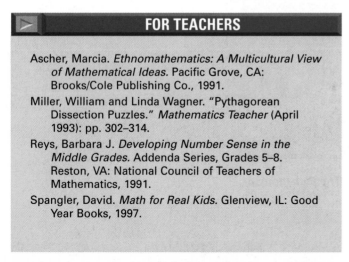

▷ FOR TEACHERS

Ascher, Marcia. *Ethnomathematics: A Multicultural View of Mathematical Ideas.* Pacific Grove, CA: Brooks/Cole Publishing Co., 1991.

Miller, William and Linda Wagner. "Pythagorean Dissection Puzzles." *Mathematics Teacher* (April 1993): pp. 302–314.

Reys, Barbara J. *Developing Number Sense in the Middle Grades.* Addenda Series, Grades 5–8. Reston, VA: National Council of Teachers of Mathematics, 1991.

Spangler, David. *Math for Real Kids.* Glenview, IL: Good Year Books, 1997.

▷ FOR STUDENTS

Cleary, Beverly. *Dear Mr. Henshaw.* New York, NY: William Morrow & Co., 1993.

Cossi, Olga. *Water Wars.* New York, NY: New Discovery Books (Macmillan Publishing Company), 1993.

Hoff, Mary and Rodgers, Mary M. *Our Endangered Planet: Groundwater.* Minneapolis, Minn.: Lerner Publications Company, 1991.

Sauvain, Philip. *The Way It Works: Water.* New York, NY: New Discovery Books (Macmillan Publishing Company), 1992.

SECTION 7B

Rational Numbers

▶ **Geography Link** ▶ **Consumer Link** ▶ **www.mathsurf.com/8/ch7/water**

Will There Be A Drop To Drink?

"Water, water everywhere, and all the boards did shrink. Water, water everywhere, nor any drop to drink."

—Samuel Taylor Coleridge, *The Rime of the Ancient Mariner* (1772–1834)

When the poet wrote these lines, he was talking about sailors adrift in a sea of salt water.

Although about $\frac{37}{50}$ of Earth's surface is water, only about 3% of all Earth's water is fresh water. Approximately $\frac{4}{5}$ of all Earth's fresh water is locked in glacial ice. Of the remaining fresh water, only about 5% is available as surface water in streams and lakes. Most fresh water is underground.

As the human population increases, more fresh water is needed to grow food and for people to drink. Like the sailors in Coleridge's poem, we may be surrounded by water but lacking in fresh water to drink.

Your body is about 70% water. Compare this to $\frac{37}{50}$.

If the earth warms, how would it affect water?

Do you think there was more fresh water in the poet Coleridge's lifetime? Explain.

343

Where are we now?

In Section 7A, students used divisibility and patterns to learn more about numbers. They learned how to

- use patterns and rules to determine multiples and divisibility.
- find the greatest common factor of numbers.
- find the least common multiple of numbers.

Where are we going?

In Section 7B, students will

- use the LCM and GCF to work with rational numbers.
- add and subtract rational numbers.
- multiply and divide rational numbers.

Theme: Water

World Wide Web

If your class has access to the World Wide Web, you might want to use the information found at the Web site address given. The interdisciplinary links relate to topics discussed in this section.

Resources
Teaching Tool Transparency 20: Map of the World

About the Page

This page introduces the theme of the section, water, and uses rational numbers to describe amounts of water on the Earth's surface.

Ask ...

- How do you use water on a daily basis?

- How important do you think water is to the survival of Earth's inhabitants, including people? Possible answer: Without water, neither Earth nor its inhabitants would exist.

Extensions

The following activities do not require access to the World Wide Web.

Geography

Emphasize that approximately $\frac{4}{5}$ of all Earth's freshwater is locked in glacial ice. Have students do research to find what would happen if this ice would melt.

Consumer

Discuss the different sources of water that are available today and why many people drink bottled water instead of tap water.

Answers for Questions

1. Possible answer: 70% < $\frac{37}{50}$, which is 74%.

2. Possible answer: Glacial ice could melt, resulting in more fresh water and flooding.

3. Answers may vary.

Connect

On page 361, students will use rational numbers to determine how water is used by various countries in the world.

Objective

- **Compare and order rational numbers.**

Vocabulary

- **Rational numbers, terminating decimal, repeating decimal**

Materials

- **Explore: 2 sheets of paper per student**

NCTM Standards

- **1, 2, 4–6, 9**

► Review

Replace each ● with <, >, or = to compare each pair of numbers.

1. 1216 ● 1206   >
2. 57,831 ● 57,899   <
3. 0.120 ● 0.0125   >
4. 1.06 ● 1.30   <
5. 3 ● –5   >
6. – 9 ● –11   >

Available on Daily Transparency 7-4

► Lesson Link

Discuss rational numbers with the class. Have students name situations where rational numbers are used in everyday life.

1 Introduce

Explore

The Point
Students make and use paper models to compare fractions.

Ongoing Assessment
Check that students fold the sheets of paper correctly in Steps 1 and 2 and that they label the creases correctly in Steps 1 and 3.

7-4 Defining Rational Numbers

You'll Learn …

■ to compare and order rational numbers

… How It's Used

Quiltmakers use rational numbers every day in order to make precise measurements and to fit patterns together.

Vocabulary

rational numbers

terminating decimal

repeating decimal

▶ **Lesson Link**   You have seen how the LCM and GCF are used when working with fractions. Now you will apply these rational numbers. ◄

Explore | Fractions

Crease Please

Materials: 2 sheets of paper per student

1. Fold one sheet of paper in half three times. Unfold and label each crease $\frac{1}{8}, \frac{2}{8}, \frac{3}{8}, \frac{4}{8}, \frac{5}{8}, \frac{6}{8}, \frac{7}{8}, \frac{8}{8}$.

2. Fold a different sheet of paper into thirds twice.

3. Label each crease from left to right, using $\frac{1}{9}, \frac{2}{9}, \frac{3}{9}, \frac{4}{9}, \frac{5}{9}, \frac{6}{9}, \frac{7}{9}, \frac{8}{9}, \frac{9}{9}$.

4. On each sheet of paper, write all fractions in lowest terms.

5. Use the folded paper to find which number in each pair is greater.

   a. $\frac{1}{8}$, $\frac{1}{9}$ b. $\frac{7}{8}$, $\frac{8}{9}$ c. $\frac{1}{4}$, $\frac{2}{9}$ d. $\frac{3}{8}$, $\frac{1}{3}$ e. $\frac{1}{2}$, $\frac{5}{9}$

6. Compare answers with your group. How would you determine the greater number without the creased papers?

7. Discuss how you would use the LCM to compare the numbers.

Learn | Defining Rational Numbers

Rational numbers are numbers that can be written as a ratio of two integers, and the denominator is not zero. Integers, fractions, and many decimals are rational numbers.

Integers	Fractions	Decimals
$-17 = \frac{-17}{1}$ and $4 = \frac{4}{1}$	$\frac{3}{2}$ and $-4\frac{3}{5} = \frac{-23}{5}$	$-0.75 = \frac{-3}{4}$ and $6.7 = \frac{67}{10}$

344   Chapter 7 • Number Sense, Rational Numbers, and Irrational Numbers

---

► MEETING INDIVIDUAL NEEDS

Resources

7-4 Practice
7-4 Reteaching
7-4 Problem Solving
7-4 Enrichment
7-4 Daily Transparency
   Problem of the Day
   Review
   Quick Quiz
Technology Master 27
Chapter 7 Project Master

Learning Modalities

Visual   Have students use 10 × 10 grids to help them change fractions to decimals.

Kinesthetic   Use counters or play money to compare decimals and fractions.

Social   In **Explore**, partners work together in comparing the size of the fractions.

English Language Development

Write the words *terminating* and *repeating* on the board. Explain that *terminating* means "ending" and *repeating* means "occurring over and over again." Then illustrate both words using terminating and repeating decimals.

Example 1

Compare $\frac{5}{9}$ and $\frac{7}{12}$.

$\frac{5}{9}\ \square\ \frac{7}{12}$

$\frac{20}{36} < \frac{21}{36}$ Write the fractions with a common denominator and compare the numerators.

$\frac{5}{9} < \frac{7}{12}$ Write the original fractions.

Example 2

Water has different freezing points at different altitudes. List the freezing points in increasing order.

Altitude (ft)	−1100	1030	0 (sea level)	−1120	1200
Freezing Point (°C)	−1.1	1.03	0	−1.12	1.2

−1.1   1.03   0   −1.12   1.2
  ↓   ↓   ↓   ↓   ↓
−1.10   1.03 0.00 −1.12 1.20   Write with same number of decimal places.

−1.12 −1.10 0.00 1.03 1.20   Write the numbers in increasing order.

A **terminating decimal** has a fixed number of digits.

$\frac{5}{8} = 0.625$

A **repeating decimal** has a repeating digit or repeating group of digits.

$\frac{1}{3} = 0.\overline{333} = 0.\overline{3}$

$\frac{5}{7} = 0.714285714\ldots = 0.\overline{714285}$

The bar indicates the repeating digits.

Both terminating decimals and repeating decimals are rational numbers.

7-4 • Defining Rational Numbers   **345**

DID YOU KNOW?

Numbers such as π ≈ 3.141592654… and √2 ≈ 1.414213562… are not rational numbers, because as decimals they do not repeat or terminate. 0.$\overline{3}$ is read as "point three repeating."

MATH EVERY DAY

▶ Problem of the Day

Scott's Seven Seas Shop is having a grand opening. Every customer that enters the store will get a special shopping bag. Every seventh customer also gets a free mug. Every 17th customer also gets a free pen and pencil set. Every 70th customer also gets a certificate for a 17% discount on merchandise. Which customer will be the first to get all four items?
1190th customer

Available on Daily Transparency 7-4

An Extension is provided in the transparency package.

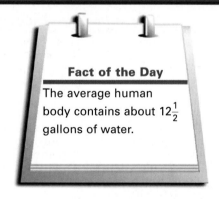

Fact of the Day

The average human body contains about $12\frac{1}{2}$ gallons of water.

Mental Math

Do these mentally.

1. − 8 + 40   32

2. 18 + − 29   −11

3. Write $\frac{16}{24}$ in lowest terms. $\frac{2}{3}$

4. Write $\frac{20}{32}$ in lowest terms. $\frac{5}{8}$

For Groups That Finish Early

If the numerators are the same, how can you compare two fractions by looking at the denominators? The fraction with the greater denominator is the smaller number.

Follow Up

Discuss students' answers for Step 6. Ask volunteers to share their answers for Step 7.

Answers for Explore

1–3. Check students' work.

4. 1st sheet: $\frac{1}{8}, \frac{1}{4}, \frac{3}{8}, \frac{1}{2}, \frac{5}{8}, \frac{3}{4}, \frac{7}{8}$, 1;

  2nd sheet: $\frac{1}{9}, \frac{2}{9}, \frac{1}{3}, \frac{4}{9}, \frac{5}{9}, \frac{2}{3}, \frac{7}{9}, \frac{8}{9}$, 1

5. a. $\frac{1}{8}$ b. $\frac{8}{9}$

  c. $\frac{1}{4}$ d. $\frac{3}{8}$

  e. $\frac{5}{9}$

6. Possible answer: Rewrite fractions with the same denominator.

7. Find the LCM of the two denominators to rewrite the fractions.

2 Teach

Learn

Point out to students the root word *ratio* in the term *rational number*. Emphasize that a rational number is the ratio of two integers.

Alternate Examples

1. Compare $\frac{5}{6}$ and $\frac{7}{8}$.
   Write the fractions with a common denominator.
   $\frac{5}{6} = \frac{20}{24}$ $\frac{7}{8} = \frac{21}{24}$
   Compare the numerators.
   $\frac{20}{24} < \frac{21}{24}$
   Write the original fractions to show the comparison.
   $\frac{5}{6} < \frac{7}{8}$

2. On each Friday in July, the Wolf River was the following number of feet above or below flood stage. List these numbers in increasing order and put them on a number line.

   3   2.5   −1.3   1.25   0
   Write each number with the same number of decimal places.
   3.00   2.50   −1.30   1.25   0.00
   Write the numbers in increasing order.

   −1.30   0.00   1.25   2.50   3.00

   ![number line from -2 to 3 with points]
   −2   −1   0   1   2   3

Alternate Examples

3. Write each fraction as a decimal. State whether it is terminating or repeating.

   a. $\frac{3}{8}$

   Enter 3 ÷ 8 = to get *0.375*.
   $\frac{3}{8}$ = 0.375 is a terminating decimal.

   b. $\frac{2}{3}$

   Enter 2 ÷ 3 = to get *0.6666667*.
   $\frac{2}{3}$ = $0.\overline{6}$ is a repeating decimal.

   Put a bar over 6 to show it repeats.

4. The *HMS Edinburgh* was carrying 465 bars of gold, weighing a total of 4.5 tons, when the ship sank in the Barents Sea in 1942. In 1981, from September to October, about 0.927 of these bars were salvaged from the wreck. What fraction of gold bars was recovered during this time?

   Read 0.927 as 927 thousandths.
   0.927 = $\frac{927}{1000}$ Write as a fraction.
   The fraction is already written in lowest terms.
   $\frac{927}{1000}$ of the gold aboard the *HMS Edinburgh* was recovered.

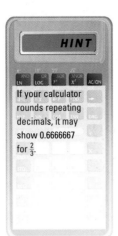

HINT

If your calculator rounds repeating decimals, it may show 0.6666667 for $\frac{2}{3}$.

▶ **History Link**

The *Atocha* sank off the Florida Keys during a hurricane. More than 300 years later, in the 1970s, treasures worth $400 million were recovered.

Example 3

Write each fraction as a decimal. State whether it's terminating or repeating.

a. $\frac{7}{25}$ b. $\frac{4}{9}$

a. Enter 7 ÷ 25 = to get *0.28*

$\frac{7}{25}$ = 0.28 is a terminating decimal.

b. Enter 4 ÷ 9 = to get *0.44444444*

$\frac{4}{9}$ = $0.\overline{4}$ is a repeating decimal.   Put a bar over the 4 to show it repeats.

Try It

Write each fraction as a decimal. State whether it's terminating or repeating.

a. $\frac{5}{6}$ **b.** $\frac{1}{8}$ **c.** $\frac{3}{4}$ a. $0.8\overline{3}$; R   b. 0.125; T   c. 0.75; T

Example 4

About 0.019 of the people on the Spanish ship *Atocha* survived the devastating wreck of September 4, 1622.

What fraction of the people aboard the *Atocha* survived?

The *Treasure Salvors'* crew searched for 15 years to finally discover the *Atocha's* treasure.

0.019   Read 0.019 as 19 thousandths.

0.019 = $\frac{19}{1000}$ Write as a fraction.

$\frac{19}{1000}$ of the people aboard the *Atocha* survived.

Try It

Write each decimal as a fraction or mixed number.

a. 0.15   **b.** 2.6   **c.** 0.046

a. $\frac{15}{100}$ or $\frac{3}{20}$ b. $2\frac{60}{100}$ or $2\frac{3}{5}$ c. $\frac{46}{1000}$ or $\frac{23}{500}$

MEETING MIDDLE SCHOOL CLASSROOM NEEDS

Tips from Middle School Teachers

Here's a challenge my students enjoy. I ask them to find all the rational numbers between 3.8 and 3.9. Some students take the easy road and only find a few decimals, but others work a long time before they believe that the possibilities are infinite.

Health Connection

Meat is frozen for storage between the temperatures of –20 and –30 degrees Celsius. Bacteria do not grow at these temperatures but bacteria already in the meat do survive. That's why it is important to cook meats thoroughly to avoid the chance of Salmonella food poisoning.

Team Teaching

Work with a science teacher to examine rational numbers used in his or her subject area. For example, the diameter of a polio virus is 28 nanometers. A nanometer is 1 millionth of a millimeter, so a polio virus is 0.000028 millimeter in diameter.

Example 5

Write $0.\overline{15}$ as a fraction in lowest terms.

$\text{Let } n = 0.\overline{15}$ Let a variable equal the repeating decimal.

$100 \times n = 100 \times 0.\overline{15}$ Multiply by 10^2 because 2 digits repeat.

$100n - n = 15.\overline{15} - n$ Subtract n.

$99n = 15.\overline{15} - 0.\overline{15}$ Substitute. Recall that $n = 0.\overline{15}$

$\dfrac{99n}{99} = \dfrac{15}{99}$ Divide by 99 to solve for n.

$n = \dfrac{15}{99} = \dfrac{5}{33}$ Write fraction in lowest terms.

Remember

$n = 1n = 1 \times n$

[Page 146]

Try It

Write each fraction in lowest terms.   **a.** $2.\overline{13}$ **b.** $0.\overline{24}$ a. $2\dfrac{13}{99}$ b. $\dfrac{8}{33}$

To compare two noninteger numbers, write both as decimals or as fractions with common denominators.

Example 6

Harry watched Old Faithful shoot steaming water into the air reaching a height of 42.2 meters. Sure enough, being faithful to its name, about 76 minutes later Fred saw it display its burst of beauty, this time at a height of $42\frac{1}{3}$ meters. Compare these two heights. Who saw the geyser shoot higher?

Compare 42.2 and $42\frac{1}{3}$.   Write the fraction as a decimal.

Compare 42.2 and 42.33.   Compare decimals.

The geyser shot higher when Fred was watching.

Try It

a. Compare -4.3 and $-4\frac{1}{3}$.   **b.** Compare 2.07 and $2\frac{1}{7}$.

     $-4\frac{1}{3} < -4.3$ $2.07 < 2\frac{1}{7}$

Check | Your Understanding

1. How can you tell if a fraction will be a terminating or repeating decimal?

2. Explain how to write $0.\overline{33}$ as a fraction.

Alternate Examples

5. Write $0.\overline{1}$ as a fraction in lowest terms.

Let $n = 0.\overline{1}$	Let a variable equal the repeating decimal.
$10 \times n = 10 \times 0.\overline{1}$	Multiply by 10 because 1 digit repeats.
$10n - n = 1.\overline{1} - n$	Subtract n.
$9n = 1.\overline{1} - 0.\overline{1}$	Substitute.
$9n = 1$	Subtract.
$\dfrac{9n}{9} = \dfrac{1}{9}$	Divide by 9 to solve for n.
$n = \dfrac{1}{9}$	

6. Compare $-\frac{3}{5}$ and -0.50.

$-\dfrac{3}{5} = -0.60$	Write the fraction as a decimal.
$-0.60 < -0.50$	Compare the decimals.
$-\dfrac{3}{5} < -0.50$	Compare the fraction and decimal.

3 Practice and Assess

Check

The following fractions are in lowest terms and the only prime factors of each denominator are 2 and 5.

$$\frac{1}{5}, \frac{3}{10}, \frac{7}{25}, \frac{8}{125}, \frac{53}{250}$$

Have students use a calculator to show that each fraction equals a terminating decimal.

The following fractions are in lowest terms and each denominator contains at least one prime factor other than 2 or 5.

$$\frac{1}{3}, \frac{4}{15}, \frac{8}{75}, \frac{9}{88}, \frac{51}{130}$$

Have students use a calculator to show that each fraction equals a repeating decimal.

Answers for Check Your Understanding

1. Possible answer: If a fraction is expressed in lowest terms and the denominator is a product of powers of 2 and 5, then the fraction will be a terminating decimal. If the fraction is in lowest terms and the denominator is a product of powers of 3 and 6, the fraction will be a repeating decimal.

2. See steps in Example 5 on page 347.

Assignment Guide

- **Basic**
  1–5, 10,15, 20, 23–25, 27, 28, 33, 34, 37, 38, 40

- **Average**
  1, 6–8, 11, 12, 16, 17, 21, 23, 27–31, 35, 36, 39, 41

- **Enriched**
  1, 7–9, 13, 14, 16, 18, 19, 22–23, 26–28, 31, 32, 35, 37, 42

Exercise Notes

■ Exercise 23

Science Whales are also marine mammals. A sperm whale can remain underwater for up to 2 hours.

Exercise Answers

20.

21.

22.

24. $12\frac{4}{5}$

25. Ana

26. Call: $\frac{43}{100}$; Alarm Clock: $\frac{22}{100} = \frac{11}{50}$;

Other: $\frac{19}{100}$; Kids: $\frac{16}{100} = \frac{4}{25}$

Reteaching

Activity

Materials: Graph paper

- Work in groups of three. Each person should mark off a 10 × 10 square on graph paper.

- One person should shade $\frac{1}{2}$ of his or her square, a second person should shade $\frac{3}{5}$, and the third person should shade $\frac{27}{50}$.

- Use your drawings to compare the fractions. Which is largest? Which is smallest? Write the fractions in order from greatest to least.
$\frac{3}{5}, \frac{1}{2}, \frac{3}{5}, \frac{27}{50}, \frac{1}{2}$

7-4 Exercises and Applications

PRACTICE 7-4

Practice and Apply

1. **Getting Started** Compare and order $\frac{-2}{3}, \frac{5}{6}, 0, \frac{-4}{7}, \frac{9}{10}, \frac{-1}{5},$ and $\frac{1}{6}$.
   a. Find the LCD (use the LCM).   1. a. 210
   b. Write all fractions with the LCD.
   b. $-\frac{140}{210}, \frac{175}{210}, \frac{0}{210}, -\frac{120}{210}, \frac{189}{210}, -\frac{42}{210}, \frac{35}{210}$
   c. List in order from least to greatest.
   c. $-\frac{140}{210}, -\frac{120}{210}, -\frac{42}{210}, \frac{0}{210}, \frac{35}{210}, \frac{175}{210}, \frac{189}{210}$

Replace each ☐ with >, <, or = to compare each pair of numbers.

2. $3.04 \boxed{>} 3.005$ 3. $-0.8 \boxed{<} -0.0789$ 4. $-0.28 \boxed{<} -0.2$ 5. $0.009 \boxed{<} 0.01$

6. $-\frac{3}{5} \boxed{<} 0.51$ 7. $\frac{7}{12} \boxed{>} \frac{1}{2}$ 8. $-4.03 \boxed{<} \frac{-32}{8}$ 9. $\frac{5}{8} \boxed{<} \frac{3}{4}$

Write each fraction as a decimal and state whether it is repeating or terminating.

10. $\frac{1}{5}$ 11. $\frac{11}{25}$ 12. $\frac{4}{33}$ 13. $\frac{2}{7}$ 14. $\frac{-4}{9}$ $-0.\overline{4}$; R
    0.2; T   0.44; T $0.\overline{12}$; R $0.\overline{285714}$; R

Write each decimal as a fraction or mixed number in lowest terms.

15. 0.45 $\frac{9}{20}$ 16. -0.3003 17. 4.56 $4\frac{14}{25}$ 18. $0.\overline{21}$ $\frac{7}{33}$ 19. $2.\overline{3}$ $2\frac{1}{3}$ 16. $-\frac{3003}{10,000}$

Compare each group of numbers and order them on a number line.

20. $-\frac{3}{4}, -\frac{1}{3}, -\frac{5}{9}, 0, -1$ 21. $-0.\overline{12}, 0.8\overline{3}, 1, -\frac{3}{5}$ 22. $6\frac{2}{3}, 6.7, 6.\overline{23}$

23. **Science** Marine mammals, like the porpoise and the sea cow, get oxygen by breathing air, not from the water through gills, as fish do. A sea cow can stay underwater for $\frac{9}{30}$ hour. A porpoise can be underwater for $\frac{1}{4}$ hour. Which marine mammal can stay underwater longer? **The sea cow**

porpoise

sea cow

24. The largest species of beaked whales is Baird's beaked whale, also called the giant bottlenose whale. The female can grow to be as long as 12.8 m. Express this length as a mixed number in lowest terms.

25. Ana spent 2.4 hours on her homework, while Lance spent $2\frac{1}{4}$ hours on his. Who spent more time on homework?

PRACTICE

Name _____

Practice 7-4

Defining Rational Numbers

Use >, <, or = to compare each pair of numbers.

1. $\frac{7}{8} \bigcirc 0.82$ 2. $1.03 \bigcirc 1.029$ 3. $\frac{-3}{6} \bigcirc 0.4$ 4. $\frac{3}{5} \bigcirc \frac{4}{7}$

5. $\frac{8}{3} \bigcirc 2.6$ 6. $0.4 \bigcirc \frac{2}{5}$ 7. $2.34 \bigcirc 2.43$ 8. $0.4 \bigcirc \frac{5}{12}$

9. $-0.63 \bigcirc \frac{-5}{7}$ 10. $\frac{8}{25} \bigcirc 0.32$ 11. $\frac{-3}{16} \bigcirc -0.2$ 12. $1.333 \bigcirc \frac{4}{3}$

Write each fraction as a decimal and state whether it is repeating or terminating.

13. $\frac{5}{8}$ 0.625; terminating   14. $-\frac{7}{10}$ -0.7; terminating

15. $\frac{16}{33}$ 0.48; repeating   16. $\frac{6}{7}$ 0.857142, repeating

17. $\frac{21}{80}$ 0.2625; terminating   18. $-\frac{5}{6}$ -0.83; repeating

Write each decimal as a fraction or mixed number in lowest terms.

19. 0.36 $\frac{9}{25}$ 20. 0.375 $\frac{3}{8}$ 21. 1.24 $1\frac{6}{25}$ 22. $0.\overline{8}$ $\frac{8}{9}$

23. 0.54 $\frac{6}{11}$ 24. 0.13 $\frac{13}{100}$ 25. $2.\overline{4}$ $2\frac{4}{9}$ 26. $7.\overline{6}$ $7\frac{2}{3}$

Compare each group of numbers and order them on a number line.

27. $0.7, 0.\overline{7}, \frac{3}{4}, \frac{7}{8}$ 28. $\frac{3}{5}, 1.2, \frac{5}{3}, 0.\overline{3}$ 29. $-0.5, -\frac{2}{3}, -\frac{1}{2}, -\frac{3}{8}$

30. $8.2, 8.2\overline{5}, 8.\overline{3}, 8\frac{1}{4}$ 31. $0.6, -0.5, \frac{1}{2}, -\frac{4}{5}$ 32. $-2\frac{2}{3}, -2\frac{2}{5}, -2.1, -2.25$

33. During the 1992 Summer Olympic Games, the top three scorers for the women's long jump were Inessa Kravets ($23\frac{3}{8}$ ft), Jackie Joyner-Kersee ($23\frac{5}{24}$ ft), and Heike Drechsler ($23\frac{7}{16}$ ft). Write these women's names in order from the longest jump to the shortest.
Heike Drechsler, Inessa Kravets, Jackie Joyner-Kersee

34. **Social Science** In 1990, 21.5% of the world's population lived in China. What fraction is this? $\frac{43}{200}$

RETEACHING

Name _____

Alternative Lesson 7-4

Defining Rational Numbers

Rational numbers are numbers that can be written as a ratio of two integers, and the denominator is not zero. Rational numbers include integers, fractions, and many decimals.

A **terminating decimal** has a fixed number of digits. A **repeating decimal** has a repeating digit or repeating group of digits. For example, 0.25 is a terminating decimal, and $0.\overline{6}$ is a repeating decimal. The bar over the 6 indicates the repeating digit.

— Example 1 —

Write $\frac{5}{8}$ as a decimal and state whether it is repeating or terminating.

Divide the numerator by the denominator. $5 \div 8 = 0.625$

Determine if there is a remainder.   There is no remainder, so it is a terminating decimal.

Since $\frac{5}{8} = 0.625$, it is a terminating decimal.

Try It Write each fraction as a decimal and state whether it is repeating or terminating.

a. $\frac{5}{6}$ 0.83; repeating.   b. $\frac{3}{4}$ 0.75; terminating.

— Example 2 —

Write 0.2 as a fraction in lowest terms.

Step 1: Let a variable equal the repeating decimal.   Let $n = 0.\overline{2}$

Step 2: Multiply both sides by 10^1, or 10, because one digit repeats. The exponent is the number of repeating digits. $10 \times n = 10 \times 0.\overline{2}$

Step 3: Subtract n from both sides. $10n - n = 2.\overline{2} - n$

Step 4: Substitute for n on one side of the equation. $9n = 2.2 - 0.2$

Step 5: Divide each side by 9 to solve for n. $\frac{9n}{9} = \frac{2}{9}$

Step 6: Write the fraction in lowest terms, if necessary. $n = \frac{2}{9}$

So, $0.\overline{2} = \frac{2}{9}$.

Try It Write each decimal as a fraction in lowest terms.

c. 0.06 $\frac{3}{50}$ d. 0.7 $\frac{7}{10}$ e. $0.\overline{7}$ $\frac{7}{9}$ f. $0.1\overline{6}$ $\frac{1}{6}$

26. Change the percents given in the graph to fractions and arrange them in order from greatest to least.

How Kids Wake Up
Other methods 19%
Parents call to them 43%
Use an alarm 22%
Wake themselves up 16%

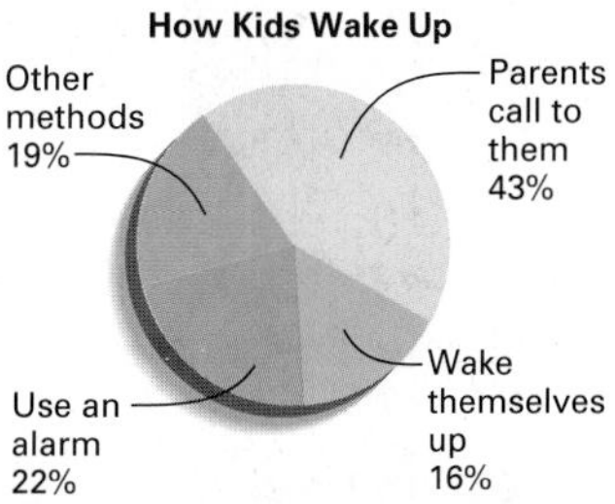

27. History The Greek mathematician Archimedes approximated π to be between $3\frac{10}{71}$ and $3\frac{1}{7}$. Write each as a decimal. 3.14084507; 3.14285714

28. **Test Prep** Which is listed from least to greatest? C

Ⓐ $-3, -3\frac{2}{3}, -3.7$ Ⓑ $\frac{1}{2}, \frac{1}{3}, \frac{1}{4}$

Ⓒ $-0.875, -\frac{4}{5}, 0$ Ⓓ $0.\overline{6}, 0.1\overline{6}, \frac{1}{6}$

29. Science Because a camel's hump stores fat and not water, a camel can lose up to 37.5% of its body weight. What fraction of the camel's weight is this? $\frac{3}{8}$

Problem Solving and Reasoning

30. Communicate Explain how to find a number between $\frac{2}{5}$ and 0.42.

Number Sense Find a number that is between each pair.

31. $\frac{1}{4}$ and $\frac{1}{5}$ **32.** $0.\overline{12}$ and $0.\overline{13}$ **33.** $\frac{-7}{8}$ and $\frac{-7}{9}$

34. Journal The decimal conversions of $\frac{1}{7}, \frac{2}{7}, \frac{3}{7}, \frac{4}{7}, \frac{5}{7}$, and $\frac{6}{7}$ display a very interesting pattern. Convert the fractions and describe the pattern.

Mixed Review

Write an algebraic expression for each situation. *[Lesson 3-3]*

35. 12 increased by a number $12 + n$ **36.** 8 subtracted from twice a number $2n - 8$

37. Number of inches in k yards $36k$ **38.** The number of sides in s squares $4s$

Solve each percent problem. *[Lesson 6-2]*

39. What is 75% of 200? 150 **40.** What is 10% of 50? 5

41. 50% of what number is 20? 40 **42.** 6 is 60% of what number? 10

Project Progress

As you keep track of your gains and losses, find places to use negative numbers. Consider whether or not your calculations would be more efficient if all your numbers were written as decimals or all as fractions.

Problem Solving
Understand
Plan
Solve
Look Back

PROBLEM SOLVING

Name ______________________ **Extend Your Thinking 7-4**

Decision Making

Nathan is looking for a part-time job. He has the following choices.

Job I Deliver daily and weekend newspapers to 75 customers. Delivery needs to be completed by 7:00 A.M. It takes about 1 hour to deliver 60 newspapers. The pay is 10¢ per delivery.

Job II Assistant at the grocery store. Duties include bagging groceries, price checking, and bringing in shopping carts from the parking lot. Hours vary, between 12–18 hours each week, with 3 hours after school twice a week and the rest on weekends. The hourly pay is $4.75.

Job III Cashier at a restaurant for 10–14 hours per week. The hours would be one weekend day for 8 hours and 1–3 weekday evenings from 5:00 to 7:00 P.M. The pay is $4.50 per hour.

1. How much can Nathan earn per week at each job? If necessary, give a range.
Job I: $52.50; Job II: $57.00–$85.50; Job III: $45.00–$63.00.

2. Name an advantage of accepting each job. Possible answer:
Job I: Would not interfere with after-school activities.
Job II: Variety of duties; May earn the most money.
Job III: Work inside; Gain experience handling money.

3. Name a disadvantage of accepting each job. Possible answer:
Job I: Early morning hours; Work in the dark.
Job II: Could interfere with homework.
Job III: Too routine, boring.

4. Which job would you choose if you were Nathan? Explain. Possible answer:
Job III because of the hours, it would fit in with school and sleep schedules the best.

ENRICHMENT

Name ______________________ **Extend Your Thinking 7-4**

Decision Making

Nathan is looking for a part-time job. He has the following choices.

Job I Deliver daily and weekend newspapers to 75 customers. Delivery needs to be completed by 7:00 A.M. It takes about 1 hour to deliver 60 newspapers. The pay is 10¢ per delivery.

Job II Assistant at the grocery store. Duties include bagging groceries, price checking, and bringing in shopping carts from the parking lot. Hours vary, between 12–18 hours each week, with 3 hours after school twice a week and the rest on weekends. The hourly pay is $4.75.

Job III Cashier at a restaurant for 10–14 hours per week. The hours would be one weekend day for 8 hours and 1–3 weekday evenings from 5:00 to 7:00 P.M. The pay is $4.50 per hour.

1. How much can Nathan earn per week at each job? If necessary, give a range.
Job I: $52.50; Job II: $57.00–$85.50; Job III: $45.00–$63.00.

2. Name an advantage of accepting each job. Possible answer:
Job I: Would not interfere with after-school activities.
Job II: Variety of duties; May earn the most money.
Job III: Work inside; Gain experience handling money.

3. Name a disadvantage of accepting each job. Possible answer:
Job I: Early morning hours; Work in the dark.
Job II: Could interfere with homework.
Job III: Too routine, boring.

4. Which job would you choose if you were Nathan? Explain. Possible answer:
Job III because of the hours, it would fit in with school and sleep schedules the best.

Exercise Notes

■ Exercise 28

Test Prep Choice A is wrong because $-3 > -3\frac{2}{3}$. Choice B is wrong because $\frac{1}{2} > \frac{1}{3}$. Choice D is wrong because $0.\overline{6} > 0.16$.

■ Exercise 29

Error Prevention Some students will fail to first convert the percent to a decimal.

■ Exercises 31–33

One number that is between two given numbers is their mean.

Project Progress

You may want to have students use Chapter 7 Project Master.

Exercise Answers

30. Possible answer: Convert $\frac{2}{5}$ to 0.40 and choose a number between 0.40 and 0.42, such as 0.41.
31. Possible answer: $\frac{11}{50}$
32. Possible answer: 0.125
33. Possible answer: $-\frac{62}{72}$
34. $0.\overline{142857}$; $0.\overline{285714}$; $0.\overline{428571}$; $0.\overline{571428}$; $0.\overline{714285}$; $0.\overline{857142}$. Each is a repeating decimal with the same digits in the same order, but in different places.

Alternate Assessment

You may want to use the *Interactive CD-ROM Journal* with this assessment.

Journal Have students write definitions for the following terms: *rational number, terminating decimal, repeating decimal.*

▶ Quick Quiz

1. Compare these fractions. $\frac{6}{7}$ and $\frac{4}{9}$ $\frac{6}{7} > \frac{4}{9}$
2. Write these fractions as decimals and state whether the decimals are repeating or terminating.
   a. $\frac{3}{8}$ 0.375; terminating
   b. $\frac{2}{3}$ $0.\overline{6}$; repeating
   c. $\frac{4}{11}$ $0.\overline{36}$; repeating
3. Compare $\frac{1}{8}$ and 0.130.
   $\frac{1}{8} < 0.130$

Available on Daily Transparency 7-4

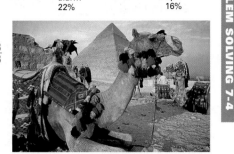

7-5
Lesson Organizer

Objective
- Add and subtract rational numbers.

NCTM Standards
- 1, 2, 4–7, 9

▶ Review
Find the LCD and write all fractions with the LCD.

1. $\frac{2}{3}, \frac{3}{5}, -\frac{1}{4}$ $\frac{40}{60}, \frac{36}{60}, -\frac{15}{60}$

2. $\frac{2}{7}, -\frac{5}{14}, \frac{1}{4}$ $\frac{8}{28}, -\frac{10}{28}, \frac{7}{28}$

Add or subtract.

3. $5681 + 75{,}930$ $81{,}611$

4. $7803 - 620$ 7183

Available on Daily Transparency 7-5

▶ Lesson Link
Discuss when it might be necessary to add or subtract rational numbers in real life. Suggestions might include working with different kinds of measurements, such as finding a combined distance or finding how much heavier one object is than another.

1 Introduce

Explore
You may wish to use Lesson Enhancement Transparency 28 with **Explore**.

The Point
Students explore how rational numbers are used by hydrologists as they study the salinity of large bodies of water.

Ongoing Assessment
In Step 3 check that students realize that for this problem they may ignore the denominators while doing the first part of the calculations. They can find 30% of 32 and 70% of 37 and then add 9.6 + 25.9. There are 35.5 parts salt per 1000 parts ocean water in the mixture.

7-5   Add and Subtract Rational Numbers

You'll Learn ...
- to add and subtract rational numbers

... How It's Used
Telephone repair people add and subtract integers, fractions, and decimals when they make adjustments during a repair after a storm.

▶ **Lesson Link**   You have learned about the types of rational numbers. Now you will add and subtract rational numbers. ◀

Explore | Rational Numbers

Hydro ≈ Water

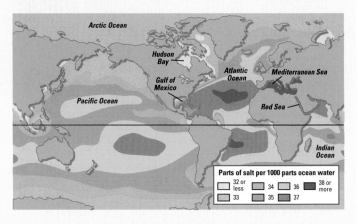

Arctic Ocean

Hudson Bay

Atlantic Ocean

Mediterranean Sea

Gulf of Mexico

Pacific Ocean

Red Sea

Indian Ocean

Parts of salt per 1000 parts ocean water
☐ 32 or less   ☐ 34   ☐ 36   ■ 38 or more
☐ 33   ☐ 35   ☐ 37

Oceans have different amounts of salt and salinity in them. A hydrologist might study the map to understand the varied salinity of the oceans. The "saltiest" oceans are shown in purple.

1. What is the salinity of the Hudson Bay? The Mediterranean Sea? The Red Sea?

2. Name the body of water with the highest salinity; the lowest salinity. Express the salinity of each as a fraction.

3. What would the salinity be if you made a mixture of 30% water with $\frac{32}{1000}$ salinity and 70% water with $\frac{37}{1000}$ salinity?

4. The average salinity of the ocean is $\frac{34.5 \text{ parts salt}}{1000 \text{ parts ocean water}}$. With your group, discuss how hydrologists would arrive at this number.

5. Discuss some reasons for the variation of salinity in the oceans.

MEETING INDIVIDUAL NEEDS

Resources
7-5 Practice
7-5 Reteaching
7-5 Problem Solving
7-5 Enrichment
7-5 Daily Transparency
      Problem of the Day
      Review
      Quick Quiz
Lesson Enhancement Transparency 28
Technology Master 28

Learning Modalities

Visual   In **Explore**, students see a map of the regions of the world where the salinity of seawater is highest.

Logical   Have students hypothesize why the water near frozen ice packs in Antarctica is very salty. When the extreme cold freezes freshwater to form ice, salt is left behind. The unfrozen seawater in that area is saltier.

Social   In **Explore**, students work in pairs to compare their ideas on the salinity of oceans and answer questions using rational numbers.

English Language Development

To help students remember the names of each place in a decimal, use a place-value chart. Have students read the numbers aloud to help them see, hear, pronounce, and understand the different meanings of ten, tens, and tenths, hundred, hundreds, and hundredths, and so on.

Learn Add and Subtract Rational Numbers

Adding and subtracting decimals is similar to adding and subtracting integers. Align the decimal points.

Example 1

Subtract 32.74 − 12.678.

$$\begin{array}{r} 32.740 \\ -12.678 \\ \hline 20.062 \end{array}$$

32.740 Align decimal points and write with the same number of decimal places.

20.062 Subtract.

Try It

Add or subtract each of the following.

a. 84.6 + 27.03 **111.63** **b.** 55 − 18.25 **36.75**

c. 309.1 − (−217.95) **d.** −0.66 + 4.4 **3.74**
527.05

Use a common denominator to add and subtract fractions with unlike denominators.

Example 2

The Osage orange tree produces large spherical fruits, which vary from $3\frac{2}{3}$ inches to $5\frac{1}{12}$ inches in diameter. What is the range in size of the fruit?

The fruit of the Osage orange tree is not edible. It is named after the Osage Indians who used its yellow wood for bows and wagon wheels.

Subtract $5\frac{1}{12} - 3\frac{2}{3}$.

Write fractions with a common denominator.

$$5\frac{1}{12} = 5\frac{1}{12} = 4\frac{13}{12} \quad \text{Rename } 5\frac{1}{12}.$$

$$-3\frac{2}{3} = -3\frac{8}{12} = -3\frac{8}{12}$$

$$\overline{\hspace{3cm}} \quad 1\frac{5}{12} \quad \text{Subtract.}$$

The range in diameter is $1\frac{5}{12}$ inches. Estimate. Since $5 - 3\frac{1}{2} = 1\frac{1}{2}$, the answer is reasonable.

> ▶ **Science Link**
>
> Plants such as the orange tree use their fruits to disperse their seeds.

Study TIP
You will usually make fewer mistakes if you don't skip steps.

MATH EVERY DAY

▶ Problem of the Day

Ancient Egyptians used hiero-glyphics to write unit fractions.

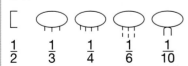

$$\frac{1}{2} \qquad \frac{1}{3} \qquad \frac{1}{4} \qquad \frac{1}{6} \qquad \frac{1}{10}$$

What symbol would they write for each of the following?

1. $\frac{1}{5}$ 2. $\frac{1}{8}$ 3. $\frac{1}{20}$

Available on Daily Transparency 7-5

An Extension is provided in the transparency package.

Fact of the Day

About 9 million tons of gold are in solution, more or less evenly distributed in the world's oceans. But it occurs in concentrations of only 0.000004 mg/kg.

Estimation

Estimate each answer.

1. 0.52 + 0.31 0.8

2. 25.8 − 9.7 16

3. 153.77 + 201.6 350

4. 1.02 − 0.48 0.5

For Groups That Finish Early

Describe what a salinity of 0.035 means. With this salinity, how much salt would be in 1000 ounces of water? Since 0.035 = $\frac{35}{1000}$, there are 35 parts salt for each 1000 parts water; 1000 ounces of water would contain 35 ounces of salt.

Follow Up

Ask volunteers to share their answers for Step 5. Discuss their answers. Students may conclude that in warmer climates, more of the ocean water evaporates, leaving behind the salt, so in these parts of the world the oceans are saltier.

Answers for Explore

1. 32 or less; 38 or more; 37.

2. Possible answers: Mediterranean Sea, $\geq \frac{19}{500}$; Hudson Bay, $\leq \frac{4}{125}$.

3. $\frac{71}{2000}$

4. Answers may vary.

5. Answers may vary.

2 Teach

Learn

Remind students that adding or subtracting decimals is like adding or subtracting whole numbers, but students have to be careful to align the decimal points.

Alternate Examples

1. Subtract 42.52 − 31.735.

$$\begin{array}{r} 42.520 \\ -\ 31.735 \\ \hline 10.785 \end{array}$$

Align decimal points and write with the same number of decimal places. Subtract.

2. Raccoons generally measure from $29\frac{3}{4}$ inches to $38\frac{3}{8}$ inches long, including their tail. What is the range in length of raccoons?

Subtract $38\frac{3}{8} - 29\frac{3}{4}$.
Write fractions with LCD.

$$38\frac{3}{8} = 38\frac{3}{8} = 37\frac{11}{8} \quad \text{Rename } 38\frac{3}{8}.$$

$$-29\frac{3}{4} = -29\frac{6}{8} = -29\frac{6}{8}$$

$$\overline{\hspace{3cm}} \quad 8\frac{5}{8} \quad \text{Subtract.}$$

The range in length is $8\frac{5}{8}$ inches.

Alternate Examples

3. Find $5\frac{3}{4} - (-2\frac{5}{9})$.

   Write fractions with a common denominator.
   $$5\frac{3}{4} - (-2\frac{5}{9}) = 5\frac{27}{36} - (-2\frac{20}{36})$$

   Add the opposite of $-2\frac{20}{36}$ and rename the result. $5\frac{27}{36} + 2\frac{20}{36}$

   $$= 7\frac{47}{36} = 8\frac{11}{36}$$

4. Christy passes Todd's house on the way to school. From Christy's house to Todd's house is $3\frac{3}{8}$ miles. From Christy's house to school is $6\frac{1}{3}$ miles. Using Christy's route, how far is it from Todd's house to school?

   Solve the equation $n + 3\frac{3}{8} = 6\frac{1}{3}$.

   Add $-3\frac{3}{8}$ to both sides.
   $$n + 3\frac{3}{8} + (-3\frac{3}{8}) = 6\frac{1}{3} + (-3\frac{3}{8})$$
   Simplify. Rewrite each fraction using the LCD.
   $$n + 0 = 6\frac{8}{24} + (-3\frac{9}{24})$$
   Rewrite $6\frac{8}{24}$ as $5\frac{32}{24}$ and subtract.
   $$5\frac{32}{24} + (-3\frac{9}{24}) = 2\frac{23}{24}$$

   It is $2\frac{23}{24}$ miles from Todd's house to school.

3 Practice and Assess

Calculating with positive and negative fractions is similar to calculating with positive and negative integers.

Example 3

Find $4\frac{5}{8} - (-3\frac{3}{5})$.

$$4\frac{5}{8} - (-3\frac{3}{5}) = 4\frac{25}{40} - (-3\frac{24}{40})$$ Write fractions with a common denominator.

$$4\frac{25}{40} + 3\frac{24}{40} = 7\frac{49}{40} = 8\frac{9}{40}$$ Add the opposite of $-3\frac{24}{40}$ and rename the result.

Try It

Add or subtract.   **a.** $5\frac{3}{5} - 3\frac{2}{20}$ $2\frac{1}{2}$ **b.** $7\frac{1}{6} + (-1\frac{1}{3})$ $5\frac{5}{6}$

Example 4

Problem Solving TIP

Here's a good thing to know when you see fraction coefficients:
$\frac{3}{7}x = \frac{3x}{7}$.

Jan and Hillary jog $6\frac{1}{5}$ miles from their house to the park daily. If they take a water break after $2\frac{1}{3}$ miles, how much farther do they have to jog to get to the park?

Solve the equation $n + 2\frac{1}{3} = 6\frac{1}{5}$.

$$n + 2\frac{1}{3} = 6\frac{1}{5}$$

$$n + 2\frac{1}{3} + (-2\frac{1}{3}) = 6\frac{1}{5} + (-2\frac{1}{3})$$ Add $-2\frac{1}{3}$ to both sides.

$$n + 0 = 6\frac{3}{15} + (-2\frac{5}{15})$$ Simplify and rewrite fractions.

$$n = 5\frac{18}{15} + (-2\frac{5}{15}) = 3\frac{13}{15}$$ Rewrite $6\frac{3}{15}$ as $5\frac{18}{15}$ and subtract.

They have to jog $3\frac{13}{15}$ miles more to get to the park.

Try It

Find n for each of the following.   **a.** $n + \frac{3}{4} = -4\frac{1}{2}$ $-5\frac{1}{4}$ **b.** $n - 10\frac{5}{8} = 3\frac{7}{12}$ $14\frac{5}{24}$

Check Your Understanding

1. Why do you use the LCD when you add and subtract fractions?

2. How is adding negative fractions similar to adding negative integers?

MEETING MIDDLE SCHOOL CLASSROOM NEEDS

Tips from Middle School Teachers

To help my students compute with rational numbers, I have them use a checklist and ask themselves: Have I found the LCD before attempting to add or subtract fractions? Have I reduced answers to lowest terms? Did I use the proper sign before the answer? By checking the list before completing their work, students are more confident about the outcome.

Cultural Connection

Around A.D. 1, Liu Hsin of China was known to have used decimal fractions. In India, 600 years later, decimal notation was in use. Between 1050 and 1059, the decimal system was introduced to Spain by the Arabs. By 1548, a book by the Flemish mathematician Simon Stevin explained how to use decimal fractions.

Science Connection

Ninety-nine percent of all the dissolved matter in the oceans is made up of only 11 major elements. However, just two elements, chlorine and sodium, account for ten times more dissolved matter than all the other elements combined. Seawater contains 18.98 parts per thousand of chlorine and 10.56 parts per thousand of sodium.

7-5 Exercises and Applications

Practice and Apply

1. **Getting Started** Add $\frac{4}{5} + \frac{5}{6}$.
   a. Write each fraction using the LCD. $\frac{24}{30}, \frac{25}{30}$
   b. Add the numerators and write the result over the LCD. $\frac{49}{30}$
   c. Write in lowest terms. $1\frac{19}{30}$

Add or subtract each of the following. Write each answer in lowest terms.

2. $0.3124 + 0.214$ 3. $-127.123 - 33.59$ 4. $45.34567 + 28.13$ 5. $124.16 - (-39.98)$

6. $\frac{2}{3} + \frac{4}{3}$ 2 7. $\frac{12}{20} - \frac{17}{20}$ $-\frac{1}{4}$ 8. $\frac{3}{9} - \left(-\frac{3}{9}\right)$ $\frac{2}{3}$ 9. $\frac{-4}{5} + \frac{4}{6}$ $\frac{-2}{15}$ 10. $\frac{9}{10} - \frac{3}{12}$ $\frac{13}{20}$

11. $7\frac{3}{5} + 2\frac{4}{5}$ $10\frac{2}{5}$ 12. $8\frac{2}{3} - \left(-5\frac{1}{3}\right)$ 14 13. $7\frac{1}{7} - 2\frac{4}{7}$ $4\frac{4}{7}$ 14. $9\frac{1}{6} - 3\frac{5}{6}$ $5\frac{1}{3}$ 15. $-12\frac{4}{5} - 1\frac{11}{12}$ $-14\frac{43}{60}$

Solve each equation.
16. $n = 1\frac{1}{3}$ 17. $n = -1\frac{1}{2}$ 18. $n = 1\frac{3}{35}$ 19. $n = 11\frac{1}{4}$

16. $n = \frac{3}{4} + \frac{7}{12}$ 17. $2\frac{1}{2} - n = 4$ 18. $n + \left(-\frac{2}{7}\right) = \frac{4}{5}$ 19. $n - 12 = -\frac{6}{8}$

20. **Geography** The United States, Russia, China, and India use about 0.45 of the world's daily consumed fresh water. What fraction of fresh water is consumed by other countries? $\frac{55}{100} = \frac{11}{20}$

21. Venus orbits the sun at an average of 21.75 miles per second, while Earth orbits the sun at an average of 18.46 miles per second. How much faster is the orbital speed of Venus? **3.29 miles per second**

22. Alexandro weighed a bag of jelly beans at the candy store and the scale read 0.65 pounds. He added on a bag of sour candies and the scale then read 1.13 pounds. How much do the sour candies weigh? **0.48 pounds**

23. **Science** Use the circle graph to determine what fraction of Earth's surface is fresh water. About $\frac{71}{100}$ of Earth's surface is salt water, and about $\frac{6}{25}$ is land. $\frac{1}{20}$

24. **Social Studies** If $\frac{7}{25}$ of the households in the United States have three or more television sets, what fraction of households have fewer than three television sets? $\frac{18}{25}$

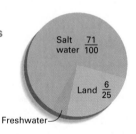

Salt water $\frac{71}{100}$

Land $\frac{6}{25}$

Freshwater

7-5 • Add and Subtract Rational Numbers   **353**

2. 0.5264
3. −160.713
4. 73.47567
5. 164.14

■ Exercise 28

Problem-Solving Tip This exercise requires working backward. Suggest that students start with $\frac{1}{3}$, change it to a fraction with a different denominator, and then write that fraction as a sum of two fractions. For example,

$$\frac{1}{3} = \frac{1}{3} \times \frac{4}{4} = \frac{4}{12}$$

$$\frac{4}{12} = \frac{3}{12} + \frac{1}{12} = \frac{1}{4} + \frac{1}{12}$$

Finally they can write the word problem for this sum.

■ Exercise 30

Error Prevention Some students may not change the percents to decimals. Remind them to do this before proceeding. The difference will be in decimal form. The exercise asks for the answer as a fraction. Students should write the fraction in lowest terms.

Exercise Answers

27. Answers may vary.

28. Answers may vary.

Alternate Assessment

 You may want to use the *Interactive CD-ROM Journal* with this assessment.

Journal Have students write five short paragraphs explaining how to find the answer to each of the following:

1. **1.235 − 0.46** Align decimal points. Write each number with same number of decimal places. Then subtract to get 0.775.

2. $3\frac{2}{5} - 2\frac{3}{4}$ Write fractions with common denominator. Rename $3\frac{8}{20}$ as $2\frac{28}{20}$. Then subtract to get $\frac{13}{20}$.

3. $\frac{1}{3} + \frac{1}{8}$ Find the LCD. Then add to get $\frac{11}{24}$.

4. **x + 10 = −7** Subtract 10 from both sides of the equation. $x = -17$

► Quick Quiz

1. Add $\frac{3}{8}$ and $\frac{3}{4}$. $1\frac{1}{8}$

2. Subtract: 0.065 − 0.06 **0.005**

3. Subtract: $9\frac{3}{8} - (-4\frac{3}{5})$ $13\frac{39}{40}$

Available on Daily Transparency 7-5

PROBLEM SOLVING 7-5

25. **Test Prep** Which of these is equivalent to $8\frac{8}{15}$? **B**

Ⓐ $8\frac{4}{7}$ Ⓑ $7\frac{23}{15}$ Ⓒ $7\frac{15}{23}$ Ⓓ $7\frac{15}{8}$

Problem Solving and Reasoning

26. **Health** A set of quadruplets were born in Great Britain on April 10, 1988, weighing $2\frac{9}{16}$ lb, $2\frac{1}{8}$ lb, $2\frac{1}{4}$ lb, and $2\frac{5}{16}$ lb. What was the average weight of the babies?

27. Write a paragraph to explain why having the same number of decimal places is similar to having fractions with common denominators.

28. **Communicate** Write a word problem that would require subtracting fractions with unlike denominators and that has $\frac{1}{3}$ as an answer. Explain how you decided on the numbers used in your word problem.

29. **Algebra** Ana's stock rose $\frac{3}{4}$ of a point Wednesday, rose $\frac{3}{8}$ of a point Thursday, and fell $1\frac{1}{4}$ points Friday. Write an algebraic expression for the situation and find the overall change in her stock for these three days.

30. **Math Reasoning** A wetland is a location other than a river, lake, or open ocean in which the soil is saturated with water. In 1900, 39.4% of Florida was wetlands. In 1990, 30.6% of Florida was wetlands. What fraction of wetlands was lost from 1900 to 1990? $\frac{11}{125}$

Mixed Review

Solve each equation. *[Lesson 3-4]*

31. $x - 10 = 7$ $x = 17$ 32. $4 + y = 14$ $y = 10$

33. $-10 - k = 44$ $k = -54$ 34. $9 + p = -17$ $p = -26$

35. $-r + 2.4 = 7.3$ $r = -4.9$ 36. $j = 88 - 2$ $j = 86$

37. $n + (-2.9) = -5.1$ $n = -2.2$ 38. $64 - t = 38$ $t = 26$

Find the percent of increase in each situation. Round to the nearest whole percent. *[Lesson 6-4]*

39. A pair of in-line skates wholesales for $150.00 and retails for $215.00. **43%**

40. There were 16 jazz band members and now there are 20. **25%**

354 *Chapter 7 • Number Sense, Rational Numbers, and Irrational Numbers*

26. $2\frac{5}{16}$ lb

29. $x = \frac{3}{4} + \frac{3}{8} - 1\frac{1}{4} = -\frac{1}{8}$

► PROBLEM SOLVING

Name _____

Guided Problem Solving 7-5

GPS **PROBLEM 29, STUDENT PAGE 354**

Ana's stock rose $\frac{3}{4}$ of a point Wednesday, rose $\frac{3}{8}$ of a point Thursday, and fell $1\frac{1}{4}$ points Friday. Write an algebraic expression for the situation and find the overall change in her stock for these three days.

— Understand —

1. Underline the number of points the stock rose.

2. Circle the number of points the stock fell.

3. What two things are you asked to do? Write an algebraic expression and find the overall change in stock price.

— Plan —

4. Would a rising stock price be a positive or a negative number? Positive.

5. Would a falling stock price be a positive or a negative number? Negative.

— Solve —

6. Write an expression for the change in stock price.
Possible answer: $\frac{3}{4} + \frac{3}{8} + (-1\frac{1}{4})$

7. Simplify your expression. $-\frac{1}{8}$

8. What is the overall change in stock price. Down $\frac{1}{8}$ of a point.

— Look Back —

9. How could you have used a calculator to find the answer? Would this be easier? Explain. Possible answer: Change fractions to decimals. Yes, less chance for calculation error.

SOLVE ANOTHER PROBLEM

Joe's stock rose $\frac{5}{8}$ of a point Monday, fell $\frac{7}{8}$ of a point Tuesday, and fell $2\frac{1}{2}$ points Wednesday. Write an algebraic expression for the situation and find the overall change in his stock for these three days.
$(+\frac{5}{8}) + (-\frac{7}{8}) + (-2\frac{1}{2}) = -2\frac{3}{4}$; Down $2\frac{3}{4}$ points.

► ENRICHMENT

Name _____

Extend Your Thinking 7-5

Visual Thinking

For each set below, show how you would rearrange the counters in the first diagram to make the arrangement in the second diagram in only four moves. Draw a diagram to show each movement.

Possible answers: Items 1 and 2

1. For each move, move two adjacent counters. After the first move, move two different counters to the vacant position.

Start: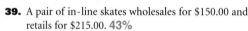

Finish:

First Move

Second Move

Third Move

Fourth Move

2. For each move, move only one counter. Each counter must touch at least one other counter.

Start: Finish:

First Move   Second Move

Third Move   Fourth Move

3. Try to solve Item 2 using only two moves.

Multiply and Divide Rational Numbers

▶ **Lesson Link** You have learned how to add and subtract rational numbers, and now you will learn how to multiply and divide rational numbers. ◀

Explore | Multiplication and Division

Hauling H₂O

Materials: Calculator

The bottled-water company delivers water in two sizes: 5-gallon bottles that sell for $8.00 and 3-gallon bottles that sell for $5.50.

Your delivery truck carries 195 bottles on a delivery-truck route, 66.$\overline{66}$% of which are 5-gallon bottles.

1. How many 5-gallon bottles are on your truck before delivery? How many 3-gallon bottles?

2. What is the total value of bottled water on a full delivery truck?

3. Compare your answers with your group and discuss how you used 66.$\overline{66}$%.

4. The company is having a special promotion: If you buy four bottles you get the fifth bottle free. If during the year you use 24 three-gallon bottles, how much money would you save with this special deal?

5. If you use 24 three-gallon bottles a year, how many total gallons of water is this? How many 5-gallon bottles would this be?

6. Which would be more economical for you, buying 3-gallon bottles or 5-gallon bottles? Why?

7-6 • Multiply and Divide Rational Numbers **355**

You'll Learn ...

■ to multiply and divide rational numbers

... How It's Used

Caterers, who are responsible for covering their expenses, use rational numbers to ensure they make a profit.

▶ Review

Multiply each number by 10, 100, and 1000.

1. **0.567** 5.67, 56.7, 567

2. **0.6** 6, 60, 600

Find the reciprocal of each number.

3. 16 $\frac{1}{16}$ 4. $\frac{2}{11}$ $\frac{11}{2}$

Write each mixed number as an improper fraction.

5. $1\frac{2}{3}$ $\frac{5}{3}$ 6. $5\frac{1}{5}$ $\frac{26}{5}$

Available on Daily Transparency 7-6

▶ Lesson Link

In this lesson students will learn how to multiply and divide rational numbers. They will use previously learned skills, such as multiplying and dividing integers, multiplying and dividing by powers of ten, finding reciprocals, and writing mixed numbers as improper fractions.

1 Introduce

Explore

The Point
Students explore multiplying and dividing rational numbers, including how to compute with 66.$\overline{66}$%.

Answers for **Explore** on next page.

MEETING INDIVIDUAL NEEDS

Resources

7-6 Practice

7-6 Reteaching

7-6 Problem Solving

7-6 Enrichment

7-6 Daily Transparency
   Problem of the Day
   Review
   Quick Quiz

Teaching Tool
Transparencies 2, 3

Technology Master 29

 Interactive CD-ROM Lesson

Learning Modalities

Kinesthetic Have students make a poster showing a mixed number "changing its appearance" and becoming an improper fraction.

Musical Challenge students to make up a rap song that describes the rules for division of fractions.

Individual Have students do research to find three interesting facts about fractions and freshwater.

Challenge

According to federal law, the length of a United States flag must be 1.9 times its width. Draw three legal U.S. flags of different sizes.

Check in Step 1 that students find 66.66% of 195 correctly. Some students might use the decimal equivalent 0.6666..., others might use the fraction $\frac{2}{3}$.

For Groups That Finish Early

Discuss how you might use your calculator to find 66.6% of 195. Possible answers: Enter 195 $\boxed{\times}$ 66.66666666 $\boxed{\%}$ $\boxed{=}$; Enter 195 $\boxed{\times}$ 2 $\boxed{\div}$ 3 $\boxed{=}$.

Follow Up

Ask volunteers to share their answers for Step 3. Have them explain how they found the answers to Steps 4–6. Discuss their answers.

Answers for Explore

1. 130; 65

2. $1397.50

3. $66.\overline{66}\% = \frac{2}{3}$

4. $22.00 and you get an extra bottle.

5. 72 gallons; $14\frac{2}{5}$ bottles

6. 5-gallon bottles; They cost less per gallon.

2 Teach

Learn

Remind students that multiplying or dividing decimals is similar to multiplying or dividing whole numbers, but students have to be careful to place the decimal point correctly in the answer.

Alternate Examples

1. On an electric bill, customers are charged $0.12419 for each kilowatt-hour of electricity used. A family used 462 kilo-watt-hours last month. How much did they have to pay for electricity?

0.12419	5 decimal places
× 462	0 decimal places
57.37578	5 decimal places

The total cost for electricity for a month was $57.38.

2. Divide 18.87 by –0.3.

$-0.3\overline{)18.87}$

Multiply the divisor by a power of 10 to make it a whole number. Multiply the dividend by the same power of 10.

$-3\overline{)188.7}$

Divide. Put the decimal point and minus sign in the quotient.

$$\begin{array}{r} -62.9 \\ -3\overline{)188.7} \end{array}$$

Learn | Multiply and Divide Rational Numbers

To multiply decimals, first multiply as with integers. Then count the total number of decimal places in the factors. Show this total number of decimal places in the product.

Example 1

Study TIP

Learn things your way when you study. Put new vocabulary and ideas into your own words.

The average American household of 2.5 people uses 5230.4 gallons of water a month. The cost per gallon is $0.0025. Determine the average monthly bill for water usage.

Multiply 5230.4 × 0.0025.

$$\begin{array}{r} 5230.4 \quad \leftarrow \text{1 decimal place} \\ \times 0.0025 \quad \leftarrow \text{4 decimal places} \\ \hline 261520 \\ +1046080 \\ \hline 13.07600 \quad \leftarrow \text{5 decimal places} \end{array}$$

The average monthly bill is $13.076, or $13.08.

Try It

Multiply each.

a. -24×0.15 b. -7.99×-7.03
        −3.6   56.1697

Example 2

Divide -16.92 by 0.3.

$0.3\overline{)-16.92}$

$3\overline{)-169.2}$ Multiply the divisor by a power of 10 to make it a whole number. Multiply the dividend by the same power of 10.

$$\begin{array}{r} -56.4 \\ 3\overline{)-169.2} \end{array}$$ Divide. Put the point and negative sign in the quotient.

Try It

Divide each.

a. $3.36 \div 1.5$ b. $-60 \div 0.88$
        2.24   −68.18

MATH EVERY DAY

▶ Problem of the Day

Phil has some quarters, dimes, nickels, and pennies. He has twice as many dimes as quarters and four fewer nickels than pennies. In all, he has $4 in change. How many coins does he have? Possible answer: 40 (8 quarters, 16 dimes, 6 nickels, 10 pennies)

Available on Daily Transparency 7-6

An Extension is provided in the transparency package.

Fact of the Day

A dripping faucet will waste 1000 gallons or more of water in one year.

Mental Math

Do these mentally.

1. $\frac{3}{8} \times \frac{2}{8}$ $\frac{3}{32}$

2. $1\frac{1}{2} \times 5$ $7\frac{1}{2}$

3. $\frac{1}{4} \div \frac{1}{4}$ 1

4. $-3\frac{1}{2} \div \frac{1}{2}$ −7

To multiply with mixed numbers, first rewrite them as improper fractions. Multiply numerators; then multiply denominators.

Example 3

A four-person household uses about $242\frac{1}{2}$ gallons of water daily. About $\frac{3}{50}$ of daily water comes from the bathroom sink. How many gallons of water is this?

Write $242\frac{1}{2}$ as an improper fraction and multiply.

$$\frac{3}{50} \times 242\frac{1}{2} = \frac{3}{50} \times \frac{485}{2} = \frac{1455}{100}$$

Write $\frac{1455}{100}$ as a mixed number in lowest terms.

$$\frac{1455}{100} = 14\frac{55}{100} = 14\frac{11}{20}$$

$14\frac{11}{20}$ gallons of water comes from the bathroom sink daily.

Try It

Multiply. **a.** $8\frac{3}{4} \times \frac{-5}{12}$ $-3\frac{31}{48}$ **b.** $6 \times 3\frac{2}{3}$ 22

Dividing by a mixed number is the same as multiplying by its reciprocal. The product of a number and its reciprocal is 1.

$\frac{3}{4}$ and $\frac{4}{3}$ are reciprocals because $\frac{3}{4} \times \frac{4}{3} = 1$.

Example 4

Divide $2\frac{5}{6} \div \frac{1}{3}$.

$2\frac{5}{6} \div \frac{1}{3} = \frac{17}{6} \div \frac{1}{3}$ Write $2\frac{5}{6}$ as an improper fraction.

$\frac{17}{6} \times \frac{3}{1} = \frac{17 \times 3}{6 \times 1} = \frac{51}{6}$ Change divisor to its reciprocal and multiply.

$8\frac{3}{6} = 8\frac{1}{2}$ Write as a mixed number in lowest terms.

Try It

Divide. **a.** $-2\frac{1}{2} \div \frac{-5}{8}$ 4 **b.** $\frac{9}{10} \div \frac{1}{5}$ $4\frac{1}{2}$

Test Prep

Stay smart! Review what you've learned earlier in the school year; you never know when you'll need it.

Estimation

Since there are 3 thirds in 1, 6 thirds in 2, and 9 thirds in 3, an estimate for the number of thirds in $2\frac{5}{6}$ is 9.

Alternate Examples

3. Mr. Johnson keeps track of his mileage and the gasoline he uses each time he fills his gas tank. He found that he uses about $42\frac{2}{5}$ gallons of gasoline per month. If $\frac{3}{4}$ of the gasoline is used for work-related trips, how many gallons of gasoline are used for this purpose?

Write $42\frac{2}{5}$ as an improper fraction and multiply:

$\frac{3}{4} \times 42\frac{2}{5} = \frac{3}{4} \times \frac{212}{5} = \frac{636}{20}$

Write the answer as a mixed number in lowest terms:

$\frac{636}{20} = 31\frac{16}{20} = 31\frac{4}{5}$

4. Find $4\frac{5}{8} \div \frac{1}{4}$.

Write $4\frac{5}{8}$ as an improper fraction.

$4\frac{5}{8} \div \frac{1}{4} = \frac{37}{8} \div \frac{1}{4}$

Change divisor to its reciprocal and multiply:

$\frac{37}{8} \times \frac{4}{1} = \frac{37 \times 4}{8 \times 1} = \frac{148}{8}$

Write the answer in lowest terms:

$18\frac{4}{8} = 18\frac{1}{2}$

MEETING MIDDLE SCHOOL CLASSROOM NEEDS

Tips from Middle School Teachers

I have an index-card file case with problems and exercises grouped according to skills involved. When my class is working on division of fractions and decimals, I ask volunteers to take a card with a division of decimals or division of fractions problem and explain how to do the computation to the class. This practice reviews students' math skills and helps them improve their communication skills.

Geography Connection

Deserts cover about $\frac{1}{7}$ of the earth's land. The Sahara desert in Africa covers $3\frac{1}{2}$ million square miles while all of the North American deserts cover only about 500,000 square miles. Ask how many times larger the Sahara Desert is than all of the North American deserts. 7 times

Cultural Connection

According to the U.S. Bureau of Census, the total population of those over five years of age in the United States in 1990 was 230,445,777. Of those, 31,844,979 spoke a language other than English at home. Of the latter, 17,339,172 spoke Spanish. Students may find out what part of the population of their community speaks a language other than English at home.

Students see two methods of solving a problem requiring division of fractions. One method uses a calculator and changes each fraction to a decimal before finding the quotient. The other method works with the fractions. Students can decide which of the two methods is easier for them.

A third method not shown would be to find a common denominator and divide the numerators.

$$\frac{15}{4} \div \frac{3}{2} = \frac{15}{4} \div \frac{6}{4} =$$

$$15 \div 6 = 2\frac{3}{6} = 2\frac{1}{2}$$

Answers for What Do You Think?

1. Possible answer: $\frac{15}{4}$ is the same as $15 \div 4$; $\frac{3}{2}$ is the same as $3 \div 2$.

2. Possible answer: Write as decimals: $3.75 \div 1.5$.

3 Practice and Assess

Check

Be sure students understand that they should change mixed numbers to improper fractions before they multiply or divide.

Answers for Check Your Understanding
1. Multiply: Rewrite them as improper fractions, multiply numerators, then multiply denominators.

   Divide: Rewrite them as improper fractions, change the divisor to its reciprocal and multiply.

2. Express the numbers as a fraction, then switch the numerator and denominator.

Randy and Mary are putting $3\frac{3}{4}$ liters of pasta sauce into 1.5-liter jars. How many 1.5-liter jars do they need?

Randy thinks ...

First, I'll write everything as a fraction. $3\frac{3}{4} = \frac{15}{4}$. Also,

$1.5 = \frac{3}{2}$. I think of fractions as "minidivision expressions."

$$\frac{15}{4} \div \frac{3}{2} = (15 \div 4) \div (3 \div 2)$$

I'll use my calculator. ⌈ 15 ÷ 4 ⌉ ÷ ⌈ 3 ÷ 2 ⌉ = 2.5

Since there is no such thing as 2.5 jars, we need 3 jars.

Mary thinks ...

I need to rewrite $3\frac{3}{4}$ as an improper fraction. $3\frac{3}{4} = \frac{15}{4}$

I'll convert the decimal to a fraction. $1.5 = \frac{15}{10} = \frac{15 \div 5}{10 \div 5} = \frac{3}{2}$

Now I'll set up my division expression and divide. $\frac{15}{4} \div \frac{3}{2} = \frac{15}{4} \times \frac{2}{3} = \frac{15 \times 2}{4 \times 3} = \frac{30}{12}$

$\frac{30}{12} = 2\frac{1}{2}$. We'll need to round $2\frac{1}{2}$ jars to 3 jars.

What do you think?

1. Explain the meaning of Randy's phrase "minidivision equations."

2. Describe another way of dividing $3\frac{3}{4} \div \frac{3}{2}$.

Check   **Your Understanding**

1. Explain how to multiply and divide with mixed numbers.

2. Describe how to determine the reciprocal of a number.

358   *Chapter 7 • Number Sense, Rational Numbers, and Irrational Numbers*

7-6 Exercises and Applications

Practice and Apply

1. **Getting Started** Divide $3\frac{1}{4} \div \frac{1}{6}$.
   a. Rewrite the mixed number as an improper fraction. $\frac{13}{4}$
   b. Multiply by the reciprocal of the divisor. $\frac{78}{4}$

2. -0.615
3. 0.0072
4. 0.6396
5. 0.032
6. 0.93

Multiply or divide each of the following. Write each answer in lowest terms.

2. -1.23×0.5
3. 0.009×0.8
4. 2.46×0.26
5. $4\overline{)0.128}$
6. $-3.2\overline{)-2.976}$

7. $\frac{1}{5} \times \frac{5}{9}$ $\frac{1}{9}$
8. $\frac{7}{8} \times \frac{2}{3}$ $\frac{7}{12}$
9. $3 \times -\frac{7}{9}$ $-2\frac{1}{3}$
10. $\frac{3}{5} \times \frac{8}{9}$ $\frac{8}{15}$
11. $\frac{1}{2} \times \frac{1}{3}$ $\frac{1}{6}$

12. $-7\frac{6}{7} \times -11$ $86\frac{3}{7}$
13. $\frac{13}{23} \times 2\frac{4}{5}$ $1\frac{67}{115}$
14. $\frac{3}{6} \div \frac{-1}{2}$ -1
15. $\frac{4}{8} \div \frac{7}{9}$ $\frac{9}{14}$
16. $4 \div \frac{2}{3}$ 6

17. $\frac{4}{7} \div \frac{4}{9}$ $1\frac{2}{7}$
18. $8 \div \frac{1}{4}$ 32
19. $30 \div \frac{1}{5}$ 150
20. $-3\frac{1}{2} \div \frac{3}{4}$ $-4\frac{2}{3}$
21. $\frac{1}{6} \div 3\frac{4}{5}$ $\frac{5}{114}$

22. **Science** The oceans cover about 7.5 million square miles of Earth's surface. If $\frac{3}{25}$ of the oceans are capped with glacial ice, what is the approximate area of the glaciers on our planet? **900,000 square miles**

23. **Geography** The Antarctic ice sheet covers an area $1\frac{1}{2}$ times the area of the 48 contiguous states, which is 3,016,345 square miles. What is the area of the Antarctic ice sheet? $\approx$ **4,524,518 square miles**

24. The Dall's porpoise is one of the fastest swimmers in the species. It can travel up to 50 kilometers per hour. At this speed, how far would this porpoise travel in $\frac{3}{4}$ hour? **37.5 kilometers**

25. **Algebra** Some cacti can store 100 gallons of water over a 4-month rainy season. Write an expression with fractions that states the average amount of water stored each rainy month. $\frac{1}{4} \times 100$ **gallons**

26. The eighth-grade class budgeted $1420 for the graduation dinner. Each person's dinner will cost $6.75. What is the greatest number of people that can attend the dinner? **210**

27. **Test Prep** Choose the expression that results in the product with the greatest absolute value. **A**
   Ⓐ $3 \times \frac{1}{2}$ Ⓑ $3 \times \frac{1}{3}$ Ⓒ $3 \times \frac{1}{4}$ Ⓓ $3 \times \frac{1}{5}$

7-6 • Multiply and Divide Rational Numbers   **359**

7-6 Exercises and Applications

Assignment Guide

■ **Basic**
1, 2–20 evens, 23–27 odds, 28–29, 31–34, 39–42

■ **Average**
1–21 odds, 22, 25–28, 30, 31, 34–38, 43

■ **Enriched**
3–21 odds, 22–31, 37–41 odds

Exercise Notes

■ **Exercises 2–6**

Estimation Students should estimate answers to check that the computed answers are reasonable.

■ **Exercise 6**

Error Prevention Watch for students who may not remember that they should multiply the divisor by a power of 10 to make it a whole number and that they must also multiply the dividend by the same power of 10.

Reteaching

Activity

Materials: Plain $8\frac{1}{2}$ by 11-inch paper, ruler, colored pencils

- Work in pairs. You and your partner will make a picture to show $\frac{2}{3} \times \frac{3}{4}$.

- Divide a sheet of paper lengthwise into 4 equal parts. Shade 3 of the parts to show $\frac{3}{4}$.

- Divide the same sheet of paper widthwise into 3 equal parts. Shade 2 of these parts a different color to show $\frac{2}{3}$. The portion of the paper shaded in both colors shows $\frac{2}{3} \times \frac{3}{4}$. Count the equal parts in this area. What fraction of the whole paper is shaded in both colors? $\frac{6}{12}$ or $\frac{1}{2}$

- Repeat this activity for $\frac{3}{5} \times \frac{2}{3}$. $\frac{3}{5} \times \frac{2}{3} = \frac{2}{5}$

> ## PRACTICE

Name _____

Practice 7-6

Multiply and Divide Rational Numbers

Multiply or divide each of the following. Write each answer in lowest terms.

1. $97.98 \times (-0.2)$ -19.596
2. 7.039×0.04 0.28156
3. $-0.1 \times (-4.1)$ 0.41
4. -0.05×0.014 -0.0007

5. $0.17\overline{)8.126}$ 47.8
6. $-3.6\overline{)32.256}$ -8.96
7. $-0.5\overline{)-423.55}$ 847.1
8. $2.7\overline{)-19.899}$ -7.37

9. -0.06×5.89 -0.3534
10. 4×0.478 1.912
11. $-5.8 \times (-7.2)$ 41.76
12. $0.008 \times (-12.22)$ -0.09776

13. $-5.5\overline{)-34.1}$ 6.2
14. $8.58\overline{)-0.1716}$ -0.02
15. $0.091\overline{)8.6541}$ 95.1
16. $-0.87\overline{)-4.524}$ 5.2

17. $\frac{3}{8} \times \frac{5}{6}$ $\frac{5}{16}$
18. $\frac{4}{9} \times \frac{6}{7}$ $\frac{8}{21}$
19. $\frac{4}{5} \times \frac{11}{12}$ $\frac{11}{15}$

20. $\frac{1}{2} \div \frac{7}{9}$ $\frac{9}{14}$
21. $\frac{3}{5} \div \frac{7}{8}$ $\frac{24}{35}$
22. $\frac{5}{7} \div \frac{15}{28}$ $1\frac{1}{3}$

23. $\frac{1}{5} \times 7\frac{1}{8}$ $1\frac{17}{40}$
24. $3 \times 6\frac{5}{9}$ $19\frac{2}{3}$
25. $2 \times 2\frac{1}{5}$ $4\frac{2}{5}$

26. $1\frac{2}{3} \div 3\frac{4}{5}$ $\frac{25}{57}$
27. $1\frac{3}{5} \div 2\frac{6}{7}$ $\frac{49}{100}$
28. $1 \div 14\frac{1}{2}$ $\frac{2}{29}$

29. $4\frac{3}{7} \times 1\frac{1}{4}$ $5\frac{15}{28}$
30. $1\frac{6}{7} \times (-5)$ $-9\frac{2}{7}$
31. $\frac{2}{5} \times 6\frac{3}{10}$ $2\frac{13}{25}$

32. $1\frac{1}{2} \div (-8)$ $-\frac{3}{16}$
33. $3\frac{1}{2} \div \frac{5}{7}$ $4\frac{9}{10}$
34. $-8\frac{1}{2} \div 9$ $-\frac{17}{18}$

35. $-3 \times 7\frac{2}{3}$ -23
36. $1\frac{1}{5} \times 5\frac{1}{6}$ $6\frac{1}{5}$
37. $6\frac{1}{4} \times 4\frac{1}{10}$ $25\frac{5}{8}$

38. $1\frac{11}{14} \div 2\frac{1}{7}$ $\frac{5}{6}$
39. $16 \div 1\frac{2}{5}$ $11\frac{3}{7}$
40. $2\frac{5}{8} \div 7\frac{1}{2}$ $\frac{7}{20}$

41. **Social Science** In 1994, about $\frac{27}{140}$ of the federal budget was spent on national defense. About $\frac{1}{28}$ of the money spent on defense was used for military personnel. What fraction of the federal budget was spent on military personnel? **About $\frac{27}{500}$**

42. **Geography** The area of Columbia is about $1\frac{1}{4}$ times the area of Venezuela, which is about 352,000 square miles. What is the area of Columbia? **About 440,000 mi²**

> ## RETEACHING

Name _____

Alternative Lesson 7-6

Multiply and Divide Rational Numbers

You can multiply and divide rational numbers written as fractions and mixed numbers by first rewriting the mixed numbers as improper fractions. Then, multiply numerators and multiply denominators.

Dividing by a fraction or mixed number is the same as multiplying by the reciprocal of the divisor. The product of a number and its reciprocal is 1.

Example 1

Find $3\frac{1}{4} \times 2\frac{3}{5}$.

Step 1: Write mixed numbers as improper fractions. $3\frac{1}{4} \times 2\frac{3}{5} = \frac{13}{4} \times \frac{13}{5}$

Step 2: Multiply numerators and multiply denominators. $= \frac{169}{20}$

Step 3: Write as a mixed number in lowest terms. $= 8\frac{9}{20}$

So, $3\frac{1}{4} \times 2\frac{3}{5} = 8\frac{9}{20}$.

Try It Multiply. Write each answer in lowest terms.

a. $2\frac{1}{2} \times 3\frac{2}{5}$ $8\frac{1}{2}$
b. $4\frac{1}{8} \times 1\frac{1}{3}$ $5\frac{1}{2}$
c. $2\frac{3}{10} \times 1\frac{1}{4}$ $2\frac{7}{8}$

d. $5\frac{1}{3} \times 2\frac{3}{4}$ $14\frac{2}{3}$
e. $6\frac{1}{4} \times 2\frac{1}{5}$ $13\frac{3}{4}$
f. $3\frac{9}{10} \times 3\frac{1}{3}$ 13

g. $1\frac{2}{5} \times 2\frac{2}{5}$ $3\frac{9}{25}$
h. $1\frac{1}{3} \times 1\frac{1}{6}$ $1\frac{5}{9}$
i. $1\frac{1}{4} \times 1\frac{2}{3}$ $2\frac{1}{12}$

Example 2

Find $3\frac{1}{2} \div 12$.

Step 1: Write the mixed number as an improper fraction. $3\frac{1}{2} \div 12$

Step 2: Change the divisor to its reciprocal. $\downarrow \quad \downarrow$

Step 3: Multiply numerators and multiply denominators. $\frac{7}{2} \times \frac{1}{12} = \frac{7}{24}$

Step 4: Write as a mixed number in lowest terms. $\frac{7}{24}$ is in lowest terms.

So, $3\frac{1}{2} \div 12 = \frac{7}{24}$.

Try It Divide. Write each answer in lowest terms.

j. $5 \div \frac{3}{4}$ $6\frac{2}{3}$
k. $2\frac{1}{4} \div 1\frac{3}{8}$ $1\frac{7}{11}$
l. $2\frac{4}{5} \div \frac{1}{2}$ $5\frac{3}{5}$

m. $1\frac{3}{5} \div \frac{3}{10}$ $5\frac{1}{3}$
n. $3\frac{1}{4} \div \frac{7}{8}$ $3\frac{5}{7}$
o. $3\frac{1}{6} \div 2$ $1\frac{7}{12}$

p. $3 \div 2\frac{7}{10}$ $1\frac{1}{9}$
q. $1\frac{2}{3} \div 1\frac{1}{3}$ $1\frac{1}{4}$
r. $6\frac{1}{2} \div 3\frac{1}{4}$ 2

Problem-Solving Tip Suggest that students model this problem on their calculators so they can see what happens with each step.

■ **Exercise 30**

Extension All the freshwater lakes in the world hold about 30,000 cubic miles of water. What fraction of this is in the Great Lakes? $\frac{5439}{30000} = \frac{1813}{10000}$ or 0.1813

■ **Exercise 31**

Problem-Solving Tip You may wish to use Teaching Tool Transparencies 2 and 3: Guided Problem Solving, pages 1–2.

■ **Exercise 32**

Extension Does multiplication of positive integers satisfy the closure property? Of negative integers? Yes since (+) (+) = (+); No since (−) (−) = (+)

Exercise Answers

28. $28\frac{3}{4}$ inches; Possible answer: Convert the mixed number to an improper fraction, multiply by 10, and simplify.

29. No; Possible answer: It is missing the necessary parentheses for the correct order of operations.

31. No; Possible answer: If both of the numbers are < 1, their product would have to be < 1.

32. Multiplication of even numbers satisfies the closure property. Multiplication of odd numbers satisfies the closure property.

Alternate Assessment

Portfolio Students might place the diagrams from the Reteaching activity, along with an explanation of each diagram, in their portfolios.

▶ **Quick Quiz**

1. Multiply 4540.2 by $0.034. $154.37

2. Divide 15.46 by 0.2. 77.3

3. A family of three uses about $182\frac{1}{2}$ gallons of water daily. $\frac{1}{20}$ of this water is used for washing clothes. How many gallons of water is this? $9\frac{1}{8}$

4. Find $3\frac{3}{8} \div \frac{1}{5}$. $16\frac{7}{8}$

Available on Daily Transparency 7-6

Problem Solving and Reasoning

PROBLEM SOLVING 7-6

28. **Communicate** Some say that the average ratio of inches of snow to inches of water is 10 to 1. If the snow is equivalent to $2\frac{7}{8}$ inches of water, how many inches of snow are there? Explain your reasoning.

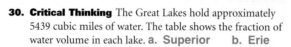

29. **Math Reasoning** Will the following calculator key strokes correctly evaluate $\frac{1}{2} \div \frac{3}{4}$? 1 ÷ 2 ÷ 3 ÷ 4 =. Explain your reasoning.

30. **Critical Thinking** The Great Lakes hold approximately 5439 cubic miles of water. The table shows the fraction of water volume in each lake. **a. Superior   b. Erie**

   a. Which lake is the largest?   b. Smallest?

   c. What is the approximate volume of each lake?

Great Lake	Superior	Michigan	Huron	Erie	Ontario
Volume Part	$\frac{53}{100}$	$\frac{11}{50}$	$\frac{4}{25}$	$\frac{1}{50}$	$\frac{7}{100}$

c. $2,882\frac{2}{3}$ mi³; $1,196\frac{3}{5}$ mi³; $870\frac{1}{4}$ mi³; $108\frac{4}{5}$ mi³; $380\frac{3}{4}$ mi³

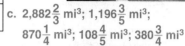

31. **Choose a Strategy** The product of two positive numbers is greater than one. Can both of these numbers be less than one? Describe your strategy and how you used it.

32. **Math Reasoning** Multiplication of integers satisfies the *closure property* because if you multiply any two integers the product will be an integer. Does multiplication of even numbers satisfy the closure property? Multiplication of odd numbers? If not, give an example.

Problem Solving

STRATEGIES

- Look for a Pattern
- Make an Organized List
- Make a Table
- Guess and Check
- Work Backward
- Use Logical Reasoning
- Draw a Diagram
- Solve a Simpler Problem

Mixed Review

Solve each equation. *[Lesson 3-5]*

33. $9x = 81$ 34. $\frac{x}{4} = 16$ $x = 64$ 35. $-x = 44$ 36. $18x = 3$ $x = \frac{1}{6}$
   $x = 9$ $x = -44$

37. $-5x = 205$ 38. $20x = -140$ 39. $x \div 7 = 3$ 40. $4 \cdot x = 88$
   $x = -41$ $x = -7$ $x = 21$ $x = 22$

Find the percent of decrease. Round to the nearest whole percent. *[Lesson 6-5]*

41. Price of a video game that was $54.00 and marked down to $36.00 **33%**

42. If there were 120 apples in the basket and 30 were eaten **25%**

43. Price of a skateboard that was $26.00 before sale of $5.00 off **19%**

360 *Chapter 7 • Number Sense, Rational Numbers, and Irrational Numbers*

▷ **PROBLEM SOLVING**

Name _____

Guided Problem Solving 7-6

GPS **PROBLEM 28, STUDENT PAGE 360**

Some say that the average ratio of inches of snow to inches of water is 10 to 1. If the snow is equivalent to $2\frac{7}{8}$ inches of water, how many inches of snow are there? Explain your reasoning.

Possible answers: Items 4, 7, 8

— **Understand** —
1. What are you asked to find? How many inches of snow are equivalent to $2\frac{7}{8}$ inches of water.

2. What is the average ratio of inches of snow to water? __10 to 1__

— **Plan** —
3. Write $2\frac{7}{8}$ as a decimal. __2.875__

4. Let x represent inches of snow. Write a proportion for the problem using 10 to 1 and x. $\frac{10}{1} = \frac{x}{2.875}$

— **Solve** —
5. Solve for x. __28.75__

6. How many inches of snow is equivalent to $2\frac{7}{8}$ inches of water? __28.75 in.__

7. Explain your reasoning. Proportion shows the relationship between inches of snow and rain. Solving the proportion will give the missing measurement.

— **Look Back** —
8. How could you have found the answer using an improper fraction? Convert the mixed number, write the proportions, and simplify.

▢ **SOLVE ANOTHER PROBLEM**

The average ratio of inches of rain to inches of snow is 1 to 10. How many inches of rain is equivalent to $16\frac{1}{2}$ inches of snow? Explain your reasoning.

1.65 in.; $\frac{1}{10} = \frac{x}{16.5}$; x = 1.65; Proportion shows the relationship between inches of rain and snow. Solving the proportion will give the missing measurements.

▷ **ENRICHMENT**

Name _____

Extend Your Thinking 7-6

Visual Thinking

Four figures in each row are identical. Circle the letter of the figure that is different.

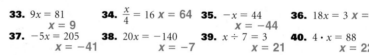

1.
   a.   b.   c.   d.   e.

2.
   a.   b.   c.   d.   e.

3.
   a.   b.   c.   d.   e.

4.
   a.   b.   c.   d.   e.

5.
   a.   b.   c.   d.   e.

You have learned how to work with rational numbers. Now you will apply what you have learned to understand how water is used by the world.

Will There Be a Drop to Drink?

Materials: Calculator

Some of the most beautiful cities in the world are located near water. The oceans cover at least 70% of Earth's surface.

We've all heard, "Don't leave the water running!!" Why? It must be an important resource.

Use your calculator to compare data about water usage. You will compare how much water is used for industrial, agricultural, and household purposes.

1. The United States gets $\frac{37}{50}$ of its freshwater from surface sources and the other part from underground sources. What part of our freshwater comes from underground?

2. Use the table below to discuss how the former Soviet Union, United States, and China use water. How does each country use its freshwater resources? What fractional part is used for household consumption?

	Industry	Agriculture	Household
Former Soviet Union	$\frac{9}{20}$	$\frac{51}{100}$	?
United States	$\frac{29}{50}$	$\frac{17}{50}$	?
China	$\frac{1}{20}$	$\frac{93}{100}$	?

3. On a worldwide basis water uses are allocated as follows: $\frac{1}{10}$ for domestic use, $\frac{1}{10}$ for industrial use, and $\frac{4}{5}$ for agricultural use. Does this allocation account for all of the world's water usage?

4. Discuss how the world uses water compared to the three countries mentioned above.

361

Will There Be a Drop to Drink?

The Point
In *Will There Be a Drop to Drink?* on page 343, students learned about the actual amount of fresh water on the Earth's surface. Now they will apply rational numbers to learn how water is used by the world.

Materials
Calculator

Resources
Teaching Tool Transparency 24: Fraction Calculator

About the Page

• Be sure students understand how to use a calculator to change fractions to decimals.

• Be sure students understand how to compare decimals.

• Point out to students that there is more than one way to find the answers to these questions. To emphasize this point, have students who used different methods share their work with the class.

Ongoing Assessment
Check that students' calculations with rational numbers are correct.

Extension

Have students represent some of the data presented in this feature in a visual to emphasize a specific point.

Answers for Connect

1. $\frac{13}{50}$ or 26%

2. Possible answers: The former Soviet Union and China use most of their water for agriculture. The U.S. uses most of its water for industry.
$\frac{1}{25}, \frac{2}{25}, \frac{1}{50}$

3. Yes.

4. Answers may vary.

Section 7B Review

Review Correlation

Item(s)	Lesson(s)
1–14	7-4
15, 16	7-5
17–18	7-6
19–22	7-5
23–31	7-6

Test Prep

Test-Taking Tip

Tell students that on multiple-choice tests sometimes one of the possible answers is "none of these." If such a choice is given, and seems to be the correct choice, students should recheck their work to be sure.

Answers for Review

1.

2.

3.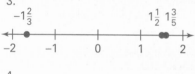

4.

Compare each group of numbers and order them on a number line.

1. $-1.07, 1.05, -1$
2. $\frac{-2}{3}, \frac{2}{6}, \frac{-1}{3}$
3. $1\frac{1}{2}, 1\frac{3}{5}, -1\frac{2}{3}$
4. $1.5, -\frac{3}{4}, 1\frac{3}{4}$

Write each fraction as a decimal and determine whether it's terminating or repeating.

5. $\frac{3}{4}$ 6. $-\frac{5}{6}$ 7. $11\frac{5}{7}$ 8. $-\frac{3}{9}$ 9. $4\frac{7}{10}$ **7.** $11.\overline{714285}$; R
   0.75; T $-0.8\overline{3}$; R $-0.\overline{3}$; R 4.7; T

Write each decimal as a fraction or mixed number.

10. -2.34 11. 3.005 12. -0.451 13. $0.\overline{364}$ 14. $2.\overline{11}$
   $-2\frac{17}{50}$ $3\frac{1}{200}$ $-\frac{451}{1000}$ $\frac{364}{999}$ $2\frac{1}{9}$

Calculate.
   7.42 7.99275 -0.1326 313.9375
15. $0.3 + 7.12$ 16. $8 - 0.00725$ 17. $3.4 \times (-0.039)$ 18. $100.46 \div 0.32$

19. $\frac{1}{6} + \left(-\frac{1}{8}\right)$ $\frac{1}{24}$ 20. $8\frac{1}{2} + 2\frac{3}{4}$ $11\frac{1}{4}$ 21. $3 - 1\frac{3}{8}$ $1\frac{5}{8}$ 22. $\frac{2}{3} - \left(-\frac{5}{7}\right)$ $1\frac{8}{21}$

23. $\frac{4}{9} \times \frac{-3}{8}$ $-\frac{1}{6}$ 24. $3\frac{1}{4} \times \frac{6}{7}$ $2\frac{11}{14}$ 25. $5 \div \frac{1}{3}$ 15 26. $-4\frac{1}{5} \div -2\frac{2}{3}$ $1\frac{23}{40}$

Solve.

27. $\frac{2}{3} = \frac{4}{5} + x$ 28. $\frac{-3}{4} = -\frac{1}{3} - x$ 29. $\frac{6}{7} + \frac{-3}{7} = x$ **27.** $x = -\frac{2}{15}$

30. A number is divided by -6, multiplied by $\frac{3}{4}$, and added to $6\frac{1}{2}$. The result is 18.5. What is the number? Explain how you solved this problem. $-96; \left(\frac{x}{-6} \times \frac{3}{4}\right) + 6\frac{1}{2} = 18\frac{1}{2}$

   28. $x = 1\frac{1}{12}$

   29. $x = \frac{3}{7}$

Test Prep

When taking multiple choice tests, express fractions in lowest terms.

31. Tina swam four laps in $3\frac{3}{10}$ minutes. The swim-team record for the distance is $2\frac{9}{10}$ minutes. How far is Tina from matching the team record? **D**

   Ⓐ $\frac{1}{10}$ minute Ⓑ $\frac{1}{5}$ minute Ⓒ $\frac{3}{10}$ minute Ⓓ None of these

Resources

Practice Masters
   Section 7B Review
Assessment Sourcebook
   Quiz 7B
 TestWorks
   Test and Practice Software

PRACTICE

Name _____

Practice

Section 7B Review

Compare each group of numbers and order them on a number line.

1. $\frac{3}{4}, \frac{5}{6}, 0.\overline{8}, 0.8$ 2. $5\frac{1}{3}, 5\frac{1}{5}, 5.25, 5.\overline{4}$ 3. $-\frac{5}{8}, -\frac{3}{7}, -0.\overline{6}, -0.5$

Write each fraction as a decimal and determine whether it's terminating or repeating.

4. $\frac{5}{7}$ 0.714285; repeating 5. $-\frac{7}{8}$ -0.875; terminating

Write each decimal as a fraction or mixed number.

6. 0.68 $\frac{17}{25}$ 7. $0.\overline{6}$ $\frac{2}{3}$ 8. $-8.\overline{36}$ $-8\frac{4}{11}$

Calculate.

9. $5.63 + 2.073$ 10. $9.6 - 3.176$ 11. 8.36×7.4
   7.703 6.424 61.864

12. $7\frac{5}{8} + 3\frac{5}{6}$ $11\frac{11}{24}$ 13. $1\frac{3}{5} \times 2\frac{1}{6}$ $3\frac{11}{18}$ 14. $10\frac{2}{3} - 8\frac{1}{5}$ $2\frac{7}{15}$

Solve.

15. $\frac{8}{9} = \frac{1}{6} + x$ 16. $x - \frac{3}{8} = \frac{9}{10}$ 17. $3\frac{1}{2} = x - \left(-7\frac{3}{5}\right)$
   $x = \frac{13}{18}$ $x = 1\frac{11}{40}$ $x = -4\frac{1}{10}$

18. For a party, a caterer needs to prepare twice as many chicken sandwiches as vegetarian sandwiches. There are to be 24 sandwiches altogether. Write a system of equations, using x for the number of vegetarian sandwiches and y for the number of chicken sandwiches. Then solve the system using a table or a graph to find the number of each kind of sandwich. *[Lesson 4-6]*

   $y = 2x, x + y = 24$; 8 vegetarian, 16 chicken

19. **Social Science** The population of Chattanooga, Tennessee, was about 120,000 in 1970. The population increased 42% from 1970 to 1980, and decreased 11% from 1980 to 1990. What was the population in 1990? *[Lesson 6-6]*   About 152,000

Section 7C
Irrational Numbers

Visit **www.teacher.mathsurf.com** for links to lesson plans from teachers and other professionals, NCTM information, and other sites.

LESSON PLANNING GUIDE

▶ **Student Edition**

▶ **Ancillaries***

LESSON	MATERIALS	VOCABULARY	DAILY	OTHER
Section 7C Opener				
7-7 Perfect Squares and Square Roots	geometry software, calculator	square root, radical sign, perfect square	7-7	Teaching Tool Trans. 2, 3, 22 Technology Master 30 *Interactive CD-ROM Geometry Tool*
7-8 Square Roots and Irrational Numbers	graph paper, calculator	principal square root, negative square root, irrational number, real numbers	7-8	Teaching Tool Trans. 7, 22 Technology Master 31
7-9 The Pythagorean Theorem	graph paper, scissors, markers (three different colors)	Pythagorean theorem	7-9	Teaching Tool Trans. 7 Lesson Enhancement Trans. 29 Technology Master 32 Ch. 7 Project Master *WW Math*—Middle School
Connect	calculator			Interdisc. Team Teaching 7C
Review				Practice 7C; Quiz 7C; *TestWorks*
Extend Key Ideas				
Chapter 7 Summary and Review				
Chapter 7 Assessment				Ch. 7 Tests Forms A–F *TestWorks;* Ch. 7 Letter Home
Cumulative Review, Chapters 1–7				Cumulative Review Ch. 1–7

* Daily Ancillaries include Practice, Reteaching, Problem Solving, Enrichment, and Daily Transparency. Teaching Tool Transparencies are in *Teacher's Toolkits*. Lesson Enhancement Transparencies are in *Overhead Transparency Package*.

SKILLS TRACE

LESSON	SKILL	FIRST INTRODUCED			DEVELOP	PRACTICE/ APPLY	REVIEW
		GR. 6	GR. 7	GR. 8			
7-7	Finding square roots.			**✗** p. 364	pp. 364–366	pp. 367–368	pp. 380, 383, 426, 604
7-8	Identifying irrational numbers.			**✗** p. 369	pp. 369–371	pp. 372–373	pp. 383, 431, 439, 609
7-9	Using Pythagorean theorem.			**✗** p. 374	pp. 374–376	pp. 377–378	pp. 383, 439, 449, 614

CONNECTED MATHEMATICS

The unit *Looking for Pythagoras (The Pythagorean Theorem),* from the **Connected Mathematics** series, can be used with Section 7C.

Math and Social Studies

(Worksheet pages 29–30: Teacher pages T29–T30)

In this lesson, students use squares, square roots, and the Pythagorean Theorem to determine information about the Great Pyramid.

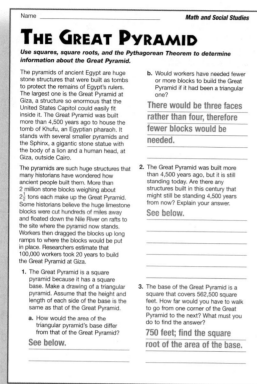

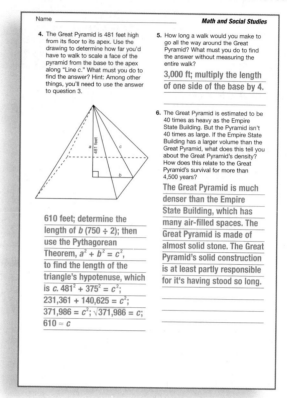

Answers

1. a. The base of the triangular pyramid would have a smaller area than that of the Great Pyramid.

2. Answers will vary depending on the opinions of students. Students can name any modern structure (such as an impressive dam, roadway, building, bridge) but must explain why they chose it. Some students may think that no modern-era structure can withstand the test of time like the Great Pyramid. This answer is acceptable, but students must give their reasoning.

BIBLIOGRAPHY

FOR TEACHERS

Ascher, Marcia. *Ethnomathematics: A Multicultural View of Mathematical Ideas.* Pacific Grove, CA: Brooks/Cole Publishing Co., 1991.

Miller, William and Linda Wagner. "Pythagorean Dissection Puzzles." *Mathematics Teacher* (April 1993): pp. 302–314.

Reys, Barbara J. *Developing Number Sense in the Middle Grades.* Addenda Series, Grades 5–8. Reston, VA: National Council of Teachers of Mathematics, 1991.

Spangler, David. *Math for Real Kids.* Glenview, IL: Good Year Books, 1997.

FOR STUDENTS

Adam, Robert. *Buildings: How They Work.* New York, NY: Sterling Publishing Company Inc., 1995.

Gardner, Robert. *Architecture.* New York, NY: Twenty-First Century Books (A Division of Henry Holt and Company, Inc.), 1994.

Glenn, Patricia Brown. *Under Every Roof: A Kids' Style and Field Guide to the Architecture of American Houses.* Washington, D.C.: The Preservation Press (National Trust for Historic Preservation), 1993.

Spinelli, Jerry. *Maniac Magee.* Boston, MA: Little, Brown, & Co., 1990.

SECTION 7C

Irrational Numbers

▶ **Social Studies Link** ▶ **Geography Link** ▶ **www.mathsurf.com/8/ch7/houses**

HOME SWEET HOME

Around the world, people live in a variety of dwellings. Whether the residence is an adobe hut on the plains, a tent in the desert, a high-rise apartment in a big city, or a house in the suburbs, it is called home. Each of these homes is based on an architect's or builder's plan. Building homes involves using numbers such as integers, decimals, or fractions.

People have different homes due to climate, culture, or landscape. In places without trees, you may find a home built of stone or mud. In the forest, you'd be able to find a log cabin. In the southwest United States, the Anasazi people carved their homes into the rock of a mountainside.

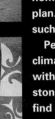
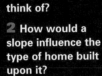

1 What are some shapes of homes that you can think of?

2 How would a slope influence the type of home built upon it?

3 How do you think the need for shelter influences mathematics?

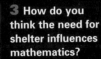

363

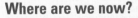

Where are we now?

In Section 7B, students explored rational numbers.

They learned how to

- use the LCM and GCF to work with rational numbers.

- add and subtract rational numbers.

- multiply and divide rational numbers.

Where are we going?

In Section 7C, students will

- learn about square roots and perfect squares.

- explore irrational numbers.

- solve problems using the Pythagorean theorem.

- Take square roots and identify perfect squares.

Vocabulary

- Square root, radical sign, perfect square

Materials

- Explore: Geometry software, calculator

NCTM Standards

- 1, 2, 4–7, 9, 13

 Review

1. Find each power.

   a. 2^2 4   b. $(-2)^2$ 4
   c. 5^2 25   d. $(-5)^2$ 25

2. Find the prime factorization of each number.

   a. 4 2^2 b. 9 3^2
   c. 25 5^2 d. 49 7^2

Available on Daily Transparency 7-7

▶ **Lesson Link**

Have students describe a situation in which they might multiply a number by itself. Ask them how they might find the length of the side of a square when they know the area of the square.

1 Introduce

 Explore

The Point

Students contrast the lengths of the sides of squares whose areas are perfect squares with those whose areas are not.

Ongoing Assessment

Check that in Step 4 students plot the area as the x-coordinate and the length of a side as the y-coordinate.

For Groups That Finish Early

Can you find any other squares with areas other than 1, 4, 9, 16, 25, or 36 that have sides with whole-number lengths?

364   Chapter 7

7-7 Perfect Squares and Square Roots

You'll Learn …

■ to take square roots and identify perfect squares

… How It's Used

Mechanical engineers use square roots to design bridges.

Vocabulary

square root

radical sign

perfect square

▶ **Lesson Link** You have learned about exponents and powers. Now you will learn about square roots and perfect squares. ◀

Explore | Perfect Squares

Drawing Square Conclusions

Materials: Geometry software, Calculator

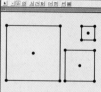

1. Draw a square. Use the measurement tool to determine the area and the length of a side.

2. Make a table to record each measurement. Your table will be used to record the side length and area of six different squares.

3. Draw squares with areas 1, 4, 9, 16, 25, and 36 square units. Use the measurement tool to verify each area and determine the side length. Record the measurements in your table.

4. Plot the data on a coordinate grid. Use the area as the x-coordinate and the side length as the y-coordinate. Connect the points and determine whether the graph is a curved or straight line.

5. Draw a square with an area of 21 and determine the length of a side.

6. Discuss how the squares with areas 1, 4, 9, 16, 25, and 36 differ from the square with area 21.

Learn | Perfect Squares and Square Roots

The **square root** of a number N is the number that when multiplied by itself gives the number N. The symbol for the square root is the **radical sign**.

You have seen the exponent ^{2} used as $5^2 = 5 \times 5 = 25$.

The inverse of x^2 is $\sqrt{x}$ used as $\sqrt{25} = 5$ because $5 \times 5 = 25$.

A **perfect square** is a number with an integer square root such as 9, 16, and 25.

364 Chapter 7 • Number Sense, Rational Numbers, and Irrational Numbers

---

MEETING INDIVIDUAL NEEDS

Resources

7-7 Practice

7-7 Reteaching

7-7 Problem Solving

7-7 Enrichment

7-7 Daily Transparency
      Problem of the Day
      Review
      Quick Quiz

Teaching Tool Transparencies 2, 3, 22

Technology Master 30

 Interactive CD-ROM Geometry Tool

Learning Modalities

Kinesthetic In the Reteaching Activity, students use a grid to show the square formed when the lengths of the sides are whole numbers.

Social In **Explore**, students work in pairs to plot the pairs of data and to graph the data pairs on a coordinate plane.

English Language Development

Explain that the word *root* can refer to the primary source, or origin, of something. Thus we can think of the *root* of a square as the number used to produce the square. Explain that $\sqrt{81} = 9$ is read "the square root of 81 equals 9."

Example 1

Use the square root key $\sqrt{x}$ on your calculator to determine whether each of the numbers is a perfect square.

a. 222   **b.** 169   **c.** 351.56

Enter 222 $\sqrt{x}$ *14.89966443*   222 is not a perfect square.

Enter 169 $\sqrt{x}$ *13*   169 is a perfect square.

Enter 351.56 $\sqrt{x}$ *18.74993333*   351.56 is not a perfect square.

Try It

Use your calculator to determine whether each number is a perfect square.

a. 729   **b.** 864   **c.** 1444   **d.** 1064.15
  Yes   No   Yes   No

You can use the square root to find the side length of a square if you only know the area.

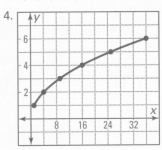

A calculator finds square roots quickly, but the display may not show all of the digits.

Example 2

Ed pours a foundation with an area of 144 ft² for a square shed. How many feet of lumber does Ed need to frame one side of this foundation? To frame the entire foundation?

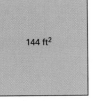

144 ft²

Enter 144 $\sqrt{x}$ *12*

Enter 4 $\times$ 12 $=$ *48*

Ed needs 12 feet of lumber to frame one side and 48 feet total.

▶ **Industry Link**

Foundations can be made by pouring cement into a frame. Some cements have sand in them.

Try It

Evaluate:

a. $2 \times \sqrt{36}$ 12   **b.** $3 \times \sqrt{49}$ 21   **c.** $5 \times \sqrt{100}$ 50   **d.** $7 \times \sqrt{169}$ 91

MATH EVERY DAY

▶ Problem of the Day

Maxine made a square quilt from 100 small squares. Each square around the border contained 4 small flowers. The rest of the quilt was plain. How many small flowers are on the quilt? 144 small flowers

Available on Daily Transparency 7-7

An Extension is provided in the transparency package.

Fact of the Day

The Biltmore House in Ashville, NC, one of the largest homes in the world, contains 250 rooms. It was built in the 1890s by George Vanderbilt for $4,400,000.

Estimation

Estimate each square root.

1. $\sqrt{65}$ 8

2. $\sqrt{105}$ 10

3. $\sqrt{23}$ 5

Follow Up

Ask volunteers to share their answers for Step 6. Ask if they can name the next three squares in the 1, 4, 9, 16, 25, 36 group. Squares with areas of 49, 64, and 81.

Answers for Explore

1. Answers may vary.

2. Answers may vary.

3. 1; 2; 3; 4; 5; 6

4.

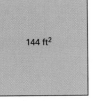

Curved line.

5. Possible answer: ≈ 4.6

6. Possible answer: The first square has sides with whole-number lengths.

2 Teach

Learn

You may wish to use Teaching Tool Transparency 22: Scientific Calculator with this lesson.

Be sure students can locate the $\sqrt{x}$ key on their calculators. On some calculators the [INV] key may have to be pressed before the $\sqrt{x}$ key is pressed.

Alternate Examples

1. Use the square root key $\sqrt{x}$ on your calculator to determine whether each of the numbers is a perfect square.

   a. 204   b. 576   c. 1521

   a. Enter 204 $\sqrt{x}$ *14.28285686*
      204 is not a perfect square.
   b. Enter 576 $\sqrt{x}$ *24*
      576 is a perfect square.
   c. Enter 1521 $\sqrt{x}$ *39*
      1521 is a perfect square.

2. Erica has a square garden that she wants to enclose with a fence. The area of the garden is 196 ft². How long will one side of the fence be? How many feet of fencing will she need for the entire garden?

   Enter 196 $\sqrt{x}$ *14*

   Enter 4 $\times$ 14 $=$ *56*

   Erica needs 14 feet of fencing for one side and 56 feet to enclose the entire garden.

3. State the two consecutive integers that $\sqrt{21}$ is between. Determine $\sqrt{21}$.

The perfect squares nearest to 21 are 16 and 25.
$\sqrt{16} < \sqrt{21} < \sqrt{25}$ because $16 < 21 < 25$.
$4 < \sqrt{21} < 5$, so $\sqrt{21}$ is between 4 and 5.
Enter 21 $\boxed{\sqrt{x}}$ 4.582575694. So, $\sqrt{21} \approx 4.58$

4. Find $\sqrt{\dfrac{81}{25}}$.

$\sqrt{\dfrac{81}{25}} = \dfrac{\sqrt{81}}{\sqrt{25}}$ Rewrite as two square roots.

$= \dfrac{9}{5} = 1\dfrac{4}{5}$ Take the square roots. Write in lowest terms.

3 Practice and Assess

Check

Be sure that students understand that they can find the square of a number using a calculator.

Answers for Check Your Understanding

1. If you know the area of a square, you can find its side length by taking the square root.

2. Yes; A square root of a perfect square is always an integer.

You can estimate the square root of a number that is not a perfect square by using the nearest perfect squares.

Example 3

ESTIMATION

It can be okay to round a calculator reading to a nearest decimal place.

a. 3 and 4; 3.2
b. 4 and 5; 4.6
c. 5 and 6; 5.5
d. 8 and 9; 8.9

State the two consecutive integers that $\sqrt{7}$ is between. Determine $\sqrt{7}$.

The perfect square numbers nearest to 7 are 4 and 9.

$\sqrt{4} < \sqrt{7} < \sqrt{9}$ because $4 < 7 < 9$.

$2 < \sqrt{7} < 3$, so $\sqrt{7}$ is between 2 and 3.

The side of the red square is between 2 and 3.

Enter 7 $\boxed{\sqrt{x}}$ *2.645751311*   So $\sqrt{7} \approx 2.65$.

Try It

State the two consecutive integers that the square root is between. Use your calculator to find each square root to the nearest tenth.

a. $\sqrt{10}$ **b.** $\sqrt{21}$ **c.** $\sqrt{30}$ **d.** $\sqrt{80}$

To find the square root of a fraction, find the square root of the numerator and the denominator.

Example 4

Find $\sqrt{\dfrac{64}{49}}$.

$\sqrt{\dfrac{64}{49}} = \dfrac{\sqrt{64}}{\sqrt{49}}$ Rewrite as two square roots.

$= \dfrac{8}{7} = 1\dfrac{1}{7}$ Take the square roots. Write in lowest terms.

Try It

Find each of the square roots.

a. $\sqrt{\dfrac{25}{64}}$ $\dfrac{5}{8}$ **b.** $\sqrt{\dfrac{100}{625}}$ $\dfrac{10}{25}$ **c.** $\sqrt{\dfrac{121}{324}}$ $\dfrac{11}{18}$ **d.** $\sqrt{\dfrac{36}{225}}$ $\dfrac{6}{15}$

Check   Your Understanding

1. Describe how taking a square root is similar to finding the side of a square.

2. Will the square of any integer be a perfect square? Explain.

366   *Chapter 7 • Number Sense, Rational Numbers, and Irrational Numbers*

MEETING MIDDLE SCHOOL CLASSROOM NEEDS

Tips from Middle School Teachers

I have a number of brain teasers on file that involve squares and square roots that I write on the board before class. For example, "What even number between 1 and 10 when squared and subtracted from 100 equals the square of the next even number between 1 and 10?" (6; $6^2 = 36$ and $100 - 36 = 64 = 8^2$) Students have added many other similar brain teasers to my file.

Team Teaching

Have other teachers in your group explain how squares and square roots are used in their subject areas. For example, a science teacher might discuss situations in which formulas that involve squares must be solved, similar to the formula in Exercise 23.

Cultural Connection

The ancient Egyptians and Babylonians used a formula to estimate square roots that was based on the nearest perfect square.

$\sqrt{a^2 + b} \approx a + \dfrac{b}{2a}$

For example, to approximate $\sqrt{35}$, use the fact that $35 = 6^2 - 1$ so in the formula, $a = 6$ and $b = -1$; $\sqrt{35} \approx 6 + \dfrac{-1}{2 \times 6}$; $35 \approx 5.9167$. Using a calculator,

$\sqrt{35} \approx 5.9161$.

PRACTICE 7-7

Practice and Apply

1. **Getting Started** Find the square root of $\sqrt{\dfrac{9}{144}}$.
   a. Write the square roots of the numerator and the denominator. $\dfrac{\sqrt{9}}{\sqrt{144}}$
   b. Take each square root. $\dfrac{3}{12}$
   c. Write the fraction in lowest terms. $\dfrac{1}{4}$

State whether or not each number is a perfect square.

2. 130 **No** 3. 49 **Yes** 4. 289 **Yes** 5. 1000 **No** 6. 225 **Yes**

Find the two consecutive integers that each is between.

7. $\sqrt{34}$ **5 and 6**   8. $\sqrt{52}$ **7 and 8**   9. $\sqrt{70}$ **8 and 9**   10. $\sqrt{110}$ **10 and 11**   11. $\sqrt{27}$ **5 and 6**

Determine each square root and write in lowest terms.

12. $\sqrt{\dfrac{64}{121}}$ $\dfrac{8}{11}$ 13. $\sqrt{\dfrac{36}{16}}$ $1\dfrac{1}{2}$ 14. $\sqrt{\dfrac{169}{144}}$ $1\dfrac{1}{12}$ 15. $\sqrt{\dfrac{81}{225}}$ $\dfrac{3}{5}$ 16. $\sqrt{\dfrac{1}{9}}$ $\dfrac{1}{3}$

17. **Social Studies** The Great Pyramid of Khufu has a square base that covers about 53,000 m². About how long is each side of the base? **≈ 230.22 meters**

18. **Patterns** List the first ten perfect squares. How do the numbers in the list increase? Describe the pattern.

19. Architects can design homes using a computer application. According to the floorplans, the living room of a new house being built is 85 square feet. State two consecutive integers that $\sqrt{85}$ is between.

20. Angela built a square dog house that is 33 in. long on each side for her new beagle puppy. What is the area of the floor for the puppy to sleep on? **1089 in²**

21. The area of the square window above the door on Dmitri's house in Santorini, Greece, is 144 in². How long is one side of the window? **12 in.**

22. **Algebra** Write a formula for finding the length of the side of a square with area x. $y = \sqrt{x}$

7-7 • Perfect Squares and Square Roots **367**

Assignment Guide

■ **Basic**
1–5, 7–10, 12–14, 17–19, 23–28 evens, 30–32, 36, 37, 39

■ **Average**
1, 4–6, 9–11, 14–16, 20–24, 27–29, 33–35, 38–40

■ **Enriched**
2–16 evens, 18–29, 34, 35, 39, 40

Exercise Notes

■ **Exercises 7–11**

Estimation Point out that in these exercises students are actually performing the first step in finding an estimate for each square root.

Exercise Answers

18. 1, 4, 9, 16, 25, 36, 49, 64, 81, 100; Possible answer: As the numbers increase by one, their squares increase by 3, 5, 7, 9, 11, 13, 15, 17, 19.

19. 9, 10

PRACTICE

Name _____

Practice 7-7

Perfect Squares and Square Roots

State whether or not each number is a perfect square.

1. 20 **No**   2. 16 **Yes**   3. 60 **No**   4. 110 **No**

5. 76 **No**   6. 4 **Yes**   7. 64 **Yes**   8. 9 **Yes**

9. 36 **Yes**   10. 32 **No**   11. 50 **No**   12. 200 **No**

13. 160 **No**   14. 625 **Yes**   15. 1 **Yes**   16. 144 **Yes**

17. 45 **No**   18. 25 **Yes**   19. 12 **No**   20. 400 **Yes**

Find the two consecutive integers that each is between.

21. $\sqrt{175}$ **13, 14**   22. $\sqrt{30}$ **5, 6**   23. $\sqrt{135}$ **11, 12**

24. $\sqrt{6}$ **2, 3**   25. $\sqrt{53}$ **7, 8**   26. $\sqrt{21}$ **4, 5**

27. $\sqrt{111}$ **10, 11**   28. $\sqrt{3}$ **1, 2**   29. $\sqrt{580}$ **24, 25**

30. $\sqrt{90}$ **9, 10**   31. $\sqrt{200}$ **14, 15**   32. $\sqrt{12}$ **3, 4**

33. $\sqrt{42}$ **6, 7**   34. $\sqrt{408}$ **20, 21**   35. $\sqrt{910}$ **30, 31**

Determine each square root and write in lowest terms.

36. $\sqrt{\dfrac{25}{36}}$ $\dfrac{5}{6}$ 37. $\sqrt{\dfrac{25}{400}}$ $\dfrac{1}{4}$ 38. $\sqrt{\dfrac{4}{36}}$ $\dfrac{1}{3}$ 39. $\sqrt{\dfrac{9}{64}}$ $\dfrac{3}{8}$

40. $\sqrt{\dfrac{81}{144}}$ $\dfrac{3}{4}$ 41. $\sqrt{\dfrac{1}{4}}$ $\dfrac{1}{2}$ 42. $\sqrt{\dfrac{64}{25}}$ $\dfrac{8}{5}$ 43. $\sqrt{\dfrac{81}{36}}$ $\dfrac{3}{2}$

44. $\sqrt{\dfrac{4}{100}}$ $\dfrac{1}{5}$ 45. $\sqrt{\dfrac{4}{9}}$ $\dfrac{2}{3}$ 46. $\sqrt{\dfrac{64}{400}}$ $\dfrac{2}{5}$ 47. $\sqrt{\dfrac{121}{400}}$ $\dfrac{11}{20}$

48. $\sqrt{\dfrac{16}{49}}$ $\dfrac{4}{7}$ 49. $\sqrt{\dfrac{81}{225}}$ $\dfrac{3}{5}$ 50. $\sqrt{\dfrac{36}{121}}$ $\dfrac{6}{11}$ 51. $\sqrt{\dfrac{49}{144}}$ $\dfrac{7}{12}$

52. A square cake pan has an area of 529 cm². How long is each side of the pan? **23 cm**

53. In the Japanese art of origami, square paper is folded to create animals and other objects. If a sheet of origami paper has area 324 cm², what is the length of each edge of the paper? **18 cm**

RETEACHING

Name _____

Alternative Lesson 7-7

Perfect Squares and Square Roots

The **square root** of a number N is the number that when multiplied by itself gives the number N. The symbol for the square root is the **radical sign** $\sqrt{}$. The square root of 9 is 3 because $3 \times 3 = 3^2 = 9$.

A **perfect square** is a number with an integer square root. For example 4 and 49 are perfect squares because their square roots are 2 and 7.

You can use the square root key on a calculator to find the square root of a number. You can find an estimated square root of a number that is not a perfect square by finding which two perfect squares it is between.

─── Example 1 ───

State whether or not 250 is a perfect square. Use a calculator.

Enter 250 $\boxed{\sqrt{}}$. The result is 15.811388.

250 is not a perfect square because 15.811388 is not an integer square root.

Try It Use a calculator to determine whether each number is a perfect square.

a. 576 **Yes.**   b. 1200 **No.**   c. 2401 **Yes.**

d. 900 **Yes.**   e. 1521 **Yes.**   f. 1875 **No.**

─── Example 2 ───

Find the two consecutive integers that $\sqrt{14}$ is between. Use your calculator to find $\sqrt{14}$ to the nearest tenth.

Determine the perfect square numbers that 14 falls between:
14 falls between 9 and 16.

$\sqrt{9} < \sqrt{14} < \sqrt{16}$ because $9 < 14 < 16$.

Find the square root of the perfect squares: $\sqrt{9} = 3$ and the $\sqrt{16} = 4$.

$3 < \sqrt{14} < 4$, so $\sqrt{14}$ is between 3 and 4.

Using a calculator, you find $\sqrt{14} = 3.7416574$, so $\sqrt{14} \approx 3.7$.

Try It Find two consecutive integers that each square root is between. Use a calculator to find each square root to the nearest tenth.

g. $\sqrt{42}$ **6 and 7; 6.5**   h. $\sqrt{88}$ **9 and 10; 9.4**

i. $\sqrt{63}$ **7 and 8; 7.9**   j. $\sqrt{75}$ **8 and 9; 8.7**

k. $\sqrt{30}$ **5 and 6; 5.5**   l. $\sqrt{130}$ **11 and 12; 11.4**

m. $\sqrt{97}$ **9 and 10; 9.8**   n. $\sqrt{152}$ **12 and 13; 12.3**

Reteaching

Activity

Materials: Graph paper

• Work with a partner. On graph paper draw squares in which the lengths of the sides are whole numbers.

• Find the area of each square. Write the area inside the square.

• Compare your squares with those of other groups. How many different squares can you draw that have sides with whole-number lengths and that have areas of 100 or less? What are the areas? 10 different squares; Areas of 1, 4, 9, 16, 25, 36, 49, 64, 81, 100.

Exercise Notes

■ Exercise 23

Science The formula in this exercise really applies only to objects in a vacuum, where there is no air resistance. A skydiver experiences considerable air resistance, so the formula would give only an approximate falling time.

■ Exercise 24

Test Prep Since $20^2 = 400$, B is the only reasonable answer.

■ Exercise 28

Problem-Solving Tip You may wish to use Teaching Tool Transparencies 2 and 3: Guided Problem Solving, pages 1–2.

Exercise Answers

27. Possible answers: $(1 \cdot 2 \cdot 3 \cdot 4) + 1 = 25 = 5^2$; $(2 \cdot 3 \cdot 4 \cdot 5) + 1 = 121 = 11^2$; $(3 \cdot 4 \cdot 5 \cdot 6) + 1 = 361 = 19^2$; $(5 \cdot 6 \cdot 7 \cdot 8) + 1 = 1681 = 41^2$; $(6 \cdot 7 \cdot 8 \cdot 9) + 1 = 55^2 = 3025$

30–35.

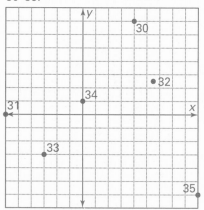

Alternate Assessment

Ongoing Throughout the lesson check that students are correctly entering data into their calculators and that they can interpret the calculator displays correctly.

► Quick Quiz

1. Which of these are perfect squares?

   63   36   324   225
   36, 324, 225

2. Find each square root.

   $\sqrt{81}$ $\sqrt{529}$ $\sqrt{361}$
   9, 23, 19

3. State two consecutive integers that $\sqrt{69}$ is between.
   8 and 9

4. Find $\sqrt{\dfrac{121}{16}}$. $2\dfrac{3}{4}$

Available on Daily Transparency 7-7

368   Chapter 7

PROBLEM SOLVING 7-7

23. **Science** The formula $t = \dfrac{\sqrt{d}}{4}$ shows how to find the time (t), in seconds, that it takes a falling object to free-fall a given distance (d), in feet. Find the falling time for a skydiver to fall 900 feet before opening the parachute. **7.5 seconds**

24. **Test Prep** Which is the length of a side of a square with an area of 324 in²? **B**

   Ⓐ 162 in.   Ⓑ 18 in.   Ⓒ 81 in.   Ⓓ 104,976 in.

900 ft

Problem Solving and Reasoning

25. **Measurement** The Daryma family of Mongolia live in a round tent called a *yurt* that has a floor area of 64π ft². What is the radius of their tent? (Area of a circle = πr^2)
   8 feet

26. **Journal** Explain how you would estimate $\sqrt{12}$ using perfect squares.
   Answers may vary.

27. **Number Sense** A method for finding perfect squares involves multiplying four consecutive whole numbers and adding 1 to their product. For instance, $(4 \cdot 5 \cdot 6 \cdot 7) + 1 = 841$ and $\sqrt{841} = 29$. Find five perfect squares using this method.

28. **Choose a Strategy** Find the area of the yellow portion in the diagram. Could the area be rearranged into another perfect square? Draw a diagram to support your answer. **16; Yes; Result is a 4-by-4 square.**

29. **Communicate** If you multiply a perfect square by a perfect square, is the answer a perfect square? Support your answer with an example.
   Yes; $25 \cdot 36 = 5^2 \cdot 6^2 = 5 \cdot 5 \cdot 6 \cdot 6 = (5 \cdot 6) \cdot (5 \cdot 6) = 30^2$

Problem Solving STRATEGIES

- Look for a Pattern
- Make an Organized List
- Make a Table
- Guess and Check
- Work Backward
- Use Logical Reasoning
- Draw a Diagram
- Solve a Simpler Problem

Mixed Review

Plot each point on a coordinate grid. *[Lesson 2-6]*

30. $(4, 7)$ 31. $(-6, 0)$ 32. $(5.5, 2.5)$

33. $(-3, -3)$ 34. $(0, 1)$ 35. $(9, -6)$

Write each rate or ratio as a fraction. *[Lesson 5-1]*

36. 9 to 5 $\dfrac{9}{5}$ 37. 11:66 $\dfrac{11}{66}$ 38. 45 miles per hour $\dfrac{45 \text{ mi}}{1 \text{ hr}}$

39. Number of feet in a yard $\dfrac{3 \text{ ft}}{1 \text{ yd}}$ 40. Number of minutes in an hour $\dfrac{60 \text{ min}}{1 \text{ hr}}$

368 *Chapter 7 • Number Sense, Rational Numbers, and Irrational Numbers*

> **PROBLEM SOLVING**

Name _____

Guided Problem Solving 7-7

GPS PROBLEM 23, STUDENT PAGE 368

The formula $t = \dfrac{\sqrt{d}}{4}$ shows how to find the time (t), in seconds, that it takes a falling object to free-fall a given distance (d), in feet. Find the falling time for a skydiver to fall 900 feet before opening the parachute.

— Understand —

1. What does the t in the formula $t = \dfrac{\sqrt{d}}{4}$ stand for?   **Time in seconds.**

2. What does the d in the formula $t = \dfrac{\sqrt{d}}{4}$ stand for?   **Distance in feet.**

3. You are asked to find how long it takes to fall how many feet?   **900 feet.**

— Plan —

4. What is the first step in solving the formula?   **b**
   a. Divide d by 4.   b. Find the square root of d.

5. What is the second step in solving the formula?   **Divide $\sqrt{d}$ by 4.**

6. What number will you substitute in the formula?   **900 for d.**

7. Which is a reasonable time?   **c**
   a. 900 seconds   b. 30 seconds   c. 8 seconds

— Solve —

8. Solve using the formula. $t = 7.5$

9. How many seconds does it takes to free-fall 900 feet.   **7.5 seconds.**

— Look Back —

10. If your answer and your estimate are not close, how can you determine if your answer is reasonable?   **Possible answer: Recalculate answer and estimate. Then compare.**

SOLVE ANOTHER PROBLEM

Find the falling time for a skydiver to fall 1600 feet before opening the parachute.
   10 seconds.

> **ENRICHMENT**

Name _____

Extend Your Thinking 7-7

Critical Thinking

A physics class was separated into groups. Each group was asked to build a bridge from balsa wood that would support a minimum of 600 pounds.

Edna, Kaya, and Chim used the expression $1000(99 - 70\sqrt{2})$ pounds to calculate the maximum safe load for the bridge they were building. They used 1.4 for $\sqrt{2}$ and found that their bridge was a winner.

Complete the table below using different approximations for $\sqrt{2}$. Round your answer to the nearest thousandth.

	Approximation of $\sqrt{2}$	Maximum Safe Load of Bridge (in pounds)
1.	1.4	1,000.000
2.	1.41	300.000
3.	1.414	20.000
4.	1.4142	6.000
5.	1.41421	5.300
6.	1.414213	5.090
7.	1.4142135	5.055

8. Will the group's bridge support at least 600 pounds? Explain.   **Possible answer: No, because 600 is much greater than 5.055.**

9. Why did the group's calculation appear to be accurate, but in actuality was not correct?   **Possible answer: The approximation of $\sqrt{2}$ used in the original calculation was too imprecise and resulted in an inaccurate value for the safe load.**

10. What do you notice about the calculated load as the approximation of $\sqrt{2}$ is rounded to a larger decimal value?   **Possible answer: The change between the calculated safe loads becomes smaller.**

Square Roots and Irrational Numbers

▶ **Lesson Link** You have learned about perfect squares and square roots. You will now learn about other square roots and other types of numbers. ◄

Explore | Irrational Numbers

Is That Rational?

Materials: Graph paper, Calculator

Recall that a rational number is a ratio such as $\frac{a}{b}$, where a and b are both integers.

1. Draw a square that is closest to 10 square units on graph paper.

2. Draw the next larger square.

3. Find the length of a side of each square.

4. Try to find a rational number $\frac{a}{b}$ so that $\left(\frac{a}{b}\right)^2 = 10$. Use a calculator. List the numbers you tried and the square of each number.

5. Did you find a rational number that has a square of 10? If not, what is the closest rational number you found?

9 sq. units   16 sq. units

Learn | Square Roots and Irrational Numbers

You know that $\sqrt{9} = 3$ because $3^2 = 9$. You also know that $(-3)^2 = 9$, so it must be true that $\sqrt{9}$ is also -3.

The positive square root is called the **principal square root**. The negative square root is the **negative square root**.

Principal Square Root ($\sqrt{\ }$)	Negative Square Root ($-\sqrt{\ }$)	Both Square Roots ($\pm\sqrt{\ }$)
$\sqrt{9} = 3$	$-\sqrt{9} = -3$	$\pm\sqrt{9} = \pm3$

-9 does not have a square root because $-9 = (-3)(3)$.

It is important to know that $-\sqrt{9} \neq \sqrt{-9}$.

Both square roots of a number have the same absolute value.

You'll Learn ...
■ to identify square roots that are irrational numbers

... How It's Used
Opticians know the difference between an irrational square root and a rational square root. They use square roots when dealing with very complex prescriptions.

Vocabulary
principal square root

negative square root

irrational number

real numbers

MEETING INDIVIDUAL NEEDS

Resources

7-8 Practice

7-8 Reteaching

7-8 Problem Solving

7-8 Enrichment

7-8 Daily Transparency
   Problem of the Day
   Review
   Quick Quiz

Teaching Tool
Transparencies 7, 22

Technology Master 31

Learning Modalities

Musical Have students make up a song or rap rhythm using the ideas of rational numbers and irrational numbers.

Visual Have students create a poster that shows the difference between rational and irrational numbers.

Social In **Explore**, students work in pairs to investigate whether the side length of a 10-square-unit square is rational.

Inclusion

Students with physical impairments may have difficulty using a calculator. Pair these students with classmates who are able to assist them. Also, a variety of calculators may be used to address individual student needs. A large numeric keypad could help students with fine motor skill difficulties. Or, a talking calculator will enable the visually-impaired student to hear the number entered into the calculator. Remind students to include new vocabulary in their notebooks.

Lesson Organizer

Objective
■ **Identify square roots that are irrational numbers.**

Vocabulary
■ **Principal square root, negative square root, irrational number, real numbers**

Materials
■ **Explore: Graph paper, calculator**

NCTM Standards
■ **1–7, 9**

▶ Review

1. Find the absolute value of each of the following.

   |0| 0 |17| 17 |−289| 289

2. Write each of the following as a decimal.

   $\frac{4}{9}$ 0.$\overline{4}$ $\frac{2}{3}$ 0.$\overline{6}$ $\frac{1}{7}$ 0.$\overline{142857}$

3. Write the following rational numbers in the form $\frac{a}{b}$.

   25 $\frac{25}{1}$ $3\frac{1}{3}$ $\frac{10}{3}$ 49.8 $\frac{498}{10}$

Available on Daily Transparency 7-8

▶ **Lesson Link**

Students will explore square roots of numbers that are not perfect squares.

1 Introduce

Explore

You may wish to use Teaching Tool Transparencies 7: $\frac{1}{4}$-inch Graph Paper and 22: Scientific Calculator with **Explore**.

The Point
Students estimate the square root of 10.

Ongoing Assessment
Check that the squares students draw in Step 1 are reasonable and that the square in Step 2 is correct.

For Groups That Finish Early

What is the closest rational number you found that has a square of 10? Now find a closer number.

Follow Up

Ask volunteers to share their answer for Step 5. Then have them find $\sqrt{10}$ on their calculators. Ask them to compare their estimate to the calculator value.

Answers for Explore

1–5. See student responses.

2 Teach

Learn

Make sure students understand that a positive number has two square roots—one positive and the other negative. But a positive number has only one principal square root—the positive square root. It is not correct to write $\sqrt{9} = \pm 3$. It is correct to write $\sqrt{9} = 3$ and $-\sqrt{9} = -3$; it is also correct to write $\pm\sqrt{9} = \pm 3$.

Alternate Examples

1. Riva's family has a square piece of land that they want to use for a vegetable garden. The area of the land is 289 ft². How many feet of picket fence will they need to fence the land on one side?

   Find $\sqrt{289}$.
   $\pm\sqrt{289} = \pm 17$

   Since length cannot be a negative value, –17 does not work. So the length of the picket fence is 17 ft.

2. Use your calculator to determine whether each square root is rational or irrational.

   a. $-\sqrt{224}$ b. $\sqrt{361}$

   Enter 224 $\boxed{\sqrt{x}}$ $\boxed{+/-}$. 4.96662954
   $-\sqrt{224}$ is irrational.

   Enter 361 $\boxed{\sqrt{x}}$. 19
   $\sqrt{361}$ is rational.

► **History Link**

On September 16, 1620, 35 pilgrims left England on the *Mayflower*.

Example 1

In the 1600s, when pilgrims first settled in New England, their houses were very plain. Here is a square floor plan with an area of 900 ft². What is the length of one side of this structure?

Find $\sqrt{900}$.

$\pm\sqrt{900} = \pm 30$

-30 does not work because length cannot be a negative value.

The length of the structure is 30 feet.

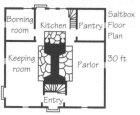

Saltbox Floor Plan
Borning room, Kitchen, Pantry, Keeping room, Parlor, 30 ft, Entry

A number that cannot be expressed as a repeating or terminating decimal is an **irrational number**.

An integer that is not a perfect square has an irrational square root.

Together, the rational and irrational numbers make up the **real numbers**.

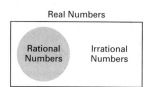

Real Numbers

Rational Numbers   Irrational Numbers

Example 2

Use your calculator to determine whether each square root is rational or irrational.

a. $-\sqrt{723}$ b. $\sqrt{256}$

Enter 723 $\boxed{\sqrt{x}}$ $\boxed{+/-}$. -26.88865932 $-\sqrt{723}$ is irrational.

Enter 256 $\boxed{\sqrt{x}}$. 16 $\sqrt{256}$ is rational.

Try It

Use your calculator to determine whether or not the following are irrational. If it is rational, then find the square root.

a. $\sqrt{167}$ b. $-\sqrt{900}$ c. $\pm\sqrt{5476}$ d. $\sqrt{59841}$
Irrational   Rational; –30   Rational; ±74   Irrational

MATH EVERY DAY

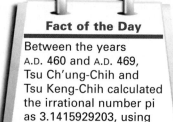

► Problem of the Day

What are the next three letters in each sequence?
1. J, F, M, A, M, J
2. S, M, T, W, T
1. J, A, S (months)
2. F, S, S (days of week)

Available on Daily Transparency 7-8

An Extension is provided in the transparency package.

Fact of the Day

Between the years A.D. 460 and A.D. 469, Tsu Ch'ung-Chih and Tsu Keng-Chih calculated the irrational number pi as 3.1415929203, using a circle 3 m across.

Mental Math

Do these mentally.

1. 30×152 4560

2. 12×60 720

3. $\frac{1}{8} \times \frac{1}{5}$ $\frac{1}{40}$

4. $\frac{1}{2} \times \frac{8}{10}$ $\frac{2}{5}$

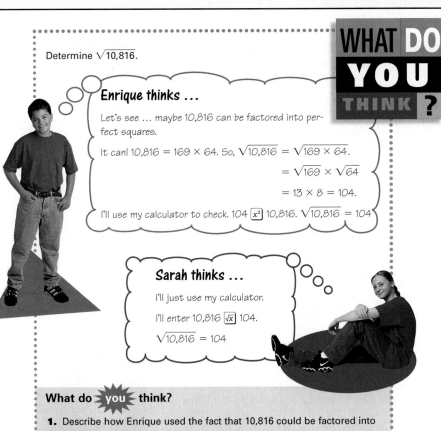

Determine $\sqrt{10,816}$.

Enrique thinks ...

Let's see ... maybe 10,816 can be factored into perfect squares.

It can! $10,816 = 169 \times 64$. So, $\sqrt{10,816} = \sqrt{169 \times 64}$.

$= \sqrt{169} \times \sqrt{64}$

$= 13 \times 8 = 104$.

I'll use my calculator to check. 104 $\boxed{x^2}$ $10,816$. $\sqrt{10,816} = 104$

Sarah thinks ...

I'll just use my calculator.

I'll enter $10,816$ $\boxed{\sqrt{x}}$ 104.

$\sqrt{10,816} = 104$

What do **you** think?

1. Describe how Enrique used the fact that 10,816 could be factored into perfect squares.

2. Sarah and Enrique both used their calculators. How did they use their calculators differently to get the same answer?

3. Describe how Enrique and Sarah could use mental math to check their calculator answers.

Check | Your Understanding

1. Explain the difference between the principal and negative square roots.

2. Explain the difference between $-\sqrt{9}$ and $\sqrt{-9}$. What does your calculator show when you enter 9 $\boxed{+/-}$ $\boxed{\sqrt{x}}$?

7-8 • Square Roots and Irrational Numbers **371**

WHAT DO YOU THINK?

Students use two methods of finding a square root. Both methods are correct, and the second is clearly easier. However, the first method might be useful if a calculator is not available or if the number is so large it exceeds the calculator's capacity.

Answers for What Do You Think?

1. He took the square root of each of the perfect squares and then multiplied them together.

2. Enrique used his calculator to check his answer; Sarah used the square root key to get the answer.

3. Possible answer: $\sqrt{4 + 9} \neq \sqrt{4} + \sqrt{9}$.

3 Practice and Assess

Check

Be sure that students understand that all positive numbers have a principal and a negative square root. But in some real world situations a negative value does not make sense.

Answers for Check Your Understanding

1. The principal root is positive and the negative root is negative.

2. $-\sqrt{9} = -3$; $\sqrt{-9}$ is not possible; Error.

3. Possible answer: They could think $100 \times 100 = 10,000$, so the answer of 104 is reasonable.

MEETING MIDDLE SCHOOL CLASSROOM NEEDS

Tips from Middle School Teachers

I like to introduce the subject of irrational numbers with pi, one of the most famous irrational numbers and certainly one with which my students are familiar. First I have the students trace or draw a circle with a compass on a stiff piece of paper. I have them carefully cut out the circle and make one tick mark on the edge. Then I have them roll the circle on its edge, using the tick mark as a reference point, to measure the circumference. I also have them measure the diameter. Using the equation π = circumference ÷ diameter, I then invite my students to share and compare the ratios they have found. Interested students carry the activity one step farther by dividing the circumference by the diameter to find several digits of pi.

Cultural Connection

Between the years A.D. 190 and A.D. 209 the mathematician Liu Hui of China used polygons of up to 3072 sides to calculate pi up to 3.14159.

History Connection

As mathematics has advanced, so has the computation of pi. In very early times, 3 was used to approximate pi. In about the third century B.C., pi was approximated using 3.14. By A.D. 200, 3.1416 was used. In 1995, a group of mathematicians calculated pi to the ten billionth (10,000,000,000) digit.

Lesson 7-8 **371**

Assignment Guide

■ **Basic**
1–4, 6–15, 22, 23, 28–29, 30, 34, 37, 38, 42

■ **Average**
1, 5–18, 24, 26, 28–29, 31, 35, 39, 42

■ **Enriched**
1, 7–11, 17–21, 25, 27–29, 32, 33, 36, 37, 40–42

Exercise Notes

■ **Exercise 7**

Error Prevention Some students may mistake the pattern in this decimal for a repeating pattern. If they do so, ask them to name the repeating digits. Although the 2 and 0s seem to repeat, there is always one more 0 in the next step. So there is really no repeating sequence.

■ **Exercises 12–21**

Estimation Students should estimate the square roots to ensure the calculator results are correct since it is easy to press the wrong keys.

■ **Exercise 28**

Error Prevention Errors may occur by careless reading of the instructions. Remind students to find the square root of the pendulum *before* doubling.

Exercise Answers

1. b. Irrational
2. Rational
3. Irrational
4. Irrational
5. Irrational
6. Rational
7. Irrational
8. Rational
9. Irrational
10. Irrational
11. Rational

Reteaching

Activity

Materials: Calculator

• Work in groups of two. You and your partner should take turns giving each other a number.

• Use the calculator to determine the square root of each number. Tell if the square root is rational or irrational.

7-8 Exercises and Applications

PRACTICE 7-8

Practice and Apply

1. **Getting Started** Use your calculator to determine whether $\sqrt{95}$ is rational or irrational.
   a. Enter 95 $\boxed{\sqrt{x}}$. **9.7467943**
   b. Determine if this is rational or irrational.

Identify each number as rational or irrational.

2. $\sqrt{4}$ 3. $\sqrt{17}$ 4. $\sqrt{20}$ 5. $\sqrt{200}$ 6. $0.12\overline{3}$

7. $0.202002000\ldots$ 8. $\sqrt{\dfrac{9}{25}}$ 9. π 10. $\sqrt{3}$ 11. $0.\overline{3}$

Use a calculator to find each square root and round to the nearest thousandth.

12. $\sqrt{2}$ 13. $\sqrt{15}$ 14. $\sqrt{29}$ 15. $\sqrt{99}$ 16. $\sqrt{147}$

17. $\sqrt{252}$ 18. $\sqrt{1000}$ 19. $\sqrt{2000}$ 20. $\sqrt{1600}$ 21. $\sqrt{456}$
   15.875   **31.623**   **44.721**   **40**   **21.354**

12. 1.414
13. 3.873
14. 5.385
15. 9.950
16. 12.124

Geometry Find the side length of each of the squares with the given area.

22. 45 in^2 23. 30 in^2 24. 36 cm^2 25. 42.25 m^2 **6.5 m**
   $\approx$ **6.71 in.** $\approx$ **5.48 in.**   **6 cm**

26. **History** The term *radical* is taken from the Arabic word *jidr*, meaning "plant-root." In Arabic math texts, a square number was thought of as growing out of a root number. For example, 49 grows out of 7, the jidr. What would the jidr be of 196? **14**

27. **Geography** The Shikushi family in Japan has a square home with four square rooms measuring 121 ft^2 each. Removable, sliding paper screens separate the rooms. In the summer, they remove the screens to allow breezes to go through and the house becomes one large room. What would the dimensions of this large room be? **22 ft × 22 ft**

Cabbage seed splitting open

28. **Science** You can find the number of seconds that it takes a pendulum to swing back and forth. First, find the square root of the pendulum's length in meters, then double it. How long will it take a pendulum that is 1.2 meters long to swing back and forth?

2.19 seconds

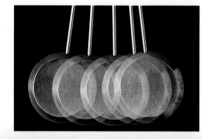

PRACTICE

Name _____

Practice 7-8

Square Roots and Irrational Numbers

Identify each number as rational or irrational.

1. $2.717711777\ldots$ 2. 75   3. $\sqrt{36}$
   Irrational   _Rational_   _Rational_

4. $6.18181818\ldots$ 5. 18.7   6. $\dfrac{4}{7}$
   Rational   _Rational_   _Rational_

7. 13.61324 8. $\sqrt{21}$ 9. $\sqrt{\dfrac{49}{64}}$
   Rational   _Irrational_   _Rational_

Use a calculator to find each of the square roots and round to the nearest thousandth.

10. $\sqrt{35}$ **5.916** 11. $\sqrt{23}$ **4.796** 12. $\sqrt{50}$ **7.071** 13. $\sqrt{44}$ **6.633**

14. $\sqrt{27}$ **5.196** 15. $\sqrt{18}$ **4.243** 16. $\sqrt{69}$ **8.307** 17. $\sqrt{56}$ **7.483**

18. $\sqrt{79}$ **8.888** 19. $\sqrt{39}$ **6.245** 20. $\sqrt{314}$ **17.720** 21. $\sqrt{73}$ **8.544**

22. $\sqrt{62}$ **7.874** 23. $\sqrt{108}$ **10.392** 24. $\sqrt{48}$ **6.928** 25. $\sqrt{1200}$ **34.641**

Geometry Find the side length of each of the squares with the given area.

26. $150 \text{ in}^2 \approx$ **12.247 in.** 27. 144 m^2 **12 m** 28. $14 \text{ cm}^2 \approx$ **3.742 cm**

29. 18.49 ft^2 **4.3 ft** 30. 2.89 km^2 **1.7 km** 31. 94.09 yd^2 **9.7 yd**

32. 49 mm^2 **7 mm** 33. 0.2025 mi^2 **0.45 mi** 34. $85 \text{ cm}^2 \approx$ **9.220 cm**

35. 40.96 in^2 **6.4 in.** 36. $111 \text{ m}^2 \approx$ **10.536 m** 37. 169 ft^2 **13 ft**

38. A square card table has a tabletop with area 1350 in^2. Find the length of each side. **About 36.7 in.**

39. **Science** The formula $t = \sqrt{\dfrac{d}{4.9}}$ gives the time (t), in seconds, for an object to free fall a distance (d), in meters. A rock is dropped from a 35-m-high cliff. How soon will it hit the beach below? **About 2.67 sec**

RETEACHING

Name _____

Alternative Lesson 7-8

Square Roots and Irrational Numbers

A number such as 25 has two square roots 5 and −5, because $5 \times 5 = 25$ and $(-5) \times (-5) = 25$.

The positive square root is called the **principal square root**, and it is indicated by $\sqrt{}$, so $\sqrt{25} = 5$.

The negative square root is indicated by $-\sqrt{}$, so $-\sqrt{25} = -5$.

Both square roots are indicated by $\pm\sqrt{}$, so $\sqrt{25} = \pm 5$.

An **irrational number** is a number that cannot be expressed as a repeating or terminating decimal. An integer that is not a perfect square has an irrational square root.

— **Example**

Use a calculator to find each square root of each number. Round square roots to the nearest thousandth, if necessary. Tell whether the number is rational or irrational.

a. $\sqrt{225}$
$\sqrt{225} = 15$
Since 15 is an integer, $\sqrt{225}$ is rational.

b. $\sqrt{300}$
$\sqrt{300} = 17.320508 \approx 17.321$,
Since 17.320509 cannot be written as a terminating or a repeating decimal, $\sqrt{300}$ is irrational.

Try It Use a calculator to find each square root and round to the nearest thousandth. Tell whether the number is rational or irrational.

a. Write $\sqrt{3}$ as shown on the calculator screen. **1.7320508**

b. Round the $\sqrt{3}$ in to the nearest thousandth. **1.732**

c. Can the decimal in Item a be written as terminating or repeating decimal? **No.**

d. Is the $\sqrt{3}$ rational or irrational? **Irrational.**

	Square Root	Rational or Irrational		Square Root	Rational or Irrational
e. $\sqrt{81}$	9	Rational.	f. $\sqrt{103}$	10.149	Irrational.
g. $\sqrt{841}$	29	Rational.	h. $\sqrt{957}$	30.935	Irrational.
i. $\sqrt{1111}$	33.332	Irrational.	j. $\sqrt{490}$	22.136	Irrational.
k. $\sqrt{1000}$	31.623	Irrational.	l. $\sqrt{1521}$	39	Rational.

29. **Test Prep** In Italy, the Pellegrini family lives in a five-room house that has a floor area of 1292 ft². If the house has a square base, what would be the length of a wall? **A**

Ⓐ 35.94 ft   Ⓑ 40.94 ft

Ⓒ 12.92 ft   Ⓓ 84.94 ft

1292 ft²

Problem Solving and Reasoning

30. Is the square root of 2000 twice the square root of 1000? Explain. **No; $\sqrt{2000} \approx 44.72$; $\sqrt{1000} \approx 31.62$; $2 \times 31.62 \neq 44.72$.**

31. Critical Thinking List the first ten perfect squares and their factors. Examine the number of factors for each. What conclusions can you draw about the number of factors of perfect squares?

32. Estimation Using the formula $d = \sqrt{1.5h}$, where d = distance, in miles, to the horizon and h = the height, in feet, of the viewer's eyes above the ground, you can find how far you can see to the horizon. If Sandy climbed a live oak tree so that her eyes were 32 feet above the ground, how far ahead could she see? **About 6.9 miles**

33. Communicate The restaurant at the top of the Eiffel Tower in Paris is 980 feet high. Use the formula in Exercise 32 to determine how far the diners can see. If the Eiffel Tower was twice as high, could they see twice as far? Explain. **38.3 miles; No; They would see about 54.2 miles.**

h=height

d=distance to horizon

Mixed Review

Find the value of y when $x = 8$ for each of the following. *[Lesson 4-1]*

34. $y = x - 2$ **35.** $4x + 7 = y$ **36.** $2x = 6 + y$ **37.** $y = x + 9$
    $y = 6$ $y = 39$ $y = 10$ $y = 17$

Make a table of five pairs of coordinates for each equation. Use 0, 1, 2, 3, 4, and 5 for x. *[Lesson 4-1]*

38. $y = x + 5$ **39.** $y = x - 3$ **40.** $y = 2x + 1$ **41.** $x = y + 4$

42. Which of the tables is an equivalent ratio table? *[Lesson 5-2]* **The one on the right**

x	2	4	6	8
y	3	5	7	9

x	3	6	9	12
y	9	18	27	36

7-8 • Square Roots and Irrational Numbers **373**

Exercise Notes

■ **Exercise 32**

Extension The formula in this exercise works only if h is expressed in feet. Then the result d is found in miles. If h is to be expressed in miles, the correct formula is $d = \sqrt{8000h}$. Then d is still given in miles.

Exercise Answers

31. 1; 4: 1, 2, 4; 9: 1, 3, 9; 16: 1, 2, 4, 8, 16; 25: 1, 5, 25; 36: 1, 2, 3, 4, 6, 9, 12, 18, 36; 49: 1, 7, 49; 64: 1, 2, 4, 8, 16, 32, 64; 81: 1, 3, 9, 27, 81; 100: 1, 2, 4, 5, 10, 20, 25, 50, 100. Possible answer: They all have an odd number of factors.

38–41. See page C1.

Alternate Assessment

Performance Have students work in small groups to write paragraph answers to these questions.

1. Why does every positive number have both a principal square root and a negative square root? Since a negative number squared is a positive number, the square root of a positive number may be either positive or negative.

2. When is a number irrational? When it cannot be expressed as a repeating or terminating decimal. An integer that is not a perfect square has an irrational square root.

> ### Quick Quiz
>
> 1. Which of these numbers is irrational?
> $\sqrt{16}$ $\sqrt{300}$ $\sqrt{121}$ $\sqrt{300}$
>
> 2. Determine whether these numbers are rational or irrational.
> $\sqrt{324}$ rational
> $\sqrt{330}$ irrational
>
> 3. Find the square roots of these numbers.
> $-\sqrt{400}$ −20 $\pm\sqrt{784}$ ±28
>
> Available on Daily Transparency 7-8

Name _____

GPS PROBLEM 28, STUDENT PAGE 372

Guided Problem Solving
7-8

You can find the number of seconds that it takes a pendulum to swing back and forth. First, find the square root of the pendulum's length in meters, then double it. How long will it take a pendulum that is 1.2 meters long to swing back and forth?

— **Understand** —
1. What are you asked to find? **The number of seconds it takes a 1.2 meter long pendulum to swing back and forth.**

2. What is the pendulum's length? **1.2 meters.**
3. Underline the steps to use in finding the number of seconds.

— **Plan** —
4. How can you find the square root of a number using a calculator? **Enter the number, then press the $\sqrt{x}$ (square root) key.**

5. How would you double a number? **Multiply by 2.**

— **Solve** —
6. Use a calculator to find the square root of 1.2. Round the answer to the nearest thousandth. **1.095**

7. Double the square root of 1.2. **2.19**

8. How long will it take a 1.2 meter pendulum to swing back and forth? **≈ 2.19 seconds.**

— **Look Back** —
9. Why is it important to follow the steps in order? What happens if you switch the order? **Possible answer: If the order changes, the answer is different.**

SOLVE ANOTHER PROBLEM

How long will it take a pendulum that is 9.6 meters long to swing back and forth?
≈ 6.196 seconds.

Name _____

Extend Your Thinking
7-8

Patterns in Numbers

Use your calculator to find the square root of each integer below. Round each answer to the nearest thousandth. The first ten are done for you.

N	$\sqrt{N}$	N	$\sqrt{N}$	N	$\sqrt{N}$
2	1.414	12	3.464	22	4.690
3	1.732	13	3.606	23	4.796
4	2.000	14	3.742	24	4.899
5	2.236	15	3.873	25	5.000
6	2.449	16	4.000	26	5.099
7	2.646	17	4.123	27	5.196
8	2.828	18	4.243	28	5.292
9	3.000	19	4.359	29	5.385
10	3.162	20	4.472	30	5.477
11	3.317	21	4.583	31	5.568

Possible answers: Items 2 and 3

1. Use the square roots in the table to find each product. Round the product to the nearest thousandth.

a. $\sqrt{2} \times \sqrt{3}$ **2.449**   b. $\sqrt{2} \times \sqrt{4}$ **2.828**   c. $\sqrt{2} \times \sqrt{5}$ **3.162**

d. $\sqrt{3} \times \sqrt{4}$ **3.464**   e. $\sqrt{3} \times \sqrt{5}$ **3.873**   f. $\sqrt{2} \times \sqrt{13}$ **5.099**

2. Look at your answers in Question 1. Compare them to the square roots of other numbers in the table. What pattern do you see?

The product of the square roots of two integers is equal to the square root of the product of the two integers.

3. Choose two sets of two numbers from the table. Multiply to see if your conjecture is true for these numbers.

$\sqrt{2} \times \sqrt{11} = 1.414 \times 3.317 = 4.690 = \sqrt{22}$;

$\sqrt{5} \times \sqrt{5} = 2.236 \times 2.236 = 5.000 = \sqrt{25}$.

Lesson 7-8 **373**

Objective

- Use the Pythagorean theorem with right triangles.

Vocabulary

- Pythagorean theorem

Materials

- Explore: Graph paper, scissors, markers (three different colors)

NCTM Standards

- 1, 2, 4–7, 9, 12, 13

► Review

1. Find the following squares.

   3^2 9 4^2 16 5^2 25

2. Find the following principal square roots.

   $\sqrt{9}$ 3 $\sqrt{16}$ 4 $\sqrt{25}$ 5

3. Add the following.

   9 + 16 = 25

Available on Daily Transparency 7-9

1 Introduce

Explore

You may wish to use Teaching Tool Transparency 7: $\frac{1}{4}$-inch Graph Paper and Lesson Enhancement Transparency 29 with **Explore**.

The Point

Students discover that if the areas of two smaller squares equal the area of a larger square, then the side measures of these squares can be used to form a right triangle.

Ongoing Assessment

Check that in Step 3 students are correctly covering the larger squares. In Step 5, check that they are correctly forming the right triangles.

You'll Learn ...

- to use the Pythagorean theorem with right triangles

... How It's Used

Bricklayers use the Pythagorean theorem to build straight walls.

Vocabulary

Pythagorean theorem

► Lesson Link You have learned about squares and square roots and will now apply what you have learned to solving problems about right triangles. ◄

Explore   Pythagorean Theorem

Squeeze in the Squares (^{2}s)

Materials: Graph paper, Scissors, Markers (three different colors)

1. Use the procedures in Parts 2 and 3 for each set of squares.

a. 3 by 3	**b.** 3 by 3	**c.** 5 by 5	**d.** 6 by 6
4 by 4	8 by 8	12 by 12	8 by 8
5 by 5	10 by 10	13 by 13	10 by 10

2. Draw a set of three squares on graph paper. Shade each square with a different color and cut each one out.

3. Without overlapping, can you cover the largest square with the two smaller squares? You can cut along the graph lines of each square.

4. Does the area of the largest square equal the sum of the areas of the two smaller squares for **a**? For **b**? For **c**? For **d**?

5. Can you make a right triangle using the sides of each of the sets of squares you worked with above?

6. What relationship do you notice between the sets of squares?

Learn   The Pythagorean Theorem

The **Pythagorean theorem** states that, for every right triangle, the sum of the squares of each leg is equal to the square of the hypotenuse.

The equation for the Pythagorean theorem is $a^2 + b^2 = c^2$, a and b for the lengths of the legs and c for the hypotenuse.

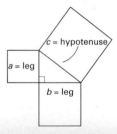

c = hypotenuse
a = leg
b = leg

374 Chapter 7 • Number Sense, Rational Numbers, and Irrational Numbers

---

Example 1

Find the missing length of the right triangle shown.

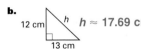

$12^2 + 5^2 = c^2$ Apply the Pythagorean theorem.

$169 = c^2$ Apply exponents. Add.

$\sqrt{169} = \sqrt{c^2}$ Take square root of both sides.

$13 = c$

The hypotenuse is 13 cm.

> **Remember**
>
> On a right triangle the legs are the sides that form the right angle. The hypotenuse is the longest side. **[Previous course]**

Try It

Find the missing length.

a. $c \approx 5$ in.

b. $h \approx 17.69$ cm

Example 2

A *tukul* is a traditional Ethiopian grass house. The length of the roof is 10 ft and the height of the roof is 6 ft. Find the distance from the wall to the center of the room.

$a^2 + 6^2 = 10^2$ Apply Pythagorean theorem.

$a^2 + 36 = 100$ Apply exponents.

$a^2 = 64$ Subtract 36 from both sides.

$\sqrt{a^2} = \sqrt{64}$ Take square root of both sides.

$a = 8$

The distance between the wall and the center of the *tukul* is 8 ft.

DID YOU KNOW?

A *tukul* is also called a *sarbet* and can be found on the high plateau of Ethiopia.

Try It

Find the missing length.

a. 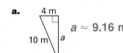 $a \approx 9.16$ m

b.  $a \approx 10.39$ ft

Sometimes the sides of a right triangle are not rational numbers.

MATH EVERY DAY

▶ Problem of the Day

You are the road manager for a small band. You are to play six towns in the next week. You determine the order of the towns. In how many different orders can you set up the tour?

720 ways

Available on Daily Transparency 7-9

An Extension is provided in the transparency package.

Fact of the Day

About four-fifths of North American Indians did not live in teepees. Only the Plains tribes used them, and only since about the 1700s.

Estimation

Estimate each answer.

1. $512 + 260 + 340$ 1100

2. $\$5.12 + \$2.60 + \$3.40$ \$11.00

3. $\frac{1}{2} + \frac{1}{4} + \frac{4}{9}$ 1

4. $0.5 + 0.25 + 0.3$ 1.1

For Groups That Finish Early

In Question 5, you found that you could make a right triangle with sides 3, 4, and 5. Use these numbers to show the relationship you discovered in Question 6.

$3^2 + 4^2 = 5^2$

Follow Up

Ask volunteers to share their answers for Steps 4, 5, and 6. Have them explain how they found the answers to these steps.

Answers for Explore

1–3. No answer required.

4. a. Yes   b. No
   c. Yes   d. Yes

5. a. Yes   b. No
   c. Yes   d. Yes

6. The sets that cover without overlapping are the ones that make right triangles.

2 Teach

Learn

Alternate Examples

1. Find the missing length of the hypotenuse in this right triangle.

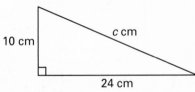

$10^2 + 24^2 = c^2$ Apply the Pythagorean theorem.

$676 = c^2$ Apply exponents. Add.

$\sqrt{676} = \sqrt{c^2}$ Take square root of both sides.

$26 = c$
The hypotenuse is 26 cm.

2. The top of a water slide is to be 8 ft high, and the length of the slide is to be 17 ft. Find the length of the horizontal base of the slide.

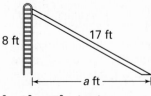

$a^2 + 8^2 = 17^2$ Apply Pythagorean theorem.

$a^2 + 64 = 289$ Apply exponents.
$a^2 = 225$ Subtract 64 from both sides.
$\sqrt{a^2} = \sqrt{225}$ Take square root of both sides.
$a = 15$
The horizontal base is 15 ft long.

3. A barn roof covers a span that is 32 feet across. The peak of the roof is 23 feet above the walls. Find the length of each side of the slanted roof using the Pythagorean theorem.

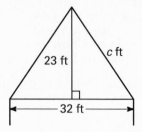

$16^2 + 23^2 = c^2$ Apply Pythagorean theorem.

$785 = c^2$ Apply exponents. Add.

$\sqrt{785} = \sqrt{c^2}$ Take square root of both sides.

$\approx 28.0179 = c$

The length of each side of the slanted roof is about 28 ft.

4. If you have a right triangle with both legs having the length of $\sqrt{5}$ inches, what is the length of the hypotenuse?

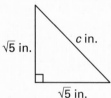

$(\sqrt{5})^2 + (\sqrt{5})^2 = c^2$ Apply Pythagorean theorem.

$5 + 5 = c^2$ Apply exponents. Add.

$10 = c^2$

$\sqrt{10} = \sqrt{c^2}$ Take square root of both sides.

$\sqrt{10} = c$

The hypotenuse is $\sqrt{10}$, or about 3.16, inches long.

3 Practice and Assess

Check

Be sure that students understand that the Pythagorean theorem applies only to right triangles.

Answers for Check Your Understanding

1. Right triangles.

2. Possible answer: The square root is used when solving for the missing side.

Read questions carefully and determine the necessary information to solve the question.

Example 3

The second story of an Austrian chalet is triangular. The floor is 18 ft across. The center of the floor to the highest point on the ceiling is 12 ft. Find the length of the slanted roof.

$18 \div 2 = 9$ Find the length of the base of the triangle.

$9^2 + 12^2 = c^2$ Apply Pythagorean theorem.

$225 = c^2$ Apply exponents. Add.

$\sqrt{225} = \sqrt{c^2}$ Take square root of both sides.

$15 = c$

The length of the roof is approximately 15 ft.

Example 4

What is the length of the hypotenuse?

$(\sqrt{3})^2 + (\sqrt{3})^2 = c^2$ Apply Pythagorean theorem.

$3 + 3 = c^2$ Apply exponents.

$6 = c^2$ Add.

$\sqrt{6} = \sqrt{c^2}$ Take square root of both sides.

$\sqrt{6} = c$

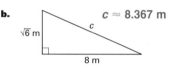

The hypotenuse is $\sqrt{6}$ units.

Try It

Find the missing length.

a. $a \approx 17.69$ in.   b.   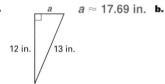 $c \approx 8.367$ m

Check Your Understanding

1. For what types of triangles does the Pythagorean theorem apply?

2. Explain how square roots are used with the Pythagorean theorem.

376   Chapter 7 • Number Sense, Rational Numbers, and Irrational Numbers

---

MEETING MIDDLE SCHOOL CLASSROOM NEEDS

Tips from Middle School Teachers

I like to have my students brainstorm ideas for real-life usage of the Pythagorean theorem, especially since it has many applications. To get them started, I ask them how it can be used to help them figure out if they can move a couch through a hallway that has a turn in it. Then I have my baseball fans explain how the theorem can be used to relate the distance between second base and home plate and between third base and first base. When students think about it, they often find many examples of the Pythagorean theorem in their lives.

Cultural Connection

The Pythagorean theorem has been discovered by people in many cultures. The ancient Chinese and Greeks deduced the theorem. Some ancient Egyptians and Babylonians knew of special cases of the theorem, and may have also known the general property.

Fine Arts Connection

The Wizard of Oz is a classic movie that many students have seen. Near the end of the movie, the scarecrow makes a statement that "the sum of the square roots of any two sides of an isosceles triangle is equal to the square root of the remaining side." This can be proved wrong in class using the Pythagorean theorem and any right isosceles triangle.

7-9 Exercises and Applications

Practice and Apply

1. **Getting Started** Find the missing length of the triangle shown.
   a. Apply the Pythagorean theorem. $12^2 + 16^2 = c^2$
   b. Apply exponents and simplify. $144 + 256 = c^2$; $400 = c^2$
   c. Take the square root of both sides. $c = 20$ cm

16 cm c
12 cm

PRACTICE 7-9

Find the length of the missing side for each right triangle.

2. $a = 27$

a 45
36

3. $a \approx 21.07$

a 40
34

4. $c = 65$
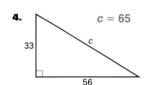
33 c
56

5. **Geometry** A flag shop is constructing flags for the Solomon Islands. If the rectangular flags are to be 4 ft by 6 ft, what would the length of the yellow stripe be? $\approx$ **7.2 ft**

Solomon Islands

6. **Social Studies** If the flags being made for Jamaica are the same size as the Solomon Island flags, what length of yellow fabric is necessary for each Jamaican flag? $\approx$ **14.4 ft**

Jamaica

7. **Science** Sunset Crater, a volcano in Arizona, has an altitude of 1200 ft. If you stand at the base of the slope—which is 2000 ft from the peak—how far are you standing from the pipe? **1600 ft**

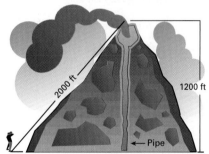
2000 ft
1200 ft
← Pipe

8. **Estimation** Paul has a 12 ft ladder to use to fix the leaking roof of his garage. If the base of the ladder is placed at least 4 ft from the garage to make climbing safe, is the ladder long enough for Paul to reach the 10 ft garage roof? **Yes**

■ **Basic**
1–4, 7–9, 11, 14–15, 17–19, 22, 23

■ **Average**
1–5, 7, 9, 10, 15, 18, 20, 21, 23, 24

■ **Enriched**
1–7, 9, 12–16, 20, 24

Exercise Notes

■ **Exercise 8**

Estimation Since the sum of the squares of 10 and 4 is less than 12 squared, the ladder is long enough to reach the garage roof.

PRACTICE

Name _____

Practice 7-9

The Pythagorean Theorem

Find the length of the missing side for each right triangle.

1.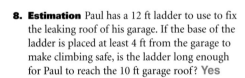
x 20
15
$x = 25$

2. x 97
72
$x = 65$

3. 144
42 x
$x = 150$

4. 44 x
125
$x = 117$

5. 45
53 x
$x = 28$

6. 12 5
x
$x = 13$

7. x 16
35
$x \approx 38.48$

8. x
12 37
$x = 35$

9. 4.8 1.4
x
$x = 5$

10. x
17
15
$x = 8$

11. 63
x 16
$x = 65$

12. 60 36
x
$x = 48$

13. 13.6 x
12.0
$x = 6.4$

14. 77
x 36
$x = 85$

15. 51
x 26
$x \approx 43.87$

16. An 8-ft ladder is leaning against a building. If the base of the ladder is 3 ft from the base of the building, how far is it up the building from the base of the ladder to the top of the ladder? **About 7.4 ft**

17. **Geography** Washington, DC, is 494 miles east of Indianapolis, Indiana. Birmingham, Alabama, is 433 miles south of Indianapolis. How far is Birmingham from Washington, DC? **About 657 mi**

RETEACHING

Name _____

Alternative Lesson 7-9

The Pythagorean Theorem

The sides of every right triangle have a special relationship. The **Pythagorean Theorem** states that the sum of the squares of each leg is equal to the square of the hypotenuse. The equation for the Pythagorean Theorem is $a^2 + b^2 = c^2$, where a and b are the lengths of the legs and c is the length of the hypotenuse. The hypotenuse is the longest side and is opposite the right angle.

— **Example** —

Find the length of the missing side of each right triangle.

a. 18 cm c
24 cm
The missing length is the hypotenuse. Solve for c.

b. 6 cm
3 cm b
The missing length is a leg. Solve for b.

Step 1: Use the Pythagorean Theorem.
a. $a^2 + b^2 = c^2$
b. $a^2 + b^2 = c^2$

Step 2: Apply the Pythagorean Theorem by substituting known values.
a. $18^2 + 24^2 = c^2$
b. $3^2 + b^2 = 6^2$

Step 3: Apply the exponent by writing the numbers in standard form.
a. $324 + 576 = c^2$
b. $9 + b^2 = 36$

Step 4: Isolate the variable squared on one side of the equation.
a. $900 = c^2$
b. $b^2 = 36 - 9$
$b^2 = 27$

Step 5: Take the square root of both sides to find the value of the variable.
a. $\sqrt{900} = \sqrt{c^2}$
$30 = c$
b. $\sqrt{b^2} = \sqrt{27}$
$b = 5.1961524$

a. The hypotenuse is 30 cm.
b. The leg is about 5.2 cm.

Try It Find the length of the missing side of each right triangle.

a. **29 in.**
20 in. c
21 in.

b. **60 cm**
100 cm
a
80 cm

Reteaching

Activity

Materials: Graph paper

• Work in groups of two.

• On graph paper draw 5 different right triangles and 2 triangles that are not right triangles.

• Measure the sides of each triangle and check whether the Pythagorean theorem applies to the triangle.

Industry Carpenters, fence installers, and concrete workers use a similar method to check that corners are formed as right angles. However, they often use a 6-, 8-, 10-foot triangle and a tape measure.

■ Exercise 16

Error Prevention Some students will find it difficult to accept that the answer to the question is "never." Suppose the length of the two equal sides is 5. Then $c^2 = 5^2 + 5^2 = 50$, so $c = \sqrt{50}$, or $5\sqrt{2}$. No matter what whole number lengths are selected for the two equal sides, the length of the hypotenuse will include $\sqrt{2}$, and will therefore be irrational.

Project Progress

You may want to have students use Chapter 7 Project Master.

Exercise Answers

14. Answers may vary.

17. Possible answers: (2, 1); (6, 3)

18. Possible answers: (2, 6); (7, 11)

19. Possible answers: (10, 6); (15, 9)

20. Possible answers: (1, 5); (3, 11)

Alternate Assessment

Project Find three numbers a, b, and c that make $a^2 + b^2 = c^2$ true. Cut three strips of cardboard with lengths of a, b, and c. Use them to demonstrate how the Pythagorean theorem can be used to form a right triangle.

▶ Quick Quiz

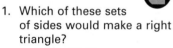

1. Which of these sets of sides would make a right triangle?
   a. 9, 11, 12 No
   b. 5, 12, 13 Yes

2. What is the length of the diagonal stripe in a flag that is 8 feet by 12 feet?
   About 14.4 feet

3. Find the missing length of each of these right triangles, where c is the length of the hypotenuse.
   a. $a = 27$, $b = 36$, $c = ?$ 45
   b. $a = ?$, $b = 56$, $c = 65$ 33

Available on Daily Transparency 7-9

PROBLEM SOLVING 7-9

9. **Test Prep** The Comanche Indians cure buffalo hides and stretch them over a wooden framework to build tepees. If the radius of a tepee is 15 ft and the hides are extended 25 ft up on the slanted sides, how high will the center of the tepee be? **C**

Ⓐ 200 ft   Ⓑ 29 ft   Ⓒ 20 ft   Ⓓ 4.5 ft

Problem Solving and Reasoning

Math Reasoning If the lengths of the sides of a triangle satisfy $a^2 + b^2 = c^2$, the triangle is a right triangle. The longest side is c, the hypotenuse. Does the set of side lengths make a right triangle?

10. 4, 5, 7 No 11. 7, 24, 25 Yes 12. 20, 21, 29 Yes 13. 5, 12, 13 Yes

14. **Communicate** The ancient Egyptians used ropes tied with knots to form a 3-4-5 triangle to help them with right angles when building the pyramids. Explain how this system would work.

15. **Measurement** A square courtyard with a diagonal walkway has an area of 81 square feet.
    GPS
    a. Find the length of the sides of the courtyard. 9 ft
    b. Find the length of the walkway. ≈ 12.728 ft

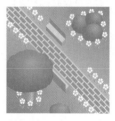

16. **Patterns** Use the Pythagorean theorem to find the length of the hypotenuse in right triangles when the legs are integer values of equal length. When do you get an integer length for the hypotenuse? **Never**

Mixed Review

Give two solution pairs for each of these equations. *[Lesson 4-2]*

17. $x = 2y$ 18. $y = x + 4$ 19. $3x = 5y$ 20. $y = 3x + 2$

Solve each proportion. *[Lesson 5-4]*

21. $\dfrac{2}{3} = \dfrac{44}{x}$ 22. $\dfrac{9}{x} = \dfrac{27{,}000}{36{,}000}$ 23. $\dfrac{x}{5} = \dfrac{20}{100}$
    $x = 66$ $x = 12$ $x = 1$

24. If a cookie recipe calls for 3 cups of sugar to make 4 dozen cookies, how many cups of sugar are needed to make 10 dozen cookies? $7\frac{1}{2}$ **cups**

Project Progress

Look back at your results from the investment period. Look for any use of irrational numbers or square roots.

Problem Solving

Understand
Plan
Solve
Look Back

▶ PROBLEM SOLVING

Name _____

Guided Problem Solving 7-9

GPS PROBLEM 15, STUDENT PAGE 378

A square courtyard with a diagonal walkway has an area of 81 square feet.
a. Find the length of the sides of the courtyard.
b. Find the length of the walkway.

— **Understand** —
1. What is the area of the square courtyard? 81 square feet.
2. What figure is formed by two sides of the courtyard and the diagonal walkway? Right triangle.
3. What part of the figure named in Item 2 represents the longest part of the walkway? Hypotenuse.

— **Plan** —
4. How can you find the length of each courtyard side? Find $\sqrt{81}$.
5. How can the Pythagorean Theorem help find the walkway length? Let the sides of the square be the legs. Solve for c.

— **Solve** —
6. What is the length of each side of the courtyard? 9 feet.
7. What is the length of the longest part of the walkway rounded to the nearest thousandth? 12.728 feet.

— **Look Back** —
8. How can you check your answer? Possible answer: Substitute answers for variables in the Pythagorean Theorem. $a^2 + b^2 = c^2$, $9^2 + 9^2 = 12.728^2$; $81 + 81 ≈ 162$.

SOLVE ANOTHER PROBLEM

A square courtyard with a diagonal walkway has an area of 324 ft². Find the length of
a. the sides of the courtyard. 18 feet.   b. the walkway. ≈ 25.5 feet.

▶ ENRICHMENT

Name _____

Extend Your Thinking 7-9

Patterns in Geometry

If the three sides of a right triangle are integers, then the measures of those sides are called **Pythagorean Triples**. A common Pythagorean Triple is 3-4-5. You can use the Pythagorean Theorem to verify that the Pythagorean Triple is correct: $3^2 + 4^2 = 5^2$.

Use the Pythagorean Theorem to see if the following numbers are Pythagorean Triples. Write yes or no.

	Pythagorean Theorem	Pythagorean Triple
1. 7-24-25	$7^2 + 24^2 \overset{?}{=} 25^2$; $49 + 576 \overset{?}{=} 625$	Yes.
2. 20-21-29	$20^2 + 21^2 \overset{?}{=} 29^2$; $400 + 441 \overset{?}{=} 841$	Yes.
3. 9-25-27	$9^2 + 25^2 \overset{?}{=} 27^2$; $81 + 625 \overset{?}{=} 729$	No.
4. 8-15-17	$8^2 + 15^2 \overset{?}{=} 17^2$; $64 + 225 \overset{?}{=} 289$	Yes.

You can make other Pythagorean Triples by multiplying each number of a triple by the same integer. For example, 6-8-10 is a Pythagorean Triple because each number in the triple 3-4-5 has been multiplied by 2.

Write two other related Pythagorean Triples. **Possible answers:**

5. 3-4-5 __9-12-15; 12-16-20__
6. 20-21-29 __40-42-58; 60-63-87__
7. 7-24-25 __14-48-50; 21-72-75__
8. 8-15-17 __16-30-34; 24-45-51__

In a Pythagorean Triple, a, b, and c are also related in this way:
$a = m^2 - n^2$, $b = 2mn$,   and $c = m^2 + n^2$
where m and n are relatively prime integers and $m > n$.

Complete this table of Pythagorean Triples.

	m	n	$a = m^2 - n^2$	$b = 2mn$	$c = m^2 + n^2$
9.	3	2	5	12	13
10.	6	5	11	60	61
11.	10	7	51	140	149

You have learned to use the Pythagorean theorem for right triangles. You will now use the Pythagorean theorem to design parts of a house.

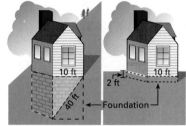

Home Sweet Home

Materials: Calculator

Some people prefer to build or fix up their own house. Measurements and calculations are crucial if you want windows to close, doors to open, stable walls, and straight floors. The Pythagorean theorem can be used for many aspects of building a house.

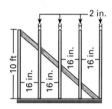

1. A foundation can keep the wooden frame of a house from rotting after years of rain, wind, and snow. Compare the two foundations shown by determining the depth of each.

2. The frame of a house is like your body's skeleton. Corner bracing can add strength to a house frame. How long is the entire length of bracing?

3. How long is a part of the bracing that is between two 10-ft-tall wood planks? Explain how you got your answer.

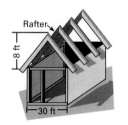

4. Rafters are the parallel beams that support a roof. What is the total length of wood used in the rafters of this roof?

5. Draw a sketch of a house that you would build for yourself and describe how you would use the Pythagorean theorem.

379

Home Sweet Home

The Point

In *Home Sweet Home* on page 363, students learned that people live in a variety of dwellings. Now students will use the Pythagorean theorem to design parts of a house.

Materials

Calculator

About the Page

- Be sure students understand how to use a calculator to find squares and square roots.

- Be sure students understand how important the Pythagorean theorem is to the aspects of building a house. Ask students if they can think of any other ways the Pythagorean theorem might be used to build a house. Possible answer: To figure out the dimensions of a staircase or ramp.

- Have students work in groups of 2 or 3 to answer Question 5. Ask each group to share their answers with the class. Discuss how each group used the answers to Questions 1–4 to answer Question 5.

Ongoing Assessment

Check that students have used the Pythagorean theorem correctly.

Extension

Have students describe other things that they might build that require the use of right angles, such as picture frames and bookcases. Suggest that they make a sketch and identify the right angles.

Answers for Connect

1. 38.7 ft; 2 ft

2. Almost 141 inches.

3. About 35 in.; Explanations may vary.

4. About 136 ft.

5. Answers may vary.

Chapter 7 Review

Section 7C Review

Review Correlation

Item(s)	Lesson(s)
1–15	7-7
16–20	7-8
21–25	7-7
26–28	7-9
29	7-8
30	7-9

Test Prep

Test-Taking Tip

Tell students that when a multiple-choice question involves a formula, they should be careful to substitute the values correctly. In many cases, one or more of the possible answers will be obtained if incorrect substitutions are made.

Answers for Review

16. Irrational

17. Rational

18. Rational

19. Rational

20. Rational

Use your calculator to determine whether each is a perfect square.

1. 1000 **No** **2.** 3025 **Yes** **3.** 686 **No** **4.** 3222 **No** **5.** 1296 **Yes**

Determine each square root and write in lowest terms.

6. $\sqrt{1296}$ 36 **7.** $\sqrt{68} \approx 8.25$ **8.** $\sqrt{\frac{49}{81}}$ $\frac{7}{9}$ **9.** $\sqrt{\frac{100}{625}}$ $\frac{2}{5}$ **10.** $\sqrt{\frac{144}{36}}$ 2

11. $-\sqrt{36}$ -6 **12.** $-\sqrt{1764}$ -42 **13.** $\pm\sqrt{12.25}$ ± 3.5 **14.** $\pm\sqrt{4096}$ ± 64 **15.** $-\sqrt{\frac{36}{4}}$ -3

Identify each number as rational or irrational.

16. $\sqrt{376}$ **17.** $\sqrt{1296}$ **18.** $0.\overline{62}$ **19.** $\frac{7}{9}$ **20.** $-\sqrt{\frac{4}{9}}$

Find the side length of a square with the given area.

21. $32\ \text{in}^2$ ≈ 5.66 in. **22.** $12\ \text{ft}^2$ ≈ 3.46 ft **23.** $441\ \text{cm}^2$ 21 cm **24.** $34\ \text{m}^2$ ≈ 5.83 m **25.** $4.25\ \text{ft}^2$ ≈ 2.06 ft

Find the missing side length of each right triangle.

26.
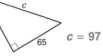
72, 65, c; $c = 97$

27. 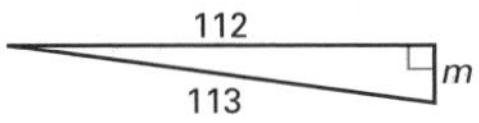
112, 113, m; $m = 15$

28.

133, 156, a; $a = 205$

29. Explain why you think it is easier for craftspeople (for example, carpenters or mechanics) to use rational numbers in their work. **Possible answer: Rational numbers are easier to measure.**

Test Prep

On a multiple-choice test you will often see a familiar formula to apply and you will have to know what the variables represent.

30. The formula $a^2 + b^2 = c^2$ satisfies all right triangles, where c is the hypotenuse. Which of the following triangles is a right triangle? **C**

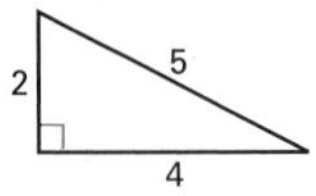

Ⓐ 2, 4, 5   Ⓑ 6, 4, 5   Ⓒ 6, 8, 10

380 *Chapter 7 • Number Sense, Rational Numbers, and Irrational Numbers*

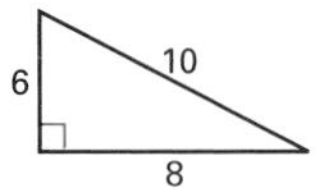

Resources

Practice Masters
   Section 7C Review

Assessment Sourcebook
   Quiz 7C

 TestWorks
   Test and Practice Software

PRACTICE

Name _____   **Practice**

Section 7C Review

Use your calculator to determine whether each is a perfect square.

1. 3823 __No__ 2. 7245 __No__ 3. 1849 __Yes__ 4. 5916 __No__

Determine each square root and write in lowest terms.

5. $\sqrt{\frac{25}{81}}$ $\frac{5}{9}$ 6. $\sqrt{49}$ __7__ 7. $\sqrt{441}$ __21__ 8. $\sqrt{\frac{100}{144}}$ $\frac{5}{6}$

9. $-\sqrt{81}$ __−9__ 10. $\sqrt{30.25}$ __5.5__ 11. $\pm\sqrt{169}$ __±13__ 12. $\sqrt{68.89}$ __8.3__

Identify each number as rational or irrational.

13. 2.141414 ... __Rational__ 14. $\frac{5}{11}$ __Rational__ 15. $5.8\overline{3}$ __Rational__

Find the side length of a square with the given area.

16. $196\ \text{ft}^2$ __14 ft__ 17. $75\ \text{m}^2$ $\approx$ __8.66 m__ 18. $116\ \text{yd}^2$ $\approx$ __10.77 yd__

19. $7.84\ \text{in}^2$ __2.8 in.__ 20. $8.4\ \text{cm}^2 \approx$ __2.90 cm__ 21. $12.8\ \text{km}^2$ $\approx$ __3.58 km__

Find the missing side of each right triangle.

22. 75, 72, ? __21__ 23. 24, 18, ? __30__ 24. 52, 20, ? __48__

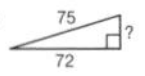

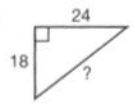

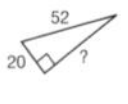

25. This graph shows the price to item ratio for oranges. How many oranges could you buy for $9? Explain your reasoning. *[Lesson 5-3]*

__22 oranges; Possible explanation:__

__(22.5, 9) is on the graph, but you can't__

__buy half an orange.__

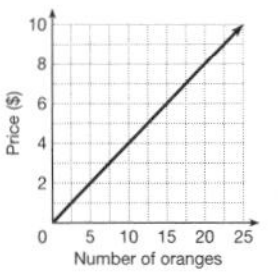

26. In 1994, 36,521,700 Americans age 25 or older had completed at least 4 years of college. This was 22.2% of all Americans age 25 or older. How many Americans were at least 25 years old in 1994? *[Lesson 6-2]* __About 164,512,000__

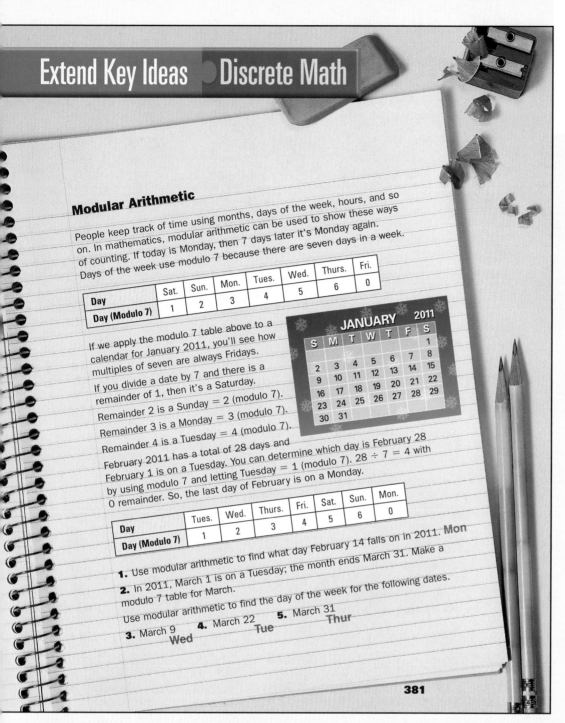

Modular Arithmetic

People keep track of time using months, days of the week, hours, and so on. In mathematics, modular arithmetic can be used to show these ways of counting. If today is Monday, then 7 days later it's Monday again. Days of the week use modulo 7 because there are seven days in a week.

Day	Sat.	Sun.	Mon.	Tues.	Wed.	Thurs.	Fri.
Day (Modulo 7)	1	2	3	4	5	6	0

If we apply the modulo 7 table above to a calendar for January 2011, you'll see how multiples of seven are always Fridays.

If you divide a date by 7 and there is a remainder of 1, then it's a Saturday.

Remainder 2 is a Sunday = 2 (modulo 7).

Remainder 3 is a Monday = 3 (modulo 7).

Remainder 4 is a Tuesday = 4 (modulo 7).

JANUARY						2011
S	M	T	W	T	F	S
						1
2	3	4	5	6	7	8
9	10	11	12	13	14	15
16	17	18	19	20	21	22
23	24	25	26	27	28	29
30	31					

February 2011 has a total of 28 days and February 1 is on a Tuesday. You can determine which day is February 28 by using modulo 7 and letting Tuesday = 1 (modulo 7). 28 ÷ 7 = 4 with 0 remainder. So, the last day of February is on a Monday.

Day	Tues.	Wed.	Thurs.	Fri.	Sat.	Sun.	Mon.
Day (Modulo 7)	1	2	3	4	5	6	0

1. Use modular arithmetic to find what day February 14 falls on in 2011. **Mon**

2. In 2011, March 1 is on a Tuesday; the month ends March 31. Make a modulo 7 table for March.

Use modular arithmetic to find the day of the week for the following dates.

3. March 9 **Wed**   4. March 22 **Tue**   5. March 31 **Thur**

Answers for Questions

2.

Day	Tues.	Wed.	Thur.	Fri.	Sat.	Sun.	Mon.
Day (mod 7)	1	2	3	4	5	6	0

Modular Arithmetic

The Point

Students use modular arithmetic to find the day of the week specific dates in given months of a particular year will fall.

About the Page

If students have difficulty conceptualizing the pattern in modular 7 arithmetic, have them draw a circle and place the numbers 0, 1, 2, 3, 4, 5, and 6 at equal intervals around the circle. This 7-hour clock may be very helpful to students with various learning styles.

Ask …

- Why is the entry for Friday in the first table 0? In this table, Saturday is the first day of the month or day 1. So Friday is considered day 7, and 7 ÷ 7 = 1 with a remainder of 0.

- Why is the entry for Monday in the second table 0? In this table, Tuesday is the first day of the month or day 1. So Monday is considered day 7, and 7 ÷ 7 = 1 with a remainder of 0.

Extension

Have students work in groups to explain how modular arithmetic can be used to find which month occurs x months from now. Have them figure out which modulo to use and to explain how to use this method of counting. Possible answers: Modulo 12; Make a two-row table. In the first row, list the names of the months, starting with the name of the next month after the current month, and ending with the name of the current month. In the second row (below each month), list the number modulo 12, starting with 1 and ending with 0. Assuming this month is June and you wanted to find out what month occurs 28 months from now, divide 28 by 12 and get the remainder (4). According to the chart, 4 or 28 months from June would be October.

Review Correlation

Item(s)	Lesson(s)
1, 2	7-1
3, 4	7-2
5, 6	7-3
7–9	7-4
10, 11	7-5
12	7-6
13–16	7-7
17, 18	7-8

For additional review, see page 682.

Chapter 7 Summary and Review

Graphic Organizer

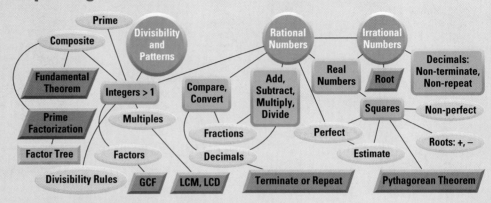

Section 7A   Number Theory

Summary

- A **prime number** is an integer greater than 1 that is only divisible by itself and 1. A **composite number** is an integer that is not prime.

- An integer is a **multiple** of a number if it is **divisible** by that number—that is, if it can be divided without a remainder. A number is divisible by each of its **factors**.

- The **Fundamental Theorem of Arithmetic** states that all integers greater than 1 can be written using **prime factorization**.

- A **common factor** of two numbers is a factor of both numbers. The largest of these is the **greatest common factor (GCF)**.

- A **common multiple** of two numbers is a multiple of both numbers. The smallest common multiple is the **least common multiple (LCM)**.

Review

1. Is 162 divisible by 2, 3, 4, 5, 6, 8, 9, or 10?
Divisible by 2, 3, 6, and 9

2. Determine the prime factorization of 924.
$924 = 2^2 \times 3 \times 7 \times 11$

3. Find the GCF of 39 and 45. **3**

4. Write $\frac{84}{112}$ in lowest terms. $\frac{3}{4}$

5. Find the LCM of 15 and 25. **75**

6. Find the LCD of $\frac{3}{15}$ and $\frac{2}{20}$. **60**

382 Chapter 7 • Number Sense, Rational Numbers, and Irrational Numbers

---

PRACTICE

Resources

Practice Masters
    Cumulative Review
    Chapters 1–7

Name _____

Practice

Cumulative Review Chapters 1–7

For each line, find the slope, the x-intercept, and the y-intercept. *[Lesson 4-5]*

1. Line through A and B   slope: $\frac{2}{3}$
   x-intercept: -3 y-intercept: 2

2. Line through B and C   slope: 2
   x-intercept: 1 y-intercept: -2

3. Line through C and D   slope: -1
   x-intercept: 4 y-intercept: 4

Complete each table to create ratios equal to the given ratio. *[Lesson 5-2]*

4.

3	6	9	42	66
7	14	21	98	154

5.

8	16	32	64	88
11	22	44	88	121

6.

9	18	27	54	81
5	10	15	30	45

7.

6	12	18	30	2
15	30	45	75	5

Estimate. *[Lesson 6-3]*

8. 63% of 12 ≈ 8 **9.** 80% of 365 ≈ 290 **10.** 35% of 67 ≈ 22

11. 12% of 582 ≈ 70 **12.** 28% of 737 ≈ 200 **13.** 125% of 89 ≈ 112

Calculate. *[Lessons 7-5 and 7-6]*

14. $6\frac{3}{4} + 7\frac{1}{3}$ $14\frac{1}{12}$ **15.** $12\frac{3}{7} - 4\frac{5}{8}$ $7\frac{45}{56}$ **16.** $3\frac{5}{6} \times 3$ $11\frac{1}{2}$ **17.** $\frac{3}{8} \div 1\frac{1}{5}$ $\frac{5}{16}$

18. $3\frac{5}{6} + 8\frac{3}{8}$ $12\frac{5}{24}$ **19.** $23\frac{4}{5} - 8\frac{1}{4}$ $15\frac{11}{20}$ **20.** $4\frac{3}{8} \times 7\frac{2}{3}$ $33\frac{13}{24}$ **21.** $8\frac{3}{4} + 2\frac{3}{8}$ $3\frac{13}{19}$

Determine the following square roots and write in lowest terms. *[Lesson 7-7]*

22. $\sqrt{361}$ 19 **23.** $\sqrt{1024}$ 32 **24.** $\sqrt{\frac{9}{16}}$ $\frac{3}{4}$ **25.** $\sqrt{\frac{36}{49}}$ $\frac{6}{7}$

26. $\sqrt{\frac{64}{121}}$ $\frac{8}{11}$ **27.** $\sqrt{\frac{100}{36}}$ $\frac{5}{3}$ **28.** $\sqrt{\frac{49}{144}}$ $\frac{7}{12}$ **29.** $\sqrt{\frac{100}{169}}$ $\frac{10}{13}$

Section 7B   Rational Numbers

Summary

- A **rational number** is a number that can be written as a ratio of two integers. Integers, fractions, terminating decimals, and repeating decimals are rational numbers.

- A **terminating decimal** has a fixed number of digits. A **repeating decimal** has a repeating digit or repeating group of digits.

- Add and subtract fractions by writing them with a common denominator.

- Use the **reciprocal** and multiply when you divide by a fraction.

Review

7. Write $\frac{3}{16}$ as a decimal and determine whether it is repeating or terminating.
0.1875; T

8. Replace ☐ with $>$, $<$, or $=$ to compare 3.806 ☐ 3.8059. **3.806 > 3.8059**

9. Write 0.12 as a fraction in lowest terms. $\frac{3}{25}$

10. Add $5.84 + 12.638$. **18.478**

11. Subtract $7\frac{8}{9} - 2\frac{5}{6}$. $5\frac{1}{18}$

12. Divide $2\frac{3}{8} \div 3\frac{1}{3}$. $\frac{57}{80}$

Section 7C   Irrational Numbers

Summary

- A **square root** of a number (N) gives N when multiplied by itself. The positive square root is the **principal square root** and its opposite is the **negative square root**.

- A **perfect square** is a number with an integer square root.

- A number that cannot be expressed as a repeating or terminating decimal is an **irrational number**. The rational and irrational numbers make up the **real numbers**.

- The **Pythagorean theorem** states that in a right triangle, the sum of the squares of the legs is equal to the square of the hypotenuse.

Review

13. State whether or not 92 is a perfect square. **No**

14. Find the square root of $\frac{25}{36}$. $\frac{5}{6}$

15. Find the two consecutive integers that $\sqrt{54}$ is between. **7 and 8**

16. What is the side length of a square with area 32 cm²? $\approx$ **5.657 cm**

17. Find $\pm\sqrt{529}$. **±23**

18. Find $-\sqrt{729}$. **−27**

Assessment Correlation

Item(s)	Lesson(s)
1–5	7-1
6–11	7-2
12–14	7-3
15–17	7-4
18, 19a	7-5
19b	7-6
20–22	7-7
23	7-8
24	7-7
25	7-8
26, 27	7-9

Answers for Assessment

9. $\frac{161}{165}$

10. $\frac{21}{47}$

11. $\frac{5}{12}$

14. Every 120 days.

Chapter 7 Assessment

1. Determine whether 615 is divisible by 2, 3, 4, 5, 6, 8, 9, or 10. **Divisible by 3 and 5**

Determine the prime factorization of each number.

2. 315   **3.** 266   **4.** 372   **5.** 213

6. Find the GCF of 24 and 64. **8**   **7.** Find the GCF of 180 and 428. **4**

2. $3^2 \times 5 \times 7$
3. $2 \times 7 \times 19$
4. $2^2 \times 3 \times 31$
5. 3×71

Write each fraction in lowest terms.

8. $\frac{54}{126}$ $\frac{3}{7}$ **9.** $\frac{322}{330}$ **10.** $\frac{63}{141}$ **11.** $\frac{75}{180}$

12. Find the LCM of 36 and 32. **288** **13.** Find the LCM of 84 and 63. **252**

14. Loaves of Breads bakery has free samples of blueberry muffins every 5 days, whole-wheat bread every 8 days, and sourdough rolls every 6 days. How often does the bakery give free samples of all three breads on the same day?

15. Determine whether $\frac{7}{11}$ is repeating or terminating as a decimal. **$0.\overline{63}$; Repeating**

16. Replace ☐ with >, <, or = to compare 3.14159 ☐ $\frac{22}{7}$. **$3.14159 < \frac{22}{7}$**

17. Write $0.\overline{15}$ as a fraction in lowest terms. **$\frac{5}{33}$**

18. Subtract $10.6724 - 3.87$. **6.8024**

19. Calculate and express each as a mixed number in lowest terms.

a. $6\frac{3}{4} + 12\frac{7}{18}$ **b.** $3\frac{5}{7} \times 7\frac{2}{13}$ **a.** $19\frac{5}{36}$ **b.** $26\frac{4}{7}$

20. State whether 150 is a perfect square. **No**

21. Find the two closest perfect squares for 89. **81, 100**

22. Estimate the square root of 150. **≈ 12.2**

23. Use a calculator to find $\sqrt{67}$ and round to the nearest thousandth. **8.185**

24. Find $\sqrt{\frac{49}{81}}$. $\frac{7}{9}$ **25.** Find $\sqrt{8} \times \sqrt{18}$. **12**

26. Decide whether side lengths 8, 15, and 17 would make a right triangle. **Yes**

27. Find the length of the missing side for the right triangle. **$x \approx 27.9$**

Performance Task

Make a poster that you could use to explain how to write a repeating decimal such as $2.\overline{7}$ as a fraction.

Performance Assessment Key

See key on page 321.

Resources
Assessment Sourcebook
Chapter 7 Tests
Forms A and B (free response)
Form C (multiple choice)
Form D (performance assessment)
Form E (mixed response)
Form F (cumulative chapter test)
TestWorks
Test and Practice Software
Home and Community Connections
Letter Home for Chapter 7
in English and Spanish

Suggested Scoring Rubric

4
- Shows all steps correctly.
- Explains all steps correctly and clearly.

3
- Shows most steps correctly, but omits some necessary steps.
- Gives a partial explanation of most steps.

2
- Shows a few steps correctly, but omits several necessary steps.
- Gives a partial explanation of some steps.

1
- Attempts to show steps and give explanations.

Performance Assessment

Choose one problem.

School Dances

Damon, a disc jockey, charges $275 for two hours and $400 for 3 hours. At school dances he charges $2 for each song requested, half of which goes toward the school's library fund. If at the spring dance, 75 songs are requested, how much will go toward the library fund? How much does Damon make per hour for a 3-hour dance? How much do you think he should charge for a dance that lasts $2\frac{1}{2}$ hours?

Telephone Dilemma

Joel's telephone is 6 ft away from the telephone jack on the same wall. The telephone jack is 8 in. above the floor. The telephone is mounted 2 ft above the floor. Will a 10 ft cord connect Joel's telephone to the telephone jack on the wall? Show your work and draw a diagram of Joel's telephone dilemma.

One Earth, One Chance

The Sierra Club used 0.074 of its donations toward outdoor activities, 0.096 toward fundraising, and 0.234 toward public education. People who donate to the Sierra Club can offer $15, $25, $35, $50, or $100. Calculate how much of each donation goes toward outdoor activities, fundraising, and public education. Create a display to show your results.

An Alternative Spud Topper

One serving of cottage cheese is 110 grams. Cottage cheese is $\frac{2}{55}$ carbohydrates, $\frac{1}{44}$ fat, and $\frac{1}{8}$ protein. How many grams of carbohydrates, fat, and protein are in one serving of cottage cheese?
4 grams carbohydrates; 2.5 grams fat; 13.75 grams protein

Cumulative Review Chapters 1-7 **385**

Answers for Assessment
- **School Dances:**
  $75; $133.33; Possible answer: $337.50, which is the average of the 2-hour and 3-hour charges.

- **One Earth, One Chance:**

Amt. Donated	$15	$25	$35	$50	$100
Outdoor Act.	$1.11	$1.85	$2.59	$3.70	$7.40
Fundraising	$1.44	$2.40	$3.36	$4.80	$9.60
Education	$3.51	$5.85	$8.19	$11.70	$23.40

- **Telephone Dilemma:**
  Answers may vary; A 10-foot cord will work.

One Earth, One Chance

4
- All calculations are correct.
- Display clearly shows all results.

3
- Most calculations are correct.
- Display shows most results.

2
- Some calculations are correct.
- Display shows few results.

1
- Few calculations are correct.
- Display is inadequate.

Telephone Dilemma

4
- All steps of work are correct.
- Diagram is complete and labeled.

3
- Most steps of work are correct.
- Diagram is complete.

2
- Steps are incomplete.
- Diagram is incomplete.

1
- Steps are incomplete and incorrect.
- Diagram is incorrect.

About Performance Assessment

The Performance Assessment options...

- provide teachers with an alternate means of assessing students.

- address different learning modalities.

- allow students to choose one problem.

Teachers may encourage students to choose the most challenging problem.

Learning Modalities
School Dances **Individual** Students follow their own instincts.
One Earth, One Chance **Logical** Students use a pattern.
Telephone Dilemma **Visual** Students draw a diagram.
An Alternative Spud Topper **Logical** Students use mathematics skills.

Suggested Scoring Rubric

See key on page 321.

School Dances

4
- Correctly answers questions about the library fund and 3-hour dance.
- Answer for question about $2\frac{1}{2}$ hour dance is logical.

3
- Correctly answers one question about the library fund and 3-hour dance.
- Answer for question about $2\frac{1}{2}$ hour dance is logical.

2
- Correctly answers one question about the library fund and 3-hour dance.
- An attempt is made to answer question about $2\frac{1}{2}$ hour dance, but answer is not logical.

1
- Incorrectly answers questions about the library fund and 3-hour dance.
- An attempt is made to answer question about $2\frac{1}{2}$ hour dance, but answer is not logical.

Rubric for **An Alternative Spud Topper** on page C1.

Chapter 8

OVERVIEW

Geometry and Measurement

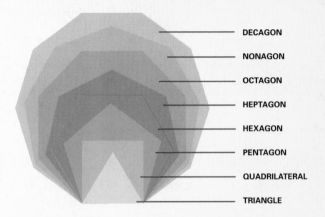

- DECAGON
- NONAGON
- OCTAGON
- HEPTAGON
- HEXAGON
- PENTAGON
- QUADRILATERAL
- TRIANGLE

Section 8A

Measurement: Students learn about customary and metric units, precision of measurements, and significant digits. Students also learn to locate positions on a map.

Section 8B

Elements of Geometry: Students learn about lines, angles, and parallel and perpendicular lines. Students classify polygons and draw views of three-dimensional figures.

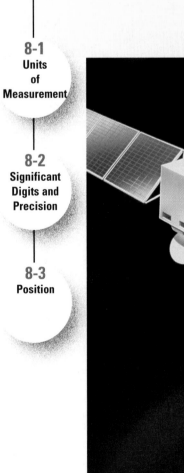

8-1
Units of Measurement

8-2
Significant Digits and Precision

8-3
Position

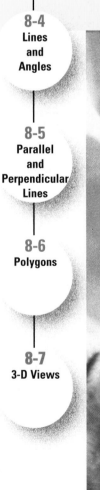

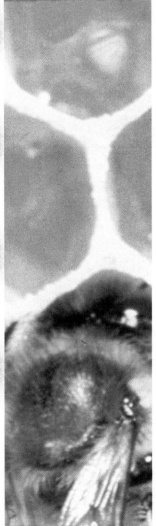

8-4
Lines and Angles

8-5
Parallel and Perpendicular Lines

8-6
Polygons

8-7
3-D Views

▶ Curriculum Standards

S T A N D A R D

			pages
1	**Problem Solving**	Skills and Strategies	388, 400, 426
		Applications	*390*, 394–395, 399–400, 405–406, 414–415, 419–420, *421*, 425–426, 430–431
		Exploration	387, 390, 396, 400, 401, 410, 416, 420, 421, 427
2	**Communication**	Oral	386, 387, 389, *391*, 393, 395, 398, *402*, 404, 409, *411*, 413, *417*, 418, *422*, 424, *428*, 429
		Written	393, 395, 398, 400, 404, 406, 413, 415, 420, 424, 426, 429, 431, 432
		Cooperative Learning	386, 390, *394*, 396, *399*, 401, *403*, 410, *412*, 416, 421, *423*, 427, *429*
3	**Reasoning**	Critical Thinking	395, *400*, 406, 426, 431
4	**Connections**	Mathematical	See Standards 5, 7, 9, 12, 13 below.
		Interdisciplinary	Career *398*, *418*, 425, *429;* Geography 394, 403, 405, 420; Health *409;* History *389, 392,* 405, 415, 431; Industry *389,* 393, 399; Science 391, 394, 397, 398, 399, 405, 407, 412, 414, 417, 419, *420,* 422, 426, 430; Social Science 387, *403;* Fine Art 386
		Technology	389, 409, 432
		Cultural	*392,* 395, 400, 403, 405, 406, 415, 420, *423*
5	**Number and Number Relationships**		390–395
7	**Computation and Estimation**		390–395, *397, 417, 422*
8	**Patterns and Functions**		*395, 415, 426,* 431
9	**Algebra**		399, 406, 410–415, 426, 435
10	**Statistics**		407
12	**Geometry**		*399,* 401–406, 409–438
13	**Measurement**		386, 387, 389–420

Italic type indicates Teacher Edition reference.

▶ Teaching Standards

Focus on Classroom Environment

The teacher has the primary role in orchestrating classroom discourse. Teachers should

- pose questions and tasks that elicit, engage, and challenge students' thinking.
- decide when and how to encourage each student to participate in discussions.
- listen carefully to students' ideas.

▶ Assessment Standards

Focus on Openness

Interviews The Openness Standard encourages an atmosphere where students review the performance of their peers, offer feedback, and work collaboratively to improve understanding. Student-student interviews provide that opportunity. In Chapter 8, students are asked to interview each other about establishing guidelines for choosing units of measure.

TECHNOLOGY

▶ For the Teacher

- **Teacher Resource Planner CD-ROM**
  Use the teacher planning CD-ROM to view resources available for Chapter 8. You can prepare custom lesson plans or use the default lesson plans provided.

- **World Wide Web**
  Visit **www.teacher.mathsurf.com** for links to lesson plans from teachers and other professionals, NCTM information, and other sites.

- **TestWorks**
  TestWorks provides ready-made tests and can create custom tests and practice worksheets.

▶ For the Parents

- **World Wide Web**
  Parents can use the Web site at **www.parent.mathsurf.com.**

▶ For the Student

- **Interactive CD-ROM**
  Lesson 8-7 has an *Interactive CD-ROM Lesson.* The *Interactive CD-ROM Journal* and *Interactive CD-ROM Geometry Tool* are also used in Chapter 8.

- **Wide World of Mathematics**
  Lesson 8-1 Middle School: Huge Mall Opens
  Lesson 8-6 Geometry: A Bridge Up for Grabs

- **World Wide Web**
  Use with Chapter and Section Openers;
  Students can go online to the Scott Foresman-Addison Wesley Web site at **www.mathsurf.comm/8/ch8** to collect information about chapter themes.

- **Jasper Woodbury Videodisc**
  Lesson 8-7: Blueprint for Success

SECTION 8A	LESSON	OBJECTIVE	ITBS Form M	CTBS 4th Ed.	CAT 5th Ed.	SAT 9th Ed.	MAT 7th Ed.	Your Form
	8-1	• Choose an appropriate unit of measurement.	✗		✗	✗	✗	
	8-2	• Identify more precise measurements.	✗		✗		✗	
	8-3	• Locate places using map coordinates and latitude and longitude.						

SECTION 8B	LESSON	OBJECTIVE	ITBS Form M	CTBS 4th Ed.	CAT 5th Ed.	SAT 9th Ed.	MAT 7th Ed.	Your Form
	8-4	• Draw, measure, and identify angles.		✗	✗	✗	✗	
	8-5	• Recognize and construct parallel and perpendicular lines.			✗	✗	✗	
	8-6	• Classify polygons.	✗	✗	✗			
	8-7	• Represent three-dimensional shapes in a drawing.			✗		✗	

Key: ITBS - Iowa Test of Basic Skills; CTBS - Comprehensive Test of Basic Skills; CAT - California Achievement Test; SAT - Stanford Achievement Test; MAT - Metropolitan Achievement Test

ASSESSMENT PROGRAM

▶ **Traditional Assessment**

QUICK QUIZZES	SECTION REVIEW	CHAPTER REVIEW	CHAPTER ASSESSMENT FREE RESPONSE	CHAPTER ASSESSMENT MULTIPLE CHOICE	CUMULATIVE REVIEW
TE: pp. 395, 400, 406, 415, 420, 426, 431	SE: pp. 408, 434 *Quiz 8A, 8B	SE: pp. 436–437	SE: p. 438 *Ch. 8 Tests Forms A, B, E	*Ch. 8 Tests Forms C, E	SE: p. 439 *Ch. 8 Test Form F

▶ **Alternate Assessment**

INTERVIEW	JOURNAL	ONGOING	PERFORMANCE	PORTFOLIO	PROJECT	SELF
TE: p. 395	SE: pp. 395, 400, 406, 408, 415, 420, 426, 434 TE: pp. 388, 415	TE: pp. 391, 396, 406, 407, 411, 416, 426, 433	SE: p. 438 *Ch. 8 Tests Forms D, E	TE: p. 400	SE: pp. 387, 400, 420 TE: p. 387	TE: p. 420

*Tests and quizzes are in *Assessment Sourcebook.* Test Form E is a mixed response test. Forms for Alternate Assessment are also available in *Assessment Sourcebook.*

 TestWorks: Test and Practice Software

MIDDLE SCHOOL PACING CHART

▶ REGULAR PACING

Day	5 classes per week
1	Chapter 8 Opener; Problem Solving Focus
2	Section **8A** Opener; Lesson **8-1**
3	Lesson **8-2**
4	Lesson **8-3**
5	**8A** Connect; **8A** Review
6	Section **8B** Opener; Lesson **8-4**
7	Lesson **8-5**
8	Lesson **8-6**
9	Lesson **8-7**
10	Technology
11	**8B** Connect; **8B** Review; Extending Key Ideas
12	Chapter 8 Summary and Review
13	Chapter 8 Assessment
14	Cumulative Review, Chapters 1–8

▶ BLOCK SCHEDULING OPTIONS

Block Scheduling for Complete Course

Chapter 8 may be presented in

- eight 90-minute blocks
- eleven 75-minute blocks

Each block consists of a combination of

- Chapter and Section Openers
- Explores
- Lesson Development
- Problem Solving Focus
- Technology
- Extend Key Ideas
- Connect
- Review
- Assessment

For details, see *Block Scheduling Handbook*.

Block Scheduling for Lab-Based Course

In each block, 30–40 minutes is devoted to lab activities including

- Explores in the Student Edition
- Connect pages in the Student Edition
- Technology options in the Student Edition
- Reteaching Activities in the Teacher Edition

For details, see *Block Scheduling Handbook*.

Block Scheduling for Interdisciplinary Course

Each block integrates math with another subject area.

In Chapter 8, interdisciplinary topics include

- Global Positioning System
- Shapes in Nature

Themes for Interdisciplinary Team Teaching 8A and 8B are

- Orbits of Satellites
- Crystals

For details, see *Block Scheduling Handbook*.

Block Scheduling for Course with *Connected Mathematics*

In each block, investigations from **Connected Mathematics** replace or enhance the lessons in Chapter 8.

Connected Mathematics topics for Chapter 8 can be found in

- *Samples and Populations*
- *Looking for Pythagoras*

For details, see *Block Scheduling Handbook*.

INTERDISCIPLINARY BULLETIN BOARD

Set Up

Prepare a bulletin board with a display containing a large map of the world and blank space in which students can place pictures.

Procedure

- Have students bring in or draw a picture of the favorite place they have visited or would like to visit.

- Have students find their favorite places on the world map, and determine the latitude and longitude to the nearest degree.

- Have students label their picture with the latitude and longitude of the location. Students may then display their pictures on the bulletin board.

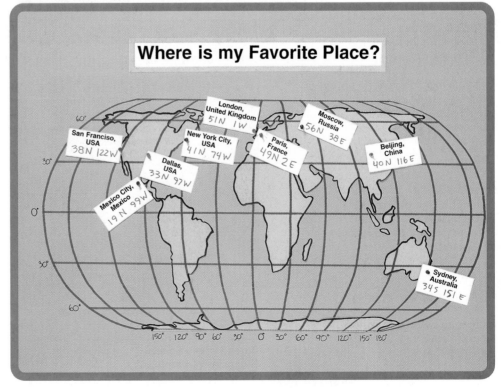

Where is my Favorite Place?

The information on these pages shows how geometry and measurement are used in real-life situations.

World Wide Web

If your class has access to the World Wide Web, you might want to use the information found at the Web site addresses given.

Extensions

The following activities do not require access to the World Wide Web.

Entertainment

Ask interested students to find out more about the America's Cup competition. Ask them to include basic information as well as any mathematical facts they find about the construction of the boats or the layout of the race course. Have the student present a short report to the class.

Science

An error in the French survey actually resulted in a meter that is slightly shorter than the definition of 1791. Have students use 1 m = 39.37 in. to find the distance from the North Pole to the equator in miles. Then have them research this distance. How do the two results compare?

Arts & Literature

Have students work in groups of three to try to find out more about the painting, such as the artist, its location, and so on. The concept of the painting is by Amanda Bishop, Bill Andreas, and Ken Done. The dimensions are 102.93 meters by 65.38 meters. The painting was created at Robb College for U.N.I.C.E.F.

People of the World

Have students find out more about the Maori people. Suggest that they investigate the *mattang* and how it worked.

Social Studies

Give students a map of Europe, Africa, Asia, or South America, and have them use four colors to color the map without making neighboring countries the same color.

8 Geometry and Measurement

Entertainment Link
www.mathsurf.com/8/ch8/ent

Entertainment

Dating back to 1851, the America's Cup is the oldest international trophy sport. In 1995, the first all-woman crew competed in the America's Cup in their yacht, America[3].

Science

In 1791, the Paris Academy of Sciences defined the meter as $\frac{1}{10,000,000}$ of the distance from the North Pole to the equator.

Arts & Literature

The largest painting in the world measures 72,437 ft[2] and is made of brightly colored squares and a smiley face. Compare that to a football field, which is only 45,000 ft[2].

386

TEACHER TALK

Meet Scott Firkins

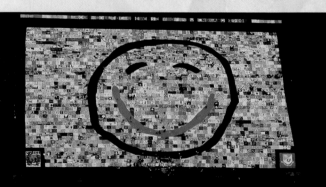

When I teach basic geometric concepts, I want students to focus on what terms mean rather than to simply memorize definitions. To get students involved I use the following two activities. First, I have them use masking tape to mark off large geometric figures on the floor. The class uses these figures to identify such things as points, segments, angles, sides, vertices, polygons, and so on.

Secondly, I have students use straws (the kind that bend work well) to make models of angles and polygons. They classify the models and we use them to make bulletin-board displays.

Burns Middle School
Owensboro, Kentucky

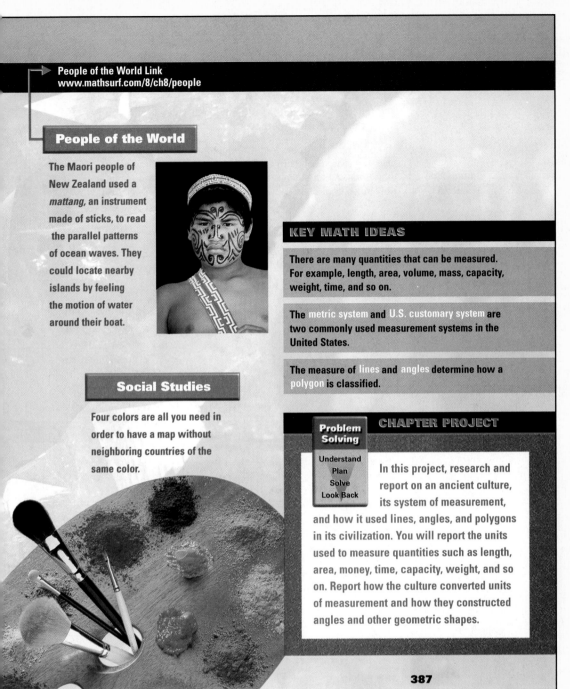

People of the World Link
www.mathsurf.com/8/ch8/people

People of the World

The Maori people of New Zealand used a *mattang*, an instrument made of sticks, to read the parallel patterns of ocean waves. They could locate nearby islands by feeling the motion of water around their boat.

Social Studies

Four colors are all you need in order to have a map without neighboring countries of the same color.

KEY MATH IDEAS

There are many quantities that can be measured. For example, length, area, volume, mass, capacity, weight, time, and so on.

The metric system and U.S. customary system are two commonly used measurement systems in the United States.

The measure of lines and angles determine how a polygon is classified.

CHAPTER PROJECT

Problem Solving
Understand
Plan
Solve
Look Back

In this project, research and report on an ancient culture, its system of measurement, and how it used lines, angles, and polygons in its civilization. You will report the units used to measure quantities such as length, area, money, time, capacity, weight, and so on. Report how the culture converted units of measurement and how they constructed angles and other geometric shapes.

387

Chapter Project

Students research and report on an ancient culture's system of measurement and its knowledge of geometry and astronomy.

Resources

Chapter 8 Project Master

Introduce the Project

- Discuss some ancient cultures that students may be interested in researching.

- Discuss possible sources of information. Be sure to consider the World Wide Web and local museums.

Project Progress
Section A, page 400 Students choose an ancient civilization and research the units of measure it used.

Section B, page 420 Students research their chosen culture's knowledge of astronomy and geometry.

Community Project

A community project for Chapter 8 is available in *Home and Community Connections*.

Cooperative Learning

You may wish to use Teaching Tool Transparency 1: Cooperative Learning Checklist with **Explore** and other group activities in this chapter.

You may choose to use this project as a performance assessment for the chapter.

Performance Assessment Key

Level 4 Full Accomplishment

Level 3 Substantial Accomplishment

Level 2 Partial Accomplishment

Level 1 Little Accomplishment

Suggested Scoring Rubric

4
- Research is thorough and of adequate depth.
- Report is clear and interesting.

3
- Research is reasonably thorough but lacking some depth.
- Report is reasonably clear.

2
- Research is not very thorough and is lacking depth.
- Report is not very clear.

1
- There is very little evidence of research and the report is not acceptable.

Solving Problems

The Point

Students focus on the multiple approaches available for solving problems.

Resources

Teaching Tool Transparency 17: Problem-Solving Guidelines

 Interactive CD-ROM Journal

About the Page

Using the Problem Solving Process

There is often more than one way to solve a problem. Students should be encouraged to use the strategy that works best for them. Discuss these steps for choosing a problem-solving strategy:

- Determine the number of choices you have to consider. If there are a limited number of choices, you may want to try *guess-and-check*.

- Think about whether you can *draw a diagram* to solve the problem. The diagram might use a placeholder box or variable to stand for the unknown quantity.

- If the problem sets limits on your choices, such as "no one can have more than 17," you may want to try *logical reasoning*. If you find you can't solve the problem using this method, you may use logical reasoning to help you make a good guess in guess-and-check.

Ask ...

- Is the guess-and-check method entirely random? No. Since 6 yielded a result that was slightly too large, the next guess was slightly less than the first guess.

- How does knowing that the box represents 2 help to solve the problem? Substitute 2 for the box in the equations for C, B, and A. This will give the number of ears of corn each person bought, which is the solution.

Answers for Problems

Joan: 15 min; Mark: 45 min; David: 60 min; Allison: 30 min

Journal

Ask students to describe a situation in which they have used one of these methods to solve a problem of their own.

Problem Solving

Understand
Plan
Solve
Look Back

Solving Problems

There is often more than one way to solve a problem. You should use the strategy that works best for you. Trying different strategies can help you decide which one suits your problem-solving style.

Problem Solving Focus

The following problem has already been solved using three different methods.

Three friends buy fresh corn at an outdoor market. Amani buys twice as much corn as Brad. Brad buys three more ears of corn than Chris. All together, Amani, Brad, and Chris buy 17 ears of corn. How much corn does each of them buy?

You know:

- There are 17 ears of corn,
- Amani has twice as many as Brad,
- Brad can't have more than eight ears of corn,
- Chris has three less than Brad.

Guess and Check	Draw a diagram	Logical Reasoning
Guess: 6 ears for Brad. $B = 6$ $A = 6 \times 2 = 12$ $C = 6 - 3 = 3$ **Check:** $6 + 12 + 3 = 21$ Too big. **Guess:** 5 ears for Brad. $B = 5$ $A = 5 \times 2 = 10$ $C = 5 - 3 = 2$ **Check:** $5 + 2 + 10 = 17$ It works.	Let $\square$ = ears Chris buys. $C = \square$ $B = \square + 3$ $A = (\square + 3) + (\square + 3)$ You have four $\square$'s and three 3's. You have four $\square$'s and 9. $17 - 9 = 8$ The four $\square$'s stand for 8 ears of corn. $8 \div 4 = 2$ Each $\square = 2$.	■ No one can have more than 17. ■ Amani must have the most. ■ Chris must have the least. ■ The other amounts are based on Brad's amount. So find Brad's amount first. $B = 5$ $A = 5 \times 2 = 10$ $C = 5 - 3 = 2$

Solve the following problem. You may use one of the above methods or a method of your own.

1 Four friends work out at a health club. Mark uses the treadmill three times as long as Joan. Allison uses it half as long as David. David uses it 15 minutes longer than Mark. All together, they use the treadmill for 2.5 hours. How long is each person on the machine?

Additional Problem

The second side of a triangle is 2 ft shorter than the first side. The third side is twice as long as the second side. The perimeter of the triangle is 34 ft. Find the length of each side.

1. Explain how you solved the problem. Answers may vary.

2. Give the answer. 10 ft, 8 ft, 16 ft

Visit **www.teacher.mathsurf.com** for links to lesson plans from teachers and other professionals, NCTM information, and other sites.

LESSON PLANNING GUIDE

▶ **Student Edition**　　　　　　　　　　　　　　　　　　　　　　▶ **Ancillaries***

LESSON		MATERIALS	VOCABULARY	DAILY	OTHER
	Chapter 8 Opener				Ch. 8 Project Master Ch. 8 Community Project Teaching Tool Trans. 1
	Problem Solving Focus				Teaching Tool Trans. 17 *Interactive CD-ROM Journal*
8-1	Units of Measurement	unsharpened pencils, paper, two optional length units	U.S. customary units, metric system	8-1	Technology Master 33 *WW Math*—Middle School
8-2	Significant Digits and Precision	meterstick	precision, significant digits	8-2	Teaching Tool Trans. 5 Ch. 8 Project Master
8-3	Position		absolute position, relative position	8-3	Teaching Tool Trans. 20, 21 Lesson Enhancement 　Transparencies 30–33
	Connect				Interdisc. Team Teaching 8A
	Review				Practice 8A; Quiz 8A; *TestWorks*

* Daily Ancillaries include Practice, Reteaching, Problem Solving, Enrichment, and Daily Transparency. Teaching Tool Transparencies are in *Teacher's Toolkits*. Lesson Enhancement Transparencies are in *Overhead Transparency Package*.

SKILLS TRACE

LESSON	SKILL	FIRST INTRODUCED			DEVELOP	PRACTICE/ APPLY	REVIEW
		GR. 6	GR. 7	GR. 8			
8-1	Converting units of measurement.	X			pp. 390–393	pp. 394–395	pp. 408, 436, 439, 455
8-2	Determining more precise measurements.			X p. 396	pp. 396–398	pp. 399–400	pp. 408, 436, 439, 460
8-3	Using map coordinates and latitude and longitude.			X p. 401	pp. 401–404	pp. 405–406	pp. 408, 437, 438, 439

CONNECTED MATHEMATICS

The unit *Samples and Population (Data and Probability),* from the **Connected Mathematics** series, can be used with Section 8A.

Math and Science/Technology

(Worksheet pages 31–32: Teacher pages T31–T32)

In this lesson, students use various units of measurement, as well as longitude and latitude to explore the orbits of satellites.

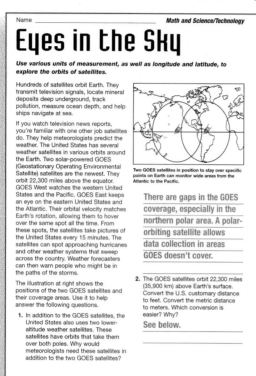

Name _____   *Math and Science/Technology*

Eyes in the Sky

Use various units of measurement, as well as longitude and latitude, to explore the orbits of satellites.

Hundreds of satellites orbit Earth. They transmit television signals, locate mineral deposits deep underground, track pollution, measure ocean depth, and help ships navigate at sea.

If you watch television news reports, you're familiar with one other job satellites do. They help meteorologists predict the weather. The United States has several weather satellites in various orbits around the Earth. Two solar-powered GOES (Geostationary Operating Environmental Satellite) satellites are the newest. They orbit 22,300 miles above the equator. GOES West watches the western United States and the Pacific. GOES East keeps an eye on the eastern United States and the Atlantic. Their orbital velocity matches Earth's rotation, allowing them to hover over the same spot all the time. From these spots, the satellites take pictures of the United States every 15 minutes. The satellites can spot approaching hurricanes and other weather systems that sweep across the country. Weather forecasters can then warn people who might be in the paths of the storms.

The illustration at right shows the positions of the two GOES satellites and their coverage areas. Use it to help answer the following questions.

Two GOES satellites in position to stay over specific points on Earth can monitor wide areas from the Atlantic to the Pacific.

1. In addition to the GOES satellites, the United States also uses two lower-altitude weather satellites. These satellites have orbits that take them over both poles. Why would meteorologists need these satellites in addition to the two GOES satellites?

   There are gaps in the GOES coverage, especially in the northern polar area. A polar-orbiting satellite allows data collection in areas GOES doesn't cover.

2. The GOES satellites orbit 22,300 miles (35,900 km) above Earth's surface. Convert the U.S. customary distance to feet. Convert the metric distance to meters. Which conversion is easier? Why?

   See below.

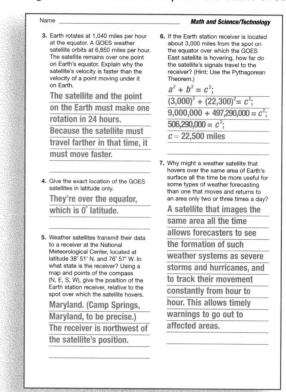

Name _____   *Math and Science/Technology*

3. Earth rotates at 1,040 miles per hour at the equator. A GOES weather satellite orbits at 6,850 miles per hour. The satellite remains over one point on Earth's equator. Explain why the satellite's velocity is faster than the velocity of a point moving under it on Earth.

   The satellite and the point on the Earth must make one rotation in 24 hours. Because the satellite must travel farther in that time, it must move faster.

4. Give the exact location of the GOES satellites in latitude only.

   They're over the equator, which is 0° latitude.

5. Weather satellites transmit their data to a receiver at the National Meteorological Center, located at latitude 38° 51′ N. and 76° 57′ W. In what state is the receiver? Using a map and points of the compass (N, E, S, W), give the position of the Earth station receiver, relative to the spot over which the satellite hovers.

   Maryland. (Camp Springs, Maryland, to be precise.) The receiver is northwest of the satellite's position.

6. If the Earth station receiver is located about 3,000 miles from the spot on the equator over which the GOES East satellite is hovering, how far do the satellite's signals travel to the receiver? (Hint: Use the Pythagorean Theorem.)

   $$a^2 + b^2 = c^2;$$
   $$(3,000)^2 + (22,300)^2 = c^2;$$
   $$9,000,000 + 497,290,000 = c^2;$$
   $$506,290,000 = c^2;$$
   $$c \approx 22,500 \text{ miles}$$

7. Why might a weather satellite that hovers over the same area of Earth's surface all the time be more useful for some types of weather forecasting than one that moves and returns to an area only two or three times a day?

   A satellite that images the same area all the time allows forecasters to see the formation of such weather systems as severe storms and hurricanes, and to track their movement constantly from hour to hour. This allows timely warnings to go out to affected areas.

Answers

2. 22,300 mi × 5,280 ft/mi = 117,744,000 feet; 35,900 km × 1,000 m/km = 35,900,000 meters; metric; To multiply by 1,000, we just move the decimal point 3 places to the right and add on the necessary number of zeros.

BIBLIOGRAPHY

► FOR TEACHERS

Battista, Michael, and Douglas H. Clements. "Constructing Geometric Concepts in Logo." *Arithmetic Teacher* 38 (Nov. 1990): 15–17.

Geddes, Dorothy. *Geometry in the Middle Grades (Addenda Series)*. Reston, VA: NCTM, 1992.

Geddes, Dorothy. *Measurement in the Middle Grades (Addenda Series)*. Reston, VA: NCTM, 1992.

Reys, Barbara. *Developing Number Sense in the Middle Grades (Addenda Series)*. Reston, VA: NCTM, 1991.

Zaslavsky, Claudia. "Symmetry in American Folk Art." *Arithmetic Teacher* 38 (Sep. 1990): 6–12.

► FOR STUDENTS

Center for Occupational Research and Development. *Applied Mathematics, Unit 3: Measuring in English and Metric Units.* Waco, TX: CORD, 1993.

Center for Occupational Research and Development. *Applied Mathematics, Unit 13: Precision, Accuracy and Tolerance.* Waco, TX: CORD, 1993.

Krupp, Robin Rector. *Let's Go Traveling.* New York, NY: Morrow Junior Books, 1992.

Wood, Jenny. *The Children's Atlas of People and Places.* Brookfield, CT: The Millbrook Press, 1993.

SECTION 8A

Measurement

▶ Industry Link   ▶ History Link   ▶ www.mathsurf.com/8/ch8/gps

Where am I? Where am I going? How do I get there? If you aren't certain about a location, you can look on a map. It hasn't always been this way.

In the past, people marked trails with stones and noted landmarks such as trees and streams. But snow and rain could interfere with this system. Stars were used for navigation, but that only worked on clear nights.

In 1978, the U.S. Department of Defense said, "We've got to have a system that really works." So since then the government has worked on something called the Global Positioning System, or GPS. There are 24 satellites orbiting the earth connected to a computer system. In a way, you could think

of the satellites as "human-made stars." GPS is accurate enough to give positions, anywhere in the world, within the width of your street, 24 hours a day.

This means that everyone will have the ability to know exactly where they are, all the time. Finally, one of humankind's basic needs will be fulfilled.

1 GPS is widely used by backpackers and sailors. What other uses can you think of for GPS?

2 GPS allows every square meter of the earth's surface to have a unique address, similar to a coordinate plane. How do you think GPS might change what we know to be a phone book?

389

Where are we now?

In Chapter 2, students explored the coordinate system; in Chapter 5, they explored rates and proportions.

They learned how to

- graph integers in the coordinate plane.

- use rates, ratios, and proportions with various measurements.

- interpret scale drawings.

Where are we going?

In Section 8A, students will

- choose appropriate units of measurement.

- determine precision in measurements.

- locate places on a map using a coordinate system and latitude and longitude.

Theme: Global Positioning System (GPS)

World Wide Web

If your class has access to the World Wide Web, you might want to use the information found at the Web site address given. The interdisciplinary links relate to topics discussed in this section.

About the Page

This page introduces the theme of the section, Global Positioning System (GPS), and compares it to earlier methods of determining location.

Ask ...

- Have you ever been lost? What did you do?

- How do the people who design parking lots and garages try to help people remember where they parked their cars?

Extensions

The following activities do not require access to the World Wide Web.

Industry

What industries would benefit from GPS technology? Possible answers: cartography (map making), freight hauling, delivery services, taxi services, motor-club services.

History

Interested students might compare early map-making methods to current ones.

Answers for Questions

1. Possible answers: Flying, boating, traveling through unmarked land (jungle or wilderness), emergency vehicles.

2. Possible answers: Addresses listed by GPS codes; Phone numbers contain all or part of a GPS code.

Connect

On page 407, students will use the concept of precision of measurements to analyze the GPS technology.

Objective
- **Choose an appropriate unit of measurement.**

Vocabulary
- **U.S. customary units, metric system**

Materials
- **Explore: Unsharpened pencils, paper, 2 optional length units**

NCTM Standards
- **1–5, 7, 13**

► Review

Find each product or quotient.

1. 3.5 × 1000 3500

2. 5.06 × 10 50.6

3. 158 ÷ 100 1.58

4. 4.7 ÷ 1000 0.0047

5. 0.8 ÷ 100 0.008

Available on Daily Transparency 8-1

► Lesson Link

Discuss the use of measurement in the Olympic games. In track and field, for instance, the metric system is used to measure running events (except the marathon), but feet and inches are used to measure the long jump, high jump, and pole vault.

1 Introduce

 Explore

The Point
Students use nonstandard units to measure objects. They observe that the measurement of an object changes when the unit changes.

8-1 Units of Measurement

► Lesson Link You've seen how numbers are used in measurement. In this lesson, you'll learn more about the units used in measurement. ◄

You'll Learn …

- to choose an appropriate unit of measurement

… How It's Used

Mask-makers use units of measurement when they mix materials to make glues or varnishes that hold the masks together.

Vocabulary

U.S. customary units

metric system

Explore | Using Units

Study Your Desk?

Materials: Unsharpened pencils, Paper, 2 optional length units

1. Lay a line of pencils across a desk. How many pencils did you use? Estimate using $\frac{1}{2}$, $\frac{1}{4}$, 0.5, or 0.25 if appropriate.

2. Measure the length of the desk with two other objects or units. Record and compare the measurements.

3. Cover the desks with sheets of paper without overlapping. How many sheets of paper did you use? This is the area of the desk in sheets of paper. What other objects or units would be appropriate for measuring the area of the desk?

4. Discuss the difference between units of length and units of area.

Learn | Units of Measurement

U.S. customary units use the inch, foot, and mile as units of length. The **metric system** uses the centimeter, meter, and kilometer as units of length.

Metric System		U.S. Customary Units	
centimeter (cm)	millimeter (mm) = 0.1 cm	inch (in.)	foot (ft) = 12 in.
	meter (m) = 100 cm		yard (yd) = 3 ft
	kilometer (km) = 1000 m		mile (mi) = 5280 ft

390 *Chapter 8 • Geometry and Measurement*

In each system of measurement you can change the units by using a ratio.

To convert from feet to inches, use the ratio $\frac{12 \text{ in.}}{1 \text{ ft}}$.

To convert from inches to feet, use the ratio $\frac{1 \text{ ft}}{12 \text{ in.}}$.

Example 1

GPS satellites orbit about 11,000 mi above the earth's surface. Convert this altitude to ft.

To convert from mi to ft, use the ratio $\frac{5,280 \text{ ft}}{1 \text{ mi}}$.

$$\frac{11,000 \text{ mi}}{1} \times \frac{5,280 \text{ ft}}{\text{mi}} = \frac{11,000 \text{ mi} \times 5,280 \text{ ft}}{1 \text{ mi}}$$

$$= \frac{11,000 \times 5,280 \text{ ft}}{1} = \frac{58,080,000 \text{ ft}}{1}$$

The satellites are about 58 million ft above the earth.

To change units within the metric system, use powers of ten.

To convert from meters to centimeters, use the ratio $\frac{100 \text{ cm}}{1 \text{ m}}$.

To convert from centimeters to meters, use the ratio $\frac{1 \text{ m}}{100 \text{ cm}}$.

Example 2

The radius of the earth is 6,371,000 m. Convert the earth's radius to km.

To convert from m to km, use the ratio $\frac{1 \text{ km}}{1,000 \text{ m}}$.

$$\frac{6,371,000 \text{ m}}{1} \times \frac{1 \text{ km}}{1,000 \text{ m}} = \frac{6,371,000 \text{ m} \times 1 \text{ km}}{1,000 \text{ m}}$$

$$= \frac{6,371,000 \text{ km}}{1,000} = 6,371 \text{ km is the earth's radius.}$$

▶ **Science Link**

The radius of the earth is the distance from its center to any point on its surface. The radius of the earth is not the same to every point on the earth's surface.

Try It

Convert each unit of length.

a. 32 km to m
32,000 m

b. 10,365 ft to mi
≈ 1.96 mi

MATH EVERY DAY

▶ **Problem of the Day**

You have four pitchers: a 9-liter pitcher, a 5-liter pitcher, a 4-liter pitcher, and a 2-liter pitcher. The 9-liter pitcher is full. How can you pour the water from pitcher to pitcher and end up with 3 liters of water in each of the three largest pitchers? Possible answer: Pitchers from largest to smallest after each pouring of water: Start, 9-0-0-0; Pour 2 liters, 7-0-0-2; Pour 4 liters, 3-0-4-2; Pour 4 liters, 3-4-0-2; Pour 1 liter, 3-5-0-1; Pour 1 liter, 3-5-1-0; Pour 2 liters, 3-3-1-2; Pour 2 liters, 3-3-3-0.

Available on Daily Transparency 8-1

An Extension is provided in the transparency package.

Fact of the Day

Though the metric system has long been legal in the United States, the United States is the last major country not to have fully converted to the metric system.

Mental Math

Do these mentally.

1. 100 yd = ____ ft 300
2. 2000 m = ____ km 2
3. 3 h 15 min = ____ min 195

Ongoing Assessment
In Steps 2 and 3, check that students have chosen an appropriate unit. Correct choices will indicate that students understand the difference between measurements of length and area.

For Groups That Finish Early
What objects could be used to measure the length and width of the classroom? The area of the floor? Possible answers: Pencils; sheets of paper.

Follow Up
Discuss the need for standardized units of measure.

Answers for Explore
1–4. Answers may vary.

2 Teach

Learn

Conversions of measurements in the metric system can be achieved simply by moving the decimal point the correct number of places. When changing from a smaller unit to a larger unit, the decimal point is moved to the left. When changing from a larger unit to a smaller unit, the decimal point is moved to the right.

Alternate Examples

1. The distance from New York City to San Francisco is about 3000 miles. Convert this distance to feet.

   Use the ratio $\frac{5280 \text{ ft}}{1 \text{ mi}}$.

   $$\frac{3000 \text{ mi}}{1} \times \frac{5280 \text{ ft}}{1 \text{ mi}} =$$

   $$\frac{3000 \text{ mi} \times 5280 \text{ ft}}{1 \text{ mi}} =$$

   15,840,000 ft

   The distance from New York to San Francisco is about 16 million feet.

2. The radius of Venus is approximately 6,350,000 m. Convert Venus's radius to km.

   Use the ratio $\frac{1 \text{ km}}{1,000 \text{ m}}$.

   $$\frac{6,350,000 \text{ m}}{1} \times \frac{1 \text{ km}}{1,000 \text{ m}} =$$

   $$\frac{6,350,000 \text{ m} \times 1 \text{ km}}{1,000 \text{ m}} = 6,350 \text{ km}$$

   The radius of Venus is about 6,350 km.

3. Determine an appropriate unit for measuring each.

   a. Mass of pencil

     Gram is a small unit of mass.

   b. Time spent in school

     Hour is a large unit of time.

   c. Weight of an apple

     Ounce is a small unit of weight.

   d. Capacity of an eyedropper

     Milliliter is a small unit of capacity.

Measurements don't just involve length. You can take measurements of area, volume, weight, time, mass, capacity, and other quantities.

The table below shows some common units of measurement. Notice that both customary and metric units are given for capacity.

DID YOU KNOW?

1 birthday card ≈ 1 oz

1 raisin ≈ 1 g

$\frac{1}{2}$ an eyedropper ≈ 1 mL

Measurement	Units		
Weight	**Ounce** (oz)	**Pound** (lb) = 16 oz	**Ton** (T) = 2000 lb
Time	**Second** (sec)	**Minute** (min) = 60 sec	**Hour** (hr) = 60 min
Mass	**Gram** (g)	**Kilogram** (kg) = 1000 g	
Capacity	Metric: U.S. Customary:	**Milliliter** (mL) **Pint** (pt) = 2 cups	**Liter** (L) = 1000 mL **Quart** (qt) = 2 pt

Units of measurement are usually expressed according to the size of the object. For example, tons are more appropriate units than ounces to indicate a car's weight. Minutes are more appropriate units than seconds to express the time it takes to cook a hard-boiled egg.

Example 3

Determine an appropriate unit for measuring each.

  a. Weight of a pencil   oz is a small unit of weight.

  b. Time it takes to take one step   sec is a small unit of time.

  c. Mass of a watermelon   kg is a large unit of mass.

  d. Capacity of a soda can   mL is a small unit of capacity.

Try It

Determine appropriate units for measuring each. **Possible answers:**

  a. Capacity of an olive jar **mL** **b.** Time it takes to brush your teeth **min**

  c. Weight of a boat **lb**   **d.** Mass of a car **kg**

Units of length, area, and volume can often be distinguished by the use of exponents.

	Length	Area	Volume
Metric	mm, cm, m, …	mm², cm², m², …	mm³, cm³, m³, …
U.S. Customary	in., ft, yd, …	in.², ft², yd², …	in.³, ft³, yd³, …

Area is expressed using square units, such as ft² (square feet). Volume is expressed using cubic units, such as m³ (cubic meters).

▶ **MEETING MIDDLE SCHOOL CLASSROOM NEEDS**

Tips from Middle School Teachers

I like to challenge my students to find some words that contain a metric prefix. Words with *centi-* might include *century, cent, centipede,* and so on. Then I ask students to define the word and explain its connection to the metric prefix.

History Connection

Ask volunteers to research and report on the origins of some standards of measurement. For example, a league originated as the distance that could be walked in one hour and an acre as the amount that could be plowed in one day. Have the volunteers share their information orally or by making and displaying small posters.

Cultural Connection

Have students from other countries discuss the use of the metric system in their native countries and how difficult it was (or is) to learn the U.S. customary units.

Example 4

Determine an appropriate unit for measuring each.

a. Distance between two cities   mi, because it is a unit of length.

b. Area of a fingernail mm^2, because it is a unit of area.

c. Volume of a stick of butter in^3, because it is a unit of volume.

d. Capacity of a carton of milk   qt, because it is a unit of capacity.

Try It

Determine an appropriate unit for measuring each. **Possible answers:**

a. Area of a classroom m^2 **b.** Volume of a sugar cube mm^3

c. Mass of a compact disc g **d.** Distance between state borders mi

Sometimes it is necessary to change units twice in order to convert to the desired unit.

Example 5

Originally, sailors who used GPS were always within 18.63 mi of the reported position. What is this distance in yd?

First, convert mi to ft. Then convert ft to yd.

$$\left(\frac{18.63 \text{ mi}}{1} \times \frac{5{,}280 \text{ ft}}{1 \text{ mi}} \right) \times \frac{1 \text{ yd}}{3 \text{ ft}} =$$

$$\left(\frac{18.63 \text{ mi} \times 5{,}280 \text{ ft}}{1 \text{ mi}} \right) \times \frac{1 \text{ yd}}{3 \text{ ft}} =$$

$$(98{,}366.4 \text{ ft}) \times \frac{1 \text{ yd}}{3 \text{ ft}} =$$

$$\frac{98{,}366.4 \text{ ft} \times 1 \text{ yd}}{3 \text{ ft}} = 32{,}788.8 \text{ yd}$$

> ▶ **Industry Link**
>
> The U.S. Coast Guard started a $14 million program to improve the precision of the civilian's GPS to be within 65 ft of the reported position.

Check   Your Understanding

1. Why do you get two different numbers when you measure the same thing using different units—for example, 550 cm and 5.5 m?

2. How do you know what units are appropriate for a length measurement? For area? For time?

Alternate Examples

4. Determine an appropriate unit for measuring each of the following.

   a. Area of football field

      yd^2, because it is a unit of area.

   b. Volume of a refrigerator

      ft^3, because it is a unit of volume.

   c. Length of newspaper

      in. (or cm), because it is a unit of length.

   d. Capacity of car's gas tank

      L (or gal), because it is a unit of capacity.

5. In a marathon, runners run approximately 26.2 miles. What is this distance in yards? First, convert miles to feet. Then, convert feet to yards.

   $$\frac{26.2 \text{ mi}}{1} \times \frac{5{,}280 \text{ ft}}{1 \text{ mi}} \times \frac{1 \text{ yd}}{3 \text{ ft}} =$$

   $$\frac{26.2 \text{ mi} \times 5{,}280 \text{ ft}}{1 \text{ mi}} \times \frac{1 \text{ yd}}{3 \text{ ft}} =$$

   $$\frac{138{,}336 \text{ ft}}{1} \times \frac{1 \text{ yd}}{3 \text{ ft}} =$$

   $$\frac{138{,}336 \text{ ft} \times 1 \text{ yd}}{3 \text{ ft}} = 46{,}112 \text{ yd}$$

3 Practice and Assess

Check

Have students compare Question 1 with the same situation for monetary units, say 550 cents and 5.50 dollars.

Answers for Check Your Understanding

1. The units cm and m are different sizes.

2. Answers may vary.

Assignment Guide

- **Basic**
  1–3, 5, 6, 8–10, 15–18, 23–26, 31–34
- **Average**
  2–14 evens, 15, 17, 18–38 evens
- **Enriched**
  1–37 odds

Exercise Notes

■ Exercise 14

Geography Although the area of Canada is larger than the area of the United States, much of northern Canada is frozen tundra that is not inhabitable.

■ Exercise 15

Error Prevention Some students may just add the numbers and divide. Remind them that all the units must be the same before finding the average.

Reteaching

Activity

Materials: 27 cubes of the same size

- Organize into groups of three.

- Use the 27 cubes to build the largest cube possible.

- Describe each of the following for the cube you built: its length, width, and height; the area of one of its faces; its volume. The length, width, and height are each 3 units, where the unit is the length of one edge of one of the 27 smaller cubes; The area of one face is 9 square units, where the square unit is one face of one of the 27 smaller cubes; The volume is 27 cubic units, where the cubic unit is one of the 27 smaller cubes.

394   Chapter 8

8-1 Exercises and Applications

Practice and Apply

1. **Getting Started** The highest point in the world is Mount Everest, at 29,028 ft. Express this altitude in miles.

    a. Write the ratio of miles to feet with ft in the denominator. $\dfrac{1\,mi}{5280\,ft}$

    b. Multiply the ratio by 29,028 ft. ≈ **5.5 mi**

What U.S. customary unit would you use for each measurement?

2. The volume of earth removed during an archaeological dig **yd³ or ft³**

3. The distance traveled in one day by a flock of geese **mi**

4. The area of a sail on a sailboat **ft² or yd²**

What metric unit would you use for each measurement?

5. A single dose of cough syrup **mL**

6. The distance from the top of a diving board to the water surface **m**

7. The mass of your backpack containing your books **kg**

Convert each measurement.

8. 7.8 m to cm **780 cm**
9. 2500 L to mL **2,500,000 mL**
10. 2.5 hr to min **150 min**

11. 64 oz to lb **4 lb**
12. 5 ft 4 in. to in. **64 in.**
13. 10 pt to qt **5 qt**

14. **Geography** The area of the United States is 3,536,341 mi² and Canada is 3,851,809 mi². Which country has a larger area and by how many square miles? **Canada; 315,468 mi²**

15. **Science** For a geology experiment, a group of students measure the mass of a piece of copper. Their results were 15.64 g, 15.69 g, 15.67 g, 0.01566 kg, and 0.01564 kg. What is the average of the students' measurements? **15.66 g**

PRACTICE

Name _____

Practice **8-1**

Units of Measurement

What U.S. customary unit would you use for each measurement?

1. The weight of a whale ___**ton**___
2. The length of a freeway ___**mile**___

3. The capacity of a punch bowl ___**quart**___
4. The area of a window ___**square inch**___

What metric unit would you use for each measurement?

5. The width of a computer monitor ___**centimeter**___
6. The amount of gasoline in a car ___**liter**___

7. The mass of a feather ___**gram**___
8. The volume of a closet ___**cubic meter**___

Convert each measurement.

9. 38 min to sec ___**2280 sec**___
10. 72 ft to in. ___**864 in.**___
11. 684 m to cm ___**68,400 cm**___

12. 25 lb to oz ___**400 oz**___
13. 46.3 kg to g ___**46,300 g**___
14. 384 mL to L ___**0.384 L**___

15. 64 qt to cups ___**256 cups**___
16. 84 mi to ft ___**443,520 ft**___
17. 1632 m to km ___**1.632 km**___

18. 3000 lb to T ___**1.5 T**___
19. 14.86 g to kg ___**0.01486 kg**___
20. 2136 min to hr ___**35.6 hr**___

21. A group of students ran one lap around a track. Their times were 132 sec, 1.83 min, 118 sec, 1.97 min, and 101 sec. Give the average time in seconds. ___**115.8 sec**___

22. The smallest street-legal car in the United States is 7 ft 4.75 in. long. Convert this length to inches. ___**88.75 in.**___

RETEACHING

Name _____

Alternative Lesson **8-1**

Units of Measurement

U.S. customary units use the inch, foot, and mile as units of length.

> 1 foot (ft) = 12 inches (in.)
> 1 yard (yd) = 3 ft
> 1 mile (mi) = 5280 ft

The **metric system** uses the millimeter, centimeter, meter, and kilometer as units of length.

> 1 millimeter (mm) = 0.1 centimeter (cm)
> 1 meter (m) = 100 cm
> 1 kilometer (km) = 1000 m

When writing the ratio in fraction form, write the measure you are converting to as the numerator and the measure you are converting from as the denominator. Another way to convert measures is to multiply or divide by the conversion fact.

—— Example 1 ——

Convert 2.9 miles to feet.

You know that 1 mi = 5280 ft.
Since you are converting from a larger unit of measure to a smaller unit, you will multiply.   2.9 × 5280 = 15,312

So, 2.9 mi = 15,312 ft.

Try It Convert each measurement.

   a. Write the conversion fact for converting feet to miles. ___**1 mi = 5280 ft**___

   b. Will you multiply or divide the number of feet by the conversion fact? ___**Divide.**___

   c. 7920 ft = ___**1.5**___ mi
   d. 5.1 mi = ___**26,928**___ ft

   e. 147 in. = ___**12¼**___ ft
   f. 156 yd = ___**468**___ ft

—— Example 2 ——

Convert 17,300 meters to kilometers.

You know that 1 km = 1000 m.
Since you are converting from a smaller unit of measure to a larger unit, you will divide.   17,300 ÷ 1000 = 17.3

So, 17,300 m = 17.3 km.

Try It Convert each measurement.

   g. 23,400 m = ___**23.4**___ km
   h. 13.4 km = ___**13,400**___ m

   i. 8.9 m = ___**890**___ cm
   j. 460 cm = ___**4.6**___ m

16. The stopwatch on the right shows the 1995 Boston Marathon record set by Cosmas N'Deti of Kenya in hours, minutes, and seconds. How much time is this in seconds? **7762 sec**

17. **Test Prep** Which of these would be an appropriate unit for the area of a rose petal? **A**

Ⓐ cm²   Ⓑ ft²   Ⓒ mm³   Ⓓ in³

Problem Solving and Reasoning

18. **Critical Thinking** Mont Blanc, the highest peak in the Alps, is 4,807 m above sea level. A climber on Mont Blanc is 88 m from the top. What is her altitude in meters? In kilometers? **4719 m; 4.719 km**

19. **Journal** The *cubit* is an ancient unit of measurement defined as the distance from a king's elbow to the tip of his middle finger, about 18 in. What is the problem with this definition? Why do you think standardized measurement units were developed?

20. **Communicate** How would you use proportions to change inches to yards? Give an example.

21. **Measurement** What customary unit would be most appropriate for measuring the area of the GPS display used in agriculture. **in²**

22. **Math Reasoning** The Grand Canyon, in Arizona, is 217 miles long. What is this length in yards? Inches? Compare the numerical values of the three measurements. Describe the relationship between these numerical values and the units of measurement associated with them.

Mixed Review

State whether each number is prime or composite. *[Lesson 7-1]*

23. 27 **C**   **24.** 91 **C**   **25.** 37 **P**   **26.** 63 **C**

27. 49 **C**   **28.** 72 **C**   **29.** 1755 **C**   **30.** 363 **C**

Find the GCF of each pair of numbers. *[Lesson 7-2]*

31. 14, 42 **14**   **32.** 16, 64 **16**   **33.** 17, 71 **1**   **34.** 33, 90 **3**

35. 21, 66 **3**   **36.** 13, 169 **13**   **37.** 82, 16 **2**   **38.** 9, 261 **9**

Exercise Notes

■ Exercise 16

Problem-Solving Tip Students may convert the hours and minutes to seconds and then add; or they may convert the hours to minutes, add the minutes, and then convert the minutes to seconds.

■ Exercise 17

Test Prep Students should eliminate choices C and D because cubic units are measures of volume, not area.

Exercise Answers

19. Possible answer: This distance may vary from king to king and the king's arm is not readily available for everyone to use when needed; So that everyone can use the same units and measuring can be precise.

20. Multiply by $\frac{1\ ft}{12\ in.} \times \frac{1\ yd}{3\ ft}$;

Possible answer:

$72\ in. \times \frac{1\ ft}{12\ in.} \times \frac{1\ yd}{3\ ft} = 2\ yd$

22. 381,920 yd; 13,749,120 in.; 217 < 381,920 < 13,749,120; Possible answer: The numerical value associated with the largest unit of measure is the smallest number.

Alternate Assessment

Interview Have pairs of students use a tape recorder to interview each other on what guidelines each uses when determining the units to use to make a particular measurement.

▶ PROBLEM SOLVING

Name _____

GPS PROBLEM 15, STUDENT PAGE 394

Guided Problem Solving 8-1

For a geology experiment, a group of students measure the mass of a piece of copper. Their results were 15.64 g, 15.69 g, 15.67 g, 0.01566 kg, and 0.01564 kg. What is the average of the students' measurements?

— Understand —

1. What are you asked to find? **Average of five measurements.**

2. Underline the measurements of the copper piece.

— Plan —

3. How do you find the average of a set of numbers? **Find the sum of the numbers and divide by the number of addends.**

4. To convert from kilograms to grams, which ratio will you use? **a**

   a. $\frac{1000\ g}{1\ kg}$ b. $\frac{1\ kg}{1000\ g}$

— Solve —

5. Convert the measurements from kilograms to grams.

   a. 0.01566 kg **15.66 g**   b. 0.01564 kg **15.64 g**

6. What is the sum of the measures in grams? **78.3 g**

7. What is the average mass? **15.66 g**

— Look Back —

8. How could you Work Backward to check your answer? **Multiply the average mass by 5, then subtract each of the five masses. The result should be zero.**

SOLVE ANOTHER PROBLEM

For a math activity, a group of students measured the length of piece of string. Their results were 234.4 cm, 235 cm, 2.34 m, and 2.348 m. What is the average of the students' measurements? **234.55 cm**

▶ ENRICHMENT

Name _____

Extend Your Thinking 8-1

Visual Thinking

Analyze the shapes on the grid to find the pattern. Then complete the missing section in the center.

Describe the pattern. **Possible answer: The pattern is 1-2-2-1-2-1-1-2 and goes from left to right in odd rows and right to left in even rows.**

▶ Quick Quiz

Choose an appropriate unit for measuring each of the following:

1. Distance from classroom to gymnasium **feet, yards, or meters**

2. Area of a desktop **square inches or square centimeters**

Convert each measurement.

3. 25 km to meters **25,000**

4. A time of 2:05:10 to seconds **7510**

Available on Daily Transparency 8-1

Objective

■ **Identify more precise measurements.**

Vocabulary

■ **Precision, significant digits**

Materials

■ **Explore: Meter stick**

NCTM Standards

■ **1–4, 13**

► **Review**

Which measurement is stated in a smaller unit?

1. 2.5 m or 2.54 m 2.54 m

2. $3\frac{1}{2}$ in. or $3\frac{3}{8}$ in. $3\frac{3}{8}$ in.

3. 3 ft 10 in. or 4 yd 3 ft 10 in.

Available on Daily Transparency 8-2

► **Lesson Link**

Remind students that in Lesson 8-1 they learned that measurement is not exact. An acceptable maximum error is $\pm\frac{1}{2}$ of the smallest unit. So the smaller the unit, the more accurate the measurement.

1 Introduce

Explore

The Point
Students discover that measurements of the same objects may have various degrees of precision, and they discuss which measurement is most precise.

Ongoing Assessment
In Step 1, check that students remeasure the distance using each unit of measure.

For Groups That Finish Early
Use a yardstick to measure the distance from the floor to the top of your desk to the nearest yard, half yard, foot, half foot, and inch. Which is the most exact?

8-2 Significant Digits and Precision

You'll Learn …

■ to identify more precise measurements

… How It's Used

Farmers use precise measurements when they analyze the quality of their soil.

Vocabulary

precision

significant digits

▶ **Lesson Link**   Now you'll apply what you know about units of measurement to calculate with measurements using significant digits. ◀

Explore Precision

How Close Can You Get?   **Materials:** Meter stick

1. Measure the distance from the floor to the top of your desk. Record the length to the nearest 1 m, nearest 0.5 m, nearest 1 cm, nearest 0.5 cm, and nearest 1 mm.

2. Compare your measurements with those of others in the group. Did you all get the same numbers? Why or why not?

3. Calculate the height of two desks atop one another using each measurement. (Hint: Multiply by 2.) Do the same for five desks.

4. Which heights are the most exact? Discuss your reasoning.

5. With your group, invent a technique of determining the most accurate measurement from a group of measurements.

Learn Significant Digits and Precision

The **precision** of a measurement is determined by the unit of measure. The smaller the unit of measure, the more precise the measurement.

Example 1

Determine the more precise height of the national Capitol dome, 287 ft or 96 yd?

Choose the measurement with smaller units.

The foot (ft) is smaller than the yard (yd).

287 ft is the more precise measurement.

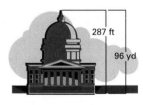

287 ft

96 yd

When you compare measurements with the same unit, the more precise measurement can be determined by the decimal places.

396 *Chapter 8 • Geometry and Measurement*

> **MEETING INDIVIDUAL NEEDS**

Resources	**Learning Modalities**
8-2 Practice	**Individual** Have students write their own summaries of precision and significant digits.
8-2 Reteaching	
8-2 Problem Solving	
8-2 Enrichment	**Visual** When discussing the four rules for determining significant digits, write examples on the chalkboard or overhead to help illustrate the point described by each rule.
8-2 Daily Transparency	
Problem of the Day	
Review	
Quick Quiz	**Inclusion**
Teaching Tool Transparency 5	Visually impaired students may have difficulty distinguishing small units on a measuring instrument. Pair these students with students who have normal vision for activities that involve measuring.
Chapter 8 Project Master	

Example 2

Using GPS, a geologist finds the distance between two mountain peaks. Which measurement is most precise, 1068 m, 1067.52 m, or 1067.5 m?

Choose the measurement to the smallest decimal place.

1067.52 m is the most precise measurement.

Try It

For each pair of measurements, determine the more precise measurement.

a. 0.5 mi, 2638 ft   **b.** 2 m, 197.5 cm   **c.** 36 in., 35.75 in.
      2638 ft   **197.5 cm**   **35.75 in.**

The greatest possible error of any measurement is $\frac{1}{2}$ or 0.5 of the smallest unit used.

The paper clip is 2.8 cm long.

The greatest possible error is +0.05 cm or −0.05 cm.

The digits that represent the actual measurement are **significant digits** . The last significant digit in a measurement is an estimated digit. These are rules for determining the number of significant digits.

1. All nonzero digits (1–9) are significant.

2. Zeros between nonzero digits are significant.

3. Zeros to the right of a decimal point and to the right of a nonzero digit are significant.

4. Zeros to the right of a decimal point and to the left of a nonzero digit are not significant.

Example 3

Determine the number of significant digits in each measurement.

a. 420.040 m   **b.** 0.00420 m

4, 2, and 4 are significant. Apply Rule 1.   4 and 2 are significant.

All zeros are significant. Apply Rules 2, 3, and 4. The last zero is significant.

6 significant digits.   3 significant digits.

Try It

Determine the number of significant digits in each measurement.

a. 0.0050 m **2**   **b.** 3.05607 kg **6**   **c.** 3000 mi **1**   **d.** 11.050 in. **5**

Have the class make a list of guidelines for determining the most precise measurement.

Answers for Explore

1–5. Answers may vary.

2 Teach

Learn

You may wish to use Teaching Tool Transparency 5: Number Lines with Mixed Practice.

Precision refers to the unit being used for a particular measurement. *Accuracy* refers to the number of significant digits in a particular measurement.

Alternate Examples

1. Determine the more precise height of a bookcase: 46 inches or 4 feet.

   Since inches is a smaller unit than feet, 46 inches is the more precise measurement.

2. Which measurement is the most precise, 48.5 ft, 48 ft, or 48.58 ft?

   Choose the measurement that is given to the smallest decimal place. 48.58 ft is the most precise measurement.

3. Determine the number of significant digits in each measurement.

   a. 150.060 ft

      1, 5, and 6 are significant (Rule 1); all the zeros are significant (Rules 2 and 3); 6 significant digits

   b. 350,000 km

      3 and 5 are significant (Rule 1); two of the zeros are significant (Rule 4); 4 significant digits

▶ Science Link

Geologists study movement of the earth's crust by surveying land and mapping altitudes at various locations.

MATH EVERY DAY

▶ Problem of the Day

Use just the digits 1, 4, and 8 to fill in the table below. Each number reading across and down must be a perfect square. Also, the first row must be the same as the first column, the second row the same as the second column, and the bottom row the same as the last column.

Possible answers:

8 4 1   4 4 1   1 4 4
4 8 4   4 8 4   4 8 4

1 4 4   1 4 4   4 4 1
Available on Daily Transparency 8-2

An Extension is provided in the transparency package.

Fact of the Day

Since 1983, the meter has been defined as the distance traveled by light in a vacuum in $\frac{1}{299{,}792{,}458}$ of a second.

Estimation

Estimate to the nearest whole number.

1. $\sqrt{50}$ 7

2. $\sqrt{7}$ 3

3. $\sqrt{88}$ 9

Alternate Examples

4. A mountain climber has ascended 2564.75 ft up a 3000-ft mountainside. How much farther does the mountain climber have to go to reach the top?

   The answer will be given to the ones place.

   ```
     3000.
   − 2564.75    Subtract.
     435.25     Round to the
                nearest one.
   ```

   The climber has 435 ft to climb.

5. A rectangular rug is custom made to be 5.25 ft by 3.875 ft. Use significant digits to express the area of the rug.

   The answer will have 3 significant digits. Enter 5.25 ×̄ 3.875 =̄ 20.34375. The area of the rug is 20.3 ft².

3 Practice and Assess

Check

Have students discuss why the sum or difference of two measurements is given to the least precise place value of the two measurements. Also, have students explain why the product or quotient of two measurements is given with as many significant digits as the least precise measurement.

Answers for Check Your Understanding

1. Possible answer: The smaller the unit (such as mm) of measure, the more precise the measurement.

2. Possible answer: The number with the fewest significant digits determines how many significant digits the answer will have.

Adding and subtracting measurements require that the answer be as precise as the least precise value of the two measurements.

Example 4

▶ **Science Link**

An *ornithologist* is someone who studies birds.

To study the toucan, an ornithologist trekked to 6540.75 ft altitude in South America. The ornithologist wants to be at 9455 ft to observe the flocks of toucans. How much higher in altitude does the ornithologist have to go?

The answer will be given to the ones place.

```
  9455.
− 6540.75    Subtract.
  2914.25 ≈ 2914
```

The ornithologist has to climb 2914 ft.

Remember

To round a number, look at the decimal place to the right.

If the digit to the right is ≤ 4, then round down.

If the digit to the right is ≥ 5, then round up.

[Previous course]

Multiplying and dividing measurements require that the answer have as many significant digits as the value in the operation with the least number of significant digits.

Example 5

A rectangular sandbox is built with the lengths 4.75 ft and 3.125 ft. Use significant digits to express the area of the sandbox.

The answer will have 3 significant digits.

Enter: 4.75 ×̄ 3.125 =̄ *14.84375*

The area of the sandbox is 14.8 ft².

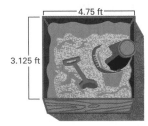

Try It

Calculate and give the number of significant digits in each answer.

a. 11.4 g + 2.65 g   b. 32.06 mL − 22.3 mL   **a. 14.1 g; 3**

c. 2.3 in. × 20.3 in.   d. 32.5 m ÷ 1.5   **9.8 mL; 2**

     47 in.; 2   **22 m; 2**

Check | Your Understanding

1. Describe how precision is affected by the unit of measurement used.

2. How do significant digits affect the calculation of measurements?

MEETING MIDDLE SCHOOL CLASSROOM NEEDS

Tips from Middle School Teachers

I try to help my students understand the importance of significant digits and precision by presenting them with real-life examples. I often bring in newspaper clippings that refer to numbers. I point out how some numbers need to be as precise as possible, such as a price listed in an advertisement or an exchange rate for foreign currency. I then point out numbers that are easier to understand and remember because they are *not* as precise, such as a population estimate *or* the annual sales in millions of dollars by a large company.

Career Connection

Have students research how precision and significant digits are important to carpenters, machinists, and tool-and-die makers. Have them share their information with the class.

Team Teaching

Work with a science teacher to point out how precision and significant digits are used and applied in scientific measurements and calculations.

Practice and Apply

1. **Getting Started** Determine the number of significant digits in 407.050.
   a. Count the number of nonzero digits. **3**
   b. Count the number of significant zeros. **3**
   c. Add the total number of significant digits from **a** and **b**. **6**

Determine the number of significant digits in each measurement.

2. 0.074 m **2**   3. 0.0056 km **2**   4. 57.048 mi **5**   5. 11.050 in. **5**

Determine which measurement is more precise.

6. 1 yd, 37 in. **37 in.**   7. 235 cm, 230 cm **235 cm**   8. 18 in., $17\frac{11}{16}$ in. **$17\frac{11}{16}$ in.**   9. 0.3 L, 0.25 L **0.25 L**

10. **Science** A measurement of 0.088 m is converted to cm. How many significant digits does the measurement have before conversion? How many after? **2; 2**

11. **Industry** A jet pilot completes a test flight which, according to the on-board GPS-based clock, lasts 2.75 hr. Another test flight on the next day lasts 0.55 hr. Using significant digits, how much total flight time did the pilot log for the two days? **3.30 hr**

Calculate and give each answer with the correct number of significant digits.

12. 8.4 g + 5.20 g **13.6 g**   13. 45 mi − 0.9 mi **44 mi**

14. 9.79 cm × 9.5 cm **93 cm²**   15. 32.8 m × 1.5 m **49 m²**

16. **Test Prep** Determine the most precise measurement. **D**
   Ⓐ 89 ft   Ⓑ 89.0 ft   Ⓒ 90 ft   Ⓓ 88.999 ft

17. **Algebra** The formula for converting temperatures from Fahrenheit to Celsius is $C = \frac{5}{9}(F - 32)$. The normal daily low temperature in Everglades National Park is 56°F. What is this temperature in °C, using significant digits. **13°C**

18. **Measurement** One leg of a right triangle is measured at 1.38 cm, the other at 0.67 cm. What is the length of the hypotenuse? Use significant digits. **1.5 cm**

PRACTICE 8-2

8-2 Exercises and Applications

Assignment Guide

■ **Basic**
1–9, 11–16, 19–21, 23–36

■ **Average**
3, 5, 9–38

■ **Enriched**
5, 9–38

Exercise Notes

■ **Exercise 16**

Test Prep Students should first look for the choice with the smallest unit. Since the units are all the same, they should then look for the choice with the smallest decimal place.

■ **Exercise 18**

Geometry Students will need to remember the Pythagorean theorem, $a^2 + b^2 = c^2$, where a and b are the lengths of the legs of a right triangle, and c is the length of the hypotenuse.

PRACTICE

Name _____

Practice **8-2**

Significant Digits and Precision

Determine the number of significant digits in each measurement.

1. 1.063 in. **4**   2. 12,000 g **2**   3. 634 yd **3**   4. 8300 qt **2**

5. 0.0037 sec **2**   6. 10.9 kg **3**   7. 2.030 pt **4**   8. 4.87 hr **3**

Underline the more precise measurement.

9. 23 oz, <u>20.7 oz</u>   10. <u>1830 g</u>, 2.5 kg   11. 160 qt, <u>137 qt</u>

12. 63.7 L, <u>63.70 L</u>   13. 3.7 T, <u>5610 lb</u>   14. 47 qt, <u>83 pt</u>

15. <u>58.3 cm</u>, 4.6 m   16. 12 L, <u>1735 mL</u>   17. 61 lb, <u>63.7 lb</u>

18. <u>3.008 pt</u>, 0.95 pt   19. 7.3 min, <u>516 sec</u>   20. <u>2.7 mL</u>, 12 mL

Calculate each and give the answer with the correct number of significant digits.

21. 6.35 oz + 4.2 oz **10.6 oz**   22. 83 g − 1.8 g **81 g**   23. 6.25 in. × 15.85 in. **99.1 in²**

24. 4.20 yd × 8.64 yd **36.3 yd²**   25. 21 cm × 5360 cm **110,000 cm²**   26. 8137 hr − 500 hr **7600 hr**

27. 5.382 m × 8 m **40 m²**   28. 6.4 ft × 4300 ft **28,000 ft²**   29. 30 mi × 165 mi **5000 mi²**

30. 2.713 mL + 8.4 mL **11.1 mL**   31. 50 lb − 4.6 lb **45 lb**   32. 6.83 km × 10.3 km **70.3 km²**

33. **Geography** Boundary Peak in Nevada is 13,000 ft high. Guadalupe Peak in Texas is 8749 ft high. How much higher than Guadalupe Peak is Boundary Peak? Use the correct number of significant digits. **4000 ft**

34. A rectangular swimming pool has length 98 ft and width 33.5 ft. Use significant digits to express the area of the pool. **3300 ft²**

RETEACHING

Name _____

Alternative Lesson **8-2**

Significant Digits and Precision

The **precision** of the measurement is determined by the unit of measure. The smaller the unit of measure, the more precise the measurement. If the same unit is used in two measurements, then the measurement to the smallest decimal place is more precise.

Significant digits are the digits that represent the actual measurement. The last significant digit in a measurement is an estimated digit. To determine when digits are significant, use these rules:

1. All nonzero digits (1–9) are always significant.

2. Zeros between nonzero digits are significant.

3. Zeros to the right of the decimal point and to the right of a nonzero digit are significant.

4. When the zero in a whole number is underlined, then it and any zeros to its left are significant.

— **Example 1** —

Determine which measurement in each set is more precise.

a. 3 yd, 110 in.   **b.** 45.12 cm, 45.2 cm

a. Since the units of measure are different, the measurement with the smaller unit of measure is more precise. An inch is smaller than a yard, so 110 in. is more precise than 3 yd.

b. Since the units of measure are the same, the measurement with the smaller decimal place is more precise. Since 45.12 has the smaller decimal place, 45.12 cm is more precise than 45.2 cm.

Try It Write the more precise measurement.

a. 1.6 mi, 8448 ft **8448 ft**   **b.** 8.9 km, 8.87 km **8.87 km**

c. 2 ft, 13 in. **13 in.**   **d.** 5.64 cm, 56.2 cm **5.64 cm**

— **Example 2** —

Determine the number of significant digits in 26,000 ft.

Apply Rule 1: the 2 and 6 are significant. Apply Rule 4: the underlined 0 in the tens place and the 0 to its left, the hundreds digit, are significant.

So, there are 4 significant digits: 2, 6, 0, and 0.

Try It Write the number of significant digits in each. Circle the digits.

e. ④.0⑨0 km **4 digits.**   **f.** ①0.0⓪0 **3 digits.**   **g.** ①④⑨.⓪① **5 digits.**

Reteaching

Activity

Materials: Yardstick, 3 yard-long strips of cardboard

• Work in groups of three.

• Put the 1-yard mark on one strip. Put the 1-foot, 2-foot, and 3-foot marks on another strip. Put the inch marks (1–36) on the third strip.

• Measure the height or length of several objects, first with the "yard" strip, then with the "foot" strip, and finally with the "inch" strip. Record the measurements.

• Compare your measurements. Which is most precise? Why?

Exercise Notes

■ **Exercises 23–30**

Review with students how to find the LCM for a pair of numbers.

■ **Exercises 32 and 33**

Remind students that a bar over a digit or group of digits indicates that the digit or digits repeat.

Project Progress

You may want to have students use Chapter 8 Project Master.

Exercise Answers

21. 5; Judges wish to determine the best scorers among many fine gymnasts.

31.

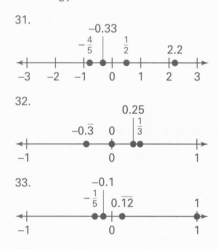

32.

33.

Alternate Assessment

Portfolio Have students find a newspaper or magazine article that mentions at least one measurement. The students should determine the number of significant digits in the measurement.

▶ **Quick Quiz**

Determine the number of significant digits in each measurement.

1. 42.0230 m **6**

2. 1050 ft **3**

Give the answer with the correct number of significant digits.

3. 41 ft − 26.8 ft **14 ft**

4. 8.50 in. × 6.0 in. **51 in²**

5. 17.06 m ÷ 8.31 **2.05 m**

Available on Daily Transparency 8-2

400   Chapter 8

Problem Solving and Reasoning

19. **Math Reasoning** An Olympic marathon covers 42.2 km of distance through the streets of the host city, followed by a 400 m lap around the main stadium. What is the total distance of the race, in meters? Use significant digits. **42,600 m**

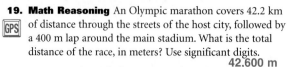

20. **Communicate** The hypotenuse of a right triangle with two equal sides measures 4.04 ft. Find the length of each leg, using significant digits. How could you use an algebraic equation to solve this? Explain. **2.86 ft**

21. **Journal** The following are the points for the women's gymnastics gold, silver, and bronze medal winners in the 1996 Olympics: 39.255, 39.075, 39.067. How many significant digits are there? Why do you think it is important to be this precise?

22. **Operation Sense** An all-terrain vehicle's GPS indicates that it has traveled 76.34 mi in 2.18 hr. Using significant digits, what is the vehicle's average speed? **35.0 mph**

PROBLEM SOLVING 8-2

Mixed Review

Find the LCM for each pair of numbers. *[Lesson 7-3]*

23. 3, 7 **21** 24. 10, 40 **40** 25. 5, 11 **55** 26. 36, 48 **144**

27. 8, 26 **104** 28. 480, 160 **480** 29. 12, 10 **60** 30. 27, 36 **108**

Order each group of numbers on a number line. *[Lesson 7-4]*

31. $-\frac{4}{5}, -0.33, 2.2, \frac{1}{2}$ 32. $-0.\overline{3}, 0, \frac{1}{3}, 0.25$ 33. $1, -\frac{1}{5}, 0.\overline{12}, -0.1$

Write each as a fraction or mixed number in lowest terms. *[Lesson 7-4]*

34. 0.85 $\frac{17}{20}$ 35. 2.17 $2\frac{17}{100}$ 36. $0.\overline{6}$ $\frac{2}{3}$ 37. 0.5 $\frac{1}{2}$ 38. -8.012 $-8\frac{3}{250}$

Project Progress

Choose an ancient civilization, then research what units of measurement it used. Investigate units that measured such quantities as time, money, length, area, volume, and weight.

Problem Solving

Understand
Plan
Solve
Look Back

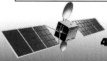

400 *Chapter 8 • Geometry and Measurement*

▷ **PROBLEM SOLVING**

Name _____

Guided Problem Solving 8-2

GPS PROBLEM 19, STUDENT PAGE 400

An Olympic marathon covers 42.2 km of distance through the streets of the host city, followed by a 400 m lap around the main stadium. What is the total distance of the race, in meters? Use significant digits.

— **Understand** —
1. What are you asked to find? **Total distance of race in meters.**

2. What is the length of the part of the race through the streets? **42.2 km**

3. What is the length of the lap in the stadium? **400 m**

— **Plan** —
4. How many meters are in a kilometer? **1000 m**

5. Convert 42.2 km to meters. **42,200 m**

6. Which operation will you use to find the total distance of the marathon? **Addition.**

— **Solve** —
7. Write an equation to find the total distance of the marathon.
42,200 + 400 = 42,600

8. What is the total distance? **42,600 m**

9. What are the significant digits in the total distance? **4, 2, 6, 0**

— **Look Back** —
10. What are two ways to convert 42.2 km to meters? **Set up a proportion and solve; move decimal to multiply by a power of ten.**

SOLVE ANOTHER PROBLEM

A bicycle race covers 34.8 km over winding country roads and 500 m in the final straight stretch across the finish line. What is the total distance of the race, in meters? **35,300 m**

▷ **ENRICHMENT**

Name _____

Extend Your Thinking 8-2

Critical Thinking

For any measurement the **greatest possible error (GPE)** is one half the unit of measure.

For example, if the length of any object measures 5 in. to the nearest inch, the unit of measure is 1 in. The greatest possible error is one half of one inch, or $\frac{1}{2}$ in. The measurement range is $5 \pm \frac{1}{2}$, which is between $4\frac{1}{2}$ in. and $5\frac{1}{2}$ in.

If the length of an object measures 6.1 cm to the nearest 0.1 cm, the unit of measure is 0.1 cm. The greatest possible error is one half of 0.1 cm, or 0.05 cm. The measurement range is 0.1 ±0.05 cm, which is between 6.05 cm and 6.15 cm.

For each measurement below, name the unit of measure, the greatest possible error, and the range of measurement.

		Unit of Measure	GPE	Range of Measurement
1.	19 mm	1 mm	0.5 mm	18.5 mm–19.5 mm
2.	20.8 m	0.1 m	0.05 m	20.75 m–20.85 m
3.	54.75 m	0.01 m	0.005 m	54.745 m–54.755 m
4.	25 in.	1 in.	0.5 in.	24.5 in.–25.5 in.
5.	4.1 ft	0.1 ft	0.05 ft	4.05 ft–4.15 ft
6.	62.85 mi	0.01 mi	0.005 mi	62.845 mi–62.855 mi
7.	30 g	1 g	0.5 g	29.5 g–30.5 g
8.	54.8 mg	0.1 mg	0.05 mg	54.75 mg–54.85 mg

9. Janie was making a birdhouse. She said the range of measurement for one of the boards was 20.505 cm– 20.515 cm. What was her measurement of the length of the board? **20.51 cm**

10. Carlos wanted a GPE of ±0.05 m for the measurements of his bookcases. How many centimeters is equal to his GPE? **±5 cm**

11. Manuela is writing the specifications for a new product. The GPE was ±0.005 g. The lowest measure is 10.565 g. What is the largest measure? **10.575 g**

12. Pate mixed two liquids in his chemistry class. He measured each liquid to the nearest mL. What was his GPE? **0.5 mL**

Position

▶ Lesson Link You've learned units for describing distance, mass, and other measurements. Now you'll learn how position and orientation are described. ◀

Explore | Position

Can the Guide Guide?

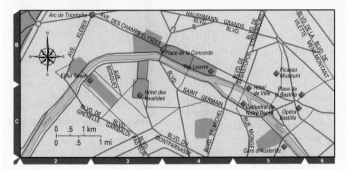

1. Use the map of Paris to name three landmarks southeast of Place de la Concorde, where the guillotine was during the French Revolution.

2. How far is the Eiffel Tower from the Hôtel des Invalides, which contains Napoleon's tomb?

3. Have one person in the group secretly write down the names of three landmarks on the map. This person will be the "guide" and will conduct a tour from the Arc de Triomphe.

4. The guide must lead the group to the three secret landmarks, in order, by giving only verbal directions. The guide can use information such as direction, distance, and street names.

5. The other members in the group try to identify each of the landmarks after the guide has given the directions. If the tour group cannot determine a landmark based on the guide's directions, then the guide must provide new directions to that landmark.

6. What are some ways that people describe where things are in your town? Your state? The country? The world?

You'll Learn ...

■ to locate places using map coordinates and latitude and longitude

... How It's Used

Police officers can locate places on a map quickly so they can arrive at an emergency promptly.

Vocabulary

absolute position

relative position

MEETING INDIVIDUAL NEEDS

Resources

8-3 Practice
8-3 Reteaching
8-3 Problem Solving
8-3 Enrichment
8-3 Daily Transparency
    Problem of the Day
    Review
    Quick Quiz

Teaching Tool Transparencies 20, 21

Lesson Enhancement Transparencies 30, 31, 32, 33

Learning Modalities

Individual Have students reflect on how their knowledge of maps and locations on a map has been enhanced.

Visual Point out that the parallels of latitude do not intersect. But the great circles of longitude all intersect at the poles.

Kinesthetic Students can use real maps and a globe when applying the lesson concepts.

Inclusion

Some students may have a difficult time reading the maps due to the condensed nature of the type and graphics. It might be helpful to have larger copies of the maps available for these students.

Objective

■ **Locate places using map coordinates and latitude and longitude.**

Vocabulary

■ **Absolute position, relative position**

NCTM Standards

■ **1–4, 12, 13**

▶ Review

Give the coordinates of each point.

1. A (3, –1)   2. B (0, 3)

3. C (–1, 2)   4. D (–2, –3)

5. Find the distance from A to C. 5

Available on Daily Transparency 8-3

▶ Lesson Link

Discuss with students another unit of measure, degrees. Ask students for instances when degrees are used. Mention and discuss lines of latitude and longitude if students do not suggest them.

1 Introduce

Explore

You might wish to use Lesson Enhancement Transparency 30 with **Explore**.

The Point
Students practice giving or following directions to various landmarks identified on a map of Paris.

Ongoing Assessment

Observe the groups at Step 4. Check that correct and clear directions are being given. Also check that directions are being followed.

For Groups That Finish Early

Use the map to determine the distance between landmarks. Then suppose the landmarks were ordered pairs on a coordinate plane. Now what is the distance between landmarks? What observations can be made? Possible answer: The distance on a coordinate plane is less than the distance on the map, since distance on the coordinate plane can be calculated as the length of a line segment while distance on the map can be calculated along streets.

Follow Up

Discuss students' responses to Step 6. Emphasize the need for a uniform method for describing position.

Answers for Explore

1. Answers may vary.

2. About $\frac{5}{8}$ mile

3–6. Answers may vary.

2 Teach

Learn

You might wish to use Lesson Enhancement Transparencies 31, 32, and 33 and Teaching Tool Transparencies 20: Map of World and 21: Map of United States with this lesson.

On local maps, the grid lines are arbitrary lines determined by the map maker. On world maps, the grid lines are lines of latitude and longitude.

Alternate Examples

1. Use the map for Example 1 to answer the following.

   a. What Interstate highway runs north and south through I-3?

   Find I on the vertical axis and 3 on the horizontal axis. Interstate highway 610 runs north and south through I-3.

   b. Give the map coordinates of the Astrodome.

   The Astrodome is in J-4.

Learn | Position

You use a grid to identify the location of places on a map. It is similar to a mathematical coordinate grid because it has horizontal and vertical coordinates.

Example 1

Use the map to answer the following.

a. What university is located in J-4?

b. Give the map coordinates of Memorial Park.

a. Find J on the vertical axis and 4 on the horizontal axis. Rice University is in J-4.

b. Memorial Park is in I-3 and I-4.

Absolute position of a location is given as coordinates, whereas the **relative position** of a location is given in relationship to another place.

Example 2

Use the map to answer the following.

a. Give the position of Hart Plaza relative to John F. Kennedy Square.

b. Give the absolute position of Hart Plaza using the map coordinates.

a. Hart Plaza is three blocks southeast of John F. Kennedy Square.

b. Hart Plaza is between G-4 and H-4.

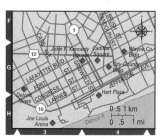

Try It

Use the map to answer the following.

a. Give the position of the zoo relative to the Kickapoo River. **4 blocks east**

b. Give the absolute position of Bradley Park using the map coordinates. **C-17**

MATH EVERY DAY

▶ Problem of the Day

In Abu Simbel, Egypt, huge stone statues of Pharaoh Ramses II can be seen from the Nile River. These are over 3300 years old. They have survived 50 years less than 50 times the length of the reign of Ramses II. How long did Ramses II reign? 67 years $(3300 = 50x - 50)$

Available on Daily Transparency 8-3

An Extension is provided in the transparency package.

Fact of the Day

The word *latitude* derives from the Latin *latus,* meaning "wide," and *longitude* derives from the Latin *longus,* meaning "long."

Mental Math

Find these mentally.

1. The number of degrees between 30° N and 18° N. 12°

2. The number of degrees between 10° E and 26° E. 16°

3. The number of degrees between 10° N and 15° S. 25°

World maps usually show positions using lines of latitude and longitude. Both of these measurements use degrees as their units.

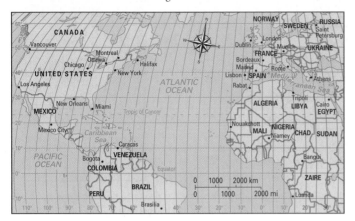

Remember

Latitude and longitude are the imaginary lines we use to locate places on the earth. Latitude lines run east and west. Longitude lines run north and south.

[Page 90]

Example 3

Use the map above to answer the following to the nearest 5°.

a. What country occupies 55° N, 65° W?

Find 55° north of the equator.

Find 65° west of 0° longitude.

Canada occupies 55° N, 65° W.

b. Give the latitude and longitude of Bordeaux, France.

Identify the longitude.

Identify the latitude.

Bordeaux is 45° N, 0°.

▶ **Geography Link**

The *prime meridian* is 0° longitude and runs through Greenwich, England.

Example 4

A sailing crew uses GPS to navigate the oceans. Its GPS receiver reports its position as 10° S, 30° W. What country is nearest to the crew?

Find 10° S, 30° W.

Brazil is the closest country.

Try It

Use the map above to answer the following to the nearest 5°.

a. What country occupies 0°, 55° W? **Brazil**

b. Give the latitude and longitude of New Orleans, Louisiana. **30° N, 90° W**

2. Use the map for Example 2 to answer the following.

   a. Give the position of the Joe Louis Arena relative to the Detroit News.

      The Joe Louis Arena is about five blocks southeast of the Detroit News.

   b. Give the absolute position of Cadillac Square using the map coordinates.

      Cadillac Square is in G-4.

3. Use the map above Example 3 to answer the following.

   a. What country occupies 28° N, 5° E?

      Find 28° north of the equator. Find 5° east of 0° longitude. Algeria occupies 28° N, 5° E.

   b. Give the latitude and longitude of Luanda to the nearest 5°.

      Identify the latitude. Identify the longitude. Luanda is 10° S, 15° E.

4. A sailing crew reports their position as 20° N, 95° W. What country is nearest to them?

   Find 20° N, 95° W. Mexico is the closest country.

▷ **MEETING MIDDLE SCHOOL CLASSROOM NEEDS**

Tips from Middle School Teachers

I like to introduce this type of lesson by taking a local map (the telephone book is often a good source for this) and enlarging it to post in front of the class. I ask a volunteer to point out the location of our school and to read the coordinates that give its location. After repeating this for a few local landmarks, I use a country or world map to find the location of our town and other well-known cities.

Cooperative Learning

Have students work in pairs to plan a trip around the world, with the limitations of traveling no more than 20° of longitude and 15° of latitude during each leg of the journey. Have each pair of students record their stops, along with the absolute position of each location.

Social Science Connection

Have students bring in newspaper articles about current events involving a major city or country. Then find the geographic location on a map and give the absolute position using latitude and longitude.

Remind students that determining distances on a map is often useful in real-life situations. Ask volunteers to share ideas about situations where they have found this skill helpful.

Answers for What Do You Think?

1. Shauna used the scale of the map as a ratio.

2. Shauna estimated the $1\frac{1}{8}$ in. between Dallas and Omaha. Kele estimated the distance between latitude lines.

3 Practice and Assess

Check

For Question 2, the equator can be compared to the *x*-axis because both determine horizontal positions. The prime meridian can be compared to the *y*-axis because both determine vertical positions.

Answers for Check Your Understanding

1. Possible answer: The distances between longitude lines are not uniform on a map grid since they converge at the poles.

2. Possible answer: Both sets of axes run vertically and horizontally.

Use the map to give the position of Dallas relative to Omaha.

Shauna thinks ...

It looks like the map scale is 250 miles to a half inch. I'll measure the distance between Dallas and Omaha in inches. Then I'll multiply that by $\frac{500 \text{ mi}}{\text{in.}}$ and round my answer to the nearest tens place.

$$1\frac{1}{8} \text{ in.} \times \frac{500 \text{ mi}}{\text{in.}} = \frac{9}{8} \text{ in.} \times \frac{500 \text{ mi}}{\text{in.}} = 562.5 \text{ mi}$$

Dallas is about 560 mi south of Omaha.

Kele thinks ...

The map scale shows that 2° latitude is about 140 mi. Dallas and Omaha are about 8° latitude apart.

I'll multiply. $8 \times \frac{140}{2} = 560 \text{ mi}$

Dallas is almost 560 mi south of Omaha.

 **TIP**

Be prepared! Look for ways to apply what you already know to new situations.

What do  **think?**

1. How did Shauna use a ratio to answer the question?

2. Explain how Shauna and Kele used estimation.

Check | Your Understanding

1. How is a map grid different from a coordinate grid?

2. Describe how latitude and longitude are similar to the *x*- and *y*-axes.

8-3 Exercises and Applications

Practice and Apply

1. **Getting Started** Give the map coordinates of the International Peace Garden. **10C**

2. What hospital is located in 9D? **Pioneer Valley Hospital**

3. What airport is located in 9E? **Salt Lake City Municipal Airport No. 2**

4. What is the position of Pioneer Valley Hospital relative to Salt Lake City Municipal Airport No. 2? **One grid north**

5. **History** Founded in 1847, Salt Lake City built its streets in a perfect grid. What is the position of the Valley Fair Mall relative to West Ridge Golf Course? **Northeast**

6. **Geography** What is the absolute position of Katmandu using latitude and longitude? **27° N, 85° E**

7. **Geography** How many degrees of latitude are between Thimphu and Dhaka? How many degrees of longitude? **4° latitude; ≈ 1° longitude**

8. **Logic** The tropic of Cancer is at $23\frac{1}{2}°$ N latitude. The tropic of Capricorn is the same distance south of 0° latitude. At what latitude is the tropic of Capricorn? **$23\frac{1}{2}°$ S**

9. **Science** Geologists think that the Himalayan mountains were formed when India collided with Asia almost 100 million years ago. The highest point in the world is located at 28.0° N, 86.6° E. What is its name? **Mt. Everest**

10. **Test Prep** How many degrees latitude is it from Jacksonville, Florida, to Key West? **A**

    Ⓐ 6° Ⓑ 1° Ⓒ 3° Ⓓ 12°

11. How many miles are between Jacksonville, Florida, and Key West? **About 395 mi**

12. How many kilometers are between Cape Canaveral and Tallahassee? **About 425 km**

13. How many miles are between Tampa and Miami? **About 200 mi**

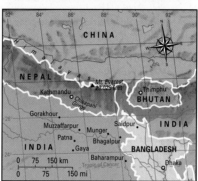

PRACTICE 8-3

PRACTICE

Name _____

Practice 8-3

Position

1. What city is located at 24°N and 104.5°W?
   Durango

2. What is the position of Ciudad Mante relative to Mexico City?
   About 230 mi north

3. What is the position of Guadalajara relative to Veracruz?
   About 480 mi northwest

4. What is the absolute position of Monterrey using latitude and longitude?
   About 25.5°N, 100.5°W

5. How many degrees of latitude are between Durango and Veracruz?
   About 5°

6. How many degrees of longitude are between San Pedro and Mexico City?
   About 4°

7. Locate the position 23°N, 95°W, on the map. Is this location in Mexico, in the Pacific Ocean, or in the Gulf of Mexico?
   Gulf of Mexico

Tell what state contains each location.

8. 40°N, 105°W **Colorado**
9. 32°N, 100°W **Texas**
10. 47°N, 110°W **Montana**
11. 45°N, 100°W **South Dakota**
12. 35°N, 95°W **Oklahoma**

RETEACHING

Name _____

Alternative Lesson 8-3

Position

A map has a grid with horizontal and vertical coordinates. The **absolute position** of a location is given as coordinates, whereas the **relative position** of a location is given in relationship to another place.

Example 1

Use the map to answer the following.

a. What university is located in B-2?

b. Give the map coordinates of the King County International Airport.

a. Find B on the vertical axis and 2 on the horizontal axis. Move right from the B. Move up from the 2. Look for the university that falls in the intersection. Seattle Pacific University is in section B-2.

b. Find the airport on the map. Move left from the airport to the vertical axis and read the scale. It is D. Go back to the airport. Move to the horizontal axis and read the scale. It is 3. King County International Airport is located in D-3.

Try It Use the map above to answer the following.

a. What park is located in C-3? **Seward Park.**

b. Give the map coordinates of Port Madison Suquamish Indian Reservation? **A-1.**

Example 2

Use the map to give the position of the Tampa Theatre relative to Teco Plaza.

Tampa Theatre is one block northeast of Teco Plaza.

Try It Use the map to give each relative position.

c. City Hall Plaza relative to the U. S. Court House.
   3 blocks southeast.

d. Bus station relative to Teco Plaza
   4 blocks northeast.

8-3 Exercises and Applications

Assignment Guide

- **Basic**
  1–10, 16, 19, 21–24, 27–30

- **Average**
  3–16, 20, 21–31 odds

- **Enriched**
  3, 4, 7–20, 23, 26, 29, 32

Exercise Notes

■ **Exercise 7**

Error Prevention Be sure that students use the dot associated with each location for determining its position, rather than where the name is situated on the map.

■ **Exercise 9**

Science It is believed that at one time India was not attached to the Asian continent. The "collision" refers to the collision of the tectonic plates on which India and Asia were located. The earth's surface consists of tectonic plates that are drifting almost imperceptibly.

■ **Exercise 10**

Test Prep Students responding with B may have found the difference in the two locations' longitudinal positions.

Reteaching

Activity

Materials: Outline map of the world

- Highlight the equator and the prime meridian using a bright color.

- Highlight the lines of latitude and longitude in another color, and label each line with its correct degree measure.

- Insert one additional line of latitude and longitude between each pair of highlighted lines.

- Label the position of your hometown with its latitude and longitude.

■ Exercise 16

There are several approaches students may take.

The proportion $\frac{5}{300} = \frac{11}{x}$ may be used; or students may reason that 1° is about 60 miles and multiply 11 by 60.

Exercise Answers

14. Durango and Presa de las Adjuntas

17. Possible answer: Distance between longitude lines decreases as you get closer to the north and south poles because they all intersect at the poles.

18. (−3, 5) is 3 units to the left and 5 units up from (0, 0).

19. East

Alternate Assessment

Ongoing Assessment Exercises 6, 7, and 14 provide opportunities to assess whether students are understanding the main concepts of the lesson.

► Quick Quiz

Refer to the map of Salt Lake City on page 405.

1. Give the map coordinates of the Cottonwood Medical Center. E-10

2. What golf course is located in D-9? West Ridge Golf Course

Refer to the map of central Mexico on page 406.

3. What city lies near 19° N, 99° W? Mexico City

4. Give the absolute position of Matehuala, Mexico, using latitude and longitude, to the nearest degree. 24° N, 101° W

Available on Daily Transparency 8-3

Problem Solving and Reasoning

14. Critical Thinking Name a lake and a city in Mexico that are approximately on the same latitude and 375 miles away from each other.

15. What kind of measuring device would you invent to measure distances and directions while traveling? How precise should it be? Make a sketch of it and describe how it would work. **Answers may vary**

16. Communicate The west coast of Cuba is at 85° W and the east coast of Cuba is at 74° W. If at that latitude, a 5° change in longitude represents about 300 mi, how far is it from coast to coast? Explain your answer. **660 mi; 1° = about 60 miles, so** $11° \times \dfrac{60\ mi}{1°} = 660\ mi$

17. Math Reasoning There is 111 km between each degree longitude at the equator. The distance between longitudes changes as you travel toward the polar regions. Describe how this distance changes and explain why it changes.

18. Algebra Describe the relative position of (−3, 5) with respect to the origin (0, 0) on a coordinate grid.

19. Math Reasoning Kachina hiked 1 mile east, turned right, and walked $\frac{3}{4}$ mile. After a lunch break, she walked in the same direction 1.25 miles, turned left, and continued her hike. What direction is Kachina facing?

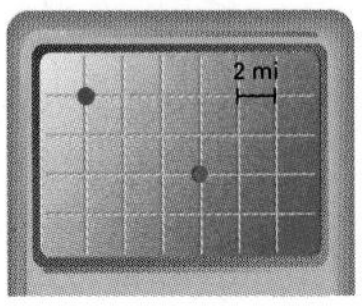

20. Math Reasoning A backpacker uses her GPS receiver to find out how much farther she needs to travel. The red dot on the GPS receiver screen shows where she is. The blue dot shows her destination. How far is that point from her current position? **≈ 7.2 mi**

Mixed Review

Find each unit rate. *[Lesson 5-5]*

21. 220 mi in 4 hr **55 mi/hr**
22. 18 birds in 9 nests **2 birds per nest**
23. $48 for 8 hr **$6 per hr**
24. $3.99 for 3 lb **$1.33 lb**
25. 32 children in 14 homes **≈ 2.3 children per home**
26. $100 for 10 CDs **$10 each**

Add or subtract. *[Lesson 7-5]*

27. 1.024 + 2.091 **3.115**
28. 0.041 − 0.144 **−0.103**
29. 42.1 + 98.156 **140.256**
30. $\frac{4}{5} + 1\frac{1}{2}$ **$2\frac{3}{10}$**
31. $5\frac{1}{3} - 2\frac{2}{3}$ **$2\frac{2}{3}$**
32. $9\frac{1}{4} + 2\frac{9}{10}$ **$12\frac{3}{20}$**

406 Chapter 8 • Geometry and Measurement

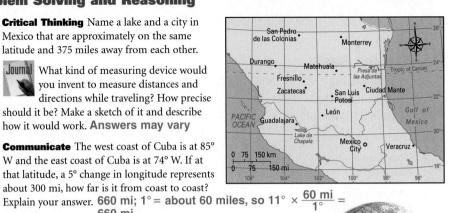

► PROBLEM SOLVING

Name _____

Guided Problem Solving 8-3

GPS PROBLEM 16, STUDENT PAGE 406

The west coast of Cuba is at 85° W and the east coast of Cuba is at 74° W. If at that latitude, a 5° change in longitude represents about 300 mi, how far is it from coast to coast? Explain your answer.

Possible answer: Item 9

— **Understand** —

1. What is the longitude at the west coast? **85° W**

2. What is the longitude at the east coast? **74° W**

— **Plan** —

4. Given the longitude, which operation will you use to find the distance across Cuba in degrees? **Subtraction.**

5. How many miles is represented by a 1° change in longitude at that latitude? **60 miles.**

6. Which operation will you use to find the distance across Cuba in miles? **Multiplication.**

— **Solve** —

7. How many degrees is it between the west and east coasts of Cuba? **11°**

8. What is the distance in miles between the west and east coasts of Cuba? **660 miles.**

9. Explain your answer. **If 1° is about 60 miles, then 11° is 11 · 60, or 660 miles.**

— **Look Back** —

10. Show how you could find the answer by writing and solving a proportion. **Let** x **= miles,** $\frac{5}{300} = \frac{11}{x}$**, 5**$x$ **= 11 · 300,** x **= 660.**

SOLVE ANOTHER PROBLEM

Possible explanation:

The west coast of Australia is at 113° E and the east coast of Australia is at 153° E. If at that latitude, a 10° change in longitude represents about 625 mi, how far is it from coast to coast? Explain your answer.

2500 mi; if 1° is about 62.5 miles, then 40° is (40 · 62.5) mi.

► ENRICHMENT

Name _____

Extend Your Thinking 8-3

Decision Making

The Carters decided to spend a three-day weekend in neighboring Ohio. They wanted to spend at least one day visiting either a museum or a zoo. They would leave from their Indianapolis home.

Amy listed some of the attractions of the state and made the list below.

Cedar Point Amusement Park in Sandusky
Kings Island Amusement Park near Cincinnati
Ohio Caverns in West Liberty
Cincinnati Museum of Natural History in Cincinnati
Cincinnati Zoo and Botanical Garden
Miamisburg Mound in Miamisburg
Cleveland Children's Museum
Ohio State University in Columbus
Columbus Zoo

1. Circle each attraction on the map. **Possible answers: Items 2–4**

2. Which attractions would you advise the Carters to visit? Keep in mind travel time between attractions. Explain. **Ohio Caverns, Columbus Zoo, Ohio State University, Miamisburg Mound. The attractions are relatively near each other. They could be visited in less than 3 days.**

3. Which roads would be the best for the Carters to travel? Explain. **Interstate 70 from Indy to U.S. 68 for a visit to Ohio Caverns. Then U.S. 33 to Columbus. On the way home, Interstate 70 to Miamisburg. Interstate 70 home.**

4. Write a schedule for the Carters that includes when they will travel and when they will visit each attraction. **Day 1: Home → Ohio Caverns → Columbus**
Day 2: Ohio State University → Columbus Zoo
Day 3: Columbus → Miamisburg Mound → Home.

Section 8A Connect

You've learned about precision and have converted units of measurement. Now you'll use this knowledge to learn more about GPS.

Where in the World Am I?

The Navstar GPS is controlled by the U.S. military at Falcon Air Force Base in Colorado. In 1995, there were 24 satellites orbiting the earth to enable people all over the world to navigate.

There are two types of Global Positioning Systems. The Precise Positioning Service (PPS) is only for the U.S. Department of Defense. The Standard Positioning Service (SPS) is for the general public.

The PPS is encoded and needs a decoder to be used. The SPS is not encoded and is used by fishing boats, cars, airplanes, and backpackers.

Types of GPS		
GPS-Determined Measurements	PPS Precision	SPS Precision
Distance in any direction N, S, E, or W	Within 17.8 m	Within 100 m
Altitude	Within 27.7 m	Within 156 m
Time (1,000,000,000 ns = 1 sec)	Within 100 ns	Within 340 ns

1. Which GPS service is more precise? Discuss your reasoning.

2. Why would there be two levels of precision for GPS service?

3. One GPS satellite has an orbit approximately 93,305 mi long and completes the orbit in 12 hr. How fast does a GPS satellite travel?

4. Suppose a ship is 200 km east of Boston. If a GPS satellite is 17,500 km directly above Boston, what is the distance between the GPS satellite and the ship? Use the Pythagorean theorem.

5. Some say that a GPS receiver in a backpack could someday help guide blind people. Discuss some other possible applications for GPS.

407

Where in the World Am I?

The Point
In *Where in the World Am I?* on page 389, students read about the Global Positioning System. Now they will use what they know about precision measurements and converting units to learn more about the Global Positioning System.

About the Page

- In Question 4, since the satellite is "directly above" Boston, a right angle is formed.

- In Question 4, suppose the ship is only 100 km east of Boston. What is the distance between the satellite and the ship? Is the difference about the same as if the ship were 300 km east? 17,500.286 km; the distance is less

Ongoing Assessment
Check students' answers for Question 1. Though the measurements for both types of GPS are given in meters, the precision is different because the measurements are given to different decimal places.

Extension

Refer to Question 4. If the ship's captain has determined the ship is 2000 m east of Boston using SPS, what is the actual range of distance it could be east of Boston? What is the actual range of distance it could be east of Boston if PPS were used? (1900 to 2100 m; 1982.2 to 2017.8 m)

Review Correlation

Item(s)	Lesson(s)
1–9	8-1
10–22	8-2
23	8-3
24	8-2
25	8-1

Test Prep

Test-Taking Tip
Discuss the following with students. When converting from smaller to larger units, there will be a *smaller* number of the larger units. Conversely, when converting from larger to smaller units, there will be a *larger* number of smaller units. For a conversion from millimeters to centimeters, the number of centimeters must be smaller than the number of millimeters.

Answers for Review
24. Possible answer: No, because the zero isn't underlined.

Section 8A Review

What metric unit would you use for each measurement?

1. The amount of water in an aquarium **Liter**

2. The lenth of the diagonal of a television screen **cm**

3. The area of your hand **cm²**

Convert each measurement.

4. 0.79 ft to yd
   ≈ 0.26 yd
5. 245 min to hr
   ≈ 4.08 hr
6. 500 mL to L
   0.5 L
7. 2500 L to mL
   2,500,000 mL
8. 1.48 km to m
   1480 m
9. $1\frac{3}{4}$ lb to oz
   28 oz

Determine the number of significant digits in each measurement.

10. 409 g **3** 11. 0.006 mm **1** 12. 2300 lb **2** 13. 0.0510 mL **3** 14. 72.0 in² **3**

Determine which measurement is more precise.

15. 0.5 gal, 1.89 L
    1.89 L
16. 6.2 cm, 6.20 cm
    6.20 cm
17. 3499 in., 3500 in.
    3499 in.
18. 201 cm, 2 m
    201 cm

Calculate and give each answer with the correct number of significant digits.

19. 8.4 g + 5.20 g
    13.6 g
20. 45 mi − 0.9 mi
    44 mi
21. 9.79 cm × 9.5 cm
    93 cm²
22. 32.8 m × 2.4 m
    79 m²

23. If 22° N, 76° E is in India, what country is 39° N, 90° E in? **China**

24. [Journal] A distance is measured as 6.35 km and recorded as 6350 m. Could someone think there are four significant digits in this measurement? Explain.

Test Prep

When you convert units of measurement on a multiple choice test, the possible answers can have the same number of significant digits. Make sure your answer has the decimal point in the proper place.

25. An eyelash is 11.3 mm long. How many cm is this? **C**
    Ⓐ 1130 cm   Ⓑ 113 cm   Ⓒ 1.13 cm   Ⓓ 0.0013 cm

Resources

Practice Masters
   Section 8A Review

Assessment Sourcebook
   Quiz 8A

TestWorks
Test and Practice Software

PRACTICE

Name _____

Practice

Section 8A Review

What metric unit would you use for each measurement?

1. The mass of a television set
   kilogram
2. The area of a football field
   square meters

Convert each measurement.

3. 75 in. to ft
   6.25 ft
4. 21 hr to min
   1260 min
5. 258 cm to m
   2.58 cm
6. 3.8 T to lb
   7600 lb

Determine the number of significant digits in each measurement.

7. 5.360 mL **4** 8. 748 lb **3** 9. 21,000 ft **2** 10. 0.0075 hr **2**

Underline the more precise measurement.

11. 26.4 cm, 8.39 cm 12. 216 ft, 3106 in. 13. 4100 lb, 6123 lb

Calculate each and give the answer with the correct number of significant digits.

14. 2100 cm − 418 cm **1700 cm** 15. 41.3 in. × 84 in. **3500 in²**

Geography Tell what country contains each location.

16. 30° N, 5° E **Algeria**
17. 15° N, 20° E **Chad**
18. 20° N, 5° W **Mali**
19. 10° N, 8° E **Nigeria**

20. The American International Building is 950 ft tall, and the Statue of Liberty is 152 ft tall. If a scale model of New York City includes a 75 in. replica of the America International Building, how tall is the model Statue of Liberty? *[Lesson 5-6]* **12 in.**

21. Explain the difference between the GCF and the LCM. *[Lessons 7-2 and 7-3]*
    Possible answer: The GCF of two numbers is the greatest number that is a factor of both numbers, and the LCM is the smallest positive number that is a multiple of both numbers.

Visit **www.teacher.mathsurf.com** for links to lesson plans from teachers and other professionals, NCTM information, and other sites.

LESSON PLANNING GUIDE

▶ **Student Edition**

▶ **Ancillaries**

LESSON		MATERIALS	VOCABULARY	DAILY	OTHER
	Section 8B Opener				Teaching Tool Trans. 18
8-4	Lines and Angles	wax paper, compass, scissors	angle, vertex, line, line segment, endpoints, ray, straight angle, right angle, acute angle, obtuse angle, complementary, supplementary, congruent, angle bisector	8-4	Lesson Enhancement Trans. 34 Technology Master 34
8-5	Parallel and Perpendicular Lines	geometry software	parallel, perpendicular, perpendicular bisector, transversal, interior angle, exterior angle, alternate angle, corresponding angle, vertical angle	8-5	Lesson Enhancement Trans. 35 Ch. 8 Project Master Technology Masters 35–37 *Interactive CD-ROM Geometry Tool*
8-6	Polygons	geoboard, rubber bands	polygon, vertex, triangle, quadrilateral, pentagon, hexagon, heptagon, octagon, Venn diagram, equilateral triangle, isosceles triangle, scalene triangle, parallelogram, rectangle, rhombus, square, trapezoid, diagonal, regular polygon, convex polygon, concave polygon	8-6	Teaching Tool Trans. 18 Lesson Enhancement Transparencies 36–38 Technology Master 38 *WW Math—Geometry*
8-7	3-D Views	10 multilink cubes		8-7	Teaching Tool Trans. 9 Technology Master 39 *Interactive CD-ROM Lesson*
	Technology	geometry software			*Interactive CD-ROM Geometry Tool*
	Connect	scissors, tape			Interdisc. Team Teaching 8B
	Review				Practice 8B; Quiz 8B; *TestWorks*
	Chapter Summary and Review				
	Chapter Assessment				Ch. Tests Forms A–F *TestWorks;* Ch. 8 Letter Home
	Cumulative Review, Chapters 1–8				Cumulative Review Ch. 1–8

SKILLS TRACE

LESSON	SKILL	FIRST INTRODUCED			DEVELOP	PRACTICE/ APPLY	REVIEW
		GR. 6	GR. 7	GR. 8			
8-4	Drawing, measuring, classifying angles.	✗			pp. 410–413	pp. 414–415	pp. 437, 439, 465, 675
8-5	Finding angles made by parallel lines.		✗		pp. 416–418	pp. 419–420	pp. 434, 437, 439, 471
8-6	Classifying polygons.	✗			pp. 421–424	pp. 425–426	pp. 434, 439, 480, 559
8-7	Drawing three-dimensional figures.			✗ p. 427	pp. 427–429	pp. 430–431	pp. 434, 437, 486, 512

CONNECTED MATHEMATICS

The unit *Looking for Pythagoras (The Pythagorean Theorem),* from the **Connected Mathematics** series, can be used with Section 8B.

INTERDISCIPLINARY TEAM TEACHING

Math and Science/Technology
(Worksheet pages 33–34: Teacher pages T33–T34)

In this lesson, students use gem crystal shapes to work with nets and 3-D views of solid objects.

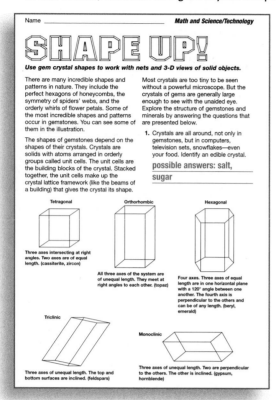

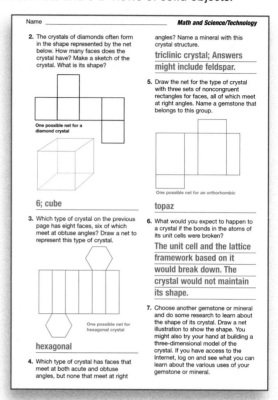

BIBLIOGRAPHY

▶ FOR TEACHERS

Battista, Michael, and Douglas H. Clements. "Constructing Geometric Concepts in Logo." *Arithmetic Teacher* 38 (Nov. 1990): 15–17.

Geddes, Dorothy. *Geometry in the Middle Grades (Addenda Series).* Reston, VA: NCTM, 1992.

Geddes, Dorothy. *Measurement in the Middle Grades (Addenda Series).* Reston, VA: NCTM, 1992.

Reys, Barbara. *Developing Number Sense in the Middle Grades (Addenda Series).* Reston, VA: NCTM, 1991.

Zaslavsky, Claudia. "Symmetry in American Folk Art." *Arithmetic Teacher* 38 (Sep. 1990): 6–12.

▶ FOR STUDENTS

Center for Occupational Research and Development. *Applied Mathematics, Unit 8: Working with Shapes in Three Dimensions.* Waco, TX: CORD, 1993.

Center for Occupational Research and Development. *Applied Mathematics, Unit 7: Working with Shapes in Two Dimensions.* Waco, TX: CORD, 1993.

Symes, R.F. and Harding, R.R. *Crystal and Gem.* New York, NY: Alfred A. Knopf, Inc., 1991.

Elements of Geometry

▶ Science Link ▶ Health Link ▶ www.mathsurf.com/8/ch8/nature

Bzzzt... Beeometry

Look around you. Look out the window. What shapes do you see? Circles? Rectangles? Triangles? Nature contains many shapes, some rare and some very common. One shape that appears over and over is the hexagon, which has six sides.

Why are hexagons so common? For one thing, hexagon-shaped surfaces don't break easily. Perhaps that is why the wax combs inside a beehive are hexagons. The cells in a comb are used for raising young bees and for storing honey. They are built with almost mathematical accuracy, to provide the maximum strength and storage space with the minimum use of materials. Bees construct these structures entirely by instinct. Various plant cells are also hexagonal-shaped.

The star shape also appears in nature frequently. You have probably seen a picture of a starfish. You may find other star shapes in nature in star fruits, in the cross section of an orange, and in the petals of some flowers.

409

1 Try to draw a section of a honeycomb with pentagons, or five-sided shapes. What happens?

2 Make a list of things in nature that you know exhibit geometric shapes.

Where are we now?

In Section 8A, students explored different measurements.

They learned how to

• choose appropriate units of measurement.

• determine precision in measurements.

• locate places on a map using a coordinate system and latitude and longitude.

Where are we going?

In Section 8B, students will

• measure, draw, and classify angles.

• recognize and draw parallel and perpendicular lines.

• classify polygons.

• draw plans for three-dimensional shapes.

In Chapters 9 and 11, students will apply their knowledge of lines, angles, and polygons to area, volume, congruence, and tessellations.

Theme: Shapes in Nature

World Wide Web

If your class has access to the World Wide Web, you might want to use the information found at the Web site address given. The interdisciplinary links relate to topics discussed in this section.

Resources
Teaching Tool Transparency 18: Power Polygons

About the Page

This page introduces the theme of the section, shapes in nature, and discusses the frequent appearance of the hexagon and pentagon in nature.

Ask …
What makes the hexagon such a useful shape? Hexagons can be arranged so that there are no spaces between them.

Extensions

The following activities do not require access to the World Wide Web.

Science
Have students find other occurrences of geometric shapes in nature. You might suggest that they bring actual pictures or drawings of their findings to class for a bulletin board display.

Health
Many remedies for medical conditions can be found in nature. Ask students if they have ever seen an aloe plant and used the secretions from the leaf to soothe a burn? Have interested students investigate this and other natural alternatives to medication.

Answers for Questions
1. It is not possible.

2. Possible answers: Tortoise shells, giraffe spots, beehives.

Connect

On page 433, students will use parallel and perpendicular lines, angles, and polygons to make a three-dimensional cube.

Lesson Organizer

Objective

- Draw, measure, and identify angles.

Vocabulary

- Angle, vertex, line, line segment, endpoints, ray, straight angle, right angle, acute angle, obtuse angle, complementary, supple-mentary, congruent, angle bisector

Materials

- Explore: Sheet of wax paper, compass, scissors

NCTM Standards

- 1–4, 9, 12, 13

➤ Review

Solve each equation.

1. $x + 38 = 90$ 52

2. $x + 78.4 = 90$ 11.6

3. $x + 38 = 180$ 142

4. $x + 90 = 180$ 90

5. $x + 115.3 = 180$ 64.7

Available on Daily Transparency 8-4

▶ Lesson Link

Degrees are used to measure angles, as well as latitude and longitude, as studied in the previous lesson. Angle measure is important in geometry, as well as in statistics, since the measure of each central angle must be known in order to construct a circle graph.

1 Introduce

Explore

You might wish to use Lesson Enhancement Transparency 34 with **Explore**.

The Point
Students repeatedly fold a circle to construct a tool for measuring angles.

8-4   Lines and Angles

You'll Learn ...

■ to draw, measure, and identify angles

... How It's Used

Lighting technicians know how to set a dramatic mood by staging lights at various angles.

Vocabulary

angle

vertex

line

line segment

endpoints

ray

straight angle

right angle

acute angle

obtuse angle

complementary

supplementary

congruent

angle bisector

▶ Lesson Link   You have learned how to use various units of measurement. Now you will learn about lines and angles. ◀

An **angle** is formed when two lines (or line segments, or rays) meet at one point, called the **vertex**. Angles are usually measured in degrees.

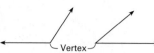

There are 360° in a complete circle.

Explore   Angles

The Angle in Creases

Materials: Sheet of wax paper, Compass, Scissors

1. Use your compass to draw the largest circle possible on the sheet of wax paper. Cut out the circle.

2. Fold the circle in half by lining up the edge of your circle. Fold the circle in half again.

3. Fold the circle in half two more times.

4. Each time you folded the circle, you made an angle. What part of the circle was located at the vertex of each angle?

5. The full circle shows 360°. When you fold the full circle in half, you make a 180° angle. What is the resulting angle measure if you fold this in half?

6. What is the number pattern that results each time an angle is folded in half? Write an algebraic equation for this.

7. If each quarter of the circle is 90°, what is the angle measure of three-quarters of a circle? How did you arrive at your answer?

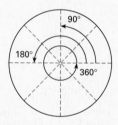

8. On your circle, label as many creases as you can with the appropriate angle measure.

9. Use your circle as a measuring tool to approximate the measure of angles you can find in your classroom.

▶ MEETING INDIVIDUAL NEEDS

Resources

8-4 Practice

8-4 Reteaching

8-4 Problem Solving

8-4 Enrichment

8-4 Daily Transparency
    Problem of the Day
    Review
    Quick Quiz

Lesson Enhancement Transparency 34

Technology Master 34

Learning Modalities

Logical   Have students discover the following relationship for complementary and supplementary angles: As the measure of one angle increases, the measure of the other decreases, and vice versa.

Visual   For Exercises 22–27 on page 414, students may want to trace the figure onto another piece of paper and extend the lines, so that they are more easily able to measure the angles.

Musical   Have students compose a song incorpo-rating the vocabulary of this lesson.

English Language Development

Relate the new mathematical vocabulary to ordinary meanings of the same words. Have students give real-world examples of the words in everyday contexts, and compare the meanings in those contexts for similarities with the mathematical meanings. You might provide magazines and newspapers and have students cut out and highlight pictures that display the terms in this lesson.

Learn | Lines and Angles

In geometry, a straight **line** extends infinitely in both directions. A line that includes points A and B is written as $\overleftrightarrow{AB}$.

A **line segment** is part of a straight line that includes its endpoints. A line segment with **endpoints** C and D is written as $\overline{CD}$.

$\overline{CD}$ measures $1\frac{1}{4}$ in. and is written as $m\overline{CD} = 1\frac{1}{4}$ in.

A **ray** has one endpoint and extends infinitely in only one direction. A ray with endpoint M that includes another point, N, is written as $\overrightarrow{MN}$.

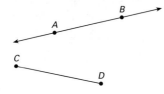
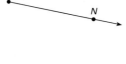
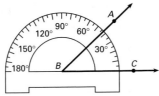

You will often see an angle drawn as two rays that meet at one point.

An angle is measured with a protractor. The angle shown is written as $\angle ABC$, where B is the vertex and A and C are on opposite sides of the angle.

$\angle ABC$ measures 43° and is written as $m\angle ABC = 43°$.

Example 1

Molybdenite is a mineral used to strengthen metal alloys. Use a protractor to measure the angle in the specimen shown.

The angle is 115°.

DID YOU KNOW?

Molybdenite can be found in California, Colorado, and Washington.

Try It

Use a protractor to measure each angle.

a. 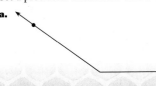 145°

b. 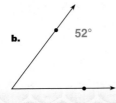 52°

MATH EVERY DAY

▶ Problem of the Day

In a pet store, there are cats, dogs, and birds. There are twice as many cats as dogs. There are 260 legs among the animals, but only 76 heads. How many of each type of animal are there? 18 dogs, 36 cats, 22 birds

Available on Daily Transparency 8-4

An Extension is provided in the transparency package.

Fact of the Day

The many editions of *The Elements* by the Greek geometer Euclid have resulted in more printed copies than any other book except religious scriptures.

Mental Math

Do these mentally.

1. 90 − 42 = ____ 48
2. 90 − ____ = 74 16
3. 180 − 85 = ____ 95
4. 180 − ____ = 124 56

Ongoing Assessment
Check students' angle measures at Step 8. Incorrect angle measures may indicate that the student did not fully understand the purpose of **Explore**.

For Groups That Finish Early
Determine the fractional part of a circle represented by each angle measure: 120°, 45°, 135°, 210°, 22.5°, and 315°. $\frac{1}{3}, \frac{1}{8}, \frac{3}{8}, \frac{7}{12}, \frac{1}{16}, \frac{7}{8}$

Follow Up
Discuss students' responses to Step 6. Is there a consensus about the pattern?

Answers for Explore
1–3. Answers may vary.

4. The center

5. 90°

6. 360, 180, 90, 45, . . . $y = \frac{x}{2}$, where x = angle measure.

7. 270°; 90 × 3

8–9. Answers may vary.

2 Teach

Learn

The order of the two points used to name a line or a line segment may be reversed and still name the same line or segment. However, the two points used to name a ray cannot be reversed. The first letter denotes the endpoint and the second letter indicates the direction.

Alternate Examples

1. Clark and Maple Streets intersect as shown. Use a protractor to measure the larger angle formed.

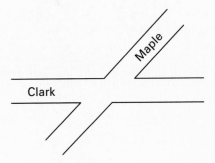

The angle is 135°.

Alternate Examples

2. Classify the angle formed by the hour hand and minute hand at 9:00.

$m\angle LMN$ on the clock is 90°.
$\angle LMN$ is a right angle.

Some angles can be classified as one of four types, depending on their measurements.

If $m\angle ABC = 180°$, then $\angle ABC$ is a **straight angle**.

If $m\angle ABC = 90°$, then $\angle ABC$ is a **right angle**.

If $0° < m\angle ABC < 90°$, then $\angle ABC$ is an **acute angle**.

If $90° < m\angle ABC < 180°$, then $\angle ABC$ is an **obtuse angle**.

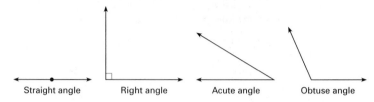

Straight angle   Right angle   Acute angle   Obtuse angle

▶ **Science Link**

In one colony, there may be as many as 80,000 worker bees and only one queen.

Example 2

Classify the angle found in honeycomb.

$m\angle RST$ in the honeycomb is $> 90°$.

$\angle RST$ is obtuse.

Try It

Classify the angle found in bee wings.
Acute

Two angles with measures that have a sum of 90° are **complementary** angles.

$\angle ABD$ is a right angle, so

$\angle ABC$ is the complement of $\angle CBD$.

Two angles with measures that have a sum of 180° are **supplementary** angles.

$\angle GHJ$ is a straight angle, so

$\angle GHI$ is the supplement of $\angle IHJ$.

412   *Chapter 8 • Geometry and Measurement*

MEETING MIDDLE SCHOOL CLASSROOM NEEDS

Tips from Middle School Teachers

I find that some students have difficulty positioning a protractor correctly and/or determining which scale to read. I find using a demonstration protractor on the overhead projector helpful as well as pairing students who understand the technique with those that do not.

Cooperative Learning

Have small groups of students brainstorm to find real-life examples of supplementary and complementary angles. For example, intersections of streets, cross braces on fences or other structures, and tile patterns on floors or walls.

Science Connection

A *parsec* is a distance used by astronomers and is equal to about 19.2 million miles. A parsec is determined by an angle measuring 1 second ($\frac{1}{3600}$ degree). When the sides of this angle pass through the Earth and the Sun, the vertex of the angle is 1 parsec away from the Earth.

Example 3

Find the measure of the complement of ∠DBE.

90° − 38.5° = 51.5°

The complement of ∠DBE is 51.5°.

Example 4

Find the measure of the supplement of ∠XYZ.

180° − 94° = 86°

The supplement of ∠XYZ is 86°.

Try It

Find each angle measure.

a. Supplement of 132.7° **b.** Complement of 18° **72°**
   47.3°

In geometry, two figures are **congruent** if they have the same shape and size.

An **angle bisector** divides an angle into two congruent angles. $\overrightarrow{KW}$ is the angle bisector of ∠PKB.

∠PKW ≅ ∠WKB states that the two angles are congruent.

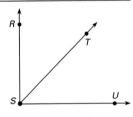

Example 5

Is $\overrightarrow{ST}$ an angle bisector?

Measure both angles with your protractor.

m∠RST = 45° and m∠TSU = 45°

∠RST ≅ ∠TSU, so $\overrightarrow{ST}$ is an angle bisector.

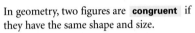

Check   Your Understanding

1. Do all acute angles have possible complements? Explain.

2. Describe how to find a supplementary angle; a complementary angle.

Study TIP

When possible, invent formulas to help you understand math definitions. For example, $C = 90°$ − angle.

Alternate Examples

3. Find the measure of the complement of ∠ABC.

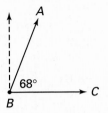

90° − 68° = 22°
The complement of ∠ABC is 22°.

4. Find the measure of the supplement of ∠QRS.

180° − 172° = 8°
The supplement of ∠QRS is 8°.

5. Is $\overrightarrow{EG}$ an angle bisector?

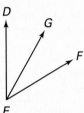

Measure both angles with your protractor.
m∠DEG = 30° and m∠FEG = 30°.
∠DEG ≅ ∠FEG, so $\overrightarrow{EG}$ is an angle bisector.

3 Practice and Assess

Check

For Question 1, remind students that acute angles have measures *less than 90°*.

Answers for Check Your Understanding

1. Yes; Since it is less than 90°, the difference between its measure and 90° is the measure of its complement.

2. 180° − the angle = the supplement;
90° − the angle = the complement

Assignment Guide

■ **Basic**
1–9, 13–15, 18–20, 22–25, 28–30, 33, 34, 37, 41–51

■ **Average**
4–26 evens, 28–51

■ **Enriched**
5–27 odds, 28–51

Exercise Notes

■ **Exercises 22–27**

Error Prevention Which scale to use on a protractor depends on the direction of the initial side of the angle. Remind students that if an angle appears acute, its measure has to be less than 90°.

■ **Exercise 33**

Test Prep Students answering incorrectly need to be reminded that all four angles in a square are right angles.

Exercise Answers

2. Obtuse   3. Acute

4. Right   5. Acute

6. Obtuse   7. Acute

8. Acute   9. Straight

10. Obtuse   11. Obtuse

28. 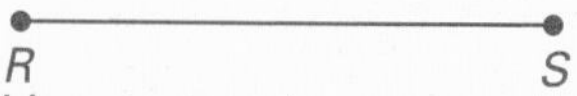
R ————————— S
Line segment

29.
T ———— V ———→
Ray

30.
←——— S ———— T ———→
Line

31.
R ———— V ———→
Ray

Activity

Materials: Protractor

• Use a protractor to draw three 90° (right) angles.

• For each 90° angle, draw a ray between the sides of the angle with its endpoint at the vertex of the angle. Then measure the two newly created angles.

• Find the sum of each pair of angles. **90°**

414   Chapter 8

8-4 Exercises and Applications

PRACTICE 8-4

Practice and Apply

1. **Getting Started** State whether ∠FDE and ∠BAC are congruent.

   a. Measure ∠FDE. Measure ∠BAC. **53°; 53°**

   b. Are the measures equal? **Yes**

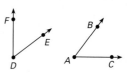

Classify each angle measurement as right, straight, obtuse, or acute.

2. 112°   3. 28°   4. 90°   5. 60°   6. 179.5°

7. 6°   8. 45°   9. 180°   10. 90.5°   11. 140°

Find the measure of the complement of each angle measure.

12. 45° **45°** 13. 22° **68°** 14. 85° **5°** 15. 9.1° **80.9°** 16. 17.6° **72.4°**

Find the measure of the supplement of each angle measure.

17. 120° **60°** 18. 39° **141°** 19. 90° **90°** 20. 175° **5°** 21. 60° **120°**

Use a protractor to measure each angle.

22. ∠HEK **75°**   23. ∠GEK **135°**   24. ∠FEG **45°**

25. ∠JEF **162°**   26. ∠FEK **180°**   27. ∠HEF **105°**

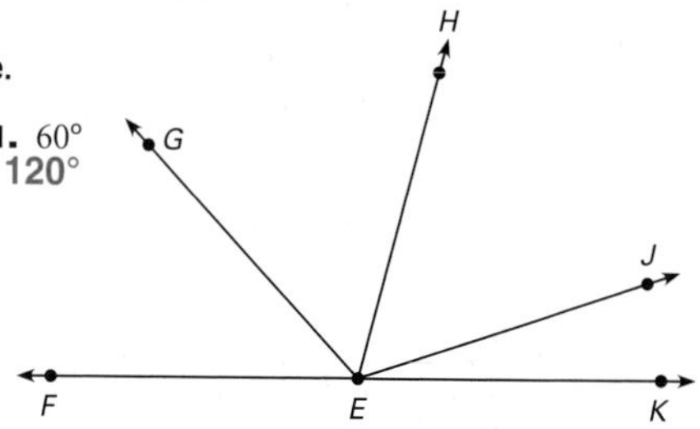

Identify each as a ray, line, or line segment and draw each.

28. $\overline{RS}$ 29. $\overrightarrow{TV}$ 30. $\overleftrightarrow{ST}$ 31. $\overrightarrow{RV}$

32. **Science** Gypsum, a mineral found in North America, is shown at the right. What kind of angles do you see?
Acute and obtuse

33. **Test Prep** Two sides of a square meet to form what kind of angle? **C**

   Ⓐ Acute   Ⓑ Obtuse   Ⓒ Right   Ⓓ Straight

34. What is the measure of the two resulting angles after a 120° angle is bisected? **60°**

35. What is the measure of the two resulting angles after a 314° angle is bisected? **157°**

PRACTICE

Name _____

Practice 8-4

Lines and Angles

Classify each angle measurement as right, straight, obtuse, or acute.

1. 27° __Acute__   2. 90.2° __Obtuse__   3. 100° __Obtuse__

4. 89° __Acute__   5. 153° __Obtuse__   6. 180° __Straight__

7. 74° __Acute__   8. 90° __Right__   9. 4° __Acute__

Find the measure of the complement of each angle measure.

10. 82° __8°__   11. 31° __59°__   12. 7° __83°__   13. 64° __26°__

14. 35° __55°__   15. 0.7° __89.3°__   16. 50° __40°__   17. 12° __78°__

Find the measure of the supplement of each angle measure.

18. 34° __146°__   19. 100° __80°__   20. 67° __113°__   21. 125° __55°__

22. 2.3° __177.7°__   23. 53° __127°__   24. 176° __4°__   25. 84° __96°__

Use a protractor to measure each angle.

26. ∠ABC __127°__   27. ∠CDE __75°__

28. ∠BDE __110°__   29. ∠BCD __92°__

30. ∠EDF __70°__   31. ∠BDC __35°__

32. ∠CBD __53°__   33. ∠BDF __180°__

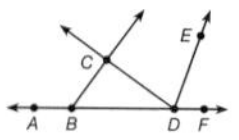

Identify each as a ray, line, or line segment and draw each. **Possible drawings:**

34. $\overleftrightarrow{JK}$ __Line__   35. $\overrightarrow{ML}$ __Ray__   36. $\overline{PQ}$ __Line segment__

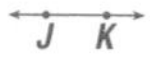

J ——— K    L ——— M    P ——— Q

37. a. Measure ∠WXY and ∠XYZ in the parallelogram shown at the right.

   m∠WXY = __104°__   m∠XYZ = __76°__

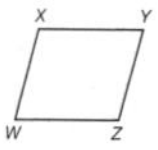

   b. Are these angles complementary, supplementary, or neither? __Supplementary__

RETEACHING

Name _____

Alternative Lesson 8-4

Lines and Angles

An **angle** is formed when two lines meet at one point called the **vertex.** An angle can be classified according to its measurement.

A **straight angle** measures 180°. A **right angle** measures 90°. An **acute angle** measures less than 90° and greater than 0°. An **obtuse angle** measures greater than 90° and less than 180°.

Complementary angles are two angles with measures that have a sum of 90°. **Supplementary** angles are two angles with measures that have a sum of 180°.

—— Example 1 ——

Classify each angle measurement as right, straight, obtuse, or acute.

   a. 180°

   a. Since the angle measures 180°, it is a straight angle.

   b. Since the angle measures less than 90° and greater than 0°, it is an acute angle.

Try It Classify each angle measurement as right, straight, obtuse, or acute. Use your protractor to draw each angle and compare it to the angles above if you need help.

   a. 150° __Obtuse.__   b. 49° __Acute.__

   c. 180° __Straight.__   d. 90° __Right.__

—— Example 2 ——

Find the measure of the complement and the supplement to ∠ABC .

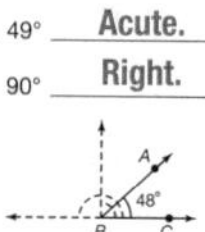

Subtract from 90° to find the measure of the complementary angle.

Subtract from 180° to find the measure of the supplementary angle.

$90° - 48° = 42°$

$180° - 48° = 132°$

The complement of ∠ABC measures 42°. The supplement of ∠ABC measures 132°.

Try It Find each angle measure.

   e. Complement of 33°. __57°__   f. Supplement of 95°. __85°__

   g. Complement of 87°. __3°__   h. Supplement of 121°. __59°__

36. History Measure the obtuse angle above the entrance to Saint Peter's Basilica, constructed during the 1500s in Rome. **130°**

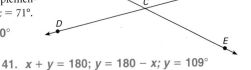

Problem Solving and Reasoning

37. Math Reasoning Pilots often use the numbers on a clock face to indicate angles. "Twelve o'clock" means "dead ahead." Suppose one pilot radios another, "Bogies at two o'clock!" At what angle have enemy planes been spotted? **60°**

38.  In Al Held's 1992 acrylic painting *Ima Ima II* how many acute angles can you find? How many obtuse angles? How many right angles? How do you think the kinds of angles in the painting affect the mood the painting creates?

39. Communicate Explain how to construct two line segments, one 6 cm and the other 3.5 cm long, meeting to form a 30° angle.

40. Math Reasoning A wheel has six equally spaced spokes that form six congruent angles. If each of these angles is to be bisected, what will the angle measure be between spokes?

Geometry In the figure at the right, $m\angle ACB = 140°$.

41. Algebra Two angles are supplementary. One angle measures x degrees, the other y degrees. Write an equation expressing that these angles are supplementary, and solve this equation for y. Find y if $x = 71°$.

42. What is $m\angle ACD$? What is $m\angle BCE$? **40°; 40°**

43. How are $\angle ACD$ and $\angle BCE$ related?

41. $x + y = 180; y = 180 - x; y = 109°$

Mixed Review

Solve each rate and proportion. *[Lesson 5-6]*

44. $0.60 each cup = $\underline{\$4.80}$ for 8 cups

45. 60 mi/hr = $\underline{240}$ mi in 4 hr

46. $\underline{4}$ ft per sec = 36 ft in 9 sec

47. $24 for 3 hr = $\underline{\$8}$ per hr

Add or subtract, writing each answer in lowest terms. *[Lesson 7-5]*

48. $\frac{3}{5} + \frac{1}{4}$ $\underline{\frac{17}{20}}$ **49.** $5\frac{2}{3} - 2\frac{2}{3}$ **3** **50.** $6.902 + 0.53$ **7.432** **51.** $36.17 - 8.66$ **27.51**

Exercise Notes

■ **Exercise 36**

Cultural The original St. Peter's Basilica was built around 330 A.D. by Constantine I. Located within Vatican City in Rome, the church was named for the disciple Peter.

■ **Exercise 37**

Error Prevention Students may measure using a ray directed at 3 o'clock, since this is horizontal. For this situation, a ray directed at 12 o'clock is the initial side from which the angle should be measured.

Exercise Answers

38–39. Answers may vary.

40. 30°

43. They are congruent. The same two lines form the sides for both angles.

Alternate Assessment

You may want to use the *Interactive CD-ROM Journal* with this assessment.

Journal Have students write in their own words the definitions of the terms introduced in this lesson: angle, vertex, line, line segment, endpoints, ray, straight angle, right angle, acute angle, obtuse angle, complementary, supplementary, congruent, and angle bisector.

▶ Quick Quiz

1. Draw ray *AB*.

2. What classification is a 65° angle? Acute

3. What classification is a 138° angle? Obtuse

4. Find the measure of the supplement of a 60° angle. 120°

5. Find the measure of the complement of a 40° angle. 50°

Available on Daily Transparency 8-4

▶ PROBLEM SOLVING

Name _____

Guided Problem Solving 8-4

GPS PROBLEM 41, STUDENT PAGE 415

Two angles are supplementary. One angle measures *x* degrees, the other *y* degrees. Write an equation expressing that these angles are supplementary, and solve this equation for *y*. Find *y* if *x* = 71°.

— **Understand** —
1. What kind of angles are the two angles? **Supplementary.**
2. What are the measures of the two angles? **x° and y°.**
3. Underline what you are asked to do.

— **Plan** —
4. What does it mean that angles are supplementary?
The sum of their measures is 180°.
5. Which is a reasonable measure for one of two supplementary angles if the other angle measures 71°? **b**
   a. Less than 90° b. Between 90° and 180° c. Greater than 180°

— **Solve** —
6. Use the measures of the two angles to write an equation showing the sum of two supplementary angles. **x + y = 180**
7. Solve the equation in Item 6 for *y*. **y = 180 − x**
8. Substitute 71 for *x* in the equation in Item 7. Solve for *y*. **y = 109°**

— **Look Back** —
9. Use a protractor to draw a 71° angle. Label it ∠x. Then draw the supplement of ∠x and label it ∠y. Measure ∠y.
109°

SOLVE ANOTHER PROBLEM

Two angles are complementary. One angle measures *x* degrees, the other *y* degrees. Write an equation expressing the fact that these angles are complementary, and solve this equation for *y*. Find *y* if *x* = 29°.
x + y = 90; y = 90 − x; y = 61°

▶ ENRICHMENT

Name _____

Extend Your Thinking 8-4

Patterns in Numbers

Scientists at Los Alamos, New Mexico developed the idea of lucky numbers. These numbers can be found by following these instructions.

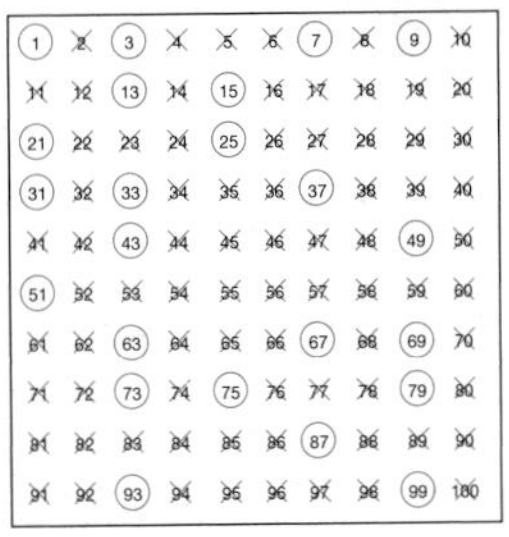

1. Circle the first number. Start with 1, cross out every second number.

2. The first number after 1 that has not been crossed out is 3. Circle it. Start with 1 and cross out every third number that has *not* been crossed out. Since 1 and 3 are not crossed out, 5 is the third number. Continuing from there, you will cross out 5, 11, 17 …

3. The first number after the 3 that has not been crossed out is 7. Circle it. Start with 1 and cross out every seventh number that has *not* been crossed out. Remember that 1, 3, and 7 are not crossed out, so include them in the pattern.

4. What pattern do you see in the numbers that are crossed out?
Possible answer: In each set of remaining numbers, each number that is being crossed out occupies a position that is a multiple of the last number circled.

5. Continue crossing out numbers until the sieve is complete. Which of the numbers are considered to be lucky numbers?
1, 3, 7, 9, 13, 15, 21, 25, 31, 33, 37, 43, 49, 51, 63, 67, 69, 73, 75, 79, 87, 93, 99

6. Which of the lucky numbers are also prime numbers?
3, 7, 13, 31, 37, 43, 67, 73, 79

- **Recognize and construct parallel and perpendicular lines.**

Vocabulary

- **Parallel, perpendicular, perpendicular bisector, transversal, interior angle, exterior angle, alternate angle, corresponding angle, vertical angle**

Materials

- **Explore: Geometry software**

NCTM Standards

- **1, 2, 4, 12, 13**

► Review

Find the supplement of each angle measure.

1. 35°   145°

2. 90°   90°

3. 112°   68°

4. 84.7°   95.3°

Available on Daily Transparency 8-5

► Lesson Link

Draw a pair of parallel lines on the board and ask students to classify them, if they can. Repeat with a pair of perpendicular lines. If no one volunteers the correct terms, supply them.

1 Introduce

Explore

The Point

Students use geometry software to study the pairs of angles formed by parallel lines cut by a transversal.

Ongoing Assessment

Check students' responses to Step 3. If they have more than two different measures, either their lines were not quite parallel or their measurements were not accurate.

8-5 Parallel and Perpendicular Lines

You'll Learn ...

■ to recognize and construct parallel and perpendicular lines

... How It's Used

Weavers create parallel and perpendicular designs on their looms.

Vocabulary

parallel

perpendicular

perpendicular bisector

transversal

interior angle

exterior angle

alternate angle

corresponding angle

vertical angle

▶ **Lesson Link**   You have learned about several types of angles. Now you will apply this knowledge to identify more types of angles. ◀

Lines in a plane that never intersect are **parallel**. $\overleftrightarrow{AB}$ and $\overleftrightarrow{CD}$ are parallel. This is written as $\overleftrightarrow{AB} \parallel \overleftrightarrow{CD}$.

Lines that form a right angle are **perpendicular**. $\overleftrightarrow{QR}$ is perpendicular to $\overleftrightarrow{AB}$, written as $\overleftrightarrow{QR} \perp \overleftrightarrow{AB}$. $\overleftrightarrow{QR}$ is perpendicular to $\overleftrightarrow{CD}$, written as $\overleftrightarrow{QR} \perp \overleftrightarrow{CD}$.

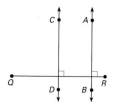

A **perpendicular bisector** is perpendicular to a line segment so that the line segment is divided into two congruent parts. For example, $\overleftrightarrow{CD}$ is a perpendicular bisector of $\overline{QR}$.

Explore   Transversals

Crisscross

Materials: Geometry software

1. Draw two parallel lines. Now draw a third line crossing the parallel lines at a slant. Label the eight angles in your diagram.

2. Measure the angles in your diagram until you find two that are congruent. State that the angles are congruent using the ≅ symbol.

3. Complete measuring all the angles in your diagram. How many different angle measures did you find?

4. Identify as many congruent pairs of angles as you can.

5. Identify as many supplementary pairs of angles as you can.

6. Are there any complementary angles?

7. Rotate the third line until it forms right angles with the parallel lines. How many right angles are there in total?

8. Draw a line segment so one of the other lines is a perpendicular bisector.

9. Discuss what you noticed about the angles in your figure.

MEETING INDIVIDUAL NEEDS

Resources

8-5 Practice

8-5 Reteaching

8-5 Problem Solving

8-5 Enrichment

8-5 Daily Transparency

Problem of the Day

Review

Quick Quiz

Lesson Enhancement Transparency 35

Chapter 8 Project Master

Technology Masters 35, 36, 37

 Interactive CD-ROM Geometry Tool

Learning Modalities

Verbal   Have pairs of students describe to each other their definitions for all the new vocabulary in this lesson.

Kinesthetic   Have students use masking tape to construct, on the floor, a large model of a pair of parallel lines and a transversal. Then have them actually stand on pairs of various angles—corresponding, alternate interior, and so on.

Challenge

At a hunter's campsite, a bear took the hunter's supplies. The hunter chased the bear one mile due south, then one mile due east, and one mile due north. Oddly, the hunter ended up right back at the campsite. What color was the bear? White, since the only place this could have happened is at the North Pole. (The path described is also possible near the South Pole, but there are no bears in Antarctica.)

Learn — Parallel and Perpendicular Lines

A line that crosses two or more other lines is a **transversal**. A transversal of two separate lines forms eight angles.

The four angles between the two lines are **interior angles**.

Angles 3, 4, 5, and 6 are interior angles.

The four angles outside the two lines are **exterior angles**.

Angles 1, 2, 7, and 8 are exterior angles.

Alternate angles are on opposite sides of the transversal. They are both interior or both exterior.

Alternate angles are congruent if the transversal crosses two parallel lines.

Angles 1 and 8, and 2 and 7 are alternate exterior angles.

Angles 3 and 6, and 4 and 5 are alternate interior angles.

Corresponding angles are on the same side of the transversal and are congruent when the transversal crosses parallel lines.

Angles 1 and 5, 2 and 6, 3 and 7, and 4 and 8 are corresponding angles.

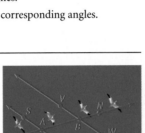

Example 1

In the diagram, $\overleftrightarrow{ST} \parallel \overleftrightarrow{VW}$. Identify both pairs of alternate interior angles.

First identify all interior angles.

∠SAN, ∠TAN, ∠VBM, and ∠WBM

Match the interior angles that are on opposite sides of the transversal $\overleftrightarrow{MN}$.

∠SAN and ∠WBM are alternate interior angles.

∠TAN and ∠VBM are alternate interior angles.

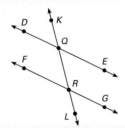

> **► Science Link**
>
> Many birds migrate each year by flying to a warmer climate.

Try It

In the diagram, $\overleftrightarrow{DE} \parallel \overleftrightarrow{FG}$. Identify both pairs of alternate exterior angles.
∠DQK and ∠GRL; ∠KQE and ∠FRL

8-5 • Parallel and Perpendicular Lines   **417**

MATH EVERY DAY

► Problem of the Day

1. Name two parallel lines in the figure below.

2. Name two perpendicular lines in the figure below.

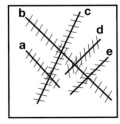

Answers 1. d and e
2. a and d

Available on Daily Transparency 8-5

An Extension is provided in the transparency package.

Fact of the Day

Parallel is derived from two Greek words meaning "beside one another," while *perpendicular* is from a Latin word meaning "plumb line" or "to hang."

Estimation

Estimate each of the following.

1. 27% of 57   14 or 15

2. 82% of 193   160

3. What percent of 74 is 38?   50%

4. What percent of 15 is 10?   67%

For Groups That Finish Early
In your drawing for Step 3, draw a third line parallel to the other two lines. Predict the measures of the newly created four angles before measuring them.

Follow Up
Discuss students' responses to Step 4. Sort the pairs of congruent angles into groups based upon the positions of the angles with respect to the parallel lines and the line crossing them. How many groups are there? 4

Answers for Explore

1–2. Answers may vary.

3. Two

4. 12 pairs of congruent angles.

5. 16 pairs

6. Answers may vary.

7. 8

8–9. Answers may vary.

2 Teach

Learn

You might wish to use Lesson Enhancement Transparency 35 with this lesson.

Help students connect the relative positions of pairs of angles to their descriptions. *Interior* angles are *inside* the parallel lines, *exterior* angles are *outside* the parallel lines, *alternate* angles are on opposite sides of the transversal, and *corresponding* angles are in the same relative position with regard to the parallel lines and the transversal.

Alternate Examples

1. In the diagram, $\overleftrightarrow{FG} \parallel \overleftrightarrow{MN}$. Identify both pairs of alternate interior angles.

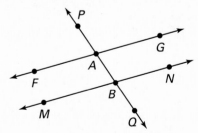

First identify all interior angles.
∠FAB, ∠GAB, ∠MBA, ∠NBA.
Match the interior angles that are on opposite sides of the transversal $\overleftrightarrow{PQ}$.
∠FAB and ∠NBA are alternate interior angles.
∠GAB and ∠MBA are alternate interior angles.

Alternate Examples

2. In the diagram, $\overrightarrow{FG} \parallel \overrightarrow{MN}$. Find $m\angle GAP$.

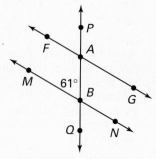

∠MBA and ∠NBA are supplementary angles.
$m\angle NBA = 180° - m\angle MBA = 180° - 61° = 119°$.
∠NBA and ∠GAP are corresponding angles, so ∠NBA ≅ ∠GAP.
$m\angle GAP = 119°$

3. Use the diagram to determine $m\angle 3$.

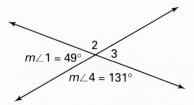

Identify the angle vertical to ∠3.
∠3 and ∠1 are vertical angles, so $m\angle 3 = m\angle 1$.
$m\angle 3 = 49°$

3 Practice and Assess

Check

In Question 1, the situation described will also make corresponding angles not congruent. Will the vertical angles still be congruent? Yes.

Answers for Check Your Understanding

1. When the first two lines are not parallel.

2. It remains the same.

3. All interior and exterior angles are 90° because the transversal is perpendicular.

Example 2

In the diagram, $\overleftrightarrow{AC} \parallel \overleftrightarrow{DF}$.

Find $m\angle DYE$.

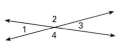

∠AXE and ∠CXE are supplementary angles.

$m\angle AXE = 180° - m\angle CXE = 180° - 68° = 112°$

∠AXE and ∠DYE are corresponding angles so ∠AXE ≅ ∠DYE.

$m\angle DYE = 112°$

When two lines intersect they form two pairs of **vertical angles**. Vertical angles are congruent.

Angles 1 and 3, and 2 and 4 are vertical angles.

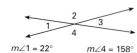

$m\angle 1 = m\angle 3$ $m\angle 2 = m\angle 4$

Example 3

Use the diagram to determine $m\angle 2$.

Identify the angle vertical to ∠2.

∠2 and ∠4 are vertical angles, so $m\angle 2 = 158°$.

$m\angle 2 = 158°$

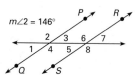

$m\angle 1 = 22°$ $m\angle 4 = 158°$

Try It

In the diagram, $\overline{PQ} \parallel \overline{RS}$. Find each angle measure.

$m\angle 2 = 146°$

a. $m\angle 4$ b. $m\angle 6$ c. $m\angle 5$
   146°   146°   34°

Check Your Understanding

1. Describe a situation in which alternate interior angles formed by a transversal are not congruent.

2. What does the definition of *parallel* tell you about the distance between parallel lines?

3. Suppose a transversal is perpendicular to two parallel lines. What are the angle measures for all interior and exterior angles? Explain.

MEETING MIDDLE SCHOOL CLASSROOM NEEDS

Tips from Middle School Teachers

A local map is often a great source of parallel and perpendicular lines and transversals. I first copy the map and highlight major parallel streets in one color, major perpendicular streets in a second color, and one or two major transversal streets in a third color. Then I use intersections to illustrate the angle terminology used with these lines. If students are familiar with the intersections, it makes the term even more vivid.

Team Teaching

Invite an art teacher to your class to discuss the works of Piet Mondrian, a Dutch artist who used parallel and perpendicular lines in his paintings. Interested students can use their knowledge of parallel and perpendicular lines to imitate this style in works of their own. Display such student art in the class.

Career Connection

Plumb lines, spirit levels, and try squares are tools used by carpenters to aid in finding the vertical, horizontal, and perpendicular. Have volunteers interested in carpentry explain the three tools, providing a demonstration of their use in building an item such as a bookcase.

8-5 Exercises and Applications

Practice and Apply

1. **Getting Started** $\overleftrightarrow{XT} \parallel \overleftrightarrow{BW}$. Find the measures of all angles in the diagram.

   a. Identify all angles with a measure of 60°. **4; 6; 8**

   b. Identify all angles with a measure of 120°. **1; 3; 5**

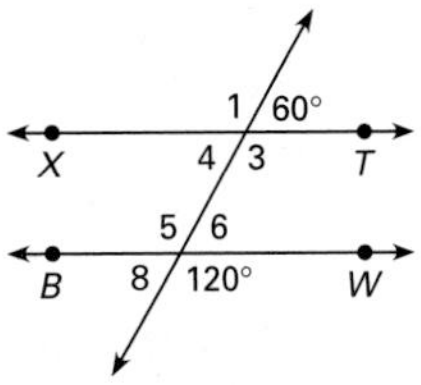

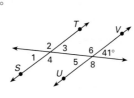

In the figure shown at right, $\overleftrightarrow{EF} \parallel \overleftrightarrow{GH}$. Use the figure for Exercises 2–10.

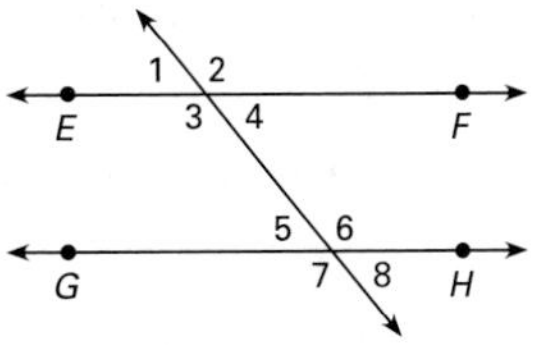

2. Name all alternate interior angles. **3 and 6; 4 and 5**

3. Name all alternate exterior angles. **1 and 8; 2 and 7**

4. Name two pairs of corresponding angles.
   Possible answers: 1 and 5; 2 and 6; 3 and 7; 4 and 8

5. Name two pairs of vertical angles.
   Possible answers: 1 and 4; 2 and 3; 5 and 8; 6 and 7

If $m\angle 6 = 130°$, find each angle measure.

6. $m\angle 5$ **50°** 7. $m\angle 7$ **130°** 8. $m\angle 3$ **130°** 9. $m\angle 2$ **130°** 10. $m\angle 1$ **50°**

In the figure on the right, $\overleftrightarrow{ST} \parallel \overleftrightarrow{UV}$. Use the figure to find the measure of each angle.

11. $m\angle 4$ **139°** 12. $m\angle 1$ **41°**

13. What kind of angles are $\angle 2$ and $\angle 8$? **Alternate exterior angles**

14. **Test Prep** How many angles are formed when a transversal crosses three parallel lines? **C**

   Ⓐ 8 Ⓑ 6 Ⓒ 12 Ⓓ 16

15. **Science** Movement along a fault usually causes earthquakes. What is the angle of the fault plane to the layers in the side of the hill? **47°**

Complete each statement to make it true.

16. _____ lines intersect at a 90° angle. **perpendicular**

17. _____ lines never intersect. **parallel**

18. A _____ intersects a line segment at 90° and divides it into two equal lengths. **perpendicular bisector**

19. Vertical angles are always _____. **congruent**

PRACTICE 8-5

Assignment Guide

■ **Basic**
1–14, 16–19, 23, 26–30

■ **Average**
2–5, 8–24, 27–31 odds

■ **Enriched**
2–5, 8–24, 26–30 evens

Exercise Notes

■ **Exercise 14**

Test Prep Have students sketch this situation if they are having difficulty.

■ **Exercise 15**

Science A fault is a fracture in the earth's crust. Movement of a fault, which can cause an earthquake, may occur up and down or parallel to the fault. One of the most active faults in the United States is California's San Andreas Fault.

PRACTICE

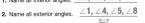

Parallel and Perpendicular Lines

In the figure shown at right, $\overleftrightarrow{PQ} \parallel \overleftrightarrow{RS}$. Use the figure for Exercises 1–7.

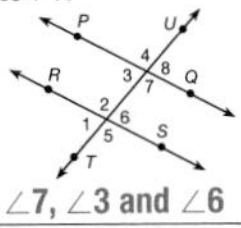

1. Name all interior angles. $\angle 2, \angle 3, \angle 6, \angle 7$

2. Name all exterior angles. $\angle 1, \angle 4, \angle 5, \angle 8$

3. Name the transversal. $\overleftrightarrow{TU}$

4. Name two pairs of alternate interior angles. $\angle 2$ and $\angle 7$, $\angle 3$ and $\angle 6$

5. Name two pairs of alternate exterior angles. $\angle 1$ and $\angle 8$, $\angle 4$ and $\angle 5$

6. Name four pairs of corresponding angles.
   $\angle 1$ and $\angle 3$, $\angle 2$ and $\angle 4$, $\angle 5$ and $\angle 7$, $\angle 6$ and $\angle 8$

7. If $m\angle 6 = 75°$, find each angle measure.

   $m\angle 1 = $ **75°** $m\angle 2 = $ **105°** $m\angle 3 = $ **75°** $m\angle 4 = $ **105°**

   $m\angle 5 = $ **105°** $m\angle 7 = $ **105°** $m\angle 8 = $ **75°**

In the figure on the right, $\overleftrightarrow{VW} \parallel \overleftrightarrow{XY}$. Use the figure to find the measure of each angle.

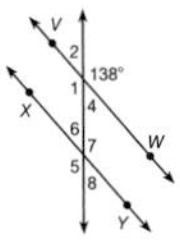

8. $m\angle 1 = $ **138°** 9. $m\angle 2 = $ **42°**

10. $m\angle 4 = $ **42°** 11. $m\angle 5 = $ **138°**

12. $m\angle 7 = $ **138°** 13. $m\angle 8 = $ **42°**

Complete each statement to make it true.

14. When a transversal crosses **parallel** lines, the alternate exterior angles are congruent.

15. Two pairs of congruent angles called **vertical** angles are formed whenever two lines intersect.

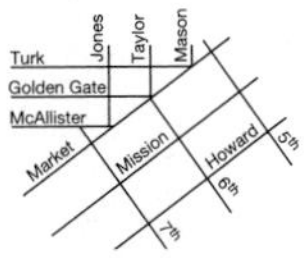

The map shows some streets in downtown San Francisco. Use it for Exercises 16–17.

16. Name the streets that are parallel to Market. **Mission, Howard**

17. Name the streets that are perpendicular to Market. **5th, 6th, 7th**

RETEACHING

Parallel and Perpendicular Lines

A **transversal** is a line that crosses two or more lines. Line a is a transversal. A transversal of two separate lines forms eight angles.

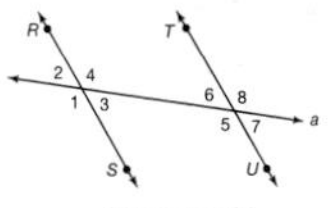

The **interior angles** are the four angles between the two lines. The **exterior angles** are the four angles outside the two lines. **Alternate angles** are on opposite sides of the transversal. They are both exterior or both interior angles and are congruent when the transversal crosses parallel lines.
Corresponding angles are on the same side of the transversal and are congruent when the transversal crosses parallel lines.

The list below names these angles in the diagram.

$\overleftrightarrow{RS}$ is parallel to $\overleftrightarrow{TU}$.

Alternate interior angles	Alternate exterior angles	Corresponding angles
$\angle 3$ and $\angle 6$	$\angle 1$ and $\angle 8$	$\angle 1$ and $\angle 5$ $\angle 2$ and $\angle 6$
$\angle 4$ and $\angle 5$	$\angle 2$ and $\angle 7$	$\angle 3$ and $\angle 7$ $\angle 4$ and $\angle 8$

— Example —

In the diagram, $\overleftrightarrow{JK}$ and $\overleftrightarrow{LM}$ are parallel. Identify both pairs of alternate exterior angles.

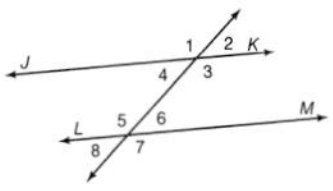

Identify all exterior angles.
Since they are all outside the parallel lines, $\angle 1, \angle 2, \angle 7$ and $\angle 8$ are exterior angles.

Identify all alternate angles.
Since they are all on opposite sides of the transversal, $\angle 1$ and $\angle 2$, $\angle 7$ and $\angle 8$, $\angle 4$ and $\angle 6$, $\angle 3$ and $\angle 5$, are alternate angles.

Match the exterior angles that are on opposite sides of the transversal.

$\angle 1$ and $\angle 7$, and $\angle 2$ and $\angle 8$ are alternate exterior angles.

Try It In the diagram, $\overleftrightarrow{AB}$ and $\overleftrightarrow{CD}$ are parallel.

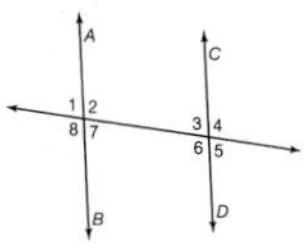

   a. Name all the alternate interior angles.
   $\angle 2$ and $\angle 6$, $\angle 3$ and $\angle 7$.

   b. Name all the alternate exterior angles.
   $\angle 1$ and $\angle 5$, $\angle 4$ and $\angle 8$.

   c. Name all the corresponding angles.
   $\angle 1$ and $\angle 3$, $\angle 2$ and $\angle 4$, $\angle 5$ and $\angle 7$, $\angle 6$ and $\angle 8$.

Reteaching

Activity

Materials: Protractor, straightedge

- Draw two parallel lines on a sheet of notebook paper, with 5 or 6 ruled spaces between them.

- Use a straightedge to draw a transversal.

- Carefully measure the angles, and note which are congruent and which are supplementary.

Exercise Notes

■ Exercise 21

Science A rainbow, which is actually a full circle, occurs when the sun's rays shine upon falling rain and are bent, or refracted, by the raindrops.

Exercise Answers

21. Answers may vary.

Project Progress

You may want to have students use Chapter 8 Project Master.

Alternate Assessment

Self Assessment Have students evaluate themselves on how well they understand the angle relationships when a transversal crosses parallel lines. They might record their evaluation on an audio or video tape.

► Quick Quiz

The diagram shows two parallel lines crossed by a transversal.

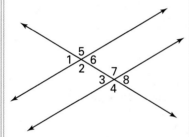

1. Name two pairs of corresponding angles. Any two of 1 and 3, 2 and 4, 5 and 7, 6 and 8.

2. Name two pairs of vertical angles. Any two of 1 and 6, 2 and 5, 3 and 8, 4 and 7.

3. Name two pairs of alternate interior angles. 2 and 7, 3 and 6

4. If $m\angle 1 = 32°$, find $m\angle 7$. 148°

Available on Daily Transparency 8-5

PROBLEM SOLVING 8-5

20. **Geography** In midtown Manhattan, almost all streets are either parallel or perpendicular—except for Broadway. What kind of angles are formed at the intersection of Broadway and 7th Avenue? **Vertical angles**

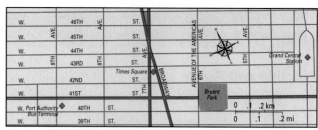

Problem Solving and Reasoning

21. **Journal** When you see a rainbow, the sun is behind you and the rain is in front of you. The points in the red arc of a rainbow form a 42° angle with the sun's rays. Use words such as *parallel*, *transversal*, and *alternate interior angles* to describe what is happening in the diagram.

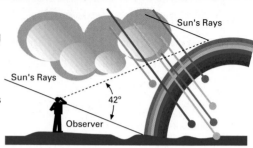

22. **Communicate** If two lines are both perpendicular to the same line, what is the relationship between those two lines? Explain. **They are parallel to each other.**

23. **Measurement** $\overleftrightarrow{KP} \parallel \overleftrightarrow{VF}$. Find the measure of each numbered angle.

24. **Geometry** $\overleftrightarrow{KP} \parallel \overleftrightarrow{VF}$. Find the sum of the angles of the triangle. How does this sum relate to a straight angle? **180°; The degrees are the same.**

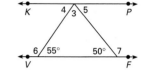

23. $m\angle 3 = 75°$; $m\angle 4 = 55°$; $m\angle 5 = 50°$; $m\angle 6 = 125°$; $m\angle 7 = 130°$

Mixed Review

Solve each proportion. [*Lesson 5-7*]

25. $\dfrac{1 \text{ in.}}{40 \text{ ft}} = \dfrac{x \text{ in.}}{160 \text{ ft}}$ 26. $\dfrac{1 \text{ in.}}{x \text{ mi}} = \dfrac{3 \text{ in.}}{36 \text{ mi}}$ 27. $\dfrac{2 \text{ cm}}{1 \text{ km}} = \dfrac{10 \text{ cm}}{x \text{ km}}$
    $x = 4$ $x = 12$ $x = 5$

Multiply or divide, then write each answer in lowest terms. [*Lesson 7-6*]

28. $\dfrac{1}{2} \times \left(-\dfrac{4}{9}\right) -\dfrac{2}{9}$ 29. $\dfrac{7}{8} \div \dfrac{8}{9}$ $\dfrac{63}{64}$ 30. 5.072×1.54 31. $5.2\overline{)9.256}$ 1.78
                              7.81088

Project Progress

As you learn more about a culture, find out how it charted the stars and planets. A culture's knowledge of astronomy can be related to its knowledge of geometry.

Problem Solving

Understand

Plan

Solve

Look Back

420 *Chapter 8 • Geometry and Measurement*

► PROBLEM SOLVING

Name _____

Guided Problem Solving 8-5

GPS PROBLEM 23, STUDENT PAGE 420

$\overleftrightarrow{KP} \parallel \overleftrightarrow{VF}$. Find the measure of each numbered angle.
Possible answer: Item 6

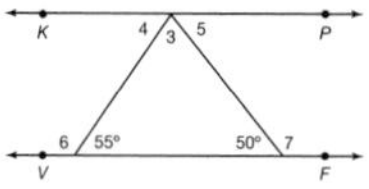

— Understand —

1. What polygon is shown in the diagram? **Triangle.**

2. Two sides of the polygon intersect parallel lines. What are these lines called? **a**
   a. Transversals   b. Corresponding lines   c. Perpendicular lines

— Plan —

3. What is the sum of the measures of the angles of a triangle? **180°**

4. What is true about the measures of alternate interior angles? **Equal.**

5. Name an alternate interior angle for the 55° angle. **∠4** The 50° angle. **∠5**

6. What is true about the measures of supplementary angles? **Sum is 180°.**

7. Name an angle supplementary to the 55° angle. **∠6** The 50° angle. **∠7**

— Solve —

8. Write the measure   a. of ∠3. **75°**   b. of ∠4. **55°**
   c. of ∠5. **50°**   d. of ∠6. **125°**   e. of ∠7. **130°**

— Look Back —

9. What is another way to find the measure of ∠3? **∠3, ∠4, and ∠5 form a straight angle. Subtract $m\angle 4$ and $m\angle 5$ from 180°.**

SOLVE ANOTHER PROBLEM

$\overleftrightarrow{AB} \parallel \overleftrightarrow{CD}$. Find the measure of each numbered angle.
∠1 = 110°; ∠2 = 120°;
∠3 = 70°; ∠4 = 50°;
∠5 = 60°

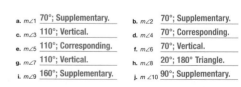

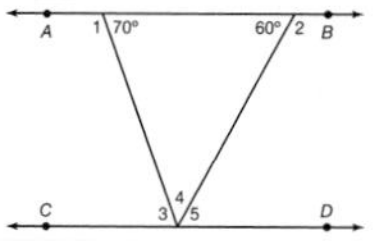

► ENRICHMENT

Name _____

Extend Your Thinking 8-5

Critical Thinking

Use your knowledge of corresponding, vertical, interior, exterior, complementary, and supplementary angles and your knowledge of the angles of triangles to find the measure of each angle below.

1. Find each measure.
$\overleftrightarrow{AB}$ and $\overleftrightarrow{CD}$ are parallel.
Explain.

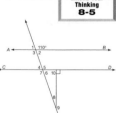

Possible explanations given.

   a. $m\angle 1$ **70°; Supplementary.**   b. $m\angle 2$ **70°; Supplementary.**
   c. $m\angle 3$ **110°; Vertical.**   d. $m\angle 4$ **70°; Corresponding.**
   e. $m\angle 5$ **110°; Corresponding.**   f. $m\angle 6$ **70°; Vertical.**
   g. $m\angle 7$ **110°; Vertical.**   h. $m\angle 8$ **20°; 180° Triangle.**
   i. $m\angle 9$ **160°; Supplementary.**   j. $m \angle 10$ **90°; Supplementary.**

2. Find the measures of ∠1 through ∠8.
$\overleftrightarrow{JK}$ and $\overleftrightarrow{LM}$ are parallel.

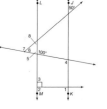

   a. $m\angle 1$ **90°; Alt. Interior.**
   b. $m\angle 2$ **90°; Supplementary.**
   c. $m\angle 3$ **90°; Right Angle.**
   d. $m\angle 4$ **100°; Alt. Interior.**
   e. $m\angle 5$ **80°; Supplementary.**
   f. $m\angle 6$ **50°; 180° Triangle.**
   g. $m\angle 7$ **130°; Supplementary.**
   h. $m\angle 8$ **50°; Alt. Exterior.**

Polygons

► **Lesson Link** You've learned about line segments and angles. Now you're ready to learn about shapes made from them. ◄

A **polygon** is a closed figure formed by three or more points joined by line segments (sides). A **vertex** of a polygon is a point at which two sides intersect.

Explore   Polygons

Getting in Shape

Materials: Geoboard™, Rubber bands

1. Wrap a rubber band around any three pegs on the Geoboard™ to outline a polygon with three sides.

2. How many unique three-sided polygons can you outline?

3. How many vertices does a three-sided polygon have?

4. How many unique four-sided polygons can you outline?

5. How many vertices does a four-sided polygon have?

6. How many unique five-sided polygons can you outline? How many six-sided polygons?

7. How many vertices do five- and six-sided polygons have?

8. Discuss the relationship between number of sides and number of vertices a polygon has.

Learn   Polygons

A polygon is classified by the number of sides it has.

Number of Sides	3	4	5	6	7	8
Polygon	Triangle	Quadrilateral	Pentagon	Hexagon	Heptagon	Octagon
Example	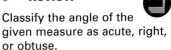					

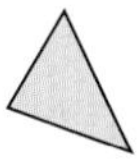

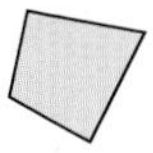

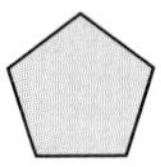

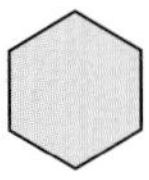

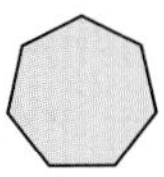

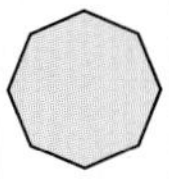

You'll Learn ...

■ to classify polygons

... How It's Used

People who make stained glass use polygons in their designs.

Vocabulary

polygon
vertex
triangle
quadrilateral
pentagon
hexagon
heptagon
octagon
Venn diagram
equilateral triangle
isosceles triangle
scalene triangle
parallelogram
rectangle
rhombus
square
trapezoid
diagonal
regular polygon
convex polygon
concave polygon

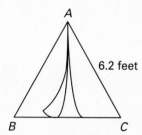
A **Venn diagram** shows a relationship by visually grouping things into sets.

Three important types of triangles are shown in the Venn diagram to the right.

An **equilateral triangle** has three congruent sides.

An **isosceles triangle** has at least two congruent sides.

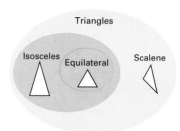

A **scalene triangle** has no congruent sides. All sides have different lengths.

A triangle has the same number of congruent sides as it has congruent angles.

The sum of a triangle's angle measures always equals 180°.

Example 1

An isosceles triangle can be seen in the shape of the tail on a humpback whale. What is the length of $\overline{FG}$?

$m\overline{FG} = m\overline{DF}$ because △DFG is isosceles.

$m\overline{FG} = 6.6$ ft

Example 2

In the scalene triangle shown, find the missing angle measure.

$32° + 76° + x = 180°$ Write an equation.

$108° + x = 180°$ Add.

$x = 72°$ Subtract 108° from both sides.

Try It
△ABC is equilateral.

a. Determine the length of $\overline{BC}$. **5 in.**

b. Determine the length of $\overline{AC}$. **5 in.**

c. Determine all angle measures of triangle ABC. **60°, 60°, 60°**

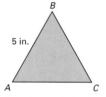

422 Chapter 8 • Geometry and Measurement

MATH EVERY DAY

► Problem of the Day

You are to throw six darts at a target with these numbers: 40, 39, 24, 23, 17, 16. Assume all six darts hit the target. What numbers must you hit to score exactly 100 points? 16, 16, 17, 17, 17, 17

Available on Daily Transparency 8-6

An Extension is provided in the transparency package.

Fact of the Day

Tiny ice crystals that have six sides stick together to form snowflakes, each of which has its own intricate pattern base on the shape of a regular hexagon.

Estimation

Estimate each product.

1. 38 × 41   1600

2. 82 × 37   3200

3. 87 × 18   1800

4. 392 × 12   4000

5. 52 × 71   3500

A Venn diagram can show the types of quadrilaterals.

A **parallelogram** is a quadrilateral with two pairs of parallel sides.

A **rectangle** is a quadrilateral with four right angles.

A **rhombus** is a parallelogram with four equal sides.

A **square** is a rectangle with four equal sides.

A **trapezoid** is a quadrilateral with exactly one pair of parallel sides.

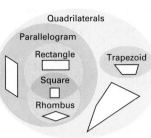

The Venn diagram shows that a rectangle is a type of parallelogram.

Example 3

Determine $m\angle ABC$ in parallelogram $ABCD$.

A parallelogram has two pairs of parallel sides, so $\overline{AB} \parallel \overline{CD}$ and $\overline{AD} \parallel \overline{BC}$.

$\angle ADC \cong \angle BCK \cong \angle PBR \cong \angle ABC$
They are all corresponding or vertical angles.

$m\angle ADC = m\angle ABC = 56°$

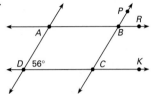

A **diagonal** of a polygon connects two vertices that do not share a side.

Example 4

In the trapezoid:

$\angle ADC \cong \angle BCD$ and $\angle DAB \cong \angle CBA$.

Measure $\angle ACD$ and $\angle BDC$ formed by the diagonals, $\overline{AC}$ and $\overline{BD}$.

$m\angle ACD = 54°$ and $m\angle BDC = 54°$

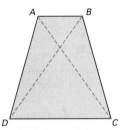

Try It

a. Determine $m\angle RST$ in parallelogram $QRST$. 114°

b. Determine $m\angle TQR$ in parallelogram $QRST$. 114°

c. Identify the diagonal line segment. $\overline{QS}$

8-6 • Polygons **423**

2. In the scalene triangle shown, find the missing angle measure.

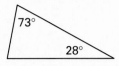

$73° + 28° + x = 180°$ Write an equation.
$101° + x = 180°$ Add.
$x = 79°$ Subtract 101° from both sides.

The missing angle measure is 79°.

3. Determine $m\angle MNP$ in parallelogram $MNPQ$.

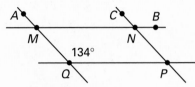

A parallelogram has two pairs of parallel sides, so $\overline{MN} \parallel \overline{QP}$ and $\overline{MQ} \parallel \overline{NP}$.

$\angle MQP \cong \angle NMA \cong \angle BNC \cong \angle MNP$. They are all corresponding or vertical angles.
$m\angle MQP = m\angle MNP$
$m\angle MNP = 134°$

4. In the trapezoid, $\angle EHG \cong \angle FGH$ and $\angle HEF \cong \angle GFE$. Measure $\angle GFH$ and $\angle FHG$ formed by the diagonals, $\overline{EG}$ and $\overline{FH}$.

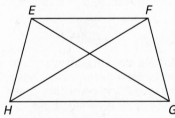

$m\angle GFH = 75°$ and $m\angle FHG = 30°$.

---

5. Describe and classify the figure. Be as specific as possible.

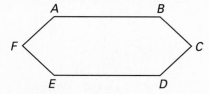

Hexagon, six sides	How many sides?
Irregular	Regular or not?
Convex	Concave or convex?

6. Find the sum of the measures of the angles in the polygon.

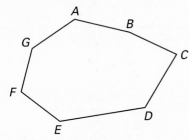

The polygon has seven sides. Substitute $k = 7$ in $180°(k - 2)$. $180°(5) = 900°$. The sum of the angle measures in a heptagon is 900°.

3 Practice and Assess

Check

To help students answer the questions, draw examples of hexagons, octagons, and pentagons that have pairs of parallel sides.

Answers for Check Your Understanding

1. A hexagon can.

2. No; Angle measures will all be the same, but two regular hexagons can have different side lengths.

All sides and all angles are congruent on a **regular polygon**.

Equilateral Triangle	Square	Regular Pentagon	Regular Hexagon	Regular Heptagon	Regular Octagon

All diagonals of a **convex polygon** are on the inside of the figure.

At least one diagonal of a **concave polygon** is outside the figure.

Example 5

Describe and classify each figure. Be as specific as possible.

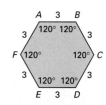

Heptagon, seven sides	How many sides?
Irregular	Regular or not?
Concave	Concave or convex?

Test Prep

Create a list of math formulas to use as a study tool.

The sum of angle measures in a polygon with k sides always equals $180°(k - 2)$.

Example 6

Find the sum of the angles in a pentagon.

A pentagon has five sides. Substitute $k = 5$ in $180°(k - 2)$.

$180°(3) = 540°$. The sum of the angles is 540°.

Try It

Describe and classify the figure on the right. Be as specific as possible.
Regular convex hexagon

Check Your Understanding

1. What polygons, besides parallelograms, have parallel sides? Explain.

2. Do all regular hexagons have the same measurements? Explain.

424 Chapter 8 • Geometry and Measurement

8-6 Exercises and Applications

Practice and Apply

1. **Getting Started** Find the measure of the missing angle.
  a. Add 61° + 23°. **84°**
  b. Subtract the sum from 180°. **96°**

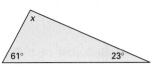

Identify the polygon outlined in each photograph. Be as specific as possible.

2.  **3.**   **4.** **Square** **5.** **Irregular convex octagon**

2. Regular convex pentagon

3. Irregular convex hexagon

Decide whether each statement is true or false.

6. All squares are parallelograms. **7.** Some trapezoids are parallelograms.

8. All rectangles are squares. **9.** An isosceles triangle can have three equal sides.

Find the measure of the missing angle.

10. 67° 74° **39°** **11.** 57° 52° **71°** **12.** 50° 40° **90°** **13.** 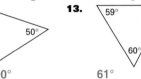 59° 60° **61°**

Determine the sum of all angles in each polygon.

14. Quadrilateral **360°** **15.** Hexagon **720°** **16.** Heptagon **900°** **17.** Octagon **1080°**

18. **Test Prep** Which figure can have only one right angle? **D**
  Ⓐ Parallelogram Ⓑ Square Ⓒ Trapezoid Ⓓ Right triangle

19. **Career** A lapidary, a craftsperson who cuts and polishes precious stones, cuts along the flat side of a crystal. What shapes appear on each of the crystal faces?
  a. Triangles and rectangles
  b. Pentagons and hexagons

a.   **b.**
Amythest   Garnet

Assignment Guide
- **Basic**
  1–19, 25–28, 30–32, 34–36
- **Average**
  4–25, 26–36 evens
- **Enriched**
  4–25, 27–37 odds

Exercise Notes
- **Exercises 6–9**

Error Prevention Students may find it helpful to refer to the Venn diagrams on pages 422 and 423 to answer these questions.

- **Exercise 18**

Test Prep If a parallelogram has one right angle, then it has four right angles and is a rectangle. A square by definition has four right angles. A trapezoid cannot have just one right angle. If it has one right angle, then it must have two because interior angles on the same side of a transversal must be supplementary.

Exercise Answers
6. True
7. False
8. False
9. True

PRACTICE 8-6

▶ PRACTICE

Name _____

Practice 8-6

Polygons

Identify each polygon. Be as specific as possible.

1. **Rectangle**   2. **Regular hexagon**  3. **Trapezoid**

4. **Regular pentagon**   5. **Parallelogram**  6. **Irregular octagon**

Decide whether each statement is true or false.

7. All squares are parallelograms. **True** 8. All quadrilaterals are parallelograms. **False**

9. Some rhombuses are rectangles. **True** 10. Some scalene triangles are isosceles. **False**

Find the measure of the missing angle.

11. **103°**   12. **50°**   13. **59°**   14. **35°**
72° 25° 52° 31° 58° x x 75° 70°

Determine the sum of all angles in each polygon.

15. nonagon (9-sided polygon) **1260°** 16. decagon (10-sided polygon) **1440°** 17. dodecagon (12-sided polygon) **1800°**

18. Name the polygon that describes the shape of a stop sign.
Regular octagon   STOP

▶ RETEACHING

Name _____

Alternative Lesson 8-6

Polygons

Triangles can be classified according to the measures of their sides. The sum of the measures of the angles in any triangle is 180°.

The sum of the angle measures in a polygon with *k* sides always equals $180°(k - 2)$.

— **Example 1** —
Find the measure of the missing angle.

Write the equation to show the sum of the measures: $m\angle x + m\angle y + m\angle z = 180°$.

 88° 46°

Substitute the known measures into the equation. $x + 88 + 46 = 180$
Add. $x + 134 = 180$
Subtract 134° from each side. $x = 46$
The third angle of the triangle measures 46°.

Try It Find the measure of each missing angle.

a. **50°** 68° 62° b. **75°** 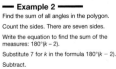 82° 23°

— **Example 2** —
Find the sum of all angles in the polygon.

Count the sides. There are seven sides.

Write the equation to find the sum of the measures: $180°(k - 2)$.

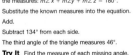

Substitute 7 for *k* in the formula $180°(k - 2)$. $x = 180(7 - 2)$
Subtract. $= 180(5)$
Multiply. $= 900$
The sum of the angles is 900°.

Try It Find the sum of all the angles in each polygon.

c. **720°**  d. **1080°**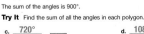

Reteaching

Activity

Materials: Two coat hangers, cardboard, string, scissors

- Organize into groups of four.
- Refer to the Venn diagrams on pages 422 and 423. Make two mobiles—one that shows the relationships among triangles and one that shows the relationships among quadrilaterals.

22 Answers may vary.

23. A concave polygon must have at least 4 sides.

25.

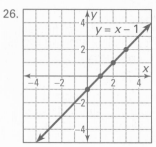
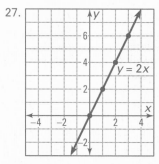

The length of the third side could be 4 in. or 7 in.; There are two possible triangles.

26.

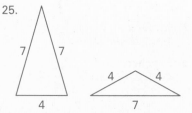

27.

$y = 2x$

28–29. See page C1.

Alternate Assessment

Ongoing Assessment Exercises 6–9 will reveal how well students understand the relationships among triangles and among quadrilaterals.

▶ **Quick Quiz**

1. Two angles of a triangle measure 40° and 70°. What is the measure of the third angle? What kind of triangle is it? **70°; isosceles**

2. Find the sum of the angles of a hexagon. **720°**

Tell whether each statement is true or false.

3. Some parallelograms are squares. **True**

4. All equilateral triangles are isosceles. **True**

5. All rhombuses are squares. **False**

Available on Daily Transparency 8-6

426 **Chapter 8**

PROBLEM SOLVING 8-6

20. Science Name the stars of the Big Dipper that form the vertices of a polygon. Name the polygon.

21. Algebra In astronomy, constellations are often identified by connecting stars with imaginary line segments. How many stars are required to make a polygon with *n* sides? ***n***

20. Megrez, Pheoda, Merak, Dubhe; irregular quadrilateral

Problem Solving and Reasoning

22.  Use the vocabulary from this lesson to describe what the orange and starfruit have in common and how they are different. Compare each fruit to a polygon and identify where the sides and vertices are.

23. Critical Thinking Recall that a concave polygon has at least one diagonal outside the figure. Try to draw a concave triangle, concave quadrilateral, concave pentagon, concave hexagon, and so on. Distinguish between polygons with an odd number of sides and an even number of sides. What conclusion can you make based on your drawings?

24. Algebra Use the $(k - 2)180°$ formula and the distributive property to find each of the angle measurements in the regular nonagon (nine-sided polygon) shown. **140°**

25. Choose a Strategy Draw an isosceles triangle with side lengths of 4 in. and 7 in. Determine the length of the third side. Is this the only possible isosceles triangle that has the side lengths 4 in. and 7 in? Explain.

Mixed Review

Graph each equation. Use 0, 1, 2, and 3 as *x* values. *[Lesson 4-3]*

26. $y = x - 1$ **27.** $y = 2x$ **28.** $y = \frac{1}{3}x$ **29.** $y = 3x - 3$

Find each square root and write in lowest terms. *[Lesson 7-7]*

30. $\sqrt{36}$ **6**   **31.** $\sqrt{49}$ **7**   **32.** $\sqrt{100}$ **10**   **33.** $\sqrt{169}$ **13**

34. $\sqrt{\frac{16}{64}}$ $\frac{1}{2}$ **35.** $\sqrt{\frac{144}{9}}$ **4**   **36.** $\sqrt{\frac{49}{36}}$ $1\frac{1}{6}$ **37.** $\sqrt{\frac{9}{121}}$ $\frac{3}{11}$

426 *Chapter 8 • Geometry and Measurement*

▶ **PROBLEM SOLVING**

Name _____

Guided Problem Solving 8-6

GPS **PROBLEM 25, STUDENT PAGE 426**

Draw an isosceles triangle with side lengths of 4 in. and 7 in. Determine the length of the third side. Is this the only possible isosceles triangle that has the side lengths 4 in. and 7 in.? Explain.

Possible answer: Item 5

— **Understand** —

1. What defines an isosceles triangle? **2 sides with equal lengths.**

— **Plan** —

2. If only *one* side measures 4 in., what will be the measures of the other two sides? **7 in.; 7 in.**

3. If only *one* side measures 7 in., what will be the measures of the other two sides? **4 in.; 4 in.**

4. Use a compass and a ruler to draw one of the triangles on another sheet of paper. Draw a segment. Set the compass to one of your measures. Place the compass on each endpoint and draw two intersecting arcs above it. Connect the three points.

— **Solve** —

5. Measure the sides. One side should measure 4 in. and another side should measure 7 in. What is the measure of the third side? **7 in. or 4 in.**

6. Repeat the procedure in Item 4 to draw different triangles. How many triangles can you draw? Explain. **2 triangles; Since two sides must be the same length, there are only two different combinations for the sides.**

— **Look Back** —

7. How can you use the relationship between the measures of the sides of a triangle to determine whether or not you can draw an isosceles triangle with any given measures? **Check that the sum of the measures of any two sides is greater than the measure of the third side.**

SOLVE ANOTHER PROBLEM

Draw an isosceles triangle with side lengths of 2 cm and 5 cm. Determine the length of the third side. Is this the only possible isosceles triangle that has the side lengths 2 cm and 5 cm? Explain. **Possible answer: 2 cm, 5 cm, 5 cm; One triangle is possible.**

▶ **ENRICHMENT**

Name _____

Extend Your Thinking 8-6

Patterns in Geometry

You have learned about triangular and square numbers. The first four numbers in each pattern are shown in these two dot arrangements.

$T_1 = 1$ $T_2 = 3$ $T_3 = 6$ $T_4 = 10$ $S_1 = 1$ $S_2 = 4$ $S_3 = 9$ $S_4 = 16$

There are also dot arrangements formed by other polygons, such as the pentagonal and hexagonal arrangements shown below.

$P_1 = 1$ $P_2 = 5$ $P_3 = 12$ $P_4 = 22$

$H_1 = 1$ $H_2 = 6$ $H_3 = 15$ $H_4 = 28$

1. Sketch the next two dot arrays for the pentagonal and hexagonal numbers above. Write the results in the table below.

Number	1st	2nd	3rd	4th	5th	6th	7th	8th	9th	10th
Triangular	1	3	6	10	15	21	28	36	45	55
Square	1	4	9	16	25	36	49	64	81	100
Pentagonal	1	5	12	22	35	51	70	92	117	145
Hexagonal	1	6	15	28	45	66	91	120	153	190

2. List at least three number patterns that can be found by studying the numbers in the table. Then complete the table. **Possible answer: The increase for each number in one column is the same. Each change between pentagonal numbers is 3 more than the preceding change, while the change for hexagonal numbers is 4 more.**

3-D Views

▶ Lesson Link In Lesson 8–6, you learned about two-dimensional shapes. Now you will learn how to visualize three-dimensional shapes. ◀

You'll Learn ...

■ to represent three-dimensional shapes in a drawing

... How It's Used

Sculptors use preliminary sketches to plan the designs of their 3-D sculptures.

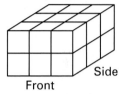

Explore | 3-D Views

Centimeter Cubist

Materials: 10 multilink cubes

You are an artist who makes sculptures from cubes. Before creating the sculptures, you draw preliminary sketches. Sketch your idea by creating: (1) three views: front, right, and top; or (2) one base plan.

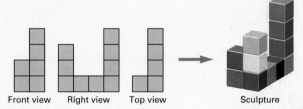

Front view   Right view   Top view

Sculpture

The illustrations show the two ways of sketching an idea for a sculpture and the resulting piece.

1. Draw a base plan for a different sculpture. The numbers in your squares should have a sum of 10.

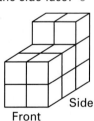

Base plan   Sculpture

2. Using your base plan, draw the three views of your planned sculpture.

3. Build your sculpture based on your sketches.

4. Build a group member's sculpture based on his or her sketches.

5. Did he or she build your sculpture correctly? Did you build his or hers correctly?

6. If you were going to create a 20-foot-tall sculpture, why would you sketch your ideas instead of immediately building it?

7. Discuss some other ways of planning 3-D objects by using drawings.

MEETING INDIVIDUAL NEEDS

Resources

8-7 Practice
8-7 Reteaching
8-7 Problem Solving
8-7 Enrichment
8-7 Daily Transparency
    Problem of the Day
    Review
    Quick Quiz
Teaching Tool Transparency 9
Technology Master 39
 Interactive CD-ROM Lesson

Learning Modalities

Kinesthetic For Exercises 1–3 on page 430, students can use the multilink cubes to recreate the figures from the text. This will help them observe the different views.

Individual Students can reflect on their own ability to visualize three-dimensional figures, and how this lesson has helped to improve their ability.

Inclusion

Allow students who have perceptual disabilities to use the multilink cubes during testing.

8-7

Lesson Organizer

Objective

■ Represent three-dimensional shapes in a drawing.

Materials

■ Explore: 10 multilink cubes

NCTM Standards

■ 1–4, 12

▶ Review

In each figure, the only hidden cubes are those needed to support visible cubes.

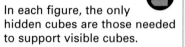

Side
Front

How many cubes are in

1. the top layer? 9

2. the front layer? 6

3. the side face? 6

Side
Front

How many cubes are in

4. the side face? 7

5. the bottom layer? 6

Available on Daily Transparency 8-7

---

1 Introduce

Explore

You may wish to use Teaching Tool Transparency 9: Isometric Dot Paper with this lesson.

The Point
Students create sculptures from multilink cubes by following a base plan and sketch of three views.

Ongoing Assessment
Check students' sculptures in Step 3. To successfully complete Steps 4–7, Step 3 must be done correctly.

2 Teach

Learn

A base plan is a top view of a cube structure. The number of cubes in each stack is written in the corresponding square.

Alternate Examples

1. Draw a base plan of the 3-D object shown. There are no hidden cubes.

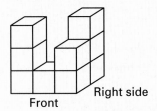

Front   Right side

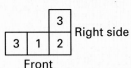

	3	
3	1	2

Right side

Front

There are two columns that are 3 cubes tall.
There is one column that is 2 cubes tall.
There is one column that is 1 cube tall.

2. Draw the right, front, and top views of the 3-D object shown. The only hidden cubes are those needed to support others.

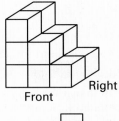

Front   Right

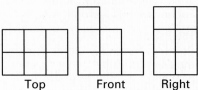

Top   Front   Right

Learn   3-D Views

When you visualize a 3-D object, it is helpful to make a sketch. For shapes built from cubes, you can draw a base plan to show the height of several stacks of cubes. You can also represent a 3-D object by drawing the right, front, and top views.

Example 1

Draw a base plan of the 3-D object shown.

Front   Right side

There are two columns that are 3 cubes tall.

There are two columns that are 2 cubes tall.

There is one column that is 1 cube tall.

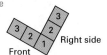

Front   Right side

Drawing the right view, front view, and top view of a 3-D object shows how the object appears from different views.

Example 2

Draw the right, front, and top views of the 3-D object shown.

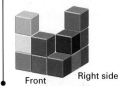

The front has two stacks of 3 cubes.

The right has one stack of 3 cubes.

There are four stacks that use only 1 cube.

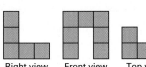

Right view   Front view   Top view

Try It

Use the drawing on the right for the following.

a. Draw a base plan.

b. Draw the right view.

c. Draw the front view.

d. Draw the top view.

Front   Right side

428   *Chapter 8 • Geometry and Measurement*

MATH EVERY DAY

A net shows the surface of a 3-D figure as if it were unfolded.

Draw a net for the galena crystal shown at right.

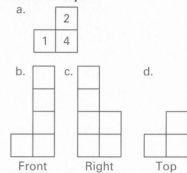

WHAT DO YOU THINK?

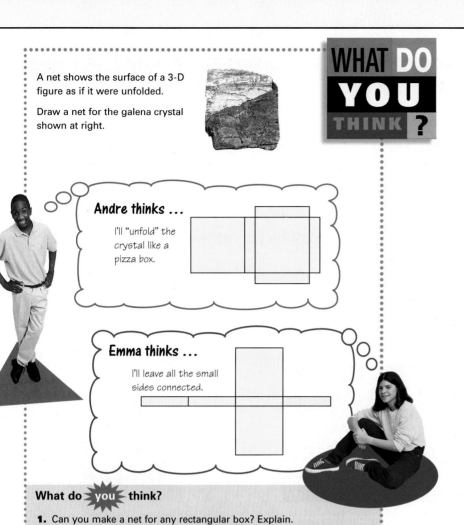

Andre thinks ...

I'll "unfold" the crystal like a pizza box.

Emma thinks ...

I'll leave all the small sides connected.

What do you think?

1. Can you make a net for any rectangular box? Explain.

2. Is there only one possible net for a rectangular box? Explain.

1. What would result if you had to build something from only a front view and top view?

2. What would result if you had to build something from a base plan without numbers?

MEETING MIDDLE SCHOOL CLASSROOM NEEDS

Tips from Middle School Teachers

I find that dry-food boxes can help students better visualize nets, and the printing on the boxes also helps students see how the faces relate to each other. I bring in several boxes made of thin cardboard, such as cereal boxes. Then I have students carefully cut them apart to make nets. If possible, I bring in two or more identical boxes so students see there is more than one possible net for a rectangular box.

Cooperative Learning

Give groups of three students around 100 multilink cubes. Have them build a mega-figure and then draw the base plan and top, front, and side views.

Career Connection

Have students find out how machinists and tool-and-die makers use top, front, and side views when drawing plans. Have them share the information with the class.

---

2. (continued)
The left side has two stacks of 3 cubes.
The middle row has two stacks of 2 cubes.
The right side has two stacks of 1 cube.

Answers for Try It

a.

	2	
1	4	

b.   c.   d.

Front   Right   Top

WHAT DO YOU THINK?

Students see two ways of forming a net for a rectangular solid, and discover there are other nets possible.

Answers for What Do You Think?

1. Possible answer: Yes, it takes 6 sides.

2. No; There is more than one way to make a net.

3 Practice and Assess

Check

For Question 1, ask students what information for creating the figure would be lacking. You might draw the front and top views of several figures on the board and have students construct them to realize that many figures are possible. The missing information is the heights of the cubes.

Answers for Check Your Understanding

1. You wouldn't know how deep to build the figure.

2. You wouldn't know how tall to build the figure.

8-7 Exercises and Applications

Assignment Guide

■ **Basic**
1–10, 12–21

■ **Average**
2–12, 13–21, odds

■ **Enriched**
2–12, 14–20, evens

Exercise Answers

1. a.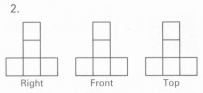

2.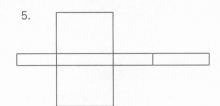
Right   Front   Top

3.

3	4	3
2	1	2

4.

4	4	4	4	4	4
4	2	2	2	2	4
4	2	2	2	2	4
4	2	2	2	2	4
4	2	2	2	2	4

5.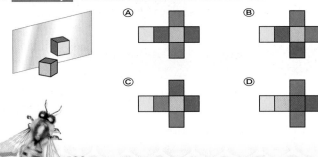

Reteaching

Activity

Materials: 12 blocks of the same size

• Work in groups of four.

• Build a 3-D object with the blocks.

• Draw a base plan for the object. Draw front, right, and top views for the object.

Practice and Apply

1. **Getting Started** Draw a base plan using the illustration shown.
    a. Draw the top view.
    b. Count the number of cubes in each column and label each square in the view.

2. Draw the right, front, and top views for the 3-D object shown.

3. Draw a base plan for the cube tower shown.

4. This chair design is called the Kubus Chair. Draw a base plan for it.

5. **Science** Amethyst, the February birthstone, is a purple type of quartz crystal. The crystal shown is rectangular. Draw a net for a rectangular prism.

6. **Test Prep** Which net would make the solid shown? **B**

Ⓐ Ⓑ Ⓒ Ⓓ

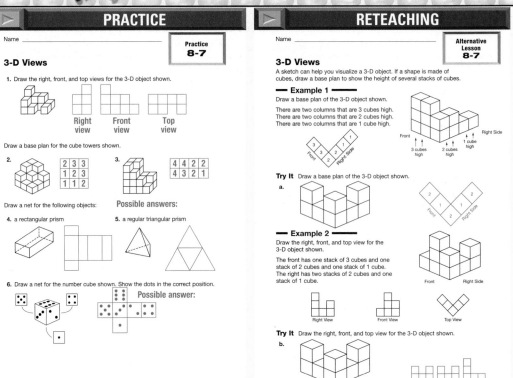

PRACTICE

Practice 8-7

3-D Views

1. Draw the right, front, and top views for the 3-D object shown.
Right view   Front view   Top view

Draw a base plan for the cube towers shown.

2.

2	3	3
1	2	3
1	1	2

3.

4	4	2	2
4	3	2	1

Draw a net for the following objects: **Possible answers:**

4. a rectangular prism

5. a regular triangular prism

6. Draw a net for the number cube shown. Show the dots in the correct position. **Possible answer:**

RETEACHING

Alternative Lesson 8-7

3-D Views

A sketch can help you visualize a 3-D object. If a shape is made of cubes, draw a base plan to show the height of several stacks of cubes.

— **Example 1** —
Draw a base plan of the 3-D object shown.

There are two columns that are 3 cubes high.
There are two columns that are 2 cubes high.
There are two columns that are 1 cube high.

Try It Draw a base plan of the 3-D object shown.
a.

— **Example 2** —
Draw the right, front, and top view for the 3-D object shown.

The front has one stack of 3 cubes and one stack of 2 cubes and one stack of 1 cube.
The right has two stacks of 2 cubes and one stack of 1 cube.

Right View   Front View   Top View

Try It Draw the right, front, and top view for the 3-D object shown.
b.

Front View Right View Top View

History Shown is a photograph of Ft. McHenry in Baltimore, Maryland, where Francis Scott Key wrote "The Star-Spangled Banner" during the War of 1812.

7. Draw a top view of Ft. McHenry.

8. What general shape does this remind you of? **A pentagon**

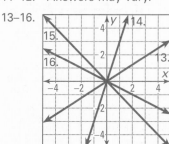

Problem Solving and Reasoning

9. Critical Thinking Which net matches the 3-D figure? **A**

 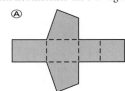 
Ⓐ   Ⓑ

10. Patterns Construct a solid shape by gluing or taping together a copy of the net shown. What do you get? **A rectangular box**

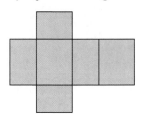

11. Math Reasoning Gems can be cut in different ways. The picture shows the top view of one type of faceted cut. Sketch how you think the right and front views look.

12. Communicate A ziggurat is a type of pyramid with terraces. The photo at the right shows Chichén Itzá, the Mayan ziggurat. Describe how you would draw a net for this shape?

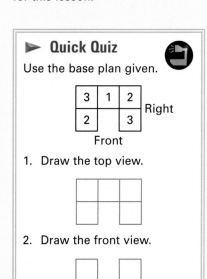

Mixed Review

Draw a line through the origin with the given slope.
[Lesson 4-4]

13. $\frac{5}{8}$ **14.** 3 **15.** -1 **16.** $-\frac{1}{2}$

Identify each number as rational or irrational. *[Lesson 7-8]*

17. $\sqrt{10}$ **18.** $0.\overline{6}$ **19.** $\sqrt{19}$ **20.** $\sqrt{225}$ **21.** 0.2323

8-7 • 3-D Views   **431**

Exercise Answers

7.

11–12.   Answers may vary.

13–16.

17. Irrational

18. Rational

19. Irrational

20. Rational

21. Rational

Alternate Assessment

Portfolio Have students select and place in their portfolios drawings they feel are the best they made for this lesson.

▶ **Quick Quiz**

Use the base plan given.

3	1	2
2		3

Right
Front

1. Draw the top view.

2. Draw the front view.

3. Draw the right view.

Available on Daily Transparency 8-7

▶ **PROBLEM SOLVING**

Name _____

Guided Problem Solving 8-7

GPS **PROBLEM 9, STUDENT PAGE 431**

Which net matches the 3-D figure?

A   B

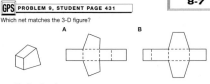

— Understand —
1. How many sides of the 3-D figure can you see? **3 sides.**
2. Which polygons make up these sides? **Quadrilateral, 2 rectangles.**
3. How many sides of each net can you see? **6 sides.**
4. Which polygons make up these sides? **2 quadrilaterals, 4 rectangles.**

— Plan —
5. How are the two nets alike? **Have 4 rectangles.**
6. How do the nets differ? **Shape of quadrilaterals, size of rectangles.**

— Solve —
7. Choose one of the differences between the nets and compare that characteristic to the solid. Which net matches the solid? **Net A.**

— Look Back —
8. Which difference between the nets is the easiest to use to compare to the solid? Explain. **Possible answer: Quadrilateral; the difference in shape is more obvious.**

SOLVE ANOTHER PROBLEM

Which net matches the 3-D figure? **Net B.**

A   B

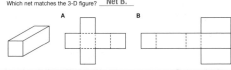

▶ **ENRICHMENT**

Name _____

Extend Your Thinking 8-7

Visual Thinking
Circle the letter of the 3-D figure on the right that can be made by the net on the left

1.

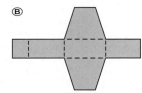

a.   b.   ⓒ.   d.

2.

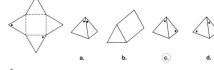

ⓐ.   b.   c.   d.

3.

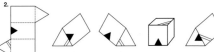

a.   ⓑ.   c.   d.

4.

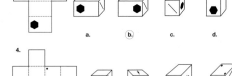

a.   ⓑ.   c.   d.

Lesson 8-7   431

Using Geometry
Software
- Drawing Side and Top
Views

The Point
Students use geometry software
to construct top and side views of
a square nut.

Materials
Geometry software

Resources

*Interactive CD-ROM
Geometry Tool*

About the Page

If students are not familiar with
the geometry software, you may
want to demonstrate some of the
important features.

Ask ...
- Have you ever used nuts and
bolts? How?

- What shape do the nuts have?
Usually they are square or
hexagonal.

Answers for Try It

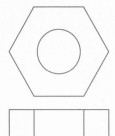

On Your Own
For the third question, you might
point out that many architects,
engineers, and industrial designers use Computer-Aided Design
(CAD) programs.

Answers for On Your Own
- It probably uses a distance
formula.

- Possible answer: Using the software because you can get more
precise drawings.

- Possible answer: Just like the
geometry software.

TECHNOLOGY

Using Geometry Software • Drawing Side and Top Views

Problem: Construct the top and side views of a square nut.
You can use dynamic geometry software to help with this exercise.

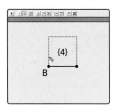

1 Use the **Regular
Polygon** tool to
construct a square.
Use the **Measure**
menu to find the
length of each side
and the measure of
each angle.

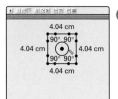

3 Use the **Circle** tool
to draw a circle
inside the square.
The circle will have
the same center as
the square. Hide
the diagonal line
segments and you'll
have the top view of
your square nut.

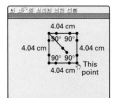

2 Use the **Segment**
tool to draw two
diagonals between
opposite pairs of
vertices. This
shows the center of
the square.

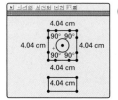

4 Draw a rectangle
with length the
same as a side of
the square. This is
the side view of the
square nut.

Solution: Length measurements may vary.

ON YOUR OWN

TRY IT

What would the top and side views of a
hexagonal nut look like?

▶ How do you think the geometry software calculates the
lengths of the sides of your construction?

▶ Is it easier to construct these views using geometry
software or by hand? Explain.

▶ How do you think an architect's design program can
help you construct these views?

In this section, you'll have a chance to apply your creativity to what you've learned about flat and three-dimensional shapes.

Bzzzt... Beeometry

Materials: Paper, Scissors, Tape

Draw six congruent squares on a sheet of paper, in order to construct a net for a "geometry cube."

You will design the net with drawings and labels from Exercises 1–6.

1. On one square, draw a line, line segment, or a ray.

2. On another square, draw any angle and label its measure.

3. On another square, draw parallel or perpendicular lines.

4. On another square, draw parallel lines with a transversal and label all angle measurements.

5. On another square, draw any polygon and include its classification.

6. On the last square, write "roll again."

7. How many pairs of parallel lines are on your net?

8. How many pairs of perpendicular lines are on your net?

9. How many acute angles are on your net? Obtuse angles?

10. How many right angles are on your net?

11. Classify all of the polygons on your net.

12. Cut out your net and use tape to make a "geometry cube."

13. All the group members will roll their cubes. If a cube lands on "roll again," then that player must roll the cube again.

14. When all cubes say other than "roll again," each player must create a drawing that uses each figure shown on the cubes.

433

Bzzzt... Beeometry

The Point
In *Bzzzt... Beeometry* on page 409, students were introduced to various geometric shapes. Now, they create a net for a "geometry cube" by using their knowledge of lines, angles, and polygons.

Materials
Paper, scissors, tape

About the Page

- **Ask students what is being created.** A cube, which is a six-sided, three-dimensional figure.

- **Why is a net being made?** So that the drawings can be made on a flat surface. The net can then be folded to make the cube.

Ongoing Assessment
Check that students have drawn the net correctly before they make their drawings for Questions 1–6.

Extension

Have students replace the drawing on one side of their cube with their own idea, then repeat Steps 13 and 14.

Answers for Connect
1–14. Answers may vary.

Review Correlation

Item(s)	Lesson(s)
1–8	8-4
9–16	8-5
17–20	8-6
21	8-7
22	8-4

Test Prep

Test-Taking Tip

Tell students that when taking a test they should be told where they can do their scratch work. If they are not told, they should ask before proceeding.

REVIEW 8B

Section 8B Review

Use the illustration to classify each angle as right, straight, obtuse, or acute.

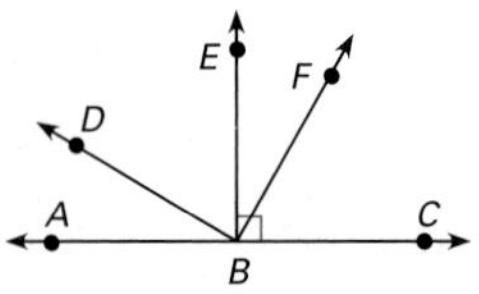

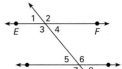

1. ∠ABD   **2.** ∠DBF   **3.** ∠FBC

4. ∠EBF   **5.** ∠ABE   **6.** ∠ABC

7. Find the angle measure complementary to 57.5°. **32.5°**

8. Find the angle measure supplementary to 108°. **72°**

1. A	2. R	3. A
4. A	5. R	6. S

$\overleftrightarrow{EF} \parallel \overleftrightarrow{GH}$. If $m\angle 3 = 130°$, find each angle measure.

9. $m\angle 2$ **130°**   **10.** $m\angle 7$ **130°**   **11.** $m\angle 6$ **130°**   **12.** $m\angle 8$ **50°**

Match each pair of angles with the angle classification.

13. ∠6 and ∠7 **d**   **A.** Alternate interior angles

14. ∠5 and ∠4 **a**   **B.** Alternate exterior angles

15. ∠1 and ∠8 **b**   **C.** Corresponding angles

16. ∠3 and ∠7 **c**   **D.** Vertical angles

Identify the polygon in each photograph. Be as specific as possible.

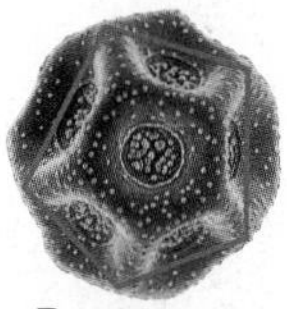

17.   **18.**   **19.**   **20.**

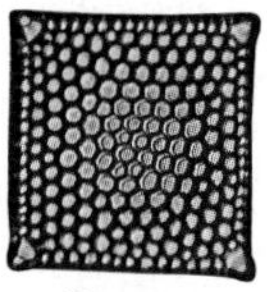

Pentagon   Triangle   Parallelogram   Square

21. State the difference between a top view and a base view of a 3-D figure. **Their shapes are the same but the base plan has the number of units stacked up written on it.**

Test Prep

On a multiple choice test, you need to know the difference between a line and a line segment. Both may appear in the answer choices of a single question. **D**

22. $\overrightarrow{CD}$ is   Ⓐ A line.   Ⓑ A line segment.   Ⓒ An angle.   Ⓓ A ray.

Resources

Practice Masters
   Section 8B Review

Assessment Sourcebook
   Quiz 8B

   TestWorks
   Test and Practice Software

PRACTICE

Name _____

Practice

Section 8B Review

Use a protractor to measure each angle. Classify each angle as right, straight, obtuse, or acute.

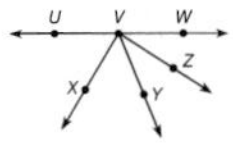

1. ∠UVX **58°; acute**   **2.** ∠XVZ **90°; right**

3. ∠WVY **67°; acute**   **4.** ∠UVW **180°; straight**

5. ∠UVY **113°; obtuse**   **6.** ∠XVW **122°; obtuse**

7. Find the angle measure complementary to 23.8°. **66.2°**

8. Find the angle measure supplementary to 81°. **99°**

Use figure at right to answer Exercises 9–16.
$\overleftrightarrow{JK} \parallel \overleftrightarrow{LM}$. If $m\angle 2 = 70°$, find each angle measure.

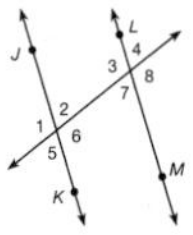

9. $m\angle 4$ **70°**   **10.** $m\angle 7$ **70°**

11. $m\angle 5$ **70°**   **12.** $m\angle 3$ **110°**

Match each pair of angles with the angle classification.

13. ∠6 and ∠8 **C**   **A.** alternate interior angles

14. ∠3 and ∠6 **A**   **B.** alternate exterior angles

15. ∠4 and ∠7 **D**   **C.** corresponding angles

16. ∠1 and ∠8 **B**   **D.** vertical angles

Identify each polygon. Be as specific as possible.

17. **Rhombus**   **18.** **Irregular pentagon**   **19.** **Isosceles triangle**

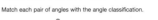

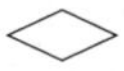

20. The largest hotel lobby is the 160 ft by 350 ft lobby at the Hyatt Regency in San Francisco. What is the largest scale that could be used to make a scale drawing of this lobby on an 8-in. by 10-in. sheet of paper? *[Lesson 5-7]*   **1 in. = 35 ft**

21. Geography Tucson, Arizona, is about 75 miles south and 70 miles east of Phoenix. What is the distance from Phoenix to Tucson? *[Lesson 7-9]*   **About 103 mi**

Extend Key Ideas ▶ Algebra

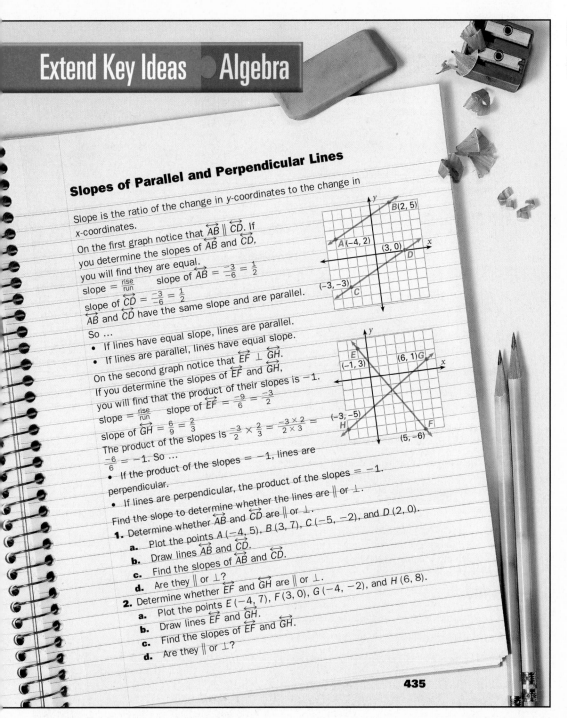

Slopes of Parallel and Perpendicular Lines

Slope is the ratio of the change in y-coordinates to the change in x-coordinates.

On the first graph notice that $\overleftrightarrow{AB} \parallel \overleftrightarrow{CD}$. If you determine the slopes of $\overleftrightarrow{AB}$ and $\overleftrightarrow{CD}$, you will find they are equal.

slope = $\frac{rise}{run}$ slope of $\overleftrightarrow{AB} = \frac{-3}{-6} = \frac{1}{2}$

slope of $\overleftrightarrow{CD} = \frac{-3}{-6} = \frac{1}{2}$

$\overleftrightarrow{AB}$ and $\overleftrightarrow{CD}$ have the same slope and are parallel.

So ...
- If lines have equal slope, lines are parallel.
- If lines are parallel, lines have equal slope.

On the second graph notice that $\overleftrightarrow{EF} \perp \overleftrightarrow{GH}$. If you determine the slopes of $\overleftrightarrow{EF}$ and $\overleftrightarrow{GH}$, you will find that the product of their slopes is −1.

slope = $\frac{rise}{run}$ slope of $\overleftrightarrow{EF} = \frac{-9}{6} = \frac{-3}{2}$

slope of $\overleftrightarrow{GH} = \frac{6}{9} = \frac{2}{3}$

The product of the slopes is $\frac{-3}{2} \times \frac{2}{3} = \frac{-3 \times 2}{2 \times 3} = \frac{-6}{6} = -1$. So ...

- If the product of the slopes = −1, lines are perpendicular.
- If lines are perpendicular, the product of the slopes = −1.

Find the slope to determine whether the lines are ‖ or ⊥.

1. Determine whether $\overleftrightarrow{AB}$ and $\overleftrightarrow{CD}$ are ‖ or ⊥.
   a. Plot the points $A(-4, 5)$, $B(3, 7)$, $C(-5, -2)$, and $D(2, 0)$.
   b. Draw lines $\overleftrightarrow{AB}$ and $\overleftrightarrow{CD}$.
   c. Find the slopes of $\overleftrightarrow{AB}$ and $\overleftrightarrow{CD}$.
   d. Are they ‖ or ⊥?

2. Determine whether $\overleftrightarrow{EF}$ and $\overleftrightarrow{GH}$ are ‖ or ⊥.
   a. Plot the points $E(-4, 7)$, $F(3, 0)$, $G(-4, -2)$, and $H(6, 8)$.
   b. Draw lines $\overleftrightarrow{EF}$ and $\overleftrightarrow{GH}$.
   c. Find the slopes of $\overleftrightarrow{EF}$ and $\overleftrightarrow{GH}$.
   d. Are they ‖ or ⊥?

435

Answers for Questions

1. a–b.

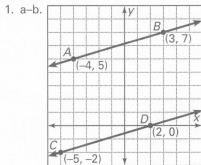

c. $\frac{2}{7}, \frac{2}{7}$

d. ‖

2a–b.

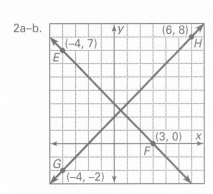

c. −1, 1

d. ⊥

Slopes of Parallel and Perpendicular Lines

The Point
Students discover that the slopes of parallel lines are the same and that the slopes of perpendicular lines have a product of −1.

About the Page

- Vertical lines are parallel, even though their slopes are undefined.

- The slopes of $\overleftrightarrow{AB}$ and $\overleftrightarrow{CD}$ could have been calculated as $\frac{3}{6} = \frac{1}{2}$ if the coordinates had been subtracted in the reverse order.

- The slopes of $\overleftrightarrow{EF}$ and $\overleftrightarrow{HG}$ could have been calculated as $\frac{9}{-6} = \frac{3}{-2}$ and $\frac{-6}{-9} = \frac{2}{3}$ if the coordinates had been subtracted in the reverse order.

Ask ...
- How are the slopes calculated? The numerator is the difference in the y-coordinates; The denominator is the difference in the x-coordinates.

- How can you tell if two lines are parallel? Their slopes will be equal.

- How can you tell if two lines are perpendicular? Their slopes will have a product of −1.

Extension

Have students find the coordinates of the vertices of a rectangle that has a slanted orientation. Have them verify that their figure is a rectangle using the slopes of the sides.

435

Review Correlation

Item(s)	Lesson(s)
1, 2	8-1
3, 4	8-2
5, 6	8-3
7	8-4
8	8-7
9	8-4, 8-5
10	8-4
11	8-6

For additional review, see page 683.

Answers for Review

8.

3	4	3	4
1	2	3	4

Chapter 8 Summary and Review

Graphic Organizer

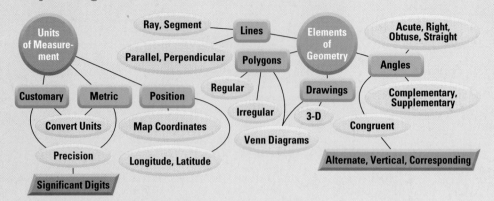

Section 8A   Measurement

Summary

- **U.S. customary units** use the inch, foot, and mile as units of length; ounce, pound, and ton for weight; and pint and quart for capacity.

- The **metric system** uses the centimeter, meter, and kilometer as units of length; gram and kilogram for mass; and milliliter and liter for capacity.

- The units and number of decimal places determine the **precision** of a measurement. The **significant digits** represent the actual measurement. Significant digits are used when calculating with measurements.

- **Absolute position** is given as coordinates. **Relative position** is given in relationship to another place.

- World maps usually show position using **latitude** (degrees north or south of the equator) and **longitude** (degrees east or west of the prime meridian).

Review

1. What metric unit would you use for the capacity of a car's gas tank? **Liter**

2. Convert 12 lb to oz. **192 oz**

3. Determine which measurement is more precise: 438 ft or 137 yd. **438 ft**

436 Chapter 8 • Geometry and Measurement

Resources

Practice Masters
    Cumulative Review
    Chapters 1–8

PRACTICE

Name _____

Practice

Cumulative Review Chapters 1–8

Solve each proportion. *[Lesson 5-4]*

1. $\frac{15}{21} = \frac{x}{35}$ $x = \underline{25}$
2. $\frac{33}{t} = \frac{48}{64}$ $t = \underline{44}$
3. $\frac{45}{33} = \frac{105}{p}$ $p = \underline{77}$
4. $\frac{k}{54} = \frac{36}{81}$ $k = \underline{24}$

5. $\frac{n}{26} = \frac{40}{65}$ $n = \underline{16}$
6. $\frac{85}{51} = \frac{15}{r}$ $r = \underline{9}$
7. $\frac{30}{48} = \frac{u}{104}$ $u = \underline{65}$
8. $\frac{45}{c} = \frac{27}{66}$ $c = \underline{110}$

Find the percent of increase or decrease. Round to the nearest whole percent. *[Lessons 6-4 and 6-5]*

9. old: 7.3   new: 11.4   **56% increase**
10. old: 27.6   new: 21.8   **21% decrease**
11. old: 384   new: 400   **4% increase**
12. old: $129.95   new: $113.60   **13% decrease**

13. old: 16.4   new: 12.8   **22% decrease**
14. old: $84.30   new: $89.90   **7% increase**
15. old: 57   new: 42   **26% decrease**
16. old: 38   new: 157   **313% increase**

Determine whether the given number is divisible by 2, 3, 4, 5, 6, 8, 9, or 10. *[Lesson 7-1]*

17. 532   **2, 4**
18. 817   **None**
19. 486   **2, 3, 6, 9**
20. 860   **2, 4, 5, 10**
21. 178   **2**
22. 135   **3, 5, 9**

Use a protractor to measure each angle. Classify each angle as right, straight, obtuse, or acute. *[Lesson 8-4]*

23. ∠BAD   **65°; acute**
24. ∠BCD   **65°; acute**
25. ∠ABC   **90°; right**
26. ∠ABD   **35°; acute**
27. ∠ADC   **140°; obtuse**
28. ∠BDC   **60°; acute**

Identify each polygon. Be as specific as possible. *[Lesson 8-6]*

29. **Trapezoid**
30. **Regular pentagon**
31. **Scalene triangle**

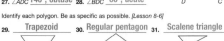

Section 8A   Measurement *continued*

4. Calculate 8.45 cm × 4.267 cm. Write your answer using the correct number of significant digits. **36.1 cm²**

5. To the nearest degree, determine the latitude and longitude of Columbus, Ohio. **40° N, 83° W**

6. What is the position of Springfield, Illinois relative to Madison, Wisconsin? **About 235 mi south**

Section 8B   Elements of Geometry

Summary

- An **angle** is formed when two lines meet at one point, called the **vertex**.

- A **line** extends infinitely in both directions. A **line segment** is part of a line with two **endpoints**. A **ray** has only one endpoint.

- An angle can be classified as **acute, right, obtuse,** or **straight.** **Complementary** angles have a sum of 90°. **Supplementary** angles have a sum of 180°.

- **Parallel** lines (∥) never intersect. **Perpendicular** lines (⊥) form 90° angles.

- A line crossing two other lines is a **transversal**. Together they form **interior angles** and **exterior angles**.

- A **polygon** is formed by three or more segments meeting at **vertices**. On a **regular polygon,** all sides and all vertex angles are congruent.

- A regular triangle is called **equilateral**. An **isosceles triangle** has at least two congruent sides, and a **scalene triangle** has none.

- A **quadrilateral** has four sides. Quadrilaterals include **rectangles, rhombuses, squares, parallelograms,** and **trapezoids**.

7. Complement: 52°; Supplement: 142°

9. a. $\overline{AB}$ and $\overline{CD}$

   b. $\overline{AB}$ and $\overline{BC}$ (or $\overline{BC}$ and $\overline{CD}$)

Review

7. Find the complementary angle and the supplementary angle of 38°.

8. Draw a base plan for the cube tower.

9. In the figure shown, which
   a. Segments are ∥ ?
   b. Segments are ⊥ ?
   c. Angle is a supplement to ∠A? **∠D**

10. Classify 150° as a right, straight, obtuse, or acute angle. **Obtuse**

11. Find the sum of the angles of a pentagon. **540°**

Assessment Correlation

Item(s)	Lesson(s)
1, 2	8-1
3, 4	8-2
5, 6	8-3
7, 8	8-4
9, 10	8-5
11, 12	8-6
13, 14	8-7

Answers for Assessment

9. a. Possible answer: ∠3 and ∠6 or ∠4 and ∠5
   b. ∠1 and ∠4
   c. ∠1 and ∠5

13.

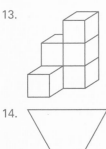

14.

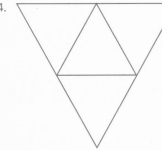

Chapter 8 Assessment

1. What metric unit would you use for the length of your school? **Meter**

2. Convert 17 ft 3 in. to inches. **207 in.**
   3. Is 25.8 lb or 98.4 oz more precise? **98.4 oz**

4. Calculate 8.29 gal + 25.9 gal using significant digits. **34.2 gal**

5. How many degrees of latitude are between Calgary and Victoria? How many degrees of longitude? **About 2.6°; About 9.3°**

6. What is the position of Regina relative to Winnipeg? **About 350 mi west**

7. Classify 100° as a right, straight, obtuse, or acute angle. **Obtuse**

8. Find the complementary angle and the supplementary angle of 54°. **Complement: 36°; Supplement: 126°**

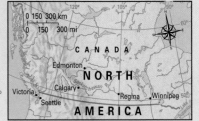

9. In the figure, name a pair of
   a. Alternate interior angles.
   b. Vertical angles.
   c. Corresponding angles.

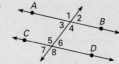

10. Name all angles that are supplementary with ∠2. ($\overleftrightarrow{AB} \parallel \overleftrightarrow{CD}$) **∠1, ∠4, ∠5, and ∠8**

11. Determine whether or not each polygon appears to be regular. Tell whether or not it is convex.

a.   **Irregular, concave**

b. **Regular, convex**

c.   **Irregular, convex**

12. Classify the shape of this polygon by the number of sides. Then find the sum of the angles. **Hexagon; 720°**

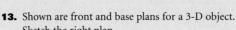

13. Shown are front and base plans for a 3-D object. Sketch the right plan.

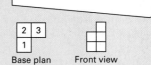

Base plan   Front view

14. Draw a net for the figure shown. (Each face is an equilateral triangle.)

Performance Task

Construct each figure using paper, scissors, and tape. Then unfold each one to find a net.

a.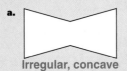
b.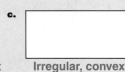
c.

Performance Assessment Key

See key on page 387.

Resources

Assessment Sourcebook
Chapter 8 Tests
  Forms A and B (free response)
  Form C (multiple choice)
  Form D (performance assessment)
  Form E (mixed response)
  Form F (cumulative chapter test)

TestWorks
Test and Practice Software

Home and Community Connections
  Letter Home for Chapter 8
  in English and Spanish

Suggested Scoring Rubric

4 • Completes all three nets accurately and neatly.

3 • Completes two of the three nets accurately and neatly or completes all three nets but they lack some accuracy and neatness.

2 • Completes one of the three nets accurately and neatly or completes two of the three nets but they are lacking in accuracy and neatness.

1 • Completes one of the nets but it is lacking in accuracy and neatness.

Multiple Choice

Choose the best answer.

1. Evaluate $(2 + 5)^2 - 8$. *[Lesson 2-7]* **C**

   Ⓐ 19   Ⓑ 21   Ⓒ 41   Ⓓ 57

2. Solve $5x + 13 = -22$. *[Lesson 3-6]* **B**

   Ⓐ $x = -9$ Ⓑ $x = -7$
   Ⓒ $x = -5$ Ⓓ $x = -2$

3. Find the solution of the system $y = 4x - 8$ and $y = -2x + 16$. *[Lesson 4-6]* **A**

   Ⓐ $(4, 8)$ Ⓑ $(3, 10)$ Ⓒ $(8, 4)$ Ⓓ $(5, 12)$

4. Solve the proportion for x: $\frac{x}{160} = \frac{45}{96}$. *[Lesson 5-4]* **C**

   Ⓐ 27   Ⓑ 36   Ⓒ 75   Ⓓ $341.\overline{3}$

5. Find 32% of 625. *[Lesson 6-4]* **B**

   Ⓐ 216   Ⓑ 200
   Ⓒ 1953.125   Ⓓ 20,000

6. Which is divisible by 9? *[Lesson 7-1]* **A**

   Ⓐ 438,633   Ⓑ 482,963
   Ⓒ 748,164   Ⓓ 914,286

7. Find the LCM of 42 and 90. *[Lesson 7-3]* **D**

   Ⓐ 6   Ⓑ 66   Ⓒ 210   Ⓓ 630

8. Subtract $\frac{11}{12} - \frac{5}{18}$. *[Lesson 7-5]* **A**

   Ⓐ $\frac{23}{36}$ Ⓑ $\frac{33}{10}$ Ⓒ $\frac{46}{72}$ Ⓓ $\frac{43}{36}$

9. Find the missing side length. *[Lesson 7-9]* **C**

   Ⓐ 17   Ⓑ 161
   Ⓒ $\sqrt{161}$ Ⓓ 289

10. Which of the following is an irrational number? *[Lesson 7-8]* **C**

    Ⓐ 3   Ⓑ $\frac{1}{3}$ Ⓒ $\sqrt{221}$ Ⓓ $\sqrt{289}$

11. Which unit is best for the height of a building? *[Lesson 8-1]* **D**

    Ⓐ Kilogram   Ⓑ Centimeter
    Ⓒ Liter   Ⓓ Meter

12. Calculate 8.23 ft × 7.8 ft and give the answer with the correct number of significant digits. *[Lesson 8-2]* **A**

    Ⓐ 64 ft^2 Ⓑ 64.2 ft^2
    Ⓒ 64.19 ft^2 Ⓓ 64.194 ft^2

13. Classify $\angle CAE$. *[Lesson 8-4]* **C**

    Ⓐ Obtuse
    Ⓑ Straight
    Ⓒ Acute
    Ⓓ Right

14. If $\overleftrightarrow{AB}$ and $\overleftrightarrow{CD}$ are parallel, which of the following best describes the pair $\angle 1$ and $\angle 2$? *[Lesson 8-5]* **C**

    Ⓐ Complementary
    Ⓑ Congruent
    Ⓒ Supplementary
    Ⓓ Vertical

15. Which is **not** a parallelogram? *[Lesson 8-6]* **D**

    Ⓐ Rectangle   Ⓑ Rhombus
    Ⓒ Square   Ⓓ Trapezoid

16. All sides and angles are congruent on a *[Lesson 8-6]* **A**

    Ⓐ regular polygon
    Ⓑ concave polygon
    Ⓒ triangle
    Ⓓ straight angle

Cumulative Review Chapters 1–8   **439**

About Multiple-Choice Tests

The Cumulative Review found at the end of Chapters 2, 4, 6, 8, 10, and 12 can be used to prepare students for standardized tests.

Students sometimes do not perform as well on standardized tests as they do on other tests. There may be several reasons for this related to the format and content of the test.

• Format
Students may have limited experience with multiple-choice tests. For some questions, such tests are harder because having options may confuse the student.

• Content
A standardized test may cover a broader range of content than normally covered on a test, and the relative emphasis given to various strands may be different than given in class. Also, some questions may assess general aptitude or thinking skills and not include specific pieces of mathematical content.

It is important not to let the differences between standardized tests and other tests shake your students' confidence.

Chapter

9

▶ OVERVIEW

Area and Volume

Section 9A

Perimeter, Area, and Surface Area: Students find the area and perimeter of polygons. They dilate rectangles and predict their perimeter and area. Finding the area and circumference of circles is covered as is finding the surface area of prisms, cylinders, pyramids, and cones.

9-1
Perimeter and Area of Polygons

9-2
Scale and Area

9-3
Circles

9-4
Surface Area of Prisms and Cylinders

9-5
Surface Area of Pyramids and Cones

Section 9B

Volume: Students find the volume of rectangular prisms. They also dilate regular prisms and predict their volume. Finding the volume of prisms, cylinders, pyramids, and cones is also covered.

9-6
Volume of Rectangular Prisms

9-7
Scale and Volume

9-8
Volume of Prisms and Cylinders

9-9
Volume of Pyramids and Cones

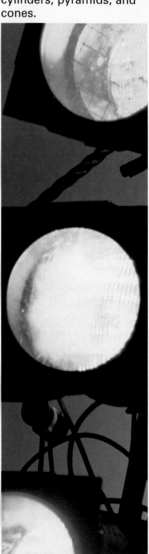

Curriculum Standards

pages

1	**Problem Solving**	Skills and Strategies	442, *449*, 455, 465, 479, 482, 486, 496
		Applications	448–449, 454–455, 459–460, 464–465, 470–471, 479–480, 485–486, 490–491, 495–496
		Exploration	441, 444, 450, 455, 456, 461, 466, 476, 481, 487, 492, 496
2	**Communication**	Oral	440–441, 443, 447, 450, 453, 456, *462, 467*, 469, 475, *477, 482*, 484, *488*, 489, 492–494
		Written	453, 455, 460, 465, 471, *480*, 484, *496*, 499
		Cooperative Learning	441, 444, *446, 448, 449*, 450, *454*, 455, 456, *459*, 461, *463, 464*, 466, *468, 470*, 476, *479*, 481, *485*, 487, *490*, 492, *495*, 496
		Critical Thinking	449, *460*, 465, 471, 480, *491*, 496
3	**Reasoning**	Mathematical	See Standards 5–9, 12, 13 below.
4	**Connections**	Interdisciplinary	Career 446, 448, *458*, 459, 463, *483, 489;* Consumer 455, *475*, 486; Fine Arts 440, *443*, 452, 454, *460*, 470; Geography 460, 479, 495; History 458, *468*, 478, *494, 495;* Industry *465, 475, 483, 489*, 490, *491;* Literature *443*, 464; Science *440*, 441, 448, 454, 459, *463*, 464, *478*, 480, 483, 485, 490, 495; Social Science *440*, 441, 471; Sports *485*
		Technology	440, 444, 450, 456, 465, 472, 475, 481, 497
		Cultural	440, 441, *458*
5	**Number and Number Relationships**		445–460, 462–471, 476–480, 482–496
6	**Number Systems and Number Theory**		445–449, 450–460, 462–471, 476–480, 482–496
7	**Computation and Estimation**		442, 445–460, 462–471, 476–480, 482–497
8	**Patterns/Functions**		450, 452, 455, 471, *480*, 486
9	**Algebra**		445–460, 462–471, 476–480, 482–496
10	**Statistics**		452, 481
12	**Geometry**		444–473, 476–480, 483–497, 499
13	**Measurement**		443–473, 476–498

S T A N D A R D

Italic type indicates Teacher Edition reference.

Teaching Standards

Focus on Diversity

Students come from various cultural, socioeconomic, and linguistic backgrounds. Respect for this diversity should be a cornerstone of all classroom discourse. Teachers should

- acknowledge that differences exist without favoring certain groups.

- promote tolerance of all groups toward each other.

Assessment Standards

Focus on Learning

Self Assessment The Learning Standard encourages students' growth as independent learners by giving opportunities for reflection on their progress and judging the quality of their work. Most alternative-assessment activities can be extended to include a self-assessment component. Self assessment in Chapter 9 gives students the opportunity to evaluate what they learned

- about the area and circumference of a circle.

- about the volume of prisms and cylinders.

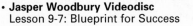

TECHNOLOGY

For the Teacher

- **Teacher Resource Planner CD-ROM**
  Use the teacher planning CD-ROM to view resources available for Chapter 9. You can prepare custom lesson plans or use the default lesson plans provided.

- **World Wide Web**
  Visit **www.teacher.mathsurf.com** for links to lesson plans from teachers and other professionals, NCTM information, and other sites.

- **TestWorks**
  TestWorks provides ready-made tests and can create custom tests and practice worksheets.

For the Parent

- **World Wide Web**
  Parents can use the Web site at **www.parent.mathsurf.com**.

For the Student

- **Interactive CD-ROM**
  Lesson 9-7 has an *Interactive CD-ROM Lesson.* The *Interactive CD-ROM Journal* and *Spreadsheet/Grapher Tool* are also used in Chapter 9.

- **Wide World of Mathematics**
  Lesson 9-1 Middle School: Huge Mall Opens
  Lesson 9-2 Geometry: Seeing with Your Hands
  Lesson 9-3 Geometry: Warp Speed at the Arena
  Lesson 9-4 Geometry: Gateway Arch
  Lesson 9-8 Middle School: Chunnel

- **World Wide Web**
  Use with Chapter and Section Openers;
  Students can go online to the Scott Foresman-Addison Wesley Web site at **www.mathsurf.comm/8/ch9** to collect information about chapter themes.

- **Jasper Woodbury Videodisc**
  Lesson 9-7: Blueprint for Success

SECTION 9A	LESSON	OBJECTIVE	ITBS Form M	CTBS 4th Ed.	CAT 5th Ed.	SAT 9th Ed.	MAT 7th Ed.	Your Form
	9-1	• Find the area and perimeter of polygons.	✗	✗	✗	✗	✗	
	9-2	• Dilate rectangles and predict the resulting perimeters and areas.			✗		✗	
	9-3	• Find the area and circumference of circles.		✗		✗	✗	
	9-4	• Find surface area of prisms and cylinders.						
	9-5	• Find the surface area of pyramids and cones.						

SECTION 9B	LESSON	OBJECTIVE	ITBS Form M	CTBS 4th Ed.	CAT 5th Ed.	SAT 9th Ed.	MAT 7th Ed.	Your Form
	9-6	• Determine the volume of rectangular prisms.		✗		✗	✗	
	9-7	• Dilate rectangular prisms and predict their volume.					✗	
	9-8	• Find the volume of prisms and cylinders.						
	9-9	• Find the volume of pyramids and cones.						

Key: ITBS - Iowa Test of Basic Skills; CTBS - Comprehensive Test of Basic Skills; CAT - California Achievement Test; SAT - Stanford Achievement Test; MAT - Metropolitan Achievement Test

ASSESSMENT PROGRAM

▶ **Traditional Assessment**

	QUICK QUIZZES	SECTION REVIEW	CHAPTER REVIEW	CHAPTER ASSESSMENT FREE RESPONSE	CHAPTER ASSESSMENT MULTIPLE CHOICE	CUMULATIVE REVIEW
	TE: pp. 449, 455, 460, 465, 471, 480, 486, 491, 496	SE: pp. 474, 498 *Quiz 9A, 9B	SE: pp. 500–501	SE: p. 502 *Ch. 9 Tests Forms A, B, E	*Ch. 9 Tests Forms C, E	SE: p. 503 *Ch. 9 Test Form F; Quarterly Test Ch. 1–9

▶ **Alternate Assessment**

	INTERVIEW	JOURNAL	ONGOING	PERFORMANCE	PORTFOLIO	PROJECT	SELF
	TE: p. 471	SE: pp. 455, 460, 471, 474, 491 TE: pp. 455, 465, 480, 496	TE: pp. 444, 450, 457, 461, 467, 473, 476, 481, 488, 493, 497	SE: pp. 502, 503 TE: p. 449 *Ch. 9 Tests Forms D, E	TE: p. 486	SE: pp. 441, 455, 496 TE: p. 441	TE: pp. 460, 491

*Tests and quizzes are in *Assessment Sourcebook.* Test Form E is a mixed response test. Forms for Alternate Assessment are also available in *Assessment Sourcebook.*

 TestWorks: Test and Practice Software

REGULAR PACING

Day	5 classes per week
1	Chapter 9 Opener; Problem Solving Focus
2	Section **9A** Opener; Lesson **9-1**
3	Lesson **9-2**
4	Lesson **9-3**
5	Lesson **9-4**
6	Lesson **9-5**
7	Technology
8	**9A** Connect; **9A** Review
9	Section **9B** Opener; Lesson **9-6**
10	Lesson **9-7**
11	Lesson **9-8**
12	Lesson **9-9**
13	**9B** Connect; **9B** Review
14	Extend Key Ideas
15	Chapter 9 Summary and Review
16	Chapter 9 Assessment
17	Cumulative Review, Chapters 1–9
18	Quarterly Test, Chapters 1–9

▶ BLOCK SCHEDULING OPTIONS

Block Scheduling for *Complete Course*

Chapter 9 may be presented in

- thirteen 90-minute blocks
- fifteen 75-minute blocks

Each block consists of a combination of

- Chapter and Section Openers
- Explores
- Lesson Development
- Problem Solving Focus
- Technology
- Extend Key Ideas
- Connect
- Review
- Assessment

For details, see *Block Scheduling Handbook*.

Block Scheduling for *Lab-Based Course*

In each block, 30–40 minutes is devoted to lab activities including

- Explores in the Student Edition
- Connect pages in the Student Edition
- Technology options in the Student Edition
- Reteaching Activities in the Teacher Edition

For details, see *Block Scheduling Handbook*.

Block Scheduling for *Interdisciplinary Course*

Each block integrates math with another subject area.

In Chapter 9, interdisciplinary topics include

- Theater
- Packages

Themes for Interdisciplinary Team Teaching 9A and 9B are

- Shopping Center Design Problems
- Packaging of Food Products

For details, see *Block Scheduling Handbook*.

Block Scheduling for *Course with Connected Mathematics*

In each block, investigations from **Connected Mathematics** replace or enhance the lessons in Chapter 9.

Connected Mathematics topics for Chapter 9 can be found in

- *Thinking with Mathematical Models*

For details, see *Block Scheduling Handbook*.

INTERDISCIPLINARY BULLETIN BOARD

Set Up

Separate the bulletin board into 8 sections. Label each section with one of the following titles: Rectangle, Square, Triangle, Circle, Prism, Cylinder, Pyramid, Cone. In each section, put a line drawing of the figure and include the appropriate formulas. Also, put a photo in each section illustrating a real-world example of the given figure.

Procedure

Have students work in groups to illustrate one section of the bulletin board. Suggest that they look in magazines or newspapers for real-world examples of their shape or just sketch different views of their shape. They should include the appropriate formulas.

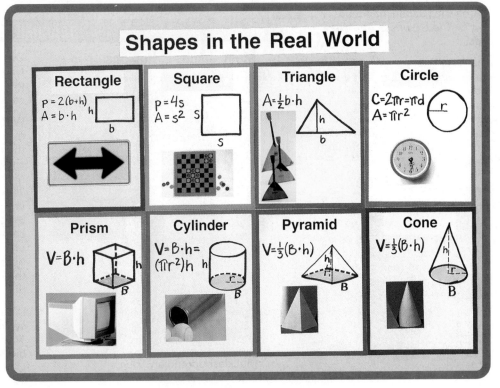

The information on these pages shows how area and volume are used in real-life situations.

World Wide Web

If your class has access to the World Wide Web, you might want to use the information found at the Web site addresses given.

Extensions

The following activities do not require access to the World Wide Web.

Arts & Literature

Bring in some examples of cubism art. Explain that cubist art analyzes the subject matter in terms of basic geometric shapes and tries to show the subject matter from several different viewpoints at the same time. Encourage interested students to draw their own cubist art.

People of the World

Students might do some additional research on Srinivasa Ramanujan to find out what contributions he has made to mathematics.

Entertainment

Students who would like to know more about the world's largest Ferris wheel, Cosmoclock 21 in Yokohama City, Japan, can read about it in *The Guinness Book of Records*.

Science

Have interested students find out more about Eratosthenes's experiment and then illustrate it on a poster board. A book that would be very helpful to them in their research is entitled *How Math Works* by Carol Vorderman (Dorling Kindersley, 1996). Students should look on page 135.

Social Studies

Have students do additional research on pyramids to find other interesting mathematical facts that were known to the ancient Egyptian pyramid builders. The ancient Egyptians also understood the relationship between the height of a pyramid and the size, angle, and slope of each of its triangular walls.

9 Area and Volume

Arts & Literature Link
www.mathsurf.com/8/ch9/arts

Entertainment Link
www.mathsurf.com/8/ch9/ent

Arts & Literature

The cubism art movement was largely attributed to European artists Pablo Picasso and George Braque.

Entertainment

Yokohama City, Japan, is the home of the world's largest Ferris Wheel, which boasts a diameter of 328 feet.

People of the World

Indian mathematician, Srinivasa Ramanujan (1887–1920), developed a formula for calculating a decimal approximation for π. Sixty-seven years after his death, computers, using a formula very similar to his, calculated the value of π to more than 100 million decimal places.

440

TEACHER TALK

Meet James E. Hopkins

Director of Education
Muckleshoot Indian Tribe
Auburn, Washington

One of the most sacred experiences in Native American cultures is the sweat lodge. It is used for cleansing the body, soul, and spirit.

When teaching circles, I have students make a model of a sweat lodge and find the circumferences and areas of the circles involved. A sweat lodge with a radius of 7 feet is made by putting 12 to 14 ten-foot long willow shoots upright in a circle and burying the ends in 8-inch holes. The willows are bent to the center, tied, and covered with blankets or hides. The door has a two-foot opening facing east, and a fire pit in the center of the lodge is 15 inches in diameter.

Detailed information about building a sweat lodge can be found in *The Indian Tipi: Its History, Construction, and Use*, by Reginald and Gladys Laubin, University of Oklahoma Press, 1957/1977.

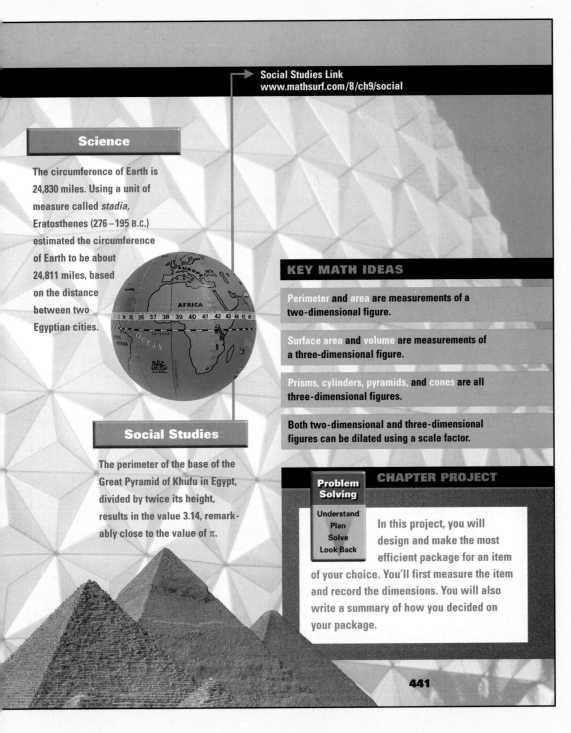

Social Studies Link
www.mathsurf.com/8/ch9/social

Science

The circumference of Earth is 24,830 miles. Using a unit of measure called *stadia*, Eratosthenes (276–195 B.C.) estimated the circumference of Earth to be about 24,811 miles, based on the distance between two Egyptian cities.

Social Studies

The perimeter of the base of the Great Pyramid of Khufu in Egypt, divided by twice its height, results in the value 3.14, remarkably close to the value of π.

KEY MATH IDEAS

Perimeter and area are measurements of a two-dimensional figure.

Surface area and volume are measurements of a three-dimensional figure.

Prisms, cylinders, pyramids, and cones are all three-dimensional figures.

Both two-dimensional and three-dimensional figures can be dilated using a scale factor.

CHAPTER PROJECT

Problem Solving
- Understand
- Plan
- Solve
- Look Back

In this project, you will design and make the most efficient package for an item of your choice. You'll first measure the item and record the dimensions. You will also write a summary of how you decided on your package.

441

Chapter Project

Students choose an item and then design and make the most efficient package possible for the item.

Materials

Any item of students' choice to package; packaging supplies such as cardboard, scissors, and tape

Resources

Chapter 9 Project Master

Introduce the Project

- Show students an unusually shaped item. Discuss the shapes your object exhibits.

- Display the packaging materials that you might use to package your item.

- Discuss with students what they should consider when deciding how to package the item. For example, an item might fit nicely in a triangular-prism box, but it might be harder and more expensive to make such a box.

Project Progress

Section A, page 455 Students identify the shapes their item exhibits. They then measure the perimeter and area of the sides of their item (2-D measurement).

Section B, page 496 Students determine the volume of their item. They describe the relationship between the dimensions of their package and the dimensions of their item.

Community Project

A community project for Chapter 9 is available in *Home and Community Connections*.

Cooperative Learning

You may want to use Teaching Tool Transparency 1: Cooperative Learning Checklist with **Explore** and other group activities in this chapter.

You may choose to use this project as a performance assessment for the chapter.

Performance Assessment Key

Level 4 Full Accomplishment

Level 3 Substantial Accomplishment

Level 2 Partial Accomplishment

Level 1 Little Accomplishment

Suggested Scoring Rubric

4
- Measurement and design techniques indicate an excellent understanding of perimeter, area, and volume.
- Written summary shows extremely thoughtful consideration of the procedure.

3
- Measurement and design techniques indicate a reasonable understanding of perimeter, area, and volume.
- Written summary shows thoughtful consideration of the procedure.

2
- Measurement and design techniques indicate a weak understanding of perimeter, area, and volume.
- Written summary shows little consideration of the procedure.

1
- Item package and written summary indicate only a remote understanding of the purpose of the project.

Checking for a Reasonable Answer

The Point
Students focus on deciding if an answer to a division problem needs to be rounded to correctly answer the question.

Resources
Teaching Tool Transparency 17: Problem-Solving Guidelines

 Interactive CD-ROM Journal.

About the Page

Using the Problem-Solving Process
An important skill in successful problem solving is the ability to determine whether an answer to a division problem needs to be rounded, and, if so, if it should be rounded up or down. Discuss the following steps for deciding how and when to round an answer:

- Read the problem carefully to determine exactly what it is asking you to find.

- Use common sense.

Ask …
- Do you know exactly what the problem is asking you to find?

- In Exercise 3, did you make sure to take all of the information in the problem into consideration? In this problem, you also have the price of the individual pins versus the boxed dozen pins to consider.

Answers for Problems
1. Too low because 14 people need the 62nd table.

2. Too low because ten books require the 12th box.

3. Too low because 45 boxes is less expensive.

4. Too low because the graduates and 23 chaperones need a total of 24 buses.

Journal

Ask students to write a division problem in which three different questions can be asked: one requiring rounding the answer up, one requiring rounding down, and one that does not require rounding.

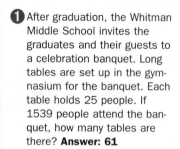

Problem Solving

Understand
Plan
Solve
Look Back

Checking for a Reasonable Answer

When you *look back* to check your answer to a problem, it is important to evaluate whether rounding is reasonable. Deciding whether to round up or down often depends upon common sense and what you are asked to solve.

Problem Solving Focus

Each of the problems below gives the answer, but the answer may not be accurate enough for the situation. State if each answer is "close enough," "too low," or "too high," and explain why.

1 After graduation, the Whitman Middle School invites the graduates and their guests to a celebration banquet. Long tables are set up in the gymnasium for the banquet. Each table holds 25 people. If 1539 people attend the banquet, how many tables are there? **Answer: 61**

2 The printing company delivers the yearbooks in boxes that contain 48 books each. There are 538 graduates. If each one gets a book, how many boxes will be delivered? **Answer: 11**

3 Each graduate receives a souvenir pin with the name of the school and the year of their graduation. The pins are packed in boxes of a dozen, and cost $28.00 a box. Individual pins cost $3.00. How many boxes should the school buy? **Answer: 44 plus 10 individual pins**

4 The day before graduation, the school takes all the graduates to an amusement park. They are taken to the park in buses that each hold 24 people. An adult chaperone will ride on each bus. How many buses should the school request? **Answer: 22**

442

Additional Problem

Each of the 538 graduates is allowed to invite four people to the graduation. If graduation invitations come in boxes of 25, how many boxes should the school purchase? 87 boxes (86 boxes would be not quite enough)

Section 9A

Perimeter, Area, and Surface Area

Visit **www.teacher.mathsurf.com** for links to lesson plans from teachers and other professionals, NCTM information, and other sites.

▶ Student Edition

LESSON PLANNING GUIDE

LESSON	MATERIALS	VOCABULARY
Chapter 9 Opener		
Problem Solving Focus		
Section 9A Opener		
9-1 Perimeter and Area of Polygons	geometry software	perimeter, area
9-2 Scale and Area	Dynamic geometry software	dilation, scale factor
9-3 Circles	Dynamic geometry software	circumference, center, radius, diameter, π (pi), inscribed, circumscribed
9-4 Surface Area of Prisms and Cylinders	tape, scissors	polyhedron, face, edge, vertex, surface area, prism, base, cylinder
9-5 Surface Area of Pyramids and Cones	scissors, tape, ruler	pyramid, height, slant height
Technology	geometry software	
Connect	drawing paper, ruler, compass, drawing pens	
Review		

▶ Ancillaries

DAILY	OTHER
	Ch. 9 Project Master Ch. 9 Community Project Teaching Tool Trans. 1
	Teaching Tool Trans. 17 *Interactive CD-ROM Journal*
9-1	Teaching Tool Trans. 2, 3, 10, 18 Lesson Enhancement Trans. 39 *CD-ROM Geometry Tool* *WW Math—Middle School*
9-2	Chapter 9 Project Master *CD-ROM Geometry Tool* *WW Math—Geometry*
9-3	*CD-ROM Geometry Tool* *WW Math—Geometry*
9-4	Lesson Enhancement Trans. 40 *WW Math—Geometry*
9-5	Lesson Enhancement Transparencies 41, 42
	CD-ROM Geometry Tool
	Teaching Tool Trans. 15, 16 Interdisc. Team Teaching 9A
	Practice 9A; Quiz 9A; *TestWorks*

SKILLS TRACE

LESSON	SKILL	FIRST INTRODUCED			DEVELOP	PRACTICE/ APPLY	REVIEW
		GR. 6	GR. 7	GR. 8			
9-1	Finding area and perimeter of polygons.	✗			pp. 444–447	pp. 448–449	pp. 474, 500, 502, 517
9-2	Dilating rectangles and predicting perimeter and area of rectangles.		✗		pp. 450–453	pp. 454–455	pp. 474, 500, 502, 522
9-3	Finding area and circumference of circles.	✗			pp. 456–458	pp. 459–460	pp. 501, 527, 559, 675
9-4	Finding surface area of prisms and cylinders.	✗			pp. 461–463	pp. 464–465	pp. 474, 501, 502, 536
9-5	Finding surface area of pyramids and cones.			✗ p. 466	pp. 466–469	pp. 470–471	pp. 501, 541, 559, 630

CONNECTED MATHEMATICS

The unit *Thinking with Mathematical Models (Representing Relationships),* from the **Connected Mathematics** series, can be used with Section 9A.

INTERDISCIPLINARY TEAM TEACHING

Math and Science/Technology
(Worksheet pages 35–36: Teacher pages T35–T36)

In this lesson, students use calculation of perimeter and surface area to solve design problems in a shopping center.

Name _____ *Math and Science/Technology*

Use calculation of perimeter and surface area to solve design problems in a shopping center.

There are more than 30,000 shopping centers in the United States. About 2,000 of them are completely enclosed centers called malls. Malls are fairly recent additions to the shopping scene. The first one opened in 1956 in Edina, Minnesota. The idea was to keep shoppers warm and dry in severe winter weather. Modern malls have expanded this idea to keep shoppers happy, comfortable, and amused, so they will stay and shop.

Chances are you've spent some time in a mall this month. In fact, a typical American probably spends at least two hours a month in a mall. Shopping center planners would like that amount of time to increase, because the more time you spend in a shopping center, the more money you are likely to spend. Shopping center planners study the way people shop and design malls to encourage people to spend their time there. For example, the designers know that most people won't walk more than 600 feet in a mall. If people think the walk down the mall is too long, they're less likely to visit. Mall planners break up a shopper's line of sight with fountains, trees, or bending corridors so shoppers can't see how far they really have to walk. Designers add food courts because research shows that shoppers who can snack will stay and shop longer. Researchers have even learned how fast most people walk past the store windows (about 4 feet per second), so store owners know they've got just a few seconds to grab your attention and get you inside.

Planning a mall requires more than psychology. It also involves architectural planning. Plants and trees in the mall must get enough light. The air conditioning system must be large enough to cool every space. The walkways must be strong enough to support the weight of crowds, furniture, and merchandise.

The diagram below shows the floorplan of a small mall. Use it to do calculations and solve planning problems.

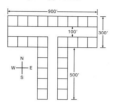

1. What are some of the things that mall designers would have to consider when planning a mall?

   Accept all reasonable answers, including parking, lighting inside the mall, plumbing and bathrooms, placement of escalators and stairways, and the locations of stores and restaurants.

Name _____ *Math and Science/Technology*

2. With the exception of the entrance, the mall designers have decided to plant trees every six feet around the outside of the mall. How many trees will they need?

   550 trees

3. The central walkway of the mall will be covered with marble tile. How much tile (in square feet) must be ordered to cover this area?

   150,000 square feet;
   $(100 \times 900) + (100 \times 600) = 150,000$

4. The owner of a store wants to give his walls and ceilings two coats of Mellow Yellow paint. He doesn't have to paint the wall that fronts on the mall corridor because it's glass. The store has ceilings that are 20 feet high. If each gallon of Mellow Yellow covers 400 square feet of surface, how many gallons of paint will he have to buy?

   80; surface area =
   $3(20 \times 100) + (100 \times 100) = 16,000 \text{ ft}^2$; $16,000 \text{ ft}^2 \div 400 \text{ ft}^2/\text{gal} = 40 \text{ gal} \times 2 \text{ coats} = 80 \text{ gal}$

5. The shopping center planners would like to place a circular fountain halfway up the north-south corridor of the mall. If at least 20 feet will be needed for a walkway between the fountain and each wall nearby, what is the maximum area of the fountain? Use $\pi = 3.14$

   2,827 square feet; $100 - 40 = 60$ foot diameter; $r = 30$ feet; $A = \pi r^2$; $A = 3.14(30)^2 \approx 2,826$

6. If the shopping center costs $50 million to build, what is the cost per square foot? Round to the nearest dollar.

   $119.05 per square foot;
   $(500 \times 300) + (900 \times 300) = 420,000 \text{ ft}^2$; $\$50,000,000 \div 420,000 \text{ ft}^2 = \$119.05/\text{ft}^2$

7. What occupations might be involved in planning a mall?

   Answers might include: architects, construction workers, plumbers, electricians, landscapers, engineers, and salespeople.

8. Visit a local mall. Make a floor plan of its corridors. In what ways is it similar to, or different from, the mall described in this activity?

   Possible answers should address such items as design, length, width, construction materials, structures such as fountains and gardens, length of uninterrupted walkways, area, distance from walls to structures.

BIBLIOGRAPHY

FOR TEACHERS

Brockett, Oscar G. *History of the Theater.* 7th ed. Needham Heights, MA: Allyn & Bacon, 1995.

Brown, John Russell, ed. *The Oxford Illustrated History of Theater.* New York, NY: Oxford University Press, 1995.

Holden, Alan. *Shapes, Space, and Symmetry.* Mineola, NY: Dover, 1991.

Ogilvy, Charles S. *Excursions in Geometry.* Mineola, NY: Dover, 1990.

Parker, Wilford O. and R. C. Wolf. *Scene Design and Stage Lighting.* 6th ed. Austin, TX: Holt, Rinehart, 1990.

FOR STUDENTS

Cassady, Marsh. *The Theater and You.* Colorado Springs, CO: Meriwether, 1992.

Cassin-Scott, Jack. *Amateur Dramatics.* New York, NY: Sterling Publishing Company, 1992.

Sitarz, Paula Gaj. *The Curtain Rises: A History of Theater from Its Origins in Greece and Rome through the English Restoration.* White Hall, VA: Shoe Tree Press, 1991.

Sitarz, Paula Gaj. *The Curtain Rises: A History of European Theater from the Eighteenth Century to the Present.* Volume II. Cincinnati, OH: Betterway Books, 1993.

SECTION 9A

Perimeter, Area, and Surface Area

▶ Fine Arts Link   ▶ Literature Link   ▶ www.mathsurf.com/8/ch9/theater

Radio City Music Hall opened on December 27, 1932, as the first building of Rockefeller Center in New York City. S. L. "Roxy" Rothafel conceived the building and was determined to make Radio City the world's biggest theatrical environment in his time. Rothafel designed the interior of the music hall to feature a golden arch and ceiling that gives the appearance of a huge sunset.

Virtually everything about Radio City is big and impressive. The stage itself is still one of the largest and best equipped theatrical stages in the world. The stage measures 144 feet wide by 60 feet deep. It features a revolving turntable, 43 feet in diameter, and three stage elevators, each 70 feet long. Each elevator is capable of being lowered 27 feet into the basement or raised 13 feet above the level of the stage. In fact, the elevator system—and the hydraulics that run it—became the design prototype for the elevators in U.S. aircraft carriers during World War II.

The Great Stage

1 What mathematical measurements might the original architects and engineers have used to design Radio City Music Hall?

2 What mathematical measurements of the great stage might set designers for a production company want to know? How might these be used?

3 How might mathematics be used in producing a 45-minute stage show?

443

Where are we now?

In Grade 7, students explored perimeter, area, and volume.

They learned how to

- find perimeter and circumference.

- find the area of polygons and circles.

- find the surface area of solids.

- find the volume of prisms and cylinders.

Where are we going?

In Grade 8, Section 9A, students will

- find the perimeter and area of polygons.

- dilate rectangles and predict their perimeter and area.

- find the area and circumference of circles.

- find the surface area of prisms, cylinders, pyramids, and cones.

Theme: Theater

World Wide Web

If your class has access to the World Wide Web, you might want to use the information found at the Web site address given. The interdisciplinary links relate to topics discussed in this section.

About the Page

This page introduces the theme of the section, theater, and discusses the importance of measurement in designing theaters and stages like Radio City Music Hall.

Ask …

- Did you ever hear of Radio City Music Hall before? Where?

- Why do you think the stage has a revolving turntable?

Extension

The following activities do not require access to the World Wide Web.

Fine Arts

Ask students if they have ever seen a professionally produced play. If they have, ask them to describe the set. Was it elaborate or simple? How did it affect their impression of the play?

Literature

The Globe Theater in London burned during a performance of *Henry VIII* by William Shakespeare. Ask interested students to research this theater.

Answers for Questions

1. Possible answer: Ceiling height and size of room for acoustics, height of stage.

2. Possible answer: Width and depth of stage, distance from stage to audience; To decide how large to make the sets.

3. Possible answer: To measure actors and their clothing sizes, to time the show, to measure angles of lighting.

Connect

On page 473, students will design their own stage set for a school play.

Objective
- **Find the area and perimeter of polygons.**

Vocabulary
- **Perimeter, area**

Materials
- **Explore: Geometry software**

NCTM Standards
- **1–6, 7, 9, 12**

> **Review**

Fill in the blanks.

1. All polygons with 3 sides are called ___. triangles

2. All polygons with 4 sides are called ___. quadrilaterals

3. A regular quadrilateral is a ___. square

4. A ___ polygon has all its sides and all its angles congruent. regular

Available on Daily Transparency 9-1

▶ **Lesson Link**

You may wish to use Teaching Tool Transparency 10: Dot Paper and 18: Power Polygons with this lesson.

1 Introduce

Explore

The Point
Students use geometry software to discover patterns between the number of sides of a regular polygon, the length of a side, and the perimeter of the polygon.

Ongoing Assessment
Check that students are using the geometry software correctly. Check students' tables in Step 2 for correct headings and entries.

9-1 Perimeter and Area of Polygons

You'll Learn ...
■ to find the area and perimeter of polygons

... How It's Used
Landscapers use perimeter and area to determine the amount of materials needed for a garden.

Vocabulary
perimeter
area

▶ **Lesson Link** You've looked at units of measurement and many kinds of polygons. Now you'll determine perimeter and area of polygons. ◀

The **perimeter** (p) is the distance around a figure.

The perimeter of the figure to the right is 35 centimeters.

Explore   Perimeter

Side by Side

Materials: Geometry software

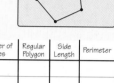

1. Use your geometry software to draw regular polygons with 3, 4, 5, and 6 sides. Make two different polygons for each number of sides.

2. On paper, make a table with the following headings: Number of Sides, Regular Polygon, Side Length, and Perimeter.

Number of Sides	Regular Polygon	Side Length	Perimeter

3. For each regular polygon, measure the length of a side and the perimeter. Use these measurements to complete the table.

4. Look for a pattern in the data from your table. In a regular polygon, what is the relationship between the number of sides, the side length, and the perimeter? State the rule for this relationship.

5. Test your rule to see if it works with regular polygons that have more than 6 sides.

Learn   Perimeter and Area of Polygons

You can calculate the perimeter of any figure by adding all the side lengths.

You can calculate the perimeter of rectangles and squares using a formula.

444 *Chapter 9 • Area and Volume*

▶ **MEETING INDIVIDUAL NEEDS**

Resources

9-1 Practice
9-1 Reteaching
9-1 Problem Solving
9-1 Enrichment
9-1 Daily Transparency
    Problem of the Day
    Review
    Quick Quiz
Teaching Tool
Transparencies 2, 3, 10, 18
Lesson Enhancement
Transparency 39

Interactive CD-ROM Geometry Tool

Wide World of Mathematics Middle School: Huge Mall Opens

Learning Modalities

Kinesthetic Have students use geoboards and rubber bands to determine perimeter and area of triangles and parallelograms. Show them how both whole and partial units need to be counted.

Visual Shade the interior region of a geometric figure to represent its area. Show the same figure without the shading to represent the perimeter of the figure.

Social In **Explore**, students work with partners to investigate perimeter.

Inclusion

To differentiate between perimeter and area, outline any two-dimensional geometric figure on the floor with masking tape. Have students walk around the figure to "experience" perimeter. Then have them cover the interior of the figure with paper to show area and to emphasize the difference between area and perimeter.

Remind students to add new vocabulary to their reference notebook.

The perimeter of a rectangle is two times the base (b) plus two times the height (h).

$$p = 2b + 2h = 2(b + h)$$

The perimeter of a square is four times the length of a side (s).

$$p = 4s$$

Example 1

A large theater will have an orchestra pit, where a full orchestra will play the music for a musical or opera. What is the perimeter of the orchestra pit shown?

Add all side lengths.

$$10 + 40 + 10 + 13 + 65 + 13 = 151 \text{ ft}$$

The perimeter of the orchestra pit is 151 ft.

Examples

2 Use a formula to find the perimeter of the rectangle.

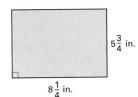

$$p = 2(b + h)$$
$$p = 2\left(8\frac{1}{4} + 5\frac{3}{4}\right) = 2 \cdot (14) = 28$$

The perimeter is 28 in.

3 Find the perimeter of the L-shaped figure.

First, find x. $x = 15 - 3$
$$x = 12$$
$$p = 3 + 4 + x + 3 + 15 + 7$$
$$p = 3 + 4 + 12 + 3 + 15 + 7 = 44$$

The perimeter is 44 m.

Try It

a. Use a formula to find the perimeter of the square. **2.12 in.**

b. Find the perimeter of the L-shaped figure. **22 m**

MATH EVERY DAY

▶ Problem of the Day

When cutting along the grid lines, there are six different ways to cut a 4-by-4 square into congruent halves. One way is shown. Show the other five ways.

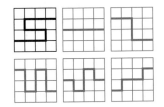

Available on Daily Transparency 9-1

An Extension is provided in the transparency package.

Fact of the Day

The word *theater* comes from the Greek word *theatron*, which means "a place for seeing."

Mental Math

Do these mentally.

1. $10 + 4 + 2 + 6 + 7 + 4$ 33

2. $2 + 9 + 5 + 3 + 12 + 9$ 40

3. $8 + 5 + 3 + 16 + 2 + 14$ 48

For Groups That Finish Early

Do you think the rule you wrote in Step 4 would work for all polygons? Test it to find out. No, the rule only works for regular polygons.

Answers for Explore

1–3. See students' work.

4. $n \times l$ = perimeter of regular polygon with n = number of sides and l = side length.

5. $n \times l$ does work for all regular polygons.

2 Teach

Learn

You may wish to use Lesson Enhancement Transparency 39 with this lesson.

Alternate Examples

1. A large piece of stage scenery is being built with the shape and size shown. What is the perimeter of the scenery?

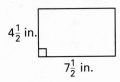

Add all side lengths. $7 + 50 + 7 + 10 + 62 + 10 = 146$ ft
The perimeter is 146 ft.

2. Use a formula to find the perimeter of the rectangle.

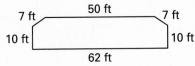

$$p = 2(b + h)$$
$$p = 2(7\frac{1}{2} + 4\frac{1}{2}) = 2 \cdot (12) = 24$$

The perimeter is 24 in.

3. Find the perimeter of the T-shaped figure.

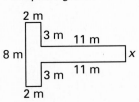

First, find x. $x = 8 - 3 - 3$
$$x = 2$$
$$p = 2 + 8 + 2 + 3 + 11 + x + 11 + 3$$
$$p = 2 + 8 + 2 + 3 + 11 + 2 + 11 + 3 = 42$$

The perimeter is 42 m.

4. The auditorium at South High School has a stage that measures 35 ft by 30 ft. What is the area of the stage?

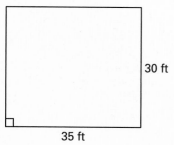

30 ft

35 ft

$A = b \cdot h$
$A = 35 \cdot 30$ Substitute and solve.
$A = 1050 \text{ ft}^2$

5. Find the area of the parallelogram.

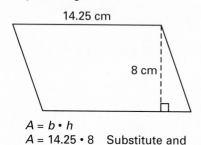

14.25 cm

8 cm

$A = b \cdot h$
$A = 14.25 \cdot 8$ Substitute and solve.
$A = 114 \text{ cm}^2$

▶ **Career Link**

People in the theater refer to the side of the stage that is to the audience's right as *stage right*.

The **area** (A) of a polygon is the number of square units contained in that polygon. You can calculate the area of rectangles and squares using a formula.

The area of a rectangle is the base (b) times the height (h). $A = b \cdot h$

The area of a square is the length of a side (s) squared. $A = s^2$

Example 4

The New York State Theater has scenery-storage areas in each wing. Each is 40 ft by 35 ft. What is the area of one of these storage areas?

$A = b \cdot h$
$A = 40 \cdot 35$ Substitute and solve.
$A = 1400 \text{ ft}^2$

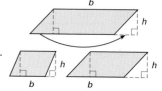

35 ft

40 ft

You can use the formula for the area of a rectangle to find the area of other polygons.

In a parallelogram, the height (h) is the perpendicular distance between the bases (b).

The area of a parallelogram is the length of the base (b) times the height (h):
$A = b \cdot h$.

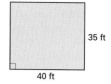

Example 5

Find the area of the parallelogram.

$A = b \cdot h$
$A = 13.5 \cdot 7.5$ Substitute and solve.
$A = 101.25 \text{ cm}^2$

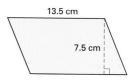

13.5 cm

7.5 cm

Try It

Find the area of each polygon.

a. $4\frac{1}{3}$ yd $10\frac{5}{6}$ yd^2

$2\frac{1}{2}$ yd

b.   34.4375 cm^2

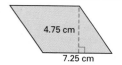

4.75 cm

7.25 cm

MEETING MIDDLE SCHOOL CLASSROOM NEEDS

Tips from Middle School Teachers

I keep stressing the difference between linear and two-dimensional (area) measures. Perimeter is a linear measure. I illustrate this by showing a polygon made of straws which represent line segments. If all the straws that make up the polygon are placed end-to-end, my students can see that the perimeter is a linear measure. Similarly, I illustrate area by showing a polygon covered with 1-inch squares.

Cooperative Learning

Have students work in small groups on a project to create a cartoon character out of polygons. After each group has created their character, have them trade with another group and challenge them to determine the perimeter and area of the figure.

Team Teaching

Make sure that the other teachers on your team know that the students have been studying perimeter and area so that they can point out when these concepts are used in their subject areas.

The height of a triangle is the perpendicular distance between the base and the opposite vertex.

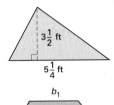

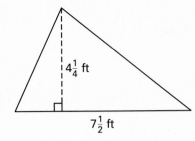
The area of a triangle is $A = \frac{1}{2}b \cdot h$.

The area of a triangle is $\frac{1}{2}$ the area of a rectangle or parallelogram.

Example 6

Find the area of the triangle.

$A = \frac{1}{2}b \cdot h$

$A = \frac{1}{2} \cdot 5\frac{1}{4} \cdot 3\frac{1}{2} = \frac{1}{2} \cdot \frac{21}{4} \cdot \frac{7}{2}$ Substitute and solve.

$A = \frac{147}{16} = 9\frac{3}{16}$ ft²

The area of a trapezoid is $A = \frac{1}{2}h(b_1 + b_2)$.

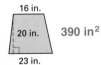

Example 7

Find the area of the trapezoid.

$A = \frac{1}{2}h(b_1 + b_2)$

$A = \frac{1}{2} \cdot 12(10 + 15)$ Substitute and solve.

$A = \frac{1}{2} \cdot 12 \cdot 25 = 150$ cm²

Try It

Find the area of each polygon.

a.
17.5 mm
105 mm²
12 mm

b.
16 in.
20 in.   390 in²
23 in.

Check   Your Understanding

1. Describe the difference between the perimeter and the area of a polygon.

2. Which formula would you use to find the area of a rhombus?

Alternate Examples

6. Find the area of the triangle.

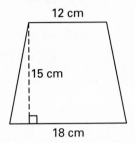
$4\frac{1}{4}$ ft

$7\frac{1}{2}$ ft

$A = \frac{1}{2}b \cdot h$ Substitute and solve.

$A = \frac{1}{2} \cdot 7\frac{1}{2} \cdot 4\frac{1}{4} = \frac{1}{2} \cdot \frac{15}{2} \cdot \frac{17}{4}$

$= \frac{255}{16}$

$A = 15\frac{15}{16}$ ft²

7. Find the area of the trapezoid.

12 cm

15 cm

18 cm

$A = \frac{1}{2}h(b_1 + b_2)$ Substitute and solve.

$A = \frac{1}{2} \cdot 15(12 + 18) = \frac{1}{2} \cdot 15 \cdot 30$

$A = 225$ cm²

3 Practice and Assess

Check

Remind students that a rhombus is a parallelogram with four congruent sides.

Answers for Check Your Understanding

1. Perimeter measures length. Area uses square units.

2. The formula for the area of a parallelogram, $A = b \times h$.

Assignment Guide

- **Basic**
  1, 2–14 evens, 15, 16, 18, 19, 20–34 evens

- **Average**
  1, 3–15 odds, 16–19, 21–33 odds

- **Enriched**
  3–15 odds, 16–19, 21–25, 27, 33, 34

Exercise Notes

- **Exercise 1**

Error Prevention When using $A = \frac{1}{2}b \cdot h$, some students will multiply both the b and the h by $\frac{1}{2}$. Remind students that each factor is multiplied only once. This may be a good time to review the Distributive Property.

- **Exercise 15**

Career A set designer begins by studying the play as a whole. The scenic demands specific to a play are then analyzed.

Reteaching

Activity

Materials: Geoboards with large rubber bands or graph paper if geoboards are not available

- Work with a partner.

- Take turns using a rubber band to form triangles on your geoboard (or drawing them on graph paper). After each triangle is formed, have your partner count units and partial units to determine the perimeter and area of the triangles.

- Then have your partner apply the correct formula to determine the perimeter and area of the triangles. Check that the numbers are close.

- Repeat Steps 2 and 3 for other geometric figures discussed in this lesson.

- Now, work together to write your own definitions of perimeter and area.

448   Chapter 9

9-1 Exercises and Applications

Practice and Apply

1. **Getting Started** Find the area of the triangle.
   a. Use the formula $A = \frac{1}{2}b \cdot h$. $A = \frac{1}{2}(5.5) \cdot 4$
   b. Solve. $A = 11$

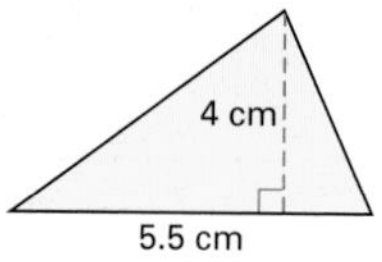

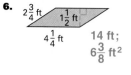
4 cm / 5.5 cm

Find the perimeter and area of each polygon.

2.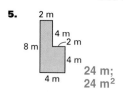
$h = 16$ in.; $b = 21$ in.
74 in.; 336 in²

3.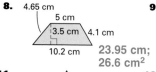
25 cm; 39.0625 cm²
6.25 cm

4.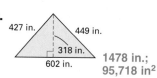
427 in. / 449 in. / 318 in. / 602 in.
1478 in.; 95,718 in²

5. 2 m / 4 m / 2 m / 8 m / 4 m / 4 m
24 m; 24 m²

6.
$2\frac{3}{4}$ ft / $1\frac{1}{2}$ ft / $4\frac{1}{4}$ ft
14 ft; $6\frac{3}{8}$ ft²

7.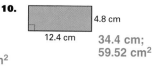
6 cm / 7.2 cm / 5 cm / 8 cm
≈ 35.2 cm; ≈ 52 cm²

8. 4.65 cm / 5 cm / 3.5 cm / 4.1 cm / 10.2 cm
23.95 cm; 26.6 cm²

9.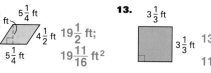
16.1 m / 16.1 m / 14.75 / 16.1 m / 16.1 m
64.4 m; 237.475 m²

10.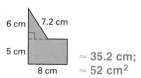
4.8 cm / 12.4 cm
34.4 cm; 59.52 cm²

11. 4.5 cm / 5.25 cm / 5.25 cm / 5.25 cm
15.75 cm; 11.8125 cm²

12. $3\frac{3}{4}$ ft / $5\frac{1}{4}$ ft / $4\frac{1}{2}$ ft / $5\frac{1}{4}$ ft
$19\frac{1}{2}$ ft; $19\frac{11}{16}$ ft²

13. $3\frac{1}{3}$ ft / $3\frac{1}{3}$ ft
$13\frac{1}{3}$ ft; $11\frac{1}{9}$ ft²

14. **Science** A halogen floor light is designed to give maximum light in a triangular shape. What is the area of maximum light for this bulb? 135 ft²

15. **Career** A set designer wants to make a parlor room 16 ft by 24 ft.
    a. How much tape does he need to mark out the room on the stage? 80 ft
    b. How much carpet does he need to cover the whole floor? 384 ft²

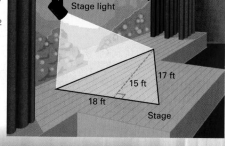
Stage light / 17 ft / 15 ft / 18 ft / Stage

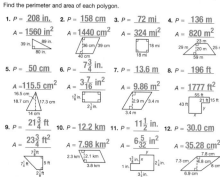

448 *Chapter 9 • Area and Volume*

---

16. **Test Prep** Niambi is carpeting the floor of her room, which is 9 ft by 13 ft. How much carpet will she have to buy to cover the entire floor? **B**

Ⓐ 22 ft Ⓑ 117 ft^2 Ⓒ 44 ft^2 Ⓓ 484 ft

Use the figure to the right for Exercises 17–19.

4 cm
2 cm
x
4 cm
y
6 cm
11 cm

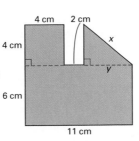

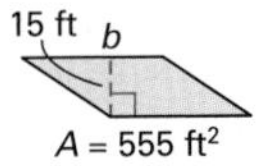

17. What is the value of y? What is the value of x? **5; ≈ 6.4**

18. Find the areas of the square, the rectangle, and the triangle. Find the total area. **16 cm^2, 66 cm^2, 10 cm^2, 92 cm^2**

19. Find the perimeter of the figure. **≈ 47.4 cm**

Problem Solving and Reasoning

Algebra Find the missing dimension in each figure.

20.

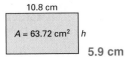

10.8 cm
A = 63.72 cm²
h

5.9 cm

21.

15 ft
b
A = 555 ft²

37 ft

22.

s
s
A = 21.16 m²

4.6 m

23. a. The figure to the right is a regular pentagon. Find the perimeter. **20 cm**

b. Communicate How could you find the area of the pentagon? Explain. **Find the area of the triangle and multiply it by 5.**

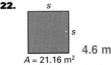

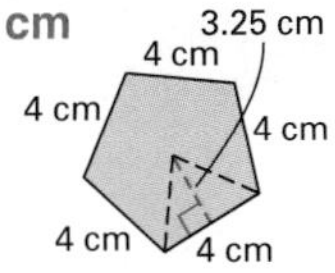

3.25 cm
4 cm
4 cm
4 cm
4 cm
4 cm

24. Critical Thinking Draw a polygon made by connecting a trapezoid, a triangle, and a parallelogram. Label the bases and heights. Find the perimeter and the total area of your figure.

25. Choose a Strategy A stage crew wants to design a room that is 48 m^2.

a. List four pairs of possible dimensions. **6 by 8, 4 by 12, 3 by 16, and 2 by 24**

b. Which of your dimensions has the smallest perimeter? The largest? **6 m by 8 m; 2 by 24**

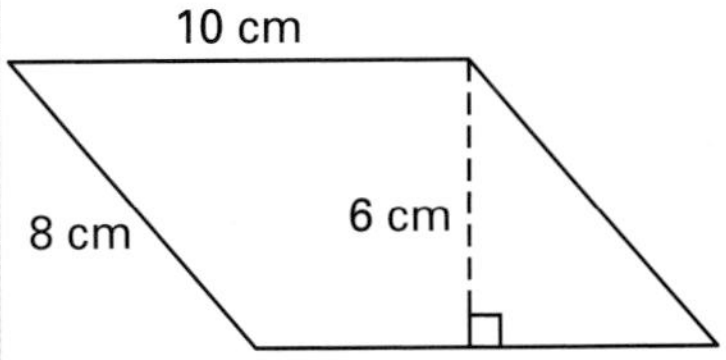

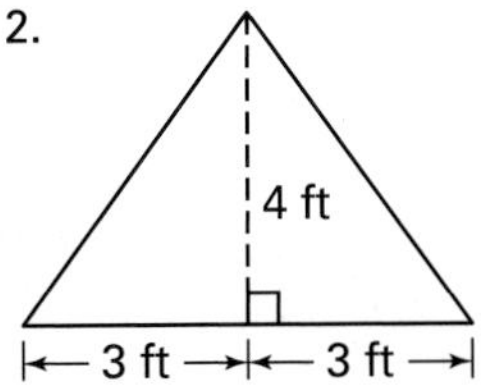

Problem Solving STRATEGIES

- Look for a Pattern
- Make an Organized List
- Make a Table
- Guess and Check
- Work Backward
- Use Logical Reasoning
- Draw a Diagram
- Solve a Simpler Problem

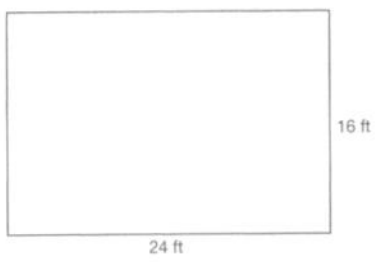

Mixed Review

Write each fraction or decimal as a percent. *[Lesson 6-1]*

26. $\frac{3}{4}$ **75%** **27.** 0.09 **9%** **28.** $\frac{9}{5}$ **180%** **29.** 1.42 **142%** **30.** 0.0038 **0.38%**

Use the Pythagorean theorem ($c^2 = a^2 + b^2$) to decide whether each set of lengths would make a right triangle. *[Lesson 7-9]*

31. 2, 3, 5 **No** **32.** 3, 4, 5 **Yes** **33.** 6, 8, 10 **Yes** **34.** 5, 7, 11 **No**

PROBLEM SOLVING 9-1

Exercise Notes

Exercise 16

Test Prep Students can eliminate choices A and D because the wrong unit for area is given. Choice C is wrong because 9 × 13 cannot be an even number.

Exercise 25

Problem-Solving Tip You may wish to use Teaching Tool Transparencies 2 and 3: Guided Problem Solving, pages 1–2.

Exercise 25b

Extension For a given perimeter, the rectangle that encloses the largest area is a square. For example, for a perimeter of 24, the square with side 6 encloses an area larger than any other rectangle with perimeter 24. Have students experiment with rectangles to discover this fact.

Exercise Answers

24. Answers may vary.

Alternate Assessment

Performance Have students work in pairs to calculate the perimeters and areas of various areas and objects within the classroom. Each pair should draw a diagram of a part of the room and label it with appropriate dimensions and areas.

Quick Quiz

Find the area of each polygon.

1.

10 cm
8 cm
6 cm

60 cm^2

2.

4 ft
3 ft
3 ft

12 ft^2

Available on Daily Transparency 9-1

PROBLEM SOLVING

Name ____________ **Guided Problem Solving 9-1**

GPS PROBLEM 15, STUDENT PAGE 448

A set designer wants to make a parlor room 16 ft by 24 ft.

a. How much tape does he need to mark out the room on the stage?

b. How much carpet does he need to cover the whole floor?

Possible answers: Items 5 and 10

— Understand —

1. What are the dimensions of the parlor room? 16 ft by 24 ft.

2. Will the designer use the tape to mark the perimeter or the area of the room? Perimeter.

3. Will the carpet cover the perimeter or area of the room? Area.

— Plan —

4. Draw a sketch of the room. Label each measure.

Possible answer:

16 ft
24 ft

5. What is the formula for the perimeter of a rectangle? $P = 2b + 2h$.

6. What is the formula for the area of a rectangle? $A = b \cdot h$.

7. What is a reasonable area for the room? d

a. 80 ft^2 b. 160 ft^2 c. 200 ft^2 d. 400 ft^2

— Solve —

8. How much tape will be needed to mark out the room on the stage? 80 ft

9. How much carpet will be needed to cover the whole floor? 384 ft^2

— Look Back —

10. What is another way to find the perimeter? Add lengths of the sides.

SOLVE ANOTHER PROBLEM

An interior designer is designing a room 21 ft by 28 ft.

a. How much wallpaper border does she need to place a strip at the top of the walls around the entire room? 98 ft

b. How much carpet does she need to cover the whole floor? 588 ft^2

ENRICHMENT

Name ____________ **Extend Your Thinking 9-1**

Visual Thinking

Count the cubes in each picture. There are no hidden spaces and each cube sits on another cube unless shown otherwise.

1.

14

2.

23

3.

20

4.

25

5.

13

6.

20

7.

27

8.

15

9.

39

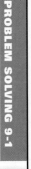

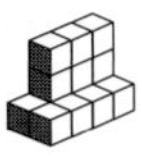

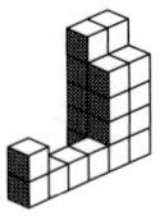

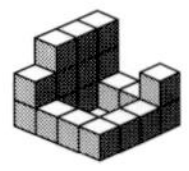

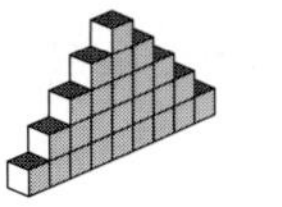

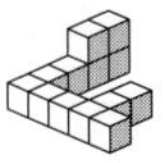

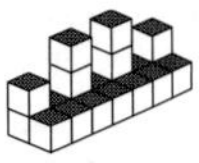

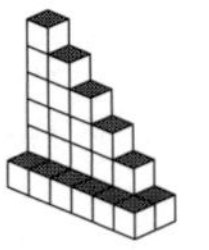

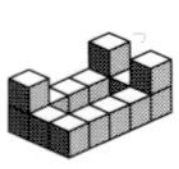

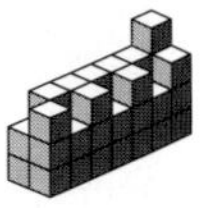

Lesson Organizer

Objective

- Dilate rectangles and predict the resulting perimeters and areas.

Vocabulary

- Dilation, scale factor

Materials

- Explore: Dynamic geometry software

NCTM Standards

- 1, 2, 4–9, 12, 13

▶ Review

Write the formula for each of the following.

1. Perimeter of a rectangle
   $p = 2b + 2h$

2. Perimeter of a square
   $p = 4s$

3. Area of a rectangle
   $A = b \cdot h$

4. Area of a square $A = s^2$

5. Area of a triangle
   $A = \frac{1}{2} b \cdot h$

Available on Daily Transparency 9-2

▶ Lesson Link

Discuss with students what is meant by the term *scale drawing*. A scale drawing of an object is a reduction or enlargement.

1 Introduce

Explore

The Point
Students use geometry software to investigate the effects doubling the dimensions of a geometric figure has on the figure's perimeter and area.

Ongoing Assessment
In Step 4, check that students have answered the question correctly. If they are having difficulties, suggest that they try Steps 3 and 4 again.

9-2   Scale and Area

▶ **Lesson Link**
You know how to find perimeter and area of some polygons. Now you'll see how scaling a polygon affects the perimeter and area. ◀

You'll Learn …

- to dilate rectangles and predict the resulting perimeters and areas

… How It's Used

Directors need to be aware of the area of a scene to plan the movement of the actors and location of scenery and props.

Vocabulary

dilation

scale factor

Explore   Scaling a Rectangle

Expanding Dimensions

Materials: Dynamic geometry software

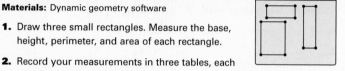

1. Draw three small rectangles. Measure the base, height, perimeter, and area of each rectangle.

2. Record your measurements in three tables, each with four columns.

3. Drag one base of each rectangle until you double the height. Record the new dimensions in your table.

4. Drag one height of each rectangle until you double the base. Record the new perimeter and area. How do the perimeter and area measurements of each rectangle compare?

5. Discuss any conclusions regarding what you found about doubling the dimensions, perimeter, and area.

Base	Height	Perimeter	Area

Learn   Scale and Area

A **dilation** is a proportional reduction or enlargement of a figure. The ratio of the original and new dimensions is called the **scale factor**.

$$\frac{10}{4} = 2.5 \qquad \frac{5}{2} = 2.5$$

The scale factor is 2.5 for the dilation.

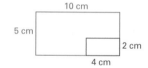

▶ MEETING INDIVIDUAL NEEDS

Resources

9-2 Practice
9-2 Reteaching
9-2 Problem Solving
9-2 Enrichment
9-2 Daily Transparency
   Problem of the Day
   Review
   Quick Quiz
Chapter 9 Project Master

 Interactive CD-ROM Geometry Tool

 Wide World of Mathematics Geometry: Seeing with Your Hands

Learning Modalities

Logical   In **Explore**, students use geometry software to investigate how doubling the dimensions of a rectangle affects the rectangle's perimeter and area.

Kinesthetic   In **Reteaching**, students use algebra unit tiles for hands-on practice with scale factors and dilation.

Verbal   Have students identify a real-world application of *dilation*. How is this application of the term similar to the mathematical application? Students are probably familiar with the term *dilation* as it applies to the pupil of the eye. When the pupil dilates, it enlarges. In mathematics, a dilation may be either an enlargement or a reduction.

English Language Development

Some students may be confused by the word *scale* thinking that it must have something to do with weight. Make sure to mention that *scale*, in the sense that we are using it, has nothing to do with weight or weighing.

You can use the scale factor to find the dimensions of the dilated figure. The blue triangle is dilated by a scale factor of $\frac{2}{3}$.

$$h = \frac{2}{3} \cdot 4 = 2.\overline{6} \text{ cm} \qquad b = \frac{2}{3} \cdot 3 = 2 \text{ cm}$$

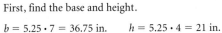
4 cm

3 cm

Examples

1 A theater-in-the-round is where the stage is in the middle of the audience. A model of this stage will be made by reducing it by a scale factor of $\frac{1}{10}$. Find the area and perimeter of the model's main stage.

6 ft
9 ft

First, find the base and height.

$$b = \frac{1}{10} \cdot 9 = \frac{9}{10} \qquad h = \frac{1}{10} \cdot 6 = \frac{6}{10} = \frac{3}{5}$$

$$p = 2\left(\frac{9}{10}\right) + 2\left(\frac{3}{5}\right) = \frac{9}{5} + \frac{6}{5} = \frac{15}{5} = 3 \quad \text{Find the perimeter.}$$

$$A = \left(\frac{9}{10}\right) \cdot \left(\frac{3}{5}\right) = \frac{27}{50} \qquad \text{Find the area.}$$

The model will show the main stage with $p = 3$ units and $A = \frac{27}{50}$ units^2.

2 The rectangle shown will be dilated by a scale factor of 5.25. Find the resulting perimeter and area.

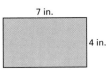
7 in.
4 in.

First, find the base and height.

$$b = 5.25 \cdot 7 = 36.75 \text{ in.} \qquad h = 5.25 \cdot 4 = 21 \text{ in.}$$

$$p = 2(36.75) + 2(21) = 115.5 \text{ in.} \quad \text{Find the perimeter.}$$

$$A = (36.75) \cdot (21) = 771.75 \text{ in}^2 \quad \text{Find the area.}$$

Try It

Determine the scale factor used to dilate the blue rectangle. **5**

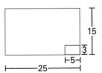
15
3
25
5

9-2 • Scale and Area **451**

MATH EVERY DAY

▶ **Problem of the Day**

You have 12 coins. One coin is fake and weighs slightly less than the real coins. Using a balance scale, how many weighings will you need to make to find the fake coin? 3 weighings; Put 6 coins on each side of the scale. Then put 3 coins from the lighter stack on each side of the scale. One of the 3 coins on the lighter side is counterfeit. Put 2 of these 3 coins on the scale. If they balance, the coin not on the scale is fake. If they do not balance, the lighter coin is counterfeit.

Available on Daily Transparency 9-2

An Extension is provided in the transparency package.

Fact of the Day

In one of the largest scale models of the solar system, in Peoria, IL, the sun has a diameter of 36 ft. Pluto is about 40 miles away.

Estimation

Estimate.

1. $1\frac{3}{8} + 2\frac{1}{2} + \frac{1}{4}$ 4

2. $2\frac{5}{8} + \frac{3}{4} + 3\frac{2}{8}$ 7

3. $2\frac{1}{3} + 1\frac{2}{3} + 4\frac{1}{2}$ $8\frac{1}{2}$

For Groups That Finish Early
Make one large rectangle and repeat Steps 3 and 4. Does your conclusion change? No

Answers for Explore

4. New perimeter is 2 × the original perimeter. New area is 4 × the original area. Difference between new perimeter and perimeter in Step 3 is 2b. New area is 2 × area in Step 3.

5. Possible answer: If b and h of a rectangle are scaled up by a factor of 2, then the perimeter is scaled by a factor of 2 and the area by a factor of 4.

2 Teach

Learn

Alternate Examples

1. A rectangular piece of stage background scenery has a base of 10 m and a height of 6 m. A model of the scenery will be made by reducing the dimensions by a scale factor of $\frac{1}{50}$. Find the area and perimeter of the model scenery.

First, find the base and height.

$$b = \frac{1}{50} \cdot 10 = \frac{10}{50} = \frac{1}{5}$$

$$h = \frac{1}{50} \cdot 6 = \frac{6}{50} = \frac{3}{25}$$

$$p = 2\left(\frac{1}{5}\right) + 2\left(\frac{3}{25}\right) \quad \text{Find the perimeter.}$$

$$= \frac{2}{5} + \frac{6}{25}$$

$$= \frac{10}{25} + \frac{6}{25} = \frac{16}{25}$$

$$A = \left(\frac{1}{5}\right) \cdot \left(\frac{3}{25}\right) = \frac{3}{125} \quad \text{Find the area.}$$

For the model, $p = \frac{16}{25}$, or 0.64 m, and $A = \frac{3}{125}$, or 0.024 m^2.

2. Dilate the triangle by a scale factor of 4.5. Find the resulting perimeter and area.

First, find the base, height, and other side. Then find the perimeter and area.

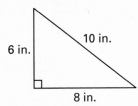
10 in.
6 in.
8 in.

$$b = 4.5 \cdot 8 = 36 \text{ in.}$$

$$h = 4.5 \cdot 6 = 27 \text{ in.}$$

$$s = 4.5 \cdot 10 = 45 \text{ in.}$$

$$p = 36 + 27 + 45 = 108 \text{ in.}$$

$$A = \frac{1}{2}(36) \cdot (27) = 486 \text{ in}^2$$

Lesson 9-2 **451**

Alternate Examples

3. Use a spreadsheet to observe the effect on the perimeter and area if a parallelogram with base 18 cm, adjacent sides of 10 cm, and height of 8 cm is dilated by a scale factor of 1.5 and the resulting parallelograms are repeatedly dilated by a scale factor of 1.5. Find b and h for each dilated parallelogram.

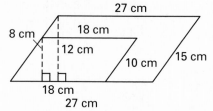

Use $p = 2(b_1 + b_2)$ and $A = b \cdot h$ to find perimeter and area.
The perimeter increases by a factor of 1.5.
The area increases by 1.5^2, or 2.25 times.

Base	Adjacent side	Height	Perimeter	Area
18	10	8	56	144
27	15	12	84	324
40.5	22.5	18	126	729
60.75	33.75	27	189	1640.25
91.125	50.625	40.5	283.5	3690.5625

4. The park district has a rectangular stage measuring 12 ft by 9 ft. They want to enlarge the stage by a scale factor of 2.5. What will the new area of the stage be?

$A = (2.5)^2 \cdot (12 \cdot 9)$
$= (6.25) \cdot (108) = 675 \text{ ft}^2$
The new area will be 675 ft^2.

Remember

When working with geometric shapes, b and h are variables for *base* and *height*.

[Page 445]

▶ **Fine Arts Link**

A *thrust stage* allows some of the audience to view part of a performance from the side.

Example 3

Use a spreadsheet to observe the effect on the perimeter and area if a 3 in. by 5 in. rectangle is dilated by a scale factor of 3.

Find b and h for each dilated rectangle.

Use $p = 2(b + h)$ and $A = b \cdot h$

The perimeter increases by a factor of 3.

The area increases by 3^2, or 9 times.

	A	B	C	D
1	Base	Height	Perimeter	Area
2	5	3	16	15
3	15	9	48	135
4	45	27	144	1215
5	135	81	432	10935

A pattern of dilated rectangles emerges with scale factors 1, 2, and 3.

Scale Factor	Perimeter	Area
1	$1 \cdot 15 = 15$	$1^2 \cdot 15 = 15$
2	$2 \cdot 15 = 30$	$2^2 \cdot 15 = 60$
3	$3 \cdot 15 = 45$	$3^2 \cdot 15 = 135$

Scale Factor	p	A
1	$1 \cdot p$	$1^2 \cdot A$
2	$2 \cdot p$	$2^2 \cdot A$
3	$3 \cdot p$	$3^2 \cdot A$

This pattern can be used for any polygon.

You can use this fact to find the new perimeter or area of any dilation.

For a dilation with scale factor x,

1. The new perimeter is $x \cdot p$, and

2. The new area is $x^2 \cdot A$.

Example 4

A community theater wants to enlarge its thrust stage by a scale factor of 1.25. What will the new area of the thrust stage be?

$A = (1.25)^2 \cdot (13 \cdot 8)$
$= (1.5625) \cdot (104) = 162.5 \text{ ft}^2$

The new area will be 162.5 ft^2.

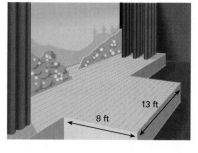

Try It

Find the new area and perimeter of a 4 m by 5 m rectangle that is dilated by a scale factor of $1\frac{3}{4}$. $p = 31\frac{1}{2}$ m and $A = 61\frac{1}{4}$ m^2

452 Chapter 9 • Area and Volume

MEETING MIDDLE SCHOOL CLASSROOM NEEDS

Tips from Middle School Teachers

When I teach scale models, I ask students to bring in models they have at home to share with the class. I encourage students to guess how many times the dimensions of the model would need to be increased or decreased to make it the same size as the original figure.

Team Teaching

Have the science teachers on your team share scale models they may use with your class. Ask the science teacher to challenge the students to guess the scale factor.

Fine Arts Connection

William Shakespeare, 1564–1616, English dramatist and poet, is generally considered the greatest of all playwrights. He wrote at least 37 plays, which traditionally have been divided into comedies, histories, and tragedies. Shakespeare's plays have been produced more times than those of any other playwright in the world.

An 8 cm by 6 cm rectangle is dilated by a scale factor of $\frac{1}{2}$. Find the perimeter and area of the new rectangle.

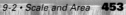

6 cm

8 cm

Seung thinks ...

First, I'll find the perimeter and area of the original rectangle.

$p = 2(8 + 6) = 28$ cm $A = 6 \cdot 8 = 48$ cm^2

Then, I'll multiply by the scale factor to find the new perimeter and multiply by the square of the scale factor to find the area.

$p = \frac{1}{2} \cdot 28 = 14$ cm

$A = \left(\frac{1}{2}\right)^2 \cdot 48 = \frac{1}{4} \cdot 48 = 12$ cm^2

Sarah thinks ...

I'm going to find the new base and height. Then I'll calculate the perimeter and area.

New base: $\frac{1}{2} \cdot 8 = 4$ cm   New height: $\frac{1}{2} \cdot 6 = 3$ cm

$p = 2(b + h) = 2 \cdot (4 + 3) = 14$ cm

$A = b \cdot h = 4 \cdot 3 = 12$ cm^2

What do you think?

1. Why doesn't Sarah multiply by $\frac{1}{4}$ when she calculates the new area?

2. In what circumstances might you choose Sarah's method? Seung's?

Check | Your Understanding

1. What is a dilation?

2. What happens when you dilate a figure by a scale factor less than 1? Greater than 1? Equal to 1?

Students are presented with two correct methods for finding the perimeter and area of a scaled rectangle. The methods are equivalent because multiplication is commutative and associative, and multiplication is distributive over addition. Students can decide which method would be better to use under certain circumstances.

Answers for What Do You Think?
 1. Possible answer: She doesn't multiply by $\frac{1}{4}$ when she calculates the new A because she's already found the new b and h.

 2. Possible answer: Use Sarah's method if you need to know the new b and h. Use Seung's if you don't need to know the new b and h.

3 Practice and Assess

Check

Remind students that a dilation is a *proportional* reduction or enlargement of a figure.

Answers for Check Your Understanding
 1. Possible answer: A reduction or enlargement of a figure.

 2. Scale factor < 1: reduction; Scale factor > 1: enlargement; Scale factor = 1: same size.

Assignment Guide

■ **Basic**
1, 2–6 evens, 8–11,
12–26 evens

■ **Average**
1, 3–7 odds, 8–11, 13–27 odds

■ **Enriched**
3–7 odds, 8–11, 14–18,
21–27 odds

Exercise Notes

■ **Exercise 5**

Error Prevention Watch for students who find the perimeter by using the base and height rather than the base and the adjacent side.

■ **Exercise 10**

Science Many microscopes magnify by 4X, 10X, and 40X using their three standard objective lenses. When these lenses are used in combination with a 10X ocular lens, magnifications of 40X, 100X, and 400X are possible. Zoom objective lenses can increase magnification from 100X to 500X.

Reteaching

Activity

Materials: Algebra unit tiles

• Work with a partner.

• Form a rectangle with the algebra unit tiles, and find its perimeter and area.

• State a scale factor you want the figure dilated by and change the figure to the new size.

• Find the perimeter and area of the dilated figure.

454 **Chapter 9**

9-2 Exercises and Applications

Practice and Apply

1. **Getting Started** Find the area of the triangle when it is dilated by a scale factor of 4.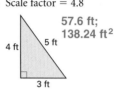

   a. Multiply each dimension by the scale factor 4. $b = 16.8$ cm; $h = 24$ cm

   b. Use the formula $A = \frac{1}{2}b \cdot h$, using the new dimensions. **201.6 cm²**

Find the perimeter and area of each polygon after the given dilation.

2. Scale factor = 3
   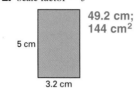
   49.2 cm;
   144 cm²

3. Scale factor = 4.8
   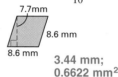
   57.6 ft;
   138.24 ft²

4. Scale factor = 0.5
   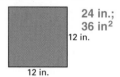
   24 in.;
   36 in²

5. Scale factor = 1.5

   42 m;
   81 m²

6. Scale factor = $\frac{1}{10}$
   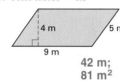
   3.44 mm;
   0.6622 mm²

7. Scale factor = 0.25
   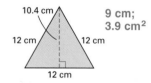
   9 cm;
   3.9 cm²

Fine Arts A Shakespearean theater group wants to buy material for its new rectangular stage. On the model, the stage is 40 cm by 100 cm. The scale factor reads 25.

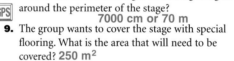

8. What is the minimum length of a string of lights around the perimeter of the stage?
   7000 cm or 70 m

9. The group wants to cover the stage with special flooring. What is the area that will need to be covered? **250 m²**

10. **Science** The rectangular cells of an onion are viewed under a microscope that enlarges each cell by the scale factor 360. If each plant cell appears to be 6 cm, what is the size of the specimen? $\frac{1}{60}$ cm

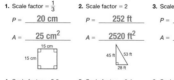

PRACTICE

Name _____

Practice 9-2

Scale and Area

Find the perimeter and area of each polygon after the given dilation.

1. Scale factor = $\frac{1}{3}$
   P = **20 cm**
   A = **25 cm²**

2. Scale factor = 2
   P = **252 ft**
   A = **2520 ft²**

3. Scale factor = 0.8
   P = **112 m**
   A = **604.8 m²**

4. Scale factor = 3.6
   P = **75.6 ft**
   A = **272.16 ft²**

5. Scale factor = 0.4
   P = **8.32 cm**
   A = **4.032 cm²**

6. Scale factor = 1.8
   P = **180 yd**
   A = **1620 yd²**

7. Scale factor = 4
   P = **18 in.**
   A = **19$\frac{1}{4}$ in²**

8. Scale factor = 7.5
   P = **252 cm**
   A = **2646 cm²**

9. Scale factor = $\frac{1}{2}$
   P = **28$\frac{1}{4}$ in.**
   A = **41$\frac{1}{16}$ in²**

10. Carolyn's construction business has been hired to provide new carpet and baseboard for a rectangular hotel lobby. A floor plan, drawn at a scale factor of $\frac{1}{20}$, measures 3 ft × 1$\frac{3}{4}$ ft.

   a. What is the area of the carpet for the lobby? **2100 ft²**

   b. The length of baseboard required is equal to the perimeter of the lobby. How much baseboard is needed? **190 ft**

RETEACHING

Name _____

Alternative Lesson 9-2

Scale and Area

A **dilation** is a proportional reduction or enlargement of a figure. The ratio of the original and new dimensions is called the **scale factor.**

— **Example 1** —
Find the scale factor for the dilation.

Write the ratio of the new dimensions to the original dimensions.

$\frac{\text{New base}}{\text{Original base}} = \frac{6}{4} = 1.5$ $\frac{\text{New height}}{\text{Original height}} = \frac{4.5}{3} = 1.5$

The scale factor for the dilation is 1.5.

Try It Find the scale factor for the dilation.

   a. Write the ratio of new base to original base. $\frac{5}{7.5} = \frac{2}{3}$

   new height to original height. $\frac{3}{4.5} = \frac{2}{3}$

   b. Write the scale factor as a ratio of two whole numbers. $\frac{2}{3}$

— **Example 2** —
Find the area and the perimeter for the rectangle after the rectangle is dilated by a scale factor of 8.

Step 1: Find the base and height of the dilated rectangle by multiplying the dimensions of the original figure by the scale factor. $b = 8 \cdot 5 = 40$ $h = 8 \cdot 2 = 16$

Step 2: Substitute the new dimensions in the area and the perimeter formulas.
Area: $A = 40 \cdot 16 = 640$ cm²   Perimeter: $P = 2(40 + 16) = 2 \cdot 56 = 112$ cm

The area of the dilated figure is 640 cm² and the perimeter is 112 cm.

Try It Find the area and the perimeter for the square after the square is dilated by a scale factor of $\frac{1}{5}$.

   c. Multiply by the scale factor to find the dimensions of the dilated square.
   Base: $\frac{1}{5} \cdot 5 = 1$ Height: $\frac{1}{5} \cdot 5 = 1$

   d. Substitute the new dimensions to find the area. **1 m²**

   e. Substitute the new dimensions to find the perimeter. **4 m**

11. **Test Prep** Determine the scale factor of a dilation of the red figure to the blue figure. **A**

Ⓐ 2.5 Ⓑ 2 Ⓒ $\frac{1}{2}$ Ⓓ 6.25

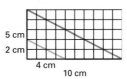

5 cm
2 cm
4 cm
10 cm

Problem Solving and Reasoning

Number Sense Decide whether the scale factor will produce a dilation that is an enlargement or a reduction.

12. Scale factor = $\frac{3}{4}$ **Reduction**
13. Scale factor = 4.5 **Enlargement**
14. Scale factor = 0.01 **Reduction**

12 in.
5 in.

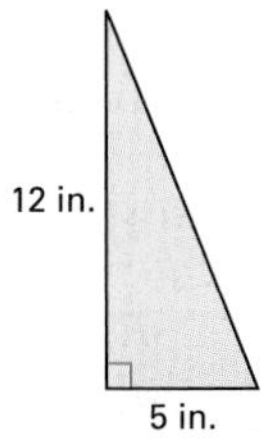

15. Math Reasoning Using the right triangle as shown, what is the effect on the perimeter and area if you double only one of the two dimensions? **Perimeter increases slightly, but the area doubles.**

16. Communicate Create a rectangle and describe the effects on the perimeter and area if you double only one of its dimensions. **The area doubles but the perimeter is less than double.**

The background curtains on the stage of a theater are 1250 ft². The production company wants to make a model of the stage using a scale factor of $\frac{1}{25}$.

17. Measurement Find the area of the curtains in the model. **2 ft²**

18. Patterns What is a possible set of dimensions for the curtains in the stage model? **Possible answer: 2 ft by 1 ft**

19. Journal Write an explanation of how to find the perimeter and area of a polygon after a dilation by scale factor = k.

Mixed Review

Solve each. *[Lesson 6-2]*

20. What number is 15% of 90? **13.5**
21. 40% of 200 is what number? **80**
22. What percent of 39 is 13? **$33\frac{1}{3}$%**
23. 100 is 25% of what number? **400**

Convert each unit. *[Lesson 8-1]*

24. 3 hr to min **180 min**
25. 150 cm to m **1.5 m**
26. 42 kg to g **42,000 g**
27. 196 in. to ft **$16\frac{1}{3}$ ft**

Project Progress

Identify the shapes that your item exhibits, such as squares, circles, triangles, or pentagons. Measure the perimeter and area of the sides of your chosen item.

Problem Solving
Understand
Plan
Solve
Look Back

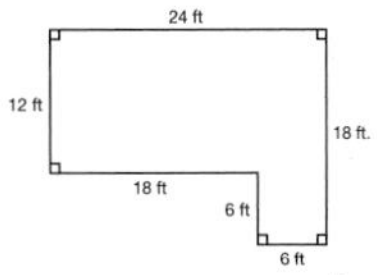

PROBLEM SOLVING 9-2

Exercise Notes

Exercise 11

Test Prep If students chose B or C, they are mistakenly comparing sides of the same triangle instead of the ratio of the sides of the original figure to the dilated figure.

Exercise 18

Consumer Many theater groups use their stage curtains as a source of income by selling blocks of advertising space on them to local businesses. Before the show starts, when the curtain is down, the advertisers have a "captive audience" to view their ads.

Project Progress

You may want to have students use Chapter 9 Project Master.

Exercise Answers

19. Answers may vary.

Alternate Assessment

You may want to use the *Interactive CD-ROM Journal* with this assessment.

Journal Have students write a problem that requires making a dilation by a scale factor. Then they should explain how to solve the problem.

Quick Quiz

1. Find the perimeter of the rectangle below after it is dilated by a scale factor of 0.25.

4 m
12 m

8 m

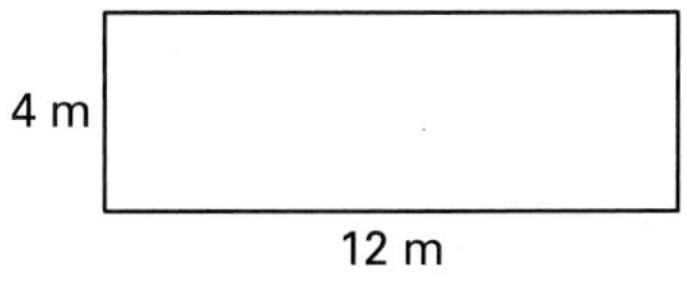

2. Find the area of the rectangle in Question 1 after it is dilated by a scale factor of 0.25. 3 m²

Available on Daily Transparency 9-2

PROBLEM SOLVING

Name ________________ **Guided Problem Solving 9-2**

GPS PROBLEM 8, STUDENT PAGE 454

A Shakespearean theater group wants to buy material for its new rectangular stage. On the model, the stage is 40 cm by 100 cm. The scale factor reads 25. What is the minimum length of a string of lights around the perimeter of the stage? Possible answers: Items 4 and 9

Understand

1. What figure is the stage? Rectangle.
2. What are the model's dimensions? 40 cm by 100 cm.
3. What is the scale factor? 25

Plan

4. What is the formula for the perimeter of a rectangle? $P = 2(b + h)$
5. How can you find the dimensions of the stage given the dimensions of the model and the scale factor? Multiply each dimension by the scale factor.

Solve

6. One dimension of the model is 40 cm. What is this dimension of the actual stage? 1000 cm
7. What is the other dimension of the actual stage? 2500 cm
8. What is the minimum length of a string of lights around the perimeter of the stage? 7000 cm or 70 m

Look Back

9. What is another way to find the length of the lights? Find the perimeter of the model, then multiply it by the scale factor. [2 · (40 + 100) · 25 = 7000]

SOLVE ANOTHER PROBLEM

A model of a stage is 100 cm by 50 cm. The scale factor reads 20. What is the minimum length of raised trim that can be used around the perimeter of the stage? 6000 cm or 60 m

ENRICHMENT

Name ________________ **Extend Your Thinking 9-2**

Decision Making

Sabrina wants to cover some of the floors in her house with square ceramic tiles. She has picked out four kinds of tiles. The floors she will tile are shown in the drawing below.

24 ft
12 ft
18 ft
18 ft
6 ft
6 ft

1. What is the area of the floors to be tiled? 324 ft²
2. Complete the table to find the cost of tiling the floor.

Tile size	Quality	Cost per tile	Tiles needed	Total cost
9 in. square	Better	$0.60	576	$345.60
9 in. square	Best	$0.75	576	$432.00
12 in. square	Good	$1.25	324	$405.00
12 in. square	Best	$1.75	324	$567.00

2. What things might Sabrina consider when deciding which tile she will purchase? Possible answer: Cost, quality of tile, size preference of tiles, work involved in cutting tiles.
3. Which kind of tile would you recommend that Sabrina buy? Why? Check students' answers.
4. Sabrina could pay a friend to lay the tile for her. The friend would charge $250. What would be the advantages and disadvantages of having the friend complete the tiling? Possible answer: Adv: Doesn't have to do the work or clean-up. Disadv: Quality control, scheduling of work.

Objective

- Find the area and circumference of circles.

Vocabulary

- Circumference, center, radius, diameter, π (pi), inscribed, circumscribed

Materials

- Explore: Dynamic geometry software

NCTM Standards

- 1, 2, 4–7, 9, 12

▶ Review

1. Find the perimeter of the parallelogram below.

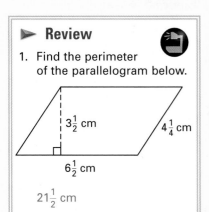

$3\frac{1}{2}$ cm $4\frac{1}{4}$ cm

$6\frac{1}{2}$ cm

$21\frac{1}{2}$ cm

2. Find the area of the parallelogram in Question 1.

$22\frac{3}{4}$ cm²

Available on Daily Transparency 9-3

▶ Lesson Link

Have students name some circular objects they see every day. Ask students when they think it might be helpful to know the circumference or area of these circular objects.

1 Introduce

Explore

The Point

Students use geometry software to discover relationships between the radius, circumference, and area of a circle.

9-3 Circles

You'll Learn …

■ to find the area and circumference of circles

… How It's Used

Set builders often work with the measurements of circular objects for the stage.

Vocabulary

circumference
center
radius
diameter
π (pi)
inscribed
circumscribed

▶ Lesson Link You've seen how to measure the distance around a polygon and its area. Now you'll do the same for circles. ◀

The distance around a circle is the **circumference** (*C*).

The **center** of a circle is a point that is the same distance from all points on the circle.

A **radius** (*r*) of a circle is the segment or distance from the center of the circle to any point on the circle.

Explore   A Circle's Ratio

Circle Search

Materials: Dynamic geometry software

1. Draw a circle. Draw a line segment from the circle to its center to show the radius.

2. Measure the radius (*r*), circumference (*C*), and area (*A*) of the circle. Make a table to record the data. Leave space for a total of ten columns in your table.

3. Drag the circle until it is about $\frac{1}{2}$ of its original area. Record the results in your table. Drag the circle again, but double the original area.

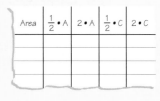

Area	$\frac{1}{2} \cdot A$	$2 \cdot A$	$\frac{1}{2} \cdot C$	$2 \cdot C$

4. Drag the circle until it has about $\frac{1}{2}$ of its original circumference. Record the results in your table. Drag the circle again, but double the original circumference.

5. Label the last two columns of your table $\frac{C}{2r}$ and $\frac{A}{r^2}$. Calculate these ratios and record them in your table. How do these two ratios compare?

6. From the data in your table, discuss any relationships between the radius, circumference, and area of a circle.

MEETING INDIVIDUAL NEEDS

Resources

9-3 Practice
9-3 Reteaching
9-3 Problem Solving
9-3 Enrichment
9-3 Daily Transparency
  Problem of the Day
  Review
  Quick Quiz

Interactive CD-ROM Geometry Tool

Wide World of Mathematics Geometry: Warp Speed at the Arena

Learning Modalities

Visual Students sketch inscribed and circumscribed figures in Exercises 2 and 3 on page 459.

Kinesthetic In **Reteaching**, students work in pairs to measure the circumference and diameter of a variety of circular objects. They also estimate π.

Social In **Explore**, students work in small groups to discover the relationships between the radius, circumference, and area of a circle.

Challenge

Circle of Sim Puzzle: Have pairs of students draw a circle and then mark six equally spaced points on the circumference. Each of the two players uses a different colored pencil and they take turns drawing a line joining any two points on the circle. Players must, however, avoid forming a triangle with their color. If they do form a triangle, they will lose.

Learn — Circles

The **diameter** of a circle is the segment or distance of the segment that passes through the center and has both endpoints on the circle.

$2r = d$
$r \quad r$

Example 1

Find the diameter of a circle with radius $2\frac{3}{4}$ in.

$2\frac{3}{4}$ in.

$d = 2r = 2\left(2\frac{3}{4}\right)$

$d = \frac{2}{1} \cdot \frac{11}{4} = \frac{22}{4} = 5\frac{1}{2}$ in.

The diameter is $5\frac{1}{2}$ in.

For every circle, the ratio of the circumference to the diameter is represented by the Greek letter **π (pi)**. In calculations, $\pi \approx 3.14$ is often used.

$\frac{C}{d} = \pi$ Solve the ratio to find the circumference formula.

$C = \pi d = \pi(2r)$ $d = 2r$.

$C = 2\pi r$ The formula for circumference is $C = 2\pi r$.

Example 2

Radio City Music Hall, where the Rockettes perform, features a revolving turntable 43 ft in diameter. Find the circumference of Radio City Music Hall's turntable.

$C = 2\pi r = \pi d$

$C \approx (3.14) \cdot 43 = 135.02$ ft

The circumference is ≈ 135 ft.

> **Remember**
>
> $\approx$ means "approximately equal to." **[Previous course]**

Try It

a. Find the radius of a circle with diameter 3.46 m. **1.73 m**

b. Find the circumference of a circle with diameter 3.46 m. $\approx$ **10.86 m**

3.46 m

MATH EVERY DAY

▶ Problem of the Day

Study the pattern below.

$1 + 2 + 1 = 4 = 2 \times 2 = 2^2$
$1 + 2 + 3 + 2 + 1 = 9 = 3 \times 3 = 3^2$
$1 + 2 + 3 + 4 + 3 + 2 + 1 = 16 = 4 \times 4 = 4^2$

Continue the pattern. What is the sum of the seventh row in the pattern? **64 ($8 \times 8 = 8^2$)**

Available on Daily Transparency 9-3

An Extension is provided in the transparency package.

Fact of the Day

The first theater in the American colonies opened in Williamsburg, Virginia, in 1716. The first vaudeville theater in the U.S., the Gaiety Museum, opened in Boston in 1883.

Mental Math

Do these mentally.

1. $2(1\frac{1}{2}$ cm)   **3 cm**

2. $2(4\frac{3}{4}$ ft) $9\frac{1}{2}$ **ft**

3. $2(10\frac{1}{4}$ m) $20\frac{1}{2}$ **m**

Ongoing Assessment
For Steps 3 and 4, make sure students understand that they are performing two procedures in each step.

For Groups That Finish Early
How does the circumference of a circle compare to the perimeter of a rectangle? Both measurements represent the "distance around."

Follow Up
Have students create a visual that displays the relationships between the radius, the circumference, and the area of a circle.

Answers for Explore
1–4. See students' work.

5. Both ratios $\approx$ 3.14 ...

6. Possible answer: $C = 2\pi r$ and $A = \pi r^2$

2 Teach

Learn

Pi is approximately 3.14. It has been calculated to millions of decimal places, but cannot be expressed exactly as a decimal.

Alternate Examples

1. Find the radius of a circle with diameter $4\frac{1}{2}$ in.

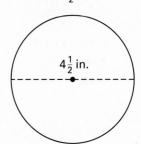

$4\frac{1}{2}$ in.

$r = d \div 2$
$r = 4\frac{1}{2} \div 2 = 2\frac{1}{4}$

The radius is $2\frac{1}{4}$ in.

2. The world's largest Ferris wheel in Yokohama City, Japan, has a diameter of 328 ft. Find its circumference.

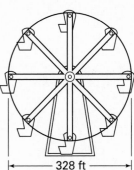

328 ft

$C = 2\pi r = \pi d$
$C \approx (3.14) \cdot 328 \approx 1029.92$ ft
The circumference $\approx$ 1029.92 ft.

3. Chad's new igloo-style tent has a floor diameter of 8 ft. What is the floor area of a tent this size?

First, find the radius.
$d = 8$ ft, so $r = 4$ ft
$A = \pi r^2$
$A = \pi(4)^2 = 16\pi$ ft^2
$\approx (16 \cdot 3.14)$ ft^2
$A \approx 50.24$ ft^2

4. Determine whether the octagon circumscribes or inscribes the circle.

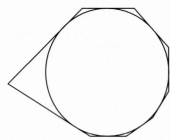

The octagon is outside the circle and one point of each of its sides is on the circumference.

The octagon circumscribes the circle.

3 Practice and Assess

Check

Emphasize that the ratios in Exercise 2 are the same for all circles, regardless of size.

Answers for Check Your Understanding

1. Possible answers: Perimeter and circumference are both distances around a figure; Perimeter of a polygon can be determined taking the sum of side lengths, circumference cannot.

2. $\frac{A}{r^2} = \pi$ and $\frac{C}{d} = \pi$

$\frac{A}{r^2} = \pi$ π is also the ratio of the area of a circle to the radius squared.

$A = \pi r^2$ The formula for the area of a circle is $A = \pi r^2$.

Example 3

▶ **History Link**

In the 1800s, Major Culberson reported a Blackfoot tepee made of 40 skins that would fit 100 people.

In the mid-1800s, the Blackfoot people used 6 buffalo skins to build tepees that had 10 ft diameter floors. What is the floor area of a tepee this size?

First, find the radius. 5 ft $= r$

$A = \pi r^2$

$A = \pi(5)^2 = 25\pi$ ft^2

$\approx (25 \cdot 3.14)$ ft^2

$A \approx 78.5$ ft^2

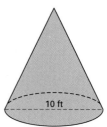

10 ft

A polygon inside a circle with all its vertices on the circumference is **inscribed** in the circle.

A polygon outside a circle with one point of each side on the circle is **circumscribed** about the circle.

Example 4

Determine whether the pentagon circumscribes or inscribes the circle.

The pentagon is inside the circle and all the vertices are on the circumference. The pentagon is inscribed in the circle.

Try It

     ≈ 50.24 cm^2

a. Find the area of a circle with $r = 4$ cm.

b. Does the square circumscribe the circle?   **Yes**

Check | Your Understanding

1. How are perimeter and circumference alike? How are they different?

2. What are the two ratios that equal π?

MEETING MIDDLE SCHOOL CLASSROOM NEEDS

Tips from Middle School Teachers

Some students think that π is a variable because it is represented by a symbol. I remind them that π is an exact value that is found by dividing the circumference of a circle by its diameter. The value is a nonrepeating, nonterminating decimal, so it is easier to write the symbol π. In our calculations we will use 3.14 as the approximation for π.

Cultural Connection

The ancient Chinese, Babylonians, Egyptians, and Greeks all realized that a circle's circumference is always equal to the product of the diameter and a certain number, which they named π. The ancient Chinese used 3 as the value of π. About 1650 B.C., the Egyptian astronomer Ptolemy calculated a value of π equal to 3.1416.

Career Connection

Costume designers are responsible for designing, and either making or purchasing costumes for the production. They usually begin their preparations by being involved in many meetings with the director and various production people to discuss their understanding of the script and how it should be translated in the costuming. There is often a considerable amount of research involved in regard to the representation of the period of time being presented. They must take many factors into consideration when planning their costume choices, including the colors and patterns used on the walls of the set and the lighting.

9-3 Exercises and Applications

Practice and Apply

1. **Getting Started** Find the area of the circle shown. Use π = 3.14.
   a. Find the radius. **4 cm**
   b. Find the area. **≈ 50.24 cm²**

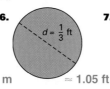
8 cm

Sketch each figure.

2. Square inscribed in a circle
3. Pentagon circumscribed about a circle

Find the circumference of each circle. Use π = 3.14.

4. 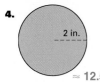 2 in.
   ≈ 12.56 in.

5. 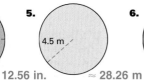 4.5 m
   ≈ 28.26 m

6. 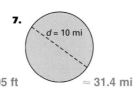 $d = \frac{1}{3}$ ft
   ≈ 1.05 ft

7. 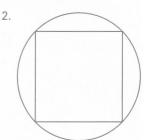 $d = 10$ mi
   ≈ 31.4 mi

Find the area of each circle. Use π = 3.14.

8. 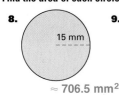 15 mm
   ≈ 706.5 mm²

9. 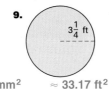 $3\frac{1}{4}$ ft
   ≈ 33.17 ft²

10. 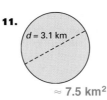 $d = 2.65$ cm
    ≈ 5.5 cm²

11. 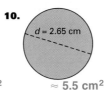 $d = 3.1$ km
    ≈ 7.5 km²

12. **Science** The earth's circumference is approximately 25,000 mi. Find the approximate diameter of the earth. **7960 mi**

25,000 mi

13. **Career** A costume designer is making costumes for an Elizabethan play. An actress's neck has a 14 in. circumference. The ruff (collar) will be made from a circle with a 6.2 in. radius. How much lace is needed to accent the circumference of the ruff? **≈ 39 in.**

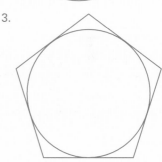
Queen Elizabeth I of England (1533–1603)

14. **Algebra** A circle has an area of 42 cm². Write an equation and solve for *r*, the radius. **πr² = 42; r ≈ 3.66 cm**

PRACTICE 9-3

9-3 • Circles **459**

9-3 Exercises and Applications

Assignment Guide

■ **Basic**
1, 2, 4–14 evens,
16, 17–21 odds, 22–30 evens

■ **Average**
3, 5–11 odds, 12, 14–20,
23–29 odds

■ **Enriched**
3, 5–11 odds, 12–14, 16–18,
20, 21–29 odds

Exercise Answers

2.

3.

PRACTICE

Name _____

Practice
9-3

Circles

Sketch each figure.

1. Octagon inscribed in a circle
2. Hexagon circumscribed about a circle

Find the circumference of each circle. Use π = 3.14.

3. **25.12 cm** $r = 4$ cm
4. **34.54 in.** $d = 11$ in.
5. **52.752 m** $r = 8.4$ m
6. **19.625 ft** $d = 6\frac{1}{4}$ ft

Find the area of each circle. Use π = 3.14.

7. **226.865 mi²** $d = 17$ mi
8. **530.66 in²** $r = 13$ in.
9. **70.84625 ft²** $d = 9\frac{1}{2}$ ft
10. **162.7776 km²** $r = 7.2$ km

11. **75.3914 cm²** $r = 4.9$ cm
12. **≈ 0.4416 ft²** $d = \frac{3}{4}$ ft
13. **0.5024 cm²** $r = 0.4$ cm
14. **≈ 371.354 in²** $d = 21\frac{3}{4}$ in.

15. **Science** Saturn is surrounded by hundreds of rings of tiny particles in orbit about the planet. The innermost rings have a circumference of about 260,000 mi. Find the radius. **About 41,400 mi**

16. A round clock face has a diameter of 15 in. Find the area. **About 177 in²**

RETEACHING

Name _____

Alternative
Lesson
9-3

Circles

The **center** of a circle is a point that is the same distance from all points on the circle.

A **radius** (*r*) of a circle is the segment or distance from the center of the circle to any point on the circle. The **diameter** (*d*) of a circle is the segment or distance of the segment that passes through the center and has both endpoints on the circle. The diameter is two times the radius.

The distance around a circle is the **circumference** (*C*). The ratio of the circumference to the diameter of a circle is represented by the Greek letter π **(pi)**. When you calculate, you can use π ≈ 3.14.

The following formulas are used for circles.
$$d = 2r \qquad C = 2\pi r \text{ or } C = \pi d \qquad A = \pi r^2$$

— **Example** —

Find the circumference and area of a circle with radius 3.7 m. Use π = 3.14.

Write the formula.	$C = 2\pi r$	$A = \pi r^2$
Substitute.	$C \approx 2 \cdot 3.14 \cdot 3.7$	$A \approx 3.14 \cdot 3.7 \cdot 3.7$
Solve.	$C \approx 23.236$ m	$A \approx 3.14 \cdot 13.69 \approx 42.9866$ m²

The circumference is ≈ 23.236 m, and the area is ≈ 42.99 m².

Try It Find the circumference and the area of a circle with a radius of 6 in. Use π = 3.14.

	Circumference	Area
a. Write each formula.	$C = 2\pi r$	$A = \pi r^2$
b. Substitute.	$C = 2 \cdot 3.14 \cdot 6$	$A \approx 3.14 \cdot 6^2$
c. Solve.	$C \approx 37.68$	$A \approx 113.04$
d. Write in correct units.	≈ 37.68 in.	≈ 113.04 in²

Find the circumference and the area of each circle. Write the circumference first.

e. 4 m
   25.12 m; 50.24 m²

f. 1.5 m
   9.42 m; 7.065 m²

g. 10 m
   62.8 m; 314 m²

Reteaching

Activity

Materials: Calculator; tape measure; circular objects such as jar lids, saucers, tin cans, and so on.

• Work with a partner.

• Make a table with three column heads: circumference, diameter, and $\frac{C}{d}$.

• Working with your partner, take turns measuring the circumference and diameter of each circular object as carefully as possible. Write the measurements on your table.

• Now use your calculator to compute the third column. What number is the result in each case? **≈ 3.14 or pi**

Lesson 9-3 **459**

■ Exercise 16

Test Prep Students can immediately eliminate choices B and D since π should not be in an answer that is an approximation. Then, by approximating r^2, students can also eliminate choice A since it is about equal to the approximation of r^2 before it is multiplied by π.

■ Exercise 17

Fine Arts This great theater in Athens, Greece, was dedicated to Dionysus, god of wine in Greek mythology. In fact, the concept of tragedy in Greek drama came from a ceremony that honored Dionysus.

Exercise Answers

17. The circumference for a full circle would be 188.4 ft so for a semicircle it would be half of that plus 60 ft, or 154.2 ft; The area of a full circle would be 2826 ft², so the area of a half-circle would be 1413 ft².

18. Possible answer: When $r = 5$, $p = 31.4$, and $A = 78.5$. When $r = 10$, $p = 62.8$, and $A = 314$. When r is doubled, p is doubled and A is quadrupled.

20. The octagon because the area between the polygon and the circle is smallest.

Alternate Assessment

Self Assessment Give students the opportunity to evaluate what they have learned about finding the circumference and area of circles. Was there anything about the lesson that they found especially difficult? Was there something that they found particularly helpful to them in learning the concepts?

► Quick Quiz

1. Find the circumference of the circle below.

$d = 3.5$ m

10.99 m

2. Find the area of the circle in Question 1. 9.616 m²

Available on Daily Transparency 9-3

---

15. **Geography** In the U.S. Midwest some farmers use a circular irrigation method. Suppose the length of an irrigation arm is 500 ft. What is the area of the irrigated circle? ≈ **785,000 ft²**

16. **Test Prep** A circle has a radius of 4.5 m. Which is the best approximation for the area of this circle? **C**

    Ⓐ 20.25 m²   Ⓑ 20.25π m²
    Ⓒ 63.6 m²   Ⓓ 63.6π m²

Problem Solving and Reasoning

17. **Communicate** A theater owner wants to design a Greek style semicircular stage with a radius of 30 ft. Explain how to find the perimeter and area of the stage. Include an illustration. [GPS]

18. **Number Sense** Investigate what happens to the perimeter and area of a circle when you double the radius. Give an example and write about your conclusions.

19. **Journal** TV and FM radio signals have a line-of-sight range, which means mountains can interfere. A radio tower has a broadcast range with a 23 mi radius. How much area does the broadcast cover? ≈ **1661 mi²**

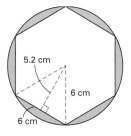

Theater of Dionysos in Athens, Greece

20. **Math Reasoning** A regular pentagon, hexagon, and octagon circumscribe a circle with a radius of 5 in. Which polygon has an area measurement closest to the area of the circle. Explain.

21. **Geometry** A hexagon is inscribed in the circle.
    a. Find the area of the triangle. **15.6 cm²**
    b. Find the area of the hexagon. **93.6 cm²**
    c. Find the area of the circle. ≈ **113.04 cm²**
    d. Find the area of the shaded region. **19.4 cm²**

    5.2 cm   6 cm   6 cm

Mixed Review

Estimate each percent. *[Lesson 6-3]*

22. 34 out of 198 **15%**   23. 67 out of 97 **70%**   24. 49 out of 76 **64%**   25. 2 out of 19 **10%**

Give the number of significant digits in each number. *[Lesson 8-2]*

26. 104.96 **5**   27. 5.0401 **5**   28. 0.0006 **1**   29. 105 **3**   30. 20.40 **4**

460   *Chapter 9 • Area and Volume*

PROBLEM SOLVING 9-3

► PROBLEM SOLVING

Name _____

Guided Problem Solving 9-3

[GPS] PROBLEM 17, STUDENT PAGE 460

A theater owner wants to design a Greek style semicircular stage with a radius of 30 ft. Explain how to find the perimeter and area of the stage. Include an illustration.

Possible answers: Items 7 and 8

— Understand —

1. Underline what you are asked to explain.

2. What figure is the stage? __Semicircle.__

— Plan —

3. Draw the shape of the stage. Label the radius.

   ← 30 ft →

4. The area of the stage is what fraction of the area of a circle? $\frac{1}{2}$

5. The curved part of the stage is what fraction of the circumference of a circle? $\frac{1}{2}$

6. How can you find the measure of the straight part? __Multiply radius by 2.__

— Solve —

7. Explain how to find the perimeter of the stage. __Divide circumference of circle by 2. Add 2 times the radius to the quotient.__

8. Explain how to find the area of the stage. __Divide area of a circle by 2.__

— Look Back —

9. Follow the steps in your explanations to find the area and perimeter of the stage. Write each measure. Are your explanations complete?
   Perimeter = 154.2 ft; Area = 1413 ft²

SOLVE ANOTHER PROBLEM

The area of a semicircular section with a radius of 15 ft and the area of a square whose one side is the diameter of the semicircle make up a stage. Explain how to find the perimeter and area of the stage. Include an illustration.

Possible answer:

← 15 ft →

Perimeter: Divide circumference of circle by 2. Add to 3 times twice the radius. Area: Divide area of circle by 2 and add the quotient to area of the square.

► ENRICHMENT

Name _____

Extend Your Thinking 9-3

Critical Thinking

Use your knowledge of area, perimeter, and circumference to find the perimeters and areas of the irregular figures below.

Find the perimeter of each figure.

1.   3 cm / 3 cm / 3 cm / 3 cm   **15.42 cm**

2.   1 km / 1 km / 1 km / 1 km / 1 km / 1 km   **8.71 km**

3.   3 m / 3 m   **28.26 m**

Find the area of each shaded region.

4.   2 mm / 8 mm   **19.44 mm²**

5.   10 m / 10 m / 10 m   **214 m²**

6.   1 dm / 1 dm / 1 dm / 1 dm / 1 dm   **18.84 dm²**

7. A quadrilateral is circumscribed about the circle. The radius of the circle is 6 cm. Each side of the polygon is perpendicular to the radius shown. Find the area of the shaded region.

   7 cm / 12 cm / 15 cm / 20 cm

   48.96 cm

Surface Area of Prisms and Cylinders

▶ Lesson Link You know how to find the area of flat figures, such as polygons and circles. Now you'll learn about the surface area of 3-D figures. ◀

A **polyhedron** is a 3-D figure that is composed of polygons. Each polygon surface is called a **face**.

The **edge** of a polyhedron is where two faces meet.

A **vertex** of a polyhedron is the intersection of three or more faces.

The **surface area** (*SA*) of a polyhedron is the sum of the areas of all the faces.

Three Polyhedrons

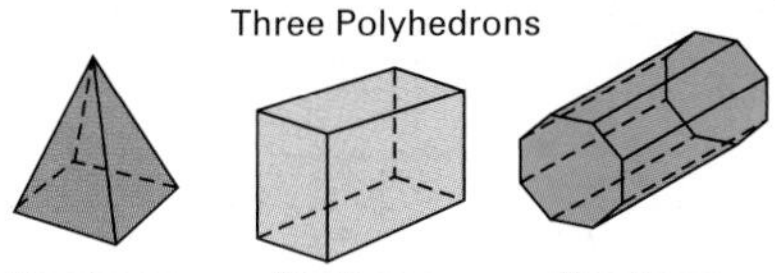

Five faces:
4 triangles
1 square

Six faces:
6 rectangles

Ten faces:
2 octagons
8 rectangles

You'll Learn ...
■ to find surface area of prisms and cylinders

... How It's Used
Interior designers use surface area to figure the amount of material to cover solid objects.

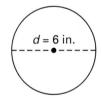

Vocabulary
polyhedron
face
edge
vertex
surface area
prism
base
cylinder

Explore Prisms

Surfing the Surface

Materials: Four sheets of 8.5 in. by 11 in. paper, Tape, Scissors

1. Find the area of one sheet of paper.

2. Make 3-D figures using one sheet of paper for each.

Figure a: Roll paper so opposite edges can be taped together.

Figure b: Fold paper into equal thirds and tape edges together.

Figure c: Fold paper into equal fourths and tape edges together.

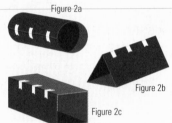

Figure 2a

Figure 2b

Figure 2c

3. Is the surface area of each of these figures greater than, less than, or equal to the area of the original sheet of paper? Explain.

4. What shapes are needed to complete the surface of each figure? Draw these shapes and calculate their areas. Tape them onto the appropriate figures.

5. Rank the three solids in total surface area from least to greatest. Justify your ranking.

MEETING INDIVIDUAL NEEDS

Resources

9-4 Practice
9-4 Reteaching
9-4 Problem Solving
9-4 Enrichment
9-4 Daily Transparency
    Problem of the Day
    Review
    Quick Quiz
Lesson Enhancement
Transparency 40

 Wide World of Mathematics Geometry: Gateway Arch

Learning Modalities

Kinesthetic In **Explore**, students make 3-D figures out of paper and analyze them in terms of total surface area.

Visual Students sketch nets for various 3-D figures as they work through the Examples and Exercises.

Verbal Have students discuss the similarities and the differences between prisms and cylinders.

Inclusion

For some students, the concept of surface area may require more instruction at the concrete level. Show the students the difference between 2-D and 3-D figures. Draw a square on the board, then show students a cube. Draw a circle, then show them a sphere. Give students the opportunity to handle 3-D figures such as cylinders, cubes, and prisms as often as possible.

Remind students to add new vocabulary and examples to their reference notebook.

Objective
■ **Find surface area of prisms and cylinders.**

Vocabulary
■ **Polyhedron, face, edge, vertex, surface area, prism, base, cylinder**

Materials
■ **Explore: Four sheets of 8.5 in. by 11 in. paper, tape, scissors**

NCTM Standards
■ **1–7, 9, 12**

▶ Review

1. Find the area of the rectangle.

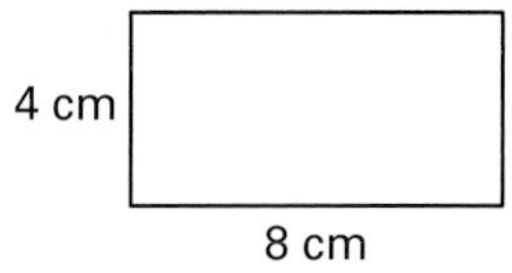

4 cm

8 cm

32 cm²

2. Find the area of the circle.

d = 6 in.

28.26 in²

Available on Daily Transparency 9-4

▶ Lesson Link

Use a closed cereal box to point out the terms *polyhedron, face, edge, vertex,* and *surface area.*

1 Introduce

Explore

The Point
Students make 3-D figures and analyze them.

Ongoing Assessment
In Step 4, check that students make each base correctly.

Lesson 9-4   **461**

Experiment with making another polyhedron from a single sheet of paper. Calculate the total surface area.

Follow Up

Allow students to explain their answers for Step 5.

Answers for Explore

1. $93\frac{1}{2}$ in²

2. a–c. See students' work.

3. Each surface area = area of original sheet of paper as long as they don't overlap. Each figure is made of only one sheet of paper.

4. Two circles for Figure a each have area ≈ 9.6 in² or ≈ 5.7 in².
   Two triangles for Figure b each have area ≈ 5.8 in² or ≈ 3.5 in².
   Two squares for Figure c each have area ≈ 7.6 in² or ≈ 4.5 in².

5. Answers may vary.

2 Teach

Learn

You may wish to use Lesson Enhancement Transparency 40 with this lesson.

Alternate Examples

1. Find the surface area of a wood box that is 25 in. by 15 in. by 3 in.

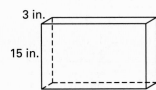

First, sketch a net; then find the area of each of the six faces.

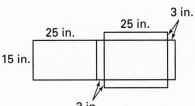

Two faces are 25 in. by 15 in.
$A = b \cdot h = 25 \cdot 15 = 375$ in²
Two faces are 25 in. by 3 in.
$A = b \cdot h = 25 \cdot 3 = 75$ in²
Two faces are 15 in. by 3 in.
$A = b \cdot h = 15 \cdot 3 = 45$ in²
The surface area is
$SA = 2(375 + 75 + 45)$
$= 990$ in².

Learn   **Surface Area of Prisms and Cylinders**

A **prism** is a polyhedron that has two congruent faces that are parallel polygons. Each parallel, congruent face is called a **base**.

A net helps you find the surface area because it shows all faces as flat polygons.

Example 1

Find the surface area of the rectangular prism.

First, sketch a net; then find the area of each face. There are three different rectangular faces.

Two faces are 30 cm by 24 cm.
$A = b \cdot h = 30 \cdot 24 = 720$ cm²

Two faces are 30 cm by 5 cm.
$A = b \cdot h = 30 \cdot 5 = 150$ cm²

Two faces are 24 cm by 5 cm.
$A = b \cdot h = 24 \cdot 5 = 120$ cm²

The surface area of the rectangular prism is
$SA = 2(720 + 150 + 120) = 1980$ cm².

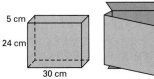
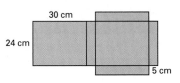

Try It

Find the surface area of a rectangular prism that is 1 in. by 2 in. by 3 in. **22 in²**

462   *Chapter 9 • Area and Volume*

MATH EVERY DAY

▶ Problem of the Day

There are 3 boxes labeled *dimes, pennies,* and *dimes and pennies.* One box has 3 dimes, one box has 3 pennies, and one box has 1 dime and 2 pennies. Each box is mislabeled. How many coins must you draw to decide which box is which? Draw one coin from the box labeled *dimes and pennies.* Since the boxes are mislabeled, the box should be labeled for the coin you drew. The labels on the remaining boxes are switched.

Available on Daily Transparency 9-4

An Extension is provided in the transparency package.

Fact of the Day

One of the world's smallest optical prisms has sides of 0.001 in. It was created at the National Institute of Standards and Technology in Boulder, CO.

Estimation

Estimate.

1. 22,596 + 21,485   44,000

2. 46,411 − 34,326   12,000

3. 57,088 + 13,478   70,000

Example 2

A 24 in. wide ramp from a stage to the audience floor needs to be built. The stage is 6 in. above the audience floor. The ramp will extend 8 in. away from the stage. What is the surface area of the ramp?

Find the area of each face.

Each triangle has $b = 8$ in. and $h = 6$ in.

$A = \frac{1}{2}(b \cdot h) = \frac{1}{2}(8 \cdot 6) = \frac{1}{2}(48) = 24$ in^2

One face is 6 in. by 24 in. with $A = 144$ in^2.

One face is 8 in. by 24 in. with $A = 192$ in^2.

One face is 10 in. by 24 in. with $A = 240$ in^2.

The surface area is

$SA = 2(24) + 144 + 192 + 240 = 624$ in^2.

► **Career Link**

Large theater companies have house crews that consist of carpenters, electricians, and other craftspeople to help design and build the setting for a performance.

A **cylinder** is a 3-D figure with two congruent circles for bases.

Notice the base of the rectangle is the circumference of a circle. The height of the rectangle is the height of the cylinder.

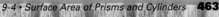

Try It

a. Find the area of each circle of the cylinder. $A \approx 50.2$ in^2

b. Find the area of the cylinder's side. $A \approx 150.7$ in^2

c. Find the surface area of the cylinder. $SA \approx 251$ in^2

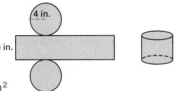

Check Your Understanding

1. How many length measurements do you need to find the surface area of a prism? A cylinder? Draw a diagram to explain.

2. How many faces would a pentagonal prism have? A hexagonal prism?

MEETING MIDDLE SCHOOL CLASSROOM NEEDS

Tips from Middle School Teachers

When I teach surface area, I don't underestimate the importance of visualization. For example, even the most abstract thinkers in class may need to see models. For this reason, I have available identical pairs of containers of many different shapes. As a class, we open one container of each pair to make a net and compare the net to the other container.

Cooperative Learning

(Materials: 12 unit cubes) Challenge a group of students to build figures of 12 cubic units in at least 10 different ways. Have them sketch each figure and find its surface area.

Science Connection

Prisms made of glass or quartz form an important class of optical elements. They are used in a variety of instruments to change the direction of a beam of light. Periscopes and some telescopes use prisms. In a spectrometer, a prism changes the direction of a beam of light by refraction—meaning that it bends the light as it passes through the prism. If a beam of white light, which contains all the wavelengths of visible light, passes through a prism, refraction forms a band of colors called a spectrum.

Additional Examples

2. A storage bin in the shape of a triangular prism whose bases are right triangles is being built to store actors' makeup. What is the surface area of the bin if it has the dimensions shown below?

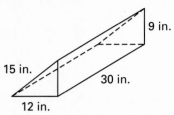

Sketch the net, then find the area of each face.

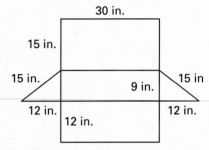

Each triangular base has $b = 12$ in. and $h = 9$ in.

$A = \frac{1}{2}(b \cdot h) = \frac{1}{2}(12 \cdot 9) =$

$\frac{1}{2}(108) = 54$ in^2

One face is 9 in. by 30 in. with $A = 270$ in^2.

One face is 12 in. by 30 in. with $A = 360$ in^2.

One face is 15 in. by 30 in. with $A = 450$ in^2.

The surface area is $SA = 2(54) + 270 + 360 + 450 = 1188$ in^2.

3 Practice and Assess

Check

Make sure students realize that a prism has two congruent bases that can have the shape of *any* polygon.

Answers for Check Your Understanding

1. Triangular or rectangular prism: 3; Cylinder: 2

2. Pentagonal prism: 7 faces; Hexagonal prism: 8 faces

Assignment Guide

- **Basic**
  1, 2–6 evens, 8–11, 13–27 odds
- **Average**
  1, 3–7 odds, 8–15, 16–26 evens
- **Enriched**
  3–7 odds, 8–15, 16–26 evens

Exercise Notes

■ **Exercise 8**

Literature "Hansel and Gretel" was part of a collection of folk tales retold in the early 1800s by Jakob and Wilhelm Grimm.

Exercise Answers

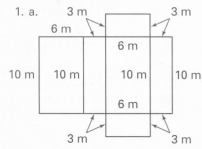

1. a.

b. 3 × 6 = 18; 3 × 10 = 30, and 6 × 10 = 60
c. 216 m²

2–7. See page C1.

Reteaching

Activity

Materials: Box with a sealed top, ruler, scissors

- Work in groups of three.

- Label the six faces on the box as *top*, *bottom*, *left*, *right*, *front*, and *back*.

- Cut the box apart along the edges. How many rectangles do you end up with? Are any of the rectangles the same size? If so, which ones?
  6; Top = bottom; left = right; front = back.

- Use a ruler to find the dimensions of the rectangles. Mark the dimensions on the rectangles. Then find the area of each rectangle.

- Now compute the surface area of the rectangular prism by adding the areas of the six rectangles.

9-4 Exercises and Applications

Practice and Apply

1. **Getting Started** Find the surface area of the rectangular prism.
   a. Draw the net for the prism. Label the dimensions for each face.
   b. Find the area of each face.
   c. Find the sum of the areas.

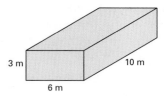

Sketch a net for each, then find the surface area.

2. 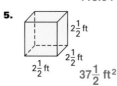 6.5 m, 5.4 m, 1.8 m **113.04 m²**

3. 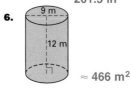 4.3 in., 5 in., 5 in., 12 in. **201.5 in²**

4. 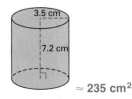 3.5 cm, 7.2 cm **≈ 235 cm²**

5. $2\frac{1}{2}$ ft, $2\frac{1}{2}$ ft, $2\frac{1}{2}$ ft **$37\frac{1}{2}$ ft²**

6. 9 m, 12 m **≈ 466 m²**

7. 5 yd, $2\frac{1}{4}$ yd, $6\frac{1}{2}$ yd **$116\frac{3}{4}$ yd**

8. **Literature** A decorative platform is being constructed for a performance of *Hansel and Gretel*. Which shape would have the greater surface area, a cube 4 ft on each side or a rectangular prism that is 8 ft by 4 ft by 2 ft?
   The rectangular prism

9. **Science** Water changes from a liquid to a solid at 32°F, the freezing point. Each section in an ice cube tray is $1\frac{1}{2}$ in. by 1 in. by 1 in. How much surface area does an ice cube from this tray have? **8 in²**

10. **Test Prep** A can has a diameter of 8 cm and a height of 15 cm. Find the area of paper for a label to cover the curved side. **D**
    Ⓐ 3014.4 cm²   Ⓑ 120 cm²
    Ⓒ 188.4 cm²   Ⓓ 376.8 cm²

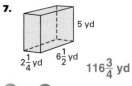

11. What is the surface area of a box that is 12 in. by $7\frac{1}{2}$ in. by 4 in.? **336 in²**

PRACTICE

Practice 9-4

Surface Area of Prisms and Cylinders

Sketch a net for each, then find the surface area. **Nets may vary**

1. SA = **292 cm²**
 8 cm, 6 cm, 7 cm; 6 cm, 6 cm, 8 cm, 7 cm, 6 cm

2. SA ≈ **123.6 in²**
 $r = 2\frac{1}{4}$ in.; ≈14.13 in., $r = 2\frac{1}{4}$ in., $6\frac{1}{2}$ in.

3. SA = **413.34 cm²**
 8.3 cm

4. SA = **324 ft²**
 6 ft, 15 ft, 9 ft, 12 ft; 9 ft, 12 ft, 15 ft, 9 ft, 6 ft, 9 ft

5. A birthday present is packaged in a tube that has length 8 in. and diameter 3 in. How much paper is needed to wrap the present? (Ignore any overlap.)
   About $89\frac{1}{2}$ in²

6. A shoebox is 4 in. tall with a 6-in. × 10-in. base. If there is no lid, how much cardboard is needed to make this box?
   188 in²

RETEACHING

Alternative Lesson 9-4

Surface Area of Prisms and Cylinders

A **polyhedron** is a 3-D figure that is composed of polygons. Each polygon surface is called a **face**. The surface area (SA) of a polyhedron is the sum of the areas of all the faces.

A **prism** is a polyhedron that has two congruent faces that are parallel polygons. Each parallel, congruent face is called a **base**.

A **cylinder** is a 3-D figure with two congruent circles for bases.

height of cylinder = height of rectangle.
circumference of circular base = base of rectangle

— Example —

Find each surface area.

Step 1: Sketch a net.

Step 2: Find the area of each base.
$A = b \cdot h$
$= 10 \cdot 4 = 40$ in²
$A = \pi r^2$
$= 3.14 \cdot 10^2 = 314$ ft²

Step 3: Find the area of the other faces.
$A = b \cdot h$
$= 10 \cdot 16 = 160$ in²
$A = b \cdot h$
$= 16 \cdot 4 = 64$ in²
$b = C = 2\pi r$
$\approx 2 \cdot 3.14 \cdot 10 \approx 62.8$ ft
$A = b \cdot h$
$\approx 62.8 \cdot 20 \approx 1256$ ft²

Step 4: Add the areas of the faces.
$SA = (2 \cdot 40) + (2 \cdot 160) + (2 \cdot 64)$
$= 528$ in²
$SA \approx (2 \cdot 314) + 1256$
≈ 1884 ft²

The surface area of the rectangular prism is 528 in² and the surface area of the cylinder is about 1884 ft².

Try It Find each surface area.

a. Sketch a net on a separate piece of paper.

b. What is the area of each base?
   15 cm²   **78.5 m²**

c. What is the area of each of the other faces?
   12 cm²   20 cm²   **785 m²**

d. Write an expression to find each surface area.
   (2 · 15) + (2 · 12) + (2 · 20)   **(2 · 78.5) + 785**

e. Evaluate to find the surface area.
   94 cm²   **942 m²**

12. The box for a videotape is 19 cm tall, 10.5 cm long, and 2.5 cm wide. It is open on one of the long and narrow sides so that the tape can be put in. What is the surface area of the box? **499 cm²**

Problem Solving and Reasoning

13. Geometry Find the surface area of the hexagonal prism. **324 cm²**

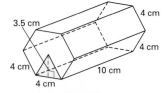

3.5 cm
4 cm
4 cm
4 cm
4 cm
10 cm

14. Number Sense Find the surface area of a cylinder with 3 m height and 1 m radius. Also, find the surface area of a cylinder with 1 m height and 3 m radius. How does the formula πr^2 affect these results?

15. Choose a Strategy A cereal company is making a jumbo-size box by doubling the dimensions of its midsize box which is 12 in. by 8 in. by 2 in. How much more cardboard will be needed to make the jumbo size? **816 in²**

GPS

Math Reasoning Determine a shortcut formula for finding the surface area.

16. A cube $6s^2$ **17.** A rectangular prism $2(bh + hw + bw)$

18. [Journal] Invent a possible surface-area problem that a set designer for a movie or play might have to solve.

19. The diameter of cylinder A is half that of cylinder B. Both have the same height.

a. Communicate Predict which will have the greater total surface area, one of cylinder B or two of cylinder A? Explain.

b. Critical Thinking Which do you think would hold more, one of cylinder B or two of cylinder A? Why?

Problem Solving
STRATEGIES
• Look for a Pattern
• Make an Organized List
• Make a Table
• Guess and Check
• Work Backward
• Use Logical Reasoning
• Draw a Diagram
• Solve a Simpler Problem

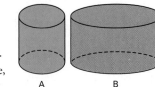

A   B

Mixed Review

Find the percent increase for each. *[Lesson 6-4]*

20. Old: 1420 New: 1562 **10%**   **21.** Old: 12.9 New: 25.8 **100%**   **22.** Old: $9.88 New: $14.82 **50%**

Classify each angle as right, straight, obtuse, or acute. *[Lesson 8-4]*

23. 130° **Obtuse**   **24.** 45° **Acute**   **25.** 90° **Right**   **26.** 180° **Straight**   **27.** 25° **Acute**

PROBLEM SOLVING 9-4

Name _____

Guided Problem Solving 9-4

GPS PROBLEM 15, STUDENT PAGE 465

A cereal company is making a jumbo-size box by doubling the dimensions of its midsize box which is 12 in. by 8 in. by 2 in. How much more cardboard will be needed to make the jumbo size?

— Understand —
1. What are the dimensions of the midsize box? __12 in. × 8 in. × 2 in.__
2. How many times greater are the dimensions of the jumbo-size box than the midsize box? __Two times.__

— Plan —
3. What are the dimensions of the jumbo-size box? __24 in. × 16 in. × 4 in.__
4. How do you find the surface area of the box? __Add areas of the faces.__
5. Draw and label a net for each box size. __Possible answer:__

— Solve —
6. How much cardboard is needed to make the midsize box? __272 in²__
7. How much cardboard is needed to make the jumbo-size box? __1088 in²__
8. How many more square inches of cardboard is needed to make the jumbo-size box than the midsize box? __816 in²__

— Look Back —
9. How does the relationship between the dimensions and surface areas of the two boxes compare to the relationship between the dimensions and area of a dilated rectangle with a scale factor of 2? __Possible answer: Dimensions multiplied by 2, SA by 2²; It is the same.__

SOLVE ANOTHER PROBLEM

A company is making a regular-size cracker box by tripling the dimensions of its sample box which is 4 in. by 3 in. by 1 in. How much more cardboard will be needed to make the regular size? __304 in²__

Name _____

Extend Your Thinking 9-4

Decision Making

You want to plant a rectangular vegetable garden in your backyard. You have 60 ft of fencing to enclose the garden and keep out some animals.

1. Find all possible whole-number dimensions for the rectangular garden. Find the area for each set of dimensions.

Dimensions	Area (ft²)	Dimensions	Area (ft²)
29 × 1	29	21 × 9	189
28 × 2	56	20 × 10	200
27 × 3	81	19 × 11	209
26 × 4	104	18 × 12	216
25 × 5	125	17 × 13	221
24 × 6	144	16 × 14	224
23 × 7	161	15 × 15	225
22 × 8	176		

2. Which garden dimensions give the greatest area? __15 × 15__
3. What other things would you consider before planting the garden? __Possible answer: Direction of sunshine, existing shade areas, trees, pet or play areas.__
4. The rectangle below represents the backyard. Choose the dimensions of the garden you prefer. Use a ruler to draw the garden in the best place. __Check students' work.__

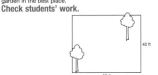

40 ft
50 ft

Exercise Notes

■ **Exercise 12**

Industry The television broadcasting industry was the first to use videotapes during the 1950's. Today, videotapes are used in the video cameras and video recorders used for home movies.

Exercise Answers

14. Possible answer: ≈ 25 m² and ≈ 75 m². The cylinder with the greater radius also has greater surface area because the radius is squared in finding the area of the circular bases.

18. Answers may vary.

19. a. The larger cylinder; It has the same area on its side as the smaller ones put together, and it has more area on the ends.

   b. The larger cylinder; The two smaller ones could be put inside it with room to spare.

Alternate Assessment

You may want to use the *Interactive CD-ROM Journal* with this assessment.

Journal Have students explain why the formulas for the surface area of a cylinder and a prism can both be given by $A = ph + 2B$, where h is the height, p is the perimeter (circumference) of a base, and B is the area of a base. Both cylinders and prisms have 2 congruent bases. The surface area includes the area of both bases ($2B$) plus the area of the lateral surface(s). Lateral area is found by multiplying distance around base (p) by the figure's height (h).

► **Quick Quiz**

1. Find the surface area of the rectangular prism.

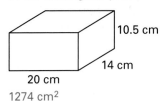

10.5 cm
14 cm
20 cm

1274 cm²

2. Find the surface area of the cylinder. Use π = 3.14.

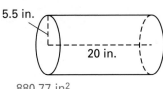

5.5 in.
20 in.

880.77 in²

Available on Daily Transparency 9-4

Surface Area of Pyramids and Cones

Objective

- Find the surface area of pyramids and cones.

Vocabulary

- Pyramid, height, slant height

Materials

- Explore: Two sheets of 8.5 in. by 11 in. paper, scissors, tape, ruler

NCTM Standards

- 1, 2, 4–7, 9, 12, 13

You'll Learn ...

■ to find the surface area of pyramids and cones

... How It's Used

Model builders know how to make polyhedrons such as pyramids and cones.

Vocabulary

pyramid

height

slant height

▶ **Lesson Link** You've worked with polyhedrons called prisms; now you'll work with polyhedrons called pyramids. ◀

A **pyramid** is a polyhedron with one base—all the other faces are triangles. The shape of the base is used to name the pyramid.

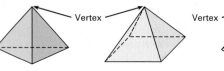

Triangular pyramid   Square pyramid   Hexagonal pyramid

Explore   Surface Area of a Pyramid

Build Your Own Pyramid

Materials: 2 sheets of 8.5 in. by 11 in. paper, Scissors, Tape, Ruler

1. Cut an 8.5 by 8.5 in. square from your sheet of paper.

2. Fold the square along each of the two diagonals, one at a time.

3. Cut out one of the V-shaped sections. Tape the cut edges together to make the pyramid.

4. Cut and attach a shape to fit on the uncovered face. Determine the surface area of your pyramid.

Step #2   Step #3

Learn   Surface Area of Pyramids and Cones

The **height** of a pyramid is the perpendicular distance from the base to the opposite vertex.

The **slant height** is the perpendicular distance from the edge of the base to the opposite vertex.

Height   Slant height

---

1. Find the area of the triangle.

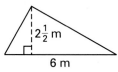

$2\frac{1}{2}$ m

6 m

7.5 m²

2. Find the area of the circle.

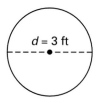

d = 3 ft

7.065 ft²

Available on Daily Transparency 9-5

▶ **Lesson Link**

Ask students to think of real-life applications that would involve finding the surface area of pyramids or cones.

1 Introduce

Explore

The Point

Students make a pyramid out of paper and calculate its surface area.

MEETING INDIVIDUAL NEEDS

Resources

9-5 Practice

9-5 Reteaching

9-5 Problem Solving

9-5 Enrichment

9-5 Daily Transparency

    Problem of the Day

    Review

    Quick Quiz

Lesson Enhancement Transparencies 41 and 42

Learning Modalities

Social In **Explore**, students work together to make pyramids out of paper and to calculate the total surface area of the pyramids.

Kinesthetic Have 3-D models of pyramids and cones available for students to actually hold and inspect.

Verbal Students are asked to write a Journal entry explaining what would happen to the surface area of a pyramid if they doubled its height.

Inclusion

Visual learners may need to have many concrete examples of surface area. Have several models of pyramids for the students to use. Have students trace each face of the pyramid onto graph paper, find the area of each face, and add to find the surface area of the pyramid.

You can find the surface area of a pyramid by looking at its net.

For a square pyramid, notice that the slant height is the height of a triangular face. The base of each triangular face is a side of the square.

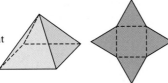

Example 1

In a play such as *Joseph and the Amazing Technicolor Dreamcoat,* which has a scene in Egypt, a square pyramid might be part of the set.

A square pyramid for a stage could have a height of 3 ft and a base area of 64 ft².

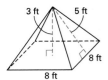

Find the surface area of this pyramid.

The pyramid base is a square with area 64 ft².

The pyramid has four triangular faces.

$A = \frac{1}{2}b \cdot h = \frac{1}{2}(8 \cdot 5) = 20$ ft²

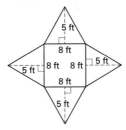

The surface area of the pyramid is

$A = 64 + 4(20) = 144$ ft².

Try It

a. What kind of pyramid is shown? **Square pyramid**

b. What is the height of the pyramid? **8 cm**

c. Use the Pythagorean theorem ($c^2 = a^2 + b^2$) to find the slant height of the pyramid. **≈ 8.5 cm**

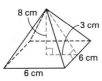

d. What is the area of the triangular face? **≈ 25.5 cm²**

e. What is the surface area of the pyramid? **≈ 138 cm²**

> ### Remember
> The Pythagorean theorem ($c^2 = a^2 + b^2$) can be used to determine the length of a side in a right triangle: a and b are legs and c is the hypotenuse.
> **[Page 374]**

MATH EVERY DAY

▶ Problem of the Day

At half-time, a band made several different arrangements. One arrangement was a square with 10 members on each side and the band leader in the center of the square. What is the least possible number of members in the band? 37;
Ten on a side, but the members at the corners are counted twice, so 10 × 4 − 4 + 1 (the leader) = 37

Available on Daily Transparency 9-5

An Extension is provided in the transparency package.

Fact of the Day

The largest pyramid ever built is located at Cholula, near Mexico City, Mexico. Built by the Toltec Indians, it is 177 ft tall and its base covers nearly 45 acres.

Mental Math

Do these mentally.

1. 970 − 170   800

2. 845 − 205   640

3. 575 − 125   450

---

2 Teach

Learn

You may wish to use Lesson Enhancement Transparencies 41 and 42 with this lesson.

Explain that a net for the pyramid is a flattened pattern for the pyramid.

Alternate Examples

1. Charlie, the owner of Charlie's Cafe, puts cardboard tents on each table to advertise his desserts. The tent is a pyramid 4 in. high with a base area of 36 in². Find the surface area of this pyramid.

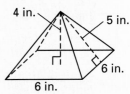

The pyramid base is a square with area 36 in².
The pyramid has four triangular faces.
$A = \frac{1}{2}b \cdot h = \frac{1}{2}(6 \cdot 5) = 15$ in²
The surface area of the pyramid is
$A = 36 + 4(15) = 96$ in².

Lesson 9-5   467

2. The triangular pyramid has an equilateral triangle base and three other faces. What is the surface area of this pyramid?

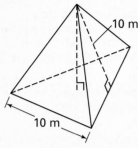

First, find the area of the base. Use the Pythagorean Theorem to find h.

$a^2 + b^2 = c^2$

$h^2 + 5^2 = 10^2$

$h^2 = 10^2 - 5^2$

$h^2 = 75$

$h \approx 8.7$ m

So $A = \frac{1}{2} bh$

$A \approx \frac{1}{2}(10)(8.7)$ Substitute

$A \approx 43.5$ m^2

Find the area of one of the three congruent triangles.

$A = \frac{1}{2}(10 \cdot 10) = 50$ m^2

The surface area of the triangular pyramid is
$SA \approx 43.5 + 3(50) \approx 193.5$ m^2.

A triangular pyramid has four triangular faces. Only one of them is the base of the pyramid. The slant height of the pyramid is the height of a triangular face that is not the base.

Example 2

The triangular pyramid has an equilateral triangle base and three other faces. What is the surface area of this pyramid?

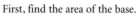

First, find the area of the base.

Use the Pythagorean theorem to find h.

$a^2 + b^2 = c^2$

$h^2 + 6^2 = 12^2$

$h^2 = 12^2 - 6^2$

$h^2 = 108$

$h \approx 10.4$ m

So $A = \frac{1}{2}bh$

$A \approx \frac{1}{2}(12)(10.4)$ Substitute.

$A \approx 62.4$ m^2

Find the area of one of the three congruent triangles.

$A = \frac{1}{2}b \cdot h$

$A = \frac{1}{2}(12 \cdot 12) = 72$ m^2

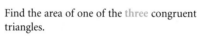

The surface area of the triangular pyramid is

$SA \approx 62.4 + 3(72) = 278.4$ m^2.

Try It

a. What is the slant height of the pyramid? **11 ft**

b. Use the Pythagorean theorem $(a^2 + b^2 = c^2)$ to find the height of the triangular base. **≈ 2.6 ft**

c. What is the area of a triangular face? **≈ 16.5 ft^2**

d. What is the surface area of the pyramid? **≈ 53.4 ft^2**

MEETING MIDDLE SCHOOL CLASSROOM NEEDS

Tips from Middle School Teachers

I find graph paper especially useful in teaching surface area. Students can work in small groups drawing the nets for a variety of figures and finding the area. Some of my students respond to challenges from others. One student can draw figures; another can find their surface area.

History Connection

Several ancient peoples, but most notably the Egyptians, used pyramids as tombs or temples. The ruins of 35 major pyramids, each of which was built to hold the body of an Egyptian king, still stand in Egypt. It is generally believed by many scholars that the pyramid shape had a religious meaning to the ancient Egyptians.

Cooperative Learning

(Materials: poster board, ruler, scissors, tape) Small groups of interested students could use the methods they have learned for constructing pyramids to produce 3-D art. Encourage them to combine various shapes to construct their creations. After they have produced their 3-D art forms, have students compute the surface area (and later the volume) of their figures. Place the figures on display in your classroom or other appropriate display areas.

A **circular cone** is a 3-D figure with a circular base and one vertex.

To find the surface area of a cone, you find the area of the base and the area of the curved surface.

The area of the curved surface is $A = \frac{1}{2}Cs$.

The area of the base is $A = \pi r^2$.

The surface area of a cone is $SA = \left(\frac{1}{2}Cs\right) + \pi r^2$.

s = slant height

Example 3

Denise needs to make a model of a cinder cone volcano for a school play. The cone should be 4 ft tall, the base 4 ft in diameter, and the slant height about 4.48 ft. She needs to know the surface area of the cone in order to buy wire mesh to make the frame. What is the surface area of this cone?

Area of curved surface $= \frac{1}{2}Cs$

$A = \frac{1}{2}(2\pi \cdot 2)4.48 \approx 28.13$ ft^2

Area of base $= \pi r^2$

$A = \pi(2)^2 \approx 12.56$ ft^2

4 ft

$SA \approx 28.13 + 12.56$ Take the sum to find the surface area.

≈ 40.69 ft^2

Denise needs approximately 40.69 ft^2 of wire mesh.

Check | Your Understanding

1. What is the difference between the slant height and the height of a pyramid or cone?

2. How can you tell by looking at a net whether the solid is a prism, a pyramid, a cone, or a cylinder?

3. Pearl City public works department is building a cone-shaped storage bin for road salt. The cone will be 20 ft tall with a base that is 30 ft in diameter. What is the surface area of this cone?

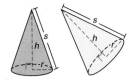

20 ft

30 ft

Use the Pythagorean Theorem to find s, the slant height.

$s^2 = 20^2 + 15^2$

$s^2 = 625$

$s = 25$

Area of curved surface $= \frac{1}{2}Cs$

$A = \frac{1}{2}(2\pi \cdot 15)25 \approx 1177.5$ ft^2

Area of the base $= \pi r^2$

$A = \pi(15)^2 \approx 706.5$ ft^2

Add to find the surface area.

$SA \approx 1177.5 + 706.5 \approx 1884$ ft^2

The surface area of the cone is approximately 1884 ft^2.

3 Practice and Assess

Check

If students are having trouble with Exercise 2, suggest that they think in terms of the number of bases shown in the net.

Answers for Check Your Understanding

1. Possible answer: The slant height is the height of a face that is not a base of the 3-D figure. The height of a pyramid or cone is perpendicular to the base of the 3-D figure.

2. Possible answer: Prisms and cylinders both have two bases, whereas pyramids and cones both have only one base. Cones and cylinders have circular bases.

Assignment Guide

■ **Basic**
1–4, 6–9, 11, 13–23 odds,
24, 25

■ **Average**
1–5, 7–10, 12, 14–22 evens,
24, 25

■ **Enriched**
1–5, 7–12, 14–20 evens, 24, 25

Exercise Notes

■ **Exercise 7**

Test Prep Some students may answer B, not realizing that you need to use π to compute the area of the base of a cone.

■ **Exercise 8**

Fine Arts One of the most coveted roles for a ballerina is the lead in the ballet *Sleeping Beauty*. This role was created in the 1890s by the French choreographer Marius Petipa, while he was the head of the Imperial Theater in St. Petersburg, Russia.

Reteaching

Materials: Models of pyramids and cones, rulers, measuring tapes

• Work in groups of three.

• Measure the models and calculate their surface areas.

• When all of the groups have had a chance to work with all of the models, compare your answers with those of other groups.

470   Chapter 9

9-5 Exercises and Applications

Practice and Apply

1. **Getting Started** Find the surface area of the triangular pyramid with the net shown.

   a. How many faces does the pyramid have? **4**

   b. What is the area of the pyramid's base? **252 ft²**

   c. What is the area of each of the other faces? **252 ft² each**

   d. Take the sum of the areas of the faces and the base to determine the surface area of the pyramid. **1008 ft²**

21 ft / 24 ft / 21 ft / 21 ft / 21 ft

For each figure, find   a. The slant height.   b. The surface area.

2.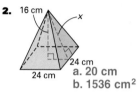
16 cm / *x* / 24 cm / 24 cm
a. **20 cm**
b. **1536 cm²**

3.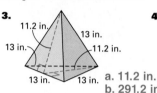
11.2 in. / 13 in. / 13 in. / 11.2 in. / 13 in. / 13 in.
a. **11.2 in.**
b. **291.2 in²**

4.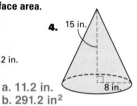
15 in. / 8 in.
a. **17 in.**
b. **≈ 628 in²**

5. An amusement park wants a square pyramid in its Ancient Wonders theme area. The pyramid is to be 8 ft high and have a 12 ft wide square base. What is the surface area of the pyramid that will be built? **384 ft²**

6. A triangular pyramid has an equilateral triangle with side length of 4 ft for a base. The height of the pyramid is 3.2 ft and the slant height is approximately 3.4 ft. What is the approximate surface area of this pyramid? **≈ 27.4 ft²**

7. **Test Prep** Which do you need to find the area of the base of a cone? **D**

   Ⓐ π   Ⓑ Radius
   Ⓒ Slant height   Ⓓ A and B

8. **Fine Arts** In a staged version of *Sleeping Beauty*, the princess wears a cone-shaped headpiece 18 in. tall. It is constructed of cardboard and wrapped with velvet fabric. How much fabric is needed to cover the cone if the actress's head has a 22 in. circumference? **≈ 201.72 in²**

Shakespeare's *Richard III*, 1949

PRACTICE 9-5

▷ PRACTICE

Name _____

Practice 9-5

Surface Area of Pyramids and Cones

For each figure, find **a.** the slant height; **b.** the surface area.

1. a. **41 cm**
   b. **1800 cm²**
   h = 40 cm / 18 cm / 18 cm

2. a. **Given**
   b. **≈ 332.4 in²**
   15 in. / 12 in. / 12 in. / 12 in.

3. a. **19.3 m**
   b. **≈ 859.1 m²**
   h = 16.8 m / r = 9.5 m

4. a. **Given**
   b. **≈ 36.93 cm²**
   5 cm / 4 cm / 4 cm / 4 cm

5. a. **15¼ in.**
   b. **155.43 in²**
   15 in. / 5½ in.

6. a. **15.7 m**
   b. **822.8 m²**
   h = 13.2 m / 17 m / 17 m

7. a. **65 mm**
   b. **≈ 10,155 mm²**
   r = 33 mm / 56 mm

8. a. **29 ft**
   b. **3920 ft²**
   h = 21 ft / 40 ft / 40 ft

9. a. **Given**
   b. **≈ 177.8 cm²**
   8.6 cm / 11.3 cm / 8.6 cm / 8.6 cm

10. **History** The largest of the Egyptian pyramids was built almost 5000 years ago. Its square base has sides of length 755 ft, and it was originally about 482 ft tall. Find the slant height and the surface area (do not include the base).

    Slant height: **About 612.2 ft**   Surface area: **About 924,000 ft²**

11. A circular cone has a surface area of 282.6 cm². The base of the cone has radius 5 cm. Find the slant height. Then use the Pythagorean Theorem to find the height of the cone.

    Slant height: **13 cm**   Height: **12 cm**

▷ RETEACHING

Name _____

Alternative Lesson 9-5

Surface Area of Pyramids and Cones

A **pyramid** is a polyhedron with one base, and all other faces are triangles. The shape of the base is used to name the pyramid.

The **height** of a pyramid is the perpendicular distance from the base to the opposite vertex. The **slant height** (*s*) is the perpendicular distance from the *edge* of the base to the opposite vertex.

A **circular cone** is a 3-D figure with a circular base and one vertex. To find the surface area of a cone, find the area of the base and the area of the curved surface.

— **Example 1** —
Find the surface area of the pyramid shown.

Step 1: Find the area of each face.
    Base $A = s^2 = 5^2 = 25$ cm²
    Each triangular face (4 in all) $A = \frac{1}{2} \cdot 5 \cdot 8 = 20$ cm²
Step 2: Add the areas of the faces. $SA = 25 + 4(20) = 105$ cm²
The surface area is 105 cm².

Try It
a. What is the area of the base? **100 ft²**
b. What is the area of each triangular face? **50 ft²**
c. How many faces are triangles? **4 faces.**
d. Find the surface area. **300 ft²**

— **Example 2** —
Find the surface area of the cone shown.

Step 1: Find the area of each surface.
    Curved surface. $A = \frac{1}{2} \cdot C \cdot s = \frac{1}{2} \cdot (3.14 \cdot 8) \cdot 5 = 62.8$ ft²
    Base. $A = \pi r^2 = 3.14 \cdot 4^2 = 50.24$ ft²
Step 2: Add the areas of the surfaces. $SA = 62.8 + 50.24 = 113.04$ ft²
The surface area of the cone is about 113.04 ft².

Try It
e. What is the area of the base? **314 ft²**
f. What is the area of the curved surface? **314 ft²**
g. What is the surface area? **628 ft²**

9. Social Studies Sioux tepees are cone-shaped. If the diameter of a tepee is 18 ft and the height is 12 ft, how much buffalo hide is needed to cover the outside surface? **≈ 423.9 ft²**

10. Algebra A square pyramid has a total surface area of 176 yd². If the slant height is 7 yd and the area of the base is 64 yd², then what is the height of the pyramid? Round your answer to the nearest hundredth place. **5.74 yd**

Problem Solving and Reasoning

11. Communicate Your classmate is confused about the difference between the height of a pyramid and the slant height. Describe the difference between the two.

For Exercises 12 and 13, refer to the square pyramid and cone of the same height, with the diameter of the cone's base equal to the side of the square base of the pyramid.

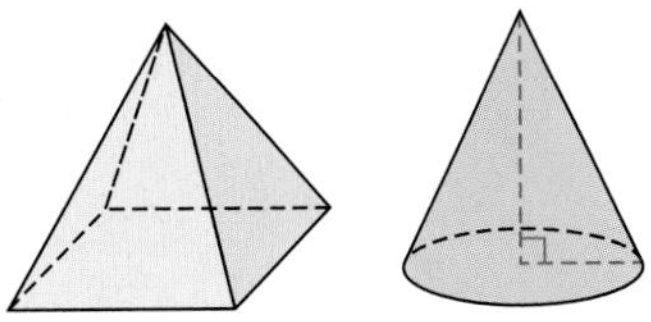

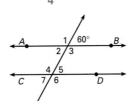

12. Math Reasoning Which is greater, the perimeter of the square base or the circumference of the circular base? **The perimeter of the square base**

13. Critical Thinking Which do you think has the greater surface area? Explain. **The pyramid**

14. [Journal] What would happen to the surface area of a pyramid if you double its height? Give an example and explain.

15. Number Sense How many faces does a hexagonal pyramid have? Octagonal pyramid? Describe the number pattern.

Mixed Review

Find the slope, *x*-intercept, and *y*-intercept for each equation. *[Lesson 4-5]*

16. $y = 2x - 1$ **17.** $y = x + 3$ **18.** $y = \frac{1}{2}x + 2$ **19.** $y = -2x - 2$, 0, 0
$2, \frac{1}{2}, -1$ $1, -3, 3$ $\frac{1}{2}, -4, 2$

20. $y = -x + 1$ **21.** $y = 3x + 0$ **22.** $y = -0.5x - 2$ **23.** $y = 4x - 5$ $4, \frac{5}{4}, -5$
$-1, 1, 1$ $3, 0, 0$ $-0.5, -4, -2$

$\overleftrightarrow{AB} \parallel \overleftrightarrow{CD}$. Use the diagram on the right to answer the questions. *[Lesson 8-5]*

24. Find the measures of all angles in the diagram.

25. Identify all interior angles. **2, 3, 4, 5**

9-5 · Surface Area of Pyramids and Cones **471**

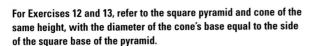
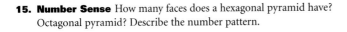
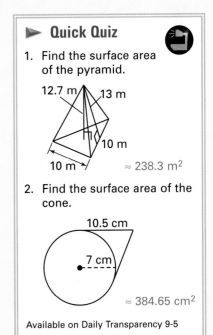

► **Quick Quiz**

1. Find the surface area of the pyramid.

  12.7 m   13 m   10 m   10 m   **≈ 238.3 m²**

2. Find the surface area of the cone.

  10.5 cm   7 cm   **≈ 384.65 cm²**

Available on Daily Transparency 9-5

Lesson 9-5   **471**

Using Geometry Software • Measuring Polygons

The Point
Students use geometry software to construct triangles and a quadrilateral.

Materials
Geometry software

Resources

 Interactive CD-ROM Geometry Tool

About the Page

If students have not used the geometry software before:

- Demonstrate how to use the polygon tool and how to select points.

- Show students the location of the Construct menu. Then demonstrate how to select "Polygon Interior."

- Show students the location of the Measure menu. Then demonstrate how to choose "perimeter" and "area" from this menu.

Ask ...
- Why do you use the polygon tool to make a triangle?
  Triangles are polygons.

- Were you able to select your three points for your triangle?

- Were you able to select "Polygon Interior" so that the software could calculate your triangle's perimeter and area for you?

Answers for Try It
  a. Answers may vary.

  b. Answers may vary.

Answers for On Your Own
- Possible answer: It adds the lengths of the sides in pixels and converts them to the chosen units.

- Possible answer: Yes; The software calculates the area instantly.

- Possible answer: It would probably change.

Using Geometry Software • Measuring Polygons

Problem: Construct a triangle. What are its perimeter and area?

You can use geometry software to answer this question.

1 Choose the Polygon Tool. Click on three different vertex points for your triangle.

2 When you return to your first point and click, your triangle will be complete.

3 Use the length tool to calculate the perimeter of the triangle.

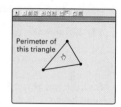
Perimeter of this triangle

4 Use the area tool to calculate the area of the triangle.

22.70 cm — Area of this triangle

Solution: The answers may vary.

TRY IT

a. Construct another triangle. What are its perimeter and area?

b. Construct a quadrilateral. What are its perimeter and area?

ON YOUR OWN

▶ How do you think geometry software calculates the perimeter of a polygon?

▶ Is it easier to find the area of a polygon using geometry software rather than a formula? Explain.

▶ Describe what would happen to the area of your triangle if you moved one of the vertices.

472

Section 9A Connect

In the beginning of Section 9A, you learned about a historical American theater hall. Now you will design a stage set for a play.

The Great Stage

Materials: Drawing paper, Ruler, Compass, Drawing pens

You and your group are in charge of designing a stage set for a school play.

The producer wants an archway that looks like a palace entrance. The archway must have a semicircular (half-circle) top and cylindrical columns for support.

You must also design rectangular steps up to a doorway in the arch.

You must decide the quantity of various materials you will use to make this archway. Do this by using what you know about area, perimeter, and surface area.

1. Each person in the group draws a sketch of each part of the design: each column, the semicircle, and the stairs. Each drawing should show the actual dimensions of the props and the drawing scale.

2. Calculate the material needed to cover the surface area of all the props.

3. Decide on the materials you would use to cover these props; for example, paint, fabric, paper, tile, and so on.

4. Make a list of the amount of materials you'll need to cover the props.

5. Decide on a layout of the stage and draw a top view of this stage plan including the props you have just designed.

6. Draw the front view of your stage plan. Identify a story line that would be appropriate for your design.

473

The Great Stage

The Point
In *The Great Stage* on page 443, students discussed stage design. Now they apply their knowledge of mathematical measurements to design a stage set for a school play.

Materials
Drawing paper, ruler, compass, drawing pens

Resources
Teaching Tool Transparencies
15: Rulers
16: Protractors

About the Page

- Make sure that students understand that their drawings are to be drawn to scale.

- Suggest that students should work together on Step 2 to calculate the surface area of the props. Make sure that everyone correctly understands the procedure.

- The decisions concerning the materials selected to cover the props should be made by the group as a whole.

- The decision on the layout of the stage should be made by the group as well, but only one drawing needs to be made.

- One student can act as secretary when the group composes the dialogue for the new stage set.

Ongoing Assessment
You might want to meet with each group at the completion of Step 2 to make sure they have calculated the surface area correctly for their chosen dimensions.

Extension

Have students design another prop of their choice, perhaps to go along with some special dialogue they have created. They should then calculate the new prop's surface area and decide on the type and amount of materials they would like to cover it.

Answers for Connect
1–6. Answers may vary.

Review Correlation

Item(s)	Lesson(s)
1	9-1
2	9-3
3	9-4
4	9-2
5	9-4, 9-5
6	9-3
7–11	9-1
12	9-4
13	9-5
14	9-4
15	9-5
16	9-3

Test Prep

Test-Taking Tip

Tell students to write legibly when writing fill-in-the-blank answers since, in most cases, if the teacher can't read it, it's automatically wrong.

Answers for Review

5. Possible answer: A prism and a cylinder have two identical ends; A pyramid and a cone come to a point at one end.

REVIEW 9A

Section 9A Review

Fill in the appropriate vocabulary term for each sentence.

1. The distance around a polygon is the _____. **Perimeter**

2. The _____ of a circle is π times the diameter. **Circumference**

3. A _____ has two parallel polygons that are the same size and shape. **Prism**

4. A reduction of a geometric figure by a scale factor is a _____. **Dilation**

5. Explain the difference between a prism and a pyramid and the difference between a cylinder and a cone.

Find the perimeter/circumference and area for each figure.

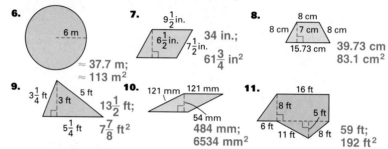

6. 6 m
≈ 37.7 m;
≈ 113 m²

7. $9\frac{1}{2}$ in. $6\frac{1}{2}$ in. $7\frac{1}{2}$ in.
34 in.;
$61\frac{3}{4}$ in²

8. 8 cm 7 cm 8 cm 15.73 cm
39.73 cm
83.1 cm²

9. $3\frac{1}{4}$ ft 3 ft 5 ft $5\frac{1}{4}$ ft
$13\frac{1}{2}$ ft;
$7\frac{7}{8}$ ft²

10. 121 mm 121 mm 54 mm
484 mm;
6534 mm²

11. 16 ft 8 ft 5 ft 6 ft 11 ft 8 ft
59 ft;
192 ft²

Find the surface area of each figure.

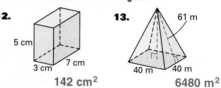

12. 5 cm 3 cm 7 cm
142 cm²

13. 61 m 40 m 40 m
6480 m²

14. 20 in. 25 in.
2198 in²

15. 18 cm 16 cm
2014 cm²

Test Prep

When using formulas on a test, always use pencil and paper to substitute and solve for a missing value.

16. The diameter of a bicycle wheel is 18 in. What is its circumference? **C**

Ⓐ 21.52 in. Ⓑ 28.52 in. Ⓒ 56.52 in. Ⓓ 85.52 in.

474 *Chapter 9 • Area and Volume*

Resources

Practice Masters
   Section 9A Review
Assessment Sourcebook
   Quiz 9A
💿 *TestWorks*
   Test and Practice Software

PRACTICE

Name _____

Practice

Section 9A Review

Fill in the appropriate vocabulary term for each sentence.

1. A **(circular) cone** is a 3-D figure with a single vertex and a circular base.

2. The circumference of a circle is 2π times the **radius**.

3. The **surface area** of a polyhedron can be found by adding the areas of all the faces.

Find the perimeter/circumference and area for each figure.

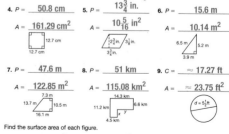

4. P = **50.8 cm**   A = **161.29 cm²**   12.7 cm 12.7 cm

5. P = **$13\frac{3}{4}$ in.**   A = **$10\frac{5}{16}$ in²** $2\frac{3}{8}$ in. $3\frac{1}{8}$ in. $3\frac{3}{4}$ in.

6. P = **15.6 m**   A = **10.14 m²**   6.5 m 5.2 m 3.9 m

7. P = **47.6 m**   A = **122.85 m²**   7.3 m 13.7 m 10.5 m 16.1 m

8. P = **51 km**   A = **115.08 km²**   14.3 km 11.2 km 6.6 km 4.5 km

9. C = **≈ 17.27 ft**   A = **≈ 23.75 ft²** $d = 5\frac{1}{2}$ ft

Find the surface area of each figure.

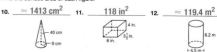

10. **≈ 1413 cm²**   40 cm 9 cm

11. **118 in²**   4 in. 6 in. $3\frac{1}{2}$ in.

12. **≈ 119.4 m²**   6.2 m 4.5 m

13. The population of Cleveland, Ohio, decreased 11.9% from 1980 to 1990. If the 1990 population was 505,600, what was the 1980 population? *[Lesson 6-5]*   **About 573,890**

14. Tell what metric unit you would use to measure the height of a cathedral. *[Lesson 8-1]*   **Possible answer: meter**

Section 9B

Volume

Visit **www.teacher.mathsurf.com** for links to lesson plans from teachers and other professionals, NCTM information, and other sites.

LESSON PLANNING GUIDE

▶ Student Edition

LESSON	MATERIALS	VOCABULARY
Section 9B Opener		
9-6 Volume of Rectangular Prisms	centimeter cubes, 8.5 in. by 11 in. paper, tape, centimeter ruler	volume
9-7 Scale and Volume	spreadsheet software	
9-8 Volume of Prisms and Cylinders	two sheets of 8.5 in. by 11 in. paper, tape, centimeter cubes, centimeter ruler	
9-9 Volume of Pyramids and Cones	scissors, tape, centimeter ruler, two sheets of 11 in. by 17 in. paper, compass, centimeter cubes	
Connect	calculator	
Review		'
Extend Key Ideas		
Chapter Summary and Review		
Chapter 9 Assessment		
Cumulative Review, Ch. 1–9		

▶ Ancillaries

DAILY	OTHER
9-6	Lesson Enhancement Transparencies 43, 44
9-7	Teaching Tool Trans. 2, 3 *Interactive CD-ROM Lesson*
9-8	Lesson Enhancement Transparencies 45, 46 *WW Math*—Middle School
9-9	Teaching Tool Trans. 2, 3 Lesson Enhancement Transparencies 47, 48 Ch. 9 Project Master
	Teaching Tool Trans. 22 Interdisc. Team Teaching 9B
	Practice 9B; Quiz 9B; *TestWorks*
	Teaching Tool Trans. 20 Lesson Enhance. Trans. 49
	Ch. 9 Tests Forms A–F *TestWorks;* Ch. 9 Letter Home
	Cumulative Review Ch. 1–9 Quarterly Test Ch. 1–9

SKILLS TRACE

LESSON	SKILL	FIRST INTRODUCED GR. 6	GR. 7	GR. 8	DEVELOP	PRACTICE/ APPLY	REVIEW
9-6	Determining volume of rectangular prisms.	✗			pp. 476–478	pp. 479–480	pp. 501, 547, 559, 650
9-7	Dilating rectangular prisms and predicting volume of rectangular prisms.			✗ p. 481	pp. 481–484	pp. 485–486	pp. 501, 552, 559, 656
9-8	Finding volume of prisms and cylinders.		✗		pp. 487–489	pp. 490–491	pp. 498, 501, 502, 662
9-9	Finding volume of pyramids and cones.			✗ p. 492	pp. 492–494	pp. 495–496	pp. 498, 501, 502, 667

CONNECTED MATHEMATICS

The unit *Thinking with Mathematical Models (Representing Relationships),* from the **Connected Mathematics** series, can be used with Section 9B.

In this lesson, students use volume to study the packaging of food products.

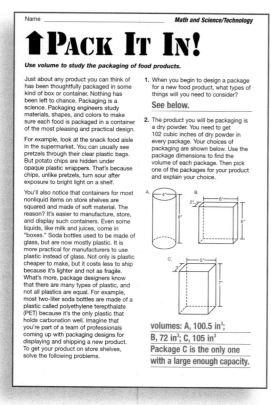

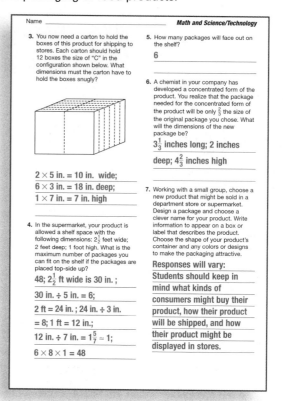

Answers

1. Accept any reasonable answers, which could include the following: Is the product solid or liquid? Is it perishable and in need of freezing or refrigeration? Is the product sensitive to light? What volume of product will each container hold? Will the product need to be heated (microwaved, baked, or immersed in boiling water) in its package? What information must be on the label? Who is the product being sold to, and what color might be most attractive to these customers? Will the package need to be opened and then resealed? Will the outside package need an inner packaging material to protect it, such as the plastic liner inside a cereal box? What is the product made of, and could it react chemically with some packaging materials?

BIBLIOGRAPHY

FOR TEACHERS

Brockett, Oscar G. *History of the Theater.* 7th ed. Needham Heights, MA: Allyn & Bacon, 1995.

Brown, John Russell, ed. *The Oxford Illustrated History of Theater.* New York, NY: Oxford University Press, 1995.

Holden, Alan. *Shapes, Space, and Symmetry.* Mineola, NY: Dover, 1991.

Ogilvy, Charles S. *Excursions in Geometry.* Mineola, NY: Dover, 1990.

Parker, Wilford O. and R. C. Wolf. *Scene Design and Stage Lighting.* 6th ed. Austin, TX: Holt, Rinehart, 1990.

FOR STUDENTS

Kohl, Herbert. *Insides, Outsides, Loops and Lines: Not Just Another Math Book.* New York, NY: W. H. Freeman, 1995.

Smoothey, Marion. *Area and Volume.* New York, NY: M. Cavendish, 1993.

VanCleave, Janice Pratt. *Janice VanCleave's Geometry for Every Kid.* New York, NY: John Wiley & Sons, 1994.

SECTION 9B | Volume

▶ **Consumer Link** ▶ **Industry Link** ▶ www.mathsurf.com/8/ch9/packages

Deliveries

The year was 1907 and business in the United States was flourishing. Few people had telephones or cars, so how were messages and packages delivered? Jim Casey, an enterprising 19-year-old from Seattle, had an idea. He borrowed $100, started the American Messenger Company, and hired other teenagers to work for him.

Jim's company did very well because of his old-fashioned values: customer courtesy, reliability, round-the-clock service, and low rates. Jim had an idea that no one else had thought of — consolidated delivery. Packages to be delivered to one neighborhood were put into a single delivery vehicle. This saved time and money.

During the 1930s Jim's company changed its name to United Parcel Service or UPS. This company now delivers over 12 million documents and packages around the world.

1 What mathematics might a package-delivery company use to keep delivery going accurately and on time?

2 Why might delivery companies set limits on overall dimensions and weight of packages?

475

Where are we now?

In Section 9A, students explored area and volume. They learned how to

- calculate the perimeter and area of polygons.

- dilate rectangles and predict their perimeter and area.

- calculate the area and circumference of circles.

- calculate the surface area of prisms, cylinders, pyramids, and cones.

Where are we going?

In Section 9B, students will

- calculate the volume of rectangular prisms.

- dilate regular prisms and predict their volume.

- calculate the volume of prisms, cylinders, pyramids, and cones.

Theme: Packages

World Wide Web

If your class has access to the World Wide Web, you might want to use the information found at the Web site address given. The interdisciplinary links relate to topics discussed in this section.

About the Page

This page introduces the theme of the section, packages, and discusses the history and philosophy of United Parcel Service (UPS).

Ask ...

- Had you ever heard the story behind UPS before?

- What were some of the steps that UPS took to become such a huge success? Customer courtesy, reliability, round-the-clock service, and low rates.

Extensions

The following activities do not require access to the World Wide Web.

Consumer

Much of what we buy comes in disposable packages. Have students find out what happens to packaging materials after they are discarded.

Industry

Most people in the U.S. have access to fresh food all year around. Have students investigate how perishable foods are packaged for shipping.

Answers for Questions

1. Possible answer: Comparing alternative delivery routes to find the fastest one.

2. Possible answer: Shipping large or heavy packages could require equipment and procedures that would slow delivery.

Connect

On page 497, students consider operating a business of their own and use their knowledge of volume to solve packaging problems.

475

■ Determine the volume of rectangular prisms.

Vocabulary

■ Volume

Materials

■ Explore: Centimeter cubes, 8.5 in. by 11 in. paper, tape, centimeter ruler

NCTM Standards

■ 1–7, 9, 12

► **Review**

Find the area of each rectangle whose dimensions are given below.

1. $b = 9\frac{1}{2}$ in., $h = 5\frac{1}{4}$ in.

   $49\frac{7}{8}$ in²

2. $b = 11.75$ cm, $h = 3.8$ cm
   44.65 cm²

3. $b = 5$ m, $h = 1.3$ m   6.5 m²

4. $b = 1.12$ ft, $h = 3.25$ ft
   3.64 ft²

Available on Daily Transparency 9-6

► **Lesson Link**

Explain that while surface area is a measure of the boundary of a solid, volume is a measure of the space inside a solid.

1 Introduce

Explore

The Point
Students make two different rectangular prisms out of the same size sheet of paper and calculate how many centimeter cubes would be needed to fill each prism.

Ongoing Assessment
For Step 2a, students will need to estimate the number of cubes required. Make sure they understand that estimation is acceptable here.

9-6   Volume of Rectangular Prisms

You'll Learn …

■ to determine the volume of rectangular prisms

… How It's Used

Volume tells you how much space a package occupies and how much it might weigh. Weight and space are important factors for a delivery company.

Vocabulary

volume

▶ **Lesson Link**   You've learned how to find the surface area of rectangular prisms. Now you'll find the volume of rectangular prisms. ◄

The **volume** is the number of cubic units in a solid.

The volume of this solid is 1 cm³.

1 cm
1 cm   1 cm

Explore   **Filling a Rectangular Prism**

Fill It Up!

Materials: Centimeter cubes, 8.5 in. by 11 in. paper, Tape, Centimeter ruler

1. Make two different rectangular prisms (without bases) by folding two 8.5 in. by 11 in. sheets of paper into equal fourths: one using the longer side and one using the shorter side. Tape the edges to form the prism.

2. Make a layer of unit cubes to cover the base of each rectangular prism.

   a. How tall is a single layer of cubes?

   b. How many cubes cover each base?

3. For each prism, how many cubes are needed to make two layers? Three layers? Four layers? Make a table to record your data.

4. a. How tall is each rectangular prism (in centimeters)?

   b. How many layers are needed to fill each prism?

5. How many cubes would fill each prism?

11 in.

$8\frac{1}{2}$ in.

Learn   **Volume of Rectangular Prisms**

The volume of a prism is found by multiplying the area of the base (B) by the prism height (h).

$V = B \cdot h$

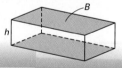

B

h

▷ **MEETING INDIVIDUAL NEEDS**

Resources	**Learning Modalities**
9-6 Practice	**Logical** In **Explore**, students experiment with making rectangular prisms out of paper and calculate how many centimeter cubes would be needed to fill the prisms.
9-6 Reteaching	
9-6 Problem Solving	
9-6 Enrichment	
9-6 Daily Transparency	**Kinesthetic** Students can make predictions as to the volume of a box and then check their prediction by filling the box with centimeter cubes.
Problem of the Day	
Review	
Quick Quiz	**Visual** Students are asked to sketch figures before calculating their volume in Exercises 8 and 9.
Lesson Enhancement Transparencies 43 and 44	

Inclusion
In Exercises 8 and 9 on page 479, students who have limited fine motor skills should be paired with students who are comfortable sketching the rectangular prisms.
Remind students to add new vocabulary to their reference notebook.

The area of the base of a polyhedron is shown by B. The length of the base of a polygon is shown by b.

Example 1

A next-day delivery service delivers a package with dimensions 12 in. by 7 in. by 30 in. What is the volume of the package?

First, draw the prism and label the dimensions.

Find the area of the rectangular base.

$B = 12 \cdot 30 = 360 \text{ in}^2$

$V = B \cdot h$

$V = 360 \cdot 7$

$V = 2520 \text{ in}^3$

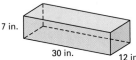

7 in. 30 in. 12 in.

The volume is 2520 in³.

Example 2

Find the height of a rectangular prism with volume 72 cm³ and base dimensions 6 cm by 3 cm.

First, find the area of the rectangular base.

$B = 6 \times 3 = 18 \text{ cm}^2$

Then use the volume formula to solve.

$V = B \cdot h$

$72 = 18 \cdot h$

$4 = h$

3 cm   6 cm

The prism has a height of 4 cm.

Try It

Find the volume of each figure.

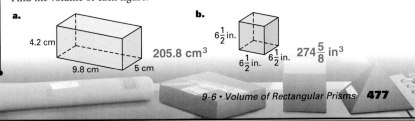

a.
4.2 cm
9.8 cm   5 cm
205.8 cm³

b.
$6\frac{1}{2}$ in.
$6\frac{1}{2}$ in. $6\frac{1}{2}$ in.
$274\frac{5}{8}$ in³

Study TIP

Are you a visual learner? If so, complement your learning style by drawing diagrams when you study.

9-6 • Volume of Rectangular Prisms **477**

MATH EVERY DAY

▶ **Problem of the Day**

One size of Post-It™ Notes is 2 in. by 3 in. These come in pads that are $\frac{13}{32}$ in. thick.

Twelve such pads are wrapped in plastic. Twelve of these plastic-wrapped groups are then put in a box. What is the volume of the box? 351 in³

Available on Daily Transparency 9-6

An Extension is provided in the transparency package.

Fact of the Day

A cubic foot of water weighs about 62 lb. Therefore, a water bed of dimensions 6 ft by $5\frac{1}{2}$ ft by 6 in. weighs over 1000 lb.

Estimation

Estimate.

1. 23 • 286 6,000

2. 32 • 108 3,000

3. 52 • 501 25,000

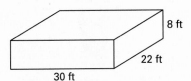
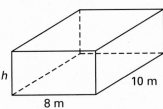
Lesson 9-6   477

Alternate Examples

3. Mishka built an L-shaped aquarium for his room. He wants to know how many gallons of water it will hold. He knows there are 231 in³ of water in 1 gallon.

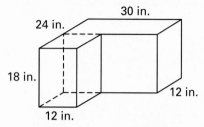

The aquarium is composed of two rectangular prisms. Find the volume of each rectangular prism.

Find the volume of the front prism, V_{front}.
$V_{front} = (12) \cdot (12) \cdot (18)$
$V_{front} = 2592$ in³

Find the volume of the rear prism, V_{rear}.
$V_{rear} = 12 \cdot 30 \cdot 18$
$V_{rear} = 6480$ in³

Find the total volume, $V_{front} + V_{rear}$.
$V_{front} + V_{rear} = 2592 + 6480 = 9072$ in³
$\frac{9072 \text{ in}^3}{231 \text{ in}^3/\text{gal}} \approx 39.3$ gal

The aquarium will hold about 39.3 gal of water.

3 Practice and Assess

Check

For Exercise 1, students might build a prism that is 2 in. by 2 in. by 2 in. using inch cubes and one that is 5 cm by 5 cm by 5 cm using centimeter cubes. Note that the prisms are about the same size but the number of cubes used differs because cubic centimeters are smaller than cubic inches.

Answers for Check Your Understanding

1. Actual volume does not change, but measuring volume in cubic centimeters would result in a larger number than using cubic inches.

2. Possible answer: Surface area uses square units, volume uses cubic units.

3. Possible answer: b is used for the base length of a polygon, whereas B is used for the base area of a polyhedron.
Area of a rectangle = bh
Area of a prism = Bh.

You can find the volume of some irregularly-shaped solids by breaking the figure into rectangular prisms.

▶ **History Link**

In 1720, it took the postal service three days to deliver a parcel from Philadelphia to New York (almost 100 miles).

Example 3

Speedy Delivery, Inc., charges by volume for irregularly-shaped packages. If it charges $170.63 for a package with the dimensions shown, how much do they charge per in³?

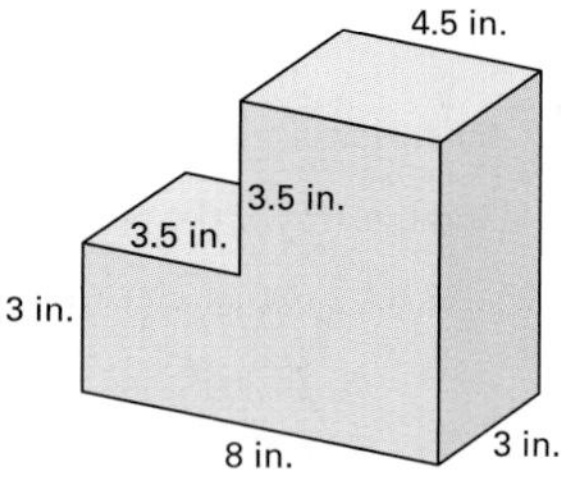

This solid is composed of two rectangular prisms.

Find the volume of each rectangular prism.

Find the volume of the bottom prism, V_{bottom}.

$V_{bottom} = (8)(3)(3)$

$V_{bottom} = 72$ in³

Find the volume of the top prism, V_{top}.

$V_{top} = (4.5)(3.5)(3)$

$V_{top} = 47.25$ in³

Find the total volume: $V_{bottom} + V_{top}$.

$V_{bottom} + V_{top} = 72 + 47.25 = 119.25$ in³

$\frac{170.63}{119.25} \approx \$1.43$ per in³

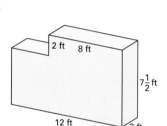

Try It

Find the volume of the figure shown.
246 ft³

Check   Your Understanding

1. Would the volume of a package change if you measured it in cubic centimeters instead of cubic inches? Explain.

2. Describe the difference between the surface area and volume of a rectangular prism.

3. In formulas for area and volume, describe the difference between b and B. Give examples of how b and B are used.

▶ MEETING MIDDLE SCHOOL CLASSROOM NEEDS

Tips from Middle School Teachers

Some of my students find it hard to transfer what they know about geometric figures in a plane to the measurement of solid figures. I find it very beneficial to use models of three-dimensional figures. Students can handle them and identify parts of figures.

Science Connection

In science and engineering, accurate recording of volumes is essential in experiments. Knowing a solid's volume can help in finding its weight, mass, pressure, and many other physical properties.

Team Teaching

You may wish to work with an art teacher to help students connect geometry and art. Students can work with perspective drawing or string art.

9-6 Exercises and Applications

Practice and Apply

1. **Getting Started** Find the volume of the rectangular prism.
   a. Multiply the length and width to determine the area of the base. **12**
   b. Multiply the area of the base by the height. **60**

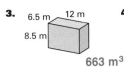

Find the volume of each figure.

2.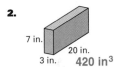
   7 in.
   3 in.
   20 in.
   420 in³

3.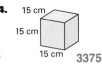
   6.5 m   12 m
   8.5 m
   663 m³

4.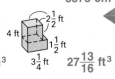
   15 cm
   15 cm
   15 cm
   3375 cm³

5.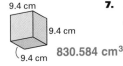
   3 yd
   $5\frac{1}{4}$ yd
   $6\frac{1}{3}$ yd
   $99\frac{3}{4}$ yd³

6. 9.4 cm
   9.4 cm
   9.4 cm
   830.584 cm³

7.
   4 ft
   $2\frac{1}{2}$ ft
   $1\frac{1}{2}$ ft
   $3\frac{1}{4}$ ft
   $27\frac{13}{16}$ ft³

Problem Solving TIP

Drawing a diagram is helpful when solving volume problems. Remember to label the dimensions.

Sketch each figure, then find its volume.

8. A box of granola cereal that measures 23 cm by 8 cm by 35 cm

9. A fly-casting pool in the park that is 30 ft wide, 40 ft long, and 5 ft deep

10. **Test Prep** A cube-shaped storage container measures $1\frac{1}{2}$ ft on each side. What is the volume of 6 such containers? **B**

    (A) $3\frac{3}{8}$ ft³   (B) $20\frac{1}{4}$ ft³   (C) $4\frac{1}{2}$ ft³   (D) None of these

11. **Geography** Falan paid $38.40 to ship a package by air from Washington, D.C., to his family in Bombay, India. The package was 18 in. by 24 in. by 20 in. What did he pay per cubic in.? **$\frac{4}{9}$ of a cent per in³**

NORTH ATLANTIC OCEAN
Washington, D.C.
AIR
Bombay, India
SOUTH ATLANTIC OCEAN
INDIAN OCEAN

12. **Number Sense** A box has base dimensions of 32 ft by 16 ft and its volume is 6144 ft³. What is the height of this box? **12 ft**

13. **Algebra** The formula for the volume of a sphere is $\frac{4}{3}\pi r^3$ where r is the radius of the sphere. What is the volume of a sphere where $r = 3$ cm? **≈ 113.04 cm³**

9-6 • Volume of Rectangular Prisms **479**

9-6 Exercises and Applications

Assignment Guide

■ **Basic**
1–10, 11–15 odds, 17–19, 21–29 odds

■ **Average**
3–9 odds, 10, 11–15 odds, 16–19, 20–28 evens

■ **Enriched**
3–9 odds, 10–14, 16–19, 20–28 evens

Exercise Answers

8. 6440 cm³

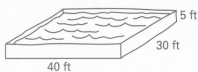
Granola cereal
35 cm
23 cm   8 cm

9. 6000 ft³

40 ft   30 ft   5 ft

Reteaching

Activity

Materials: Small box, centimeter cubes, metric ruler

• Work with a partner.

• Use your metric ruler to measure the dimensions of the box in centimeters. Using the formula you learned for volume, make a prediction about how many cubic centimeters you think would be needed to fill up the box.

• Working with your partner, fill the box with layers of centimeter cubes. If the cubes don't fit exactly, estimate how many half cubes would be needed to fill the box.

• Now take the cubes out and count them. Remember to include all half cubes. How close did you come to your prediction?

PRACTICE

Volume of Rectangular Prisms

Find the volume of each figure.

1. **16,422 in³**
   42 in.   17 in.   23 in.

2. **1728 cm³**
   12 cm   12 cm   12 cm

3. **21 ft³**
   $3\frac{1}{2}$ ft   3 ft   2 ft

4. **24 yd³**
   2 yd   6 yd   2 yd

5. **1881 in³**
   $8\frac{1}{4}$ in.   24 in. $9\frac{1}{2}$ in.

6. **389.017 cm³**
   7.3 cm   7.3 cm   7.3 cm

7. **32.487 m³**
   1.6 m   3.1 m   5.6 m   2.1 m   3.7 m

8. **1840 in³**
   8 in.   9 in.   8 in.   7 in.   10 in.

9. **56,862 mm³**
   26 mm   22 mm   48 mm   65 mm   27 mm

Sketch the figure, then find its volume.   **Drawings will vary.**

10. A cassette box that measures 1.7 cm by 7 cm by 10.9 cm
    V = **129.71 cm³**
    7 cm   1.7 cm   10.9 cm

11. A recycling bin that is 15 in. wide, $20\frac{1}{2}$ in. long and 13 in. tall
    V = **$3997\frac{1}{2}$ in³**
    Newspapers Only   13 in.   15 in. $20\frac{1}{2}$ in.

12. The lobby of the Hyatt Regency Hotel in San Francisco, California measures 350 ft by 160 ft. Its ceiling is 170 ft tall. Find the volume of a rectangular prism with these dimensions.
    9,520,000 ft³

RETEACHING

Volume of Rectangular Prisms

The **volume** is the number of cubic units in a solid. The volume of this solid is 1 cm³.
1 cm   1 cm   1 cm

The volume of a rectangular prism is found by multiplying the area of the base (B) times the height (h) of the prism. $V = B \cdot h$

—— **Example 1** ——
Find the volume of the rectangular prism shown.
Step 1: Find the area of the rectangular base.
$B = 4 \cdot 7 = 28$ in²
Step 2: Find the volume.
$V = B \cdot h = 28 \cdot 5 = 140$ in³
So, the volume of the rectangular prism is 140 in³.
5 in.   7 in.   4 in.

Try It Find the volume of each rectangular prism.
a. Find the area of the base. **20 cm²**
b. Find the volume. **200 cm³**
10 cm   4 cm   5 cm
c. Find the area of the base. **100 in²**
d. Find the volume. **1000 in³**
10 in.   10 in.   10 in.

—— **Example 2** ——
Find the height of the rectangular prism with volume 225 cm³ and base dimensions 5 cm by 5 cm.
Step 1: Find the area of the rectangular base.
$B = 5 \cdot 5 = 25$ cm²
Step 2: Substitute in the volume formula to find the height.
$V = B \cdot h \rightarrow 225 = 25 \cdot h$
$9 = h$
The height of the rectangular prism is 9 cm.
h cm   5 cm   5 cm

Try It Find the height of each figure. The volume is 960 in³.
e. Find the area of the base. **120 in²**
f. Substitute in the volume formula to find the height. **8 in.**
h in.   12 in.   10 in.

Lesson 9-6 479

15. 125 cm³; $V = s^3$

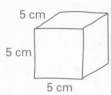
5 cm

5 cm

5 cm

16. Answers may vary.

17–18.

L	W	H	V	A
1	1	36	36	146
1	2	18	36	112
1	3	12	36	102
1	4	9	36	98
1	6	6	36	96
2	2	9	36	80
2	3	6	36	72
3	3	4	36	66

19. The prism with dimensions 1 in. × 1 in. × 36 in. has the greatest surface area. The prism with dimensions 3 in. × 3 in. × 4 in. has the least.

21. Both items have a volume of 648 in³. The book will not fit because of its 9 in. length.

Alternate Assessment

You may want to use the *Interactive CD-ROM Journal* with this assessment.

Journal Have students answer this question in their own words: With a rectangular prism, how can you tell which face is the base? Any face of a rectangular prism can be its base.

► Quick Quiz

1. Find the volume of a cube whose edge measures 12 in. 1728 in³

2. Find the total volume of the figure.

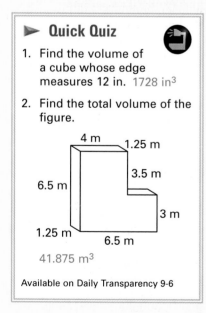
4 m
1.25 m
3.5 m
6.5 m
3 m
1.25 m
6.5 m

41.875 m³

Available on Daily Transparency 9-6

---

14. **Science** The concrete in bridges expands in the hot sun. To prevent the road from buckling, engineers build gaps, called expansion joints, between segments of the road. What is the total volume of an expansion joint that is 25 ft by 1 ft by 4 in?
$8\frac{1}{3}$ ft³

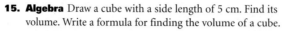

Problem Solving and Reasoning

15. **Algebra** Draw a cube with a side length of 5 cm. Find its volume. Write a formula for finding the volume of a cube.

16. **Communicate** Which formula do you prefer to use in finding the volume of a rectangular prism: $V = B \cdot h$ or $V = l \cdot w \cdot h$? Explain.

Patterns The chart at the right has been started to list all the possible sets of whole-number dimensions that make a rectangular prism with a volume of 36 ft³.

L	W	H	V
1	2	18	36
			36
			36

17. Copy and complete the chart.

18. Find the surface area of each prism.

19. Which set of dimensions has the greatest surface area? The least?

20. **Critical Thinking** An airline reserves some of its cargo space for shipping packages but limits the size of packages. A corrugated box is 48 in. by 18 in. by 36 in. Redesign the box so that it has the same volume but less surface area.
Possible answer: Dimensions 27 in. × 32 in. × 36 in.

21. **Math Reasoning** A rectangular box has dimensions of 18 in. by 6 in. by 6 in. A large coffee table book has dimensions of 18 in. by 9 in. by 4 in. Find the volume of each and determine whether the book will fit in the box. Explain.

22. **Estimation** Seth can't fit everything in his 5040 in³ suitcase. Use the photograph to estimate the volume of clothes he's trying to pack.
Possible answer: 5200 in³

Mixed Review

Check to see if the point is a solution of both equations. *[Lesson 4-6]*

23. Point $(2, -3)$ **Yes**
$y = x - 5$
$y = 2x - 7$

24. Point $(1, 3)$ **Yes**
$y = 2x + 1$
$y = 4x - 1$

25. Point $(-4, 1)$ **No**
$y = 3x + 13$
$y = -x - 5$

Find the sum of the angle measures for each polygon. *[Lesson 8-6]*

26. Triangle **180°**
27. Octagon **1080°**
28. Pentagon **540°**
29. Square **360°**

► PROBLEM SOLVING

Name _____

Guided Problem Solving 9-6

GPS PROBLEM 9, STUDENT PAGE 479

Sketch the figure. Then find the volume of a fly-casting pool in the park that is 30 ft wide, 40 ft long, and 5 ft deep.

— Understand —
1. What are you asked to find? Volume of fly-casting pool.

2. What figure is the pond? Rectangular prism.

3. What is each dimension of the pool?

   a. Width 30 ft   b. Length 40 ft   c. Depth 5 ft

— Plan —
4. Sketch the figure for the pond. Label each dimension.

5 ft
30 ft
40 ft

5. How can you find the volume of the pond? Possible answer: Multiply the area of the base (B) by the height (h).

6. How can you find the area of the bottom of the pool? Possible answer: Multiply length and width.

— Solve —
7. What is the area of the bottom of the pool? 1200 ft²

8. What is the volume of the pool? 6000 ft³

— Look Back —
9. How could you find the volume without drawing a sketch? Possible answer: Substitute values in the formula: $A = B \cdot h$.

SOLVE ANOTHER PROBLEM

Sketch the figure. Then find the volume of a fish pond at the zoo that is 20 ft wide, 25 ft long, and 3 ft deep.

3 ft
20 ft
25 ft

1500 ft³

► ENRICHMENT

Name _____

Extend Your Thinking 9-6

Patterns in Geometry

Use your knowledge of volume and surface area to find the relationship between the rectangular prisms below.

1. Find the volume and the surface area for each set of dimensions of the prisms below.

Base		Height	Volume (units³)	Surface area (units²)
length	width			
1	36	6	216	516
2	18	6	216	312
3	12	6	216	252
4	9	6	216	228
6	6	6	216	216

2. What pattern do you notice in the dimensions of the prisms?
Possible answers: Dimensions of the base change, but have an area of 36 units² while the height stays the same.

3. What is the relationship of the volume and surface area?
Possible answers: As the dimensions approach the cube, the surface area becomes less for the same volume. The cube has the same surface area as volume.

4. Repeat the analysis for four sets of dimensions with a volume of 384 units³. Was your outcome the same?
Check students' work. The outcome is the same.

Scale and Volume

▶ **Lesson Link** Now that you know about volume of a rectangular prism, you'll see how volume is affected when dimensions are scaled up or down. ◀

| **Explore** | Scaling a Rectangular Prism |

Which Dimension?

Materials: Spreadsheet software

Examine the effect on the volume of a rectangular box if you multiply one of its dimensions by a scale factor.

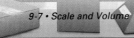

	A	B	C	D	E
1	Scale Factor	Length	Width	Height	Volume
2	1	4	3	2	?
3	2	8	3	2	?
4	3	12	3	2	?

3 in. 2 in. 4 in.

1. Use a spreadsheet to make a table similar to the one shown. Apply scale factors 1 through 5 to the length of the box. Find each volume.

2. How do the new volumes compare to the original volume?

3. Predict the volume of the box if the length is scaled by a factor of 6.

4. Make another table, but this time hold the length constant and apply the scale factor to the width. How do the resulting volumes compare to those in the first table?

5. Make a third table, this time applying the scale factor to height only. How do the resulting volumes compare to the two previous tables?

6. Make a conclusion about scaling one dimension of a rectangular box.

| **Learn** | Scale and Volume |

The volume of a rectangular prism is affected when its length measurements are scaled. The change of volume depends on whether one, two, or three dimensions are scaled.

9-7 • Scale and Volume **481**

You'll Learn ...
- to dilate rectangular prisms and predict their volume

... How It's Used
Package design involves the scaling of boxes up or down to see the effect on volume, which in turn affects weight and cost of shipping.

MEETING INDIVIDUAL NEEDS

Resources

9-7 Practice
9-7 Reteaching
9-7 Problem Solving
9-7 Enrichment
9-7 Daily Transparency
    Problem of the Day
    Review
    Quick Quiz
Teaching Tool Transparencies 2 and 3

 Interactive CD-ROM Lesson

Learning Modalities

Kinesthetic In **Explore**, students use a spreadsheet to explore the effect on the volume of a rectangular box if you multiply one of its dimensions by a scale factor.

Visual Throughout the lesson, students use diagrams to help them visualize the Examples.

Individual In **What Do You Think?**, students are encouraged to think about the two methods presented for finding the volume of a dilated prism and to decide which method they prefer.

English Language Development

Some students may be confused by the use of the word scale in *scaled up*, *scaled down*, and *scale factor*. Explain that when a dimension is scaled up, it is multiplied by a number greater than 1 (thus making the new dimension larger). When a dimension is scaled down, it is multiplied by a number less than 1 (thus making the new dimension smaller). The scale factor is the number by which the dimension is multiplied.

9-7
Lesson Organizer

Objective
- **Dilate rectangular prisms and predict their volume.**

Materials
- **Explore: Spreadsheet software**

NCTM Standards
- **1, 2, 4–7, 9, 12, 13**

▶ Review

1. Find the area of a rectangle with $b = 5$ ft and $h = 7$ ft. 35 ft²

2. Find the area of the rectangle in Exercise 1 after it is dilated by a scale factor of 2. 140 ft²

Find the volume of each rectangular prism with the following dimensions.

3. 6 m by 10 m by 13 m
   780 m³

4. 7 in. by 7 in. by 11 in.
   539 in³

Available on Daily Transparency 9-7

▶ Lesson Link

In Lesson 9-2 students used scale and area to solve problems faced by theatrical companies. Have them extend this to how scale and volume might be applied to problems in other real-life situations.

1 Introduce

| **Explore** |

The Point
Students use a spreadsheet to explore the effect on the volume of a rectangular box if one of its dimensions is multiplied by a scale factor.

Ongoing Assessment
Make sure that all students do Step 1 correctly because they use the same procedure in Steps 4 and 5.

2 Teach

Learn

Scaling one dimension of a rectangular prism changes the volume of the prism by that scale factor. Applying scale factors to two dimensions changes the volume of the prism by the product of the scale factors, and so on.

When one dimension of a rectangular prism is scaled, multiply the original volume by the scale factor to find the volume of the scaled prism.

When two dimensions of a rectangular prism are scaled, multiply the original volume by the square of the scale factor to find the volume of the scaled prism.

DID YOU KNOW?

Polystyrene foam fill for packaging can be reused and recycled.

Example 1

A delivery service charges 1¢ per in³ for foam filler to package fragile items. Suppose a breakable parcel that was originally in a 6 in. by 4 in. by 4 in. box needed to be put in a larger box. Determine the ratio of the volume of the larger box to the volume of the original box.

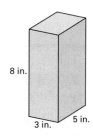

The volume of the original box is 96 in³.

a. How much is the foam filler if one 4 in. dimension is tripled?

The box is 6 in. by 12 in. by 4 in.
The volume of foam filler is
$V = 6 \cdot 12 \cdot 4$
$V = 288 \text{ in}^3$.
The cost of foam filler for a 6 in. by 12 in. by 4 in. box is $2.88.
Since $288 \div 96 = 3$, the volume of the larger box is 3 times greater than the original box.

b. How much is the foam filler if both 4 in. dimensions are tripled?

The box is 6 in. by 12 in. by 12 in.
The volume of foam filler is
$V = 6 \cdot 12 \cdot 12$
$V = 864 \text{ in}^3$.
The cost of foam filler for a 6 in. by 12 in. by 12 in. box is $8.64.
Since $864 \div 96 = 9$, the volume of the larger box is 9 times greater than the original box.

Problem Solving TIP

If you're not crunched for time, try solving a problem more than one way, just to see if you can.

Try It

a. Find the volume of a 3 in. by 5 in. by 8 in. rectangular box. **120 in³**

b. Find the volume of the same box after one dimension has been increased by a scale factor of 4. **480 in³**

c. Find the volume of the same box after two dimensions have been increased by a scale factor of 4. **1920 in³**

DELIVERED

MATH EVERY DAY

▶ Problem of the Day

The number of grooves around a dime is equal to the coin's value in cents squared less the value of the coin plus two less than triple the value of the coin. How many grooves are there around a dime? 118
$[(v^2 - v) + (3v - 2)]$

Available on Daily Transparency 9-7

An Extension is provided in the transparency package.

Fact of the Day

In *Gulliver's Travels*, the main character describes his adventures in lands where humans are "scaled" up or down from what he considers "normal."

Mental Math

Do these mentally.

1. $5 \cdot 6 \cdot 3$ 90

2. $8 \cdot 2 \cdot 2$ 32

3. $3 \cdot 4 \cdot 5$ 60

A dilation of a three-dimensional figure changes all three dimensions by the scale factor. The blue rectangular prism is a dilation of the red rectangular prism.

You can find the scale factor by using the ratio of any two corresponding dimensions.

$$\frac{4}{2} = 2 \qquad \frac{6}{3} = 2 \qquad \frac{8}{4} = 2$$

The scale factor of the dilation is 2.

The volume of the red prism is 24 cm³. So, $24 \cdot 2^3 = 24 \cdot 8 = 192$, since the scale factor is 2. The volume of the blue prism is 192 cm³.

When a prism is dilated, the volume is multiplied by the cube of the scale factor.

Example 2

A rectangular prism is 7 cm by 6 cm by 12 cm. Find the volume of the prism after a dilation by a scale factor of 22.

The original volume

$V = 7 \cdot 6 \cdot 12$

$V = 504$ cm³

The volume of the dilation

$V = (22)^3 \cdot 504$

$V = 5,366,592$ cm³

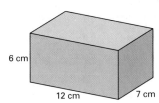

Try It

A rectangular prism has a volume of 43 ft³. Find the volume after the dilation.

a. Scale factor = 5   **b.** Scale factor = $\frac{1}{2}$ 5.375 ft³

5375 ft³

The pattern will work for the dilation of any prism with volume V.

Scale Factor	Volume of Dilated Prism
1	$1^3 \cdot V$
2	$2^3 \cdot V$
3	$3^3 \cdot V$
…	…
n	$n^3 \cdot V$

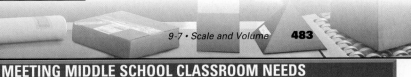

9-7 • Scale and Volume   **483**

MEETING MIDDLE SCHOOL CLASSROOM NEEDS

Tips from Middle School Teachers

When working with scale factors and volume, I use rectangular prisms made from cubes to visually illustrate how applying scale factors to more than one dimension affects the size, shape, and volume of the prism.

Career Connection

Architects deal with scale factors and volume in the course of their work all the time. If a client decides that they would like a structure to be smaller or larger, the architect must multiply the appropriate dimensions on a blueprint by a certain scale factor.

Industry Connection

When preparing a package for shipment, delivery services suggest putting at least 2 inches of cushioning material on the bottom of the carton. Each item should be wrapped with cushioning material individually and should not be touching other items or the top, bottom, or sides of the carton. More filler should be included to fill up the spaces, and an additional layer of cushioning material should be put on top.

Alternate Examples

1. The Energy Saver Insulation Service charges $1.15 per cubic foot of blown-in attic insulation. Suppose an estimate was given for insulation $\frac{1}{3}$-foot deep in a 30 × 20 foot attic. Take the ratio of the volume of each new situation below to the original volume. The original volume is 200 ft³ and costs $230.00.

   a. What would the insulation cost if the $\frac{1}{3}$-ft dimension is doubled?

   The volume is 30 ft by 20 ft by $\frac{2}{3}$ ft.
   The volume of insulation is
   $V = 30 \cdot 20 \cdot \frac{2}{3}$
   $V = 400$ ft³.

   The cost of insulation for 30 ft by 20 ft by $\frac{2}{3}$ ft is $1.15 × 400, or $460.00. Since 400 ÷ 200 = 2, the volume of insulation needed now is 2 times greater than originally needed.

   b. How much is the insulation if the $\frac{1}{3}$-ft dimension and the 20-ft dimension are both doubled?

   The volume is 30 ft by 40 ft by $\frac{2}{3}$ ft.
   The volume of insulation is
   $V = 30 \times 40 \times \frac{2}{3}$
   $V = 800$ ft³.

   The cost of insulation for 30 ft by 40 ft by $\frac{2}{3}$ ft is $1.15 × 800, or $920.00. Since 800 ÷ 200 = 4, the volume of insulation needed now is 4 times greater than was originally needed.

2. A rectangular prism is 9 cm by 5 cm by 15 cm. Find the volume of the prism after a dilation with scale factor 18.

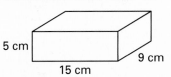

   The original volume
   $V = 9 \cdot 5 \cdot 15$
   $V = 675$ cm³

   The volume of the dilation
   $V = (18)^3 \cdot 675$
   $V = 3,936,600$ cm³

Students see two methods for finding the volume of a dilated prism. In one method each dimension is multiplied by the scale factor, and in the other method the original volume is multiplied by the scale factor cubed. Students can decide which of the two correct methods they prefer.

Answers for What Do You Think?

1. Possible answer: Steve applied the scale factor to each side length.

2. Both answers are measures of volume, which involves a cubic unit, and original dimensions are given in cm.

3 Practice and Assess

Check

You might suggest that students try a simple example to find the answers to Question 2.

Answers for Check Your Understanding

1. Possible answer: The volume will be the same regardless of which two dimensions are scaled, but surface areas could differ.

2. Possible answer: The volume increases if you use a scale factor greater than 1; Decreases with a scale factor less than 1.

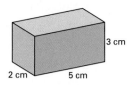

A 5 cm by 3 cm by 2 cm rectangular prism is dilated by a scale factor of 6. Find the volume of the dilated prism.

Steve thinks ...

Scale each dimension by 6.

5 cm becomes $6 \cdot 5 = 30$ cm.

3 cm becomes $6 \cdot 3 = 18$ cm.

2 cm becomes $6 \cdot 2 = 12$ cm.

The volume of a dilated prism is

$V = 30 \cdot 18 \cdot 12 = 6480$ cm^3.

Gabriella thinks ...

Find the original volume.

$V = 5 \cdot 3 \cdot 2 = 30$ cm^3.

Multiply the original volume by 6^3.

The new prism's volume is

$V = 6^3 \cdot 30 = 6480$ cm^3.

What do  **think?**

1. Describe how Steve solved the problem.

2. Why are both Steve's and Gabriella's answers given in cm^3?

Check | Your Understanding

1. If you want to scale two dimensions of a rectangular prism, does it matter which pair of dimensions you scale? Explain.

2. What happens to the volume of a rectangular prism when you dilate it by a scale factor greater than 1? Less than 1?

9-7 Exercises and Applications

Practice and Apply

1. [Getting Started] Find the volume of a rectangular prism of 360 ft^3 after a dilation of $\frac{1}{2}$.

a. Find $\left(\frac{1}{2}\right)^3$. $\frac{1}{8}$

b. Multiply this by 360 to find the new volume. **45 ft^3**

Find the volume of each prism after scaling one dimension by the indicated scale factor.

2. Scale factor = 8

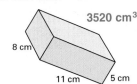
3520 cm^3

8 cm, 11 cm, 5 cm

3. Scale factor = $\frac{1}{3}$

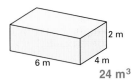
24 in., 18 in., 36 in.
5184 in^3

4. Scale factor = 0.5

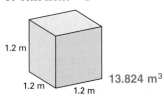
2 m, 6 m, 4 m
24 m^3

Find the volume of each figure after the dilation.

5. Scale factor = 3

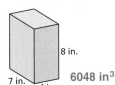
8 in., 7 in., 4 in.
6048 in^3

6. Scale factor = 0.8

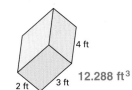
4 ft, 2 ft, 3 ft
12.288 ft^3

7. Scale factor = 2

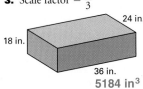
1.2 m, 1.2 m, 1.2 m, 1.2 m
13.824 m^3

8. Science Alkaline earth metals are found in many sea shells. A researcher ships some abalone shells to the lab. The delivery company charges $1.25 per cubic ft for next-day delivery. What will a $1\frac{3}{4}$ ft × $1\frac{1}{2}$ ft × 2 ft package cost for next-day service? **About $6.56**

9. [Test Prep] What is the scale factor between a cubic box that exactly fits a $3\frac{1}{2}$ in. diameter softball and one that exactly fits a 9 in. diameter basketball? **D**

Ⓐ 3   Ⓑ $31\frac{1}{2}$ Ⓒ $\frac{7}{18}$ Ⓓ $2\frac{4}{7}$

9-7 • Scale and Volume **485**

PRACTICE 9-7

9-7 Exercises and Applications

Assignment Guide

■ **Basic**
1, 2–8 evens, 9, 10, 11–15 odds, 16, 18–20

■ **Average**
1, 3–7 odds, 8–11, 13–16, 18–20

■ **Enriched**
3–7 odds, 8–15, 17–20

Exercise Notes

■ **Exercise 8**

Science An abalone is a saltwater snail found in most mild and tropical seas. It has a flat, muscular foot that allows it to attach itself to rocks. The abalone's large, rather flat shell is lined with mother-of-pearl, which is used in making costume jewelry.

■ **Exercise 9**

Sports Softballs are available with circumferences of 11, 12, 14, and 16 inches. All of the balls, with the exception of the 16-inch ball, are used with a softball mitt.

Reteaching

[Activity]

Materials: Centimeter cubes

• Work with a partner.

• With your partner, make a small rectangular prism out of centimeter cubes. Write the dimensions and the volume on a sheet of paper.

• Apply a scale factor of 2 to your prism. Write down the new dimensions and volume.

• Apply a scale factor of 3 to your original prism. Write down the new dimensions and volume.

• Do you see a pattern in regard to the volumes of the new figures with dilated lengths? What conclusion can you draw from this?

Scaling one dimension of a rectangular prism changes the volume by the scale factor.

PRACTICE

Name _____

Practice **9-7**

Scale and Volume

Find the volume of each prism after scaling one dimension by the indicated scale factor.

1. Scale factor = 3

$V =$ **2016 cm^3**
14 cm, 6 cm, 8 cm

2. Scale factor = $\frac{1}{16}$

$V =$ **32 in^3**
8 in., 8 in., 8 in.

3. Scale factor = $\frac{3}{7}$

$V =$ **126 m^3**
7 m, 14 m, 3 m

Find the volume of each figure after the dilation.

4. Scale factor = $\frac{1}{2}$

$V =$ **259.47 cm^3**
18 cm, 9.3 cm, 12.4 cm

5. Scale factor = $\frac{2}{3}$

$V =$ **$333\frac{1}{3}$ in^3**
$7\frac{1}{2}$ in., 20 in., $7\frac{1}{2}$ in.

6. Scale factor = 10

$V =$ **804,357 cm^3**
9.3 cm, 9.3 cm, 9.3 cm

7. Scale factor = $\frac{1}{10}$

$V =$ **91 mm^3**
65 mm, 35 mm, 40 mm

8. Scale factor = 3

$V =$ **$1012\frac{1}{2}$ ft^3**
2 ft, $2\frac{1}{2}$ ft, $7\frac{1}{2}$ ft

9. Scale factor = $\frac{1}{7}$

$V =$ **30 cm^3**
42 cm, 35 cm, 7 cm

10. Some sponges expand when they become wet. A dry sponge measures $\frac{3}{8}$ in. by $1\frac{3}{4}$ in. by $2\frac{3}{4}$ in. If water dilates this sponge by a scale factor of 2, find the volume of the wet sponge. **$14\frac{7}{16}$ in^3**

11. Science Every cubic foot of air weighs about 0.26 lb. Find the weight of the air in a 11-ft by 13-ft room with an 8-ft ceiling. **About 297 lb**

RETEACHING

Name _____

Alternative Lesson **9-7**

Scale and Volume

When *one* dimension of a rectangular prism is scaled, multiply the original volume by the scale factor to find the volume of the scaled prism.

When *two* dimensions of a rectangular prism are scaled, multiply the original volume by the *square* of the scale factor to find the volume of the scaled prism.

When a three-dimensional figure is dilated (all *three* dimensions are scaled), the volume is multiplied by the *cube* of the scale factor.

— Example 1 —

Find the volume of this rectangular prism after *one* dimension, the height, is scaled by a factor of 3.

10 cm, 2 cm, 5 cm

Step 1: Find the volume of the original prism.
$V = B \cdot h$
$= 2 \cdot 5 \cdot 10 = 100$ cm^3

Step 2: Find the volume of the scaled prism. Multiply the volume by the scale factor.
$V = 100 \cdot 3 = 300$ cm^3

The volume of the scaled rectangular prism is 300 cm^3.

Try It Find the volume of the prism after scaling *one* dimension by a scale factor of $\frac{1}{2}$.

6 in., 5 in., 4 in.

a. Find the volume of the original prism. **120 in^3**

b. Multiply by the scale factor to find the scaled volume. **60 in^3**

— Example 2 —

Find the volume of this rectangular prism after the prism is dilated (*three* dimensions scaled), by a scale factor of $\frac{1}{4}$.

4 cm, 4 cm, 8 cm

Step 1: Find the volume of the original prism.
$V = B \cdot h$
$= 4 \cdot 4 \cdot 8 = 128$ cm^3

Step 2: Find the volume of the scaled prism. Multiply the volume by the *cube* of the scale factor.
$V = 128 \cdot \left(\frac{1}{4}\right)^3$
$= 128 \cdot \frac{1}{64} = 2$ cm^3

The volume of the scaled rectangular prism is 2 cm^3.

Try It Find the volume of the prism after the prism is dilated by a scale factor of 5.

3 m, 10 m, 7 m

c. Find the volume of the original prism. **210 m^3**

d. Multiply by the cube of the scale factor to find the scaled volume. **26,250 m^3**

■ Exercise 14

Problem-Solving Tip Encourage students to make a table showing their solutions.

■ Exercise 15

Problem-Solving Tip You may wish to use Teaching Tool Transparencies 2 and 3: Guided Problem Solving, pages 1–2.

Exercise Answers

11. 785,000 cm³; 0.785 cm³; $\frac{1}{1,000,000}$

13. a. Speedy Shipping
    b. No; E-Z Shipping would be cheaper for a 10 in. × 10 in. × 10 in. package, for example.

15. a. $\frac{1}{30}$; Possible answer: Which makes the model 18 in. long—a suitable size for a class project.
    b. 404 in² not including the floor.
    c. 720 in³

16. a. No
    b. Yes
    c. Yes

17. a. Yes
    b. Yes
    c. Yes

20. 14

Alternate Assessment

Portfolio Encourage students to include some of the materials they created in this lesson in their portfolios. You might suggest their spreadsheet from **Explore** as a possible choice.

► Quick Quiz

1. Find the volume of a rectangular prism of 123 in³ after scaling one dimension by a scale factor of $\frac{1}{2}$. $61\frac{1}{2}$ in³

2. Find the volume of a rectangular prism of 635 ft³ after scaling two dimensions by a scale factor of 2. 2540 ft³

3. Find the volume of a rectangular prism of 245 cm³ after a dilation of 4. 15,680 cm³

4. Find the volume of a cube of 729 cm³ after a dilation of 3. 19,683 cm³

Available on Daily Transparency 9-7

---

10. **Measurement** Find the volume of the figure to the right after a dilation of 2.5. **10,703.125 cm³**

11. **Number Sense** Find the volume of the figure to the right after a dilation with a scale factor of 10. Do the same for a dilation with a scale factor of $\frac{1}{10}$. Find the ratio of these volumes.

12. **Algebra** Write a volume formula for a box with $V = 214$ cm³ after
    a. One dimension is scaled by s. $V = 214s$
    b. Two dimensions are scaled by s. $V = 214s^2$
    c. Three dimensions are scaled by s. $V = 214s^3$

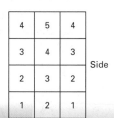

14 cm
8 cm
5 cm
9 cm
5 cm
5 cm

Problem Solving and Reasoning

13. You have a package 24 in. by 18 in. by 12 in. to ship. E-Z Shipping charges by volume $0.002 per in³, whereas Speedy Shipping charges by surface area $0.005 per in².
    a. Which company is cheaper for this package?
    b. **Communicate** Will this be true for all shapes of packages? Explain.

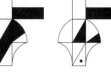

14. **Patterns** A manufacturing company wants you to design a box with 4 times the volume of its standard 12 in. × 6 in. × 4 in. box. Find as many whole-number solutions as you can.
    Answers may vary. There are 28 different whole-number solutions.

15. **Choose a Strategy** Sally wants to make a scale model of a long hut 45 ft by 25 ft by 10 ft for a social studies project.
    a. Choose a scale factor for her. Why did you select it?
    b. Find the surface area of the model hut.
    c. Find the volume of the model hut.

Problem Solving
STRATEGIES

- Look for a Pattern
- Make an Organized List
- Make a Table
- Guess and Check
- Work Backward
- Use Logical Reasoning
- Draw a Diagram
- Solve a Simpler Problem

Mixed Review

Test whether each point is a solution of the inequality. *[Lesson 4-7]*

16. $y > 2x - 5$ a. $(2, -3)$ b. $(4, 5)$ c. $(1, -2)$

17. $y \leq 3x + 1$ a. $(2, 7)$ b. $(-2, -6)$ c. $(4, -13)$

18. How many cubes are needed to build a tower with this base plan? *[Lesson 8-7]* **34**

19. How many of the cubes can be seen from a front view of the tower? *[Lesson 8-7]* **13**

20. How many cubes can be seen from a side view of the tower? *[Lesson 8-7]*

4	5	4
3	4	3
2	3	2
1	2	1

Side

PROBLEM SOLVING 9-7

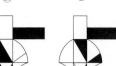
DELIVERED

► **PROBLEM SOLVING**

Name _____

Guided Problem Solving 9-7

GPS PROBLEM 13, STUDENT PAGE 486

You have a package 24 in. by 18 in. by 12 in. to ship. E-Z Shipping charges by volume $0.002 per in³ whereas Speedy Shipping charges by surface area $0.005 per in².

a. Which company is cheaper for this package?
b. Will this be true for all shapes of packages? Explain.

— **Understand** —   Possible answers: Items 10 and 11
1. Underline the dimensions of the package.
2. Circle each company's rate.

— **Plan** —
3. What formula can you use to find the volume of the package? $V = B \cdot h$
4. Sketch the net for the package.
5. What formula can you use to find the area of each face? $A = b \cdot h$
6. Which operation will you use to find the cost? **Multiplication.**

— **Solve** —
7. Find the volume of the package. **5184 in³** The surface area. **1872 in²**
8. What is the shipping cost for each company?
   a. E-Z Shipping **$10.37**   b. Speedy Shipping **$9.36**
9. Which company is cheaper for this package? **Speedy Shipping.**
10. Will this be true for all shapes of packages? Explain. **No, volume and surface area do not have a linear relationship.**

Look Back
11. Would calculations be easier if rates and measurements were converted to feet before multiplying? Explain. **Yes, smaller numbers may result in less chance for errors.**

SOLVE ANOTHER PROBLEM
Use the rates above. Is it cheaper to ship a package measuring 12 in. by 20 in. by 4 in. using E-Z Shipping or Speedy Shipping? **E-Z Shipping ($1.92 vs $3.68 for Speedy)**

► **ENRICHMENT**

Name _____

Extend Your Thinking 9-7

Visual Thinking
Circle the letters of the two figures that are identical.

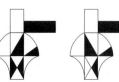

A.   B.   C.

D.   E.   F.

G.   H.   I.

Volume of Prisms and Cylinders

▶ **Lesson Link**   You've learned how to find the volume of rectangular prisms. Now you'll find the volume of other prisms and cylinders. ◀

Explore   Volume of a Cylinder

Volume in the Round

Materials: 2 sheets of 8.5 in. by 11 in. paper, Tape, Centimeter cubes, Centimeter ruler

1. Make two different cylinders, each from a sheet of paper. Roll one along the longer side and the other along the shorter side. Tape the sides together for each one.

2. Make a layer of unit cubes to cover the circular base of each cylinder.

   a. Estimate the number of cubes needed to cover each base.

   b. Calculate the area of each base by measuring the radius and then using $A = \pi r^2$ (use cm²). Compare this result with your estimate.

3. **a.** Using cm, how tall is a single layer of cubes?

   b. For each cylinder, how many cubes are needed for two layers? Three layers? Four layers?

4. **a.** Using cm, how tall is each cylinder?

   b. Estimate how many layers of cubes are needed to completely fill each cylinder. Describe how you made the estimate.

5. How many cubes will completely fill each cylinder? Discuss why you think the numbers differ.

$8\frac{1}{2}$ in.   11 in.

Learn   Volume of Prisms and Cylinders

The volume of prisms and cylinders can be found by taking the product of the base area (B) and the height (h). $V = B \cdot h$

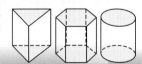

9-8 • Volume of Prisms and Cylinders   **487**

You'll Learn ...
■ to find the volume of prisms and cylinders

... How It's Used

Packages come in shapes of prisms and cylinders. The volume of these packages determine space needed for shipping.

Objective
■ **Find the volume of prisms and cylinders.**

Materials
■ **Explore: Two sheets of 8.5 in. by 11 in. paper, tape, centimeter cubes, centimeter ruler**

NCTM Standards
■ **1, 2, 4–7, 9, 12, 13**

▶ **Review**

1. Find the volume of the rectangular prism.

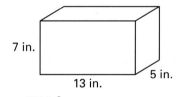

7 in.

13 in.   5 in.

455 in³

2. Find the area of a circle with diameter 10 in. Use 3.14 for π. 78.5 in²

Available on Daily Transparency 9-8

▶ **Lesson Link**

Students may think only of using rectangular boxes when packing items or shipping gifts. Tell them that in this lesson they will learn to find the volume of prisms and cylinders—two other types of boxes that can be used when packaging items for shipping.

1 Introduce

Explore

The Point
Students make two different cylinders out of the same size sheet of paper and calculate how many centimeter cubes would be needed to fill each cylinder.

MEETING INDIVIDUAL NEEDS

Resources

9-8 Practice
9-8 Reteaching
9-8 Problem Solving
9-8 Enrichment
9-8 Daily Transparency
   Problem of the Day
   Review
   Quick Quiz

Lesson Enhancement Transparencies 45 and 46

 Wide World of Mathematics Middle School: Chunnel

Learning Modalities

Logical   In **Explore**, students experiment with making cylinders out of paper and use actual centimeter cubes to estimate how many cubes would be needed to fill each cylinder.

Kinesthetic   Have student locate various prism- or cylinder-shaped objects in the classroom and find the volume of these objects.

Challenge

Have students calculate the volume of this solid figure. The diameter of the hole is 5 ft.

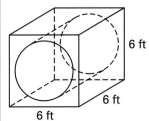

6 ft

6 ft

6 ft

The volume is 98.25 ft³.

Check that, in Step 2, students' estimates are reasonable and their calculations are correct. If students need help organizing all of their information for Step 3, suggest that they make a table.

For Groups That Finish Early

Brainstorm a list of examples of things that are stored in prism- or cylinder-shaped containers.

Follow Up

Have students share their answers to Step 4b. Then discuss Step 5.

Answers for Explore

1. See students' cylinders.
2. a. 36, 62
   b. 36.73 cm³, 62.46 cm²

3. a. 1 cm
   b. 72,124; 108, 186; 144, 248

4. a. 28 cm, 21.5 cm
   b. 28, 21.5; Each layer is 1 cm tall.

5. 1028.44, 1342.89; Multiplied area and height.

2 Teach

Learn

You may wish to use Lesson Enhancement Transparencies 45 and 46 with this lesson.

Make sure that students remember that the *B* in the formula for finding the volume of a prism or cylinder stands for the *area* of the base.

Alternate Examples

1. Mrs. Chin received a bottle of cologne as a gift. It came in a box that was a triangular prism. Find the volume of the triangular box.

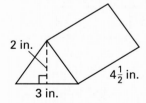

2 in.
$4\frac{1}{2}$ in.
3 in.

First, find the area of the triangular base (*B*).

$B = \frac{1}{2}(b \cdot h)$

$B = \frac{1}{2}(3 \cdot 2) = 3$ in²

Use *B* to find the volume.
$V = B \cdot h$
$V = 3 \cdot 4.5$
$V = 13.5$ in³
The volume is 13.5 in³.

For a triangular prism, the area of the base $B = \frac{1}{2}(b \cdot h)$. You may recognize this as the formula for the area of a triangle.

$B =$ *area of a prism base* and $b =$ *length of a triangular base.*

Also, there are two heights to consider—the height of the triangle and the height of the prism. Both of them are represented by the variable *h*.

Example 1

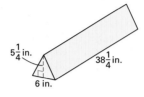

Posters can be sent through the mail in boxes that are triangular prisms. Find the volume of the triangular box.

$5\frac{1}{4}$ in.
$38\frac{1}{4}$ in.
6 in.

First, find the area of the triangular base (*B*).

$B = \frac{1}{2}(b \cdot h)$

$B = \frac{1}{2}(6 \cdot 5\frac{1}{4}) = 15\frac{3}{4}$ in²

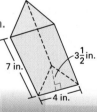

$5\frac{1}{4}$ in.
6 in.

Use *B* to find the volume.

$V = B \cdot h$

$V = 15\frac{3}{4} \cdot 38\frac{1}{4}$

$V = 15.75 \cdot 38.25$

$V = 602.4375$ in³

The volume is 602.4375 in³.

Try It

a. What is the height of the triangular base. $3\frac{1}{2}$ in.
b. What is the area of the triangular base. 7 in²
c. What is the volume of the prism. 49 in³

7 in.
$3\frac{1}{2}$ in.
4 in.

488   *Chapter 9 • Area and Volume*

MATH EVERY DAY

▶ Problem of the Day

B. J.'s favorite color is purple. Through the TV Shop-At-Home program, two different outfits are offered. Each comes in red, green, blue, purple, and orange. However, when you order the outfits, you do not get to choose the color—a color is picked at random and sent to you. If B. J. orders both outfits, what is the probability

1. that both will be purple?
2. that at least one will be purple?
1. 1 out of 25; 2. 9 out of 25

Available on Daily Transparency 9-8

An Extension is provided in the transparency package.

Fact of the Day

There are about 147.2 billion cubic feet in a cubic mile.

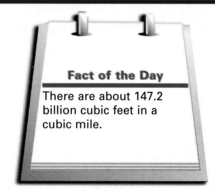

Estimation

Estimate.

1. 50,042 – 42,154   8,000
2. 74,899 – 24,766   50,000
3. 52,200 – 10,322   42,000

For a cylinder, the area of the base $B = \pi r^2$, where r = radius. The volume of a cylinder then is $V = Bh = (\pi r^2)h$.

Example 2

Find the volume of the cylinder.

First, find the area of the base (B).

$B = \pi \cdot r^2$

$B = \pi \cdot (2)^2 \approx 12.56 \text{ m}^2$

Use B to find the volume.

$V = B \cdot h$

$V \approx 12.56 \cdot 4.5$

$V \approx 56.52 \text{ m}^3$

The volume is 56.52 m^3.

Try It

Find the volume of each cylinder.

a.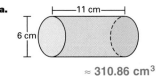

$\approx 310.86 \text{ cm}^3$

b.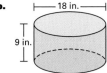

$\approx 2289.06 \text{ in}^3$

Check   Your Understanding

1. A stack of 40 nickels is $2\frac{1}{2}$ in. tall. The diameter of a nickel is $\frac{13}{16}$ in. Describe how you would find the volume of the stack of nickels.

2. Describe the similarities and differences between finding the volume of a prism and a cylinder.

3. Explain how to find the volume of a prism or cylinder with a height of zero.

4. Based on what you know about finding the volume of a triangular prism, describe how you would find the volume of a hexagonal prism.

▶ **Language Link**

A *numismatist* is someone who studies or collects coins, money, and medals.

MEETING MIDDLE SCHOOL CLASSROOM NEEDS

Tips from Middle School Teachers

To help students visualize the volume of a container, I use small food cartons and cans and dried beans. I ask each group of students to select a container and then take as many dried beans as they think will fill the container. Then they fill the container to see how well they estimated.

Career Connection

Chemists often need to accurately measure the volume of liquids in cylinder-shaped or almost cylinder-shaped test tubes and beakers in the course of their work.

Industry Connection

When a ship is fully loaded, it becomes heavier and more of it sinks below the water line, displacing a greater volume of water. If the ship is too heavy, it will become unstable. In an effort to upgrade safety standards, the Merchant Shipping Act of 1876 introduced load lines, which are marked on the side of a cargo ship's hull to show the maximum load that the ship can safely carry. The lines are called Plimsoll marks, named after Samuel Plimsoll, a member of the British Parliament that brought about their adoption.

Alternate Examples

2. Find the volume of the cylinder.

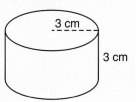

First, find the area of the base (B).
$B \approx \pi \cdot r^2$
$B = \pi \cdot (3)^2 \approx 28.26 \text{ cm}^2$
Use B to find the volume.
$V = B \cdot h$
$V \approx 28.26 \cdot 3$
$V \approx 84.78 \text{ cm}^3$
The volume is 84.78 cm^3.

Check

You may wish to demonstrate Question 1 by stacking up forty nickels.

Answers for Check Your Understanding

1. Possible answer: (1) Find the radius of the nickel. (2) Find the area of the circular face of a nickel. (3) Multiply the area by the 2.5 in.

2. Possible answer: Both use the formula $V = B \cdot h$ where B = area of the prism (cylinder) base and h = height of the prism (cylinder). A cylinder has a circular base and the prism has a polygonal base.

3. Possible answer: A prism with a height of zero is just a 2-D polygon. A cylinder with a height of zero is a 2-D circle. All 2-D shapes have zero volume.

4. Possible answer: Find the area of the hexagonal base and multiply it by the height.

9-8 Exercises and Applications

Assignment Guide

■ **Basic**
1, 2–10 evens, 11, 15–20

■ **Average**
3–7 odds, 8, 10, 11–15 odds, 16–19, 21

■ **Enriched**
3–7 odds, 8–16, 21

Exercise Notes

■ **Exercise 9**

Science Hotbeds are kept hot with either the help of electricity or fermenting manure. They are excellent places for germinating seeds as well as for raising young plants.

Exercise Answers

1. a.

b. ≈ 19.625 m²
c. ≈ 117.75 m³

Practice and Apply

1. **Getting Started** A cylinder has a diameter of 5 m and a height of 6 m.
   a. Sketch the cylinder and label the radius and height.
   b. Use the formula $A = \pi r^2$ to find the area of the base (use 3.14 for π).
   c. Multiply by the height to find the volume.

Find the volume of each solid, using 3.14 for π.

2.
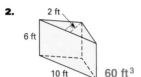
60 ft³

3.
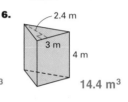
≈ 254.34 cm³

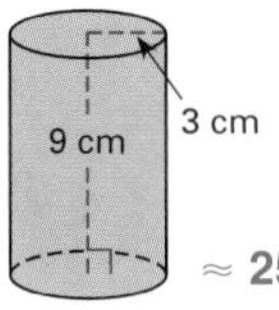

4.
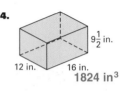
1824 in³

5.

≈ 565.2 cm³

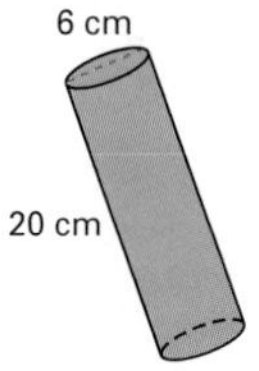

6.
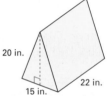
14.4 m³

7.
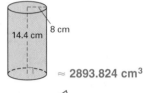
≈ 2893.824 cm³

8. **Industry** A photographic-supply company is designing a package to hold a tripod. The base of the package is an isosceles triangle with a base of 15 in. and a height of 20 in. The length of the package is 22 in. What is the volume of this package? **3300 in³**

9. **Science** A *hotbed* is a bed of soil that is enclosed in glass. The heat trapped under the glass is useful for raising seedlings. A hotbed forms the shape of a triangular prism that is 1.2 m long. The triangular base has a height of 0.3 m and a base length of 0.5 m. What is the volume of this hothouse? **0.09 m³**

PRACTICE 9-8

Reteaching

Activity

Materials: Empty cans of various sizes brought in from home, metric ruler

• Work in groups of four.

• Predict the order of the volume of the cans from least volume to greatest volume. Arrange the cans in this order.

• Now use the ruler to measure the diameter and height of each can. Use the formula for the volume of a cylinder to calculate each can's actual volume.

• How do the actual volumes compare to how you arranged the cans from least volume to greatest volume?

PRACTICE

Name _____

Practice 9-8

Volume of Prisms and Cylinders

Find the volume of each solid. Use 3.14 for π.

1. **1552.5 cm³**
2. **693 in³**
3. ≈ **773,325 mm³**
4. ≈ **4786 cm³**
5. **244\frac{3}{8} in³**
6. **36,192 mm³**
7. **38.88 m³**
8. **2400 ft³**
9. ≈ **2111 cm³**
10. **39.69 m³**
11. ≈ **45.73 yd³**
12. **879.06 cm³**

13. The attic of Karen's house has the shape of the triangular prism shown at the right. Find the volume of the attic.
6075 ft³

14. A cylindrical cookie tin has a diameter of 10 in. and a height of $3\frac{1}{2}$ in. How many cubic inches of cookies can it hold? Round your answer to the nearest cubic inch.
275 in³

RETEACHING

Name _____

Alternative Lesson 9-8

Volume of Prisms and Cylinders

The volume of prisms and cylinders is the product of the area of the base (*B*) and the height (*h*).

— Example 1 —

Find the volume of the triangular prism shown.

Step 1: Find the area of the base. Use the formula for area of a triangle.
$B = \frac{1}{2}(b \cdot h)$
$= \frac{1}{2}(6 \cdot 4) = \frac{1}{2} \cdot 24 = 12 \text{ cm}^2$

Step 2: Find the volume.
$V = B \cdot h = 12 \cdot 8 = 96 \text{ cm}^3$

The volume of the triangular prism is 96 cm³.

Try It Find the volume of the triangular prism shown.

a. What figure is the base? **Triangle.**
b. What is the area of the base? **$\frac{1}{2} \cdot 4 \cdot 3 = 6$ cm²**
c. What is the prism's height? **5 cm**
d. What is its volume? **30 cm³**

— Example 2 —

Find the volume of the cylinder shown.

Step 1: Find the area of the base. Use the formula for area of a circle.
$B = \pi r^2$
$= 3.14 \cdot 10^2 = 3.14 \cdot 100 = 314 \text{ in}^2$

Step 2: Find the volume.
$V = B \cdot h = 314 \cdot 5 = 1570 \text{ in}^3$

The volume of the cylinder is 1570 in³.

Try It Find the volume of the cylinder shown.

e. What figure is the base? **Circle.**
f. What is the area of the base? **$3.14 \cdot 5^2 = 78.5$ cm²**
g. What is the height? **20 cm**
h. What is the volume? **1570 cm³**

Find the volume of each cylinder.

i. **50.24 cm³**
j. **282.6 m³**
k. **471 ft³**

10. **Test Prep** A grain silo shaped like a cylinder is 30 ft tall and 8 ft in diameter. To the nearest hundred ft³, how many cubic ft of grain can the silo hold? **C**

Ⓐ 75,400 ft³   Ⓑ 82,400 ft³   Ⓒ 1,500 ft³   Ⓓ 7,500 ft³

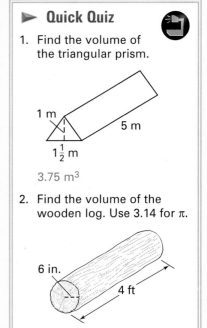

Problem Solving and Reasoning

Operation Sense Find the volume of the shaded region in each figure.

11.

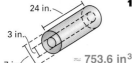
24 in.
3 in.
7 in.
≈ **753.6 in³**

12.

2 cm
6 cm
3 cm
12 cm
16 cm
1104 cm³

13. Geometry A hotel in Detroit is shaped like a cylinder with a diameter of 35 m and a height of 230 m.

   a. To the nearest m³, what is the volume of the building? **221,174 m³**

   b. The curved surface is covered with glass. How much glass is there on the surface of the hotel? **25,277 m²**

14. **Journal** A classmate is confused about the difference between the height of the triangle in the base of a triangular prism and the height of the prism. Write an explanation with an illustration to help clarify the two heights.

15. Communicate The base areas of a triangular, rectangular, and hexagonal prism are equal. Which prism do you think has the greatest volume? The least? Explain.

Mixed Review

Find the coordinates of each point. *[Lesson 2-6]*

16. A **(4, 2)**   **17.** B **(2, −3)**

18. C **(0, −1)**   **19.** D **(−5, 4)**

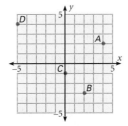

Complete each table of values. *[Lesson 4-1]*

20.

x	0	1	2	3	4	5
y = x + 7						

21.

x	0	1	2	3	4	5
y = −3x						

9-8 • Volume of Prisms and Cylinders **491**

PROBLEM SOLVING 9-8

Name _____

Guided Problem Solving 9-8

GPS PROBLEM 11, STUDENT PAGE 491

Find the volume of the shaded region in the figure.

24 in.
3 in.
7 in.

— **Understand** —

1. Which two solids make up the figure? Possible answers: Items 7 and 11 **Cylinders.**

2. What is the diameter of the inside figure? **3 in.** The outside figure? **7 in.**

3. What is the height of both figures? **24 in.**

— **Plan** —

4. What is the radius of the inside figure? **1.5 in.** The outside figure? **3.5 in.**

5. What is the formula for finding the volume of a cylinder? **V = B · h**

6. What is the formula for finding the area of the flat part of a cylinder? **A = πr²**

7. How can you find the volume of the shaded region? **Subtract volume of inside cylinder from volume of outside cylinder.**

— **Solve** —

8. What is the volume of the outside cylinder? **923.16 in³**

9. What is the volume of the inside cylinder? **169.56 in³**

10. What is the volume of the shaded region? **753.6 in³**

— **Look Back** —

11. What is another way to find the volume of the shaded space? **Find area of shaded part of the base. Multiply by cylinder's height.**

SOLVE ANOTHER PROBLEM

Find the volume of the shaded region in the figure. **2009.6 in³**

12 in. 4 in.
20 in.

Name _____

Extend Your Thinking 9-8

Critical Thinking

Use your knowledge of the volume of cylinders to answer these questions.

A
10 in.
10 in.
h

B
5 in.
20 in.
h

1. How are the dimensions of the cylinders alike? Possible answer: The height of one is the diameter of the other, and vice versa.

2. How are the dimensions of the cylinders different? Possible answer: The heights are different measures, as are the radii.

3. Predict which of the cylinders above has the greater volume. Explain. **Check students' answers.**

4. Calculate the volume of Cylinder A. **3140 in³**

5. Calculate the volume of Cylinder B. **1570 in³**

6. Which cylinder has the greater volume? Why do you think this is true? Cylinder A; Even though its height is only half the height of Cylinder B, the area of its base is four times greater, so the volume is greater.

7. Which cylinder has the greater surface area? Cylinder A; its surface area is 1256 in²; Cylinder B's surface area is 785 in².

Exercise Notes

■ **Exercise 13**

Industry Detroit is often called the *Automobile Capital of the World* or *Motor City*. More automobiles are produced in the Detroit area than anywhere else in the U.S.

Exercise Answers

14. Possible answer: With the prism sitting on one of its triangular ends, the height of a triangular base is a horizontal measurement, while the height of the prism is a vertical measurement.

15. The tallest prism will have the greatest volume; The shortest will have the least; Since the volume of a prism is the base area times the height, the volume will be proportional to height.

20.

x	0	1	2	3	4	5
y = x + 7	7	8	9	10	11	12

21.

x	0	1	2	3	4	5
y = −3x	0	−3	−6	−9	−12	−15

Alternate Assessment

Self Assessment Give students the opportunity to evaluate what they have learned about finding the volume of prisms and cylinders. Was there anything about the lesson that they found difficult? Was there something that they found particularly helpful to them in learning the concepts?

▶ **Quick Quiz**

1. Find the volume of the triangular prism.

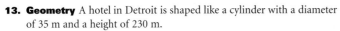
1 m
5 m
1½ m

3.75 m³

2. Find the volume of the wooden log. Use 3.14 for π.

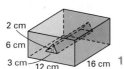
6 in.
4 ft

5425.92 in³ or 3.14 ft³

Available on Daily Transparency 9-8

■ **Find the volume of pyramids and cones.**

Materials

■ **Explore: Scissors, tape, centimeter ruler, two sheets of 11 in. by 17 in. paper, compass, centimeter cubes**

NCTM Standards

■ **1–7, 9, 12, 13**

► Review

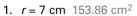

Find the area of the circle with the following radius.

1. $r = 7$ cm 153.86 cm^2

2. $r = 8\frac{1}{2}$ in. $226\frac{43}{50}$ in^2

3. Find the area of a triangle with base 9.4 ft and height 6 ft. 28.2 ft^2

4. Find the area of a rectangle with base 1.25 m and height 0.4 m. 0.5 m^2

Available on Daily Transparency 9-9

► Lesson Link

Remind students of practical applications that require finding the volume of prisms and cylinders, such as choosing boxes to pack items. Ask them to think of real-life applications that would involve finding the volume of pyramids or cones.

1 Introduce

Explore

The Point
Students use paper to make a cone and a cylinder with the same height and the same base. They then estimate the difference between the volume of the cone and the volume of the cylinder.

9-9 Volume of Pyramids and Cones

You'll Learn …

■ to find the volume of pyramids and cones

… How It's Used

A CAD operator creates drawings and 3-D models of motorcycles, cars, airplanes, and other things that require detailed engineering and design.

► **Lesson Link** You've found the volume of prisms and cylinders. Now you'll use that knowledge to find the volume of pyramids and cones. ◄

Explore   Cone to Cylinder

Cups and Cones

Materials: Scissors, Tape, Centimeter ruler, 2 sheets of 11 in. by 17 in. paper, Compass, Centimeter cubes

1. Use a compass to draw a circle with a 12.7 cm radius. Use a ruler to draw a radius on your circle. Cut out the circle.

2. Cut along the radius line that you drew.

3. Pull one edge of the cut radius until you produce a cone with a 15.2 cm diameter circular base. Use tape to keep this cone in place.

4. Measure the height of the cone.

5. Cut out a rectangle that will make a cylinder with the same height as the cone. The cylinder should also have the same diameter as the cone's base.

6. Calculate the volume of the cylinder by measuring the dimensions.

7. Estimate the volume of the cone by filling it with centimeter cubes. Record the estimate.

8. Place the cone inside the cylinder so that both of their circular bases are on the tabletop. Estimate the volume between the cylinder and the cone by filling the space with centimeter cubes. Record the estimate.

9. Discuss the relationship between the volume of the cylinder and the volume of the cone.

Cut

492 Chapter 9 • Area and Volume

Resources	Learning Modalities
9-9 Practice	**Social** In **Explore**, students work in pairs to test their estimate of the difference in volume between two figures.
9-9 Reteaching	
9-9 Problem Solving	
9-9 Enrichment	**Kinesthetic** Allow students to experiment with cones, cylinders, and materials such as dried beans or uncooked rice to further explore the relationship between these two shapes.
9-9 Daily Transparency	
Problem of the Day	
Review	**Individual** Allow students to reflect upon what they have learned about finding the volume of 3-D shapes. Answer any questions they might have about finding volume.
Quick Quiz	
Teaching Tool Transparencies 2 and 3	

Lesson Enhancement Transparencies 47 and 48

Chapter 9 Project Master

English Language Development

For students with limited English proficiency, it may be necessary to draw more diagrams and to clarify the connection between the variables in the formulas and the numbers they represent. After a formula has been derived, show several examples using the formula. Draw arrows from the numbers on the figure to respective variables.

Learn | Volume of Pyramids and Cones

The volume of a cone is $\frac{1}{3}$ the volume of a cylinder.

$V_{cone} = \frac{1}{3}(B \cdot h)$ where B is the area of the base and h is the height.

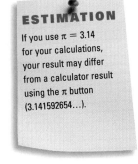

Example 1

Find the volume of the cone.

First, find the area of the circular base (B).

$B = \pi \cdot r^2$

$B = \pi \cdot 6^2 \approx 113.04$ cm^2

Use B to find the volume.

$V = \frac{1}{3}(B \cdot h)$

$V \approx \frac{1}{3}(113.04) \cdot 8$

$V \approx 301.44$ cm^3

The volume is about 301.44 cm^3.

8 cm
6 cm

ESTIMATION

If you use $\pi = 3.14$ for your calculations, your result may differ from a calculator result using the π button (3.141592654…).

Try It

Find the volume of the cone. **V ≈ 39.25 m^3**

6 m
5 m

The formula used to find B, the area of a figure's base, will depend on the shape of the base.

Finding the area of the square base will be different than finding the area of a triangular base.

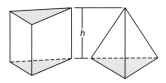

The volume of a pyramid is related to the volume of its related prism.

For a prism with volume $V = B \cdot h$, the related pyramid has volume $V = \frac{1}{3}(B \cdot h)$.

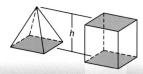

9-9 • Volume of Pyramids and Cones **493**

MATH EVERY DAY

▶ Problem of the Day

In some agricultural parts of Africa, traditional round houses with conical roofs are still used. The circular base has a 15-foot diameter and is 5 feet tall. The conical roof has a height of 4 feet above the top of the cylinder. Find the volume of such a traditional round house. Round to the nearest whole number. 1119 ft^3

Available on Daily Transparency 9-9

An Extension is provided in the transparency package.

Fact of the Day

The largest single block from a pyramid is from the Third Pyramid. It was built for King Menkaure (who is also known as Mycerinus) in Giza, Egypt and weighs 320 tons.

Mental Math

Do these mentally.

1. 50 + 45 + 15 110

2. 75 + 20 + 30 125

3. 30 + 40 + 45 115

Ongoing Assessment

Step 3, where the cone needs to be formed to have a 15.2 cm diameter circular base, is crucial. Check that students form the cone correctly. Step 4, where the height of the cone is to be measured, is also important. Check students' work at this point to make sure they are finding the height, not the slant height.

For Groups That Finish Early

Do you think that the relationship between the cone and the cylinder in Step 9 would be true for all cones and cylinders of the same height and base size? Why? Yes; Answers may vary.

Follow Up

Ask students if they are surprised about the relationship between cones and cylinders that they discovered. Have them explain why or why not.

Answers for Explore

1–3. Check students' work.

4. ≈ 10.2 cm

5. Check students' work.

6. ≈ 1844 cm^3

7. ≈ 614 cm^3

8. ≈ 1229 cm^3

9. Possible answer: The volume of a cone is $\frac{1}{3}$ the volume of a cylinder with the same height and base size.

2 Teach

Learn

You may wish to use Lesson Enhancement Transparencies 47 and 48 with this lesson.

Alternate Examples

1. Find the volume of the cone.

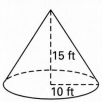

15 ft
10 ft

First, find the area of the circular base (B).

$B = \pi \cdot r^2$

$B = \pi \cdot 10^2 = 314$ ft^2

Use B to find the volume.

$V = \frac{1}{3}(B \cdot h)$

$V = \frac{1}{3}(314) \cdot 15$ ft

$V = 1570$ ft^3

The volume is 1570 ft^3.

Alternate Examples

2. Find the volume of the pyramid. Let h_t = height of the triangle.

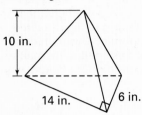

10 in.

14 in.   6 in.

$V = \frac{1}{3}B \cdot h$

$V = \frac{1}{3}(\frac{1}{2}b \cdot h_t) \cdot h$

$V = \frac{1}{3}(\frac{1}{2}(14 \cdot 6)) \cdot 10$

$V = \frac{1}{3}(42) \cdot 10 = 140 \text{ in}^3$

The volume of the pyramid is 140 in³.

3. Find the volume of the pyramid.

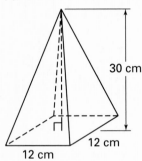

30 cm

12 cm

12 cm

$V = \frac{1}{3}B \cdot h$

$V = \frac{1}{3}(12^2) \cdot h$

$V = \frac{1}{3}(144) \cdot 30$

$V = \frac{1}{3}(144) \cdot 30 = 1440 \text{ cm}^3$

The volume of the pyramid is 1440 cm³.

3 Practice and Assess

Check

Suggest that students think about the formulas for finding the volume of a pyramid and the volume of a cone when answering Question 1.

Answers for Check Your Understanding

1. Possible answer: Each is $\frac{1}{3}$ the volume of the respective prism or cylinder.

2. Possible answer: The cylinder would have the same height and the same base diameter.

3. Yes. The slant height must increase because the vertex of the pyramid is further away from the base when the height is increased.

494   **Chapter 9**

Remember

A pyramid has only one base. **[Page 466]**

Example 2

Find the volume of the pyramid. Let h_t = height of the triangle.

$V = \frac{1}{3}B \cdot h$

$V = \frac{1}{3}(\frac{1}{2}b \cdot h_t) \cdot h$

$V = \frac{1}{3}(\frac{1}{2}(5 \cdot 12)) \cdot 15$

$V = \frac{1}{3}(30) \cdot 15 = 150 \text{ in}^3$ The volume of the pyramid is 150 in³.

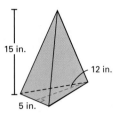

15 in.

12 in.

5 in.

Example 3

Find the volume of the pyramid.

$V = \frac{1}{3}B \cdot h$

$V = \frac{1}{3}(9^2) \cdot h$

$V = \frac{1}{3}(81) \cdot 25$

$V = \frac{1}{3}(81) \cdot 25 = 675 \text{ cm}^3$ The volume of the pyramid is 675 cm³.

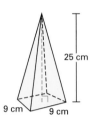

25 cm

9 cm   9 cm

Try It

Find the volume of each pyramid.

a. 5 m   5 m

6 m

50 m³

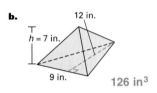

b.   12 in.

$h = 7$ in.

9 in.

126 in³

Check   Your Understanding

1. How are the volumes of pyramids and cones similar?

2. Given a cone that has a height of 18 cm and a circular base with a diameter of 8 cm, describe the cylinder that has 3 times the volume of that cone.

3. As the height of a pyramid increases does the slant height increase? Explain.

494   *Chapter 9 • Area and Volume*

MEETING MIDDLE SCHOOL CLASSROOM NEEDS

Tips from Middle School Teachers

I try to develop conceptual understanding by allowing students opportunities to discover a formula for themselves before I present it to them. Many students respond well to this approach because they want to know why the formula "works." However, I occasionally have students who simply want me to give them the formula. It is important that we allow for individual learning styles.

Team Teaching

Work with a social studies teacher when your class is studying pyramids. Have the students research Mexican and Egyptian pyramids. Students might enjoy preparing a chart listing the most famous pyramids, their locations, and their dimensions. Students can then calculate the volumes of the famous pyramids and note them on the chart.

History Connection

The Great Pyramid of Khufu, referred to in Exercise 8, was built about 2600 to 2500 B.C. for King Khufu (called Cheops by the Greeks). It is one of the ten pyramids at Giza, on the west bank of the Nile River outside of Cairo, Egypt.

Practice and Apply

1. **Getting Started** Find the volume of the pyramid.
   a. Find the area of the base. $12\frac{1}{4}$ ft^2
   b. Multiply the base area by the height and divide by 3 to find the volume.
   $16\frac{1}{3}$ ft^3

$h = 4$ ft $3\frac{1}{2}$ ft $3\frac{1}{2}$ ft

Find the volume of each solid. Use 3.14 for π.

2.
$h = 8$ in. 12 in. 12 in.
384 in^3

3.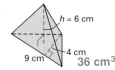
$h = 6$ cm 9 cm 4 cm
36 cm^3

4.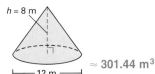
$h = 8$ m 12 m
$\approx$ 301.44 m^3

5.
$h = 7$ ft 4 ft 12 ft
56 ft^3

6. 36 mm 40 mm
$\approx$ 60,288 mm^3

7. 10 cm 6 cm
$\approx$ 94.2 cm^3

8. **Geography** The Great Pyramid of Khufu in ancient Egypt was a square pyramid 147 m high, with each side of the base 230 m. To the nearest m^3, how much limestone rock made up the pyramid? **2,592,100 m^3**

9. **Algebra** A cone with height of 25 mm is 3685 mm^3. What is the radius of the base? **$\approx$ 11.9 mm**

10. **Number Sense** Two square pyramids are each 10 inches tall. One pyramid has a 25 in^2 base and the other has a 64 in^2 base. Which pyramid has the greater volume?

11. **Science** The funnel at the right is used to put coolant, a mixture of antifreeze and water, in the radiator of a car. What is the maximum volume of coolant that the funnel can hold?

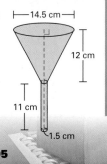
14.5 cm 12 cm 11 cm 1.5 cm

12. **Test Prep** An ice-cream company sells a prepackaged sugar cone with a 6 cm diameter with ice cream, fudge, and nuts filled to the top of the cone. To the nearest cm, what is the volume of this cone if it is 14 cm tall? **D**
   Ⓐ 301 cm^3 Ⓑ 151 cm^3 Ⓒ 603 cm^3 Ⓓ 132 cm^3

9-9 • Volume of Pyramids and Cones **495**

PRACTICE 9-9

9-9 Exercises and Applications

Assignment Guide

■ **Basic**
1, 2–8 evens, 12–16, 17–25 odds

■ **Average**
1, 3–7 odds, 8–13, 14–24 evens

■ **Enriched**
3–7 odds, 8–13, 14–24 evens

Exercise Notes

■ **Exercise 8**

Geography The Great Pyramid of Khufu was originally 147 meters tall, but it has lost some of its upper stones and it now stands at 140 meters tall. It is no longer a complete pyramid.

■ **Exercise 12**

History Ice cream cones were first served in 1904 at the World's Fair in St. Louis. A scoop of ice cream was placed inside of a thin, crispy waffle that was rolled into a cone.

Exercise Answers

10. The pyramid with 64 in^2 base.

11. 680 cm^3 (This is only an approximation, since part of the cone actually sticks into the cylinder.)

Reteaching

Activity

Materials: Pairs of containers in the shape of cylinders and cones (each pair having the same radius and height), several bags of dried beans

- Work in groups of four.

- Select a cone and cylinder of the same height and radius.

- Fill the cone with beans and pour them into the cylinder. How many times do you need to do this to fill the cylinder with beans? Three times

- Repeat the experiment using different pairs of cones and cylinders with the same height and radius. Is the result always the same as in the first experiment? Yes

---

PRACTICE

Name _____

Practice 9-9

Volume of Pyramids and Cones

Find the volume of each solid. Use 3.14 for π.

1. **2601 ft^3** $h = 27$ ft 17 ft 17 ft

2. **484.5 cm^3** $h = 17$ cm 19 cm 9 cm

3. **28.26 in^3** $h = 12$ in. $r = 1\frac{1}{2}$ in.

4. **1205.76 ft^3** $h = 18$ ft 16 ft

5. **$\approx$ 114.7 cm^3** $h = 11.5$ cm 7.3 cm 8.2 cm

6. **$\approx$ 21.1 in^3** $h = 4\frac{1}{2}$ in. $3\frac{3}{4}$ in. $3\frac{3}{4}$ in.

7. **$\approx$ 3538 ft^3** $r = 13$ ft $h = 20$ ft

8. **1650 cm^3** $h = 22$ cm 15 cm

9. **$136\frac{7}{8}$ in^3** $h = 7\frac{1}{3}$ in. $9\frac{3}{8}$ in. 12 in.

10. **110,592 ft^3** $h = 81$ ft 64 ft 64 ft

11. **7728 mm^3** $h = 46$ mm 24 mm 42 mm

12. **$\approx$ 362.9 in^3** $h = 8\frac{7}{8}$ in. $r = 6\frac{1}{4}$ in.

13. The base of a square pyramid has sides of length 15 in. If the pyramid has volume 1050 in^3, what is the height? **14 in.**

14. A special cushion designed to go in a corner is shaped like a triangular pyramid. The base is a right triangle with sides of length 42 cm, 56 cm, and 70 cm. If the height of the pillow is 64 cm, what is the volume? **25,088 cm^3**

RETEACHING

Name _____

Alternative Lesson 9-9

Volume of Pyramids and Cones

The volume of a cone is $\frac{1}{3}$ the volume of a related cylinder. You can use a formula to find the volume of a cone.
$V = \frac{1}{3}(B \cdot h)$ where B is the area of the base and h is the height.

The volume of the pyramid is one-third the volume of a related prism. You can use a formula to find the volume of a pyramid.
$V = \frac{1}{3}(B \cdot h)$ where B is the area of the base and h is the height.

— Example 1 —
Find the volume of the cone.

Step 1: Find the area of the circular base.
$B = \pi r^2$
$= 3.14 \cdot 4^2 = 3.14 \cdot 16 = 50.24$ cm^2

Step 2: Find the volume.
$V = \frac{1}{3}(B \cdot h)$
$= \frac{1}{3}(50.24 \cdot 9) = 150.72$ cm^3

The volume of the cone is 150.72 cm^3.

Try It Find the volume of the cone.

9 cm 4 cm

a. What figure is the base? **Circle.**
b. What is the area of the base? **200.96 in^2**
c. What is the height? **20 in.**
d. What is the volume? **1339.73 in^3**

20 in. 8 in.

— Example 2 —
Find the volume of the pyramid.

Step 1: Find the area of the square base. $B = s^2$
$= 6^2 = 36$ in^2

Step 2: Find the volume. $V = \frac{1}{3}(B \cdot h)$
$= \frac{1}{3}(36 \cdot 5) = 60$ in^3

The volume of the pyramid is 60 in^3.

$h = 5$ in. 6 in. 6 in.

Try It Find the volume of the pyramid.

e. What figure is the base? **Square.**
f. What is the area of the base? **25 cm^2**
g. What is the height? **5 cm**
h. What is the volume? **41.6 cm^3**

$h = 5$ cm 5 cm 5 cm

Lesson 9-9 **495**

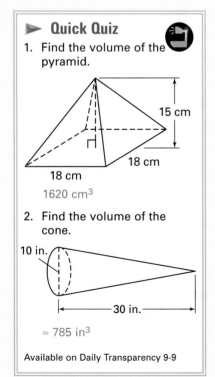
Problem Solving and Reasoning

13. **Math Reasoning** Which solid has a greater volume, the pyramid or cone?

14. **Communicate** Suppose you know the dimensions of a cone but have forgotten the formula for the volume of a cone. Describe a way you could find the volume.

15. **Algebra** Write an equation and use the Pythagorean theorem to find the height of a cone that has a slant height of 15 in. and a radius of 9 in. $h^2 + 81 = 225$ $h = 12$ in.

16. **Critical Thinking** A dinnerware factory packs its dinnerware in a pyramid-shaped box.

   a. How much cardboard is saved by using a pyramid design over a square-based prism design? ≈ **344 in²**

   b. How much volume is saved? **960 in³**

17. **Choose a Strategy** A manufacturer of cone-shaped hats wants to ship each hat in a cylinder with the same diameter and height. How much packing filler is needed for each cylinder to completely fill the package? **6280 cm³**

Mixed Review

Evaluate. *[Lesson 2-7]*

18. -5^2 **−25**   19. 4^3 **64**   20. $(-2)^5$ **−32**   21. 8^2 **64**   22. -6^0 **−1**

Determine if each ordered pair is a solution of the equation. *[Lesson 4-2]*

23. $y = 4x$ a. $(2, 8)$ b. $(4, -16)$

24. $x = y + 1$ a. $(7, 6)$ b. $(3, 2)$

25. $y = 3x - 2$ a. $(1, 1)$ b. $(2, -4)$

Problem Solving

STRATEGIES

- Look for a Pattern
- Make an Organized List
- Make a Table
- Guess and Check
- Work Backward
- Use Logical Reasoning
- Draw a Diagram
- Solve a Simpler Problem

> **Project Progress**

You should know the volume of your chosen item. Be able to describe the relationship between the dimensions of your package and the dimensions of your item. Also, look back on how you decided on the final package.

Problem Solving

Understand
Plan
Solve
Look Back

PROBLEM SOLVING 9-9

► **PROBLEM SOLVING**

Name _____

Guided Problem Solving 9-9

GPS PROBLEM 13, STUDENT PAGE 496

Which solid has a greater volume, the pyramid or cone?

— **Understand** —

1. What is the height of the cone? __12 cm__

2. What is the height of the pyramid? __12 cm__

— **Plan** —

3. What is the formula for finding the volume of a cone? $V = \frac{1}{3}(B \cdot h)$

4. What is the formula for finding the base of the cone? $A = \pi r^2$

5. What is the formula for finding the volume of a pyramid? $V = \frac{1}{3}(B \cdot h)$

6. What is the formula for finding the base of the pyramid? $A = s^2$

— **Solve** —

7. What is the volume of the cone? __78.5 cm³__

8. What is the volume of the pyramid? __100 cm³__

9. Which solid has the greater volume? __Pyramid.__

— **Look Back** —

10. How could you find the greater volume without actually calculating the volume of each figure? Explain. Possible answer: Compare area of the Bases. Since both volumes are calculated as $\frac{1}{3}(B \cdot h)$, and figures have same height, the area of the base will determine the greater volume.

SOLVE ANOTHER PROBLEM

Which solid has a greater volume, the pyramid or cone? __Pyramid.__

► **ENRICHMENT**

Name _____

Extend Your Thinking 9-9

Visual Thinking

Each of the nine squares in the "spreadsheet" should contain all of the lines and symbols from both the labeled square above it and the one to its left.

For example, if square A contained a circle and square 1 contained a dot, then the square A1 would contain both a circle and a dot in their respective positions.

1. Which of the squares is incorrect? Explain. Square B1, the diagonal from the upper left to lower right corners is missing.

_____

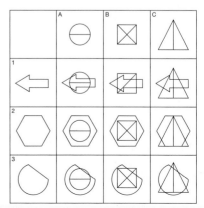

In the beginning of Section 9B, you learned how some teenagers started what is today one of the largest package-delivery companies in the world. Now you will use your knowledge of volume to solve packaging problems involved in operating a business of your own.

The Dig on Deliveries

Materials: Calculator

You and your friends have a part-time job buying used stereo-sound components and shipping them to a relative in another state who refurbishes and resells them.

The boxing, foam packing, and shipping costs come out of your pay of $25 per component. You have the three components to ship (see photos). Your local post office has the box sizes shown in the lower right chart to use for shipping.

Woofer-tube   Sub-woofer   Band-pass enclosure

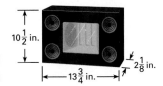

1. Determine the volume, to the nearest in³, of each sound component.

2. Choose the box size to ship each component. (You may ship more than one component per box.) Determine the volume of foam packing needed for each box.

3. The foam packing material is $0.99 per ft³. If a delivery company charges $0.002 per in³ for shipping, what is the total cost of boxing, packing, and shipping for the three components? How much profit did you make?

2 in. x 10 in. x 13 in.	$1.75
10 in. x 12 in. x 15 in.	$2.25
10 in. x 14 in. x 20 in.	$2.50
12 in. x 16 in. x 24 in.	$3.25
16 in. x 20 in. x 24 in.	$3.50

497

The Dig on Deliveries

The Point
In *The Dig on Deliveries* on page 475, students read about how teenager Jim Casey started a business. Now they will consider problems involved in operating a business of their own.

Materials
Calculator

Resources
Teaching Tool Transparency 22: Scientific Calculator

About the Page
- Remind students that they need to keep the dimensions of the box in mind as well as its volume when choosing a box.

- Students should realize that the foam packing will fill up all of the space in the box that the item does not fill.

- Note also that the foam packing is priced per cubic foot. Students will need to convert from cubic inches to cubic feet by dividing the cubic inches by 1728 in³.

Ongoing Assessment
Check that all students have made the correct box choices in Step 2 before they go on to Step 3. Remind them that the costs of shipping are deducted from their pay, so they will want to pack the boxes in the least expensive way.

Extension
You find you have two sub-woofers to send. You decide to send them in a 10 in. × 14 in. × 20 in. box. Determine your boxing, approximate packing, and shipping costs. Based on these costs, what is your profit for these two components? Then describe how you will fit two sub-woofers in this box. You may want to draw a diagram. Boxing: $2.50, Packing: ≈ $0.62, Shipping: $5.60; Profit: $41.28; Since the sub-woofer has an irregular shape, by turning one sub-woofer upside-down in the box it can slide partially under the right-side-up sub-woofer. This allows the $12\frac{1}{2}$ inch dimensions of the two sub-woofers to overlap and fit in the 14 × 20 inch space.

Answers for Connect

1. Woofer-tube: 567 in³; Possible answer for Sub-woofer: about 286 in³, if formula for the volume of a cone is used to approximate its volume; Band-pass enclosure: 307 in³

2. Possible answer: Ship the Woofer-tube and the Band-pass enclosure in one 10 in. × 12 in. × 15 in. box; 926 in³, or 0.54 ft³ of packing is needed. Ship the Sub-woofer in another 10 in. × 12 in. × 15 in. box, placing it on an angle within the box; 1514 in³, or 0.88 ft³ of packing is needed.

3. Total cost: $13.11; Profit = $61.89

(Some students may apply the formula for the volume of a cylinder to approximate the volume of the Sub-woofer as 859 in³. All answers would need to be adjusted to reflect this approximation.)

Review Correlation

Item(s)	Lesson(s)
1	9-6
2, 3	9-8
4	9-6
5, 6	9-9
7	9-6
8	9-9
9	9-8
10, 11	9-7
12	9-6, 9-8
13	9-8, 9-9
14	9-8

Test Prep

Test-Taking Tip
Tell students that when they need to obtain information from diagrams of 3-D figures on a test, they should visualize the figure in their mind to help them understand it better.

REVIEW 9B

Section 9B Review

Find the volume of each solid. Use 3.14 for π.

1.
2 in. 17 in.
$16\frac{1}{2}$ in.
561 in³

2.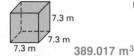
$\frac{1}{2}$ in.
1 in. 12 in.
3 in³

3.
3.2 cm
6 cm
≈ 48.2304 cm³

4.
7.3 m
7.3 m
7.3 m
389.017 m³

5. $h = 12$ m
18 m 18 m
1296 m³

6. $4\frac{1}{2}$ ft
2 ft
3 ft
$4\frac{1}{2}$ ft³

7.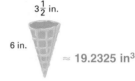
14 in.
10 in. 4 in.
560 in³

8. $3\frac{1}{2}$ in.
6 in.
≈ 19.2325 in³

9. 10.5 cm
17.5 cm
≈ 1515 cm³

Find the volume for each after the given dilation.

10. Scale factor = 10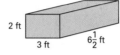
2 ft
3 ft $6\frac{1}{2}$ ft
39,000 ft³

11. Scale factor = $\frac{1}{3}$
9 in.
9 in.
9 in.
27 in³

12. Which has the greater volume: a can 16 cm in diameter and 24 cm high or a box 16 cm by 12 cm by 24 cm? **The can**

13. A model-rocket club uses the design to the right to see which student can get the most distance from a launch. What is the volume of the rocket? **50.24 in³**

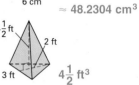
3 in.
15 in.
2 in.

Test Prep

Be careful with cylinder and cone formulas that include r for radius. The given dimensions may include a value for the diameter instead. Never use a value for the diameter in these formulas.

14. To the nearest 10 cubic cm, what is the volume of a cylinder with a diameter of 10 cm and a height of 14 cm? **C**

Ⓐ 440 cm³　　Ⓑ 4400 cm³　　Ⓒ 1100 cm³　　Ⓓ 7700 cm³

498 *Chapter 9 • Area and Volume*

Resources

Practice Masters
　Section 9B Review

Assessment Sourcebook
　Quiz 9B

　TestWorks
　Test and Practice Software

PRACTICE

Name _____

Practice

Section 9B Review

Find the volume of each solid. Use 3.14 for π.

1. **660 ft³**
11 ft　15 ft
8 ft

2. **110.592 cm³**
4.8 cm　4.8 cm
4.8 cm

3. **≈ 78.28 in³**
$h = 5\frac{1}{2}$ in.
$7\frac{3}{4}$ in.

4. **1309 ft³**
$8\frac{1}{2}$ ft
14 ft　11 ft

5. **9847.04 m³**
$r = 14$ m
16 m

6. **≈ 7.29 in³**
$h = 3\frac{1}{4}$ in.
$2\frac{1}{2}$ in.

Find the volume for each after the given dilation.

7. Scale factor = 4
$V = $ **$24\frac{1}{16}$ in³**
$\frac{5}{16}$ in.　$1\frac{1}{8}$ in.
$\frac{7}{8}$ in.

8. Scale factor = $\frac{2}{3}$
$V = $ **7.68 cm³**
3 cm
2.4 cm　3.6 cm

9. Scale factor = 0.75
$V = $ **216 in³**
8 in.
8 in.　8 in.

10. Which has the greater volume: a cone with radius 8 in. and height 12 in. or a cylinder with diameter 9 in. and height 12 in.?
Cone

11. A decorative pedestal has the shape of a prism with a square pyramid on top, as shown. What is the volume of the pedestal?
960 in³
Total height 32 in.
24 in.
6 in.

12. **Geography** Springfield, Illinois, is 193 mi due west of Indianapolis, Indiana. Jeanette drove due north from Indianapolis until she was 215 mi from Springfield. How far did she drive? *[Lesson 7-9]*
About 94.7 miles
215 mi
Springfield 193 mi Indianapolis

13. **Geography** A portion of Utah is shown. Name all cities in 2B. If none, write "None." *[Lesson 8-3]*
Knolls, Delle

Comparing Areas of Map Projections

A map shows the earth's surface on a plane. If the earth were flat, it would be easy to represent its surface on a flat sheet of paper. But the earth is a sphere, and a spherical surface is not easily flattened.

A **map projection** is an attempt to represent a spherical surface as a flat surface.

Use the facts that Greenland has an area of 840,050 mi² and Canada has an area of 3,851,809 mi² to compare the following two representations of the earth.

The **cylindrical projection** was originally ideal for navigation and is still used today. The lines of longitude and latitude appear as straight lines that intersect at right angles. The North and South Poles are greatly exaggerated.

The **conic projection** usually shows latitude lines as parts of circles, and longitude lines radiate from the North or South Pole.

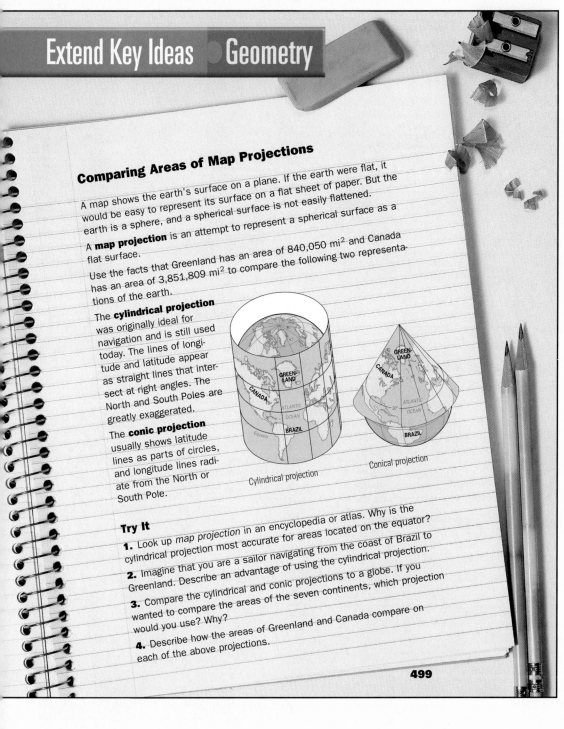

Cylindrical projection

Conical projection

Try It

1. Look up *map projection* in an encyclopedia or atlas. Why is the cylindrical projection most accurate for areas located on the equator?

2. Imagine that you are a sailor navigating from the coast of Brazil to Greenland. Describe an advantage of using the cylindrical projection.

3. Compare the cylindrical and conic projections to a globe. If you wanted to compare the areas of the seven continents, which projection would you use? Why?

4. Describe how the areas of Greenland and Canada compare on each of the above projections.

499

Answers for Try It

1. Distances and other measurements near the equator are less distorted on a cylindrical projection than on a conical projection.

2. Answers may vary.

3. Use the cylindrical projection to get a better estimate of area for continents that have the majority of their land mass near the equator. Use the conical projection to estimate the area of continents near the polar region.

4. Canada and Greenland are more exaggerated on the cylindrical projection. Canada and Greenland appear closer to their relative proportions on the conical projection.

Comparing Areas of Map Projections

The Point
Students explore two different types of map projections: cylindrical and conic.

Resources
Teaching Tool Transparency 20: Map of World
Lesson Enhancement Transparency 49

About the Page

- It is impossible to project a sphere, such as the surface of the earth, onto a flat surface with complete accuracy.

- Each type of map projection has its advantages and drawbacks.

- Different map projections are used for different purposes.

Ask ...

- When a round-topped tent is up, its sides are nice and smooth, but when you take it down, what happens? It is all wrinkled up and you need to smooth it and fold it to make it lie flat.

- Do you see how cartographers have a similar problem when they try to draw flat maps of the spherical earth? Answers may vary.

Extension

Have students measure and note the widths of Greenland and South America on a globe. Then have them measure and note these widths on a cylindrical map projection. What difference do the students find? A globe shows that Greenland is about one-fifth of the width of South America. A cylindrical, or Mercator, projection shows their widths to be about the same.

Review Correlation

Item(s)	Lesson(s)
1	9-1
2	9-2
3, 4	9-3
5	9-4
6	9-5
7	9-6
8	9-8, 9-9
9	9-8
10	9-9
11	9-7
12	9-8

For additional review, see page 684.

Chapter 9 Summary and Review

Graphic Organizer

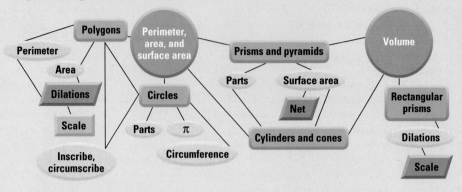

Section 9A   Perimeter, Area, and Surface Area

Summary

- The **perimeter** (p) is the distance around a figure.

- The **area** (A) of a polygon is the number of square units it contains. Area of a rectangle = bh, area of a square = s^2, and area of a triangle = $\frac{1}{2}bh$.

- The distance around a circle is the **circumference**. The **radius** is the distance from the **center** to any point on the circle. The **diameter** = $2r$. π **(pi)** is used to calculate the area of a circle.

- A **polyhedron** is a 3-D figure composed of polygonal **faces** that meet at **edges**. A **vertex** of a polyhedron is the intersection of three or more faces. **Prisms, cylinders, pyramids,** and **cones** are polyhedrons.

- The **surface area** (SA) of a polyhedron is the sum of the areas of all the faces. A net can be helpful in finding the surface area of a polyhedron.

Review

1. Find the perimeter and area of each polygon.

a. 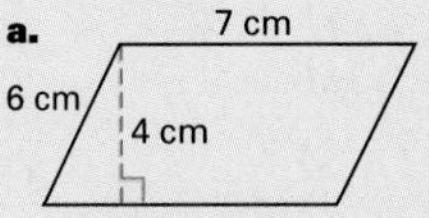
7 cm
6 cm
4 cm
26 cm; 28 cm²

b. 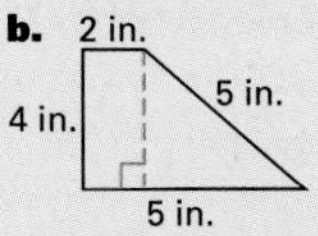
2 in.
4 in.   5 in.
5 in.
16 in.; 14 in²

2. Find the perimeter and area of

a. The polygon in Exercise 1a after a dilation of a scale factor of 3.

b. The polygon in Exercise 1b after a dilation of a scale factor of $\frac{2}{5}$.
a. 78 cm; 252 cm²
b. 6.4 in.; 2.24 in²

Resources

Practice Masters
  Cumulative Review
  Chapters 1–9

Assessment Sourcebook
  Quarterly Test Chapters 1–9

> ## PRACTICE

Name _____

Practice

Cumulative Review Chapters 1–9

Write each percent as a fraction in lowest terms and as a decimal. *[Lesson 6-1]*

1. 82% $\frac{41}{50}$; 0.82   **2.** 60% $\frac{3}{5}$; 0.60   **3.** 13% $\frac{13}{100}$; 0.13

4. 25% $\frac{1}{4}$; 0.25   **5.** 8% $\frac{2}{25}$; 0.08   **6.** 35% $\frac{7}{20}$; 0.35

Identify each number as rational or irrational. *[Lesson 7-8]*

7. $\sqrt{36}$ Rational   **8.** $\sqrt{0.64}$ Rational   **9.** $\sqrt{28}$ Irrational

10. $\sqrt{\frac{49}{81}}$ Rational   **11.** $\sqrt{12}$ Irrational   **12.** $\sqrt{\frac{144}{25}}$ Rational

In the figure shown at right, $\overleftrightarrow{VW} \parallel \overleftrightarrow{XY}$. *[Lesson 8-5]*   Possible answers:

13. Name a pair of alternate interior angles. $\angle 4, \angle 6$

14. Name a pair of corresponding angles. $\angle 3, \angle 7$

15. Name a pair of vertical angles. $\angle 1, \angle 3$

16. Name the angles that are congruent to $\angle 3$. $\angle 1, \angle 5, \angle 7$

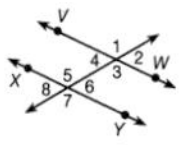

Find the perimeter and area of each polygon after the given dilation. *[Lesson 9-2]*

17. Scale factor = 4   **18.** Scale factor = 2   **19.** Scale factor = $\frac{1}{5}$

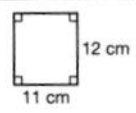

$P =$ ___184 cm___ $P =$ ___250 in.___ $P =$ ___3.2 m___

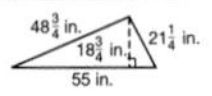

$A =$ ___2112 cm²___ $A =$ ___$2062\frac{1}{2}$ in²___ $A =$ ___0.5504 m²___

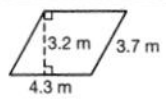

Find the volume of each solid. Use 3.14 for π. *[Lesson 9-9]*

20. ___246.96 cm³___   **21.** ___$143\frac{11}{16}$ in³___   **22.** ___≈ 151.0 m³___

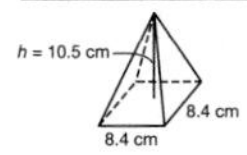

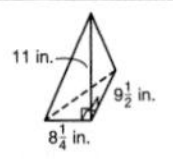

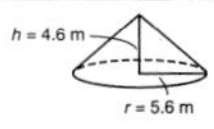

Section 9A Perimeter, Area, and Surface Area *continued*

3. For the circle shown, find the circumference and the area.
≈ **52.1 cm;** ≈ **216 cm²**

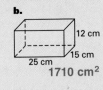
8.3 cm

4. One of the rings in a three-ring circus has a circumference of 141.3 ft. Find the diameter of the ring. ≈ **45 ft**

5. Find the surface area of each figure.

a.

7 ft
5 ft
≈ **149.2 ft²**

b.

12 cm
15 cm
25 cm
1710 cm²

6. Find the slant height and the surface area.

a.

12 in.
10 in.
10 in.
13 in.; 360 in²

b.
20 m
15 m
25 m; 1884 m²

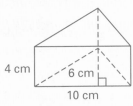
4 cm
6 cm
10 cm

b. $V \approx 83.7$ in³

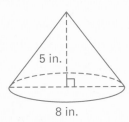
5 in.
8 in.

11. a. $V = 13.5$ m³
   b. $V = 27$ m³
12. a. $V = 24$ ft³
   b. $V = 6$ ft³

Section 9B Volume

Summary

■ The **volume** of a solid measures the space it occupies.

■ Volume (V) of a prism or cylinder $= B \cdot h$, and volume (V) of a pyramid or cone $= \frac{1}{3}B \cdot h$ where $B =$ area of the figure's base.

■ In a dilation with a scale factor of x, the volume of the solid is multiplied by x^3.

Review

7. Find the volume of each solid.

a.

5 cm
5 cm
5 cm
125 cm³

b.
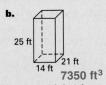
25 ft
21 ft
14 ft
7350 ft³

8. Find the volume of each solid.

a.

3 in.
$6\frac{1}{2}$ in.
≈ **184 in³**

b.
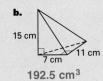
15 cm
7 cm
11 cm
192.5 cm³

9. a. Sketch a triangular prism with height 4 cm where the triangle has a base 10 cm and height 6 cm. Then find its volume.

b. Sketch a cone with diameter 8 in. and height 5 in. Then find its volume.

10. a. Find the volume of the solid in Exercise 7a after scaling two dimensions by a scale factor of $\frac{1}{5}$. **5 cm³**

b. Find the surface area and volume of the solid in Exercise 7b after a dilation of a scale factor of 7. **2,521,050 ft³**

11. Find the volume of a triangular prism where $B = 3$ m² and
a. $h = 4.5$ m
b. $h = 9$ m

12. Find the volume of a cylinder where $B = 12$ ft² and
a. $h = 2$ ft
b. $h = \frac{1}{2}$ ft

Chapter 9 Assessment

1. Refer to the parallelogram shown below.

a. Find the perimeter and area. **66 ft; 240 ft²**

b. Find the perimeter and area after a dilation of a scale factor of 4. **264 ft; 3840 ft²**

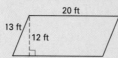

2. Refer to the triangle shown below.

a. Find the perimeter and area. **40 in.; 60 in²**

b. Find the perimeter and area after a dilation of a scale factor of $\frac{3}{4}$. **30 in.; 33.75 in²**

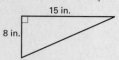

3. Find the diameter, area, and circumference of the circle at the right. **22 m; ≈ 379.94 m²; 69.08 m**

4. Which shows **a.** a square circumscribed about a circle. **b.**

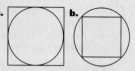

5. Refer to the rectangular prism shown below.

a. Sketch a net of the prism.

b. Find the surface area of the prism. **686 ft²**

6. Refer to the cylinder shown below.

a. Find the surface area of the cylinder. ≈ **753.6 cm²**

b. Find the volume of the cylinder. ≈ **1406.72 cm³**

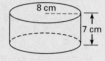

7. Refer to the pyramid shown below. Find the slant height and surface area of the pyramid. **17 m; 800 m²**

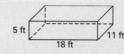

8. A disposable paper cup has the shape of a cone with diameter 5 cm and height 6 cm. How much water does the cup hold? **About 39.25 cm³**

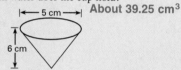

9. A simplified drawing of Monique's house is shown at the right.

a. What is the volume of the house? **5520 ft³**

b. Monique plans to paint her house. How much surface area will she cover? (Do not include the roof or the floor.) **792 ft²**

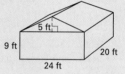

Performance Task

Make a chart showing a drawing of every kind of 3-D figure you have learned. Label each figure with its name. Show formulas for surface area and volume of each figure.

502 *Chapter 9 • Area and Volume*

Assessment Correlation

Item(s)	Lesson(s)
1, 2	9-1, 9-2
3, 4	9-3
5	9-4
6	9-4, 9-8
7	9-5
8	9-9
9	9-4

Answers for Assessment

4.

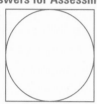

5. a. Answers may vary.

Performance Assessment Key

See key on page 441.

Resources
Assessment Sourcebook
Chapter 9 Tests
Forms A and B (free response)
Form C (multiple choice)
Form D (performance assessment)
Form E (mixed response)
Form F (cumulative chapter test)
TestWorks
Test and Practice Software
Home and Community Connections
Letter Home for Chapter 9
in English and Spanish

Suggested Scoring Rubric

4
- Makes a chart showing and labeling all 3-D figures studied.
- Includes correct formulas for surface area and volume for all of the figures.

3
- Makes a chart showing and labeling most of the 3-D figures studied.
- Includes correct formulas for surface area and volume for most of the figures.

2
- Makes a chart showing and labeling a few of the 3-D figures studied.
- Includes correct formulas for surface area and volume for a few of the figures.

1
- Makes little or no attempt to make chart.

Performance Assessment

Choose one problem.

THINK GLOBALLY, ACT LOCALLY

Find your home location on a globe of the earth. Determine the latitude and longitude of your home. Then draw a map showing the region that is within 5° latitude north or south, and within 5° longitude east or west of your home. Use the scale of the globe to determine the perimeter and area of this region.

BUILDING A CUBE THE HARD WAY

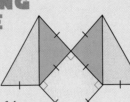

Make three copies of the net shown at the right on pieces of stiff paper. The sides shown with tick marks are all the same length. Make the patterns as large as you can, but all the same size. Cut out each net. Fold and tape each one to make three figures. Put the three figures together to make a cube. How does this three-dimensional puzzle relate to the formula for the volume of a pyramid?

Roll-to-Roll CARPETING

Dena bought a 10 ft by 8 ft piece of lime green carpet that is 1 in. thick. When the carpet is rolled up it forms a cylinder 10 ft long and $1\frac{1}{2}$ ft in diameter. What is the volume of this roll of carpet and about how many layers of carpet are there in the cylinder?

How Much Is Money?

You'll need a quarter, dime, nickel, and penny. Find the area of the circular base of each coin. Now find the height of each coin. Use this information to find the volume of each coin. Compare the ratios of coin value to volume.

Cumulative Review Chapters 1–9 **503**

About Performance Assessment

The Performance Assessment options ...

- provide teachers with an alternate means of assessing students.

- address different learning modalities.

- allow students to choose one problem.

Teachers may encourage students to choose the most challenging problem.

Learning Modalities
Think Globally, Act Locally **Visual** Students draw a map.
Building a Cube the Hard Way **Kinesthetic** Students form a cube from three pyramids.
Roll-to-Roll Carpeting **Individual** Students solve the problem on their own.
How Much Is Money? **Logical** Students explore the ratios of the value of coins compared to the coin's volume.

Suggested Scoring Rubric

See key on page 441.

Roll-to-Roll Carpeting

4
- Easily calculates the volume of the roll of carpet.
- Easily estimates the amount of layers in the cylinder.

3
- Calculates the volume of the roll of carpet.
- Estimates the amount of layers in the cylinder.

2
- Calculates the volume of the roll of carpet.
- Estimates the amount of layers in the cylinder with assistance.

1
- Shows very little understanding of calculating the volume of the roll of carpet.
- Attempts to estimate the amount of layers in the cylinder with considerable assistance.

Rubric for **How Much Is Money?** is on page C2.

Think Globally, Act Locally

4
- Easily finds home on globe, draws accurate map of region within 5° latitude and within 5° longitude, and determines the perimeter and area of the region.

3
- Finds home on globe, draws a passable map of region within 5° latitude and within 5° longitude, and determines the perimeter and area of the region.

2
- Finds home on globe with assistance, draws a poor map of region within 5° latitude and within 5° longitude but does not determine the perimeter and area of the region.

1
- Shows only a remote understanding of how to find home on globe.

Building a Cube the Hard Way

4
- Makes three copies of the net, folds and tapes them together to make three figures, and puts them together to make a cube.

3
- Makes three copies of the net, folds and tapes them together to make three figures, and is able to put them together to make a cube with assistance.

2
- With assistance, makes three copies of the net, folds and tapes them together to make three figures, and is able to put them together to make a cube.

1
- Shows only a remote understanding of what is being requested. Is only able to make the three figures and attempts to put them together to form a cube with considerable assistance.

Chapter 10

▶ **OVERVIEW**

Algebra:
Functions and Relationships

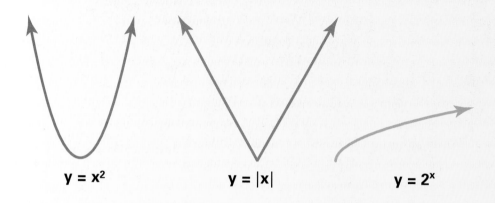

$y = x^2$ $y = |x|$ $y = 2^x$

Section 10A

Functions: Students learn how to represent linear, quadratic, and other types of functions using tables, graphs, and equations.

10-1 Functions

10-2 Linear Functions

10-3 Quadratic Functions

10-4 Other Functions

Section 10B

Polynomials: Students evaluate polynomials. Then they explore adding, subtracting, and multiplying polynomials.

10-5 Polynomials

10-6 Adding Polynomials

10-7 Subtracting Polynomials

10-8 Multiplying Polynomials and Monomials

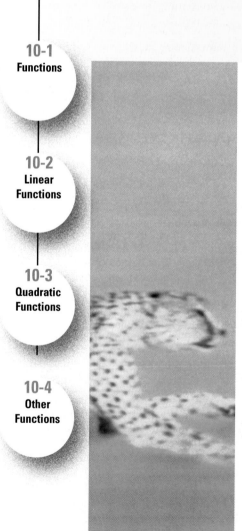

S T A N D A R D

▶ Curriculum Standards

#	Standard		pages
1	**Problem Solving**	Skills and Strategies	506, 527, 538, 541
		Applications	511, 512, 516, 517, 521, 522, 526, 527, 535, 536, 540, 541, 546, 547, 551, 552
		Exploration	505, 508, 513, 518, 523, 532, 537, 542, 548
2	**Communication**	Oral	504, 505, 507, 510, 515, 520, 525, 531, 534, 539, 545, 547, 550, 552
		Written	507, 510, *513*, 515, 518, 520, 523, 527–530, 532, 537, 539–542, 545, 550–554, 558
		Cooperative Learning	508, *511*, 513, *516*, 518, *521*, 523, *526*, 532, *535*, 537, *539*, 542, 548, *551*, *552*
3	**Reasoning**	Critical Thinking	506, 512, 517, 522, 527, 536, 541, 547, 552
4	**Connections**	Mathematical	See Standards 5, 6, 8, 9, 11–13 below.
		Interdisciplinary	Consumer *510*, 516, *525*, 526, *539*, 540; Fine Arts 504; Geography *550*; History *531*; Health *515*; Industry *520*; Science 504, 505, 507, 512, 516, 520, 522, 530, 531, 536, 544, 547, *550*; Social Science 504, 505, 531
		Technology	513, 518, 524, 525, 528, 531, 533
		Cultural	*504, 515, 525, 534*
5	**Number and Number Relationships**		548–552
6	**Number Systems and Number Theory**		547–552
7	**Computation and Estimation**		*509*, 543
8	**Patterns and Functions**		504, 505, 508–530, 532–559
9	**Algebra**		508–530, 532–559
11	**Probability**		527
12	**Geometry**		504, 511, 517, 522, 527, 532, 534–536, 539–542, 546, 547, 551, 552, 554, 557–559
13	**Measurement**		517, 522, 527, 532, 534, 535, 539–541, 544, 546, 547, 551, 552, 554, 557–559

Italic type indicates Teacher Edition reference.

▶ Teaching Standards

Focus on Inclusion

Not every child will have the same interest or capabilities in mathematics. However, the NCTM has as its goal the mathematics education of all students. This includes

- learning-disabled students.

- developmentally delayed students.

- emotionally disturbed students.

▶ Assessment Standards

Focus on Coherence

Journal The Coherence Standard seeks to align assessment with curriculum and instruction. As students move from being passive receptors of knowledge to active creators of mathematics, journal entries provide an assessment tool to document that creation. Journal writing in Chapter 10 has students

- predict rules for subtracting polynomials.

- evaluate the above predictions.

TECHNOLOGY

▶ For the Teacher

- **Teacher Resource Planner CD-ROM**
  Use the teacher planning CD-ROM to view resources available for Chapter 10. You can prepare custom lesson plans or use the default lesson plans provided.

- **World Wide Web**
  Visit **www.teacher.mathsurf.com** for links to lesson plans from teachers and other professionals, NCTM information, and other sites.

- **TestWorks**
  TestWorks provides ready-made tests and can create custom tests and practice worksheets.

▶ For the Parent

- **World Wide Web**
  Parents can use the Web site at **www.parent.mathsurf.com**.

▶ For the Student

- **Interactive CD-ROM**
  Lesson 10-3 has an *Interactive CD-ROM Lesson*. The *Interactive CD-ROM Journal* and *Interactive CD-ROM Spreadsheet/Grapher Tool* are also used in Chapter 10.

- **Wide World of Mathematics**
  Lesson 10-1 Algebra: Rube Goldberg Machines
  Lesson 10-3 Algebra: La Quebrada Divers
  Lesson 10-4 Algebra: Endangered Species
  Lesson 10-5 Algebra: Investing for College

- **World Wide Web**
  Use with Chapter and Section Openers; Students can go online to the Scott Foresman-Addison Wesley Web site at **www.mathsurf.com/8/ch10** to collect information about chapter themes.

SECTION 10A	LESSON	OBJECTIVE	ITBS Form M	CTBS 4th Ed.	CAT 5th Ed.	SAT 9th Ed.	MAT 7th Ed.	Your Form
	10-1	• Recognize a function and find the input and output values of a function.	✗	✗	✗	✗	✗	
	10-2	• Represent functions using tables, graphs, and equations.	✗	✗	✗	✗	✗	
	10-3	• Represent quadratic functions as graphs, tables, and equations.						
	10-4	• Graph and evaluate other types of functions.						

SECTION 10B	LESSON	OBJECTIVE	ITBS Form M	CTBS 4th Ed.	CAT 5th Ed.	SAT 9th Ed.	MAT 7th Ed.	Your Form
	10-5	• Evaluate polynomials.						
	10-6	• Add polynomials.						
	10-7	• Subtract polynomials.						
	10-8	• Multiply polynomials and monomials.						

Key: ITBS - Iowa Test of Basic Skills; CTBS - Comprehensive Test of Basic Skills; CAT - California Achievement Test; SAT - Stanford Achievement Test; MAT - Metropolitan Achievement Test

ASSESSMENT PROGRAM

Traditional Assessment

QUICK QUIZZES	SECTION REVIEW	CHAPTER REVIEW	CHAPTER ASSESSMENT FREE RESPONSE	CHAPTER ASSESSMENT MULTIPLE CHOICE	CUMULATIVE REVIEW
TE: pp. 512, 517, 522, 527, 536, 541, 547, 552	SE: pp. 530, 554 *Quiz 10A, 10B	SE: pp. 556–557	SE: p. 558 *Ch. 10 Tests Forms A, B, E	*Ch. 10 Tests Forms C, E	SE: p. 559 *Ch. 10 Test Form F

Alternate Assessment

INTERVIEW	JOURNAL	ONGOING	PERFORMANCE	PORTFOLIO	PROJECT	SELF
TE: p. 552	SE: pp. 512, 517, 522, 527, 536, 541, 547, 551 TE: pp. 506, 536, 541, 547	TE: pp. 508, 512, 513, 518, 523, 527, 532, 537, 542, 548, 553	SE: p. 558 TE: p. 522 *Ch. 10 Tests Forms D, E	TE: p. 536	SE: pp. 505, 527, 552 TE: p. 505	TE: p. 517

*Tests and quizzes are in *Assessment Sourcebook*. Test Form E is a mixed response test. Forms for Alternate Assessment are also available in *Assessment Sourcebook*.

TestWorks: Test and Practice Software

MIDDLE SCHOOL PACING CHART

 REGULAR PACING

Day	5 classes per week
1	Chapter 10 Opener; Problem Solving Focus
2	Section **10A** Opener; Lesson **10-1**
3	Lesson **10-2**
4	Lesson **10-3**
5	Lesson **10-4**
6	Technology
7	**10A** Connect; **10A** Review
8	Section **10B** Opener; Lesson **10-5**
9	Lesson **10-6**
10	Lesson **10-7**
11	Lesson **10-8**
12	**10B** Connect; **10B** Review; Extend Key Ideas
13	Chapter 10 Summary and Review
14	Chapter 10 Assessment, Cumulative Review, Chapters 1–10

► BLOCK SCHEDULING OPTIONS

Block Scheduling for Complete Course

Chapter 10 may be presented in

- eight 90-minute blocks
- eleven 75-minute blocks

Each block consists of a combination of

- Chapter and Section Openers
- Explores
- Lesson Development
- Problem Solving Focus
- Technology
- Extend Key Ideas
- Connect
- Review
- Assessment

For details, see *Block Scheduling Handbook*.

Block Scheduling for Lab-Based Course

In each block, 30–40 minutes is devoted to lab activities including

- Explores in the Student Edition
- Connect pages in the Student Edition
- Technology options in the Student Edition
- Reteaching Activities in the Teacher Edition

For details, see *Block Scheduling Handbook*.

Block Scheduling for Interdisciplinary Course

Each block integrates math with another subject area.

In Chapter 10, interdisciplinary topics include

- Motion
- Birds

Themes for Interdisciplinary Team Teaching 10A and 10B are

- Linear Functions
- Writing and Evaluating Polynomials

For details, see *Block Scheduling Handbook*.

Block Scheduling for Course with *Connected Mathematics*

In each block, investigations from **Connected Mathematics** replace or enhance the lessons in Chapter 10.

Connected Mathematics topics for Chapter 10 can be found in

- *Thinking with Mathematical Models*
- *Frogs, Fleas, and Painted Cubes*

For details, see *Block Scheduling Handbook*.

INTERDISCIPLINARY BULLETIN BOARD

Set Up

Put up examples of parabolas and parts of parabolas as shown. Also include some examples of real-life pictures illustrating parabolas.

Procedure

- Have students find other pictures of situations that illustrate parabolas and display these pictures on the bulletin board.

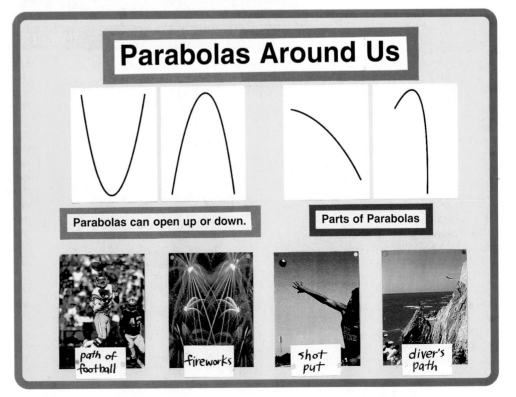

Parabolas Around Us

Parabolas can open up or down.

Parts of Parabolas

path of football

fireworks

shot put

diver's path

The information on these pages shows how functions and relationships are used in real-life situations.

World Wide Web

If your class has access to the World Wide Web, you might want to use the information found at the Web site addresses given.

Extensions

The following activities do not require access to the World Wide Web.

Entertainment

When using siteswap notation, the number of balls needed for a pattern is the average of the numbers in the siteswap. Have students research books or videos about juggling and siteswap notation.

Arts & Literature

Students might be interested in graphing the frequencies of the 12-step chromatic scale.

C	♮	261.63	G		392.00
C	#	277.18	G	#	415.31
D		293.67	A		440.16
D	#	311.11	A	#	466.16
E		329.63	B		493.88
F		349.23	C	♮	523.25
F	#	369.99			

= sharp
♮ = natural

Science

Have pairs of students research the link between Galileo's discovery of Jupiter's four largest moons and the Copernican view of the solar system.

People of the World

Have students research additional facts concerning numbers of stars, such as how many stars are visible to the naked eye. About 5000.

Social Studies

Given the following ratios of the width of a flag to its length, ask students which flag is longest for a given width. Canada

Cambodia:	≈ 1:1.7
Canada:	1:2
Egypt:	1:1.5
Switzerland:	1:1
United States:	1:1.9

Entertainment

Jugglers now use mathematics to describe *siteswaps*— how high a pin goes and in which hand it is caught.

Science

Jupiter's four largest moons— Callisto, Io, Europa, and Ganymede—were discovered by Galileo in the year 1609.

Arts & Literature

The graph of the frequencies of the 12-step chromatic scale forms an exponential curve. High C has double the frequency of middle C.

504

TEACHER TALK

Meet Dennis McElhaney

The Walker School
Marietta, Georgia

I like to begin teaching linear functions using real-world situations. Several weeks before we begin this chapter, I ask the students to find specific information about different kinds of businesses that charge for their services, especially those that charge a flat rate plus a per unit rate. An example of such a business is a parking garage that charges $2 for the first hour plus $0.50 for each additional hour. Other examples might include charges for telephone calls, costs of renting cars or other equipment, costs of appliance repairs, and so on. After students learn how to write linear equations, I have them express each charge using an equation. Then we compare the costs of the same or similar services offered by different companies.

and Relationships

Social Studies Link
www.mathsurf.com/8/ch10/social

People of the World

Astronomer Annie Jump Cannon (1863–1941) published a catalog listing more than 1000 stars according to their color spectra. It took ten volumes to contain the catalog.

Social Studies

The shape of the flag of the United States was determined in 1959 by executive order of President Dwight Eisenhower. Federal standards require that the ratio of its width to its length must be 1:1.9.

KEY MATH IDEAS

A **function** is a relationship that gives one output value for each input value.

The input is the **independent variable** and the output is the **dependent variable**.

The graph of a **linear function** is a line.

The graph of a **quadratic function** is nonlinear; it is a curve called a **parabola**.

An expression such as $2x^4 - 3x + 2$ is a **polynomial**.

Like terms have the same variable raised to the same exponent.

CHAPTER PROJECT

Problem Solving

Understand
Plan
Solve
Look Back

Find a situation you would like to model with an equation or function; for example, the height of a baseball over time as it leaves the bat, the thickness of a book given the number of pages, the value of a doll given its age. As you learn about the various models in this chapter, decide which is the best for your situation. Try to find a way to use the model for the situation you chose.

505

Chapter Project

Students use equations and functions to model a situation of their choice. After studying various models, they will choose the one most appropriate for their situation.

Resources
Chapter 10 Project Master

Introduce the Project
- Discuss different types of situations students could model with an equation.

- Review different situations with the students. Are the situations too complex to model or are they suitable?

Project Progress
Section A, page 527 Students sketch and label a graph for their chosen situations. They compare their sketches to the function models studied so far and rule out those that do not work at all.

Section B, page 552 Students decide on a model for their situations and explain how the chosen model fits or does not fit.

Community Project

A community project for Chapter 10 is available in *Home and Community Connections*.

Cooperative Learning

You may want to use Teaching Tool Transparency 1: Cooperative Learning Checklist with **Explore** and other group activities in this chapter.

PROJECT ASSESSMENT

You may choose to use this project as a performance assessment for the chapter.

Performance Assessment Key

Level 4 Full Accomplishment

Level 3 Substantial Accomplishment

Level 2 Partial Accomplishment

Level 1 Little Accomplishment

Suggested Scoring Rubric

4
- Collected data is accurate and complete.
- Chosen equation or function models the situation accurately.
- Description gives complete explanation.

3
- Collected data is adequate.
- Chosen equation or function adequately models the situation.
- Description gives good explanation.

2
- Collected data is incomplete.
- Chosen equation or model is not appropriate.
- Description is brief.

1
- Little data collected.
- Chosen equation or function is not related to situation.
- No description given.

Checking for a Reasonable Answer

The Point
Students examine solutions that are mathematically correct to see if the solutions are reasonable answers.

Resources
Teaching Tool Transparency 17: Problem-Solving Guidelines

 Interactive CD-ROM Journal

About the Page

Using the Problem Solving Process
Successful problem solving involves checking an answer to see if it makes sense for the situation in which it is presented. Discuss these steps for making sure an answer fits the situation:

- Check the answer in the context of the problem. Does it fit?

- If the answer does not fit the problem situation, can it be changed to fit?

- Is it necessary to round the answer or to omit a part of it?

- After you have refined the answer, check it in the context of the problem again.

- If the answer still does not fit, does the problem have a reasonable answer?

Ask …
- When would it be reasonable to refer to temperature as a negative number? When the temperature is below zero.

- What kind of number would not be reasonable when referring to the age of a person? Possible answers: A negative number; A very large number.

- What can an unreasonable answer tell you? Possible answers: It may indicate unreasonable numbers in a problem or a mistake in computation.

Journal

Ask students to think of and describe a real-life situation in which mathematics could be used to solve a problem. Have them describe a reasonable answer and an unreasonable answer.

Problem
Solving

Understand
Plan
Solve
Look Back

Checking for a Reasonable Answer

When you look back, it is important to check your answer to a problem to make sure that it is reasonable. Sometimes you may find that your answer is mathematically correct, but makes no sense in the real world.

Problem Solving Focus

Read each problem and its answer. Show why each is mathematically correct. Then explain whether the answer is reasonable or not.

1 Lois and Jack have the same birthday, but Jack is 15 years older than Lois. The sum of their ages is 9. How old is each one of them?
Answer: Jack is 12, Lois is −3

2 Tyra bought Jack a tie and Lois a bracelet. The bracelet was on sale, but was $39 more than Jack's tie. The bill totaled $25. How much was each gift?
Answer: Bracelet $32, tie −$7

3 There is a snowstorm on the day of their birthday party. When the guests arrive, the temperature is 12°F. By the time they leave, the storm causes a temperature drop of 18°F. What is the temperature then? **Answer: −6°F**

4 Jack makes hot soup for his guests. He empties 3 cans of soup concentrate into a pot, adds 3 cans of milk and warms the soup. He pours an 8 oz cup of soup for Lois, leaving 40 oz of soup in the pot. How much does a can hold? **Answer: 8 oz**

5 The entire party lasted two hours. If they spent 40 minutes making and eating soup, 20 minutes opening gifts, 45 minutes looking at pictures, and 25 minutes playing in the snow, how much time was left for eating cake?
Answer: −10 minutes

Answers for Problems
1. $12 - (-3) = 15$; $12 + (-3) = 9$; Not reasonable because age cannot be a negative number.

2. $(-7) + 32 = 25.00$; $32 - (-7) = 39$; Not reasonable because a price cannot be a negative number.

3. $12 - 18 = -6$; Reasonable because a temperature can be a negative number.

4. $8(3 + 3) - 8 = 40$; Reasonable

5. $120 - (40 + 20 + 45 + 25) = -10$; Not reasonable because time cannot be a negative number.

Additional Problem

Read the problem and answer the question. Show why it is mathematically correct. Then explain whether the answer is or is not reasonable.

Erin did yard work at two houses on Saturday to earn some extra money. She earned $16 at the second house. This gave her a total earnings of $12. How much did she earn at the first house?

Answer: −$4

The answer is mathematically correct because $12 − $16 = −$4. She earned −$4 at the first house. The answer is not reasonable because she would not earn a negative amount (or have to pay the owner) for work that she did.

Visit **www.teacher.mathsurf.com** for links to lesson plans from teachers and other professionals, NCTM information, and other sites.

LESSON PLANNING GUIDE

▶ Student Edition

LESSON	MATERIALS	VOCABULARY	DAILY	OTHER
Chapter 10 Opener				Teaching Tool Trans. 1 Ch. 10 Project Master Ch. 10 Community Project
Problem Solving Focus				Teaching Tool Trans. 17 *Interactive CD-ROM Journal*
10-1 Functions		function	10-1	Technology Master 50 *WW Math—Algebra*
10-2 Linear Functions	graphing utility	dependent variable, independent variable, linear function	10-2	Teaching Tool Trans. 23 Technology Master 51 *Spreadsheet/Grapher Tool* *WW Math—Algebra*
10-3 Quadratic Functions	graphing calculator	nonlinear function, quadratic function, parabola	10-3	Teaching Tool Trans. 23 Lesson Enhancement Trans. 55 Technology Master 52 *Interactive CD-ROM Lesson* *WW Math—Algebra*
10-4 Other Functions		exponential function, step function	10-4	Teaching Tool Trans. 2, 3, 23 Lesson Enhancement Trans. 56 Technology Master 53 Ch. 10 Project Master *Spreadsheet/Grapher Tool*
Technology	graphing calculator			Teaching Tool Trans. 23
Connect	graphing utility			Teaching Tool Trans. 23 Interdisc. Team Teaching 10A
Review				Prac. 10A; Quiz 10A; *TestWorks*

▶ Ancillaries

SKILLS TRACE

LESSON	SKILL	FIRST INTRODUCED			DEVELOP	PRACTICE/ APPLY	REVIEW
		GR.6	GR. 7	GR. 8			
10-1	Finding input and output values of functions.			✗ p. 508	pp. 508–510	pp. 511–512	pp. 530, 556, 559, 568
10-2	Representing linear functions with tables, graphs, and equations.			✗ p. 513	pp. 513–515	pp. 516–517	pp. 530, 556, 559, 573
10-3	Representing quadratic functions as graphs, tables, and equations.			✗ p. 518	pp. 518–520	pp. 521–522	pp. 530, 556, 559, 578
10-4	Finding outputs for and graphing exponential and step functions.			✗ p. 523	pp. 523–525	pp. 526–527	pp. 530, 556, 559, 583

CONNECTED MATHEMATICS

The unit *Thinking with Mathematical Models (Representing Relationship),* from the **Connected Mathematics** series, can be used with Section 10A.

Math and Science/Technology
(Worksheet pages 39–40: Teacher pages T39–T40)

Students use linear functions to understand how velocity, distance, and time relate to a pitched baseball.

Name _____   *Math and Science/Technology*

Quick Pitch

Use linear functions to learn about baseball pitches.

Hitting a baseball is one of the hardest skills to master in sports. It is not surprising when you realize that a batter has just a fraction of a second to swing at a small ball whizzing toward home plate at close to 100 miles per hour. In fact, it is so difficult to hit a baseball that the batting averages of even the best hitters in the game are usually not far above .333. So even baseball superstars get a hit only about one third of the times they officially come to bat.

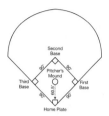

SPEED OF BASEBALL PITCHES			
Pitch	Average Speed		Time from Pitcher to Batter (sec)
	mph	feet per second	
Fastball	90	132	.46
Slider	85	125	.48
Curveball	75	110	.55
Change-up	65	95	.64
Knuckleball	65	95	.64

In addition to speed, pitchers use a few tricks to keep batters from getting hits. A pitcher who throws the ball at the same velocity and in the same spot all the time won't be successful. Even the worst hitters would adjust and begin to hit the ball hard and often. So pitchers change the speed and location of their pitches constantly, using the basic pitches listed in the table above. They also change the type of pitch they throw. Some of these pitches, like sliders, curves, and knuckleballs, don't move in a straight line but dip, swerve, and flutter.

Use the table and the diagram of the baseball diamond above to answer the questions that follow. Note: the distance from the pitcher's mound to home plate is 60 ft 6 in.

1. List two variables involved when a pitcher throws a baseball toward a hitter. Name one constant. (The variables and the constant are connected with the flight of the ball.)

The variables are the type of pitch, the velocity (speed) of the baseball, and the time the baseball takes to travel from the pitcher to the hitter. The constant is the distance from the pitcher's mound to home plate.

Name _____   *Math and Science/Technology*

2. Which of the variables identified in item 1 is the independent variable? Which is the dependent variable? Explain your answer.
See below.

3. a. What is the relationship between the speed of a pitch and the time it takes a ball to travel from pitcher to batter?
They are inversely proportional.

   b. Construct a function that expresses the relationship of velocity and distance to time in the pitching of a baseball.
   $t = \frac{d}{r}$, where t (time)
   $= \dfrac{\text{distance } d \text{ (the constant, 60' 6")}}{r \text{ (velocity or rate of speed)}}$

   c. Use the function you constructed above to find t and fill in the table on page 39.
   See below for math used to find these answers.

4. Why would changing the speed of consecutive pitches decrease the ability of a batter to hit the baseball?
See below.

5. a. An ordinary person might pitch a ball at 40 miles per hour—a pitch speed that would be very easy to hit. How long would it take a ball to get from the pitcher's mound to home plate at that speed?
1.03 seconds

   b. How much less time does it take for a fastball pitch to reach the batter than a knuckleball?
   .18 sec
   .64 − .46 = .18

   c. What is the percent of increase in time?
   $\frac{.18}{.46} \times 100 = 39\%$

6. How would you redesign the baseball diamond to help increase the batter's average?
See below.

7. The trajectory of a pitched baseball (its exact path including the way it curves) also affects the hitter's ability to hit it. What variables under the control of a pitcher would help to determine the trajectory of the baseball? Do some research to find out how the pitcher alters these variables.
Variables include the way the pitcher grips the ball, how and when the pitcher releases the ball, and the force with which the pitcher throws the ball. Accept all research, but have students list sources.

Answers

2. The velocity at which the pitcher throws the ball is the independent variable. The time the ball takes to go from the pitcher's mound to home plate is the dependent variable because it is dependent upon the velocity at which the pitcher throws the ball.

3. c. For the fastball, which travels at 90 miles/hour:
   Use the formula $t = t/r$ or $t = 60.5$ ft (pitcher's mound to home plate) 90 mi/hr (velocity of baseball)
   First, convert the velocity in mi/hr to ft/sec
   To find the number of feet in 90 miles:
   90 miles × 5,280 ft/mi = 475,200 ft
   To find the number of seconds in 1 hour:
   60 min × 60 sec/min = 3,600 sec
   Divide the distance by the time to get velocity in ft/sec 475,200 ft/3,600 sec = 132 ft/sec

Then apply the formula:
$t = d/r = 60.5$ ft/132 ft/sec = .46 sec
(Use the same procedure for the other items as well.)

4. It would decrease the ability of the batter to adjust to the speed of the ball. For example, a batter who sees two fastballs come at him at 95 miles per hour adjusts to that speed. If the next pitch is a change-up coming at him at just 60 miles per hour, his reactions are geared to a faster pitch and he is likely to swing too soon and miss the ball.

6. Accept any reasonable answer. The most obvious change would be to increase the distance between the pitcher's mound and home plate. This would increase the amount of time the batter has to observe a pitch and most likely would help him to hit better.

BIBLIOGRAPHY

▷ FOR TEACHERS

Burton, Robert. *Birdflight: An Illustrated Study of Birds' Aerial Mastery.* New York, NY: Facts on File, 1990.

Phillips, Elizabeth. *Patterns and Functions.* Addenda Series, Grades 5–8. Reston, VA: NCTM, 1991.

Short, Lester L. *The Lives of Birds: Birds of the World and Their Behavior.* New York, NY: Henry Holt and Company, Inc., 1993.

▷ FOR STUDENTS

Applied Mathematics, Unit 24: Patterns and Functions and *Unit 25: Quadratics.* Waco, TX: Center for Occupational Research and Development, 1991.

Gardner, Robert. *Experiments with Motion.* Getting Started in Science. Springfield, NJ: Enslow Publishers, Inc., 1995.

Sauvain, Philip. *Motion.* New York, NY: Macmillan Publishing Company, 1992.

A World in Motion

Motion, the act or process of changing position, surrounds us in our daily lives. Earth rotates on its axis and around the sun. When we fly kites, the wind, which is air in motion, makes our kites soar into the sky or fall to the ground. Periodic motion can be seen in the pendulum of a grandfather clock as it swings and repeats its movement regularly and exactly. We observe and experience motion in our own movements as well as in those of others, such as in a handshake, the blink of an eyelid, a walk around the block.

The graceful movements of a dancer, a football quarterback running for a touchdown, a child running in the park—each is an example of motion. Imagine a bird flying to its nest, a dog running to greet its owner, a cat licking its paws. Motion occurs each time we move or observe movement.

1 How do you think motion is affected by gravity?

2 What do you think is meant by slow motion? Motion picture? Range of motion?

3 When you are sitting still in class, is motion occurring? Explain.

507

Where are we now?

In Chapter 4, students explored linear equations.

They learned how to

- use tables and equations to represent two-variable relationships.

- examine relationships in graphs.

- analyze linear equations of the form $y = mx + b$.

Where are we going?

In Section 10A, students will

- identify functions and find the input and output values of a function.

- represent functions using tables, graphs, and equations.

- represent quadratic functions as graphs, tables, and equations.

- graph and evaluate other types of functions.

Theme: Motion

World Wide Web

If your class has access to the World Wide Web, you might want to use the information found at the Web site address given. The interdisciplinary links relate to topics discussed in this section.

About the Page

This page introduces the theme of the section, motion, and discusses motion in everyday life.

Ask …

- What kinds of units might you use when solving motion problems that involve distance? Possible answers: inches, feet, meters, miles, kilometers.

Extension

The following activities do not require access to the World Wide Web.

Science
Have interested students research Sir Isaac Newton's law of motion and prepare a report.

Geography
Suggest that students select a place they would like to visit and compare two ways in which they might travel there.

Answers for Questions

1. Possible answer: Gravity slows motion and pulls objects toward the earth.

2. Possible answers: Slow motion is motion slower than normal speed; Motion picture is a series of visual images projected at a rate to simulate movement; Range of motion defines the limits to which something may move.

3. Yes; Your heart is pumping blood, your nerves are transmitting impulses, micro-organisms are moving, and Earth is rotating on its axis.

Connect

On page 529, students will use functions to model the flight (height over time) of a pelican.

Objective

- Recognize a function and find input and output values of a function.

Vocabulary

- Function

NCTM Standards

- 1, 2, 4, 8, 9, 12

 Review

Evaluate each expression for $n = 2, 5,$ and 10.

1. $3n + 1$ 7, 16, 31

2. $5n - 8$ 2, 17, 42

3. $n^2 + 3$ 7, 28, 103

4. $\frac{20}{n} - 2$ 8, 2, 0

Available on Daily Transparency 10-1

▶ **Lesson Link**

Have students discuss when they have encountered dependent relationships in everyday life. Examples might include: A person's pay may depend on the number of hours he or she works.

1 Introduce

Explore

The Point
Students apply their own rules, or expressions, to a given input value and determine the related output. They also try to deduce another student's rules.

Ongoing Assessment
In Step 2, check that students have correctly evaluated their rules.

For Groups That Finish Early
Change the initial input to 3 and the initial output to 5. Repeat Steps 1 and 2.

Follow Up
Discuss students' answers to the question posed in Step 4. Help students conclude that some rules give exactly one output for each input. Ask them for an example of a rule that will give more than one output for a given input.

508   Chapter 10

10-1   Functions

You'll Learn ...

■ to recognize a function and to find the input and output values of a function

... How It's Used

Computer graphics artists use functions to add effects such as shading to their artwork.

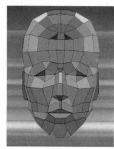

Vocabulary

function

▶ **Lesson Link**   In previous lessons, you looked at many different relationships between numbers. In this lesson, you will look at one of these relationships in which one number depends on another number. ◀

If you put whole carrots into a food processor and use the "slice" blade, you know that the result will always be sliced carrots. The result depends on the vegetable you put in and the type of blade used.

A machine that performs a duty can be used to represent relationships in mathematics. We *input* a value, apply a *rule*, and get an *output* value.

Explore   Functions

What's My Rule?

1. Here is a "rule" machine. Find as many rules as possible that will give you the output value for the given input value.

2. When the input is 4, what output does each rule give?

3. Compare your output values for an input value of 4 to another person's output values. Try to guess the rules the other person used.

4. If you used the same rule, is it possible to get two different output values if you both use 6 as the input value?

Learn   Functions

When each input value for a rule results in exactly one output value, this special relationship is called a *function*. A **function** is a relationship in which an output value depends on an input value, and gives only one output for each input. Two different input values can have the same output value, but two different output values cannot have the same input value.

508   *Chapter 10 • Algebra: Functions and Relationships*

Resources

10-1 Practice
10-1 Reteaching
10-1 Problem Solving
10-1 Enrichment
10-1 Daily Transparency
    Problem of the Day
    Review
    Quick Quiz
Technology Master 50

 Wide World of Mathematics
Algebra: Rube Goldberg Machines

Learning Modalities

Logical   For Exercise 10 on page 511, it may be helpful for students to note that as the input increases by 1, the output increases by 2. This would suggest that there is multiplication by 2 as part of the function rule. A similar situation occurs in Exercise 11 on page 511.

Kinesthetic   Graphing calculators may be used as a function machine. For Exercise 15 on page 512, students can enter the rule into the calculator and have the calculator determine the answers to Part a.

Inclusion

Some students may have difficulty seeing patterns because they do not transfer information to new situations readily. Give these students extra practice in recognizing and extending patterns. Only if they can do this without too much difficulty should they be asked to generalize.

Example 1

Ashley's salary as a dance instructor depends on the number of hours she works. If she is paid $7 an hour, what is her salary for 8 hours? 15 hours? 25 hours? If her salary was $133, how many hours did she work? Is her salary a function of the hours she works?

Input	Rule: Multiply by 7	Output
8	8×7	56
15	15×7	105
25	25×7	175

For 8 hours, her salary is $56. For 15 hours, her salary is $105. For 25 hours, her salary is $175.

To reverse multiplying by 7, you can divide by 7: $133 \div 7 = 19$. She worked 19 hours for $133.

Yes, her salary is a function of her hours worked. For each number of hours (input), there is only one value for her salary (output).

Try It

Denika is Ashley's assistant. She earns $5.50 an hour. How much does she make for 20 hours? Is her salary a function of her hours worked? If she earned $55.00, how many hours did she work? **$110; Yes; 10 hours**

Example 2

Is the cost a function of the number of items? Explain.

Input (items)	4	9	1	8	4
Output (cost)	$2.00	$4.00	$0.50	$4.00	$3.00

4 items may cost $2, or 4 items may cost $3 (for the input 4, there is more than one output). So cost is not a function of the number of items.

Try It

Is the price a function of the number of Buddy Biscuits? Explain.

Buy 4, and the 5th one is free!

Biscuits	1	2	3	4	5
Price	$0.75	$1.50	$2.25	$3.00	$3.00

Yes; For any given number of Buddy Biscuits there is only one price

10-1 • Functions **509**

MENTAL MATH

Only SIDO rules out a function (Same Input, Different Output). These situations are okay for functions: Same input, same output; Different input, same output.

MATH EVERY DAY

▶ Problem of the Day

Mr. Tao made a scale model of his home and gave it to his granddaughter for her birthday. The dimensions of the model are $\frac{1}{20}$ of the actual size. The dimensions of the actual living room are 12 feet by 15 feet. How many square yards of carpet will be needed for the living room in the model? $\frac{1}{20}$ yd²; Area of actual living room = 180 ft² = 20 yd²

Available on Daily Transparency 10-1

An Extension is provided in the transparency package.

Fact of the Day

Everything is in motion. Even when you are sitting apparently motionless, you are moving because Earth is rotating on its axis and revolving about the sun.

Estimation

Using the function rule "49% of x," estimate the output for the given input.

1. 80 40

2. 150 75

3. 1000 500

Answers for Explore

1. Possible answers: Leave input unchanged; Give output as 4; Subtract 2 and square.

2. Possible answers: 4, 4, 4

3. Answers may vary.

4. No

2 Teach

Learn

Point out that the relationship described by the rule "match a number to its square" is a function since each input gives only one output, even though 2 and –2 as inputs both give 4 for an output. But the relationship described by the rule "match a number to its square root" is not a function, since 4 as an input has both 2 and –2 as outputs.

Alternate Examples

1. The distance that Matt jogs depends on the number of minutes that he spends jogging. If he jogs at a constant rate of 0.15 mile per minute, what distance does Matt jog in 15 minutes? 30 minutes? 60 minutes? If he jogged 6 miles, how many minutes did he jog? Is the distance he jogs a function of the number of minutes he jogs?

Input	Rule: Multiply by 0.15	Output
15	15×0.15	2.25
30	30×0.15	4.5
60	60×0.15	9

For 15 minutes, he jogs 2.25 miles. For 30 minutes, he jogs 4.5 miles. For 60 minutes, he jogs 9 miles. Yes, the distance he jogs is a function of the number of minutes he jogs. For each number of minutes jogged (input), there is only one value of distance traveled (output).

2. Is the test score a function of the number of minutes spent studying? Explain.

Input (minutes)	10	20	10	40	30
Output (score)	75	80	83	75	88

Scores of 75 and 83 were obtained by studying for 10 minutes. So, test scores are not a function of minutes spent studying.

Alternate Examples

3. The number of minutes Robbi rides her bike is related to the number of miles she travels. Examine the table below. Is the relationship a function? If so, what is the rule? Explain.

Time Spent Riding (min) Input	Distance Traveled (mi) Output
15	3
25	5
40	8
50	10

There is only one output value for each input value, so the relationship is a function. The rule is "Divide the input value by 5 to get the output value."

3 Practice and Assess

Check

For Question 2, calculators in general must work exclusively with functions. How can the calculator give an answer if an input value must be matched with more than one output value? As an example, suggest the graph of $x = y^2$ and note that we graph two separate equations, $y = \sqrt{x}$ and $y = -\sqrt{x}$, both of which are functions.

Answers for Check Your Understanding

1. There can be only one output value for each input value. Examples may vary.

2. Yes; There is only one output value for each input value.

3. There is only one way to round any given number to the nearest 10, but the same number could also be rounded to the nearest 100, the nearest 1, the nearest tenth, and so on.

Example 3

Country western line dancing had a rise in popularity in 1996. The number of dancers in each row is related to the length of the dance floor. Examine the table below. Is the relationship a function? If so, what's the rule? Explain.

Floor Length (ft) Input	Dancers per Row Output
12	4
15	5
24	8
39	13

If you divide each input value by 3, you get the output value.

$12 \div 3 = 4$
$15 \div 3 = 5$
$24 \div 3 = 8$
$39 \div 3 = 13$

There is only one output value for each input value, so the relationship is a function. The rule is "Divide the input value by 3 to get the output value."

Try It

Is the relationship a function? If so, what is the rule? Explain your answer.

a.

Input	2	5	0	6	4
Output	4	25	0	36	16

Yes; Input n yields output n^2

b.

Input	1	2	3	2	1
Output	10	20	30	40	50

No; There are two output values for 1 and two output values for 2

Check Your Understanding

1. What is special about a function? Give an example of a relationship that *is* a function. Give an example of a relationship that *is not* a function.

2. The $\boxed{x^2}$ key on a calculator squares the number that you input. Is this a function? Explain.

3. Why is the rule "Round a number to the nearest 10" a function, but the rule "Round a number" is not?

MEETING MIDDLE SCHOOL CLASSROOM NEEDS

Consumer Connection

Have students find an example of a function relationship in an advertisement and explain why it is a function. For example, "25% off everything" is a function, because for every input (an original price) there is only one output (the sale price). Similarly, 3 cans for $1.99 is a function.

Cooperative Learning

Have students work in small groups to research two or three functions in an area that interests them, such as music, sports, or TV.

Team Teaching

Functions are very important in the applications of mathematics to other disciplines, especially the physical and social sciences. Ask other teachers on your team to point out relevant functions used in their disciplines. Suggest that they give students several inputs for each function, and ask students to supply appropriate outputs.

10-1 Exercises and Applications

Practice and Apply

1. **Getting Started** Answer each question for the given function machine.

   a. What number is the input value? **4**

   b. What number is the output value? **8**

   c. What is the rule? **Multiply by 3 and subtract 4**

   d. If you input 6, what is the output? **14**

4	Multiply by 3 and subtract 4	8

For the function machine shown, find the output value for each input value.

2. Input of 4 **17.75**

3. Input of −1 **−2.25**

4. Input of 10 **41.75**

5. Input of 0 **1.75**

Input	Multiply by 4 and add 1.75	Output

For the function machine shown, find the input value for each output value.

6. Output of 1 **4**

7. Output of 4 **16**

8. Output of 9 **36**

9. Output of −4 **−16**

Input	Divide by 4	Output

What is a possible rule for the input and output shown in each table?

10.

Input	Output
−1	−2
0	0
1	2
2	4

Multiply by 2

11.

Input	Output
5	9
7	13
9	17
11	21

Multiply by 2 and subtract 1

12.

Input	Output
7	0
6	0
5	0
4	0

Multiply by 0

13. **Test Prep** Which situation does **not** describe a function? **C**

   Ⓐ Distance traveled given the rate of speed.

   Ⓑ Distance traveled given the time it takes.

   Ⓒ Distance traveled given the age of the commander.

   Ⓓ They are all functions.

14. **Geometry** Is the area of a circle a function of its diameter? **Yes**

10-1 • Functions **511**

PRACTICE 10-1

Assignment Guide

■ **Basic**
1–13, 15, 17, 18, 21–25

■ **Average**
1–9 odds, 10–25

■ **Enriched**
1, 2–8 evens, 10–25

Exercise Notes

■ **Exercises 6–9**

Error Prevention Students may need to be reminded to read the question carefully. The output is given, not the input.

■ **Exercise 13**

Test Prep Point out that choices A and B refer to $d = rt$ and describe functions, but choice C does not involve a factor that affects distance.

■ **Exercise 14**

Error Prevention For students answering no, point out that while the area of a circle is πr^2, r is $\frac{d}{2}$, so that each value of d will give only one area for the circle.

Reteaching

Activity

Materials: 100 counters

• Work in groups of three.

• One student should be the function machine, another student should be the inputter, and the third student should be the recorder.

• The function machine thinks of a rule. The inputter selects a number of counters and gives them to the function machine. The function machine outputs the correct number of counters. Inputting and outputting continues for at least four trials.

• The recorder makes a table of inputs and outputs, and tries to guess the rule.

• After the rule is guessed or the recorder gives up, rotate positions so that each person in your group has at least one turn in each role.

PRACTICE

Name _____

Practice 10-1

Functions

For the function machine shown, find the output value for each input value.

1. Input of 20 **1**

2. Input of 5 **−2**

3. Input of −35 **−10**

4. Input of 13 **−0.4**

Input →	Divide by 5 and subtract 3	→ Output

For the function machine shown, find the input value for each output value.

5. Output of 6 **−1**

6. Output of 12 **5**

7. Output of −28 **−35**

8. Output of −13 **−20**

Input →	Add 7	→ Output

What is a possible rule for the input and output shown in each table?

9.

Input	1	3	5	9
Output	16	18	20	24

Add 15.

10.

Input	−1	0	1	2
Output	−5	−2	1	4

Multiply by 3 and subtract 2.

11.

Input	−8	−3	2	7
Output	7	7	7	7

Output is always 7.

12.

Input	64	4	−4	−8
Output	16	1	−1	−2

Divide by 4.

13. At Roy's Donut Shop, if you buy 1 to 4 donuts, you pay $0.50 per donut. If you buy 5 to 8 donuts, the price is $0.40 each. Roy limits each customer to 8 donuts.

   a. Complete the table by finding the *total* purchase price for each number of donuts.

Number of donuts	0	1	2	3	4	5	6	7	8
Total price ($)	0.00	0.50	1.00	1.50	2.00	2.00	2.40	2.80	3.20

   b. Is the price a function of the number of donuts? Explain. **Yes. For each number of donuts, there is only one price.**

   c. Is the number of donuts a function of the price? Explain. **No. For the input $2.00, there are two possible outputs (4 or 5 donuts).**

RETEACHING

Name _____

Alternative Lesson 10-1

Functions

A **function** is a relationship in which an output value depends on an input value, and it gives only one output for each input. Two different output values cannot have the same input value.

Example 1

Cecelia earns $3.50 per day walking her neighbor's dog. Is the amount she earns a function of the number of days she walks the dog? If so, what is the rule?

Input (days)	1	2	3	5	6	8
Output (earnings)	$3.50	$7.00	$10.50	$17.50	$21.00	$28.00

Yes, the amount earned is a function of the number of days worked. For each day (the input), there is only one value for the amount earned (the output). The rule is *Multiply by $3.50*.

Try It

a. The Student Council operates a school-supply store. Each pencil costs $0.25. Is the cost for pencils a function of the number of items? If so, what is the rule?

Input (pencils)	1	2	3	4	5
Output (cost)	$0.25	$0.50	$0.75	$1.00	$1.25

Yes. The rule is *Multiply by $0.25*.

Example 2

Is the relationship a function? If so, what is the rule?

Input	1	2	3	4	2
Output	2	4	4	8	5

The relationship is not a function. For the input value 2, there is more than one output.

Try It Is each relationship a function? If so, what is the rule?

b.

Input	1	2	3	4	5	4	10
Output	3	6	9	9	12	8	30

No. For the input value 4, there is more than one output.

c.

Input	2	4	6	8	10	20	50
Output	1	2	3	4	5	10	25

Yes. The rule is *Divide by 2*.

■ Exercise 17

If a flare was launched at an angle instead of straight up, the same relationship between height above the ground with respect to time would occur. However, the path of the flare would look different because the flare would be traveling horizontally as well as vertically.

Exercise Answers

15. a. Calories burned = minutes × 13.5; 202.5; 270; 405; 607.5
    b. About 22 min.
    c. Yes; Yes; Each input value yields only one output.

17. Yes; For any given time there is only one height.

18. Not necessarily. The squaring function gives the same output for any number and its opposite.

19. Take the absolute value.

20. Square, then subtract one.

25. Possible answer

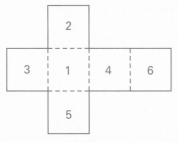

Alternate Assessment

Ongoing Exercise 15 summarizes the content of this lesson. Check that all students have successfully completed Exercise 15.

► Quick Quiz

Use the rule "multiply by 4 and subtract 3."

1. If the input is 3, what is the output? 9

2. If the output is 25, what was the input? 7

3. Does the rule describe a function? Yes

4. Write the function rule for the following inputs and outputs:

Input	3	5	6	9
Output	7	11	13	19

Multiply by 2 and add 1

Available on Daily Transparency 10–1

---

15. An average person skiing cross country at 6 mi/hr burns about 13.5 calories per min.

   a. Write a rule for how many calories would be burned by skiing 6 mi/hr. Use the rule to find the number of calories burned in 15 min; 20 min; 30 min; 45 min.

   b. To burn 300 calories, approximately how long must Donna ski?

   c. Does the number of calories burned depend on the number of minutes spent skiing? Does the relationship describe a function? Explain.

16. **Chemistry** There are three different forms, or *isotopes*, in which hydrogen atoms occur. Is the number of neutrons a function of the number of protons? **No**

	Protons	Neutrons
Hydrogen-1 (protium)	1	0
Hydrogen-2 (deuterium)	1	1
Hydrogen-3 (tritium)	1	2

Problem Solving and Reasoning

17. **Communicate** A flare is launched straight up from the ground. The table shows the relationship of the height above the ground with respect to time. Is the relationship a function? Explain.

Time (sec)	0	1	2	3	4	5
Height (m)	0	20	30	30	20	0

18. **Journal** If you are given the output of a function, would there be only one input?

Critical Thinking Guess my rule.

19.

If You Say ...	−2	−1	1	2
I Say ...	2	1	1	2

20. **GPS**

If You Say ...	3	5	6	10
I Say ...	8	24	35	99

Mixed Review

Find the percent decrease for each. *[Lesson 6-5]*

21. From 100 to 77   23%
22. From 1000 to 977   2.3%
23. From 0.3 to 0.21   30%
24. From 1000 to 10   99%

25. Draw a net for the number cube shown. (Note that numbers on opposite faces add up to 7.) *[Lesson 8-7]*

PROBLEM SOLVING

Name _____

Guided Problem Solving 10-1

GPS PROBLEM 20, STUDENT PAGE 512

Guess my rule.

If you say...	3	5	6	10
I say...	8	24	35	99

— Understand —

1. What are the input values? 3, 5, 6, 10

2. What are the output values? 8, 24, 35, 99

3. Is the relationship a function? Yes.

— Plan —

4. Can one of the following operations and a constant (the same number) be applied to each input value in the table to get each output value?

   a. Addition? No.   b. Subtraction? No.   c. Multiplication? No.

   d. Division? No.   e. Exponents (x^2, x^3...)? No.

5. Which operation and constant when applied to the input value results in a number that is closest to the output value? x^2

6. What do you need to do to your answer to Item 5 to obtain the output value? b

   a. Add 1.   b. Subtract 1.   c. Add 2.

— Solve —

7. What is the rule? Square the input value, then subtract 1.

— Look Back —

8. How can you tell that you will need to multiply or use an exponent in the function? Output value increases by a greater factor than the input value.

SOLVE ANOTHER PROBLEM

Guess my rule.

If you say...	2	3	4	8
I say...	6	11	18	66

Square the input value, then add 2.

ENRICHMENT

Name _____

Extend Your Thinking 10-1

Patterns in Algebra

Some engineers use the *Rankine* temperature scale in their work. To change a temperature from degrees Fahrenheit to degrees Rankine, you can use the formula $R = 459.67 + F$.

Scientists often use the Celsius temperature scale in their work. To change Celsius temperatures to Rankine temperatures, first change Celsius temperatures to Fahrenheit using the formula $F = \frac{9}{5}C + 32$. Then use the formula above to change to degrees Rankine.

Example: Suppose you want to change 20°C to Rankine.

   Step 1: Write as °F.   → $F = \frac{9}{5} \cdot 20 + 32$ → $F = 68°$

   Step 2: Write as °R.   → $R = 459.67 + 68$ → $R = 527.67°$

1. Complete the table.

°Celsius	°Fahrenheit	°Rankine
5	41	500.67
10	50	509.67
15	59	518.67
20	68	527.67
25	77	536.67
30	86	545.67
35	95	554.67

2. Describe the pattern that occurs as each Celsius temperature increases by 5°. Fahrenheit and Rankine temperatures increase by 9°.

3. How can you combine the two formulas to create a single formula? Substitute $\frac{9}{5}C + 32$ into the formula $R = 459.67 + F$ for F.

   So, $R = 459.67 + \frac{9}{5}C + 32$.

4. Look at the formula you created in Item 3. Predict what will happen to the Celsius and Rankine temperatures as the Fahrenheit temperatures increase by 1°. How can you verify your prediction? Fahrenheit and Rankine temperatures increase by $\frac{9°}{5}$.

   Verify by comparing temperatures only 1° apart.

Linear Functions

▶ **Lesson Link**   You have learned about special relationships called functions. In this lesson, you will represent functions in different ways. ◀

Explore | Linear Functions

Is It Possible?

Materials: Graphing utility

1. Using a graphing utility, press Y= and enter the equation Y=1.5X−1. Press GRAPH to graph the equation. Use one of the ZOOM key options to get an integer window.

2. Press TRACE. What point is shown?

3. Move along the line by pressing the left and right arrow keys. What happens to the value of *x*? Is it possible to find two points on the graph with the same *x*-coordinate but with different *y*-coordinates?

4. Graph another linear equation. Use the trace feature again. Can you find two different *y* values for the same *x*-coordinate on this graph?

Learn | Linear Functions

You have used function machines to enter an input, perform a function, and receive an output. The value of the output depended on the value of the input.

| Input *x* | Add 4 | Output *y* |

If we let *x* represent the input and *y* the output, this relationship can be represented by the function rule $x + 4 = y$ or $y = x + 4$. The output (y) depends on the input (x).

When the value of *y* depends on the value of *x*, *y* is a function of *x* and is called the **dependent variable**; *x* is called the **independent variable**.

In graphing, we use the horizontal axis (*x*-axis) for the independent variable and the vertical axis (*y*-axis) for the dependent variable.

y depends on x

You'll Learn ...

■ to represent functions using tables, graphs, and equations

... How It's Used

A printer uses linear functions to determine costs of large print jobs.

Vocabulary

dependent variable
independent variable
linear function

10-2 • *Linear Functions*   **513**

MEETING INDIVIDUAL NEEDS

Resources

10-2 Practice
10-2 Reteaching
10-2 Problem Solving
10-2 Enrichment
10-2 Daily Transparency
　　　Problem of
　　　the Day
　　　Review
　　　Quick Quiz
Teaching Tool Trans. 23
Technology Master 51

 Interactive CD-ROM Spreadsheet/ Grapher Tool

 Wide World of Mathematics Algebra: Endangered Species

Learning Modalities

Verbal   Have students write a short story in which the application of a function plays a part.

Musical   For Exercise 17 on page 517, students could consider an instrument that they play. Some instruments apply a function relationship, such as the recorder or flute, in which the tone produced is a function of how many holes are covered, or a violin, whose tone is a function of the length of the string.

Visual   Point out to students that the graph of a linear function is the same as the graph of its related linear equation.

Challenge

Describe the graph in Exercise 10 on page 516. Now suppose that any fraction of a minute is rounded up. Describe the graph of the new situation. Does the graph show a function? Line; step graph; yes.

10-2
Lesson Organizer

Objective

■ **Represent functions using tables, graphs, and equations.**

Vocabulary

■ **Dependent variable, independent variable, linear function**

Materials

■ **Explore: Graphing utility**

NCTM Standards

■ **1–4, 8, 9, 12, 13**

▶ **Review**

Find three values for *x* and *y* that satisfy each equation.

1. $y = 3x - 1$ Possible answers: (1, 2), (2, 5), (3, 8)

2. $y = 4x - 5$ Possible answers: (1, −1), (2, 3), (3, 7)

3. $2x - y = 6$ Possible answers: (5, 4), (4, 2), (3, 0)

Available on Daily Transparency 10-2

---

1 Introduce

Explore

You may wish to use Teaching Tool Transparency 23: Graphing Calculator or *Interactive CD-ROM Spreadsheet/Grapher Tool* with **Explore.**

The Point

Students use a graphing utility to graph lines and note that one value for *x* gives exactly one value for *y*.

Ongoing Assessment

Check students' results after Step 3. The second part of the question highlights the point of **Explore.**

For Groups That Finish Early

Repeat Step 4 two or three more times. Is the answer always the same?   Yes

---

Lesson 10-2   **513**

514

Follow Up

Ask the class to formulate a general statement about an equation that is a function. Possible answer: For an equation that represents a function, you cannot find two different y values for a given value of x.

Answers for Explore

1. Check students' graphs.

2. Answers may vary.

3. Increases and decreases; No

4. No

2 Teach

Learn

For a function, every value we assign to the independent variable determines one and only one value for the dependent variable. In terms of the graph of the function, this means that any vertical line intersects the graph at exactly one point.

Alternate Examples

1. Graph the equation $y = 2x + 1$. Does it describe a function? Is it a linear function?

   Make a table of input and output values.

Input	Function Rule	Output
x	$2x + 1$	y
-1	$2(-1) + 1$	-1
0	$2(0) + 1$	1
1	$2(1) + 1$	3

   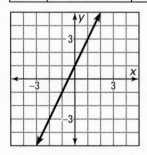

   The equation is a function, because each input (x) value has a single output (y) value. It is a linear function because the graph is a line.

2. The band is selling boxes of dried fruit for $2.50 each to raise money for a trip.

   a. Write and graph the rule that relates the money collected to the number of boxes of dried fruit sold. If after 1 day, they had collected $30, how many boxes of fruit were sold?

   Example 2 is continued on page 515.

The equation $y = 3x + 2$ is a statement that the expressions y and $3x + 2$ are equal. The function $y = 3x + 2$ means the value of y is given by the rule $3x + 2$.

Examples

1 Graph the equation $y = 3x + 2$. Does it describe a function? Is it linear?

Make a table of input and output values.

Input	Function Rule	Output
x	$3x + 2$	y
-1	$3(-1) + 2$	-1
0	$3(0) + 2$	2
1	$3(1) + 2$	5

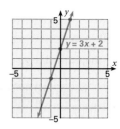

The equation is a function, because each input (x) value has a single output (y) value. It is a **linear function** because the graph is a line.

2 The swim team is sponsoring a swim-a-thon to raise money. Paula's pledges totaled $3 for each lap completed.

a. Write and graph the rule that relates the money pledged to the number of laps completed. If after fifteen minutes, Paula had raised $27, how many laps did she complete?

Let $y =$ the money pledged and $x =$ number of laps completed; the rule is then $y = 3x$.

Locate the output, or dependent value, 27 on the y-axis. Find the approximate corresponding x value: $x = 9$ laps.

b. Does the rule describe a function? Explain.

The rule describes a function because for each input value there is only one output value.

Try It

a. Graph $y = -2x$. Does it describe a linear function? Explain.

b. The Spanish club is selling T-shirts as a fund-raiser. The T-shirts sell for $4 each. Write and graph the rule that relates the money earned to the number of T-shirts sold. If after one day James had collected $36, how many T-shirts did he sell? Does the rule describe a function? Explain.

MATH EVERY DAY

▶ **Problem of the Day**

Yoshina gave the taxicab driver $8.75, which included a $1 tip. The cost of a taxicab ride was $3 for the first mile and $0.25 for each additional tenth of a mile. How far did Yoshina ride? 2.9 miles ($8.75 − $1.00 = $7.75; x is one-tenth of a mile; 7.75 = 3 + 0.25x, x = 19; distance = 2.9)

Available on Daily Transparency 10-2

An Extension is provided in the transparency package.

Fact of the Day

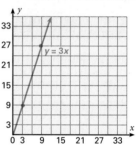

Newton's first law of motion states that an object moving in a straight line will continue to do so unless acted on by an outside force.

Mental Math

For the function $y = 100x + 6$, mentally calculate the output for the given input.

1. 3 306

2. 4.7 476

3. 2.89 295

In the weightless conditions aboard a space station, the height of a pushed pencil can be modeled by a linear function of the time since it was released. A pencil pushed downward from a height of 120 cm drops 2.5 cm per second. Make a set of output values for the function $y = -2.5x + 120$.

Tanisha thinks ...

I can find output values by using the tables in a calculator. If I enter $-2.5x$ ⊞ 120 as the function Y_1 and look at the table formed, I can find the output values.

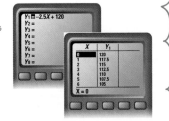

The output values are 120, 117.5, 115, 112.5, and so on.

Daniel thinks ...

I noticed that 120 is the y-intercept. I can just subtract 2.5 for each increase of 1 in the x values.

x	0	1	2	3	4	5
y	120	117.5	115	112.5	110	107.5

−2.5 −2.5 −2.5 −2.5 −2.5

What do think?

What method would you use if you wanted to know how long it would take for the pencil to hit the floor? Why?

Check | Your Understanding

1. How can you use the graph of a function to find the input value for a given output value?

2. How can you tell from a table if a relationship is a function?
   If it shows only one y value for each x value.

3. Is the graph $y = \frac{1}{2}x - 5$ the graph of a linear function? Explain.
   Yes; The graph will be a nonvertical straight line.

10-2 • Linear Functions **515**

Alternate Examples

2. (continued)

Let y = amount of money collected and x = number of boxes sold; the rule is then $y = 2.50x$. Locate the output or dependent value 30 on the y-axis. Find the corresponding x value: 12 boxes.

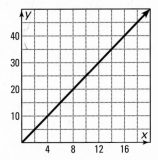

b. Does the rule describe a function? Explain.

The rule describes a function because for each input value there is only one output value.

Answers for Try It

a. Yes; The graph is a straight line.

b. Money earned = $4 × number of shirts sold; 9 shirts; Yes; The number of shirts determines the amount of money earned.

WHAT DO YOU THINK?

Ask students if there is a third way to solve the problem. Possible answer: Solve the equation $120 - 2.5x = 0$. The value of x will be the number of seconds for the pencil to hit the ground.

Answers for What Do You Think?

Possible answer: I would use Tanisha's method because I could make the calculator graph it and identify the x-intercept.

3 Practice and Assess

Check

Ask students to generalize the form for a linear function. Are all lines linear functions. $y = mx + b$; No; Vertical lines are not.

Answers for Check Your Understanding

1. If the function is linear, locate the point on the line where the y-coordinate equals the output value, then read the input from the x-coordinate.

Assignment Guide

- **Basic**
  1–9, 11–13, 17–21

- **Average**
  5–20

- **Enriched**
  5–19, 21

Exercise Answers

6.

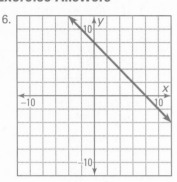

Yes

7–10. See page C2.

Reteaching

Activity

Materials: Graphing calculator

- Work with a partner.

- Graph each equation and tell if it describes a linear function. Explain why or why not.

  a. $y = -\frac{1}{2}x + 3$
     Yes; Graph is a line and each input gives exactly one output.

  b. $y = 5$
     Yes; Graph is a line and each input gives exactly one output.

  c. $y = x^2$
     No, each input has two outputs; Graph is a curve.

  d. $x = -4$
     No; Calculator gives error message; The one input gives many outputs.

516   Chapter 10

PRACTICE 10-2

10-2 Exercises and Applications

Practice and Apply

1. **Getting Started** Given the function rule $y = x + 3$,
   a. What is the dependent variable? **y**
   b. What is the independent variable? **x**
   c. Find the output values for the following input values: $x = -5$, $x = 0$, $x = 5$.
      $y = -2$, $y = 3$, $y = 8$

Given the following function rules, complete the table of values.

2. $y = 2x - 6$

Input (x)	Output (y)
−1	−8
0	−6
1	−4
2	−2
3	0

3. $y = -x + 10$

Input (x)	Output (y)
−1	11
0	10
1	9
2	8
3	7

4. $y = 3x - 5$

Input (x)	Output (y)
−1	−8
0	−5
1	−2
2	1
3	4

5. **Test Prep** Which number is the input value for $y = 1.5x - 4$, if the output value is 2? **B**

   Ⓐ −1   Ⓑ 4   Ⓒ 1   Ⓓ $1\frac{1}{3}$

Graph each linear equation. Does the equation describe a function?

6. $y = -x + 8$ 7. $y = 2x - 1$ 8. $y = 3$ 9. $x = 3$

10. **Consumer** Some airlines offer in-flight phones. The total cost to use the in-flight phone on one airline is $8 + $2 per min.

    a. Find a rule and make a table of values for the cost of 6 different call lengths.

    b. Is this relationship a function?

    c. Is the total cost dependent on the number of minutes used?

11. **Science** The distance the fastest marine animal, a killer whale, can travel is a function of the time traveled. The killer whale travels approximately 34.5 mi/hr.

    a. Write an equation to show the relationship between distance and time. **$d = 34.5t$**

    b. Use your equation to find how far the whale can travel in 2 hr, 6 hr, and 10 hr.
       69 mi, 207 mi, 345 mi

516 Chapter 10 • Algebra: Functions and Relationships

PRACTICE

Name _____

Practice 10-2

Linear Functions

Given the following function rules, complete the table of values.

1. $y = 4x - 8$

Input (x)	Output (y)
−1	−12
0	−8
1	−4
2	0
3	4

2. $y = -2x + 3$

Input (x)	Output (y)
−1	5
0	3
1	1
2	−1
3	−3

3. $y = -5x - 2$

Input (x)	Output (y)
−1	3
0	−2
1	−7
2	−12
3	−17

Graph each linear equation. Does the equation describe a function?

4. $y = -2$ **Yes**   5. $y = x - 3$ **Yes**   6. $x = 1$ **No**

Does each table of values represent a function? Explain your answer.

7.

Input (x)	−1	3	1	5	3
Output (y)	3	4	7	2	8

No; There are two possible outputs for an input of 3.

8.

Input (x)	−4	2	6	7	8
Output (y)	3	5	1	5	7

Yes; For each input value, there is only one output value.

9. **Science** The speed of sound in air is about 1088 ft/sec.
   a. Write an equation to show the relationship between distance d and time t.
      $d = 1088t$
   b. Use your equation to find how far a sound travels in 2 seconds, 5 seconds, and 10 seconds.

   2 seconds **2,176 ft**   5 seconds **5,440 ft**   10 seconds **10,880 ft**

RETEACHING

Name _____

Alternative Lesson 10-2

Linear Functions

If we let x represent the input value and y represent the output value in a function, then the output, y, depends on the input, x. In a function, the variable y is called the **dependent variable**, and the variable x is called the **independent variable**. A function that can be graphed as a straight line is called a **linear function**.

— **Example 1** —

Graph the equation $y = 2x + 1$. Does it describe a function? Is it a linear function?

First, make a table of input and output values. Then graph the ordered pairs (x, y).

Input (x)	Function Rule 2x + 1	Output (y)
−2	2(−2) + 1	−3
0	2(0) + 1	1
1	2(1) + 1	3
2	2(2) + 1	5

The equation $y = 2x + 1$ is a function. Each input (x) value has a single output (y) value. It is a linear function because the graph is a line.

Try It Graph the equation $y = -2x + 3$.

a. First, make a table of input and output values.

Input (x)	Function Rule −2x + 3	Output (y)
−1	−2(−1) + 3	5
0	−2(0) + 3	3
1	−2(1) + 3	1

b. Graph the ordered pairs.

c. Does each input (x) value have a single output (y) value? **Yes.**

d. Is it a function? **Yes.**   e. Is the graph a line? **Yes.**

f. Is it a linear function? **Yes.**   g. Label your graph.

On the same grid, graph the equation $y = x + 1$. Label your graph.

h. Is it a linear function? How do you know? **Yes. It is a straight line.**

Does each table of values represent a function? Explain your answer.

12.

Input (x)	Output (y)
−1	1
0	0
1	1
2	1
3	1

13.

Input (x)	Output (y)
−2	8
−1	4
0	0
−1	−4
−2	−8

14.

Input (x)	Output (y)
0	0
100	10
100	−10
400	20
400	−20

15. Jenny is placing an ad in the newspaper classifieds to sell her snowboard. The cost of the ad is $18 plus $6.50 for each line.

  a. Write an equation that relates the cost (c) of an ad in the classifieds to the number of lines (n) in the ad.

  b. Make a graph relating these values.

  c. Is the cost of the ad a function of the number of lines it has?

Problem Solving and Reasoning

16. Critical Thinking Isaac wondered if airlines base ticket prices on the distance flown. He found the approximate mileage between some cities and round-trip fares.

  a. Is ticket price a function of distance? Explain.

  b. What other things might affect the cost of a ticket?

Cities	Distance (mi)	Price ($)
Chicago-Baltimore	675	298
Denver-Los Angeles	1050	445
Jacksonville-Charleston	675	189
Knoxville-Buffalo	675	442
Milwaukee-Boston	1050	895
Tampa-Pittsburgh	1050	189

17. Give an example of a function in your everyday life. Explain why it is a function and define the dependent and independent variables.

Mixed Review

18. Start with 1000. What is the result of a 27% decrease followed by a 30% increase? *[Lesson 6-6]* **949**

Find the perimeter and area of each polygon. *[Lesson 9-1]*

19. An equilateral triangle with sides 4 in. long **12 in., $4\sqrt{3} \approx 6.9$ in²**

20. A 2 m by 6 m rectangle **16 m, 12 m²**

21. A parallelogram with base 23 cm and height 10 cm **Perimeter can't be determined, 230 cm²**

10-2 • Linear Functions **517**

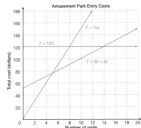

Exercise Answers

12. Yes; One output value for each input value.

13. No; Inputs −1 and −2 each have two output values.

14. No; Inputs 100 and 400 each have two output values.

15. a. $c = 6.5n + 18$

    b.
    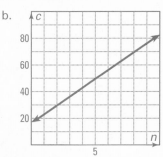

    c. Yes

16. a. No; It is possible to pay different fares for the same distance.

    b. Possible answers: Length of stay, when the ticket is purchased, frequent flyer, first class/business class/coach.

17. Answers may vary.

Alternate Assessment

Self Assessment Have students reflect on their progress in understanding linear functions and identifying independent and dependent variables. Ask them to identify any areas they still do not understand.

▶ **Quick Quiz**

Use the equation $y = 2x - 3$.

1. Which variable is the dependent variable? **y**

2. What is the output if the inputs are 2, 7, and 15? **1, 11, 27**

3. What is the input if the output is 21? **12**

4. Does this equation describe a linear function? Explain why or why not. **Yes; Graph is a line and each input gives exactly one output.**

Available on Daily Transparency 10–2

Lesson 10-2 **517**

10-3 Lesson Organizer

Objective

- Represent quadratic functions as graphs, tables, and equations.

Vocabulary

- Nonlinear function, quadratic function, parabola

Materials

- Explore: Graphing calculator

NCTM Standards

- 1–4, 8, 9, 12, 13

 Review

Evaluate each expression for $n = -2$, 2, and 5.

1. $n^2 + n - 1$ 1, 5, 29
2. $2n^2 - 3$ 5, 5, 47
3. $n^2 - 2n + 1$ 9, 1, 16

Available on Daily Transparency 10-3

1 Introduce

Explore

You might wish to use Teaching Tool Transparency 23: Graphing Calculator with **Explore**.

The Point
Students explore the output values of a quadratic function.

Ongoing Assessment
Check students' results after Step 4. This introduces the idea that the range (possible y values) may not be all the real numbers, as is the case with most linear functions.

For Groups That Finish Early
How can you change the equation $y = x^2$ so the graph of the new equation is a parabola that opens downward? Use a negative coefficient for x^2.

Follow Up
Discuss some of the characteristics of the parabola, such as the range, symmetry, and vertex.

10-3 Quadratic Functions

You'll Learn …

- to represent quadratic functions as graphs, tables, and equations

… How It's Used

Projectile motion, the motion in a launched fireworks display, can be modeled using quadratic equations.

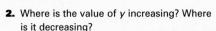

Vocabulary

nonlinear function

quadratic function

parabola

▶ **Lesson Link**   You have studied linear functions. In this lesson, you will extend many of the ideas that you learned about linear functions to another type of function. ◀

Explore   Quadratic Functions

Ups and Downs

Materials: Graphing calculator

1. Graph $y = x^2$ using the standard graphing calculator screen. Is this graph a function? Explain.

2. Where is the value of y increasing? Where is it decreasing?

3. Trace along the graph (or evaluate) to find y when x is 4. Then trace along the graph to find y when x is -4.

4. Trace along the graph to find a negative value for y. How does the function equation help to explain your findings?

5. Change the function to $y = x^2 - 4$ and graph. Does this change your answer to Question 4? Explain.

Learn   Quadratic Functions

You have already learned about linear functions; in this lesson you will look at a **nonlinear function** called a **quadratic function**. A quadratic function is a function in which the highest power of x is 2. The following are examples of quadratic functions.

$$y = x^2 \qquad y = -x^2 \qquad y = 2x^2 \qquad y = 4x^2 - 6 \qquad y = x^2 + 2x + 1$$

The graph of a linear function is a straight line; this is because equal changes in x result in equal changes in the value of y. Recall that the change in y divided by the change in x is the slope.

The graph of a quadratic function is a $\cup$ or upside-down $\cup$-shaped curve, called a **parabola** .

518   Chapter 10 • Algebra: Functions and Relationships

▶ MEETING INDIVIDUAL NEEDS

Resources

10-3 Practice

10-3 Reteaching

10-3 Problem Solving

10-3 Enrichment

10-3 Daily Transparency
      Problem of
      the Day
      Review
      Quick Quiz

Teaching Tool
Transparency 23

Lesson Enhancement
Transparency 55

Technology Master 52

 Interactive CD-ROM Lesson

 Wide World of Mathematics Algebra: La Quebrada Divers

Learning Modalities

Visual   For Exercise 16 on page 522, it may be helpful for students to draw the diagonals in a square, a hexagon, and an octagon to verify their calculations.

Kinesthetic   Graphing calculators may be helpful for students having difficulty drawing the graphs of the functions.

Verbal   Help students restate any problem they have difficulty solving.

Challenge

Have students determine the quadratic function that models the areas of all rectangles with a perimeter of 60, and graph the function. What is the maximum area possible? Let x = width of rectangle. Then $30 - x$ = length of rectangle. $A = x(30 - x)$ or $A = -x^2 + 30x$; Maximum area is 225, which occurs when the rectangle is a 15×15 square.

For quadratic functions, equal changes in x do not result in equal changes in the value of y.

Look at the graph of the quadratic function representing the height of a ball thrown into the air. As x increases by 1, y changes by different amounts.

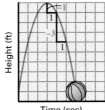

Height (ft) vs Time (sec)

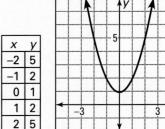
Examples

1 Make a table and graph for $y = 2x^2 + 4$. Use both positive and negative values for x. What happens to the y value as the x value increases?

x	y
−2	12
−1	6
0	4
1	6
2	12

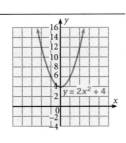

As the values of x increase, the values of y decrease until $x = 0$; then they begin to increase again.

2 Graph each function. How are the graphs alike? How are they different?

a. $y = x^2$ and $y = -x^2$

b. $y = x^2$ and $y = x^2 + 3$

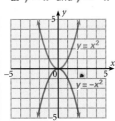

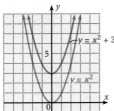

a. Both graphs are parabolas. $(0, 0)$ is part of both graphs. They are both symmetric about the y-axis.

The graph of x^2 opens upward, whereas the graph of $-x^2$ opens downward.

b. Both graphs are parabolas, open upward, and are symmetric about the y-axis.

The y-intercept of the graph of x^2 is $y = 0$, whereas the y-intercept of the graph of $x^2 + 3$ is $y = 3$.

Try It

a. Make a table and graph for $y = 2x^2 - 4$.

b. Graph $y = x^2$ and $y = 2x^2$. How are the graphs alike? How are they different?

MATH EVERY DAY

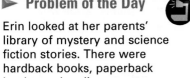

▶ Problem of the Day

Erin looked at her parents' library of mystery and science fiction stories. There were hardback books, paperback books, and audio cassettes. Every paperback book was a mystery. Half of the hardback books were mysteries. Half of all the mystery stories were paperback books. There were 40 hardback books and 30 paperback books. How many mystery stories were on audio cassettes? **10 cassettes**
(The key is that all 30 paperback books are mysteries.)

Available on Daily Transparency 10-3

An Extension is provided in the transparency package.

Fact of the Day

Newton's third law of motion states that for every action there is an equal and opposite reaction. This is the principle of rocket flight.

Mental Math

Perform these computations mentally proceeding from left to right.

1. $5 \times 6 \div 2 \div 3$ **5**

2. $4 \times (-2) \div 8 \times -1$ **1**

3. $9 \times 4 \div 3 \times 0 \times 5 \div 2$ **0**

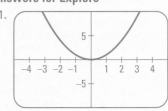
2 Teach

Learn

You may wish to use Lesson Enhancement Transparency 55 with this lesson.

Alternate Examples

1. Make a table and graph for $y = x^2 + 1$. Use both negative and positive values for x. What happens to the y values as the x values increase?

x	y
−2	5
−1	2
0	1
1	2
2	5

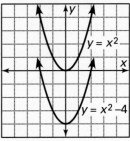

As the x values increase, the values of y decrease until $x = 0$; then they begin to increase.

2. Graph $y = x^2$ and $y = x^2 - 4$. How are the graphs alike? How are they different?

Both graphs are parabolas that open upward and are symmetric about the y-axis. The y-intercept of the graph of $y = x^2$ is $y = 0$, whereas the y-intercept of the graph of $y = x^2 - 4$ is $y = -4$. Each point of the second graph is 4 units below a corresponding point on the first graph, so the shape of the curves is the same.

Answers for Try It on page C3.

Alternate Examples

3. A ball is thrown upward vertically at a starting speed of 96 ft/sec. The height h (in feet above the starting point) that the ball will reach at the end of t seconds is modeled by the function $h = -16t^2 + 96t$. Make a table and graph using $t = 0$ to 6 seconds. Could you use values for t that are greater than 6? Why or why not?

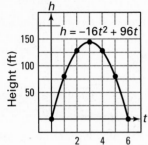

t	h
0	0
1	80
2	128
3	144
4	128
5	80
6	0

You could use values for t that are greater than 6, but it would not make sense in the problem because negative values for the height would result.

Answers for Try It

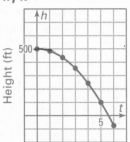

t	h
0	500
1	484
2	436
3	356
4	244
5	100
6	-76

3 Practice and Assess

Check

Answers for Check Your Understanding

1. The quadratic equation has an x^2 term. The graph will be U-shaped instead of straight.

2. The graph opens downward instead of upward.

3. Both have a y-intercept of -2 and are increasing when $x > 0$. But unlike $x - 2$, $x^2 - 2$ is curved and is increasing when $x < 0$.

4. When the x-y relationship represents a situation in which x does not make sense for negative numbers; The negative x value represents a situation that could never happen.

Sometimes when we are working real-world problems, some values do not make sense in the problem. The part of a graph that solves a problem may not look like a whole parabola.

Example 3

A pilot drops supplies to scientists working at an Antarctic Substation. Ignoring air resistance, if the drop is made from 800 ft, the function $h = -16t^2 + 800$, where t is time in sec and h is height in ft, will model the situation. Make a table and a graph using $t = 0$ to 8 sec. Could you use negative values for t or h? Why was the graph not a complete parabola?

Time (sec)	Height (ft)
0	800
1	784
2	736
3	656
4	544
5	400
6	224
7	16
8	-224
9	-496

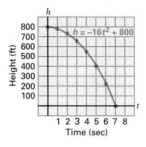

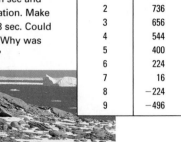

You could use negative values for t and h to see the entire graph, but it would not make sense in the problem to use negative values for time or height. Because the negative values were not used, the graph was not a parabola.

Try It

A pilot drops food to a village from a height of 500 ft. Ignoring air resistance, the function $h = -16t^2 + 500$, where t is time in sec and h is height in ft, will model the situation. Make a table and a graph using $t = 0$ to 6 sec.

Check   Your Understanding

1. How does a quadratic function differ from a linear function?

2. How does multiplying x^2 by -1 affect the graph of a quadratic function?

3. Compare the graphs of $y = x^2 - 2$ and $y = x - 2$. How are they alike? How are they different?

4. When can you ignore negative values of x? Why?

MEETING MIDDLE SCHOOL CLASSROOM NEEDS

Tips from Middle School Teachers

For problems like Exercise 5 on page 521, I also like students to see what happens if the coefficient of x^2 is $\frac{1}{2}$, $\frac{1}{4}$, or $\frac{1}{8}$. Then I help students formulate some general conclusions.

Team Teaching

Check with the science teacher on your team to see if it is possible to display some science posters about motion, perhaps about Newton's laws of motion or Einstein's theory of relativity.

Industry Connection

Many objects are shaped in such a way that their cross section is a parabola. Some of these objects are flashlight and headlight reflectors, satellite dishes and other antennas, and even some contact lenses. Have small groups of students research such objects and make a poster about them.

10-3 Exercises and Applications

Practice and Apply

Getting Started Which are graphs of linear functions? Which are graphs of quadratic functions? Which are neither?

1.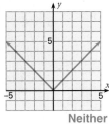
Neither

2.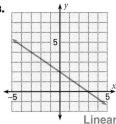
Quadratic

3.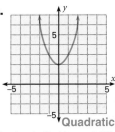
Linear

Graph each set of functions and describe the similarities and differences within the set of graphs.

4. $y = x^2$, $y = x^2 + 3$, and $y = x^2 - 3$

5. $y = x^2$, $y = 2x^2$, $y = 4x^2$, and $y = 8x^2$

6. $y = x^2$ and $y = -x^2$

7. $y = 2x^2$ and $y = -2x^2$

Match each graph with the function that describes it.

8. E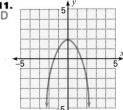

9. F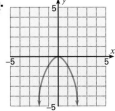

10. C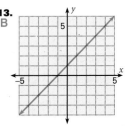

11. D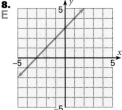

12. A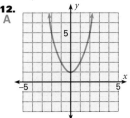

13. B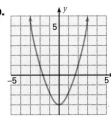

Ⓐ $y = x^2 + 1$ Ⓑ $y = x + 1$ Ⓒ $y = x^2 - 3$

Ⓓ $y = -x^2 + 2$ Ⓔ $y = x + 3$ Ⓕ $y = -x^2$

10-3 • Quadratic Functions **521**

10-3 Exercises and Applications

Assignment Guide

■ **Basic**
1–15, 18–23

■ **Average**
1–5, 8–23

■ **Enriched**
1–4, 7–23

Exercise Answers

4.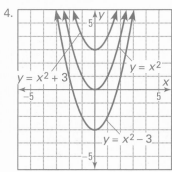

Same shape, different vertical positions.

5–7. See page C3.

Reteaching

Activity

Materials: Graphing calculator

• Work with a partner.

• Graph $y = x^2$. Then explain how the graph of each of the following equations can be found from the graph of $y = x^2$.

  a. $y = -x^2$
  Flip graph of $y = x^2$ over the x-axis.

  b. $y = x^2 + 4$
  Slide graph of $y = x^2$ up 4 units.

  c. $y = x^2 - 4$
  Slide graph of $y = x^2$ down 4 units.

  d. $y = -x^2 + 1$
  Flip graph of $y = x^2$ over the x-axis, and then slide it up 1 unit.

• Use a graphing calculator to check your answer.

PRACTICE

Name _____

Practice 10-3

Quadratic Functions

Graph each set of functions.

1. $y = x^2 - 2$, $y = x^2$, and $y = x^2 + 2$

2. $y = x^2$, $y = -2x^2$, and $y = 3x^2$

3. $y = -x^2$, $y = -x^2 + 2$ and $y = -x^2 + 5$

Match each graph with the function that describes it.

4. B
5. C
6. A

7. E
8. D
9. F

A. $y = -2x^2$ B. $y = 2x^2$ C. $y = 2x^2 - 4$
D. $y = -2x^2 + 4$ E. $y = -x^2 + 3$ F. $y = x^2 - 3$

10. For a group of n people, the formula $h = \frac{1}{2}(n^2 - n)$ gives the number of handshakes that would occur if each person shook hands once with each other person. Find the number of handshakes for each number of people.

a. $n = 1$ **0**   b. $n = 4$ **6**   c. $n = 9$ **36**   d. $n = 25$ **300**

RETEACHING

Name _____

Alternative Lesson 10-3

Quadratic Functions

Some functions are nonlinear; that is, the graph is not a straight line. A **quadratic function** is a function in which the highest power of x is 2. The graph of a quadratic function is a U- or upside-down U-shaped curve, called a **parabola**.

── Example 1 ──

Make a table and graph for $y = x^2 + 2$. Use both positive and negative values for x.

x	$x^2 + 2$	y
-2	$(-2)^2 + 2$	6
-1	$(-1)^2 + 2$	3
0	$0^2 + 2$	2

x	$x^2 + 2$	y
1	$1^2 + 2$	3
2	$2^2 + 2$	6

Try It

a. Make a table and graph for $y = x^2 - 3$. Use both positive and negative values for x.

x	$x^2 - 3$	y
-2	$(-2)^2 - 3$	1
-1	$(-1)^2 - 3$	-2
0	$0^2 - 3$	-3
1	$1^2 - 3$	-2
2	$2^2 - 3$	1

── Example 2 ──

Graph $y = x^2$ and $y = x^2 + 1$. How are the graphs alike? How are they different?

Both graphs are parabolas, and the parabolas open upward. The graphs are symmetric about the y-axis.

The y-intercepts are different. In $y = x^2$, the y-intercept is $y = 0$. In $y = x^2 + 1$, the y-intercept is $y = 1$.

Try It

b. Graph $y = x^2$ and $y = x^2 - 2$. How are the graphs alike? How are they different?

Both are parabolas, opening upward, y-intercepts are different.

Exercise Answers

14. a. At 3 and 7 seconds; $50(3) - 5(3)^2 = 50(7) - 5(7)^2 = 105$.
    b. The rocket hits the ground.

17.

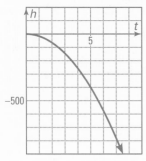

The canyon is 400 ft deep; The value is negative because the function represents height measured from the canyon's rim.

18. a. i and iii; The x^2 term is positive.
    b. i and ii; There is no constant term to shift the graph up or down.
    c. All of them, since any x value and its opposite will produce the same y value.

19. Answers may vary.

Alternate Assessment

Performance Have students do research and develop a problem involving the trajectory of some object, such as a ball or rocket, that can be represented by a quadratic function. Have students write and explain the equation that models the situation, find the maximum height reached by the object, and how long it takes for the object to hit the ground.

---

14. **Science** A toy rocket was launched into the air. The function $h = 50t - 5t^2$ models this situation, where h = height in m and t = time in sec.

    a. When is the rocket 105 m in the air? Explain.

    b. What happens at 10 sec?

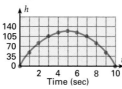

15. [Test Prep] The area of a square can be modeled by a quadratic function. Which is the function rule for the area of a square? **C**

    Ⓐ $y = 4x$ Ⓑ $y = x \cdot x \cdot x \cdot x$

    Ⓒ $y = x^2$ Ⓓ $y = 4x^2$

16. **Geometry** The formula $d = \frac{n^2 - 3n}{2}$ gives the number of diagonals (d) for a polygon with n sides.

    a. How many diagonals does a square have? **2**

    b. How many diagonals does a hexagon have? **9**

    c. How many diagonals does an octagon have? **20**

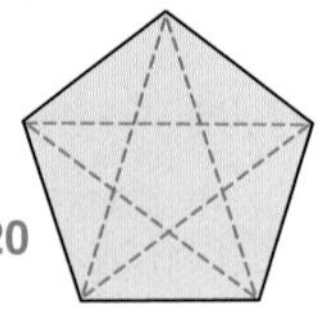

Problem Solving and Reasoning

17. **Communicate** Ossie dropped a pebble into a canyon. He heard it hit the ground 5 sec later. The function $h = -16t^2$ will model this situation. Time (t) is in sec, height (h) is in ft. Graph the function. If the pebble hits the ground in 5 sec, how deep is the canyon? Why is the value negative?

19. Journal How can you tell the shape of a parabola from its function rule?

18. **Critical Thinking** Answer each question about the functions.

    i. $y = 4x^2$ **ii.** $y = -4x^2$

    iii. $y = x^2 + 2$ **iv.** $y = 2 - x^2$

    a. Which graph(s) will open upward? How do you know?

    b. Which graphs pass through the point $(0, 0)$? How do you know?

    c. Which graphs are symmetric about the y-axis?

Mixed Review

Solve each equation. [Lesson 3-2]

20. $x + 5 = 12$ **7**   21. $y - 10 = 17$ **27**   22. $\frac{1}{3}p = 4$ **12**

23. Find the perimeter of a triangle with side lengths of 9 cm, 8 cm, and 5 cm after it is dilated by a scale factor of 3. [Lesson 9-2] **66 cm**

522 *Chapter 10 • Algebra: Functions and Relationships*

► PROBLEM SOLVING

Name _____

[Guided Problem Solving 10-3]

[GPS] **PROBLEM 14, STUDENT PAGE 522**

A toy rocket was launched into the air. The function $h = \boxed{50t - 5t^2}$ models this situation, where h = height in m and t = time in sec.

a. When is the rocket 105 m in the air? Explain.

b. What happens at 10 sec?

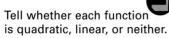

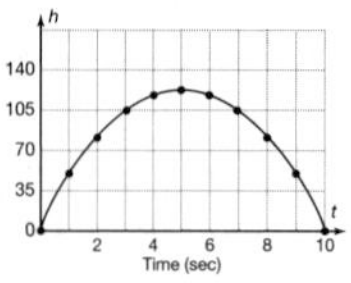

— Understand —

1. Circle the function.

2. Which axis in the graph represents height? *y-axis.*

— Plan —

3. Can there be more than one time for each height? Why? Yes, different input values can have same output value.

4. How can you find the values? Use the graph.

— Solve —

5. When is the rocket 105 m in the air? What is happening at this time? At 3 sec and 7 sec; Rocket is rising and coming back to Earth.

6. What is the height at 10 sec? What is happening to the rocket? 0 m; The rocket has come back to earth.

— Look Back —

7. Why doesn't the graph extend below the x-axis? Rocket does not penetrate the earth. It will not go lower than the launch point.

[SOLVE ANOTHER PROBLEM]

An object is launched into the air. The function $h = 80t - 16t^2$ models this situation, where h = height in ft and t = time in sec.

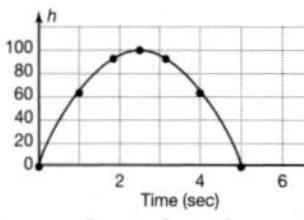

a. When is the object 64 feet in the air? Explain. At 1 sec and 4 sec; The object is rising and coming down.

b. What happens at $2\frac{1}{2}$ sec? The object is at its highest point.

► ENRICHMENT

Name _____

[Extend Your Thinking 10-3]

Critical Thinking

The graph at the right shows $y = x^2$. Compare this graph to the ones you complete below.

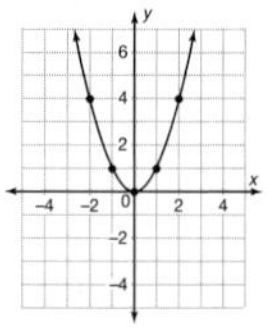

1. a. Complete the table for the equation $y = (x + 1)^2$

x	-4	-3	-2	-1	0	1	2
y	9	4	1	0	1	4	9

   b. Graph the ordered pairs. Describe how your graph compares to the graph shown for $y = x^2$.

   Graph is shifted 1 unit to the left of the y-axis.

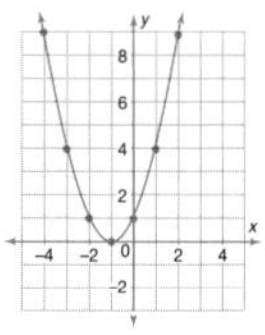

2. a. Complete the table for the equation $y = (x - 1)^2$

x	-2	-1	0	1	2	3	4
y	9	4	1	0	1	4	9

   b. Graph the ordered pairs.

   c. How does this graph compare with the graphs in Item 1 above?

   Graph is shifted 1 unit to the right of the y-axis.

   d. Describe the symmetry of this graph. Symmetrical about $x = 1$.

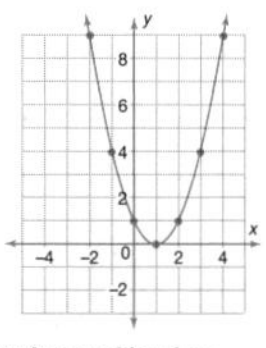

3. Describe how $y = (x - 4)^2$ and $y = (x + 3)^2$ will appear after graphing them. Possible answers: The first graph is the parabola $y = x^2$ shifted 4 units to the right. The second graph is parabola $y = x^2$ shifted 3 units to the left.

Other Functions

▶ Lesson Link In the last lesson, you looked at one type of nonlinear function, a quadratic function. In this lesson, you will look at other types of nonlinear functions. ◀

Explore Other Functions

Which Is Which?

Which graph do you think is appropriate for each situation? Explain your reasoning.

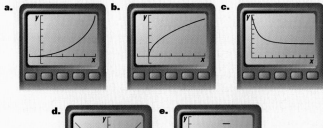

1. The temperature of a cup of cocoa that cools quickly at first, then more and more slowly as it reaches room temperature.

2. The size of a bacteria colony doubles every hour.

3. The length of the side of a square increases as the enclosed area increases linearly.

4. The output value is the input value rounded to the nearest integer.

5. The distance of a train from the station as it approaches the station and then passes the station.

10-4 • Other Functions **523**

You'll Learn ...
■ to graph and evaluate other types of functions

... How It's Used
The rate that carbon 14 decays is an exponential function that helps paleontologists determine the age of a fossil.

Vocabulary

exponential function

step function

Objective
■ **Graph and evaluate other types of functions.**

Vocabulary
■ **Exponential function, step function**

NCTM Standards
■ **1–4, 8, 9, 11–13**

▶ Review
Evaluate each expression for $n = -2, -1, 0, 1,$ and 2.

1. 2^n $\frac{1}{4}, \frac{1}{2}, 1, 2, 4$

2. $|n|$ 2, 1, 0, 1, 2

Available on Daily Transparency 10-4

---

1 Introduce

Explore

You may wish to use Lesson Enhancement Transparency 56 with **Explore**.

The Point
Students relate various situations to appropriate graphs.

Ongoing Assessment
Check students' results after Step 1 just to be sure that they are thinking and reasoning correctly.

For Groups That Finish Early
Describe another appropriate representation for each graph.

Follow Up
Discuss students' reasoning for matching graphs and situations.

Answers for Explore
1. c; The curve drops steeply at first, then less steeply.

2. a; Doubling means faster and faster growth over time.

3. b; The graph should be a parabola sitting on its side.

4. e; All x values within 0.5 of an integer produce the same y value.

5. d; The graph is linear on each side of the origin, but all y values are positive.

▷ MEETING INDIVIDUAL NEEDS

Resources

10-4 Practice
10-4 Reteaching
10-4 Problem Solving
10-4 Enrichment
10-4 Daily Transparency
   Problem of the Day
   Review
   Quick Quiz
Teaching Tool Transparencies 2, 3, 23
Lesson Enhancement Transparency 56
Technology Master 53
Chapter 10 Project Master

 Interactive CD-ROM Spreadsheet/ Grapher Tool

Learning Modalities

Individual Have students reflect on the different types of functions presented and write about a real-world application of each.

Logical For Exercise 19 on page 527, have students create a table of values for each function and determine the pattern for the output values. Noting the pattern of the output values can help to identify the type of function being used.

Visual Have students make posters that display the different types of nonlinear functions they have studied. Display the posters throughout the classroom.

Inclusion

Students with impaired vision or limited fine-motor skills may have difficulty drawing the graphs or using a graphing calculator. Use of graph paper with large squares might help.

Lesson 10-4 **523**

2 Teach

You may wish to use Teaching Tool Transparency 23: Graphing Calculator with this lesson.

A step function is the result of rounding. For example, consider the greatest integer function. When 3.5 is input, the greatest integer less than or equal to 3.5 is 3. For any value $3 \leq x < 4$, the output is 3. For $4 \leq x < 5$, the output is 4, and so on. The resulting graph looks like a flight of steps.

Alternate Examples

1. Graph the function $y = 0.8^x$ for $x \geq 0$. What is the value of y when x is 2? What is x when y is 0.512?

   Use a graphing utility. Trace to 2 on the x-axis and find the corresponding value of y, $y = 0.64$. Then trace until you find $y = 0.512$. Note that the corresponding value of x is 3.

2. In a certain organism the number of cells quadruple every hour. If the organism starts with one cell, how long will it take for there to be at least 4000 cells?

   You can find the answer from a table or a graph.

Hours (x)	0	1	2	3	4	5	6
Number (y)	1	4	16	64	256	1024	4096

   The function $y = 4^x$ can be used to model this situation. Using a graph utility, trace to find x when y is approximately 4000.

   The organism will have at least 4000 cells in approximately 6 hours.

Answers for Try It

a.

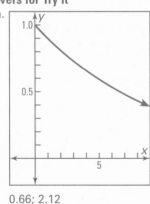

0.66; 2.12

In all linear and quadratic functions, a variable was raised to an exponent.

In many nonlinear functions, the exponent will be a variable. These nonlinear functions, such as $y = 2^x$, are called **exponential functions**.

Examples

1 Graph the function $y = 0.5^x$ for $x \geq 0$. What is the value of y when x is 2? What is x when y is 0.125?

You can use a graphing utility.

Trace to 2 on the x-axis and find the corresponding value of y, $y = 0.25$. Then trace until you find $y = 0.125$. The corresponding value of x is 3.

2 A colony of bacteria is being grown in a laboratory. The lab technicians begin with a single bacterium. Every hour, the number of bacteria doubles. How long will it take the colony to number 1000?

You can find the answer from a table or a graph.

Hours (x)	0	1	2	3	4	5	6	7	8	9	10
Number (y)	1	2	4	8	16	32	64	128	256	512	1024

The function $y = 2^x$ can be used to model this situation. Using a graphing utility, trace to find x when y is approximately 1000.

The colony will number 1000 in approximately 10 hr.

Try It

a. Graph the function $y = 0.9^x$. What is the approximate value of y when x is 4? What is the value of x when y is approximately 0.8?

b. Suppose the number of bacteria triples every hour. The function $y = 3^x$ can be used to model this situation. How long will it take the colony to number 5000? **About** $7\frac{3}{4}$ **hours**

Science Link

E. coli, the most intensely studied bacteria, has a doubling time of 20 min. This is why E. coli food poisoning must be treated quickly.

MATH EVERY DAY

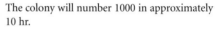

► Problem of the Day

Ten blocks are needed to make a staircase of four steps. How many blocks are needed to make ten steps? How many blocks are needed to make fifty steps?

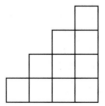

a. 55 blocks; b. 1275 blocks; The general equation is $\dfrac{n(n+1)}{2}$.

Available on Daily Transparency 10-4

An Extension is provided in the transparency package.

Fact of the Day

The rate of motion is usually referred to as *speed*. The term *velocity* describes both the speed of an object and its direction.

Estimation

Between what two consecutive whole numbers is each number?

1. $\sqrt{41}$ 6 and 7
2. $\sqrt{90}$ 9 and 10
3. $\sqrt{200}$ 14 and 15

Functions can also be made up of pieces or steps. In a **step function**, different rules may be applied to different input values. The graph of a step function is not connected.

Example 3

Wind speeds are usually given to the nearest 10 mi/hr. Graph the function that rounds a number to the nearest 10.

Numbers ending in 5 or more round up. Make a table.

x	3	5	8	14	15	18	20	24	25	34
y	0	10	10	10	20	20	20	20	30	30

The value of y is 10 for any value of $x \geq 5$ but less than 15, so this part of the graph is a flat segment.

Because 14.99 rounds to 10, whereas 15 rounds to 20, we use an open circle at $(15, 10)$ to show that the point is not included.

Try It

Graph the function that rounds a number to the nearest 100.

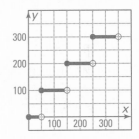

HINT

Many graphing utilities have a rounding function under the MATH key.

Check Your Understanding

1. Explain the difference between the functions $y = x^2$ and $y = 2^x$.

2. How are the graphs of $y = 2^x$ and $y = 0.5^x$ alike? How are they different?

   2. Both are exponential; 2^x is increasing while 0.5^x is decreasing

3. How can you tell from the equation that a function is exponential?

   The exponent will be a variable.

10-4 • Other Functions **525**

Alternate Examples

3. Attendance at big events is often estimated to the nearest thousand. Numbers ending in 500 or greater are rounded up, and numbers ending in less than 500 are rounded down. Graph the function that rounds a number to the nearest thousand.

   The value of y is 0 for any value $x \geq 0$ but less than 500, so this part of the graph is flat. An open circle is used at 500 because 500 rounds to 1000.

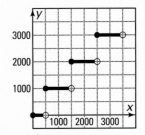

Answers for Try It

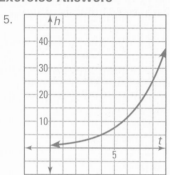

Assignment Guide

■ **Basic**
1–8, 11–16, 19, 24–26

■ **Average**
5, 6, 9–16, 18–22, 23–27 odds

■ **Enriched**
7–23, 28

Exercise Answers

5.

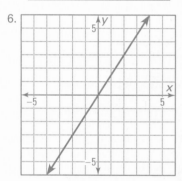

6.

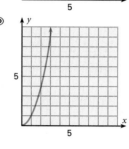

7–11. See page C3.

Reteaching

Materials: Graphing calculator

• Work with a partner.

• Use the graphing calculator to graph each equation. Then name the type of function you have graphed.

a. $y = 5x$ Linear function

b. $y = x^2 + 3$
Quadratic function

c. $y = 5^x$
Exponential function

d. $y = x$ rounded to the nearest 100
Step function

526   Chapter 10

10-4 Exercises and Applications

Practice and Apply

Getting Started Match each function to its graph.

1. $y = 2x$ **B**   **2.** $y = x^2$ **D**   **3.** $y = 2^x$ **C**   **4.** $y =$ round down to the whole number **A**

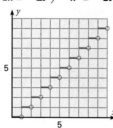

Ⓐ   Ⓑ   Ⓒ   Ⓓ

Graph each function.

5. $y = 1.5^x$ **6.** $y = 1.5x$ **7.** $y = 4x$ **8.** $y = 4^x$

9. Suppose the population of butterflies on an island doubles in size each year. If there are 1,000 butterflies now, in how many years will there be 1,000,000 butterflies? Show how this is modeled by $y = 1,000 \cdot 2^x$.

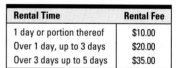

10. John bought a new bank. The first day, he put two pennies in it. Each day he doubled the number of pennies he put in. The equation $y = 2^x$ models this situation.

  a. Graph the equation.

  b. On what day did John add $0.64?

  c. What was the first day John added more than $2.00 to the bank?

11. Consumer Ready Rent-All rental charges for a VCR are as follows.

Rental Time	Rental Fee
1 day or portion thereof	$10.00
Over 1 day, up to 3 days	$20.00
Over 3 days up to 5 days	$35.00

  a. Graph the function.

  b. What kind of function is this?

PRACTICE

Name _____

Practice 10-4

Other Functions

Graph each function.

1. $y = 3x$ **2.** $y = 3^x$ **3.** $y = 0.4x$

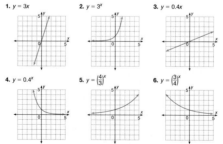

4. $y = 0.4^x$ **5.** $y = \left(\frac{4}{3}\right)^x$ **6.** $y = \left(\frac{3}{4}\right)^x$

Identify each function as linear, quadratic, exponential, or step.

7. $y = 2x + 5$ _Linear_   **8.** $y = 5^x$ _Exponential_

9. $y =$ round up to the next hundred _Step_

10. $y = 0.3^x$ _Exponential_   **11.** $y = 4x^2$ _Quadratic_

12. $y =$ multiply by 7 _Linear_   **13.** $y = x + 8$ _Linear_

14. $y = -x^2 + 3$ _Quadratic_   **15.** $y =$ round to the nearest 0.1 _Step_

16. Consumer A mail-order catalog lists the following charges for shipping and handling:

Price of Order ($)	Under 10	10 to 25	Over 25
Shipping Charge ($)	2.50	4.00	7.00

  a. Graph the function.

  b. What kind of function is this? _Step function_

RETEACHING

Name _____

Alternative Lesson 10-4

Other Functions

An **exponential function** is another kind of nonlinear function. This function has an exponent as the variable. An example of an exponential function is $y = 2^x$.

— Example —

Graph the function $y = 3^x$ for $x \geq 0$. What is the value of y when x is 2? What is x when y is about 250?

Make a table of the values for x and y. Use a calculator.

x	0	1	2	3	4	5	6
y	1	3	9	27	81	243	729

When x is 2, then $y = 9$.
When y is about 250, then x is 5.

Try It

  a. Graph the function $y = 2^x$ for $x \geq 0$. Complete the table of values for x and y.

x	1	2	3	4	5	6	7	8
y	2	4	8	16	32	64	128	256

What is the value of y when x is 8? _256_

What is x when y is about 500? _About 9._

  b. Graph the function $y = 0.5^x$ for $x \geq 0$.

x	1	2	3	4
y	0.5	0.25	0.125	0.0625

What is x when y is about 0.3? _About 2._

  c. Graph the function $y = 0.8^x$ for $x \geq 0$.

x	1	2	3	4
y	0.8	0.64	0.512	0.4096

What is the value of y when x is 3? _0.512_

What is x when y is about 0.25? _About 6._

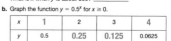

Identify each function as linear, quadratic, exponential, or step.

12. $y = 0.6^x$ **13.** $y = 0.6x^2$ **14.** $y = $ round to nearest ten   **15.** $y = 6x$
Exponential   Quadratic   Step   Linear

16. **Test Prep**   The equation $y = x^2 - 5$ describes which type of function? **B**

    Ⓐ Linear   Ⓑ Quadratic   Ⓒ Exponential   Ⓓ Step

17. Tabitha's mom started a savings account to help pay for her college education. She deposited $1000 and is receiving 7% interest compounded annually on her money. The function $A = 1000(1.07)^t$ will show the balance (A) after t years.

    a. How much money is in the account after 5 years? **$1402.55**

    b. Approximately how many years will it take to have a balance of $2000? **11 years**

18. **Chance** What are the chances that a 90% free-throw shooter will make the next 10 free throws in a row? Graph 0.9^x and find y when x is 10.

Problem Solving and Reasoning

19. **Choose a Strategy** As the value of x increases, what happens to each value?

    a. $2x$ **b.** x^2 **c.** 2^x **d.** 0.2^x

20. Give an example of a step function you might see in your everyday life. Why is it a step function?

Communicate Without graphing, describe each graph.

21. $y = 5^x$ **22.** $y = \left(\frac{1}{2}\right)^x$ **21.** Exponential, increasing

                                      22. Exponential, decreasing

Mixed Review

Write an expression for each situation. *[Lesson 3-3]*

23. Twice a number, subtracted from 10   **24.** Three times a number, plus 3
                  $10 - 2n$ $3n + 3$

Find the circumference and area of a circle with each given radius. *[Lesson 9-3]*

25. $r = 6$ m   **26.** $r = 18$ mm   **27.** $r = 2.9$ m   **28.** $r = 87$ cm
25. 12π m, 36π m²   **26.** 36π mm, 324π mm²
27. 5.8π m, 8.41π m²   **28.** 174π cm, 7569π cm²

Project Progress

Sketch and label a graph for the situation you chose. Compare your sketch to the graphs of the function models you have seen. Rule out any that do not work.

Problem Solving
Understand
Plan
Solve
Look Back

10-4 • Other Functions   **527**

Problem Solving
STRATEGIES
• Look for a Pattern
• Make an Organized List
• Make a Table
• Guess and Check
• Work Backward
• Use Logical Reasoning
• Draw a Diagram
• Solve a Simpler Problem

Exercise Notes

■ **Exercise 19**

Problem-Solving Tip You may wish to use Teaching Tool Transparencies 2 and 3: Guided Problem Solving, pages 1–2.

Project Progress

You may want to have students use Chapter 10 Project Master.

Exercise Answers

18.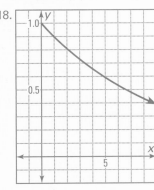
0.349, or about 35%

19. Make a table.

x	$2x$	x^2	2^x	0.2^x
0	0	0	1	1
1	2	1	2	0.2
2	4	4	4	0.04
3	6	9	8	0.008
4	8	16	16	0.0016
5	10	25	32	0.00032

   a. Increase
   b. Decrease for $x < 0$, increase for $x > 0$.
   c. Increase
   d. Decrease

20. Possible answer: Sports statistics, which change stepwise each time a player is involved in a play.

Alternate Assessment

Ongoing Discuss students' responses to Exercises 19 and 20 to see if they understand the different kinds of functions.

▶ **Quick Quiz**

Graph each function. Tell whether it is quadratic, linear, exponential, or step.

1. $y = 3^x$ Exponential

2. $y = x^2 - 3$ Quadratic

3. $y = (\frac{1}{4})^x$ Exponential

4. Parking rates: $2 for up to 1 hour, and $1 more for each additional hour or part of an hour. Step

Available on Daily Transparency 10-4

PROBLEM SOLVING

Name _____

Guided Problem Solving
10-4

GPS PROBLEM 11, STUDENT PAGE 526

Ready Rent-All rental charges for a VCR are as follows.

Rental Time	Rental Fee
One day or portion thereof	$10.00
over 1 day, up to 3 days	$20.00
over 3 days, up to 5 days	$35.00

   a. Graph the function.

   b. What kind of function is this?

— Understand —

1. What is the fee for renting a VCR for each time period?

   a. 0 hr **$0**   **b.** 5 hr **$10**   **c.** 23 hr **$10**   **d.** 25 hr **$20**

— Plan —

2. Which is the independent variable, time or rental fee? **Time.**

3. On which axis will you graph the number of days? **Horizontal, or x-axis.**

— Solve —

4. Graph the function on the grid above.

5. What kind of function did you graph? **a**

   a. Step function   **b.** Exponential function   **c.** Not a function

— Look Back —

6. How do you know what kind of function the charges are without graphing? **Possible answer: Each fee covers a range of times, so it will be step function.**

SOLVE ANOTHER PROBLEM

The video rental store rents game systems as follows.

Rental Time	Rental Fee
One day or portion thereof	$ 8.00
over 1 day up to 2 days	$12.00
over 2 days up to 4 days	$20.00

   a. Graph the function.

   b. What kind of function is this? **Step function.**

ENRICHMENT

Name _____

Extend Your Thinking
10-4

Critical Thinking
Some equations form a circle when graphed.

1. a. Complete the table below for the equation $x^2 + y^2 = 4$.

x	0	2	0	–2
y	2	0	–2	0

   b. Graph the ordered pairs. Think of the ordered pairs as part of the circumference of a circle with center (0, 0).

2. a. Complete the table below for the equation $x^2 + y^2 = 9$.

x	0	3	0	–3
y	3	0	–3	0

   b. Graph the ordered pairs. Think of the ordered pairs as part of the circumference of a circle with center (0, 0).

3. Predict what you think the graph of $x^2 + y^2 = 25$ will look like. Graph the equation to verify your prediction.
A circle with a radius of 5 and the center at (0, 0).

4. Jesse drew four circles to make a target for a computer game. The radii were 3.8 cm, 4.2 cm, and 5.6 cm. Write the equations for each given circle.
$x^2 + y^2 = 3.8^2$; $x^2 + y^2 = 4.2^2$; $x^2 + y^2 = 5.6^2$

5. Jesse used the following equations to draw circles for another computer game target: $x^2 + y^2 = 49$, $x^2 + y^2 = 6$, and $x^2 + y^2 = 25$. What is the area of the circle with the greatest diameter?
153.86 square units.

Lesson 10-4   **527**

Technology

Using a Graphing Calculator • Graphing Functions

Using a Graphing Calculator • Graphing Functions

The Point

Students use a graphing calculator's trace command to find the coordinates of different points on a graph.

Materials

Graphing calculator

Resources

Teaching Tool Transparency 23: Graphing Calculator.

About the Page

- A graphing calculator is helpful for students because it eliminates computational errors that they might make in plotting points on a graph.

- A graphing calculator helps students who are not as artistically proficient as others when drawing graphs.

- A graphing calculator is helpful when isolating a specific part of the graph. To focus in on a specific area, only the viewing window parameters need to be changed. If the graph were drawn by hand, new points would have to be plotted and the graph would have to be physically drawn again.

Ask ...

- What do the window specifications Xmin=0 and Xmax=94 mean? They mean the range of the window for x goes from 0 to 94.

- If Xscl=10, how many units does each interval on the x-axis represent? 10 units.

- In this example, you use Xmin=0, Xmax=94, Ymin=0, and Ymax=40. If you changed the window to Xmax=40, how would your view of the graph be affected? Possible answer: Only the left half of the present graph would be viewed and it would be "stretched" by a factor of approximately 2.

On Your Own

Remind students to check for reasonable answers.

Problem: The distance from Kansas City, Missouri, to Denver, Colorado, is 600 mi. How long will it take to make the trip at different rates of speed?

1 Remember that $t = \frac{d}{r}$. Time depends on the rate of speed, so use X as the rate of speed. Use the viewing window shown and enter 600/X as Y1.

2 Press GRAPH. Then press TRACE and the left and right arrow keys to find solutions.

3 If your calculator can make a table, you can use it to display solutions.

Solution: At 20 mi/hr, it would take 30 hr; at 55 mi/hr, it would take 10.9 hr.

Why does an x-value of 0 produce an error?

TRY IT

A $10,000 prize will be split evenly among the winners. How much will each person receive if there are different numbers of prizewinners? Graph the solutions.

ON YOUR OWN

► Change the range for the original problem to include negative numbers for x and y. Describe the shape of the graph. Trace to the left of 0. What are some other solutions? Do these make sense in the problem situation?

528

Answers for Try It

```
WINDOW
Xmin = 0
Xmax = 100
Xscl = 10
Ymin = 0
Ymax = 1000
Yscl = 100
```

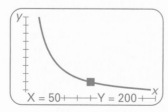

Answers for On Your Own

It is the 1st quadrant graph of $y = \frac{600}{x}$, plus its mirror image in quadrant 3. Another solution is (–20, –30). This means that at –20 mi/hr, it would take –30 hr, so negative solutions do not make sense in the problem.

Section 10A Connect

In this Connect, you will combine your knowledge of the different types of functions.

The World in Motion

Materials: Graphing utility

Kirt estimated that as a pelican swooped down toward the water, it was about 20 ft high, then 12, then 8, then 5, then 3. Then it stayed very close to the water as it flew. He used his graphing utility and found several possible function models for its height over time based upon the initial height.

He started with time at 0 sec.

   a. $y = -4x + 20$ **b.** $y = x^2 - 8x + 20$ **c.** $y = 20(0.6)^x$

1. Graph each function.

2. Which are good models for the height of the pelican? Which are not? Which do you feel is the best model? Why?

3. Do you think a step function would be a good model? Why or why not?

4. Suppose the pelican flew down to the water and immediately back up again. How would your answer to Question 2 change?

529

The World in Motion

The Point

In *The World in Motion* on page 507, students were given examples of how motion surrounds our daily lives. Now, students will choose the graph of the function that best models the height of a pelican's flight.

Materials

Graphing utility

Resources

Teaching Tool Transparency 23: Graphing Calculator

 Interactive CD-ROM Spreadsheet/Grapher Tool

About the Page

- It may help to review the differences among the three types of functions posed in this activity. The first is linear, the second is quadratic, and the third is exponential.

- Some students may benefit by seeing a rough graph of the pelican's flight. Have a student volunteer make such a graph on the chalkboard. Assume the amount of time between each height measurement is constant. Point out that this graph is a rough path of the pelican's flight because the data about time is not given.

- If students do not understand why a step function is not a good model of the pelican's flight, draw an example of a step function on the chalkboard. Compare this example to the rough graph of the pelican's flight.

Extension

Refer to Question 4. Establish which equation is a good model for the flight of the pelican. Now pose the situation where the pelican swoops back to the water, and model the flight from the water, to the sky, and back to the water. Experiment with the students to see how the equation would have to change. The coefficient of x^2 would have to be negative.

Answers for Connect

1. a.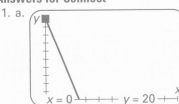

b.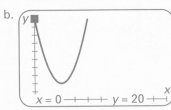

c.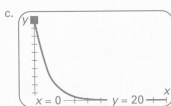

2. Possible answer: b and c; a; c is best, since the graph gives the correct starting height at $x = 0$ and descends from there to settle along the x-axis.

3. No; The pelican height changes smoothly, not in jumps.

4. b would be the best model because the curve drops down and rises back up.

Review Correlation

Item(s)	Lesson(s)
1–6	10-1
7	10-2
8–11	10-2, 10-3, 10-4
12	10-2
13, 14	10-1
15	10-2, 10-3, 10-4
16	10-2
17	10-3
18	10-4

Test Prep
Test-Taking Tip

Tell students that when checking problems in which they are computing function values, it may be helpful to mentally picture what the graph of the function looks like. This may help them determine if an answer is reasonable or not.

Answers for Review

8.
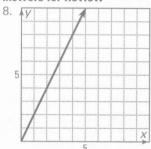

9.
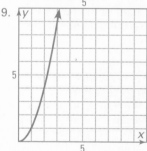

10.
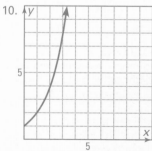

11, 13–17. See page C4.

530

Section 10A Review

For the function machine shown, find each missing value.

| Input | Multiply by 2 and subtract 8 | Output |

1. Input -1 output $\underline{-10}$
2. Input $\underline{0}$ output -8
3. Input 4   output $\underline{0}$
4. Input $\underline{1}$ output -6
5. Input 3   output $\underline{-2}$
6. Input $\underline{54}$ output 100

Test Prep

Use inverse operations to find the input value of a function.

7. Which is the input value for $y = 5x$ if the output value is -30? **C**
   Ⓐ -150 Ⓑ 6   Ⓒ -6 Ⓓ 5

Sketch an example of a graph for each type of function. **Possible answers shown.**

8. Linear   9. Quadratic   10. Exponential   11. Step

12. If y is a function of x, name the dependent variable and the independent variable.
   x independent, y dependent

Is y a function of x? Explain.

13.
x	−1	0	1	2	3
y	1	0	1	2	3

14.
x	−2	−1	0	−1	−2
y	8	4	0	−4	−8

15. Graph $y = x$, $y = x^2$, and $y = 4^x$. Describe the similarities and differences.

16. **Geology** Antarctic glaciers flow approximately 0.0005 km/hr. Write an equation to show the relationship between distance and time. Find how far a glacier travels in a week.

17. **Science** The height of a penny dropped into a well is modeled by the function $h = -16t^2$, where time (t) is in sec and height (h) is in ft.

   a. Make a table of values and graph the function, using $t = 1$ to 8 sec.

   b. If the penny hits bottom in 4 sec, how deep is the well? Why is the value of h negative?

18. A bank offers a 6% annual-interest savings account. The function $A = 1000(1.06)^t$ gives the balance (A) after t years. If $1000 is invested, how much money is in the account after 5 years? Approximately how many years will it take to have a balance of $2000? **$1338.23; 12 years**

530   *Chapter 10 • Algebra: Functions and Relationships*

Resources

Practice Masters
   Section 10A Review

Assessment Sourcebook
   Quiz 10A

   TestWorks
   Test and Practice Software

PRACTICE

Name _____

Practice

Section 10A Review

For the function machine shown, find each missing value.

1. Input 3, output $\underline{3}$
2. Input $\underline{9}$, output 5
3. Input -9, output $\underline{-1}$
4. Input $\underline{-15}$, output -3

| Input → | Divide by 3 and add 2 | → Output |

Sketch an example of a graph for each kind of function.   **Possible answers:**

5. Exponential

6. Step
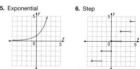

7. Quadratic

8. Is y a function of x? Explain.

x	1	0	1	2	3
y	−2	−1	0	1	2

No; There are two possible outputs for an input value of 1.

9. Graph $y = 2$, $y = 2x$, $y = x^2$, and $y = 2^x$. Describe the similarities and differences.
   Answers will vary.

10. **Science** An elephant can run about 25 mi/hr at maximum speed. If distance is a function of time, write an equation to show the relationship between distance and time. Use your equation to show how far the elephant could travel in 3 hours at this speed.   **$d = 25t$; 75 mi**

11. The population of San Francisco, California, was about 716,000 in 1970. It decreased 5.2% from 1970 to 1980, and increased 6.6% from 1980 to 1990. What was the population in 1990? *[Lesson 6-6]*   **About 724,000**

12. The floor plan of a home shows a kitchen that is $6\frac{2}{3}$ in. by 8 in. If the scale factor is 18, what is the area of the actual kitchen? *[Lesson 9-2]*   **17,280 in^2 or 120 ft^2**

Section 10B

Polynomials

Visit **www.teacher.mathsurf.com** for links to lesson plans from teachers and other professionals, NCTM information, and other sites.

LESSON PLANNING GUIDE

▶ **Student Edition**

▶ **Ancillaries***

LESSON	MATERIALS	VOCABULARY	DAILY	OTHER
Section 10B Opener				
10-5 Polynomials		polynomial, term, monomial, binomial, trinomial, degree	10-5	Technology Master 54 *WW Math*—Algebra
10-6 Adding Polynomials	algebra tiles	like terms, simplified	10-6	Teaching Tool Trans. 2, 3, 13, 14
10-7 Subtracting Polynomials	algebra tiles		10-7	Teaching Tool Trans. 13, 14 Technology Masters 55, 56
10-8 Multiplying Polynomials and Monomials			10-8	Technology Master 57 Ch. 10 Project Master
Connect	centimeter cubes			Lesson Enhancement Trans. 57 Interdisc. Team Teaching 10B
Review				Practice 10B; Quiz 10B; *TestWorks*
Extend Key Ideas				
Chapter Summary and Review				
Chapter Assessment				Ch. 10 Tests Forms A–F *TestWorks;* Ch. 10 Letter Home
Cumulative Review Chapters 1–10				Cumulative Review Ch. 1–10

* Daily Ancillaries include Practice, Reteaching, Problem Solving, Enrichment, and Daily Transparency. Teaching Tool Transparencies are in *Teacher's Toolkits*. Lesson Enhancement Transparencies are in *Overhead Transparency Package*.

SKILLS TRACE

LESSON	SKILL	FIRST INTRODUCED GR. 6	GR. 7	GR. 8	DEVELOP	PRACTICE/ APPLY	REVIEW
10-5	Evaluating polynomials.			✗ p. 532	pp. 532–534	pp. 535–536	pp. 557, 558, 559, 589
10-6	Adding polynomials.			✗ p. 537	pp. 537–539	pp. 540–541	pp. 554, 557, 559, 599
10-7	Subtracting polynomials.			✗ p. 542	pp. 542–545	pp. 546–547	pp. 554, 559, 604, 675
10-8	Multiplying polynomials.			✗ p. 548	pp. 548–550	pp. 551–552	pp. 554, 557, 559, 609

CONNECTED MATHEMATICS

The unit *Frogs, Fleas, and Painted Cubes (Quadratic Relationships),* from the **Connected Mathematics** series, can be used with Section 10B.

Math and Social Studies
(Worksheet pages 41–42: Teacher pages T41–T42)

Students use knowledge of writing and evaluating polynomials to determine the carrying capacity of a freight train.

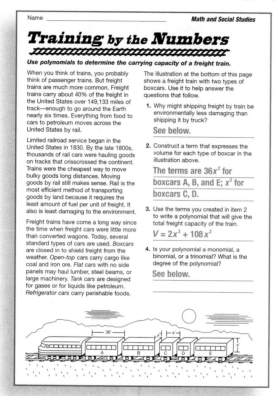

Math and Social Studies

Name _____

Training by the Numbers

Use polynomials to determine the carrying capacity of a freight train.

When you think of trains, you probably think of passenger trains. But freight trains are much more common. Freight trains carry about 40% of the freight in the United States over 149,133 miles of track—enough to go around the Earth nearly six times. Everything from food to cars to petroleum moves across the United States by rail.

Limited railroad service began in the United States in 1830. By the late 1800s, thousands of rail cars were hauling goods on tracks that crisscrossed the continent. Trains were the cheapest way to move bulky goods long distances. Moving goods by rail still makes sense. Rail is the most efficient method of transporting goods by land because it requires the least amount of fuel per unit of freight. It also is least damaging to the environment.

Freight trains have come a long way since the time when freight cars were little more than converted wagons. Today, several standard types of cars are used. *Boxcars* are closed in to shield freight from the weather. *Open-top* cars carry cargo like coal and iron ore. *Flat cars* with no side panels may haul lumber, steel beams, or large machinery. *Tank cars* are designed for gases or for liquids like petroleum. *Refrigerator cars* carry perishable foods.

The illustration at the bottom of this page shows a freight train with two types of boxcars. Use it to help answer the questions that follow.

1. Why might shipping freight by train be environmentally less damaging than shipping it by truck?

   See below.

2. Construct a term that expresses the volume for each type of boxcar in the illustration above.

   The terms are $36x^2$ for boxcars A, B, and E; x^3 for boxcars C, D.

3. Use the terms you created in item 2 to write a polynomial that will give the total freight capacity of the train.

   $V = 2x^3 + 108x^2$

4. Is your polynomial a monomial, a binomial, or a trinomial? What is the degree of the polynomial?

   See below.

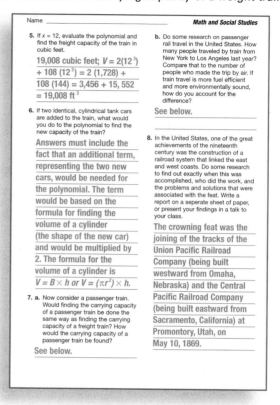

Math and Social Studies

Name _____

5. If $x = 12$, evaluate the polynomial and find the freight capacity of the train in cubic feet.

   19,008 cubic feet; $V = 2(12^3) + 108(12^2) = 2(1,728) + 108(144) = 3,456 + 15,552 = 19,008\ ft^3$

6. If two identical, cylindrical tank cars are added to the train, what would you do to the polynomial to find the new capacity of the train?

   Answers must include the fact that an additional term, representing the two new cars, would be needed for the polynomial. The term would be based on the formula for finding the volume of a cylinder (the shape of the new car) and would be multiplied by 2. The formula for the volume of a cylinder is $V = B \times h$ or $V = (\pi r^2) \times h$.

7. a. Now consider a passenger train. Would finding the carrying capacity of a passenger train be done the same way as finding the carrying capacity of a freight train? How would the carrying capacity of a passenger train be found?

   See below.

b. Do some research on passenger rail travel in the United States. How many people traveled by train from New York to Los Angeles last year? Compare that to the number of people who made the trip by air. If train travel is more fuel efficient and more environmentally sound, how do you account for the difference?

   See below.

8. In the United States, one of the great achievements of the nineteenth century was the construction of a railroad system that linked the east and west coasts. Do some research to find out exactly when this was accomplished, who did the work, and the problems and solutions that were associated with the feat. Write a report on a seperate sheet of paper, or present your findings in a talk to your class.

   The crowning feat was the joining of the tracks of the Union Pacific Railroad Company (being built westward from Omaha, Nebraska) and the Central Pacific Railroad Company (being built eastward from Sacramento, California) at Promontory, Utah, on May 10, 1869.

Answers

1. Accept all reasonable answers. Students should include the idea that many trucks would be required to haul the same amount of cargo that one train can haul. The trucks would also create more pollution than one train locomotive.

4. A binomial because it has two terms; degree 3 because the value of its largest exponent is 3.

7. a. No. The carrying capacity of the passenger train would be found by counting the number of seats per car.

b. Students can find the data they need by reading books and magazines, by checking the Internet (keywords such as: RAILROAD, AMTRAK, AIR TRAVEL), or by contacting organizations like Amtrak, United States Department of Transportation, and the Federal Aviation Administration. The numbers for cross-country fliers will be much higher than those for rail riders, largely because rail travel takes longer (three days as opposed to about six hours).

BIBLIOGRAPHY

FOR TEACHERS

Adams, Dennis, Helen Carson, and Mary Hamm. *Cooperative Learning and Educational Media: Collaborating with Technology and Each Other.* Englewood Cliffs, NJ: Educational Technology Publications, 1990.

Burton, Robert. *Birdflight: An Illustrated Study of Birds' Aerial Mastery.* New York, NY: Facts on File, 1990.

Phillips, Elizabeth. *Patterns and Functions.* Addenda Series, Grades 5–8. Reston, VA: NCTM, 1991.

Short, Lester L. *The Lives of Birds: Birds of the World and Their Behavior.* New York, NY: Henry Holt and Company, Inc., 1993.

FOR STUDENTS

Gray, Ian. *Birds of Prey.* Oxford Scientific Films. New York, NY: Mallard Press, 1990.

MacQuitty, Miranda. *Sea Birds.* Oxford Scientific Films. New York, NY: Mallard Press, 1990.

Snedden, Robert. *What Is a Bird?* San Francisco, CA: Sierra Club Books for Children, 1992.

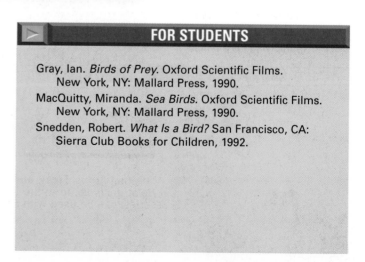

SECTION 10B

Polynomials

▶ Science Link   ▶ History Link   ▶ www.mathsurf.com/8/ch10/birds

WHICH CAME FIRST?

When we think of animals living today that are direct descendants of dinosaurs, we probably think of alligators, lizards, komodo dragons, or rhinoceroses. But we probably don't think of birds.

The earliest bird fossil found was that of Archaeopteryx, a bird that lived about 140 million years ago. It had wings with both feathers and claws, teeth, and a dinosaur-like tail. It could barely fly, and may even have climbed trees.

Today's birds are also varied in shape and form. From the ostrich, to the penguin, to the burrowing owl, to the peacock, nature has given birds colors and abilities of which we can only dream.

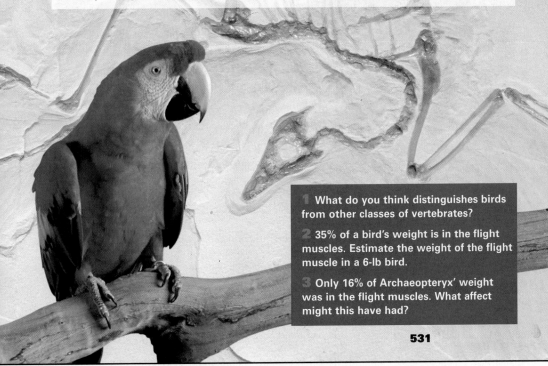

1 What do you think distinguishes birds from other classes of vertebrates?

2 35% of a bird's weight is in the flight muscles. Estimate the weight of the flight muscle in a 6-lb bird.

3 Only 16% of Archaeopteryx' weight was in the flight muscles. What affect might this have had?

531

Where are we now?

In Section 10A, students studied different kinds of functions.

They learned how to

- identify functions and find the input and output values of a function.

- represent functions using tables, graphs, and equations.

- represent quadratic functions as graphs, tables, and equations.

- graph and evaluate other types of functions.

Where are we going?

In Section 10B, students will

- evaluate polynomials.

- add polynomials.

- subtract polynomials.

- multiply monomials and polynomials.

Objective
- Evaluate polynomials.

Vocabulary
- Polynomial, term, monomial, binomial, trinomial, degree

NCTM Standards
- 1–4, 8, 9, 12, 13

► **Review**

Evaluate each expression for $n = -2$, 1, and 5.

1. $n^2 + 3n - 2$ $-4, 2, 38$

2. $2n^3 - 4n$ $-8, -2, 230$

3. $6n^0$ $6, 6, 6$

Available on Daily Transparency 10-5

► **Lesson Link**

Students have worked informally with polynomial expressions in many preceding chapters. Now they explore polynomials more formally and in greater depth.

1 Introduce

Explore

The Point
Students write a polynomial for the surface area of a box.

Ongoing Assessment
Check students' results after Step 4. Be sure that students understand that the 2 is to be replaced by x and that Steps 1–3 should be repeated.

For Groups That Finish Early
Calculate the surface area for $x = 4, 5, 6, 7, 8, 9$, and 10.   112, 150, 192, 238, 288, 342, and 400.

Follow Up
Be sure that everyone understands how the answer to Step 4 is obtained.

10-5 Polynomials

▶ **Lesson Link**   You have learned about linear functions and several nonlinear functions. Now you will learn about another type of nonlinear function. ◄

You'll Learn ...
- to evaluate polynomials

... How It's Used
Computer programmers use polynomials to program 3-D graphics for video games.

Vocabulary
polynomial
term
monomial
binomial
trinomial
degree

Explore   Polynomials

Let's Box!

1. Find the area of each square end of the box pictured above.

2. Find the area of the rectangular faces.

3. Find the surface area of the box by adding the areas of all the faces.

4. If the square ends had side length x units, write an expression that would give the surface area of the box.

5. How does the surface area change as the length of the side of the square changes? Explain your answer.

▶ **Language Link**

Poly- means many or too many.

Learn   Polynomials

A **polynomial** is an algebraic expression that is the sum of one or more parts, called **terms**. Each term is a signed number, a variable, or a number multiplied by a variable or variables. The variables can have whole-number exponents.

Polynomial: $-2x^3 - 4x^2 + 3x + 1$

Terms: $-2x^3$ $-4x^2$ $3x$ 1

532   *Chapter 10 • Algebra: Functions and Relationships*

MEETING INDIVIDUAL NEEDS

Resources
10-5 Practice
10-5 Reteaching
10-5 Problem Solving
10-5 Enrichment
10-5 Daily Transparency
Problem of the Day
Review
Quick Quiz
Technology Master 54
Wide World of Mathematics Algebra: Investing for College

Learning Modalities

Verbal   Have students write a short story in which words using the prefixes mono-, bi-, and tri- are incorporated.

Individual   In Exercise 26 on page 536, students exhibit their understanding of when an expression is a polynomial and when it is not.

English Language Development

Some students may find the vocabulary in this lesson difficult. Suggest that they make their own list of terms, with definitions and examples. Flash cards might be another way to help students master the vocabulary.

Some polynomials have special names.

monomial:	x,	$2x^3$,	-2

Monomials have one term.

binomial: $\quad x + 1, \quad 2x^3 - 7x$ **Binomials** have two terms.

trinomial: $\quad x + 3x^2 - 4x^3, \quad x^2 - 4x + 3$ **Trinomials** have three terms.

The **degree** of a polynomial with one variable is the value of the largest exponent of the variable that appears in any term.

$2x^3$, $2x^3 - 7$, and $-4x^3 + 3x^2 + x$ have degree 3

$x^2 - 4x + 3$ has degree 2

x and $x + 4$ each have degree 1

-2 has degree 0

Polynomials are usually written with the term that has the highest degree first, the next highest second, and so on. This is called writing a polynomial in descending order.

$x^4 + 3x - 2x^6 + 5$ written in descending order is $-2x^6 + x^4 + 3x + 5$.

Examples

1 Write the polynomial $x^5 + 2x - 6x^3 + 2x^2$ in descending order. What is the degree of the polynomial?

$x^5 - 6x^3 + 2x^2 + 2x$ The term with the highest degree is x^5, then $-6x^3$, then $2x^2$, and finally $2x$.

Because the largest exponent is 5, the degree of the polynomial is 5.

2 The height of a sagging highwire x m from the end can be modeled by the polynomial $15 + 0.00025x^3 - 0.375x - 0.005x^2 + 0.000004x^4$. Write this polynomial in descending order. What is the degree of the polynomial?

$0.000004x^4 + 0.00025x^3 - 0.005x^2 - 0.375x + 15$ The exponents are in order.

Since the largest exponent is 4, the degree of the polynomial is 4.

Try It

Write the trinomial $x + 2 - 4x^2$ in descending order. What is the degree of the polynomial? $-4x^2 + x + 2$, 2

MATH EVERY DAY

▶ **Problem of the Day**

Using prime numbers only, complete the magic square so that each row, column, and diagonal has a sum of 219.

		37
	73	
		43

103	79	37
7	73	139
109	67	43

Available on Daily Transparency 10-5

An Extension is provided in the transparency package.

Fact of the Day

The ostrich is the largest living bird. A full-grown ostrich stands 7 to 8 feet tall and weighs between 200 and 300 pounds.

Mental Math

Calculate each percent mentally.

1. 150% of 50   75

2. 125% of 80   100

3. 250% of 60   150

Answers for Explore

1. Each of the two has area $2^2 = 4$ units^2.

2. Each of the four has area $2(5) = 10$ units^2.

3. $2(2^2) + 4(2 \cdot 5) = 48$ units^2.

4. Possible answer: $2(x^2) + 4(x \cdot 5)$.

5. Possible answer: Increases as the length increases, since each square end gets larger and each rectangular face gets larger.

2 Teach

Learn

A number such as –2 has degree 0 because it can be written as $-2x^0$. Remind students that any number to the 0 power is 1, so $-2x^0 = -2 \cdot 1 = -2$. We usually do not write the x^0 part of a term.

Alternate Examples

1. Write the polynomial $x^3 + 5 - 4x + 2x^4$ in descending order. What is the degree of the polynomial?

   $2x^4 + x^3 - 4x + 5$.

   The term with the highest degree is $2x^4$, then x^3, then $4x$, and finally 5. Because the largest exponent is 4, the degree of the polynomial is 4.

2. Jack found that the amount of money he has saved in a savings account over the past four years can be modeled by the following polynomial, where r is 1 + the annual interest rate: $425r^1 + 250r^2 + 375r^3 + 300r^4$. Write this polynomial in descending order. What is the degree of the polynomial?

   $300(r)^4 + 375(r)^3 + 250(r)^2 + 425(r)^1$. Since the largest exponent is 4, the degree of the polynomial is 4.

Alternate Examples

3. Evaluate $x^4 - x^3 + x - 2$ for $x = -1$

$x^4 - x^3 + x - 2$
$(-1)^4 - (-1)^3 + (-1) - 2$
         Substitute -1 for x in the polynomial.
$= 1 - (-1) - 1 - 2$
         Simplify powers, then add or subtract.
$= -1$

4. The surface area of a cube can be represented by the function $SA = 6s^2$, where SA = surface area and s = the length of a side. Find the surface area of a cube with each given side length.
   a. 2 cm   b. 5 in.   c. 1.2 m

   Substitute the given side length into the equation $SA = 6s^2$.
   a. $SA = 6(2)^2 = 24$. The surface area of the cube is 24 cm^2.
   b. $SA = 6(5)^2 = 150$. The surface area of the cube is 150 in^2.
   c. $SA = 6(1.2)^2 = 8.64$. The surface area of the cube is 8.64 m^2.

3 Practice and Assess

Check

For Question 1, have students give some other words that use the prefixes. **Possible answers:** monopoly, bicycle, triangle, tripod, polygon.

Answers for Check Your Understanding

1. Mono: 1; Bi: 2; Tri: 3; Poly: many

2. Put the polynomial expression in descending order and look for the highest exponent.

3. They are the same; Put both in descending order.

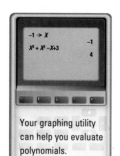

Your graphing utility can help you evaluate polynomials.

Study TIP

Understanding common prefixes and suffixes can help you learn the meanings of unfamiliar words.

Polynomials can be evaluated by replacing the variables with the given numbers and using the order of operations to simplify the expression.

Examples

3 Evaluate $x^3 + x^2 - x + 3$ for $x = -4$.

$(-4)^3 + (-4)^2 - (-4) + 3$ Substitute -4 for x in the polynomial.

$= -64 + 16 + 4 + 3$ Simplify powers, then add or subtract.

$= -41$

4 The volume of a cube can be represented by the function $V = s^3$, where V = volume and s = the length of a side. Find the volume of a cube with each given side length.

  a. 3 in.   **b.** 1.5 in.   **c.** 2 cm

Substitute the given side length into the equation $V = s^3$.

  a. $V = (3)^3 = 27$. The volume of the cube is 27 in^3.

  b. $V = (1.5)^3 = 3.375$. The volume of the cube is 3.375 in^3.

  c. $V = (2)^3 = 8$. The volume of the cube is 8 cm^3.

Try It

  a. Evaluate $x^3 - x^2 + x + 5$ for $x = 0$ and $x = -3$. **5, −34**

  b. The volume of a hemispheric birdbath is a function of the length of its radius and can be represented by the function $V = \frac{2}{3}\pi r^3$, where V = volume and r = the length of the radius. Find the volume of a birdbath with each given radius length. Use $\pi = 3.14$.

    i. 1 ft   **ii.** 4 ft   **iii.** 2.25 m
    ≈ 2.09 ft^3 ≈ 134 ft^3 ≈ 23.8 m^3

Check | Your Understanding

1. What do the prefixes *mono-*, *bi-*, *tri-*, and *poly-* mean?

2. How do you determine the degree of a polynomial?

3. Are the polynomials $3x^2 - 2 + x - x^3$ and $x - 2 - x^3 + 3x^2$ the same? How do you know?

MEETING MIDDLE SCHOOL CLASSROOM NEEDS

Tips from Middle School Teachers

The terminology in this lesson may intimidate some students. I begin the lesson by writing <u>mono</u>mial, <u>bi</u>nomial, <u>tri</u>nomial, and <u>poly</u>nomial on the board, underlining the prefixes. Then we discuss other words with these prefixes.

Team Teaching	Cultural Connection
Check with both the science and social science teachers to see if they can supply polynomials that have been used to model phenomena in their disciplines.	Have students for whom English is a second language translate the vocabulary terms in this lesson into their native languages. (For example, in Spanish *polynomial* is *polinomio*, in German it is *polynomische*, and in French it is *polynôme*.) Compare these words with the English words. Are there any similarities?

Practice and Apply

1. **Getting Started** State the number of terms in each polynomial expression.

   a. $-2x^2 + 3x + 1$ **3** **b.** $4x$ **1** **c.** $-2x^3 + 6$ **2**

Identify each expression as a monomial, binomial, or trinomial.

2. $0.75y$ **Monomial**   3. $a + 3 - 4a^2$ **Trinomial**   4. $2b^5$ **Monomial**   5. $x + 12$ **Binomial**   6. $3x^3 + 2x^2 + 9$ **Trinomial**

Write each polynomial expression in descending order, then find the degree of each polynomial.

7. $4 + 2x$
   $2x + 4; 1$

8. $2x + 4x^2 - 3$
   $4x^2 + 2x - 3; 2$

9. $x^2 - x^3 - x^4$
   $-x^4 - x^3 + x^2; 4$

10. $2x + 4x^3 + 1$
    $4x^3 + 2x + 1; 3$

Evaluate each polynomial for $x = -3$.

11. $3x + 6$ **−3**   12. $x^2 + 3x - 3$ **−3**   13. $3x^2 - 4x + 12$ **51**   14. $x^3 - 3$ **−30**

Evaluate each polynomial for $g = 2$ and for $g = 10$.

15. $g - g^2 + g^3$
    $6; 910$

16. $g^2 - 9g$
    $-14; 10$

17. $5 - g$ **3; −5**   18. $25g^2 - 4$ **96, 2496**

19. **Geometry** The surface area of a cylinder with a height of 12 in. is given by $2\pi r^2 + 24\pi r$. Find the surface area of a cylinder with a radius, r, of 2 in. $\approx$ **175.9 in²**

20. **Language Arts** The words *monomial, binomial, trinomial,* and *polynomial* use the prefixes *mono-, bi-, tri-,* and *poly-*. Find some other words that use these prefixes and give their meanings.

21. **Test Prep** Which of the following is the degree of the polynomial $5 + 3x^4 - 2x^5 + x^8$? **B**

    Ⓐ 18   Ⓑ 8   Ⓒ 5   Ⓓ 4

22. **Patterns** Evaluate each polynomial in the table for $x = 0, 1, 2,$ and 3. Describe the pattern that is formed.

	$x = 0$	$x = 1$	$x = 2$	$x = 3$
$x + 1$				
$x^2 + 2x + 1$				
$x^3 + 3x^2 + 3x + 1$				
$x^4 + 4x^3 + 6x^2 + 4x + 1$				

Assignment Guide

■ **Basic**
1–13, 15–18, 20, 21, 23, 25, 28–33

■ **Average**
2–10 evens, 11–23, 25–33

■ **Enriched**
2–10 evens, 12–14, 16–33

Exercise Notes

■ **Exercise 9**

Error Prevention Students may forget to write the negative sign in front of the x^4 term.

Exercise Answers

20. Possible answers: Monotone: one note or pitch; Bicycle: two-wheeled cycle; Trimaran: three-hulled sailboat; Polysyllabic: having several syllables.

22.

	0	1	2	3
$x + 1$	1	2	3	4
$x^2 + 2x + 1$	1	4	9	16
$x^3 + 3x^2 + 3x + 1$	1	8	27	64
$x^4 + 4x^3 + 6x^2 + 4x + 1$	1	16	81	256

For any value of x, the columns contain the next number $(x + 1)$, the next number squared, the next number cubed, and so on. The rows contain 1, 2, 3, 4, the squares of 1, 2, 3, 4, the cubes, and so on.

Reteaching

Activity

Materials: 3" by 5" note cards

• Work in groups of three.

• Using x as the variable, each group member writes 5 different monomials, each on a separate note card.

• Stack the cards upside down in a deck, shuffle them, and deal 3 cards to each group member.

• Form a polynomial in descending order with your 3 cards. Add any like terms that you have. Evaluate the polynomial for $x = 1, 2,$ and 3.

• Return the cards to the deck, and repeat the activity two more times.

PRACTICE

Polynomials

Identify each expression as a monomial, binomial, or trinomial.

1. $2x^3$ **Monomial**   2. $5y - 7$ **Binomial**   3. $x^5 - 3x^2 + 2$ **Trinomial**

4. $c^3 - 5$ **Binomial**   5. $8d + 2 - d^5$ **Trinomial**   6. $215k$ **Monomial**

Write each polynomial expression in descending order. Then find the degree of each polynomial.

7. $7 - 5x + 2x^3$ Deg.: **3**
   $2x^3 - 5x + 7$

8. $12 + 3x$ Deg.: **1**
   $3x + 12$

9. $3x + 2 + x^2$ Deg.: **2**
   $x^2 + 3x + 2$

10. $-x^3 + 2x^7$ Deg.: **7**
    $2x^7 - x^3$

11. $7x^4 - 2x^3$ Deg.: **4**
    $7x^4 - 2x^3$

12. $4x - 3 + x^5$ Deg.: **5**
    $x^5 + 4x - 3$

Evaluate each polynomial for $x = -5$.

13. $4x + 7$ **−13**   14. $-7x + 3$ **38**   15. $4x^2 + 18x$ **10**

16. $x^2 - 3x + 8$ **48**   17. x^3 **−125**   18. $x^2 - 5x + 7$ **57**

Evaluate each polynomial for $t = 3$ and for $t = 8$.

19. $t^3 - 5$
    $t = 3$: **22**
    $t = 8$: **507**

20. $-3t^2 + 12t$
    $t = 3$: **9**
    $t = 8$: **−96**

21. $56 - 9t$
    $t = 3$: **29**
    $t = 8$: **−16**

22. $5 + 8t^2 - t$
    $t = 3$: **74**
    $t = 8$: **509**

23. $8t - 4 + t^2$
    $t = 3$: **29**
    $t = 8$: **124**

24. $t^3 - 2t - 12$
    $t = 3$: **9**
    $t = 8$: **484**

25. **Science** A ball is thrown upward at a speed of 48 ft/sec. Its height h, in feet, after t seconds, is given by $h = 48t - 16t^2$. Find the height after 2 seconds. **32 ft**

26. **Geometry** The formulas $S = 4\pi r^2$ and $V = \frac{4}{3}\pi r^3$ give the surface area S and volume V of a sphere with radius r. The moon has radius 1080 mi. Find the surface area and volume. Use 3.14 for π.

    Surface area: $\approx$ **14,650,000 mi²**   Volume $\approx$ **5,274,000,000 mi³**

RETEACHING

Polynomials

A **polynomial** is an algebraic expression that is the sum of one or more parts, called **terms**. Each term is a signed number, a variable, or a number multiplied by a variable or variables. The variables can have whole-number exponents.

The **degree** of a polynomial with one variable is the value of the largest exponent of the variable that appears in any term.

Polynomial	Degree
4 and −6	0
x and $x - 5$	1
$x^2 + 3x + 2$ and $4x^2 - x$	2
x^3 and $x^3 + x^2 - 2$	3

A polynomial is usually written with the term that has the highest power first, the next highest power second, and so on. This is called writing a polynomial in descending order.

You can evaluate a polynomial by replacing the variables with numbers and simplifying the expression.

— **Example 1** —

Write the polynomial $x^2 - 6 + 4x - 10x^3$ in descending order. What is the degree of the polynomial?

The term $10x^3$ has the highest degree, then x^2, then $4x$ and finally 6.

$-10x^3 + x^2 + 4x - 6$ is written in descending order. The largest exponent is 3, so the degree of the polynomial is 3.

Try It Write each polynomial in descending order. What is the degree of the polynomial?

a. $2x + 3x^2 + 9 + x^4$ $x^4 + 3x^2 + 2x + 9$; degree is 4.

b. $5 + 3x + 6x^3 + 2x^2$ $6x^3 + 2x^2 + 3x + 5$; degree is 3.

— **Example 2** —

Evaluate $x^2 + 5x + 9$ for $x = -2$.

	$x^2 + 5x + 9$
Substitute −2 for x.	$= (-2)^2 + 5(-2) + 9$
Simplify powers, then multiply.	$= 4 + -10 + 9$
Add or subtract.	$= 3$

So, $x^2 + 5x + 9 = 3$ when $x = -2$.

Try It

c. Evaluate $x^3 + 2x^2 + 8$ for $x = 3$. **53**

d. Evaluate $x^3 + 5x + 4$ for $x = 2$. **22**

■ Exercise 24

Science Niels Bohr, a Danish physicist, won the Nobel Prize in physics in 1922 for his work on atomic structure. During World War II he worked with scientists in Los Alamos, New Mexico, on the first atomic bomb. After the war he advocated peaceful uses of nuclear energy.

■ Exercise 26

Students need to think about the part of the definition of polynomial that states that the exponents must be whole numbers. Writing a term with an exponent that is not a whole number is the way to write an expression that is not a polynomial.

Exercise Answers

25. $V = ns^3$ where s is the side length and n is the number of boxes.

27. 0, 1, 5, 14, 30; The differences are the perfect squares 1, 4, 9, 16.

Alternate Assessment

Portfolio Students might find illustrations that suggest real-life applications of polynomials, and place these in their portfolios. See Example 4, Try It on page 534, and Exercises 19 and 23–25 for examples.

▶ Quick Quiz

Consider the expression $3x - 5 + 2x^3$.

1. Rewrite the expression in descending order. What is its degree? $2x^3 + 3x - 5$; 3

2. Classify the expression. Trinomial

3. Evaluate the expression for $x = 2$. 17

4. Write a binomial that has degree 4. Possible answer: $x^4 + 1$

Available on Daily Transparency 10–5

PROBLEM SOLVING 10-5

23. **Geometry** At Epcot Center in Orlando, Florida, the Spaceship Earth is built in the shape of a sphere with a diameter of approximately 165 ft. Use $\pi = 3.14$ to answer each question.

   a. Use the formula $S = 4\pi r^2$, where S = surface area and r = radius, to find the approximate surface area. **85,486.5 ft²**

   b. Using the formula $V = \frac{4}{3}\pi r^3$, where V = volume and r = radius, find the approximate volume. **2,350,878.75 ft³**

24. **Science** Niels Bohr's model of the atom shows that electrons rotate around the nucleus in a series of orbits called *shells*. $2x^2$ represents the number of electrons in each shell, where $x = 1$ in the first shell, $x = 2$ in the second shell, and so on. How many electrons could be orbiting the nucleus in the fourth shell of an atom? **32 electrons**

Problem Solving and Reasoning

25. **Critical Thinking** The Birdseed Box uses boxes that are the same length, width, and height. Write an expression that will give the total volume of any number of boxes.

26. **Journal** Give some examples of expressions that are polynomials. Give some examples of expressions that are not polynomials and explain why they are not. **Answers may vary**

27. **Math Reasoning** The differences between terms of this sequence form a pattern.

sequence: 0   1   3   6   10   15

differences: 1   2   3   4   5

Evaluate $\frac{2n^3 + 3n^2 + n}{6}$ for $n = 0, 1, 2, 3,$ and 4 to create a sequence. Describe the pattern in the differences.

Mixed Review

Solve each equation. *[Lesson 3-4]*

28. $x + 20 = 55$ **35** 29. $88 = x - 17$ **105** 30. $x + 4\frac{1}{2} = 5\frac{1}{2}$ **1** 31. $x - 40 = 140$ **180**

Find how much fabric is needed to cover each object. *[Lesson 9-4]*

32. The cover of a photo album that is 10 in. by 13 in. by 3 in. **299 in²**

33. A gift box that is 28 cm by 28 cm by 16 cm and its lid that is 28 cm by 28 cm by 2 cm **3584 cm²**

▶ **PROBLEM SOLVING**

Guided Problem Solving 10-5

GPS PROBLEM 23, STUDENT PAGE 536

At Epcot Center in Orlando, Florida, the Spaceship Earth is built in the shape of a sphere with a diameter of approximately 165 ft. Use $\pi = 3.14$ to answer each question.

a. Use the formula $S = 4\pi r^2$, where S = surface area and r = radius to find the approximate surface area.

b. Using the formula $V = \frac{4}{3}\pi r^3$, where V = volume and r = radius, find the approximate volume.

— **Understand** —

1. What is the diameter? **≈ 165 ft**

2. Underline the value of π that you will use.

3. Write the formula for surface area. **$S = 4\pi r^2$** For volume. **$V = \frac{4}{3}\pi r^3$**

— **Plan** —

4. What is the radius of the sphere? **≈ 82.5 ft**

5. Find the value of r^2. **≈ 6806.25 ft²** Of r^3. **≈ 561,515.625 ft³**

6. Complete the equation to find the surface area. $S =$ **4 · 3.14 · 6806.25**

7. Complete the equation to find the volume. $V =$ **$\frac{4}{3}$ · 3.14 · 561,515.625**

— **Solve** —

8. Solve each equation.

   a. Surface area **85,486.5 ft²**   **b.** Volume **2,350,878.75 ft³**

— **Look Back** —

9. Why did you find r^2 and r^3 as the first step in solving both formulas? **Possible answer: To follow order of operations.**

SOLVE ANOTHER PROBLEM

A museum has an exhibit within a sphere with a diameter of approximately 40 feet. Use $\pi = 3.14$ to answer each question.

a. Use the formula $S = 4\pi r^2$, where S = surface area and r = radius to find the approximate surface area. **5024 ft²**

b. Using the formula $V = \frac{4}{3}\pi r^3$, where V = volume and r = radius, find the approximate volume. **33,493.3̄ ft³**

▶ **ENRICHMENT**

Extend Your Thinking 10-5

Visual Thinking

Draw the figure that should appear in the center circle. If a shape appears an even number of times, include it in your drawing. If a shape appears an odd number of times, do *not* include it in your drawing.

Use the circles below to create your own puzzle. Trade with a friend and solve.

Adding Polynomials

▶ **Lesson Link**   In the last lesson, you were introduced to polynomials. In this lesson, you will learn to add polynomials. ◀

Explore   Adding Polynomials

Family Reunion

Materials: Algebra tiles

1. What expression is modeled by the tiles?

2. What expression is modeled by the tiles?

3. Model the two sets of tiles above with your tiles. Combine the two sets. Remove any zero pairs. What expression remains?

4. Model $x^2 + 4x - 3$ with algebra tiles. Model $4x - 2x^2 + 1$ with more algebra tiles. Combine the two sets and remove any zero pairs. What expression remains?

5. When you combine algebra tiles, do you combine x^2 tiles with x tiles? x tiles with unit tiles? How can you apply this to adding expressions?

Learn   Adding Polynomials

Recall from the last lesson that polynomials contain terms. **Like terms** are terms that have the same variable raised to the same exponent.

For the polynomial $3x^2 + 4x^3 - 6x + 2 - 8x^3 - 2x^2$, $3x^2$ and $-2x^2$ are like terms because both contain the variable x raised to the second power; $4x^3$ and $-8x^3$ are like terms because both contain the variable x raised to the third power. Like terms can be combined using the distributive property.

$$3x^2 + -2x^2 = (3 + -2)x^2 = 1x^2 \qquad 4x^3 + -8x^3 = (4 + -8)x^3 = -4x^3$$

You'll Learn ...
■ to add polynomials

... How It's Used

Many irregularly-shaped pieces were used to renovate the Statue of Liberty.

Sometimes you will have to add polynomials in order to find the area of irregular figures.

Vocabulary
like terms

simplified

MEETING INDIVIDUAL NEEDS

Resources

10-6 Practice
10-6 Reteaching
10-6 Problem Solving
10-6 Enrichment
10-6 Daily Transparency
    Problem of the Day
    Review
    Quick Quiz
Teaching Tool Transparencies 2, 3, 13, 14

Learning Modalities

Verbal Ask students to compose a short poem or limerick to describe adding like terms in a polynomial.

Visual Have students color squares on graph paper to simulate algebra tiles. Have them use one color for positive terms and another color for negative terms in a polynomial.

Inclusion

Visually impaired students may have difficulty grouping like terms. It may be helpful for these students to first circle each type of term in the polynomial with a specific color. For example, all x^2-terms may be circled in red, all x-terms may be circled in yellow, and all whole numbers may be circled in blue. Then the student can identify like terms more easily when simplifying.

Objective
■ **Add polynomials.**

Vocabulary
■ **Like terms, simplified**

Materials
■ **Explore: algebra tiles**

NCTM Standards
■ **1–4, 8, 9, 12, 13**

▶ **Review**

Evaluate each expression.

1. $(100 + 50 + 3) + (400 + 20 + 5)$ 578

2. $(300 + 80 + 2) + (600 + 7)$ 989

3. $(500 + 90 + 8) + (200 + 20 + 2)$ 820

Available on Daily Transparency 10-6

▶ **Lesson Link**

Remind students that in Lesson 10-5 **Explore**, they used a polynomial to describe the surface area of a box. By adding polynomials, they could find the total surface area of several such boxes.

1 Introduce

Explore

You may wish to use Teaching Tool Transparencies 13: Algebra Tiles (red) and 14: Algebra Tiles (yellow) with **Explore**.

The Point
Students use algebra tiles to model adding polynomials.

Ongoing Assessment
Make sure students are finding legitimate zero pairs in their modeling. Check that students are not combining unlike tiles.

For Groups That Finish Early
Why do you think zero pairs are removed when combining the two sets of tiles? Since their sum is 0, we apply the identity property of addition.

Lesson 10-6   537

Ask volunteers to share their answers for Steps 3 and 4. Have a volunteer show the steps he or she used to add the polynomials. Discuss with the class these volunteers' answers to Step 5.

Answers for Explore

1. $2x^2 - 3x + 1$

2. $x^2 + 2x - 4$

3. $3x^2 - x - 3$

4. $-x^2 + 8x - 2$

5. No; No; Combine only like terms.

2 Teach

Learn

You may want to compare adding polynomials to adding whole numbers expressed in expanded form. For example, compare $(100 + 50 + 3) + (400 + 20 + 5)$ to $(x^2 + 5x + 3) + (4x^2 + 2x + 5)$.

Alternate Examples

1. Simplify each expression.

   List the terms in descending order. Group like terms. Combine Like terms.
   a. $8 + x + 5x^2 - 4x$
   $5x^2 + x - 4x + 8$
   $= 5x^2 + (1 - 4)x + 8$
   $= 5x^2 + (-3)x + 8$
   $= 5x^2 - 3x + 8$

   b. $2y^2 + (-9y) + 7y^2 - y$
   $2y^2 + 7y^2 + (-9y) - y$
   $= (2 + 7)y^2 + (-9 - 1)y$
   $= 9y^2 + (-10)y$
   $= 9y^2 - 10y$

2. Add the polynomials
   $6x^2 - 2x - 9$, $-4x^2 + 3$, and $x - 2$.
   $(6x^2 - 2x - 9) + (-4x^2 + 3) + (x - 2)$
   Write without parentheses:
   $= 6x^2 - 2x - 9 + -4x^2 + 3 + x - 2$
   Group like terms:
   $= (6x^2 + -4x^2) + (-2x + x) + (-9 + 3 - 2)$
   Combine like terms to simplify:
   $= (2x^2) + (-x) + (-8)$
   $= 2x^2 - x - 8$.

A polynomial is **simplified** when it contains no like terms.

Examples

1 Simplify each expression.

a. $1 + 4x + 3x^2 - 5x$ **b.** $3w^2 + (-6w) + 4w^2 - 2w$

a. $3x^2 + 4x - 5x + 1$ List the terms in descending order.

   $= 3x^2 + (4 - 5)x + 1$ Group like terms.

   $= 3x^2 + -1x + 1$ Combine like terms.

   $= 3x^2 - x + 1$ $-1x = -x.$

b. $3w^2 + 4w^2 + (-6w) - 2w$ List the terms in descending order.

   $= (3 + 4)w^2 + (-6 - 2)w$ Group like terms.

   $= 7w^2 + (-8)w$ Combine like terms.

   $= 7w^2 - 8w$

2 Add the polynomials $2x^2 - 4x - 8$, $-x^2 + 2$, and $x - 3$.

$(2x^2 - 4x - 8) + (-x^2 + 2) + (x - 3)$

$= 2x^2 - 4x - 8 + -x^2 + 2 + x - 3$ Write without parentheses.

$= (2x^2 - x^2) + (-4x + x) + (-8 + 2 - 3)$ Group like terms.

$= x^2 + (-3x) + (-9)$ Combine like terms to simplify.

$= x^2 - 3x - 9$

Polynomials can also be added vertically in columns. If there is a term missing in one of the polynomials, it can be replaced by 0 as a placeholder.

x^2	x	constant	
$2x^2$	$-4x$	-8	Arrange terms in descending order.
$-1x^2$	$+0x$	$+2$	Group like terms by aligning them vertically.
$+0x^2$	$+x$	-3	
$1x^2$	$+(-3x)$	$+(-9)$	$= x^2 - 3x - 9$ Combine like terms and simplify.

Try It

Simplify each expression.

a. $5x^2 + 12x + 2x^2 - 5x + 1$ $7x^2 + 7x + 1$

b. $-6n^2 - 3n + 2n + (-5)n^2 - 9$ $-11n^2 - n - 9$

c. Add $5x^2 + 2x - 4$, $5x - 2x^2$, and $x - 6$. $3x^2 + 8x - 10$

Problem Solving TIP

When combining like terms, just think of x^2 as apples, x as oranges, integers as bananas, and so on. You can only add apples to apples and oranges to oranges.

MATH EVERY DAY

► Problem of the Day

Pavo Nurmi of Finland won two Olympic races on July 10, 1924. He ran the 1500-meter race in 3 minutes 53.6 seconds. Less than an hour later, he ran the 5000-meter race and won in 14 minutes, 31.2 seconds. Find his average speed in kilometers per hour for both races combined. 21.2 km/hr
(6500 meters ÷ 18.413 minutes = 6.5 km ÷ 0.307 hr ≈ 21.2 km/hr)

Available on Daily Transparency 10-6

An Extension is provided in the transparency package.

Fact of the Day

If the lighting in a chicken coop simulates long days of about 14 to 16 hours, hens may begin laying eggs before the usual egg-laying age of 20 weeks.

Mental Math

Simplify these polynomials mentally.

1. $x^2 + -x^2 + 3$ 3

2. $2x + 4 + -1$ $2x + 3$

3. $x^2 + x + -x^2$ x

Example 3

Find an expression for the floor area of the chicken coop. If x is 20 ft, what is the area?

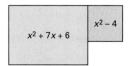

To find the floor area, add the polynomials.

$(x^2 + 7x + 6) + (x^2 - 4)$

$(x^2 + x^2) + 7x + (6 - 4)$ Group like terms.

$2x^2 + 7x + 2$ Combine like terms.

or

$\quad (x^2 + 7x + 6)$ Arrange terms in descending order.

$\underline{+\ (x^2 + 0x - 4)}$ Group like terms by aligning them vertically.

$\quad 2x^2 + 7x + 2$ Combine like terms.

When x is 20:

$2(20)^2 + 7(20) + 2$

$= 2(400) + 140 + 2$

$= 942$

The chicken coop has an area of 942 ft^2.

Try It

Find an expression for the area of the total region. What is the area when $x = 10$? $2x^2 + x - 11$; 199

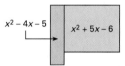

Check | Your Understanding

1. Give an example of like terms and of terms that are not alike. Explain.

2. Can the sum of two binomials be a trinomial? Explain.
   Yes, if only one pair of terms is alike

3. When you write a polynomial in descending order, what in the expression is descending? **The exponents**

MEETING MIDDLE SCHOOL CLASSROOM NEEDS

Tips from Middle School Teachers

Students may be initially confused when adding polynomials with missing terms, such as $(x^2 + 1) + (x^2 + 3x + -4)$. I ask students to first write each polynomial in descending order. Then I have them write each polynomial with the same number of terms, using $0x^2$, $0x$, 0, and so forth, when necessary. I have students draw columns on their paper and align like terms in the columns to help them with their addition.

Consumer Connection

Exercise 16 on page 540 discusses a situation in which a person carpets her family room. When viewing carpeting advertisements, students should be aware that the price of the carpeting may not cover all of the costs. For example, labor for installation may not be included. Also, the padding may not be included in the price.

Cooperative Learning

Students may gain additional practice in adding polynomials by playing the following game. Have groups of four students work together and make game cards. On separate small squares of paper or index cards, they should write polynomial terms, one term per card. A term written in black is positive and a term written in red is negative. Have the group shuffle the completed cards and work in pairs. Each student in one pair should draw three cards. They then have to "add" and simplify the polynomials. If they simplify correctly, they get one point. The pairs should take turns drawing cards for a predetermined time. At the end of this time, the pair with the most points wins.

Alternate Examples

3. Find an expression for the floor area of the studio apartment shown below. If x is 6 feet, what is the area?

To find the floor area, add the polynomials.

$(6x^2 + 7x + 2) + (x^2 + 2x)$

$= (6x^2 + x^2) + (7x + 2x) + 2$
    Group like terms.

$= 7x^2 + 9x + 2$
    Combine like terms.

or

Arrange terms in descending order, group like terms by aligning them vertically, and combine like terms.

$\quad 6x^2 + 7x + 2$

$\underline{+\ \ x^2 + 2x + 0}$

$\quad 7x^2 + 9x + 2$

When x is 6:

$7(6)^2 + 9(6) + 2 = 7(36) + 54 + 2$
$= 308.$

The studio apartment has a floor area of 308 ft^2.

3 Practice and Assess

Check

If students answer "no" to Question 2, ask them to review the examples. In Example 2, they should find two binomials that, if added, have a trinomial as a sum.

Answers for Check Your Understanding

1. Possible answer: $4x^2 + 2x^2$, $2x + x^2$; Like terms have the same exponent on the variables.

10-6 Exercises and Applications

Assignment Guide

■ **Basic**
1–15, 19, 20, 23, 27–33

■ **Average**
1–13, 15–17, 18–24 evens, 25, 27, 28–32 evens

■ **Enriched**
1–7 odds, 8–18, 21–27, 31, 33

Exercise Notes

■ **Exercise 14**

Measurement Some students may wonder why there is so much unused volume in a can of tennis balls. Remind students that the can is cylindrical, while the tennis balls are spherical, so there is unused space surrounding the top and bottom hemisphere of each tennis ball.

■ **Exercises 15**

Test Prep Some students may examine variables only and list B as the answer, while others may examine only exponents and list D as the answer. Remind these students that both conditions (same variable and same exponent) must be met for terms to be like terms.

Exercise Answers

14. a. 156 cm³

  b. 3; Taking into account the empty spaces between spherical balls and sides of the can, 4 would take up too much space.

17. $x^3 + 5x^2 + 4x^2 + 7x$;
  $x^3 + 9x^2 + 7x$; 582 ft³

Reteaching

Activity

Materials: Algebra tiles

- Work with a partner.

- Use algebra tiles to make up two original polynomials. Combine the sets of tiles and find the resulting expression.

- Exchange problems with another group. Solve the other group's problem while they are solving yours. Compare answers. Do your answers check?

PRACTICE 10-6

Practice and Apply

1. **Getting Started** Fill in the blanks.

   To simplify the polynomial $4p + 3p^2 - p + 5p^2$, write the polynomial in _____ order. Then combine _____ by using the _____ property.
   Descending   **Like terms**   **Distributive**

Simplify each, if possible. If the expression cannot be simplified, write "already simplified." Write answers in descending order.

2. $2x^2 - 4x + 8x^3 + x$
   $8x^3 + 2x^2 - 3x$

3. $4y^2 + 2y$
   Already simplified

4. $4p - 3$
   Already simplified

5. $2m^2 - 8m + 5m + 5m^2$
   $7m^2 - 3m$

6. $5b^2 - 4b + 2b^3 + (-3)b$
   $2b^3 + 5b^2 - 7b$

7. $5a - 4a + 3a + 6$
   $4a + 6$

Find each polynomial sum. Write the answers in simplest form.

8. $(2m - 6m^2) + (-2m^2 - 2m + 1)$
   $-8m^2 + 1$

9. $(2x) + (-2x^2 - 2x + 1)$
   $-2x^2 + 1$

10. $(-y^3 + 3y) + (4y^2 + 3y - 1)$ $-y^3 + 4y^2 + 6y - 1$

11. $5x^2 + 6x + 2$
    $+ 8x^2 - 2x - 9$
    $13x^2 + 4x - 7$

12. $5z^2 + 3z - 1$
    $+ -3z + 1$
    $5z^2$

13. $x^2 + 3x - 6$
    $+ 3x^2 - 4x + 15$
    $4x^2 - x + 9$

14. **Measurement** The volume of a tennis ball can is approximately 620 cm³. A tennis ball has a diameter of approximately 6.68 cm.

   a. Use the formula for the volume of a sphere, $V = \frac{4}{3}\pi r^3$, to find the approximate volume of a tennis ball. Use π = 3.14.

   b. How many tennis balls do you think will fit into one can? Explain your reasoning.

15. **Test Prep** Which of the following pairs of terms are like terms? **A**
   Ⓐ x^2 and $3x^2$ Ⓑ x^3 and $3x$ Ⓒ $7x$ and 7 Ⓓ x^2 and y^2

16. **Consumer** Carpet is sold for $9.95 per square yd. To find the area of her family room, Marjorie used the formula $A = x^2 + 2x$, where A = area in yd² and x = length of the room = 3 yd. How much did it cost Marjorie to carpet her family room? **$149.25**

17. A zoo built an aviary for its exotic birds. The total volume includes the flight space, x^3, an exercise room, $5x^2$, a private loft, $4x^2$, and a nesting box, $7x$. Write the polynomial that represents the total volume of the aviary, then simplify it. Evaluate the polynomial for $x = 6$ ft.

▷ PRACTICE

Adding Polynomials

Simplify each if possible. If the expression cannot be simplified, write "simplified." Write answers in descending order.

1. $5p^2 + 7p^2$ **12p²**

2. $3x^4 + 3x + 4x^2 + 8x$ $3x^4 + 4x^2 + 5x$

3. $9t^3 - 5t^2 - 4t^3$ $5t^3 - 5t^2$

4. $6w^3 - 4w^2 + 6w - 4$ **Simplified**

5. $7x + 9x^2 - 12x + 3$ $9x^2 - 5x + 3$

6. $4u^3 + 7u - 21u^3$ $-17u^3 + 7u$

7. $8g^5 + 3g^3 - 2g + 3$ **Simplified**

8. $3k - 9 - 2k + 35$ $k + 26$

Find each polynomial sum. Write the answers in simplest form.

9. $(3x^2 + 4x) + (x^2 + 7x - 3)$
   $4x^2 + 11x - 3$

10. $(2j - 5) + (3j^2 - 7j + 14)$
    $3j^2 - 5j + 9$

11. $(-z^3 + 8z - 2) + (2z^2 - 3z + 2)$
    $-z^3 + 2z^2 + 5z$

12. $(5s^2 - 4s + 7) + (3s^2 + 4s + 11)$
    $8s^2 + 18$

13. $(7g^2 - 5g + 4)$
    $+ (4g^2 + 7g - 6)$
    $11g^2 + 2g - 2$

14. $(-4y^2 + 2y - 3)$
    $+ (-6y - 7)$
    $-4y^2 - 4y - 10$

15. $(m^2 + 4m + 3)$
    $+ (2m^2 - m + 4)$
    $3m^2 + 3m + 7$

Find the total floor area of each birdhouse.

16. $3x^2 - 3x + 7$

17. $5x^3 + 23x + 7$

18. $3x^2 - 21x + 22$

19. A tabletop is $4x^2 - 2x + 7$ in. above the floor. A computer monitor with height $7x - 3$ in. is on the table. Write a polynomial in simplest form to represent the distance from the top of the monitor to the floor. What is the distance if $x = 3$?
    $4x^2 + 5x + 4$; 55 in.

20. If you know x^2, the square of an even number x, you can find the square of the next even number by adding $4x + 4$ to x^2. The square of 46 is 2116. Show how you can add polynomials and evaluate to find 48^2.
    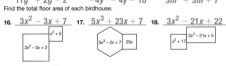
    Possible answer: $x^2 + 4x + 4 = 2116 + 4 \cdot 46 + 4 = 2304$

▷ RETEACHING

Adding Polynomials

Like terms are terms that have the same variable raised to the same exponent. You can combine like terms by using the distributive property.
$2x^3 + 4x^3 = (2 + 4)x^3 = 6x^3$ $5x^2 - 4x^2 = (5 - 4)x^2 = 1x^2 = x^2$.

A polynomial is **simplified** when it contains no like terms.

— Example 1 —

Simplify $2x + 3x^2 + 7 - 4x^2$.

Write the terms in descending order.	$= 3x^2 - 4x^2 + 2x + 7$
Group like terms.	$= (3 - 4)x^2 + 2x + 7$
Combine like terms.	$= -x^2 + 2x + 7$

So, $2x + 3x^2 + 7 - 4x^2 = -x^2 + 2x + 7$.

Try It

a. Simplify $7x + 8x^2 + 4 - 6x^2$.

   Write the terms in descending order. $8x^2 - 6x^2 + 7x + 4$

   Group and combine like terms. $(8 - 6)x^2 + 7x + 4 = 2x^2 + 7x + 4$

b. Simplify $3x + 8x^2 - 9 + 7x^3 + 3x^2$. $7x^3 + 11x^2 + 3x - 9$

— Example 2 —

Add the polynomials $(3x^2 - 2x + 3)$, $(x^2 - 7x + 7)$, and $(-2x^2 - 4)$.

Arrange in columns with each polynomial written in descending order with like terms in the same column. Use 0 as a place holder if a term is missing in any of the polynomials.

$\quad 3x^2 - 2x + 3$
$\quad\ x^2 - 7x + 7$
$+ -2x^2 + 0x - 4$
$\quad 2x^2 - 9x + 6$

The sum is $2x^2 - 9x + 6$.

Try It Add the polynomials.

c. $2x^2 + 5x - 3$
   $6x^2 + 2x + 2$
   $+ 3x^2 - 4x + 8$
   $11x^2 + 3x + 7$

d. $3x^3 - 2x^2 - 4x + 1$
   $2x^3 + 3x^2 + 0x - 2$
   $+ 2x^3 + 0x^2 - 3x - 8$
   $7x^3 + x^2 - 7x - 9$

e. $5x^3 + 3x^2 + 5x + 9$
   $2x^3 + 0x^2 + 0x - 4$
   $+ x^3 + 4x^2 + 2x + 2$
   $8x^3 + 7x^2 + 7x + 7$

f. $(2x^2 + 3x + 5)$, $(-x^2 + 8)$, and $(3x^2 - 4x + 5)$ $4x^2 - x + 18$

g. $(10x^3 + 5x^2 + 6)$, $(4x^3 + 3x - 2)$, and $(x^3 - 4x^2 + 9)$
   $11x^3 + 5x^2 + 3x + 13$

18. If you know the cube of a counting number x, x^3, you can find the cube of the next counting number by adding $3x^2 + 3x + 1$. The cube of 5 is 125. Show how you can add polynomials and evaluate to find 6^3.

Geometry Find the total area of each figure.

19.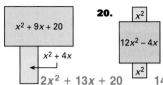
$x^2 + 9x + 20$
$x^2 + 4x$
$2x^2 + 13x + 20$

20.
x^2
$12x^2 - 4x$
x^2
$14x^2 - 4x$

21.
$x^2 + 6x + 8$
$2x^2 + 7x + 3$
$3x^2 + 13x + 11$

22.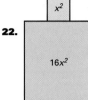
x^2
$16x^2$
$17x^2$

Problem Solving and Reasoning

23. Critical Thinking Write an expression that contains four terms and simplifies to $2x$.

24. Is simplifying an equation the same as solving it? Explain.

25. Communicate Jennifer simplified the expression $4x + 3x$ to $7x^2$. Was she correct? Explain your reasoning. **No; Should be $7x$**

26. Choose a Strategy Find the missing term. $-2x$

$(3x^2 - 6x) + (\underline{\quad\quad} - 2x^2) = x^2 - 8x$

27. Critical Thinking When asked to simplify $x^2 + x^2$, four students got the following answers. Who is correct? What do you think each of the students did to get their answer?

 a. Willard's answer is x^4.   **b.** Bryant's answer is $2x^4$.

 c. Katie's answer is $2x^2$.   **d.** Matt's answer is x^2.

> **Problem Solving**
> **STRATEGIES**
> • Look for a Pattern
> • Make an Organized List
> • Make a Table
> • Guess and Check
> • Work Backward
> • Use Logical Reasoning
> • Draw a Diagram
> • Solve a Simpler Problem

Mixed Review

Solve each equation. [Lesson 3-5]

28. $14x = 84$ **6**   **29.** $27 = \frac{3}{4}x$ **36**   **30.** $\frac{x}{5} = -60$ **−300**   **31.** $7.1x = 63.9$ **9**

Find each surface area. [Lesson 9-5]

32.
10 cm
6 cm
$\pi(12\sqrt{34} + 36)$
$\approx 332.8 \text{ cm}^2$

33.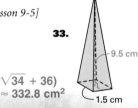
9.5 cm
1.5 cm
$2.25 + 3\sqrt{90.8125}$
$\approx 30.8 \text{ cm}^2$

10-6 • Adding Polynomials **541**

Exercise Notes

■ Exercise 23

Extension Tell students there are infinitely many 4-term expressions that can be simplified to $2x$.

■ Exercise 25

Error Prevention If students think Jennifer is correct, tell them to think of the variable in this problem as a set of concrete items, such as 5 dollars. Does 4(5 dollars) + 3(5 dollars) = 7(5 • 5 dollars)?

■ Exercise 27

Problem-Solving Tip You may wish to use Teaching Tool Transparencies 2 and 3: Guided Problem Solving, pages 1–2.

Exercise Answers

18. $x^3 + (3x^2 + 3x + 1) =$
    $x^3 + 3x^2 + 3x + 1;$
    $(5)^3 + 3(5)^2 + 3(5) + 1 =$
    $125 + 75 + 15 + 1 = 216$

23. Possible answer: $4x - 3x + 2x - x$

24. No; Simplifying means combining terms, while solving means finding the value(s) of the variable that make(s) the equation true.

27. a. Incorrect; Added exponents, forgot to add coefficients.
    b. Incorrect; Added exponents.
    c. Correct; Added coefficients but not exponents.
    d. Incorrect; Forgot to add coefficients.

Alternate Assessment

 You may want to use the *Interactive CD-ROM Journal* with this assessment.

Journal Ask students to think about the basic rules for addition and subtraction of integers and about what they learned about adding polynomials. Have them write a paragraph predicting which rules might apply to subtracting polynomials. Tell them they will check their predictions in the next lesson.

> ► **Quick Quiz**
>
> Simplify the following.
>
> 1. $4x + 6 + x^3 - 2x + 3x^2 + 1$
> $x^3 + 3x^2 + 2x + 7$
>
> 2. $3x^2 + 2y + 3x + 2 + z^2 + 7 + y$
> $3x^2 + z^2 + 3x + 3y + 9$
>
> 3. $x^2 - 9x + 6$
> $\underline{+ 4x^2 + 13}$
> $5x^2 - 9x + 19$
>
> Available on Daily Transparency 10-6

PROBLEM SOLVING

Name _____

Guided Problem Solving 10-6

GPS **PROBLEM 27, STUDENT PAGE 541**

When asked to simplify $x^2 + x^2$, four students got the following answers. Who is correct? What do you think each of the students did to get their answer?

 a. Willard's answer is x^4.   **b.** Bryant's answer is $2x^4$.

 c. Katie's answer is $2x^2$.   **d.** Matt's answer is x^2.

— Understand —

1. What polynomial are you asked to simplify? $x^2 + x^2$

2. What are you asked to find? Which student added correctly.

— Plan —

3. How do you add like terms? b
   a. Add exponents.   **b.** Add coefficients (numbers multiplying each variable).

— Solve —

4. Which student has the correct answer? Katie.

5. How did Willard find his answer? Added exponents.

6. How did Bryant find his answer? Added exponents and coefficients.

7. How did Katie find her answer? Added coefficients.

8. How did Matt find his answer? Chose one term.

— Look Back —

9. Write each term as $1x^2$. Then use the distributive property to find the sum. $1x^2 + 1x^2 = x^2(1 + 1) = 2x^2$

SOLVE ANOTHER PROBLEM

When asked to simplify $4x^3 + x^3$, three students got the following answers. Who is correct? Write how you think each student got their answer.

 a. Su-mi's answer is $4x^6$. Added exponents.

 b. Lizzie's answer is $5x^3$. Added coefficients.

 c. Mato's answer is $5x^6$. Added exponents and coefficients.

Possible answers: Items 5, 6, and 8

Correct answer: Lizzie

ENRICHMENT

Name _____

Extend Your Thinking 10-6

Decision Making

The eighth-grade class of 55 students is organizing a fundraiser to help pay for one of their class trips. They need to raise $1650. The committee has narrowed the possibilities to the following three kinds of sales.

 a. Boxes of cookies at $3 per box, profit is $1 per box

 b. Gift wrap at $5 per roll, profit is $2.50 per roll

 c. Magazine subscriptions from $15–$20 each, profit is $3 per subscription

1. How many of each item need to be sold to raise the money for the trip?

   a. Boxes of cookies 1650 boxes.   **b.** Gift wrap 660 rolls.

   c. Magazine subscriptions 550 subscriptions.

2. How many of each item will each student have to sell?

   a. Boxes of cookies 30 boxes.   **b.** Gift wrap 12 rolls.

   c. Magazine subscriptions 10 subscriptions.

3. What is the total amount of money that would be collected for each item?

   a. Boxes of cookies $4950   **b.** Gift wrap $3300

   c. Magazine subscriptions $8250 – $11,000

4. Which item might be the easiest to sell door-to-door? Why?
   Possible answer: Cookies; they are least expensive and most people like to eat cookies.

5. Which item would you prefer to sell? Explain your answer.
   Possible answer: Cookies; they are easier to sell than subscriptions and easier to carry than gift wrap.

6. Would you rather have more than one item to sell? Why?
   Possible answer: Yes. If people have more choices, they are more likely to buy at least one item.

Lesson 10-6 **541**

Objective

■ **Subtract polynomials.**

Materials

■ **Explore: Algebra tiles**

NCTM Standards

■ **1–4, 6, 8, 9, 12, 13**

► **Review**

Evaluate each expression.

1. 547 – 421 126

2. (500 + 40 + 7) –
   (400 + 20 + 1) 126

3. (500 + 40 + 7) +
   (–400 + –20 + –1) 126

Available on Daily Transparency 10-7

▶ **Lesson Link**

You may wish to remind students that in Lesson 10-6, they learned to add polynomials. In this lesson, they will learn to subtract polynomials by changing subtraction to adding the opposite.

1 Introduce

Explore

You may wish to use Teaching Tool Transparencies 13: Algebra Tiles (red) and 14: Algebra Tiles (yellow) with **Explore**.

The Point
Students use algebra tiles to model subtracting polynomials.

Ongoing Assessment
Check that students are removing the zero pairs in Step 3. Make sure students see that the results from Steps 2 and 3 are the same.

For Groups That Finish Early
What would remain if you subtracted or removed two negative *x* tiles and one positive unit tile from the original expression? What would remain if you added two positive *x* tiles and one negative unit tile to the original expression? You would have one x^2 tile and one negative *x* tile in both cases.

10-7 Subtracting Polynomials

▶ **Lesson Link** In the last lesson, you learned to add polynomials. In this lesson, you will learn to subtract polynomials. ◀

Explore | **Subtracting Polynomials**

Materials: Algebra tiles

The Buddy System

1. What expression is modeled?

2. What would remain if you subtracted or removed 1 x^2 tile and 1 negative *x* tile?
   $-2x + 1$

3. What would remain if you added 1 negative x^2 tile and 1 positive *x* tile to the original expression? Remember to remove zero pairs.
   $-2x + 1$

4. Compare the results from Steps 2 and 3. Why did this happen?

5. What would remain if you added 1 negative x^2 tile, 3 positive *x* tiles, and 1 negative unit tile to the original expression? Explain.

Learn | **Subtracting Polynomials**

Recall from previous work with algebra tiles that the following are additive inverses and make up zero pairs.

$x^2 + (-x^2) = 0$ $-x + x = 0$ $1 + -1 = 0$

In Chapter 2, you learned that the opposite of a number is called its additive inverse. When you add a number to its additive inverse, you get zero. The additive inverse of 3 is -3; of x^3, $-x^3$; of $-5x^2$, $5x^2$. You also learned that subtraction of integers is the same as adding the opposite.

$a - b$ is the same as $a + (-b)$.

MEETING INDIVIDUAL NEEDS

Resources
10-7 Practice
10-7 Reteaching
10-7 Problem Solving
10-7 Enrichment
10-7 Daily Transparency
Problem of the Day
Review
Quick Quiz
Teaching Tool Transparencies 13, 14
Technology Masters 55, 56

Learning Modalities

Kinesthetic In **Explore**, students use algebra tiles to model subtracting polynomials. Students work in pairs.

Musical Have students write a rap song about subtracting polynomials.

English Language Development

Pair English-speaking students with students who have limited English proficiency. Have these pairs of students find examples of polynomials and their additive inverses and practice reading these expressions and additive inverses aloud. Have them use *minus* for subtraction, *the opposite of* when a term contains a variable, and *negative* for a negative number.

You'll Learn …

■ to subtract polynomials

… **How It's Used**

A carpenter subtracts polynomials when calculating the amount of material needed to construct the walls if space is left for doors and windows.

Examples

1 Find the additive inverse of the polynomial $x^2 + 4x - 8$.

$-(x^2 + 4x - 8)$ Take the opposite of the polynomial.

$= -(x^2 + 4x + -8)$ Change subtraction to adding the opposite.

$= -x^2 + -4x + 8$ Take the opposite of each term in the polynomial.

$= -x^2 - 4x + 8$

When you subtract polynomials, add the opposite or additive inverse.

2 Subtract $(6x^3 + 2x^2 - 5) - (x^3 - 3x^2 + 7)$.

$(6x^3 + 2x^2 - 5) + -(x^3 - 3x^2 + 7)$ Add the opposite of the second polynomial.

$= (6x^3 + 2x^2 + -5) + -(x^3 + -3x^2 + 7)$ Change subtracting to adding the opposite.

$= (6x^3 + 2x^2 + -5) + (-x^3 + 3x^2 + -7)$ Find the opposite of all terms in the parentheses.

$= (6 + -1)x^3 + (2 + 3)x^2 + (-5 + -7)$ Group like terms.

$= 5x^3 + 5x^2 + -12$ Combine like terms.

$= 5x^3 + 5x^2 - 12$

As with addition, subtraction can be done vertically.

$(6x^3 + 2x^2 - 5) + -(x^3 - 3x^2 + 7)$ Add the opposite of the second polynomial.

$= (6x^3 + 2x^2 + -5) + -(x^3 + -3x^2 + 7)$ Change subtracting to adding the opposite.

$= (6x^3 + 2x^2 + -5) + (-x^3 + 3x^2 + -7)$ Find the opposite of all terms in the parentheses.

$$\begin{array}{r} (6x^3 + 2x^2 + -5) \\ + (-x^3 + 3x^2 + -7) \\ \hline 5x^3 + 5x^2 + -12 \end{array}$$

Group like terms by aligning them vertically.

Combine like terms.

$= 5x^3 + 5x^2 - 12$

Try It

a. Find the additive inverse of $-2x^3 + 1$. $2x^3 - 1$

b. Subtract $(4x^3 + 6x^2 - 2x) - (2x^3 - 8x + 5)$. $2x^3 + 6x^2 + 6x - 5$

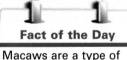

MENTAL MATH

Many steps in subtracting polynomials can be done mentally.

MATH EVERY DAY

► Problem of the Day

You spin the spinner below. On which number would you expect the spinner to stop? Why?

There is an equal chance of the spinner stopping on any number. The area is not what determines the chance. The central angles, where the spinner is attached, are all congruent (90°).

Available on Daily Transparency 10-7

An Extension is provided in the transparency package.

Fact of the Day

Macaws are a type of large, tropical parrot found in the Americas. There are about 18 species of macaws. Only a few can be trained to talk.

Estimation

Estimate each answer.

1. 0.24×409 100

2. $409 \div 0.24$ 1600

3. 51% of 5999   3000

Follow Up

Ask volunteers to share their explanations from Step 4. Then ask other volunteers to share their results from Step 5. Discuss with the class the patterns found in Steps 4 and 5.

Answers for Explore

1. $x^2 - 3x + 1$

4. Subtraction is the same as adding the opposite.

5. 0; Adding terms and their inverses gives 0.

2 Teach

Learn

Compare subtracting polynomials to subtracting whole numbers expressed in expanded form. Compare the expression 500 + 40 + 7 to $5x^2 + 4x + 7$ and the expression 400 + 20 + 1 to $4x^2 + 2x + 1$.

Alternate Examples

1. Find the additive inverse of the polynomial $3x^2 - 7x + 2$.

   $-(3x^2 - 7x + 2)$ Take the opposite of the polynomial.

   $= -(3x^2 + -7x + 2)$ Change subtracting to adding the opposite.

   $= -3x^2 + 7x + -2$ Take the opposite of each term.

   $= -3x^2 + 7x - 2$

2. Subtract $(13x^3 + 12x - 11) - (6x^3 - 9x + 2)$.

   Adding can be done horizontally by
   a. Adding the opposite of the second polynomial;
   b. Changing subtracting to adding the opposite;
   c. Finding the opposite of all terms in the parentheses;
   d. Grouping like terms;
   e. Combining like terms.

   a. $(13x^3 + 12x - 11) + -(6x^3 - 9x + 2)$
   b. $= (13x^3 + 12x + -11) + -(6x^3 + -9x + 2)$
   c. $= (13x^3 + 12x + -11) + (-6x^3 + 9x + -2)$
   d. $= (13 + -6)x^3 + (12 + 9)x + (-11 + -2)$
   e. $= 7x^3 + 21x + -13$
   $= 7x^3 + 21x - 13$.

Example 2 continues on page 544.

2. (continued)

Subtraction can be done vertically. After finding the opposite of all terms in the parentheses, group like terms by aligning them vertically.

$$(13x^3 + 12x + -11)$$
$$+ (-6x^3 + 9x + -2)$$
$$\overline{7x^3 + 21x - 13}$$

$$= 7x^3 + 21x - 13$$

3. At Bird World, the annual revenue from selling a "Canary Condo" deluxe bird cage at a price p is given by $-4p^2 - 90p + 3900$. The cost is $-1150p + 55,000$. Profit is revenue minus cost. What is the profit function for selling the cages? What is the profit when cages are sold for $100? For $150?

Revenue – Cost:
$-4p^2 - 90p + 3900 - (-1150p + 55,000)$
Change subtracting to adding the opposite:
$= -4p^2 - 90p + 3900 + 1150p - 55,000$
Group like terms:
$= -4p^2 + (-90p + 1150)p + (3900 - 55,000)$
Combine like terms:
$= -4p^2 + 1060p - 51,100$

The profit function is $-4p^2 + 1060p - 51,100$.

Evaluate for $100.
$-4p^2 + 1060p - 51,100;$
$-4(100)^2 + 1060(100) - 51,100$
$= -40,000 + 106,000 - 51,100$
$= 14,900$

Evaluate for $150.
$-4p^2 + 1060p - 51,100;$
$-4(150)^2 + 1060(150) - 51,100$
$= -90,000 + 159,000 - 51,100$
$= 17,900$

The annual profit is $14,900 when cages are priced at $100; $17,900 when they are priced at $200.

DID YOU KNOW?

Macaws sell for about $1500 each.

Examples

3 At For the Birds, the annual revenue from selling a macaw cage at a price (p) is given by $-4p^2 - 100p + 4,200$. The cost is $-1,300p + 60,000$. Profit is revenue minus cost. What is the profit function for selling the cages? What is the profit when cages are sold for $150? For $200?

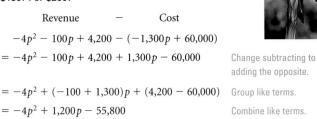

	Revenue	–	Cost

$-4p^2 - 100p + 4,200 - (-1,300p + 60,000)$

$= -4p^2 - 100p + 4,200 + 1,300p - 60,000$ Change subtracting to adding the opposite.

$= -4p^2 + (-100 + 1,300)p + (4,200 - 60,000)$ Group like terms.

$= -4p^2 + 1,200p - 55,800$ Combine like terms.

The profit function is $-4p^2 + 1,200p - 55,800$. Evaluate.

$-4p^2 + 1,200p - 55,800$	$-4p^2 + 1,200p - 55,800$
$= -4(150)^2 + 1,200(150) - 55,800$	$= -4(200)^2 + 1,200(200) - 55,800$
$= -90,000 + 180,000 - 55,800$	$= -160,000 + 240,000 - 55,800$
$= 34,200$	$= 24,200$

The annual profit is $34,200 when cages are priced at $150; $24,200 when they are priced at $200.

4 Find the unknown side length.

Add the known lengths of the sides.

$(x^2 + 4) + (2x^2 - 4x) + (3x + 1) + (2x - 3)$

$= 3x^2 + x + 2$

Subtract from the given perimeter.

$(4x^2 + 2) - (3x^2 + x + 2) = x^2 - x$

The length of the unknown side is $x^2 - x$.

$x^2 + 4$ $2x^2 - 4x$
$3x + 1$ $2x - 3$
$p = 4x^2 + 2$

Try It

$-70p^2 + 1495p - 300; 7650

a. The annual revenue from selling parakeets at a price p is given by $-70p^2 - 25p + 200$. The cost is $-1520p + 500$. What is the profit function for selling the parakeets? What is the profit when parakeets are sold for $10?

b. The perimeter is $7x^2 + 3x + 8$. Find the unknown side length. $6x - 5$

$5x + 4$ $5x^2 + 9$
$2x^2 - 8x$

MEETING MIDDLE SCHOOL CLASSROOM NEEDS

Tips from Middle School Teachers

Some students need a transition between working with algebra tiles and written expressions. For these students, I go through each term of the expression one-by-one. As I hold up the algebra tiles representing each term, I ask a volunteer to write the term on the board. Then I place the tiles under the term if the board has a ledge. Otherwise, I place them on a desk. As I use the algebra tiles to represent the expression, volunteers build the written expression for the class. As zero pairs are found, volunteers simplify the expression.

Team Teaching

Invite the science teacher to share examples of formulas with polynomials that are used in real-life problem solving. Ask the teacher to present at least one example that involves subtracting polynomials, for example, one similar to that in Exercise 25 on page 547.

Science Connection

When an object is propelled straight upward as discussed in **What Do You Think?** on page 545, a polynomial of the form $-gt^2 + vt + h$ gives the height of the object above the ground. In the polynomial, t represents time after launch in seconds, g represents the pull of gravity ($g = -5$ if measured in m/sec; $g = -16$ if measured in ft/sec), v is the velocity of the object at launch (either m/sec or ft/sec), and h is the height of the object above the ground at launch (either m or ft). Have students suggest values for g, v, and h that are reasonable for specific real-world situations.

How much higher does a clay disk propelled upwards with an initial velocity of 100 ft/sec go, over time, than one propelled at 70 ft/sec from a platform 25 ft high? Subtract $-16t^2 + 70t + 25$ from $-16t^2 + 100t$ to find out.

Ashley thinks ...

I'll write the polynomials vertically, like a regular subtraction problem.

$$
\begin{array}{rcr}
-16t^2 + 100t & & -16t^2 + 100t \\
- (-16t^2 + 70t + 25) & = & + 16t^2 - 70t - 25 \\
\end{array}
$$

Now I can combine like terms. $\longrightarrow$ $\quad 30t - 25$

My answer is $30t - 25$. It is 5 ft higher after 1 sec, 35 ft after 2 sec, and so on.

Kele thinks ...

I'll do the subtraction horizontally. $\quad (-16t^2 + 100t) - (-16t^2 + 70t + 25)$

I'll add the opposite of the second polynomial. $\quad -16t^2 + 100t + -(-16t^2 + 70t + 25)$

$$-16t^2 + 100t + (16t^2 - 70t - 25)$$

I'll group like terms. $\quad (-16 + 16)t^2 + (100 - 70)t + (-25)$

I'll combine like terms. $\quad 0t^2 \quad + \quad 30t \quad - \quad 25$

My answer is also $\quad 30t - 25$.

What do you think?

Which way would you use to subtract polynomials? Why?

Check   Your Understanding

1. How are addition and subtraction of polynomials related?

2. How do you find the additive inverse of a polynomial expression?

3. Add a polynomial expression and its inverse. Explain your result.
0; Any term plus its opposite is 0

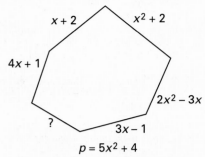

Alternate Examples

4. Find the unknown side length.

Polygon with sides labeled: $x + 2$, $x^2 + 2$, $4x + 1$, $2x^2 - 3x$, $?$, $3x - 1$

$p = 5x^2 + 4$

Add the known lengths of the sides.
$(4x + 1) + (x + 2) + (x^2 + 2) + (2x^2 - 3x) + (3x - 1) = 3x^2 + 5x + 4$

Subtract from the given perimeter:
$(5x^2 + 4) - (3x^2 + 5x + 4) = 2x^2 - 5x$

The length of the unknown side is $2x^2 - 5x$.

Students see two methods of solving a problem. In one method subtraction is performed vertically and in the other subtraction is performed horizontally. Students can decide which of the two correct methods is easier for them.

Answers for What Do You Think?

Possible answer: Ashley's way, because it is more like adding whole numbers or decimals.

3 Practice and Assess

Check

If students have difficulty with Question 1, remind them of what they discovered in **Explore** on page 542. If students do not get zero as the answer for Question 3, they may have written the additive inverse incorrectly.

Answers for Check Your Understanding

1. Subtracting is the same as adding the additive inverse.

2. Take the opposite of each term in the expression.

Assignment Guide

■ **Basic**
1–15, 16–20 evens, 21–23, 25–29 odds, 32, 33–39 odds

■ **Average**
1–15, 16–24 evens, 25–29, 32–38 evens

■ **Enriched**
1–13, 17, 19–23, 25–33, 38

Exercise Notes

■ **Exercise 5**

Error Prevention Students who write a positive sign before the $2x$ term may have incorrectly simplified the original polynomial by missing a negative sign. Have these students rewrite the problem step-by-step.

■ **Exercises 9, 11, 12, and 15**

Error Prevention Some students may become confused by the variables having different exponents but the same coefficient. These students should take their time when subtracting and simplifying, checking each step carefully to make sure it is written correctly.

Exercise Answers

13. $2v^3 - 8v^2 + 6v - 1$

14. $3g^2 + g - 2$

15. $a^3 - 6a^2 + 2a - 3$

Reteaching

Activity

Materials: Algebra tiles

• Work with a partner.

• Use algebra tiles to make up two original polynomials. Lay each set of tiles on a piece of paper indicating if the set is the first set or the second set. Subtract the second set of tiles from the first set and find the expression that remains.

• Exchange problems with another group. Solve the other group's problem while they are solving yours. Compare answers. Do your answers check?

546   Chapter 10

10-7 Exercises and Applications

Practice and Apply

1. **Getting Started** Write the additive inverse of each monomial.

a. $-x^3$ x^3 **b.** $4x^2$ **c.** $2x$ **d.** $-7x^5$ **e.** 27 -27
            $-4x^2$ $-2x$ $7x^5$

Find the additive inverse of each polynomial.

2. $3x^3 - 5x^2 + (-x) + 2$ **3.** $x^4 - 2$ **4.** $4x^2 - 12x + 9$
  $-3x^3 + 5x^2 + x - 2$ $-x^4 + 2$ $-4x^2 + 12x - 9$

5. $3x^3 - (-2x)$ **6.** $-4x^3 + 7x^2 + 13x - 2$ **7.** $-x^5 + 2x + 9x^3 - 3$
  $-3x^3 - 2x$ $4x^3 - 7x^2 - 13x + 2$ $x^5 - 2x - 9x^3 + 3$

Subtract Write your answers in simplest form.

8. $(5x^2 + 6x + 2) - (8x^2 - 2x - 9)$ **9.** $(2x) - (-2x^2 - 2x + 1)$
  $-3x^2 + 8x + 11$ $2x^2 + 4x - 1$

10. $(-y^3 + 3y) - (4y^2 + 3y - 1)$ **11.** $(2m - 6m^2) - (-2m^2 - 2m + 1)$
   $-y^3 - 4y^2 + 1$ $-4m^2 + 4m - 1$

12. $\quad (3m^2 + 3m - 5)$ **13.** $\quad (4v^3 - 3v^2 + 1)$
   $- (3m^2 + 3m - 5)$ $- (2v^3 + 5v^2 - 6v + 2)$
       0

14. $\quad (5g^2 + 4g - 7)$ **15.** $\quad (5a^3 - 4a^2 + 2a + 3)$
   $- (2g^2 + 3g - 5)$ $- (4a^3 + 2a^2 + 6)$

Geometry Find an expression for the area not covered by the bird.

16.
$x^2 - 2x$
$4x^2 + 11x - 20$
$A = 5x^2 + 9x - 20$

17.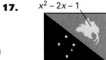
$x^2 - 2x - 1$
$11x^2 - 2x + 1$
$A = 12x^2 - 4x$

18.
$x^2 + 10$
$3x^2 + 8x - 9$
$A = 4x^2 + 8x + 1$

19.
$2x^2 + 4x + 3$
$12x^2 + 4x + 3$
$A = 14x^2 + 8x + 6$

20. **Test Prep** Which of the following polynomials is the additive inverse of the polynomial $2x^2 - 4x + 7$? **C**

Ⓐ $-2x^2 - 4x + 7$ Ⓑ $2x^2 + 4x + 7$

Ⓒ $-2x^2 + 4x + -7$ Ⓓ $-2x^2 - 4x - 7$

PRACTICE

Name _____

Practice 10-7

Subtracting Polynomials

Find the additive inverse of each polynomial.

1. $3x + 7$ $-3x - 7$ 2. $4x^2 - (-2x) - 7$ $-4x^2 - 2x + 7$

3. $x^2 + 2x + (-9)$ $-x^2 - 2x + 9$ 4. $3x^3 - 7x + 5$ $-3x^3 + 7x - 5$

Subtract. Write your answers in simplest form.

5. $(4x - 3) - (9x + 4)$ 6. $(3x^2 - 2x + 7) - (x^2 + 2x + 5)$
   $-5x - 7$ $2x^2 - 4x + 2$

7. $(4p + 7) - (p^2 + 8p - 3)$ 8. $(7t^2) - (3t^2 + 5t + 8)$
   $-p^2 - 4p + 10$ $4t^2 - 5t - 8$

9. $\ (8k^2 + 2k + 3)$ 10. $\ (5u^2 + 7u + 9)$ 11. $\ (c^3 - 2c^2 + 4)$
   $- (3k^2 - 6k + 4)$ $- (2u^2 + 3u + 9)$ $- (c^3 + 3c^2 + 8)$
   $5k^2 + 8k - 1$ $3u^2 + 4u$ $-5c^2 - 4$

Find an expression for the area of each shaded region, given the total area A of each figure.

12. $x^2 - 7x + 15$ 13. $x^2 - 4x - 13$ 14. $x^2 - 8x + 7$

$\ 4x - 9$ $\ 2x^2 - 3x + 11$ $\ 3x^2 - 5$
$A = x^2 - 3x + 6$ $A = 3x^2 - 7x - 2$ $A = 4x^2 - 8x + 2$

Find the missing side length, based on the perimeter of each figure.

15. $3x^2 - 4x - 4$ 16. $x^2 - 3x - 7$ 17. $x^2 + 3x - 9$

$2x^2 + 7$ $x^2 + 6x$ $5x + 7$
$7x - 5$ $3x + 4$ $3x^2 - 8x + 2$
                     $x^2 + 4x - 3$
$p = 5x^2 + 3x - 2$ $p = 3x^2 + 10x - 6$ $p = 4x^2$

18. **Physics** A ball is dropped from the top of a 128-foot building at the same time that Sam begins riding up on the elevator. The ball's height, in feet, is given by $-16t^2 + 128$, and Sam's height, in feet, is given by $4t$, where t is the number of seconds. Find a polynomial that tells how far above Sam that ball is after t seconds.
$-16t^2 - 4t + 128$ ft

RETEACHING

Name _____

Alternative Lesson 10-7

Subtracting Polynomials

When you subtract a polynomial from another polynomial, add the opposite of each term of the second polynomial.

— Example 1 —

Find the opposite of $-3x^2 + 6x - 2$.

Take the opposite of the polynomial. $-(-3x^2 + 6x - 2)$
Change subtraction to adding the opposite. $-(-3x^2 + 6x + (-2))$
Take the opposite of each term in the polynomial. $3x^2 - 6x + 2$

The opposite of $-3x^2 + 6x - 2$ is $3x^2 - 6x + 2$.

Try It
a. Find the opposite of $-2x^3 + 5x - 1$. $2x^3 - 5x + 1$

b. Find the opposite of $3x^2 - 3x + 8$. $-3x^2 + 3x - 8$

— Example 2 —

Subtract $3x - 10$ from $8x + 5$. Write your answer in simplest form.

$(8x + 5) - (3x - 10) = (8x + 5) + -(3x - 10)$ Add the opposite of $3x - 10$.
$= 8x + 5 + (-3x) + 10$
$= 8x + (-3x) + 5 + 10$ Group like terms.
$= 5x + 15$ Combine like terms.

The answer is $5x + 15$.

— Example 3 —

Subtract: $(7x^2 + 9x - 3) - (4x^2 + 2x + 5)$.

Write in vertical form.	Change subtracting to adding opposite.	Combine like terms.
$7x^2 + 9x - 3$	$7x^2 + 9x - 3$	$7x^2 + 9x - 3$
$- (4x^2 + 2x + 5)$	$- 4x^2 - 2x - 5$	$- 4x^2 - 2x - 5$
		$3x^2 + 7x - 8$

The answer is $3x^2 + 7x - 8$.

Try It Subtract the polynomials.

c. $\ 8x^2 - 4x + 5$ **d.** $\ -9x^2 - 4x + 10$ **e.** $\ 12x^2 - 7x + 2$
   $- (3x^2 + 6x - 1)$ $- (4x^2 + 8x - 3)$ $- (-2x^2 - 3x + 5)$
   $5x^2 - 10x + 6$ $-13x^2 - 12x + 13$ $14x^2 - 4x - 3$

f. $(5x - 9) - (8x + 5)$ $-3x - 14$ **g.** $(6x + 1) - (-4x - 5)$ $10x + 6$

h. $(4x^2 - 14x + 3) - (8x^2 + 2x - 5)$ $-4x^2 - 16x + 8$

i. $(15x - 4) - (7x^2 - 10x - 8)$ $-7x^2 + 25x + 4$

Geometry Find the missing side length, based on the perimeter of each figure.

21.
$x^2 + 2x$
$x^2 + 2x + 5$
$p = 3x^2 + 4x + 10$
$x^2 - 3x + 3$

22.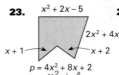
$3x + 2$
$x^2 - 4$
$x^2 - 2$
$p = 3x^2 - 10$
$x^2 - 4$

23.
$x^2 + 2x - 5$
$2x^2 + 4x$
$x + 1$ $x + 2$
$p = 4x^2 + 8x + 2$
$x^2 + 4$

24.
$3x^2 + 4x$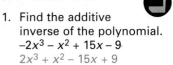
x^2
$p = 7x^2 + 7x$
$3x^2 + 3x$

25. **Physics** How much higher does a disc propelled upwards with an
initial velocity of 40 m/sec go, over time, than one propelled at 30 m/sec
from a platform 8 m high? Subtract $-5t^2 + 30t + 8$ from $-5t^2 + 40t$. $10t - 8$

Problem Solving and Reasoning

26. Critical Thinking Find two monomials with a difference of $4x^3$.

27. Communicate Josie simplified the expression $4x - 3x$ and got an
answer of 1. Was she correct? Explain your reasoning.

28. Critical Thinking What would you subtract from $8x^2$ to get $-18x^2$? $26x^2$

29. What conclusion can you make about two polynomials with a
difference of zero? Explain your answer.

30. Critical Thinking Find the missing term. $4x$

$(-2x^2 - 4x) - (\underline{} - 3x^2) = x^2 - 8x$

31. A *matrix* is a rectangular array of numbers. It can be used to add or
subtract polynomials. The first two rows show the aligned coefficients
of $x^3 - x^2 + 2x - 4$ and $2x^3 - 3x^2 + 5$. The third row shows the
sum of each pair of corresponding coefficients. Use a matrix to subtract
$x^5 - 3x^2 + 2$ from $3x^5 + 2x^4 - 2x + 3$. $2x^5 + 2x^4 + 3x^2 - 2x + 1$

$$
\begin{array}{cccc}
x^3 & x^2 & x^1 & x^0 \\
\end{array}
$$
$$
\begin{bmatrix}
1 & -1 & 2 & -4 \\
2 & -3 & 0 & 5 \\
3 & -4 & 2 & 1
\end{bmatrix}
$$

Mixed Review

32. A heron weighing 2 kg eats 340 g of food daily. What percent of its
weight does it eat daily? *[Lesson 6-2]* **17**%

Determine the prime factorization of each. *[Lesson 7-1]*

33. 90   **34.** 256 2^8 **35.** 87   **36.** 101   **37.** 375 $3 \cdot 5^3$
$2 \cdot 3^2 \cdot 5$ $3 \cdot 29$ **Already prime**

Find the volume of each. *[Lesson 9-6]*

38.
7.25 in.
7.25 in.
7.25 in.
≈ 381.08 in^3

39.
3.8 m
10.2 m   6 m
232.56 m^3

10-7 • Subtracting Polynomials **547**

PROBLEM SOLVING

Name _____

Guided Problem Solving 10-7

GPS PROBLEM 25, STUDENT PAGE 547

How much higher does a disc propelled upwards with an initial velocity
of 40 m/sec go, over time, than one propelled at 30 m/sec from a
platform 8 m high? Subtract $-5t^2 + 30t + 8$ from $-5t^2 + 40t$.

— Understand —

1. Underline the two polynomials you will use when you subtract.

— Plan —

2. Order the steps below to show how to subtract polynomials.

   __4__ Combine like terms

   __1__ Add the opposite of the second polynomial

   __3__ Group like terms.

   __2__ Find the opposite of all terms in the parentheses.

3. Write the polynomials you will subtract as an expression.

   $(-5t^2 + 40t)$ $-$ $(-5t^2 + 30t + 8)$

— Solve —

4. Use the steps in Item 2 to subtract the polynomial in Item 3.

   a. Step 1: $(-5t^2 + 40t) + -(-5t^2 + 30t + 8)$

   b. Step 2: $(-5t^2 + 40t) + (5t^2 - 30t - 8)$

   c. Step 3: $(-5 + 5)t^2 + (40 - 30)t - 8$

   d. Step 4: $10t - 8$

— Look Back —

5. Show how to write the problem vertically.
   Then solve to check your answer.

   $-5t^2 + 40t$
   $- (-5t^2 + 30t + 8)$
   _____
   $10t - 8$

   SOLVE ANOTHER PROBLEM

How much higher does a rocket propelled upwards with an initial
velocity of 36 m/sec go, over time, than one propelled at 25 m/sec
from a platform 10 m high? Subtract $-5t^2 + 25t + 10$ from $-5t^2 + 36t$. $11t - 10$

ENRICHMENT

Name _____

Extend Your Thinking 10-7

Visual Thinking

The third square in each row and each column is related to the
two squares preceding it. Compare the first two squares. Determine
which elements they have in common. The third square is composed
of their *differences*.

— Example: —

The first two squares have a small dark
square in common. Their differences are
a large circle and a large triangle. So, the
third square contains a large triangle and
a large circle, each of which is the same
size as those in squares 1 and 2.

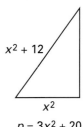

1. Draw the figure that belongs
   in each empty square.

2. Create a 9-square puzzle. Leave
   one square blank. Trade with a
   classmate and solve each others'
   puzzles.
   Check students' work.

PROBLEM SOLVING 10-7

Exercise Notes

■ **Exercise 25**

Sports In skeet shooting, clay
targets are shot into the air from
two devices. A person stands in
one of eight areas and tries to
shoot the targets. Skeet shooting
is a form of trapshooting, which
began in the late 1700s in
England. Skeet shooting and trapshooting are both part of the
Summer Games of the Olympics.

■ **Exercise 27**

Extension There is one case
where the answer would be
correct. Interested students might
enjoy figuring out that when 1 is
substituted for x, $4x - 3x$ does
equal 1.

Exercise Answers

26. Possible answer: $5x^3$, x^3

27. No; She dropped the variable.

29. The polynomials are equal.

Alternate Assessment

You may want to use the
Interactive CD-ROM Journal
with this assessment.

Journal Have students read the
Journal entry they made in
Lesson 10-6 for **Alternate
Assessment**. Have them write a
brief paragraph explaining which
of their predictions about subtracting polynomials were correct,
which were incorrect, and why
they think their results turned
out the way they did.

► **Quick Quiz**

1. Find the additive
   inverse of the polynomial.
   $-2x^3 - x^2 + 15x - 9$
   $2x^3 + x^2 - 15x + 9$

2. Subtract.
   $(7x^2 - 2x + 4) -$
   $(4x^2 - 2x - 1)$ $3x^2 + 5$

3. Find the missing side
   length, given the perimeter.

   $x^2 + 12$
   x^2
   $p = 3x^2 + 20$
   $x^2 + 8$

Available on Daily Transparency 10-7

► Review

Evaluate each expression.

1. $(2 \cdot 2)$ 4
2. $(2 \cdot 2 \cdot 2)$ 8
3. $(2 \cdot 2 \cdot 2 \cdot 2)$ 16
4. $(2 \cdot 2 \cdot 2 \cdot 2 \cdot 2)$ 32

Available on Daily Transparency 10-8

► Lesson Link

In the previous two lessons, students learned that adding and subtracting polynomials was very similar to adding and subtracting integers. In this lesson, students will see that multiplying monomials and polynomials is also very similar to multiplying integers.

1 Introduce

Explore

The Point
Students investigate multiplying powers of 2 and 3 to discover the rule of multiplying powers with the same base.

Ongoing Assessment
Check to make sure that students find the correct product of 2^3 and 2^4 (128) and of 3^2 and 3^4 (729). Otherwise, the relationship between the product and the exponents will be obscured.

For Groups That Finish Early
Test your conjecture with two other powers of 2 and 3, such as $2^2 \cdot 2^5$ and $3^2 \cdot 3^5$.

Follow Up
Ask volunteers to share their answers to Step 3. After a brief class discussion, have a volunteer write a sentence describing the relationship the class found.

10-8 Multiplying Polynomials and Monomials

You'll Learn ...
- to multiply polynomials and monomials

... How It's Used

Astrophysicists often multiply numbers in scientific notation.

► Lesson Link   In the last two lessons, you added and subtracted polynomials. In this lesson, you will learn to multiply polynomials and monomials. ◄

Explore   Multiplying Polynomials and Monomials

It's Powerful!

Compound microscopes use two or more lenses to expand the size of an image. Understanding how to multiply powers will give you an idea of how much an image can be expanded when lenses are used together.

1. Multiply 2^3 by 2^4. What is the product?

2. Is the result a power of 2? Write the result as a power of 2.

3. How does the product appear to relate to the exponents in 2^3 and 2^4?

4. Test your conjecture on the product of 3^2 and 3^4.

5. Suppose you multiply 2^3 and 100^4. Would you be able to relate the product to the exponents in the same way? Explain.

Remember

Exponential form is a base with an exponent that tells how many times the base is used as a multiplier. [Page 97]

Learn   Multiplying Polynomials and Monomials

Recall that 5^2 is the same as $5 \cdot 5$, and 5^4 is the same as $5 \cdot 5 \cdot 5 \cdot 5$.

To multiply $5^2 \cdot 5^4$, think $(5 \cdot 5)(5 \cdot 5 \cdot 5 \cdot 5)$. This is 5^6.

When you multiply two powers with the same base, add their exponents.

MULTIPLYING POWERS WITH LIKE BASES

In words: When multiplying powers with like bases, add their exponents.

In symbols: $a^m \cdot a^n = a^{m+n}$ **Example:** $x^4 \cdot x^5 = x^{4+5} = x^9$

548 Chapter 10 • Algebra: Functions and Relationships

► MEETING INDIVIDUAL NEEDS

Resources

10-8 Practice
10-8 Reteaching
10-8 Problem Solving
10-8 Enrichment
10-8 Daily Transparency
　　　Problem of
　　　the Day
　　　Review
　　　Quick Quiz
Technology Master 57
Chapter 10 Project Master

Learning Modalities

Social In **Alternate Assessment** students interview each other about the lesson concepts.

Visual Ask volunteers to make bright, colorful posters showing the rule for multiplying powers (monomials) with the same base.

Challenge

Have interested students make a game to assist others in working with polynomials. Have them make game cards that ask students to simplify, add, subtract, multiply, and find the additive inverses of polynomials. Each game card should have the answer printed upside-down or on the back of the card. The answers should be checked by students in this group. A game board should also be designed, with students encouraged to use their imagination. A nice working model of the game should be made and used in class.

Example 1

a. Multiply $6^7 \times 6^8$.

$6^7 \times 6^8 = 6^{7+8} = 6^{15}$

b. Multiply 2×2^5. (Note that 2 is 2^1.)

$2^1 \times 2^5 = 2^{1+5} = 2^6$

The methods for multiplying numerical bases, such as 6 and 2 above, can help you multiply monomials.

Example 2

a. Multiply x by x^4.

x is x^1.

$x^1 \cdot x^4 = (x)(x \cdot x \cdot x \cdot x) = x^{1+4} = x^5$

b. Multiply $2x^2(3x^3)$.

$2x^2 \cdot 3x^3 = 2 \cdot 3(x \cdot x)(x \cdot x \cdot x) = 6x^{2+3} = 6x^5$

Try It

Multiply.

a. $5^2 \times 5^4 \ 5^6$ **b.** $8^3 \times 8^0 \ 8^3$ **c.** $x^5(x^3) \ x^8$ **d.** $4x^3 \cdot -8x^3 \ {-}32x^6$

Because you can multiply a monomial times a monomial, the distributive property can help you multiply a monomial times a polynomial.

Example 3

a. Multiply $5x^2$ by $2x^3 + 6$.

$5x^2(2x^3 + 6) = 5x^2 \cdot 2x^3 + 5x^2 \cdot 6$ Use the distributive property.

$= 10x^{3+2} + 30x^2$ Multiply monomials.

$= 10x^5 + 30x^2$ Simplify.

b. Multiply $-5x^4$ by $3x + 5 - 2x^3$.

$-5x^4(3x + 5 - 2x^3)$

$= -5x^4 \cdot 3x + -5x^4 \cdot 5 + -5x^4 \cdot -2x^3$ Use the distributive property.

$= -15x^{4+1} + -25x^4 + 10x^{4+3}$ Multiply monomials.

$= -15x^5 - 25x^4 + 10x^7$ Simplify.

Try It

a. Multiply $-2x^2$ by $5x^4 + 6x$.   **b.** Multiply $2x^2$ by $3x^2 + 5x - 1$.

            $-10x^6 - 12x^3$ $6x^4 + 10x^3 - 2x^2$

10-8 • Multiplying Polynomials and Monomials   **549**

MATH EVERY DAY

▶ Problem of the Day

Ari was using his calculator when it malfunctioned and only showed the top of the digits. He challenges you to figure out what the original problem had been.

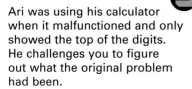

$2645 + 7973 = 10{,}618$

Available on Daily Transparency 10-8

An Extension is provided in the transparency package.

Fact of the Day

Hummingbirds' wings actually make a humming sound as they move. Although over 300 species of hummingbirds exist, only 19 species live in the United States.

Mental Math

Do these mentally.

1. $a \cdot a \cdot a \cdot a \cdot a \ a^5$

2. $a^2 \cdot a^7 \ a^9$

3. $a^0 \cdot a^4 \ a^4$

Answers for Explore

1. 128

2. Yes; 2^7

3. The exponents are added.

4. $3^2 \cdot 3^4 = 729 = 3^6$

5. No; The bases are not the same.

2 Teach

Learn

Refer to the **Review** questions on page 548 as an introduction to this section. Point out that $(2 \cdot 2)(2 \cdot 2) = 4 \cdot 4$, which is the same as $(2 \cdot 2 \cdot 2 \cdot 2) = 16$. Point out that $(2 \cdot 2)(2 \cdot 2 \cdot 2) = 4 \cdot 8$, which is the same as $(2 \cdot 2 \cdot 2 \cdot 2 \cdot 2) = 32$.

Alternate Examples

1. **a.** Multiply $4^4 \times 4^5$.

   $4^4 \times 4^5 = 4^{4+5} = 4^9$

   b. Multiply 9×9^2. (9 is 9^1.)

   $9^1 \times 9^2 = 9^{1+2} = 9^3$

2. **a.** Multiply x by x^2. (x is x^1.)

   $x^1 \cdot x^2 = (x)(x \cdot x)$
   $= x^{1+2} = x^3$

   b. Multiply $2x^3(5x^5)$.

   $2x^3 \cdot 5x^5 =$
   $2 \cdot 5(x \cdot x \cdot x)(x \cdot x \cdot x \cdot x \cdot x)$
   $= 10x^{3+5} = 10x^8$

3. **a.** Multiply $3x^2$ by $7x + 2$.

   Use the distributive property:
   $3x^2(7x + 2) = 3x^2 \cdot 7x + 3x^2 \cdot 2$
   $= 21x^{2+1} + 6x^2$ Multiply monomials.
   $= 21x^3 + 6x^2$ Simplify.

   b. Multiply $-4x^6$ by $(3x^2 + 12 - 8x^4)$.

   Use the distributive property:
   $-4x^6(3x^2 + 12 - 8x^4)$
   $= -4x^6 \cdot 3x^2 + -4x^6 \cdot 12 + -4x^6 \cdot -8x^4$
   $= -12x^{6+2} + -48x^6 + 32x^{6+4}$ Multiply monomials.
   $= -12x^8 + -48x^6 + 32x^{10}$ Simplify.
   $= -12x^8 - 48x^6 + 32x^{10}$

Alternate Examples

4. A peregrine falcon can fly as fast as 3.491×10^5 meters per hour. How many meters would it travel if it could fly constantly at this speed for 1 year (8.76×10^3 hours)?

$(3.491 \times 10^5)(8.76 \times 10^3)$

$= (3.491 \cdot 8.76) \times (10^5 \cdot 10^3)$ Group numbers and bases together.

$= 30.581 \times 10^8$ Multiply the numbers, add the exponents.

$= 3.0581 \times 10^9$ Rewrite in scientific notation.

5. Alpha Centauri, the next closest star after the sun, is about 4.31×10^0 light years away from Earth. Multiply to find how far light travels to get from Alpha Centauri to Earth. A light year is 5.87×10^{12} miles.

$(5.87 \times 10^{12}) \times (4.31 \times 10^0)$ Group numbers and bases together.

$= (5.87 \cdot 4.31) \times (10^{12} \cdot 10^0)$

$\approx 25.3 \times 10^{12}$ Multiply the numbers, add the exponents.

$\approx 2.53 \times 10^{13}$ Rewrite in scientific notation.

Light travels about 2.53×10^{13} miles to get from Alpha Centauri to Earth.

3 Practice and Assess

In Chapter 2, you studied scientific notation. The rules for multiplying powers can help you multiply two numbers written in scientific notation.

Examples

4 The smaller the bird, the faster it needs to flap its wings to stay airborne. A hummingbird flaps its wings 1.5×10^3 times per min. How many times would it flap its wings if it could stay airborne for a year (5.256×10^5 min)?

$(1.5 \times 10^3)(5.256 \times 10^5)$

$= (1.5 \cdot 5.256) \times (10^3 \cdot 10^5)$ Group numbers and bases together.

$= 7.884 \quad \times \quad 10^8$ Multiply the numbers, add the exponents.

A hummingbird would flap its wings 7.884×10^8 times, or approximately 800 million times in a year.

5 A light year, the distance light travels in a year, is 5.87×10^{12} miles. A parsec is 3.26×10^0 light years. Multiply to find how many miles are in a parsec. Write the answer in scientific notation.

$(5.87 \times 10^{12}) \times (3.26 \times 10^0)$

$= (5.87 \cdot 3.26) \times (10^{12} \cdot 10^0)$ Group numbers and bases together.

$\approx 19.1 \times 10^{12}$ Multiply. Add exponents.

$\approx 1.91 \times 10^{13}$ Rewrite in scientific notation.

There are about 1.91×10^{13} miles in a parsec.

Try It

a. Multiply 7×10^4 by 5×10^6. Write the answer in scientific notation.
3.5×10^{11}

b. In 1995, the estimated population of the U. S. was 2.6×10^8. Each person's share of the national debt is about $\$1.9 \times 10^4$. What is the national debt?
$\$4.94 \times 10^{12}$

Check Your Understanding

1. Explain how to multiply two powers with the same base. Multiply coefficients, add exponents

2. Why can't you simplify the product of w^3 and x^2?

3. When multiplying $-2x^3$ by a polynomial, how do you know what the sign of each term will be?

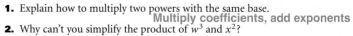

Practice and Apply

1. **Getting Started** Use these steps to multiply x^4 by x^3.

   a. Write x^4 as the product of factors. $\underline{x}\cdot\underline{x}\cdot\underline{x}\cdot\underline{x}$.

   b. Write x^3 as the product of factors. $\underline{x}\cdot\underline{x}\cdot\underline{x}$.

   c. Count the total number of x factors. $\underline{7}$.

   d. $x^4\cdot x^3 = \underline{x^7}$.

Multiply.

2. $7^2\cdot 7^7$ $\mathbf{7^9}$

3. $4^1\cdot 4^6$ $\mathbf{4^7}$

4. $c^3\cdot c^6$ $\mathbf{c^9}$

5. $2r^2\cdot 3r^4$ $\mathbf{6r^6}$

6. $(-4r^3)(5r^2)$ $\mathbf{-20r^5}$

7. $(-3d^6)(8d^4)$ $\mathbf{-24d^{10}}$

8. $(-s^2)(-s^2)$ $\mathbf{s^4}$

9. $(4f^6)(5f^9)$ $\mathbf{20f^{15}}$

10. $8y^2\cdot y^0$ $\mathbf{8y^2}$

11. $9b^3\cdot\frac{1}{3}b^2$ $\mathbf{3b^5}$

12. $4y^2(-3y^5-6)$ $\mathbf{-12y^7-24y^2}$

13. $-6t(1-t^2)$ $\mathbf{-6t+6t^3}$

14. $-2s^7(s^2+2s-1)$ $\mathbf{-2s^9-4s^8+2s^7}$

15. $5g^4(3g^3-2g^2+5g+8)$

16. $-\frac{1}{2}a^2(10a-8)$ $\mathbf{-5a^3+4a^2}$

17. $m(2m+4)$ $\mathbf{2m^2+4m}$

18. **Test Prep** Which monomial is the product of $-5x^3\cdot -5x^3$? **C**

    Ⓐ $-10x^3$ Ⓑ $25x^3$ Ⓒ $25x^6$ Ⓓ $-10x^6$

Multiply each of the following. Write your answers in scientific notation.

19. $(3.2\times 10^4)\cdot(3.1\times 10^5)$ $\mathbf{9.92\times 10^9}$

20. $(1.3\times 10^2)\cdot(2.7\times 10^6)$ $\mathbf{3.51\times 10^8}$

21. $(5.1\times 10^3)\cdot(1.6\times 10^3)$ $\mathbf{8.16\times 10^6}$

22. **GPS** Find an expression for the area of each region and the total area of the figure. Simplify if possible.

23. **Journal** Why do you add exponents when you multiply powers with the same base?

24. Find the volume of the bird house. $\mathbf{12x^3+4x^2}$

25. If each person's share of the national debt is 1.9×10^4 dollars, how much of the debt are the people in the following states responsible for?

    a. Florida: population 1.3×10^7 $\mathbf{\$2.47\times 10^{11}}$

    b. Oklahoma: population 3.1×10^6 $\mathbf{\$5.89\times 10^{10}}$

    c. Wyoming: population 4.5×10^5 $\mathbf{\$8.55\times 10^9}$

    d. California: population 3.1×10^7 $\mathbf{\$5.89\times 10^{11}}$

10-8 • Multiplying Polynomials and Monomials **551**

10-8 Exercises and Applications

Assignment Guide

■ **Basic**
1–20, 22, 23, 26, 27, 29, 33, 35

■ **Average**
1–18, 21–23, 26, 27, 29–31, 34

■ **Enriched**
1–11 odds, 12–29, 32–36 evens

Exercise Notes

■ **Exercise 1**

Error Prevention This exercise provides a review for all students about the rule for multiplying powers with like bases. If a student has trouble with this exercise, he or she has not grasped the concept of multiplying polynomials and monomials.

■ **Exercises 11 and 16**

Error Prevention This is the first time students have seen fractions as coefficients in this lesson. Suggest that students express the whole number coefficients in fraction form, for example, $9=\frac{9}{1}$.

Exercise Answers

15. $15g^7-10g^6+25g^5+40g^4$

22. $6x^2+2x$; $10x^2-4x$; $8x$; $18x^2+6x$; $34x^2+12x$

23. Possible answer: Because the number of factors represented increases additively.

> ## PRACTICE

Name _____

Practice 10-8

Multiplying Polynomials and Monomials

Multiply.

1. $3^7\cdot 3^4$ $\mathbf{3^{11}}$

2. $x^3\cdot x^5$ $\mathbf{x^8}$

3. $3t^6\cdot t^8$ $\mathbf{3t^{14}}$

4. $(5c^8)(7c^{12})$ $\mathbf{35c^{20}}$

5. $(11u^2)(3u^0)$ $\mathbf{33u^2}$

6. $(7p)(5p^3)$ $\mathbf{35p^4}$

7. $(12y^2)(3y^9)$ $\mathbf{36y^{11}}$

8. $(-5g^3)(2g)$ $\mathbf{-10g^4}$

9. $(6k^2)(-8k^4)$ $\mathbf{-48k^6}$

10. $4x(x^2+5x-3)$ $\mathbf{4x^3+20x^2-12x}$

11. $-7r(4r^7-8r^3+9)$ $\mathbf{-28r^8+56r^4-63r}$

12. $\frac{1}{3}h^2(6h^3-12h^2+15)$ $\mathbf{2h^5-4h^4+5h^2}$

13. $8v^3(-2v^2+7v-3)$ $\mathbf{-16v^5+56v^4-24v^3}$

14. $-2n^6(5n^4+3n^2+4)$ $\mathbf{-10n^{10}-6n^8-8n^6}$

15. $b^2(5b^2-8b+3)$ $\mathbf{5b^4-8b^3+3b^2}$

16. $-\frac{3}{4}q^3(-8q^2+64)$ $\mathbf{6q^5-48q^3}$

17. $20w^6(6w^8-3w^6+w^4)$ $\mathbf{120w^{14}-60w^{12}+20w^{10}}$

Multiply each of the following. Write your answers in scientific notation.

18. $(2.3\times 10^3)(1.7\times 10^4)$ $\mathbf{3.91\times 10^7}$

19. $(4.6\times 10^{11})(3.9\times 10^9)$ $\mathbf{1.794\times 10^{21}}$

20. $(3.2\times 10^3)(1.4\times 10^3)$ $\mathbf{4.48\times 10^6}$

21. $(1.6\times 10^6)(4.1\times 10^5)$ $\mathbf{6.56\times 10^{11}}$

22. $(6.8\times 10^7)(1.1\times 10^1)$ $\mathbf{7.48\times 10^8}$

23. $(8.3\times 10^{10})(7.9\times 10^8)$ $\mathbf{6.557\times 10^{19}}$

24. $(3.0\times 10^2)(1.9\times 10^7)$ $\mathbf{5.7\times 10^9}$

25. $(2.4\times 10^4)(3.1\times 10^9)$ $\mathbf{7.44\times 10^{13}}$

26. $(6.3\times 10^9)(1.4\times 10^6)$ $\mathbf{8.82\times 10^{15}}$

27. $(8.4\times 10^8)(1.0\times 10^5)$ $\mathbf{8.4\times 10^{13}}$

28. **Social Science** Japan has about 3.35×10^2 people per square kilometer of land. The area of Japan is about 3.78×10^5 km². Find the population of Japan. Give your answer in scientific notation.

    About 1.27×10^8 people

29. Multiply to find an expression for the volume of the aquarium. Simplify if possible. $\mathbf{30x^7-90x^6+120x^5}$

> ## RETEACHING

Name _____

Alternative Lesson 10-8

Multiplying Polynomials and Monomials

You can multiply two powers with the same base by adding their exponents: $a^m\cdot a^n=a^{m+n}$. To multiply a monomial times a polynomial, you can use the distributive property.

— **Example 1** —

Find each answer.

a. Multiply: $3^2\cdot 3^5$.

   $3^2\cdot 3^5=3^{2+5}=3^7$ Think: $3^2\cdot 3^5=(3\cdot 3)\cdot(3\cdot 3\cdot 3\cdot 3\cdot 3)$

b. Multiply: $x\cdot x^3$.

   $x\cdot x^3=x^{1+3}=x^4$

Try It Multiply.

a. $5^2\cdot 5^4$ $\mathbf{5^6}$

b. $10\cdot 10^3$ $\mathbf{10^4}$

c. $4^3\cdot 4^5$ $\mathbf{4^8}$

d. $3^2\cdot 3^5$ $\mathbf{3^7}$

e. $x^7\cdot x^2$ $\mathbf{x^9}$

f. $x^3\cdot x^9$ $\mathbf{x^{12}}$

g. $x^3\cdot x^2$ $\mathbf{x^5}$

h. $x^4\cdot x^3$ $\mathbf{x^7}$

i. $x^7\cdot x$ $\mathbf{x^8}$

— **Example 2** —

Multiply $3x^2$ by $-2x^2+4x-3$.

$3x^2(-2x^2+4x-3)$

$(3x^2\cdot -2x^2)+(3x^2\cdot 4x)-(3x^2\cdot 3)$ Use the distributive property.

$-6x^{2+2}+12x^{2+1}-9x^2$ Multiply monomials.

$-6x^4+12x^3-9x^2$ Simplify.

Try It

j. Multiply $5x$ and $3x^3+x^2+9$. $\mathbf{15x^4+5x^3+45x}$

k. Multiply $3x^3$ and $4x^2-5x-6$. $\mathbf{12x^5-15x^4-18x^3}$

l. Multiply $-4x^2$ and $2x^2-x-1$. $\mathbf{-8x^4+4x^3+4x^2}$

m. Multiply $6x^2$ and $2x^2+3x-7$. $\mathbf{12x^4+18x^3-42x^2}$

n. Multiply $-5x^2$ and $2x^2+4x+3$. $\mathbf{-10x^4-20x^3-15x^2}$

o. Multiply $3x$ by $4x^3+2x-5$. $\mathbf{12x^4+6x^2-15x}$

Reteaching

Activity

Materials: Graph paper

• Work with a partner.

• Draw a rectangle on graph paper. Assume that the length and width of each square is x and the area of each square is x^2.

• Write the length and width of your rectangle in terms of x.

• Find the area of your rectangle by counting squares. Then find the area by multiplying.

• Draw other rectangles and find the areas.

Lesson 10-8 **551**

Exercise Notes

■ **Exercise 27**

Extension This exercise extends multiplying powers with like bases to finding the power of a power.

■ **Exercise 29**

This exercise provides a nice conclusion to this lesson, as it requires students to apply the thinking patterns used in the lesson to a new context.

Project Progress

You may want to have students use Chapter 10 Project Master.

Exercise Answers

29. a. Subtract exponents

    b. $2^1 = \frac{8}{4} = 2$

Alternate Assessment

Interview Have students prepare questions about this lesson to ask other students. Have them interview one or more of their classmates. Hold a brief classroom discussion, sharing the answers they received. Possible questions include: What was the hardest mathematical idea to understand in this lesson? Do you feel you understood it better after practice? What was one interesting mathematical fact you learned? What was one interesting fact about birds that you learned?

► Quick Quiz

1. Multiply $a^4 \times a^7$. a^{11}

2. Multiply $6x^3$ by $(x^2 - 6x + 9)$. $6x^5 - 36x^4 + 54x^3$

3. Multiply 4×10^6 by 4×10^8. Write the answer in scientific notation. 16×10^{14}, 1.6×10^{15}

Available on Daily Transparency 10-8

---

26. **Geometry** Multiply to find an expression for the volume of the box. Simplify if possible. $15x^3 + 105x^2$

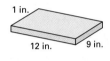

Problem Solving and Reasoning

27. **Math Reasoning** What is $(3^2)^3$? (Think of it as $3^2 \cdot 3^2 \cdot 3^2$.) What is the expanded product $(a^2)^3$? $3^6 = 729$; a^6

28. **Critical Thinking** Find an expression for the surface area of the figure at the right. $58x^2 + 54x$

29. **Communicate** When you multiplied powers with like bases, you added exponents.

    a. What do you think you would do when dividing powers with like bases?

    b. Try your conjecture on $\frac{2^3}{2^2}$

Mixed Review

Find the GCF of each set of numbers. *[Lesson 7-2]*

30. 40, 56 **8**   31. 125, 175 **25**   32. 18, 48 **6**   33. 63, 15, 126 **3**

Find the volume of each after the dilation. *[Lesson 9-7]*

34. Scale factor = 0.5   35. Scale factor = 4   36. Scale factor = $\frac{1}{3}$

25 cm / 18 cm / 10 cm   **562.5 cm³**

2.4 m / 2.4 m / 2.4 m   **884.736 m³**

1 in. / 12 in. / 9 in.   **4 in³**

Project Progress

Decide on a model. (You might also try graphing some polynomial functions, such as $y = x^3$, before you decide.) Explain how the model you chose fits or does not fit your situation.

Problem Solving

Understand
Plan
Solve
Look Back

► PROBLEM SOLVING

Name _____

Guided Problem Solving 10-8

GPS PROBLEM 22, STUDENT PAGE 551

Find an expression for the area of each region and the total area of the figure. Simplify if possible.

| 2x | 1 | 2 | 3 | 4 |
| | 3x + 1 | 5x − 2 | 4 | 4x + 5x + 2 |

— Understand —

1. What shape is each region? **Rectangle.**

2. What is the height of each region? **2x**

— Plan —

3. Number the regions from 1 to 4 starting with the region on the left.

4. Add to find the base of the entire figure. **17x + 5**

5. What is the formula to find the area of each region? **A = b · h**

— Solve —

6. Use the formula in Item 5 to find each area. Then simplify, if possible.

   a. Region 1 $(3x + 1) \cdot 2x = 6x^2 + 2x$

   b. Region 2 $(5x − 2) \cdot 2x = 10x^2 − 4x$

   c. Region 3 $4 \cdot 2x = 8x$

   d. Region 4 $(4x + 5x + 2) \cdot 2x = 8x^2 + 10x^2 + 4x = 18x^2 + 4x$

   e. Total area $(17x + 5) \cdot 2x = 34x^2 + 10x$

— Look Back —

7. What is another way to find the total area? **Add areas of four regions.**

SOLVE ANOTHER PROBLEM

| 3a | J | K | L | M |
| | 3a + 1 | 6a + 1 | 6a | 2 |

Find an expression for each region and the total area of the figure. Simplify if possible.

   a. Region J $(3a + 1) \cdot 3a = 9a^2 + 3a$

   b. Region K $(6a + 1) \cdot 3a = 18a^2 + 3a$

   c. Region L $6a \cdot 3a = 18a^2$ d. Region M $2 \cdot 3a = 6a$

   e. Total area of figure $(15a + 4) \cdot 3a = 45a^2 + 12a$

► ENRICHMENT

Name _____

Extend Your Thinking 10-8

Patterns in Numbers

1. You know that you add exponents when you multiply two expressions with the same base. For example: $7^2 \times 7^3 = 7^{2 + 3} = 7^5$. Make a conjecture about what you should do with the exponents when you divide expressions with the same base.

   Answers will vary.

2. Study the example below. What is the value of $\frac{7 \times 7 \times 7}{7 \times 7 \times 7}$? **1**

   $7^7 \div 7^3 = \frac{7 \times 7 \times 7 \times 7 \times 7 \times 7 \times 7}{7 \times 7 \times 7} = 7 \times 7 \times 7 \times 7 \times \frac{7 \times 7 \times 7}{7 \times 7 \times 7}$
   $= 7 \times 7 \times 7 \times 7$
   $= 7^4$

3. Study and continue the pattern below.

   $7^9 \div 7^3 = 7^{9 - 3} = 7^6$ $= 7 \times 7 \times 7 \times 7 \times 7 \times 7$
   $7^9 \div 7^4 = 7^{9 - 4} = 7^5$ $= 7 \times 7 \times 7 \times 7 \times 7$
   $7^9 \div 7^5 = 7^{9 - 5} = 7^4$ $= 7 \times 7 \times 7 \times 7$
   $7^9 \div 7^6 = 7^{9 - 6} = 7^3$ $= \underline{7 \times 7 \times 7}$
   $7^9 \div 7^7 = 7^{9 - 7} = \underline{7^2}$ $= \underline{7 \times 7}$
   $7^9 \div 7^8 = 7^{9 - 8} = \underline{7^1}$ $= \underline{7}$

4. Describe the pattern that you see.
   Possible answer: When you divide expressions with the same base, you subtract the exponents.

5. Extend the pattern for $7^9 \div 7^9$.
   $7^9 \div 7^9 = \frac{7 \times 7 \times 7 \times 7 \times 7 \times 7 \times 7 \times 7 \times 7}{7 \times 7 \times 7 \times 7 \times 7 \times 7 \times 7 \times 7 \times 7} = \underline{1}$

6. What do you think a^0 means? Explain. **a^0 equals 1. To get zero as an exponent, you are dividing a number by itself, such as** $7^9 \div 7^9 = 7^{9 - 9} = 7^0 = 1$.

Section 10B Connect

In this Connect, you will link your knowledge of polynomials.

Which Came First?

Materials: Centimeter cubes

Stacked boxes of eggs are to be marked "fragile." Suppose all visible sides are marked. How many boxes will be marked on 1 side? On 2 sides? Use cubes to simulate the exercise.

1. Build a 2 by 2 by 2 cube. How many small cubes did you use? If all the visible faces are marked, how many cubes will have 3 marked faces? 2 marked faces? 1 marked face? 0 marked faces? Copy the table and complete the column for the 2 by 2 by 2 cube.

2. Build a 3 by 3 by 3 cube. Complete the column for this cube. Then build a 4 by 4 by 4 cube, and so on, to finish the table. Describe any patterns you see in the table.

	Dimensions			
	$2 \times 2 \times 2$	$3 \times 3 \times 3$	$4 \times 4 \times 4$	$5 \times 5 \times 5$
Number of boxes	8	27	64	125
Number with 3 Sides Marked	8	8	8	8
Number with 2 Sides Marked	0	12	24	36
Number with 1 Side Marked	0	6	24	54
Number with 0 Sides Marked	0	1	8	27

3. For an $n \times n \times n$ cube of boxes, how many boxes are there? If all visible faces of the $n \times n \times n$ cube are marked, match the number of boxes to the correct expression.

   a. The total number of boxes iii   i. 8

   b. The number with 3 marked sides i   ii. $12(n - 2)$

   c. The number with 2 marked sides ii   iii. n^3

   d. The number with 1 marked side v   iv. $(n - 2)^3$

   e. The number with 0 marked sides iv   v. $6(n - 2)^2$

4. In a 20 by 20 by 20 cube, how many boxes would be unmarked?
   5832 cubes

553

Review Correlation

Item(s)	Lesson(s)
1–9	10-5
10–14	10-6
15	10-7
16	10-6
17	10-7
18–27	10-8
28	10-6, 10-8

Test Prep

Test-Taking Tip

If students know there is no penalty for wrong answers, then they should not leave any blank answers. They should guess at answers they don't know to eliminate as many wrong answers as possible.

Answers for Review

1. Binomial, two terms.

2. Trinomial, three terms.

3. Monomial, one term.

4. None of these, more than three terms.

REVIEW 10B

Section 10B Review

Identify each polynomial expression as a monomial, binomial, trinomial, or none of these. Explain your choice.

1. $4x^2 + x$ 2. $4x + x^5 + 2$ 3. $-2x^3$ 4. $x^3 + x^2 - x + 3$

Find the degree of each polynomial expression. Write the polynomial expression in descending order.

$5; -x^5 + x^2 - x$

5. $-6 + 8x$ 6. $2x^3 + 3x^2 - 9$ 7. $x^2 - x - x^5$ 8. $28x$ 9. $x^7 - 3$
   $1; 8x - 6$ $3; 2x^3 + 3x^2 - 9$ $1; 28x$ $7; x^7 - 3$

Simplify each if possible. If the expression cannot be simplified, write "already simplified." Write your answer in descending order.

10. $-6x^2 - 3x + 8x^3 + 2x$ 11. $8x^2 + 8x$ Already simplified
    $8x^3 - 6x^2 - x$
12. $-6y^3 + 4y + -3y^3 - 5y$ 13. $8x - 2x + 4x + 5$ $10x + 5$
    $-9y^3 - y$
14. $(2x^2 - 5x + 2) + (-4x^2 - 3x)$ 15. $(2x) - (-2x^2 - 2x + 1)$ $2x^2 + 4x - 1$
    $-2x^2 - 8x + 2$
16. $\quad (5x^2 + 3x + 1)$ 17. $\quad (5p^2 + 3p - 7)$
    $+ (3x^2 + 4x - 5)$ $- (4p^2 + 5p + 2)$ 20. $3y^3 + 6y^2 - 12y$
    $\overline{8x^2 + 7x - 4}$ $\overline{p^2 - 2p - 9}$
18. $a(a^7)$ a^8 19. $x^2 \cdot x^4$ x^6 20. $3y(y^2 + 2y - 4)$ 21. $4x^2 \cdot -5x^8$ $-20x^{10}$

22. $-2m^2(2m - 6)$ 23. $(y + 3)y$ 24. $x^5 \cdot y^5$ x^5y^5 25. $x^3(x^2 + 5)x$ $x^6 + 5x^4$
    $-4m^3 + 12m^2$ $y^2 + 3y$
26. The function $h = -5(t^2 - 5t + 10)$ can be used to find the approximate height of a launched flare in t sec. Write this function another way. $h = -5t^2 + 25t - 50$

Test Prep

When asked to multiply numbers in scientific notation, remember to group numbers together and bases together, then add exponents.

27. Which is the product of 1.2×10^6 and 4.1×10^8? **C**

    Ⓐ $5.3 \cdot 10^{14}$ Ⓑ $4.92 \cdot 10^2$

    Ⓒ $4.92 \cdot 10^{14}$ Ⓓ $4.92 \cdot 10^{48}$

28. Multiply to find the expression for each area. Add; Simplify if possible.

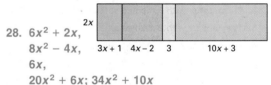

28. $6x^2 + 2x,$
    $8x^2 - 4x,$
    $6x,$
    $20x^2 + 6x; 34x^2 + 10x$

Resources

Practice Masters
   Section 10B Review

Assessment Sourcebook
   Quiz 10B

   TestWorks
   Test and Practice Software

PRACTICE

Name _____

Practice

Section 10B Review

Identify each polynomial expression as a monomial, binomial, trinomial, or polynomial. Explain your choice.

1. $3x^5 + 2x - 4$ 2. $7x^3$
   Trinomial; 3 terms   Monomial; 1 term

3. $x^7 - 2$ 4. $-4x^3 + 2x - x + 3$
   Binomial; 2 terms   Polynomial; more than 3 terms

Find the degree of each polynomial expression. Write the polynomial expression in descending order.

5. $4x + 3x^5 - 6$ Deg.: $\underline{5}$ 6. $-7 + 3x^2 - 5x$ Deg.: $\underline{2}$ 7. $8x^3 - 5x^2 + x^4$ Deg.: $\underline{4}$
   $3x^5 + 4x - 6$ $3x^2 - 5x - 7$ $x^4 + 8x^3 - 5x^2$

Simplify each if possible. If the expression cannot be simplified, write "simplified." Write your answer in descending order.

8. $5x + x^2 - 8x + x^2$ $\underline{2x^2 - 3x}$ 9. $-7k^3 - 6k^2 + 2k - 3$ $\underline{\text{Simplified}}$

10. $(\ c^2 - 7c + 11)$ 11. $(\ 15x^2 + 4x + 12)$
    $+ (4c^2 + 4c + 5)$ $- (\ 7x^2 + 5x - 3)$
    $\overline{5c^2 - 3c + 16}$ $\overline{8x^2 - x + 15}$

12. A rectangle has length $3x$ and width $2x + 1$. After a dilation of scale factor x, the area of the new rectangle is $x^2(3x)(2x + 1)$. Simplify this expression. $6x^4 + 3x^3$

13. Multiply to find an expression for each area. Simplify if possible.

    a. $\underline{24x^2 - 12x}$ b. $\underline{6x^2 + 3x}$
    c. $\underline{9x^2}$ d. $\underline{21x^2 - 15x}$ $8x - 4 \ 2x + 1 \ 3x \ 7x - 5$

14. Four students were asked their heights. The answers were 4 ft, 51 in., 55 in., and $4\frac{1}{2}$ ft. What was the average height? *[Lesson 8-1]*   52 in. or $4\frac{1}{3}$ ft

15. A 1.44-megabyte computer disk uses a circular piece of magnetic media with radius $1\frac{11}{16}$ in. Find the circumference and the area. *[Lesson 9-3]*

    Circumference: __About 10.6 in.__   Area: __About 8.94 in²__

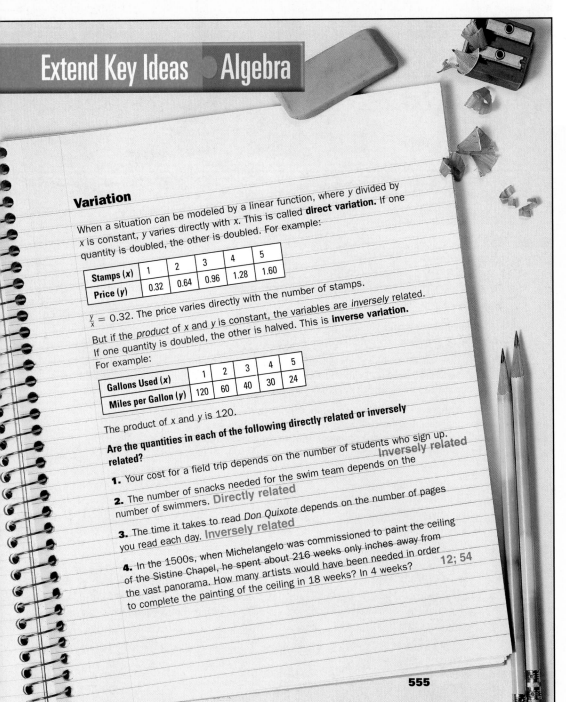

Variation

When a situation can be modeled by a linear function, where *y* divided by *x* is constant, *y* varies directly with *x*. This is called **direct variation.** If one quantity is doubled, the other is doubled. For example:

Stamps (*x*)	1	2	3	4	5
Price (*y*)	0.32	0.64	0.96	1.28	1.60

$\frac{y}{x} = 0.32$. The price varies directly with the number of stamps.

But if the *product* of *x* and *y* is constant, the variables are *inversely* related. If one quantity is doubled, the other is halved. This is **inverse variation.** For example:

Gallons Used (*x*)	1	2	3	4	5
Miles per Gallon (*y*)	120	60	40	30	24

The product of *x* and *y* is 120.

Are the quantities in each of the following directly related or inversely related?

1. Your cost for a field trip depends on the number of students who sign up. **Inversely related**

2. The number of snacks needed for the swim team depends on the number of swimmers. **Directly related**

3. The time it takes to read *Don Quixote* depends on the number of pages you read each day. **Inversely related**

4. In the 1500s, when Michelangelo was commissioned to paint the ceiling of the Sistine Chapel, he spent about 216 weeks only inches away from the vast panorama. How many artists would have been needed in order to complete the painting of the ceiling in 18 weeks? In 4 weeks? **12; 54**

555

Algebra

The Point

Students determine if quantities are directly related or inversely related.

About the Page

If students have trouble visualizing the relationships in the tables, you may want to give them a hands-on demonstration. For example, use stamps and change and pretend you are buying various amounts of stamps to show the direct variation relationship. Use 120 counters and separate the counters equally in 1, 2, 3, 4, and 5 cups to demonstrate the inverse variation relationship (the number of counters per cup is inversely proportional to the number of cups).

Ask ...

- What other situations are similar to purchasing stamps at the same price each time? Possible answers: Buying multiple boxes or cans of the same item at a store, being charged the same amount per person for a group going to a movie.

- What other situations are similar to figuring gas mileage for a car? Possible answers: Being charged for a 25-pound bag of potatoes regardless of the number or size of the potatoes inside, being charged a flat rate to park a car regardless of the number of people in the car.

Extension

Ask students to imagine they are considering buying a season pass to an amusement park. Regular admission for one day costs $11. The season pass costs $39. Have students use a direct relationship to make a table for 5 separate 1-day admissions. Then have them use an indirect relationship to make a table for using a season pass 1, 2, 3, 4, and 5 times. Describe how the price per admission changes with each visit using a season pass. 1 visit: $39.00 per visit; 2 visits: $19.50 per visit; 3 visits: $13.00 per visit; 4 visits: $9.75 per visit; 5 visits: $7.80 per visit.

Chapter 10 Summary and Review

Review Correlation

Item(s)	Lesson(s)
1, 2	10-1
3	10-2
4, 5	10-3
6	10-4
7, 8	10-5
9–11	10-6
12–14	10-7
15–17	10-8

For additional review, see page 685.

Answers for Review

3. Yes

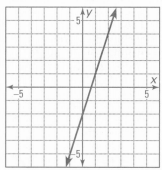

4. Possible answer: The y–intercept of $y = 2x^2$ is 0, but the y–intercept of $y = 2x^2 - 4$ is –4.

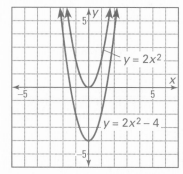

$y = 2x^2$
$y = 2x^2 - 4$

5. 64 ft

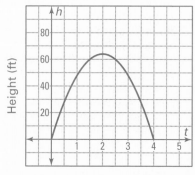

Time (seconds)

556

Chapter 10 Summary and Review

Graphic Organizer

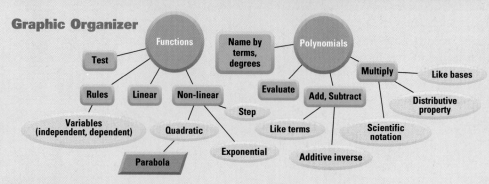

Section 10A Functions

Summary

■ A **function** is a relationship that gives one output value for each input value. Two different output values cannot have the same input value.

■ In a function, the input is the **independent variable** and the output is the **dependent variable**. To graph a function, use the x-axis for the independent variable and the y-axis for the dependent variable.

■ A function is a **linear function** if its graph is a line. A **quadratic function** is a **nonlinear function** in which the value of x is squared. Its graph is a ∪ or upside-down ∪-shaped **parabola**. In an **exponential function**, the exponent is a variable. A **step function** has a graph that is not connected.

Review

1. For the function machine shown,
   a. Find the output value for an input of -3.
      −18
   b. Find the input value for an output of 24.
      4

   | In | Multiply by 6 | Out |

2. What is a possible rule for the input and output shown in the table?
   Multiply by 3 and add 1.

Input	2	4	6	8
Output	7	13	19	25

3. Graph the equation $y = 3x - 2$. Does the equation describe a linear function?

4. Graph the functions $y = 2x^2$ and $y = 2x^2 - 4$ and explain their differences.

5. A ball was thrown. Its height (h, in ft) after t sec is given by $h = 64t - 16t^2$. Graph the function. How high did the ball go?

6. A plumber charges $25 for every half hour or portion thereof. Graph this function.

Resources

Practice Masters
  Cumulative Review
  Chapters 1–10

PRACTICE

Name _____

Practice

Cumulative Review Chapters 1–10

Add, subtract, multiply or divide each of the following. Write each answer in simplest form. *[Lessons 7-5, 7-6]*

1. $3\frac{1}{5} + 2\frac{1}{4}$ $5\frac{9}{20}$ 2. $5\frac{1}{3} - 2\frac{1}{2}$ $2\frac{5}{6}$ 3. $4\frac{3}{7} + 8\frac{1}{2}$ $12\frac{13}{14}$ 4. $6\frac{1}{5} - \frac{5}{8}$ $5\frac{23}{40}$

5. $\frac{3}{4} \times \frac{5}{7}$ $\frac{15}{28}$ 6. $2\frac{1}{2} \div 3\frac{1}{3}$ $\frac{3}{4}$ 7. $2\frac{5}{8} \times 3\frac{3}{7}$ 9 8. $8\frac{2}{3} \div 2\frac{3}{5}$ $3\frac{1}{3}$

Identify each polygon. Be as specific as possible. *[Lesson 8-6]*

9. Regular pentagon 10. Trapezoid

11. Octagon 12. Equilateral triangle

Find the surface area of each figure. *[Lesson 9-4]*

13. $821\frac{3}{4}$ in^2 14. 675.36 cm^2 15. $\approx 25{,}321$ ft^2 16. ≈ 253.2 mm^2

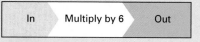

Graph each linear equation. Does the equation describe a function? *[Lesson 10-2]*

17. $x = -4$ No 18. $y = 3x$ Yes 19. $y = -2x + 1$ Yes

Add or subtract. Write the answers in simplest form. *[Lesson 10-6]*

20. $(x^2 - 5x - 6)$
    $-(3x^2 + 2x - 4)$
    $-2x^2 - 7x - 2$

21. $(2x^2 \quad + 7)$
    $+(-x^2 - 2x + 3)$
    $x^2 - 2x + 10$

22. $(5x - 3)$
    $-(4x^2 + x - 7)$
    $-4x^2 + 4x + 4$

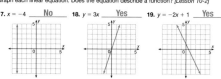

Section 10B Polynomials

Summary

- A **term** (or **monomial**) is a signed number, a variable, or a number multiplied by a variable or variables. The variables can have whole-number exponents.

- A **polynomial** is a sum of one or more terms. A **binomial** is a polynomial with two terms and a **trinomial** is a polynomial with three terms. The **degree** of a polynomial with one variable is the largest exponent in a term.

- A polynomial is written in descending order if the terms are written in order from the highest-degree term to the lowest-degree term.

- Polynomials can be evaluated by replacing the variables with the given numbers and using the order of operations rules to simplify the expression.

- **Like terms** are terms that have the same variable raised to the same exponent. A polynomial is **simplified** when it contains no like terms.

- Add polynomials by combining like terms. You can use the distributive property or add the polynomials vertically. Subtract a polynomial by adding its opposite, or additive inverse. You can find the additive inverse of a polynomial by changing the sign of each term.

- When multiplying powers with like bases, add their exponents: $a^m \cdot a^n = a^{m+n}$. This rule can be used to multiply monomials or numbers in scientific notation.

- Use the distributive property to multiply a monomial times a polynomial.

Review

7. Write $3x - 4x^3 + 5 - 7x^2$ in descending order. Find the degree of the polynomial.
$$-4x^3 - 7x^2 + 3x + 5; \ 3$$

8. **a.** Evaluate $x^3 - 4x + 3$ for $x = 3$. **18**

  b. Evaluate $2x^2 + 7x - 3$ for $x = -5$. **12**

9. Simplify. $5x^3 - 5x^2 - 3x + 14$
$$2x - 5x^2 + 4 - 5x + 10 + 5x^3$$

10. Add. $4p^2 - 1$
$$(p^2 - 5p + 7) + (3p^2 + 5p - 8)$$

11. Find the total area. $4x^2 + 2x + 5$

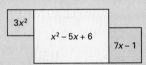

12. The perimeter is $2x^3 - 6x + 8$. Find the missing side length. $x^2 - x - 5$

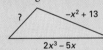

13. Find the additive inverse of the polynomial $-6x^3 + 9x^2 + 2x - 15$.
$$6x^3 - 9x^2 - 2x + 15$$

14. Subtract $(4g^2 + 7) - (3g^2 - 8g + 4)$. Write the answer in lowest terms. $g^2 + 8g + 3$

15. Find the area of a rectangle with a width of $3x^2$ and a length of $2x - 5$. $6x^3 - 15x^2$

16. Multiply $(2.3 \times 10^5) \cdot (1.8 \times 10^9)$ and write the answer in scientific notation.
$$4.14 \times 10^{14}$$

17. Multiply $-3u^3(5u^2 - 7u + 4)$.
$$-15u^5 + 21u^4 - 12u^3$$

Chapter 10 Summary and Review **557**

Answers for Review

6.

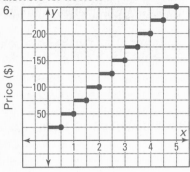

Time (hours)

Chapter 10 Assessment

Assessment Correlation

Item(s)	Lesson(s)
1–4	10-1
5	10-2
6	10-3
7	10-4
8	10-2
9, 10	10-5
11	10-7
12, 13	10-6
14	10-7
15–18	10-8
19	10-7
20	10-8

Answers for Assessment

4. No; There can be two homes with the same number of rooms but different areas.

5.
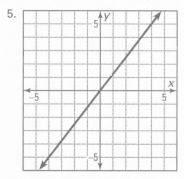

6. a. Answers may vary.

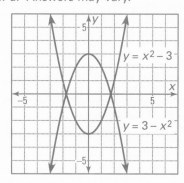

b. Answers may vary.

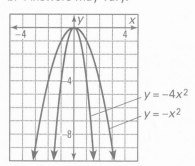

Answers for Exercises 7–8 and Performance Task on page 559.

Chapter 10 Assessment

1. For the function machine shown,
   a. Find the output value for an input of 12. **−3**
   b. Find the input value for an output of 31. **46**

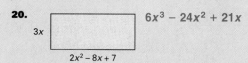
In | Subtract 15 | Out

2. What is a possible rule for the input and output shown in the table?

Input	5	7	9	11
Output	−11	−15	−19	−23

Multiply by −2 and subtract 1.

3. For the function rule $y = 4x - 7$, complete the table of values.

x	−1	0	1	2	3
y	−11	−7	−3	1	5

4. Is the area of a house (in ft^2) a function of the number of rooms in the house? Explain.

5. Graph the function $y = 1.25x$.

6. Graph each pair of functions and describe the similarities and differences.
   a. $y = x^2 - 3$ and $y = 3 - x^2$
   b. $y = -4x^2$ and $y = -x^2$

7. A call costs 15¢ for the first min, 10¢ for each additional min. The time is rounded to the next whole number before the charge is calculated. Graph the price as a function of time.

8. Graph the equation $y = -x + 4$. Does the equation describe a linear function?

9. Evaluate $2x^3 - 3x - 8$ for $x = 5$. **227**

10. Write the polynomial $2x - 3x^4 + 1 + 7x^6$ in descending order and give its degree.
    $7x^6 - 3x^4 + 2x + 1$; Degree 6

11. Find the additive inverse of the polynomial $-6x^2 + 12x - 5$. **$6x^2 - 12x + 5$**

Simplify, if possible. Write your answer in descending order.

12. $7 + 3x - 5x^3 + 6x$ **$-5x^3 + 9x + 7$**

13. $(5z^2 - 4) + (-3z^2 + 2z - 5)$ **$2z^2 + 2z - 9$**

14. $(5r^3 - 2r + 5) - (7r^2 + 3r - 2)$
    $5r^3 - 7r^2 - 5r + 7$

15. $7p^2 \cdot 3p^5$ **$21p^7$**

16. $x(3x^3 - 4x^2 + 7x)$ **$3x^4 - 4x^3 + 7x^2$**

17. $8u^5(5u^3 + 4u^2 - 3u - 2)$
    $40u^8 + 32u^7 - 24u^6 - 16u^5$

18. Multiply $(4.8 \times 10^7) \cdot (1.2 \times 10^{10})$. Write your answer in scientific notation.
    5.76×10^{17}

Find the area of each shaded region.

19.
| $2x^2 - 5x - 2$ |

A = $5x^2 + 3x - 4$

$3x^2 + 8x - 2$

20.
$3x$

$2x^2 - 8x + 7$

$6x^3 - 24x^2 + 21x$

Performance Task

A flare is shot upwards at 40 m/sec. The height after t sec is given by $h = 40t - 5t^2$. Sketch a graph of this function. Label your graph to show when the flare is rising, when it is falling, and when it hits the ground.

Performance Assessment Key

See key on page 505.

Resources

Assessment Sourcebook

Chapter 10 Tests
   Forms A and B (free response)
   Form C (multiple choice)
   Form D (performance assessment)
   Form E (mixed response)
   Form F (cumulative chapter test)

   TestWorks
   Test and Practice Software

Home and Community Connections
   Letter Home for Chapter 10
   in English and Spanish

Suggested Scoring Rubric

4
- Shows a graph with all necessary labeling.
- Graph accurately plots the function $h = 40t - 5t^2$.

3
- Shows graph but omits one or two labels.
- Graph is reasonably accurate but has a few flaws.

2
- Shows graph but omits the labels.
- Graph has some correct data points for the function but also includes incorrect data points.

1
- An attempt is made to graph the function but few or no data points are correct.

Multiple Choice

Choose the best answer.

1. Which pair of ratios does **not** form a proportion? *[Lesson 5-2]* **D**

Ⓐ $\frac{88}{121} \overset{?}{=} \frac{48}{66}$ Ⓑ $\frac{81}{36} \overset{?}{=} \frac{54}{24}$

Ⓒ $\frac{15}{35} \overset{?}{=} \frac{24}{56}$ Ⓓ $\frac{28}{40} \overset{?}{=} \frac{55}{75}$

2. 64 is 8% of which number? *[Lesson 6-2]* **D**

Ⓐ 5.12   Ⓑ 12.5   Ⓒ 80   Ⓓ 800

3. Find the quotient $\frac{5}{7} \div \frac{3}{14}$. Write the answer in lowest terms. *[Lesson 7-6]* **C**

Ⓐ $\frac{70}{21}$ Ⓑ $\frac{13}{14}$ Ⓒ $\frac{10}{3}$ Ⓓ $\frac{15}{98}$

4. How many sides does a pentagon have? *[Lesson 8-6]* **B**

Ⓐ 4   Ⓑ 5   Ⓒ 6   Ⓓ 7

5. For the pyramid shown, which of the following is equal to 384? *[Lessons 9-5, 9-7]* **D**

Ⓐ Slant height
Ⓑ Surface area
Ⓒ Volume
Ⓓ Both B and C

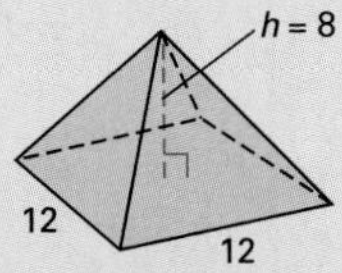

6. A circle has a diameter of 7 in. Find the approximate area of the circle. *[Lesson 9-3]* **A**

Ⓐ 38.5 in^2 Ⓑ 44.0 in^2

Ⓒ 22.0 in^2 Ⓓ 153.9 in^2

7. Find the volume of a 6 ft by 4 ft by 5 ft rectangular prism. *[Lesson 9-6]* **B**

Ⓐ 15 ft^3 Ⓑ 120 ft^3

Ⓒ 40 ft^3 Ⓓ 20 ft^3

8. What is a possible rule for the input and output shown in the table? *[Lesson 10-1]* **C**

Input	6	7	8	9
Output	14	17	20	23

Ⓐ $y = x + 8$ Ⓑ $y = \frac{1}{3}(x + 4)$

Ⓒ $y = 3x - 4$ Ⓓ $y = x - 8$

9. Which function is shown in the graph below? *[Lessons 10-2, 10-3, 10-4]* **B**

Ⓐ $y = 2x$
Ⓑ $y = x^2$
Ⓒ $y = 2^x$
Ⓓ $y = 3^x$

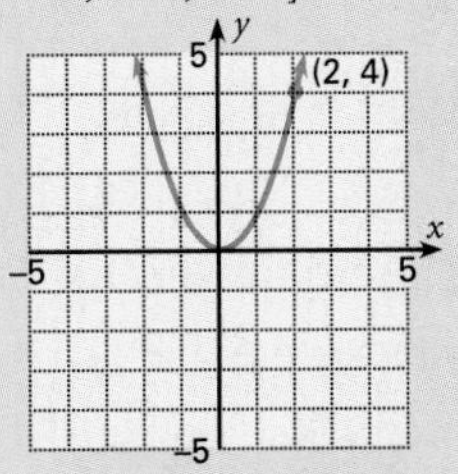

10. Which of the following is a polynomial of degree 2? *[Lesson 10-5]* **C**

Ⓐ $5x + 3$ Ⓑ $2x^3 + 7x - 4$

Ⓒ $3x^2$ Ⓓ $7x^3 - 6x + 2$

11. Which of the following shows $(3x^2 + 7x - 3) + (8x^2 + 5)$ in simplest form? *[Lesson 10-6]* **A**

Ⓐ $11x^2 + 7x + 2$

Ⓑ $8x^2 + 3x^2 + 7x + 2$

Ⓒ $-5x^2 + 7x - 8$

Ⓓ $11x^2 + 7x - 8$

12. Find the additive inverse of $4x^3 + 2x - 5$. *[Lesson 10-7]* **B**

Ⓐ $4x^3 - 2x + 5$ Ⓑ $-4x^3 - 2x + 5$

Ⓒ $-4x^3 + 2x - 5$ Ⓓ $-4x^3 - 2x - 5$

13. Find the product of $2x^3 \cdot 5x^4$. *[Lesson 10-8]* **D**

Ⓐ $7x^{12}$ Ⓑ $7x^7$ Ⓒ $10x^{12}$ Ⓓ $10x^7$

Cumulative Review Chapters 1–10 **559**

Cumulative Review Test Prep

About Multiple-Choice Tests

The Cumulative Reviews found at the end of Chapters 2, 4, 6, 8, 10, and 12 can be used to prepare students for standardized tests.

Students sometimes do not perform as well on standardized tests as they do on other tests. There may be several reasons for this related to the format and content of the test.

- **Format**
Students may have limited experience with multiple-choice tests. For some questions, such tests are harder because having options may confuse the student.

- **Content**
A standardized test may cover a broader range of content than normally covered on a test, and the relative emphasis given to various strands may be different than given in class. Also, some questions may assess general aptitude or thinking skills and not include specific pieces of mathematical content.

It is important not to let the differences between standardized tests and other tests shake your students' confidence.

Answers for Assessment, page 558

7. Step function.

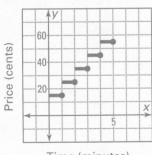

8. Yes

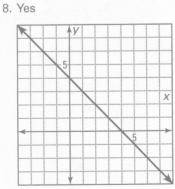

Answer for Performance Task, page 558

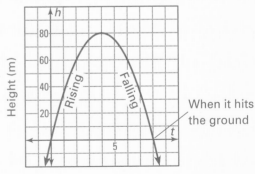

When it hits the ground

Chapter 11

Similarity, Congruence, and Transformations

▶ OVERVIEW

Section 11A

Similarity and Congruence: Students explore similar and congruent figures, trigonometric ratios, and indirect measurement.

Section 11B

Transformations: Students investigate reflections, rotations, translations, and dilations, as well as symmetry and tessellations.

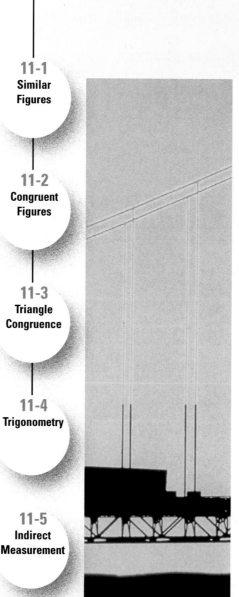
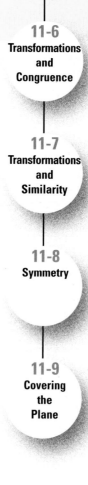

11-1
Similar Figures

11-2
Congruent Figures

11-3
Triangle Congruence

11-4
Trigonometry

11-5
Indirect Measurement

11-6
Transformations and Congruence

11-7
Transformations and Similarity

11-8
Symmetry

11-9
Covering the Plane

► Curriculum Standards

S T A N D A R D

			pages
1	**Problem Solving**	Skills and Strategies	562, 570, 583, *599*, 609
		Applications	567–568, 572, 573, 577, 578, 582, 583, 588, 598, 603, 604, 608, 609, 613, 614
		Exploration	561, 564, 569, 574, 579, 584, 594, 600, 605, 610
2	**Communication**	Oral	560–561, 563, 566, 571, 573, 576, *578*, 581, *583*, 587, 593, 597, 602, *604*, 607, 612, 614
		Written	568, 573, 578, 583, 589, 599, 604, 609, 614
		Cooperative Learning	564, *566*, *571*, 574, 579, 584, *586*, 594, *596*, 600, 605, 610
3	**Reasoning**	Critical Thinking	573, *578*, 583, *589*, 599, 604, 609
4	**Connections**	Mathematical	See Standards 5, 9, 12, 13 below.
		Interdisciplinary	Career 578; Fine Arts *593*, *602*, 606, 611; Geography *563*, 571, *596*, 602; History 576, 581, *583*, *586*, *593*, 595, *607*, 608, 613; Industry 567, 588; Literature 585; Science 561, *563*, *576*, *581*, 583, 586, 607, 609, *612*; Social Science 561, 598, 614
		Technology	562, 564, 568, 573, 579, 584, 590, 594, 604
		Cultural	560, *576*, *581*, 593, 598, 602, 606, 607, 609, *612*, 613, 615
5	**Number and Number Relationships**		589
7	**Computation and Estimation**		589, 595, *611*
8	**Patterns and Functions**		*568*, 589, *604*, 609
9	**Algebra**		572, 589, 599, 604
12	**Geometry**		560–622
13	**Measurement**		604

Italic type indicates Teacher Edition reference.

► Teaching Standards

Focus on Major Shifts

In order for students to be empowered, we need to shift toward

- connecting mathematics, its ideas, and its applications—away from treating mathematics as a body of isolated concepts and procedures.

- classrooms as mathematical communities—away from classrooms as simply a collection of individuals.

► Assessment Standards

Focus on Learning

Portfolios The Learning Standard encourages teachers to give students opportunities to reflect on their progress and to judge their work according to standards shared by both the teacher and the other students. Justifying the selection of their best works to include in a portfolio gives students the chance to be active participants in their assessment. Examples of work from Chapter 11 that students are asked to put in their portfolios include

- drawings of polygons.

- tessellations.

TECHNOLOGY

► For the Teacher

- **Teacher Resource Planner CD-ROM**
  Use the teacher planning CD-ROM to view resources available for Chapter 11. You can prepare custom lesson plans or use the default lesson plans provided.

- **World Wide Web**
  Visit **www.teacher.mathsurf.com** for links to lesson plans from teachers and other professionals, NCTM information, and other sites.

- **TestWorks**
  TestWorks provides ready-made tests and can create custom tests and practice worksheets.

► For the Parent

- **World Wide Web**
  Parents can use the Web site at **www.parent.mathsurf.com.**

► For the Student

- **Interactive CD-ROM**
  Lesson 11-4 has an *Interactive CD-ROM Lesson*. The *Interactive CD-ROM Journal, Interactive CD-ROM Geometry Tool,* and *Interactive CD-ROM Spreadsheet/Grapher Tool* are also used in Chapter 11.

- **Wide World of Mathematics**
  Lesson 11-6 Geometry: Miniature Golf
  Lesson 11-9 Geometry: Textile Works

- **World Wide Web**
  Use with Chapter and Section Openers;
  Students can go online to the Scott Foresman-Addison Wesley Web site at **www.mathsurf.com/8/ch11** to collect information about chapter themes.

- **Jasper Woodbury Videodisc**
  Lesson 11-1: The Right Angle

STANDARDIZED - TEST CORRELATION

SECTION 11A LESSON	OBJECTIVE	ITBS Form M	CTBS 4th Ed.	CAT 5th Ed.	SAT 9th Ed.	MAT 7th Ed.	Your Form
11-1	• Identify similar figures.	✗	✗	✗	✗	✗	
11-2	• Identify congruent figures.	✗	✗	✗	✗	✗	
11-3	• Identify congruent triangles.		✗				
11-4	• Use ratios in order to find missing side lengths of a right triangle.						
11-5	• Apply knowledge of geometry and trigonometric ratios.						

SECTION 11B LESSON	OBJECTIVE	ITBS Form M	CTBS 4th Ed.	CAT 5th Ed.	SAT 9th Ed.	MAT 7th Ed.	Your Form
11-6	• Move all the points of a figure and still have a congruent shape.		✗	✗	✗	✗	
11-7	• Transform a figure and have a shape that is similar to, but not congruent to, the original.		✗	✗	✗	✗	
11-8	• Recognize several types of symmetry.			✗	✗	✗	
11-9	• Create endless patterns using transformations.			✗			

Key: ITBS - Iowa Test of Basic Skills; CTBS - Comprehensive Test of Basic Skills; CAT - California Achievement Test; SAT - Stanford Achievement Test; MAT - Metropolitan Achievement Test

ASSESSMENT PROGRAM

▶ **Traditional Assessment**

QUICK QUIZZES	SECTION REVIEW	CHAPTER REVIEW	CHAPTER ASSESSMENT FREE RESPONSE	CHAPTER ASSESSMENT MULTIPLE CHOICE	CUMULATIVE REVIEW
TE: pp. 568, 573, 578, 583, 593, 599, 604, 609, 614	SE: pp. 592, 616 *Quiz 11A, 11B	SE: pp. 618–619	SE: p. 620 *Ch. 11 Tests Forms A, B, E	*Ch. 11 Tests Forms C, E	SE: p. 621 *Ch. 11 Test Form F

▶ **Alternate Assessment**

INTERVIEW	JOURNAL	ONGOING	PERFORMANCE	PORTFOLIO	PROJECT	SELF
TE: p. 578	SE: pp. 568, 573, 592, 609, 614, 616 TE: pp. 562, 568, 589	TE: pp. 564, 569, 574, 579, 584, 591, 594, 600, 605, 609, 610, 615	SE: pp. 620, 621 TE: p. 599 *Ch. 11 Tests Forms D, E	TE: pp. 573, 614	SE: pp. 561, 583, 604 TE: p. 561	TE: pp 583, 604

*Tests and quizzes are in *Assessment Sourcebook*. Test Form E is a mixed response test. Forms for Alternate Assessment are also available in *Assessment Sourcebook*.

 TestWorks: Test and Practice Software

▶ REGULAR PACING

Day	5 classes per week
1	Chapter 11 Opener; Problem Solving Focus
2	Section **11A** Opener; Lesson **11-1**
3	Lesson **11-2**
4	Lesson **11-3**
5	Lesson **11-4**
6	Lesson **11-5**; Technology
7	**11A** Connect; **11A** Review
8	Section **11B** Opener; Lesson **11-6**
9	Lesson **11-7**
10	Lesson **11-8**
11	Lesson **11-9**
12	**11B** Connect; **11B** Review; Extend Key Ideas
13	Chapter 11 Summary and Review
14	Chapter 11 Assessment Cumulative Review, Chapters 1–11

▶ BLOCK SCHEDULING OPTIONS

Block Scheduling for Complete Course

Chapter 1 may be presented in

- eight 90-minute blocks
- eleven 75-minute blocks

Each block consists of a combination of

- Chapter and Section Openers
- Explores
- Lesson Development
- Problem Solving Focus
- Technology
- Extend Key Ideas
- Connect
- Review
- Assessment

For details, see *Block Scheduling Handbook.*

Block Scheduling for Lab-Based Course

In each block, 30–40 minutes is devoted to lab activities including

- Explores in the Student Edition
- Connect pages in the Student Edition
- Technology options in the Student Edition
- Reteaching Activities in the Teacher Edition

For details, see *Block Scheduling Handbook.*

Block Scheduling for Interdisciplinary Course

Each block integrates math with another subject area.

In Chapter 11, interdisciplinary topics include

- Bridges
- Native American Arts and Crafts

Themes for Interdisciplinary Team Teaching 11A and 11B are

- Bridge Design
- Native American Art

For details, see *Block Scheduling Handbook.*

Block Scheduling for Course with *Connected Mathematics*

In each block, investigations from **Connected Mathematics** replace or enhance the lessons in Chapter 11.

Connected Mathematics topics for Chapter 11 can be found in

- *Kaleidoscopes, Hubcaps, and Mirrors*

For details, see *Block Scheduling Handbook.*

INTERDISCIPLINARY BULLETIN BOARD

Set Up

Prepare a bulletin board with a display containing several photographs of different kinds of bridges and a variety of Native American arts and crafts. Label each picture with a reference number.

Procedure

As the chapter is studied, each student should choose one of the pictures and write a paragraph or two describing how the mathematics in the chapter was used in the design of the pictured object. Encourage students to display their own photographs that reflect the mathematics studied in this chapter.

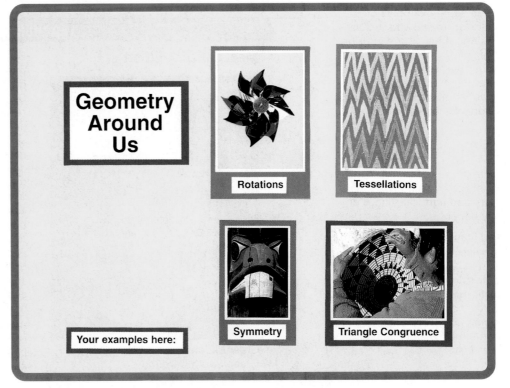

11 Similarity, Congruence, and

Entertainment Link
www.mathsurf.com/8/ch11/ent

Arts & Literature Link
www.mathsurf.com/8/ch11/arts

Entertainment

A knowledge of angles and reflections is essential to successful billiard players, as they must frequently bank their shots to avoid moving their opponents' ball.

Arts & Literature

The works of Dutch artist M. C. Escher (1898–1972) consist almost entirely of interlocking, infinitely repeating designs called tessellations, which are based on translations, rotations, and reflections.

Circle Limit III by M. C. Escher.
©1996 Cordon Art-Baarn-Holland. All rights reserved.

People of the World

Despite having asthma, Jackie Joyner-Kersee achieved world records in the heptathalon. Great athletes like her often do weight lifting training which can strengthen muscles symmetrically.

560

The information on these pages shows how reflections, rotations, and translations as well as symmetry are used in real-life situations.

World Wide Web

If your class has access to the World Wide Web, you might want to use the information found at the Web site addresses given.

Extensions

The following activities do not require access to the World Wide Web.

Entertainment

A principle that applies to both reflections and billiard playing is a familiar dictum of physical science: The angle of reflection is congruent to the angle of incidence. Students who are billiard players can explain bank shots and carom shots to the class.

People of the World

Have students interested in weight lifting training research and describe some of the exercises that work various muscle groups. Have them explain how combinations of exercises can strengthen muscles symmetrically.

Arts & Literature

Bring in some examples of Escher's art to show to the class. Books about his art are in print, and art prints are available from various sources including Dale Seymore Publications. Students who are interested can try drawing their own Escher-type art.

Science

Suggest that students work in groups of four to construct a periscope by using two small mirrors and light cardboard or heavy paper.

Social Studies

Origami is the Japanese word for *folded paper*. There are about 100 traditional origami forms. Most are depictions of such natural objects as birds, fish, and flowers. Some students who have origami pieces at home may wish to show them to the class.

TEACHER TALK

Meet Christine Elliott

Greer Middle School
Greer, South Carolina

Each year my students look forward to participating in my model bridge building competition, which extends the Section 11A Connect on page 591. After researching various kinds of bridges and testing a variety of shapes for strength and stability, students work in groups to design a bridge. The groups decide on the type of bridge they wish to build and what materials they will use. As a class, we decide on how long and how wide we want to make our bridges. Next, students make scale drawings of their bridges, which I approve, and finally they build their bridges. After the bridges are completed, we test them for load capacity. I evaluate the project based on construction, artistic design, and durability.

Students are amazed and proud of their constructions. Making the connection to success is important in motivating the middle-school learner.

Transformations

Science Link
www.mathsurf.com/8/ch11/sci

Science

A periscope uses reflections in two mirrors, enabling the viewer to see above the line of sight. The mirrors are parallel to each other and at a 45° angle to the horizon line.

KEY MATH IDEAS

Two figures are similar if they have the same shape but not necessarily the same size. Two figures are congruent if they have the same shape and size.

For an angle in a right triangle with measure x, the trigonometric ratios sin, cos, and tan can be used to find the length of a side.

A line of symmetry divides a figure into two identical halves.

A tessellation is a pattern of repeated figures that covers a plane.

Social Studies

The Japanese have long perfected the art of paper folding, called *origami*, which is a striking application of the many properties of reflections.

CHAPTER PROJECT

Problem Solving
Understand
Plan
Solve
Look Back

In this project, using a 3 in. by 5 in. card, you will make a hypsometer—a device for measuring tall objects. You will use it to measure the height of a building. After you have made the hypsometer, align it with the top and bottom of the building. Determine the distance between you and the building and you'll be able to find the height of the building. Explain how this works after you've tried it.

561

Chapter Project

Students construct a hypsometer and use it to measure the heights of tall objects in their locality.

Resources
Chapter 11 Project Master

Introduce the Project
- Show students a completed hypsometer if possible or pictures of one from a science project reference book.

- Discuss with students how the hypsometer is used.

Project Progress
Section A, page 583 Students construct a hypsometer by making measurements and following step-by-step directions.

Section B, page 604 Students plan how they will use the hypsometer by deciding which object to measure and how far away from the object they will be. They will use trigonometry to compute the height of the object they measure.

Community Project

A community project for Chapter 11 is available in *Home and Community Connections*.

Cooperative Learning

You may wish to use Teaching Tool Transparency 1: Cooperative Learning Checklist with **Explore** and other group activities in the chapter.

PROJECT ASSESSMENT

You may choose to use this project as a performance assessment for the chapter.

Performance Assessment Key

Level 4 Full Accomplishment

Level 3 Substantial Accomplishment

Level 2 Partial Accomplishment

Level 1 Little Accomplishment

Suggested Scoring Rubric

4
- Hypsometer is well constructed.
- Excellent knowledge of use of hypsometer is displayed.

3
- Hypsometer is constructed reasonably well.
- Good knowledge of use of hypsometer is displayed.

2
- Hypsometer, if constructed, is inadequate.
- Fair knowledge of use of hypsometer is displayed.

1
- Hypsometer is barely constructed.
- Virtually no knowledge of use or purpose of hypsometer is displayed.

Problem Solving Focus

Checking the Rules of the Problem

The Point
Students focus on understanding a problem and checking three given answers to determine which one meets all the stated conditions.

Resources
Teaching Tool Transparency 17: Problem-Solving Guidelines

Interactive CD-ROM Journal

About the Page

Using the Problem Solving Process
Discuss the following steps for checking an answer against the conditions of the problem.

- Read the problem to determine exactly what it is asking.

- Break the problem down into smaller parts, each stating only one condition if possible.

- Check each part of the answer against each condition of the problem.

Ask …
- Did you read the problem more than once?

- Do you know exactly what the problem is asking you to find?

Answers for Problems
1. Answer 3 is correct. Answer 1 misread the information about Colin and LuAnn, and gave them each 2 fewer than Mary rather than a total of 2 fewer; Answer 2 also misread the information about Colin and LuAnn, but interpreted it as though they each got 2 apples.

2. Answer 2 is correct. Answer 1 included the irrelevant information that Jamie gave $\frac{1}{3}$ of his tickets to his brother, and did not pay attention to the fact that Marsha not only had $\frac{1}{3}$ as many tickets as Jamie, but 6 fewer than Albert; Answer 3 is incorrect because the total number of tickets purchased does not equal 83.

Journal

Ask students to write about how they check an answer to a problem.

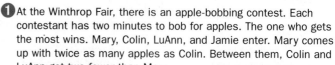

Problem Solving
Understand
Plan
Solve
Look Back

Checking the Rules of the Problem

After you have solved a problem, look back to make sure you followed the rules of the problem. If you followed all the rules, then your answer is probably correct.

Problem Solving Focus

Each problem below has three answers. State which of the three answers is correct, and which rule the other two answers didn't follow.

1 At the Winthrop Fair, there is an apple-bobbing contest. Each contestant has two minutes to bob for apples. The one who gets the most wins. Mary, Colin, LuAnn, and Jamie enter. Mary comes up with twice as many apples as Colin. Between them, Colin and LuAnn get two fewer than Mary. Jamie gets half as many as LuAnn. All together, the four bobbers get 15 apples. How many did each get?

Answer #1	Answer #2	Answer #3
M = 8	M = 8	M = 8
C = 6	C = 2	C = 4
L = 6	L = 2	L = 2
J = 3	J = 1	J = 1

2 Jamie met Marsha, Albert, and Seena at the fair. They all went over to the ticket booth, where they bought tickets to use on all of the rides at the fair. Jamie bought 3 times as many tickets as Marsha, but he gave $\frac{1}{3}$ of them to his little brother. Albert bought half as many tickets as Jamie. Seena bought 5 more tickets than Marsha. Marsha bought 6 fewer tickets than Albert. All together, they bought 83 tickets. How many did each person buy?

Answer #1	Answer #2	Answer #3
J = 24	J = 36	J = 18
M = 8	M = 12	M = 6
A = 12	A = 18	A = 12
S = 13	S = 17	S = 11

562

Additional Problem

Juan is twice as old as his sister Imelda but only $\frac{1}{3}$ as old as his father. Juan's mother is 2 years younger than Juan's father. The ages of all four family members total 88. How old is each person?

Answer #1	Answer #2	Answer #3
J = 14	J = 10	J = 12
I = 7	I = 8	I = 6
F = 42	F = 36	F = 36
M = 40	M = 34	M = 34

1. Which answer is correct? Answer 3

2. Explain why the other answers are not correct. In Answer 1, all conditions are met except the sum of the ages is 103, not 88. In Answer 2, Juan is neither twice as old as Imelda nor $\frac{1}{3}$ as old as his father.

Section 11A

Similarity and Congruence

Visit **www.teacher.mathsurf.com** for links to lesson plans from teachers and other professionals, NCTM information, and other sites.

LESSON PLANNING GUIDE

▶ **Student Edition**

▶ **Ancillaries**

LESSON	MATERIALS	VOCABULARY	DAILY	OTHER
Chapter 11 Opener				Ch. 11 Project Master Ch. 11 Community Project Teaching Tool Trans. 1
Problem Solving Focus				Teaching Tool Trans. 17 *Interactive CD-ROM Journal*
11-1 Similar Figures	Dynamic geometry software, 8-1/2 in. by 11 in. paper	similar, corresponding angles, corresponding sides, similarity ratio	11-1	Teaching Tool Trans. 19 Lesson Enhancement Trans. 58 Technology Master 58 *CD-ROM Geometry Tool*
11-2 Congruent Figures	paper, ruler, protractor, compass	congruent polygons	11-2	Teaching Tool Trans. 6, 15, 16, 19 Lesson Enhancement Trans. 59 Technology Master 59
11-3 Triangle Congruence		side-side-side, side-angle-side, angle-side-angle, side-angle-angle	11-3	Teaching Tool Trans. 19 Lesson Enhancement Trans. 60 Technology Master 60
11-4 Trigonometry	Dynamic geometry software, 8-1/2 in. by 11 in. paper, scientific calculator	adjacent leg, opposite leg, trigonometric ratios, sine, cosine, tangent	11-4	Teaching Tool Trans. 2, 3, 22 Technology Master 61 Ch. 11 Project Master *Interactive CD-ROM Lesson* *WW Math*— Geometry
11-5 Indirect Measurement	Geometry software, scientific calculator		11-5	Teaching Tool Trans. 22 Lesson Enhancement Trans. 61 *CD-ROM Geometry Tool*
Connect	toothpicks, ruler, tape, scissors			Interdisc. Team Teaching 11A
Review				Prac. 11A; Quiz 11A; *TestWorks*

SKILLS TRACE

LESSON	SKILL	FIRST INTRODUCED			DEVELOP	PRACTICE/ APPLY	REVIEW
		GR. 6	GR. 7	GR. 8			
11-1	Identifying similar figures.	✗			pp. 564–566	pp. 567–568	pp. 592, 618, 636
11-2	Identifying congruent figures.			✗ p. 569	pp. 569–571	pp. 572–573	pp. 592, 619, 642
11-3	Identifying congruent triangles.			✗ p. 574	pp. 574–576	pp. 577–578	pp. 592, 618, 650, 675
11-4	Using sine, cosine, and tangent ratios.			✗ p. 579	pp. 579–581	pp. 582–583	pp. 592, 619, 656
11-5	Making indirect measurements.		✗		pp. 584–587	pp. 588–589	pp. 592, 619, 662, 675

CONNECTED MATHEMATICS

The unit *Kaleidoscopes, Hubcaps, and Mirrors (Symmetry and Transformations),* from the **Connected Mathematics** series, can be used with Section 11A.

Math and Science/Technology

(Worksheet pages 43–44: Teacher pages T43–T44)

In this lesson, students use knowledge of triangles and basic trigonometry to explore bridge design.

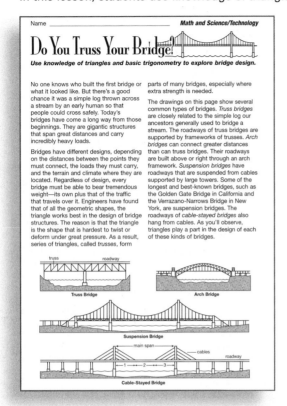

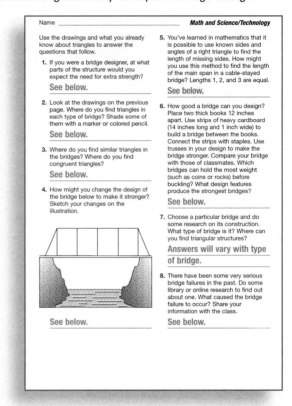

Answers

1. Accept all reasonable answers. They might include the supports that hold the bridge up, the towers, the roadway, the sides of the bridge including cables or girders.

2. Triangles can be found in the supporting trusses of the truss bridge, the arch of the arch bridge, the towers and the truss supports under the roadway of the suspension bridge, and the cables of the cable-stayed bridge.

3. Similar triangles can be found most obviously in the cables of the cable-stayed bridge. Congruent triangles are seen in the truss bridges, the arch bridge, and the towers and roadway of the suspension bridge.

4. The original bridge has boxy supports. The bridge could be strengthened by adding triangular truss supports.

5. If you know the height that the highest cable reaches, you can use the tangent funtion to find length l. Then multiply by 3, since length l = length 2 = length 3, tan y = side opposite/side adjacent

6. Allow students to create any design. Have them determine as a class the design features that were most successful and whether trusses contributed to that success.

8. There are several well-known bridge failures students might research, including the following: Tay Bridge of Scotland (1879), Tacoma Narrows Bridge of Washington State (1940), Silver Bridge of Point Pleasant, Ohio (1967).

BIBLIOGRAPHY

FOR TEACHERS

Del Grande, John and Lorna Morrow. *Geometry and Spatial Sense (Addenda Series).* Reston, VA: NCTM, 1993.

Geddes, Dorothy, et al. *Geometry in the Middle Grades (Addenda Series).* Reston, VA: NCTM, 1992.

Overstreet, Charles W. *Plains Indian and Mountain Men Arts and Crafts.* Liberty, UT: Eagle's View, 1993.

Petroski, Henry. *Engineers of Dreams: Great Bridge Builders and the Spanning of America.* New York, NY: Alfred Knopf, 1995.

Underhill, Ruth Murray. *Pueblo Crafts.* Washington, DC: Bureau of Indian Affairs, U.S. Dept. of Interior, 1994.

FOR STUDENTS

Carter, Polly. *The Bridge Book.* New York, NY: Simon & Schuster, 1992.

Center for Occupational Research and Development. *Applied Mathematics, Unit 21: Using Right Triangle Relationships.* Waco, TX: CORD, 1992.

Center for Occupational Research and Development. *Applied Mathematics, Unit 22: Using Trigonometric Functions.* Waco, TX: CORD, 1992.

Hawkes, Nigel. *Structures and Buildings.* London, England: Aladdin Books Ltd., 1994.

SECTION 11A

Similarity and Congruence

▶ **Geography Link** ▶ **Science Link** ▶ **www.mathsurf.com/8/ch11/bridges**

building is part art, part science. Engineers use science (including math!) to make sure that bridges can support the weight of the vehicles and pedestrians using them. Architects working with engineers use their artistic instincts and training to create bridges that are not only strong but pleasing to the eye.

Both strength and attractiveness are usually enhanced by a property called symmetry, which in the case of bridges means that one side is the mirror image of the other. When a symmetric bridge is made up of numerous triangles (as many bridges are), the triangles come in pairs: Each triangle on one side of a bridge has an identical twin on the other—another triangle congruent to the first one, as a mathematician would say. Later in this chapter, you will be learning more about symmetry. First, though, you will learn about congruency as well as similarity, different ways in which two triangles (and other shapes) can be alike.

Un·a·bridged

1 Why might a bridge with matching triangles on each side be stronger than one where the triangles on each side are different?

2 Why might a bridge with all vertical and horizontal bracing be less stable?

563

Where are we now?

In Grade 6 students were introduced to flips and turns, and line and point symmetry. Students extended these explorations in Grade 7 to include dilations and similar figures.

They learned how to

- draw translations, reflections, and rotations of figures in the coordinate plane.

- recognize whether a figure has line, rotational, or point symmetry.

- create similar figures by dilations.

- find missing measures in similar figures.

Where are we going?

In Grade 8, Section 11A, students will

- identify and draw similar and congruent figures.

- use similar figures and trigonometric ratios to make indirect measurements.

- apply their knowledge of geometry and trigonometric ratios to solve problems.

Theme: Bridges

 World Wide Web

If your class has access to the World Wide Web, you might want to use the information found at the Web site address given. The interdisciplinary links relate to topics discussed in this section.

About the Page

This page introduces the theme of the section, bridges, and discusses the use of symmetry in designing bridges.

Ask ...

- In what types of structures have you noticed the use of symmetry or triangles? Possible answer: Bridges

- Why do you think triangles are used in building bridges? Possible answer: The triangle is rigid; its shape cannot be changed without breaking a side. Other polygons can be bent out of shape by pushing in or pulling out their sides.

Extensions

The following activities do not require access to the World Wide Web.

Geography

Have students research the longest, shortest, widest, highest, and most unusual bridges in the world. Suggest that they show the locations of these bridges on a world map.

Science

Interested students might research the roles various scientists play in bridge building and write a brief report.

Answers for Questions

1. Possible answer: Stress will be distributed more evenly.

2. Possible answer: It could rock back and forth.

Connect

On page 591, students will build a model bridge out of toothpicks, using a design that incorporates congruent and similar triangles.

11-1
Lesson Organizer

Objective
- Identify similar figures.

Vocabulary
- Similar, corresponding angles, corresponding sides, similarity ratio

Materials
- Explore: Dynamic geometry software, $8\frac{1}{2}$ in. by 11 in. paper

NCTM Standards
- 1, 2, 4, 12

► Review

What is the base and height of the resulting rectangle if the rectangle below is dilated by each of the given scale factors?

5 cm

8 cm

1. A scale factor of 2
   16 cm; 10 cm

2. A scale factor of 0.5
   4 cm; 2.5 cm

3. A scale factor of 1
   8 cm; 5 cm

Available on Daily Transparency 11-1

1 Introduce

Explore

The Point
Students use geometry software to discover the relationship between the ratios of the sides of the original polygon and the dilated polygon.

Ongoing Assessment
For Step 3, check that students are using the measure tool and the dilate tool properly.

11-1 | Similar Figures

You'll Learn ...
- to identify similar figures

... How It's Used
Sign makers use similar figures as repetitive design elements in their work.

Vocabulary
similar
corresponding angles
corresponding sides
similarity ratio

► Lesson Link You've seen the results of scaling a rectangle. Now you'll see how angle and side measurements correspond on scale drawings. ◄

Explore | Similar Polygons

The Size Factor

Materials: Dynamic geometry software, $8\frac{1}{2}$ in. by 11 in. paper

1. With the geometry software, draw a polygon with 3, 4, or 5 sides.

2. On paper, make a table with as many columns as the polygon has sides. Label the first column "side 1," the second, "side 2," and so on.

3. Measure each side of the polygon using the measure tool, and record your measurements in your table. Use the dilate tool to shrink or enlarge your polygon. Notice that the side measurements change.

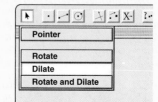

4. Record the new measurements in the appropriate columns.

5. In each column, find the ratio between the old and new measurements. What do you notice? Why do you think you got these results?

6. Use the dilate tool again and record a third set of measurements. Find the ratios between the second and third measurements for each table column. What do you notice?

7. Do you think the dilation changed the angle measurements?

Learn | Similar Figures

Two figures are **similar** if they have the same shape but not necessarily the same size.

$\triangle ABC \sim \triangle XYZ$ means $\triangle ABC$ is similar to $\triangle XYZ$.

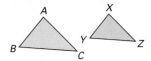

MEETING INDIVIDUAL NEEDS

Resources

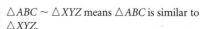

- 11-1 Practice
- 11-1 Reteaching
- 11-1 Problem Solving
- 11-1 Enrichment
- 11-1 Daily Transparency
    - Problem of the Day
    - Review
    - Quick Quiz
- Teaching Tool Transparency 19
- Lesson Enhancement Transparency 58
- Technology Master 58
- *Interactive CD-ROM Geometry Tool*

Learning Modalities

Logical In **Explore**, students use a geometry utility to experiment with dilating a polygon. They discover a pattern when comparing the ratio of each side of the original polygon to each side of the dilated polygon.

Visual Throughout the lesson, students look at the shape of figures to determine if they are similar.

Individual In Exercise 10 on page 568, students are asked to write a Journal entry about the similarity of all squares, all rectangles, and all polygons.

Inclusion

Some students may benefit from working with a set of triangle cutouts of various sizes, each of which can be matched with at least one similar triangle.

In similar figures, corresponding angles are congruent.

$\angle MLO$ and $\angle SRU$ are corresponding angles.

In similar figures, pairs of **corresponding sides** have equal length ratios.

$\overline{TU}$ and $\overline{NO}$ are corresponding sides.

When viewing two similar figures, we see that one is a scale drawing of the other.

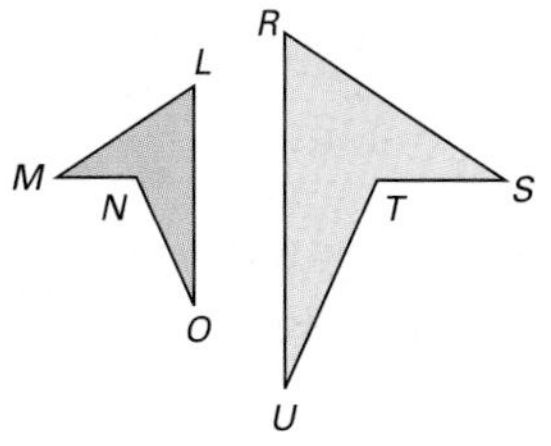

The ratio between corresponding side lengths of similar figures is the **similarity ratio**. The similarity ratio of similar figures can be compared to the scale factor of scale drawings.

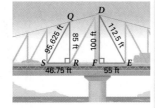

Example 1

A cantilever bridge has two cantilevers that extend from both sides of a waterway. These two cantilevers meet at the middle of the waterway.

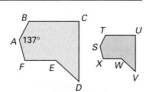

$\triangle QSR \sim \triangle DEF$. Find the similarity ratio of the two figures.

$\overline{QR}$ and $\overline{DF}$ are corresponding sides. Identify corresponding sides.

$\frac{m\overline{QR}}{m\overline{DF}} = \frac{85 \text{ ft}}{100 \text{ ft}} = \frac{17}{20}$ Take the ratio of their lengths.

The similarity ratio of $\triangle QSR$ and $\triangle DEF$ is $\frac{17}{20}$.

DID YOU KNOW?

The largest antique ever sold was London Bridge in March 1968. It sold for $2,469,600. All 11,800 tons of it was rebuilt in Havasu City, Arizona.

Example 2

The hexagons are similar. Find $m\angle XST$.

$\angle FAB$ and $\angle XST$ are corresponding angles.

So $m\angle XST = 137°$.

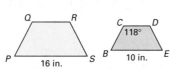

Try It

$PQRS \sim BCDE$

a. Find the similarity ratio of figure $PQRS$ to figure $BCDE$. $\frac{8}{5}$

b. Find the measure of $\angle PQR$. 118°

MATH EVERY DAY

Problem of the Day

On a 40-question test, three points are deducted for each wrong answer and five points are added for each correct answer. You answer all the questions and get a score of 0. How many questions did you get correct? 15 correct ($3x = 5y$; $x + y = 40$; $x = 25$, $y = 15$)

Available on Daily Transparency 11-1

An Extension is provided in the transparency package.

Fact of the Day

In 1874, rivets became part of Levi® jeans as the result of a joke about a prospector who carried so much ore in his pockets he had to have the pockets riveted.

Mental Math

Do these mentally.

1. $3(1\frac{1}{2})$ $4\frac{1}{2}$
2. $2(5\frac{1}{2})$ 11
3. $4(15)$ 60

For Groups That Finish Early
Draw another polygon with a different number of sides and repeat Steps 1–5. What are the results? The results are similar.

Answers for Explore
1–4. Answers may vary.

5. Possible answer: The ratio is the same for all columns, because each side was enlarged by the same factor.
6. The ratio is the same for all columns.
7. No; The angle measurements remain unchanged.

2 Teach

Learn

You may wish to use Teaching Tool Transparency 19: Tangram and Lesson Enhancement Transparency 58 with this lesson.

Another way of stating the relationship between the sides of similar figures is to say that their sides are proportional.

Alternate Examples

1. $\triangle ABC \sim \triangle STU$. Find the similarity ratio of the two figures.

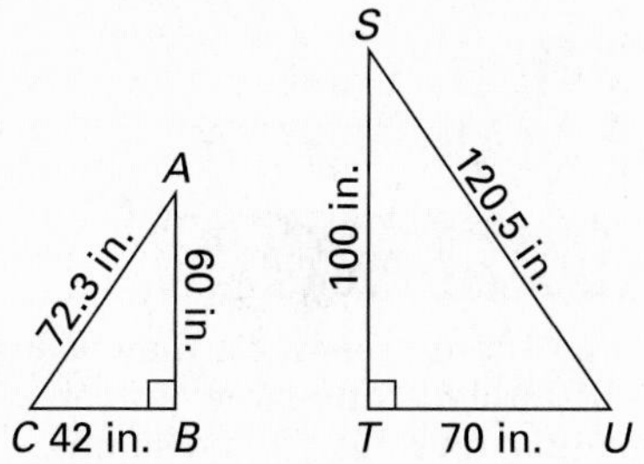

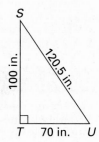

Identify corresponding sides.
$\overline{AC}$ and $\overline{SU}$ are corresponding sides.
Take the ratio of their lengths.
$\frac{m\overline{AC}}{m\overline{SU}} = \frac{72.3 \text{ in.}}{120.5 \text{ in.}} = \frac{3}{5}$

The similarity ratio of $\triangle ABC$ and $\triangle STU$ is $\frac{3}{5}$.

2. The pentagons are similar. Find $m\angle NOP$.

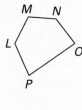

$\angle TUV$ and $\angle NOP$ are corresponding angles.
So, $m\angle NOP = 85°$.

3. Determine whether △*KLM* and △*XYZ* are similar.

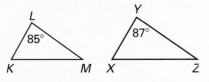

∠*KLM* is not congruent to ∠*XYZ*.
Not all corresponding angles are congruent.
△*KLM* is not similar to △*XYZ*.

4. Are the figures similar? Explain.

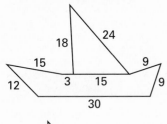

$\frac{2}{3}$ and $\frac{9}{12}$ are ratios for corresponding sides.
$\frac{2}{3} \neq \frac{9}{12}$. The figures are not similar.

3 Practice and Assess

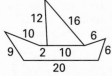

For Exercise 2, students may need to be reminded that in a regular polygon, all sides are the same length and all angles have the same measure.

Answers for Check Your Understanding

1. If the corresponding angles are congruent, the figures are not only similar but congruent; If the corresponding angles are not congruent, the figures are not similar.

2. Yes; Since in a regular pentagon all sides are the same length and all angles are congruent, the pentagons will have the same shape and are similar.

If pairs of corresponding angles are congruent, the triangles are similar.

Example 3

Determine whether △*ABC* and △*DEF* are similar.

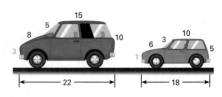

∠*CAB* ≅ ∠*FDE*

∠*ACB* ≅ ∠*DFE*

∠*ABC* ≅ ∠*DEF*

All corresponding angles are congruent.

△*ABC* ~ △*DEF*

Example 4

Are the figures similar?

$\frac{1}{3}$ and $\frac{3}{5}$ are ratios for two pairs of corresponding sides.

$\frac{1}{3} \neq \frac{3}{5}$. The figures are not similar.

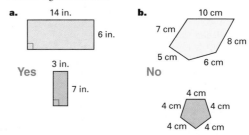

Try It

Are the figures similar?

a.

14 in.

6 in.

Yes   3 in.

7 in.

b.

10 cm

7 cm

8 cm

5 cm   6 cm

No

4 cm

4 cm   4 cm

4 cm   4 cm

Check | **Your Understanding**

1. If the ratio between all corresponding sides of two figures is 1, are the figures similar? Explain.

2. Are any two regular pentagons similar? Explain.

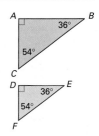

566 *Chapter 11 • Similarity, Congruence, and Transformations*

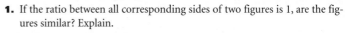

MEETING MIDDLE SCHOOL CLASSROOM NEEDS

Tips from Middle School Teachers

I always make sure that students understand that the order in which the vertices are listed in a similarity sentence indicates the correspondence between the two polygons. First I draw △*ABC* and △*DEF* on the chalkboard. Then I ask the students to help me complete the following sentence: If △*ABC* ~ △*DEF*, ∠*A* corresponds to ____ (∠*D*), ∠*B* corresponds to ____ (∠*E*), ∠*C* corresponds to ____ (∠*F*), $\overline{AB}$ corresponds to ____ ($\overline{DE}$), $\overline{AC}$ corresponds to ____ ($\overline{DF}$), and $\overline{BC}$ corresponds to ____ ($\overline{EF}$).

Team Teaching	Cooperative Learning
Ask an art teacher to suggest a project that involves the use of symmetry. The art teacher may be willing to help you assess students' work.	This activity will reinforce the concept of similarity. Have students work with a partner. Have each student draw a simple polygon, using graph paper or rulers to determine lengths of sides. Have partners trade papers. Each student should redraw the polygon, using lengths that are twice (or half) as long. Each student should explain why the new polygon is similar to the original.

11-1 Exercises and Applications

Practice and Apply

1. [Getting Started] Decide whether the triangles are similar.

   a. Write a proportion for the corresponding sides.
   b. Determine if the cross products are equal. **a.** $\dfrac{1.5}{3.0} = \dfrac{1.8}{3.6}$
   Yes, (1.5)(3.6) = (3.0)(1.8) = 5.4

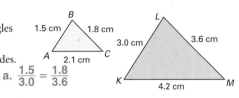

Decide whether each pair of figures is similar.

2.

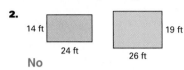

No

3.

Yes

 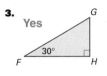

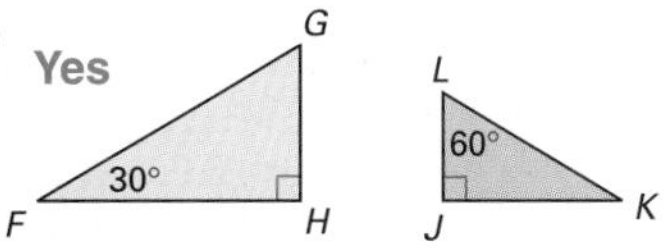

4. The two trapezoids are similar.

 a. Find x. **2.2 cm**

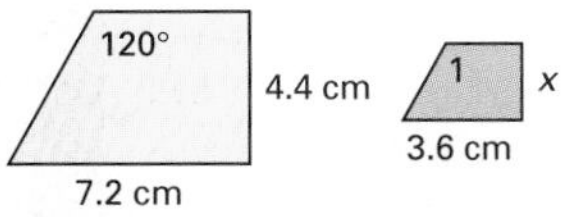

   b. Find the measure of $\angle 1$. **120°**

5. Industry The main span of New York's Brooklyn Bridge is 1595 ft long. On a blueprint for the bridge, the span measures 31.9 in. What is the scale factor of the blueprint? **1 in.:50 ft**

6. Measurement The two jeans pockets are similar. Find x, the length of the top of the smaller pocket. **4.8 in.**

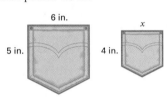

7. [Test Prep] Given that triangles ABC and DEF are similar, what is the length of side $\overline{BC}$ on $\triangle ABC$? **A**

   Ⓐ 28 mi   Ⓑ 35 mi
   Ⓒ 14 mi   Ⓓ 42 mi

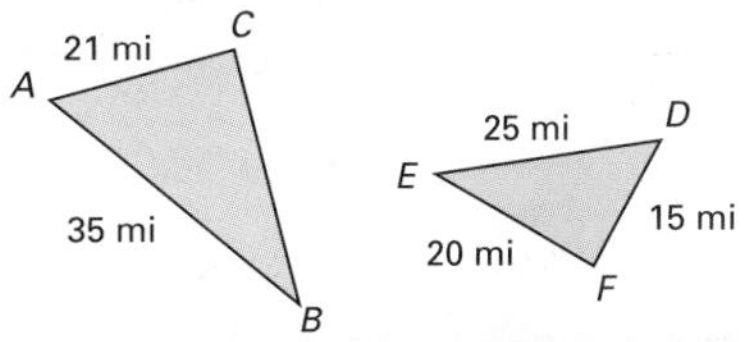

11-1 • Similar Figures **567**

PRACTICE 11-1

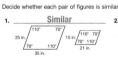
 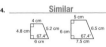

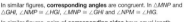
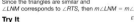 

11-1 Exercises and Applications

Assignment Guide

■ **Basic**
1–4, 6, 7, 10, 11, 14–22 evens

■ **Average**
2–4, 6–9, 13–23 odds

■ **Enriched**
2–4, 5, 7, 9–13, 17, 18, 22, 23

Exercise Notes

■ **Exercise 3**

[Error Prevention] Some students may not recognize figures as similar if the figures are oriented in such a way that corresponding sides occupy different positions. Have these students use tracing paper to check for similarity.

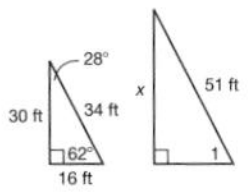

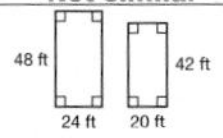

■ **Exercise 7**

Test Prep Students choosing B have matched $\overline{BC}$ and $\overline{DE}$, which are not corresponding sides.

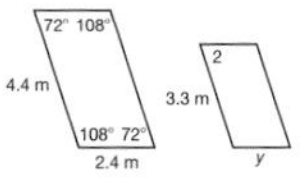

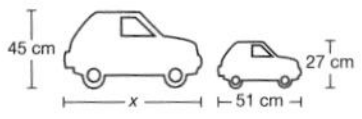

Reteaching

[Activity]

Materials: Ruler

• Work with a partner.

• Draw a polygon with 4 sides on a piece of paper.

• Make a table with columns headed "Side 1" through "Side 4."

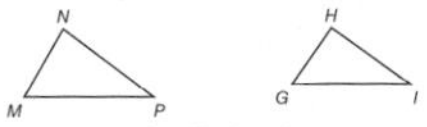

• Measure each side of your polygon and record your measurements in the table.

• Dilate the figure by a scale factor of 3. Record the measurements of each side of the new figure in the table.

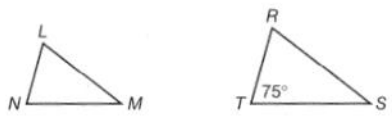

• Find the ratio between the original measurement and the dilated measurement for each side.

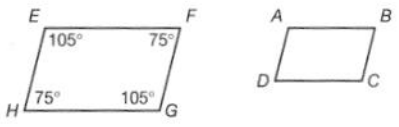

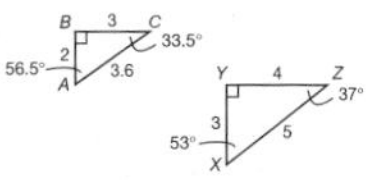

• What results do you notice? Why? The ratio is the same for all sides because each side was enlarged by the same factor.

• Dilate the original figure by a scale factor of 0.5. Record the measurements of each side of the new figure in the table. What result do you notice now? The ratio is the same for all sides, because each side was reduced by the same factor.

Lesson 11-1   567

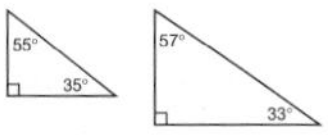

10. Yes; No; Regular polygons with the same number of sides will always be similar.

11. Each cable forms an angle of a different measurement where it intersects the road.

13. Possible answer: A scale factor less than 1 is a reduction, greater than 1 is an enlargement. Examples may vary.

14. Factors: 1, 3, 5, 9, 15, 45; Prime factors: 3, 5

15. Factors: 1, 2, 3, 6, 11, 22, 33, 66; Prime factors: 2, 3, 11

16. Factors: 1, 3, 9, 27, 81; Prime factor: 3

17. Factors: 1, 2, 3, 4, 6, 8, 12, 16, 24, 48; Prime factors: 2, 3

18. Factors: 1, 2, 4, 5, 10, 20, 25, 50, 100; Prime factors: 2, 5

Alternate Assessment

You may want to use the *Interactive CD-ROM Journal* with this assessment.

Journal Have students write about whether they think all right triangles are similar. Suggest that they include diagrams along with their explanation. Right triangles are not necessarily similar. The corresponding angles are not necessarily congruent, and the corresponding sides are not necessarily in the same ratio.

▶ Quick Quiz

$ABCD \sim JKLM$

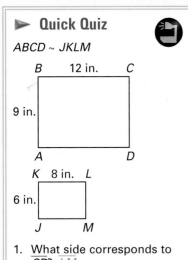

1. What side corresponds to $\overline{CD}$? *LM*

2. What angle corresponds to $\angle A$? $\angle J$

3. Find the similarity ratio of figure $ABCD$ to figure $JKLM$. $\frac{3}{2}$

Available on Daily Transparency 11-1

---

8. Quadrilateral I was shrunk and flipped to make quadrilateral II. Find the similarity ratio of I to II. **4 to 1**

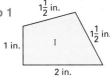

9. **Algebra** Write an algebraic expression that represents the area of the dilation of a square with an area of 64 unit^2, where the scale factor is *x*. **$64x^2$**

Problem Solving and Reasoning

10. Journal Are all squares similar? Are all rectangles similar? Which polygons do you think will always be similar?

11. **Communicate** The photo of the Pont de Brotonne in France shows how the cables that support the roadway are directly connected to the towers. A fan pattern is shown by the cables connecting several points of the roadway to several points on the tower. Tell how you know that the triangles formed by the cables on one side of a tower are not similar.

12. **Technology** Using geometry software, draw a polygon and dilate it by a scale factor of 2. Then measure the area of each polygon using the area tool. Calculate the ratio of the two areas. What is the area ratio for a scale factor of 3? **1 to 4; 1 to 9**

13. **Math Reasoning** Draw a conclusion about dilating figures using a scale factor less than 1 versus using a scale factor greater than 1. Give an example to support your conclusion.

Mixed Review

List all factors for each number and identify the prime factors. *[Lesson 7-1]*

14. 45   15. 66   16. 81   17. 48   18. 100

For the rule "add 5," find the output value for each input value. *[Lesson 10-1]*

19. 7 **12**   20. 5.5 **10.5**   21. 0.01 **5.01**   22. $\frac{3}{4}$ **$5\frac{3}{4}$**   23. −22 **−17**

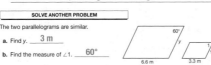

▶ PROBLEM SOLVING

Name _____

Guided Problem Solving 11-1

GPS PROBLEM 4, STUDENT PAGE 567

The two trapezoids are similar.

a. Find *x*.

b. Find the measure of ∠1.

— **Understand** — Possible answers: Items 6, 7, and 10

1. Underline the length that corresponds to *x*.

2. Circle the angle measure that corresponds to ∠1.

3. How are the two figures alike? Same shape, similar.

— **Plan** —

4. In similar figures, what is the relationship between

   a. corresponding sides? They have equal length ratios.

   b. corresponding angles? They are congruent.

5. Give the measures of two corresponding sides. 7.2 cm and 3.6 cm

6. Use the measures in Item 5 to find the similarity ratio. $\frac{7.2}{3.6}$

7. Write a proportion using the similarity ratio to find *x*. $\frac{7.2}{3.6} = \frac{4.4}{x}$

— **Solve** —

8. Find the length of *x*. 2.2 cm

9. Find the measure of ∠1. 120°

— **Look Back** —

10. What is a different strategy you could use to find the answer? Guess and Check; Use Logical Reasoning.

SOLVE ANOTHER PROBLEM

The two parallelograms are similar.

a. Find *y*. 3 m

b. Find the measure of ∠1. 60°

▶ ENRICHMENT

Name _____

Extend Your Thinking 11-1

Patterns in Geometry

A right triangle with angle measures of 30° and 60° is called a 30-60-90 triangle. A 30-60-90 triangle is actually one half of an equilateral triangle.

1. Use the Pythagorean Theorem to find the missing side of each triangle. Round your answer to the nearest tenth if necessary.

Shorter leg (opposite 30° angle)	Longer leg (opposite 60° angle)	Hypotenuse (opposite 90° angle)
1	1.7	2
2	3.5	4
3	5.2	6
4	6.9	8
5	8.7	10
6	10.4	12

2. What pattern do you notice in the columns of the table above? Possible answer: Relatively steady increase in measures: Column 1 by 1 unit. Column 2 by ≈ 1.7 units, and Column 3 by 2 units.

3. What pattern do you notice in the rows of the table above? Possible answer: Measures in Column 2 are ≈ 1.7 times those in Column 1 and Measures in Column 3 are 2 times those in Column 1.

The lengths of the sides of any 30-60-90 triangles are x, $x\sqrt{3}$ and $2x$. See how that compares to your answers to Questions 2 and 3. Use this relationship to give the answers to the questions below in terms of *y*.

4. What is the length of the shorter leg? $\frac{y}{2}$

5. What is the length of the longer leg? $\frac{y\sqrt{3}}{2}$

6. Label the legs of the triangle.

Congruent Figures

► **Lesson Link** You know how to identify similar polygons. Now you'll work with polygons with the same size and shape. ◄

Explore | Congruent Polygons

Congratulations! They're Twins!

Materials: Paper, Ruler, Protractor, Compass

1. On a sheet of paper, draw a polygon with 6, 7, or 8 sides. Do this so no one can see your work.

2. With your group, take turns describing your figure as the others try to draw an identical figure. You can use length and angle measurements to describe your figure.

3. When describing your figure, what did you say to make it easier for those who are drawing? What units of measurement did you use?

4. When taking your turn to draw, what did you find most helpful?

You'll Learn ...

■ to identify congruent figures

... How It's Used

The art of jewelry-making exhibits the use of congruent shapes.

Vocabulary

congruent polygons

Learn | Congruent Figures

Congruent polygons have the same shape and size.

To indicate congruence, write $ABCD \cong NMLK$.

  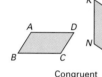

Congruent   Congruent   Not congruent

Corresponding angles of congruent figures are congruent.

$\angle DCB \cong \angle KLM$ in the congruent parallelograms.

Corresponding sides of congruent figures are congruent.

$\overline{AD} \cong \overline{NK}$ in the congruent parallelograms.

11-2 • Congruent Figures **569**

MEETING INDIVIDUAL NEEDS

Resources

11-2 Practice
11-2 Reteaching
11-2 Problem Solving
11-2 Enrichment
11-2 Daily Transparency
11-2 Daily Transparency
　　Problem of
　　the Day
　　Review
　　Quick Quiz
Teaching Tool
Transparencies 15, 16, 19
Lesson Enhancement
Transparency 59
Technology Master 59

Learning Modalities

Verbal In **Explore**, students use speaking skills when they describe a shape to their group and listening skills when they listen to other group members' descriptions of their shapes.

Visual In **Example 1**, students see how to determine if two figures are congruent by tracing one and then turning and sliding it on top of the other.

Inclusion

Some students will be able to recognize similar and congruent figures if they are side-by-side and oriented the same way, but not when the figures are turned or flipped. Ask volunteers to make pairs of cards using materials such as poster board and markers. Have them draw a figure on each card, making pairs of similar and congruent figures. Play a matching "memory" game by mixing the cards randomly so that the pictures can be oriented in any direction. Turn the cards face down, side-by-side. Allow students to pick up pairs and match cards to form similar or congruent pairs.

Objective

■ **Identify congruent figures.**

Vocabulary

■ **Congruent polygons**

Materials

■ **Explore: Paper, ruler, protractor, compass**

NCTM Standards

■ **1–4, 12**

► **Review**

List ten examples of items that have the same shape and the same size.
Possible answers: Desks, spoons, socks.

Available on Daily Transparency 11-2

► **Lesson Link**

Discuss the meaning of *identical polygons*. Emphasize that identical polygons would match exactly if one was placed on top of the other.

---

1 Introduce

Explore

You may wish to use Teaching Tool Transparencies 15: Rulers and 16: Protractor with **Explore**.

The Point

Students draw a polygon and use length and angle measurements to describe its shape to the other group members, who then try to draw an identical figure.

Ongoing Assessment

For Step 2, check that students are giving clear, accurate directions or are correctly following given directions.

For Groups That Finish Early

Draw another shape with a different number of sides and repeat Step 2.

Lesson 11-2 **569**

Follow Up
Students should discuss their answers to Steps 3 and 4.

Answers for Explore

1–2. Answers may vary.

3–4. Possible answers: Length measurements, angle measurements, left vs. right turns as you move around the figure.

2 Teach

Learn

You may wish to use Teaching Tool Transparencies 6: Cuisenaire Angle Ruler and 19: Tangram and Lesson Enhancement Transparency 59 with this lesson.

Alternate Examples

1. How would you determine whether two figures, such as the ones below, are congruent?

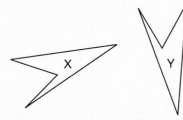

Trace one figure. Place the tracing over the other figure. If all parts of the two figures can be matched up, the figures are congruent.

2. How would you determine whether parallelogram *LMNO* and parallelogram *PQRS* are congruent?

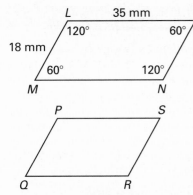

Check that corresponding angles have the same measure and that corresponding sides have the same length.

You can determine whether two figures are congruent by matching a tracing or comparing measurements.

Problem Solving TIP

Similar figures and congruent figures don't always have to be your usual polygons.

Example 1

Determine whether the two figures are congruent.

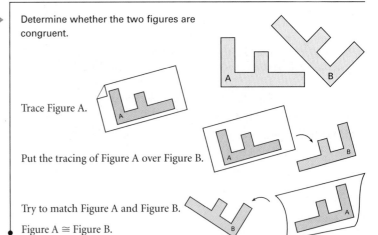

Trace Figure A.

Put the tracing of Figure A over Figure B.

Try to match Figure A and Figure B.

Figure A ≅ Figure B.

Example 2

Determine whether $\triangle ABC \cong \triangle DEF$.

First, measure $\angle DEF$, $\angle EFD$, and $\angle FDE$.

$m\angle DEF = 90° = m\angle ABC$

$m\angle EFD = 20° \neq m\angle BCA$

$m\angle FDE = 70° \neq m\angle CAB$

Measure $\overline{EF}$, $\overline{DF}$, and $\overline{DE}$.

$m\overline{EF} = 37 \text{ mm} \neq m\overline{BC}$

$m\overline{DF} = 40 \text{ mm} \neq m\overline{AC}$

$m\overline{DE} = 13 \text{ mm} \neq m\overline{AB}$

All corresponding parts are not congruent.
$\triangle ABC$ and $\triangle DEF$ are not congruent.

Try It

Determine whether the squares are congruent.
No

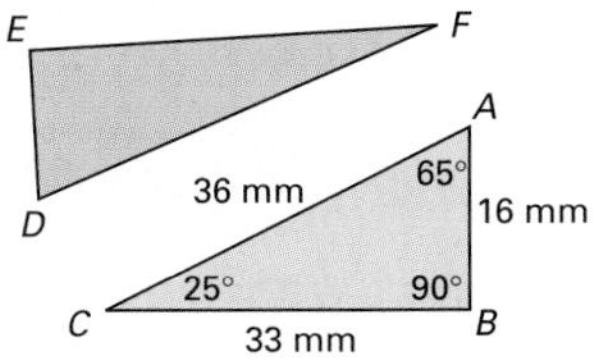

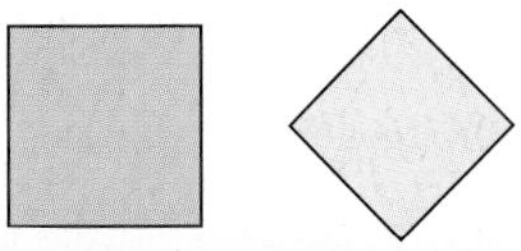

MATH EVERY DAY

Problem of the Day

Which diagonal is longer?

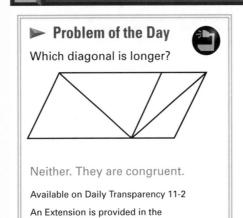

Neither. They are congruent.

Available on Daily Transparency 11-2

An Extension is provided in the transparency package.

Fact of the Day

The Forth Rail Bridge, discussed in Exercise 10 on page 573, is about 2380 m in total length and was opened in 1890.

Estimation

Estimate.

1. 57 • 412 24,000
2. 22 • 832 16,000
3. 43 • 530 20,000

Example 3

Determine whether the two hexagons are congruent.

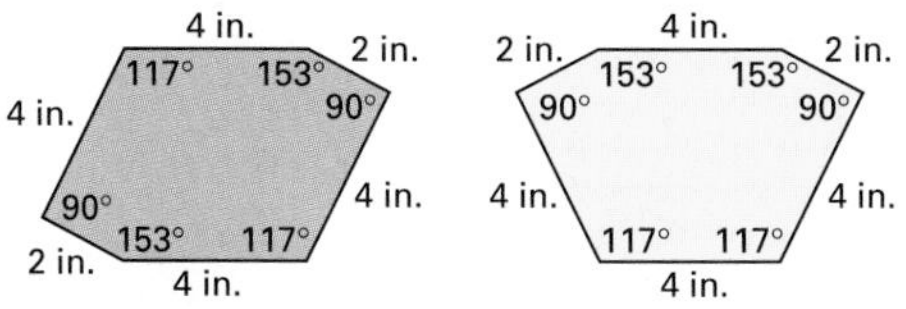

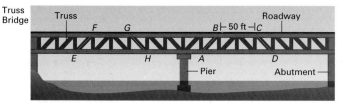

They both have the same angle and side length measures, but the measurements do not occur in the same order. The hexagons are not congruent.

If two figures are congruent and you know the measurements of one, you can find the measurements of the other figure.

Example 4

Trapezoids *ABCD* and *EFGH* are congruent. Find the length of $\overline{FG}$.

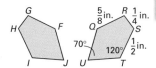

$\overline{FG}$ corresponds to $\overline{BC}$.

$m\overline{BC} = 50$ ft $\quad m\overline{FG} = 50$ ft

Try It

The two pentagons are congruent.

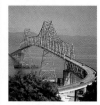

a. What side corresponds to $\overline{ST}$? $\overline{HI}$

b. Find the length of $\overline{FG}$. $\frac{5}{8}$ in.

c. Find $m\angle HIJ$. 120°

▶ Geography Link

The longest continuous truss bridge is 1232 ft and crosses the Columbia River, bridging Washington and Oregon.

Check Your Understanding

1. Are any two regular hexagons congruent? Are they similar? Explain.
2. If all the angles of an octagon are congruent to the angles of another octagon, are the octagons congruent? Explain.

Alternate Examples

3. Determine whether the two pentagons are congruent.

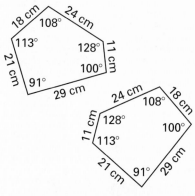

Both pentagons have the same angle measures and side lengths, but the measurements do not occur in the same order. The pentagons are not congruent.

4. Rectangles *WXYZ* and *PQRS* are congruent. Find the length of $\overline{PQ}$.

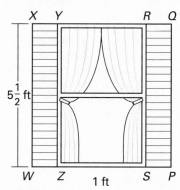

$\overline{PQ}$ corresponds to $\overline{WX}$. Since $m\overline{WX} = 5\frac{1}{2}$ ft, $m\overline{PQ} = 5\frac{1}{2}$ ft.

MEETING MIDDLE SCHOOL CLASSROOM NEEDS

Tips from Middle School Teachers

I find that all students benefit from working with manipulatives such as a geoboard. The geoboard provides students with an opportunity to construct congruent figures in a hands-on situation.

Team Teaching

Work with an art teacher to have students create a design using similar and congruent figures. Students could be inspired by looking at examples of stained glass created with geometric shapes.

Cooperative Learning

In small groups, have students use congruent figures to "design" jewelry or other pieces of art. Interested groups may use materials to make the objects they design.

3 Practice and Assess

Check

For Question 1, students may need to be reminded that in a regular polygon, all sides are the same length and all angles have the same measure.

Answers for Check Your Understanding

1. No; They may be different sizes. Yes, they both have all the same angle measures.
2. No; They may have different side lengths.

Assignment Guide

- **Basic**
  1–4, 6–8, 10, 13–21 odds
- **Average**
  2, 3, 5–10, 14–22 evens
- **Enriched**
  2, 3, 5–7, 9–13, 18, 21, 22

Exercise Notes

Exercise 1

Error Prevention Some students will read the wrong scale on a protractor when measuring angles. Before measuring, have students describe the angle as obtuse or acute and estimate the angle's measure based on their description of the angle.

Exercise 6

Test Prep Choice A can be eliminated by noting Figure 4 does not have a long extension as does Figure 2. Choice C can be eliminated by noting the "middle steps" of Figures 1 and 2 don't match. Choice D can be eliminated because the "middle steps" of Figures 3 and 4 don't match.

Exercise Answers

1. a. The corresponding sides are not congruent.
   b. The corresponding angles are congruent.

Reteaching

Activity

Materials: Window, two pieces of unruled paper, ruler

- Work with a partner.
- Draw a polygon on a piece of paper.
- Have your partner hold the polygon drawing up to a window. You put another sheet of paper over the polygon drawing and trace the vertices of the polygon on your new sheet. Then take the sheet down and draw lines to connect the vertices.
- Help your partner to do the same.
- Explain how you can check to see if your two drawings are congruent. Check if corresponding side lengths and corresponding angle measurements are equal.

572   **Chapter 11**

11-2 Exercises and Applications

Practice and Apply

1. **Getting Started** Determine whether the parallelograms are congruent.
   a. Measure the corresponding sides.
   b. Measure the corresponding angles.

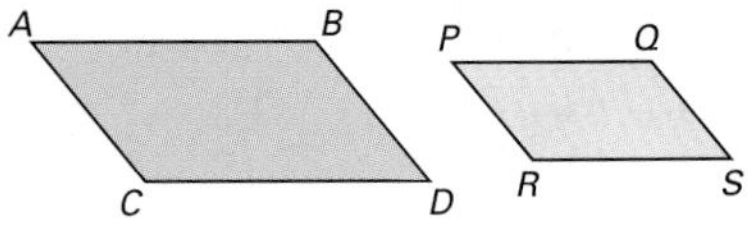

The two pentagons are congruent.

2. Find $m\angle STP$. **45°**

3. Find $m\overline{XY}$. **6 mm**

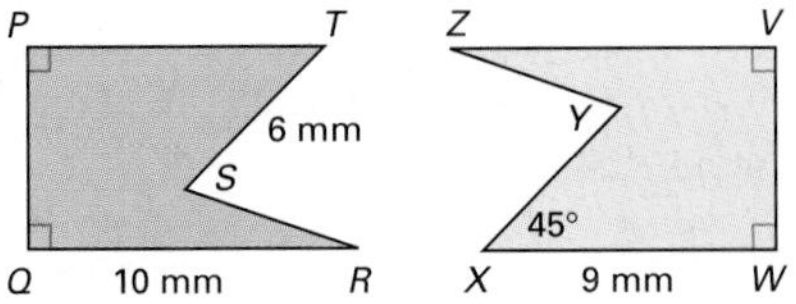

Determine whether each pair of figures is congruent.

4.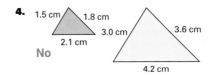
   No

5.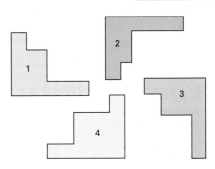
   Yes

6. **Test Prep** Two of the figures shown are congruent. Which are they? **B**
   - Ⓐ 2 and 4
   - Ⓑ 1 and 3
   - Ⓒ 1 and 2
   - Ⓓ 3 and 4

7. **Algebra** In the figure, the polygons are congruent. Find the value of *x*. **8**

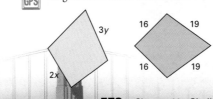

8. **Algebra** In the figure, the polygons are congruent. Find the value of *x*. **5**

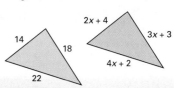

572   *Chapter 11 • Similarity, Congruence, and Transformations*

PRACTICE

Name _____

Practice 11-2

Congruent Figures

The two quadrilaterals are congruent.

1. Find $m\angle JKH$. ____68°____

2. Find $m\overline{HI}$. ____17 in.____

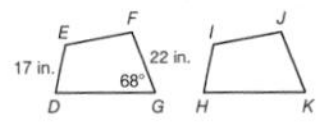

The two hexagons are congruent.

3. Find $m\angle STU$. ____115°____

4. Find $m\overline{MN}$. ____1.2 cm____

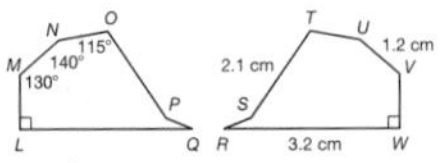

Determine whether each pair of figures is congruent.

5. ____Not congruent____   6. ____Not congruent____

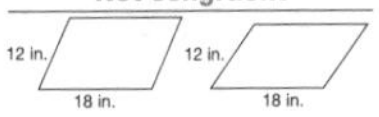

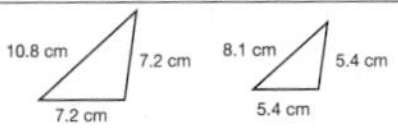

7. ____Congruent____    8. ____Congruent____

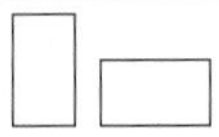

9. **Algebra** In the figure, the polygons are congruent. Find the values of *x* and *y*.

$x =$ ____12____ $y =$ ____$\frac{25}{6}$____

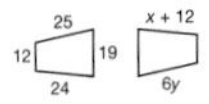

10. Construct a polygon congruent to the one shown. Label the vertices and complete the statements.   Possible answers:

$\overline{AB}$ corresponds to ____$\overline{GH}$____

$\overline{AF}$ corresponds to ____$\overline{GL}$____

$\overline{DE}$ corresponds to ____$\overline{JK}$____

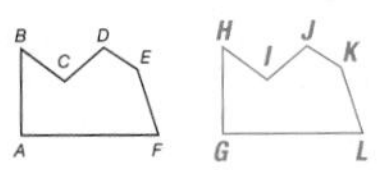

RETEACHING

Name _____

Alternative Lesson 11-2

Congruent Figures

When two figure have the same shape and size, they are **congruent**. Both the corresponding angles and the corresponding sides of congruent figures are congruent.

— Example 1 —

Determine whether the two quadrilaterals are congruent.

Measure $\angle J$, $\angle K$, $\angle L$, and $\angle M$.

$m\angle J = 90° = m\angle W$ $m\angle K = 90° = m\angle X$
$m\angle L = 90° = m\angle Y$ $m\angle M = 90° = m\angle Z$

Measure $\overline{JK}$, $\overline{KL}$, $\overline{LM}$, and $\overline{JM}$.

$m\overline{JK} = 30$ mm $m\overline{WX} = 35$ mm
$m\overline{KL} = 40$ mm $m\overline{XY} = 40$ mm
$m\overline{LM} = 30$ mm $m\overline{YZ} = 35$ mm
$m\overline{JM} = 40$ mm $m\overline{WZ} = 40$ mm

The corresponding angles of the figures are congruent. The corresponding sides are *not* congruent.

The rectangles JKLM and WXYZ are not congruent since all corresponding parts are not congruent.

Try It

a. Determine whether the two triangles are congruent. Explain.

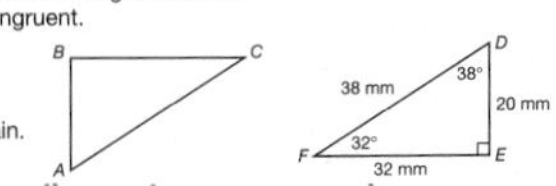

Congruent; all corresponding parts are congruent.

— Example 2 —

Parallelograms ABCD and RSTU are congruent. Find the length of $\overline{BC}$.

Find the side that corresponds to $\overline{BC}$.
$\overline{BC}$ corresponds to $\overline{ST}$.

Since $\overline{ST} = 24$ m, $\overline{BC} = 24$ m.

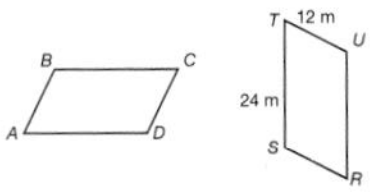

Try It

The trapezoids JKLM and PQRS are congruent.

b. Find the length of $\overline{JK}$. ____23 mm____

c. Find the length of $\overline{KL}$. ____22 mm____

d. Find the length of $\overline{JM}$. ____37 mm____

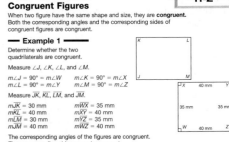
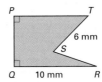

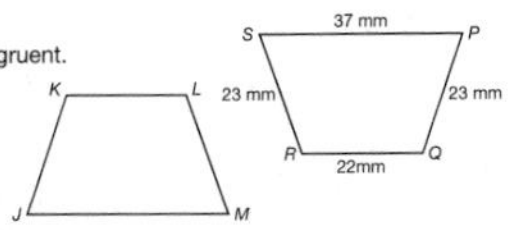

9. Geometry Construct a polygon congruent to the one shown, and describe how you did it. Label the vertices and the corresponding sides.

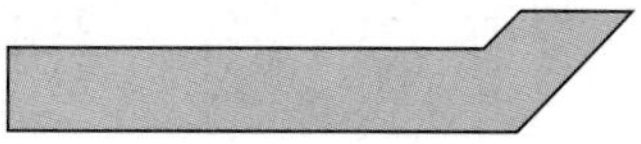

Problem Solving and Reasoning

10. Communicate The photograph shows the Forth Rail Bridge, a cantilever bridge in Scotland. Terry thinks that the highlighted triangles on the bridge are not congruent because they don't appear to be the same size in the photo. Explain the error in Terry's reasoning.

11. Technology With geometry software, construct a triangle congruent to the one shown. Measure the length of each side. Then move the vertices around until all side measures match those in the figure. (You may not be able to match them exactly; just do your best.) Now measure the angles inside the triangle, rounding to the nearest degree. How did the corresponding angles compare?

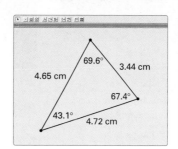

69.6° 3.44 cm
4.65 cm
67.4°
43.1° 4.72 cm

12. Math Reasoning If you are checking two triangles for congruency, do you need to measure every side and every angle? If not, how many measurements do you need?

13. Journal What steps would you perform to construct a copy of this regular octagon? Is there more than one way to do it?

4 cm

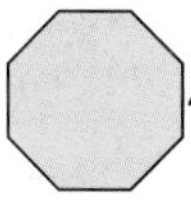

Mixed Review

Find the GCF for each pair of numbers. *[Lesson 7-2]*

14. 13, 52 **13** **15.** 16, 24 **8** **16.** 28, 49 **7** **17.** 20, 50 **10** **18.** 15, 40 **5**

Decide whether each equation describes a function. *[Lesson 10-2]*

19. $y = 2$ **Yes** **20.** $y = 3x + 2$ **Yes** **21.** $y = -4x$ **Yes** **22.** $y = |x + 1|$ **Yes**

11-2 • Congruent Figures **573**

(sidebar, rotated) PROBLEM SOLVING 11-2

Exercise Notes

■ **Exercise 12**

Error Prevention This exercise refers to the familiar Side-Side-Side, Side-Angle-Side, and Angle-Side-Angle conditions for congruency of triangles, which are considered in Lesson 11-3. However, triangles need not be congruent if they have two sides and a nonincluded angle congruent. That is, Side-Side-Angle is *not* a condition for congruency.

Exercise Answers

9. Answers may vary.

10. Terry did not consider the perspective of the photograph. If the photo was a perfect side view of the bridge, the triangles would appear congruent.

11. They are congruent.

12. Possible answer: You need to measure only two pairs of corresponding angles and one pair of corresponding sides.

13. Answers may vary.

Alternate Assessment

Portfolio Students may wish to save their drawings from **Explore** in their portfolios. They could include their own shapes, along with written instructions for drawing the shape.

▶ **Quick Quiz**

Draw a polygon congruent to *EFGH*. Label the vertices.

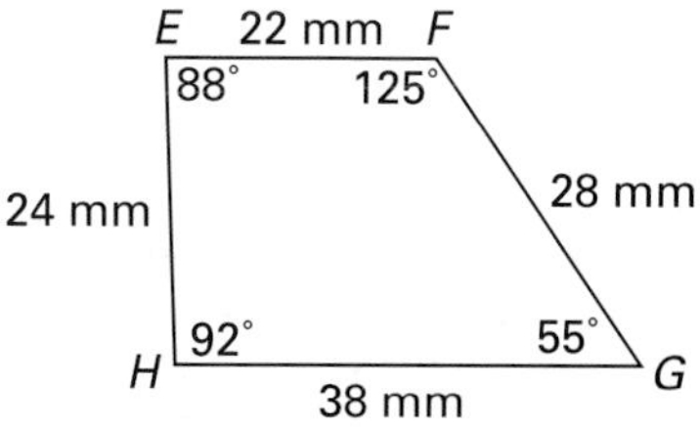

E 22 mm F
88° 125°
24 mm 28 mm
92° 55°
H 38 mm G

1. How do you know that your polygon is congruent to *EFGH*? Its sides and angles are congruent to corresponding parts of *EFGH*.

2. In your figure, which angle corresponds to ∠*FGH*? Answers may vary.

3. In your figure, which side corresponds to *HE*? Answers may vary.

Available on Daily Transparency 11-2

PROBLEM SOLVING

Name _____

Guided Problem Solving 11-2

GPS PROBLEM 7, STUDENT PAGE 572

In the figure, the polygons are congruent. Find the value of *x*.

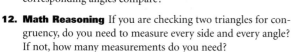

16 19
3y
2x 16 19

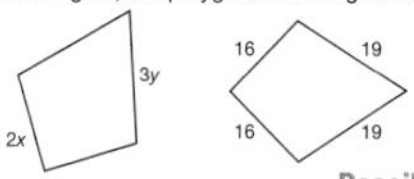

— Understand — Possible answers: Items 3, 7, and 9

1. What are the lengths of the sides of the polygon on the right? **16 and 19.**

2. What are the lengths of the sides of the polygon on the left? **2x and 3y.**

3. What makes two figures congruent? **They have the same size and shape.**

— Plan —

4. What is true about the measures of corresponding sides in congruent figures? **They are equal.**

5. What is the measure of the side corresponding to 2x? **16**

6. Write an equation using the lengths of the corresponding sides. **2x = 16**

7. How will you solve the equation? **Divide 16 by 2.**

— Solve —

8. Find the value of x. **x = 8**

— Look Back —

9. Why don't the figures look the same? **The second figure has a different orientation. It has been turned.**

SOLVE ANOTHER PROBLEM

In the figure, the polygons are congruent. Find the value of x.

3x 21
4y 18 21
18

x = 6

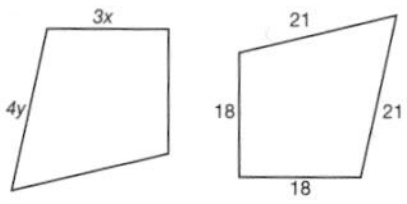

ENRICHMENT

Name _____

Extend Your Thinking 11-2

Visual Thinking

In each polygon below, length ℓ_1 corresponds to length ℓ_2 to form similar polygons. For example for the two similar rectangles $\ell_2 = 2\ell_1$. For polygon 2, construct a similar hexagon with $\ell_2 = \frac{1}{3}\ell_1$. For polygon 3, construct a similar trapezoid with $\ell_2 = 3\ell_1$. For polygon 4, construct a similar triangle with $\ell_2 = \frac{1}{4}\ell_1$.

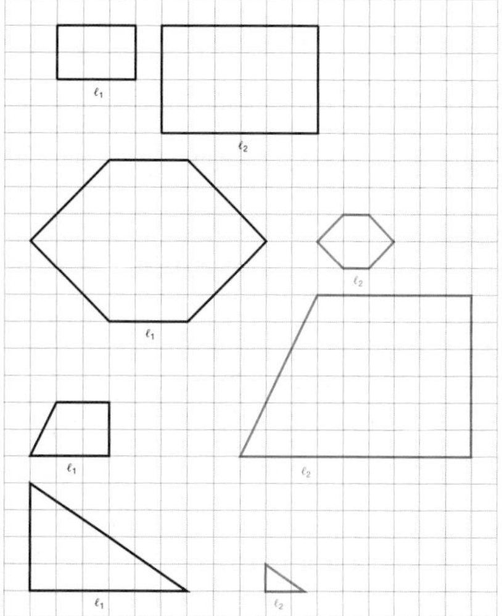

Polygon 1
ℓ_1
ℓ_2

Polygon 2
ℓ_1
ℓ_2

Polygon 3
ℓ_1 ℓ_2

Polygon 4
ℓ_1 ℓ_2

Lesson 11-2 **573**

Objective

- Identify congruent triangles.

Vocabulary

- Side-Side-Side, Side-Angle-Side, Angle-Side-Angle, Side-Angle-Angle

NCTM Standards

- 1–4, 12

► **Review**

$\triangle ABC \cong \triangle STU$ and $\overline{AC}$ corresponds to $\overline{SU}$.

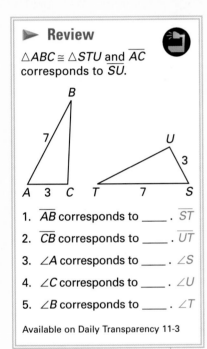

1. $\overline{AB}$ corresponds to ____ . $\overline{ST}$
2. $\overline{CB}$ corresponds to ____ . $\overline{UT}$
3. $\angle A$ corresponds to ____ . $\angle S$
4. $\angle C$ corresponds to ____ . $\angle U$
5. $\angle B$ corresponds to ____ . $\angle T$

Available on Daily Transparency 11-3

► **Lesson Link**

In Lesson 11-2 students considered the general conditions for congruence. Now they will narrow their focus and consider specific minimal conditions for triangle congruence.

1 Introduce

Explore

The Point
Students study a sketch of an old stone bridge to discover the minimum necessary conditions for triangle congruence.

Ongoing Assessment
Check students' explanations in Steps 3 and 4.

11-3   Triangle Congruence

▶ **Lesson Link**   Now that you've learned about congruent figures, you're ready to take a closer look at triangles and ways of showing their congruence. ◀

Explore   **Congruent Triangles**

You'll Learn ...

- to identify congruent triangles

... How It's Used

A percussionist can have a set of triangles. If the triangles are not congruent, then they will produce different pitches.

Vocabulary

Side-Side-Side

Side-Angle-Side

Angle-Side-Angle

Side-Angle-Angle

Stone Bridges

Below is an illustration of a stone bridge with the wooden framework used to build it. The people who built the bridge set up the wooden framework to support the stones as the bridge was built.

Because the sketch is not drawn to scale, you only know the measurements shown. You will determine whether triangles that appear to be congruent are congruent.

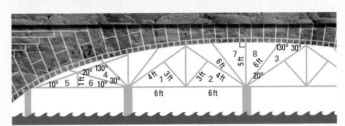

1. With triangles 1 and 2, all corresponding sides are congruent. Are the triangles congruent? Explain.

2. With triangles 3 and 4, all corresponding angles are congruent. Are the triangles congruent? Explain.

3. With the measurements given for triangles 5 and 6, do you know if they are congruent? Explain.

4. With the measurements given for triangles 7 and 8, do you know if they are congruent? Explain.

5. Discuss the minimum information necessary to determine whether or not two triangles are congruent.

MEETING INDIVIDUAL NEEDS

Resources

- **11-3** Practice
- **11-3** Reteaching
- **11-3** Problem Solving
- **11-3** Enrichment
- **11-3** Daily Transparency
    - Problem of the Day
    - Review
    - Quick Quiz
- Teaching Tool Transparency 19
- Lesson Enhancement Transparency 60
- Technology Master 60

Learning Modalities

Visual   In **Explore**, students study a sketch of an old stone bridge to discover some facts about triangle congruency.

Kinesthetic   Have students experiment with constructing congruent triangles using protractors, compasses, and rulers.

Verbal   Have students write a paragraph explaining how a surveyor, carpenter, or artist might use congruent triangles.

Challenge

Have interested students research the use and purpose of the triangle in the structure of geodesic domes. Students can present their reports to the class. Have them include illustrations or photos of geodesic domes in their presentations as examples.

Learn Triangle Congruence

You don't need every measurement to know that two triangles are congruent. Small marks are used to signify that corresponding parts are congruent.

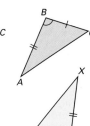

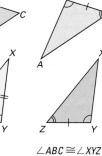

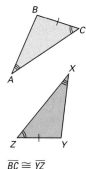

Side-Side-Side

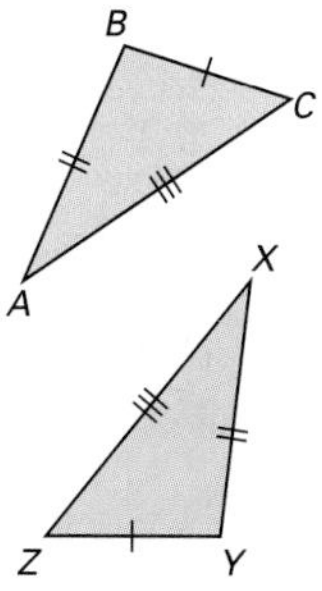

$\overline{AB} \cong \overline{XY}$
$\overline{BC} \cong \overline{YZ}$
$\overline{CA} \cong \overline{ZX}$

Side-Angle-Side

$\overline{AB} \cong \overline{XY}$
$\angle ABC \cong \angle XYZ$
$\overline{BC} \cong \overline{YZ}$

Angle-Side-Angle

$\angle ABC \cong \angle XYZ$
$\overline{BC} \cong \overline{YZ}$
$\angle BCA \cong \angle YZX$

Side-Angle-Angle

$\overline{BC} \cong \overline{YZ}$
$\angle BCA \cong \angle YZX$
$\angle CAB \cong \angle ZXY$

Test Prep

Use initials to help remember facts for a test.

SSS = Side-Side-Side

SAS = Side-Angle-Side

ASA = Angle-Side-Angle

SAA = Side-Angle-Angle

Example 1

Are the triangles congruent? If so, state the rule that justifies your answer.

Yes, because of the Side-Side-Side rule.

Try It

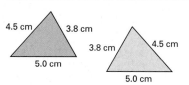

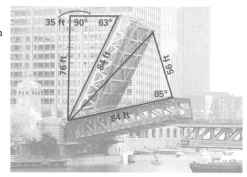

Bascule bridges, as seen along the Chicago River, open upward to let ships pass. Suppose the dimensions are as labeled.

Are the two triangles congruent? If so, state the rule that justifies your answer.

For Groups That Finish Early

If one triangle has two sides and an angle congruent to corresponding parts of another triangle, must the triangles be congruent? Give an example. No; sample example:

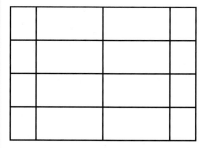

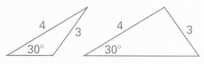

Follow Up

Volunteers from each group should take turns stating one of the conclusions that their group came to in Step 5. Check that all of the groups agree with the conclusions.

Answers for Explore

1. Yes; Having all sides congruent causes the triangles to have all angles congruent also.
2. No; Triangles with congruent angles can be different sizes.
3. No, because there is not enough information.
4. Yes, because of the angle measurements.
5. Congruencies: All sides, one pair of sides and any two pairs of angles, or one pair of angles and the adjacent pairs of sides.

2 Teach

Learn

You may wish to use Teaching Tool Transparency 19: Tangram and Lesson Enhancement Transparency 60 with this lesson.

Remind students that congruent triangles have the same shape and size.

Alternate Examples

1. Are the triangles congruent? If so, state the rule that justifies your answer.

Yes, because of the Side-Angle-Angle rule.

Answer for Try It

No.

MATH EVERY DAY

Problem of the Day

How many different-sized rectangles can you find?

24

Available on Daily Transparency 11-3

An Extension is provided in the transparency package.

Fact of the Day

Bascule bridges, as discussed on page 575, are the modern versions of drawbridges, which were built across the moats of many castles in Europe during the Middle Ages.

Mental Math

Do these mentally.

1. 500 ÷ 20 25
2. 600 ÷ 30 20
3. 900 ÷ 50 18

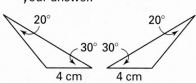

Alternate Examples

2. Are the triangles congruent? If so, state the rule that justifies your answer.

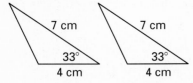

Yes, by the Side-Angle-Side rule.

3. Are the triangles congruent? If so, state the rule that justifies your answer.

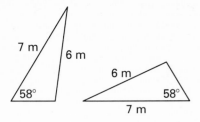

No, Side-Side-Angle is not a rule for congruency.

Answer for Try It
Yes; The SAS rule.

3 Practice and Assess

Check

For Question 2, point out the following possibilites.

- If the four congruent parts are three sides and one angle, the Side-Side-Side and Side-Angle-Side rules can be used.

- If the four congruent parts are three angles and one side, the Angle-Side-Angle or Side-Angle-Angle rules can be used.

- If the four congruent parts are two sides and two angles, the Side-Angle-Side, Side-Angle-Angle, and Angle-Side-Angle rules can be used.

Answers for Check Your Understanding

1. Triangles with congruent angles can still be different sizes.

2. Yes; At least one of the rules proving congruence on the basis of three parts will apply.

Example 2

Are the triangles congruent? If so, state the rule that justifies your answer.

Yes, because of the Side-Angle-Side rule.

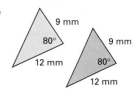

Example 3

Are the triangles congruent? If so, state the rule that justifies your answer.

No. The length measurements "2 m" do not appear on corresponding sides.

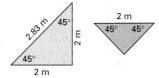

▶ **History Link**

Completed in May of 1937, the Golden Gate Bridge in California spans 6450 ft. That's more than a mile!

Try It

Suspension bridges, such as the Golden Gate Bridge in San Francisco, are used to span long distances.

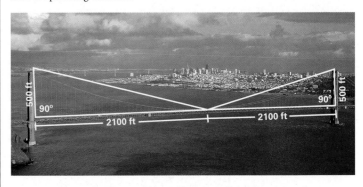

Are the two triangles shown in this bridge congruent? If so, state the rule that justifies your answer.

Check | Your Understanding

1. Why isn't there an Angle-Angle-Angle rule? Explain.

2. Suppose you know that four parts of a triangle are congruent to four corresponding parts of another triangle. Is this enough information to know that the triangles are congruent? Explain.

576 Chapter 11 • Similarity, Congruence, and Transformations

MEETING MIDDLE SCHOOL CLASSROOM NEEDS

Tips from Middle School Teachers

When teaching triangle congruence, I like to use different colored chalks to emphasize the included sides and angles of the triangles.

Cultural Connection

The art of surveying, mentioned in Exercise 11 on page 579, began in ancient Egypt. Each year, after the flooding of the Nile River had subsided, surveyors had the job of reestablishing land boundaries.

Science Connection

The triangle shape is extremely important to engineering and architecture for making rigid, strong structures. Many man-made structures are made with groups of triangles, for example, pitched roofs on houses. The triangles of wood in the roof divide the large forces that act on each triangle's top vertex into two smaller forces that act along the sides of the triangle. The roof load can then be supported equally by the walls of the house.

11-3 Exercises and Applications

Practice and Apply

1. `Getting Started` △GHI ≅ △SQR and $\overline{HI}$ corresponds to $\overline{QR}$.

a. $\overline{HG}$ corresponds to __QS__.

b. $\overline{IG}$ corresponds to __RS__.

c. ∠H corresponds to __∠Q__.

d. ∠I corresponds to __∠R__.

e. ∠G corresponds to __∠S__.

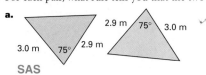

2. For each pair, what rule tells you that the two triangles are congruent?

a.

SAS

b. **ASA**

State whether each pair of triangles has congruence; if it does, give the rule that justifies your answer.

3.

Yes; SSS

4. **No**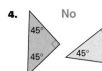

5. 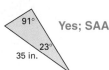 **Yes; SAA**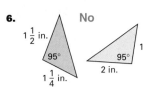

6. **No**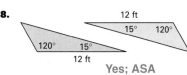

7. **Yes; SAS**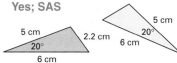

8.

Yes; ASA

9. For each rule, draw a pair of triangles that satisfy it.

a. Side-Side-Side   b. Angle-Side-Angle   c. Side-Angle-Side

PRACTICE 11-3

Assignment Guide

■ **Basic**
1–5, 7–11, 12–22 evens

■ **Average**
4–10, 11–23 odds

■ **Enriched**
2, 6–14, 18, 19, 22, 23

Exercise Notes

■ **Exercises 4 and 6**

Extension Ask students how they would change one or both of the triangles in these pairs to make the two congruent.

Exercise Answers

9. a–c. Answers may vary.

PRACTICE

Name _____

Practice **11-3**

Triangle Congruence

For each pair, what rule tells you that the two triangles are congruent?

1. Angle-Side-Angle
2. Side-Side-Side

3. Side-Angle-Side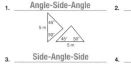
4. Side-Angle-Angle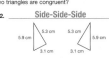

State whether each pair of triangles has congruence; if it does, give the rule that justifies your answer.

5. **No**
6. **Yes; Side-Angle-Side**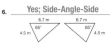

7. **Yes; Side-Angle-Angle**
8. **No**

9. A craftsman building a stained glass window determines that BC and CD are the same length. State the rule used to determine this.

Angle-Side-Angle

RETEACHING

Name _____

Alternative Lesson **11-3**

Triangle Congruence

You can tell whether two triangles are congruent if you know certain measurements of the triangles.

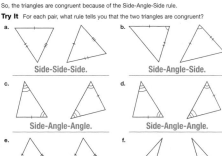

Side-Side-Side	Side-Angle-Side	Angle-Side-Angle	Side-Angle-Angle
$\overline{AB} \cong \overline{XY}$	$\overline{AB} \cong \overline{XY}$	$\angle ABC \cong \angle XYZ$	$\overline{BC} \cong \overline{YZ}$
$\overline{BC} \cong \overline{YZ}$	$\angle ABC \cong \angle XYZ$	$\overline{BC} \cong \overline{YZ}$	$\angle BCA \cong \angle YZX$
$\overline{CA} \cong \overline{ZX}$	$\overline{BC} \cong \overline{YZ}$	$\angle BCA \cong \angle YZX$	$\angle CAB \cong \angle ZXY$

— **Example** —

What rule tells you that the two triangles are congruent?

Look at the marks on the triangles. The angles are congruent. The respective sides of the sides of the angle are also congruent.

So, the triangles are congruent because of the Side-Angle-Side rule.

Try It For each pair, what rule tells you that the two triangles are congruent?

a. Side-Side-Side.
b. Side-Angle-Side.
c. Side-Angle-Angle.
d. Side-Angle-Angle.
e. Side-Side-Side.
f. Angle-Side-Angle.

Reteaching

`Activity`

Materials: Unruled paper, protractor, compass, ruler

- Work with a partner.

- Draw △ABC using any side and angle measures.

- Use your compass and ruler to draw a triangle congruent to △ABC using the Side-Side-Side rule.

- Now make congruent triangles using the Side-Angle-Side rule, the Angle-Side-Angle rule, and the Side-Angle-Angle rule.

11. The SAS rule.

12. $m\overline{EF} \approx 9.698$ or about 9.7 miles.

13. Not necessarily; The triangles are the same shape (i.e., similar) but not necessarily the same size.

14. Answers may vary.

20.

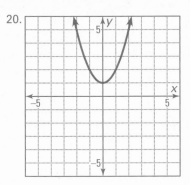

Quadratic

21–23. See page C4.

Alternate Assessment

Interview Ask students to name and explain the four rules for determining triangle congruence. They may find it helpful to draw diagrams of triangles to assist them with their explanations.

► **Quick Quiz**

State whether the triangles are congruent and, if they are, give the rule that justifies your answer.

1.

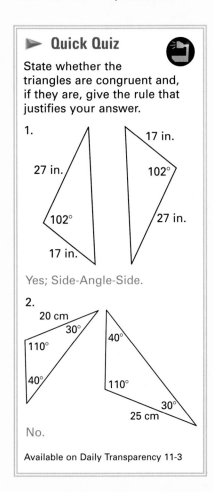

17 in.

27 in.

102°

102°

27 in.

102°

17 in.

Yes; Side-Angle-Side.

2.

20 cm
30°
110°
40°

40°
110°
30°
25 cm

No.

Available on Daily Transparency 11-3

---

10. **Test Prep** How far is it from Cauchy Square to the Weierstrasse? **C**

Ⓐ 0.20 km

Ⓑ 0.17 km

Ⓒ 0.10 km

Ⓓ Insufficient information

11. **Career** A surveyor at this native-plant preservation area concludes that the fences on the right and left sides of the land are the same length. State the rule used to determine this.

380 yd   380 yd
50°   50°
475 yd   475 yd

Problem Solving and Reasoning

12. **Communicate** Refer to the two triangles and find $m\overline{EF}$ if you can; if not, explain why not.

5.8 mi   98°   A
C   49°
7.5 mi   B

E   49°   7.5 mi
F   98°   D
6.2 mi

13. **Math Reasoning** The three angles of one triangle are congruent to the three angles of a second triangle. Are the triangles congruent? Explain.

14. **Critical Thinking** Truss bridges are built over canyons and rivers. The parts of the trusses are arranged in the form of triangles, as in the portion shown. Make a similar shape out of line segments. Then, taking as few measurements as possible (including at least one angle), finish your truss by adding a left half that is the mirror image of the right. What is the minimum number of measurements you need?

Mixed Review

Find the LCM for each pair of numbers. *[Lesson 7-3]*

15. 6, 20 **60** 16. 35, 40 **280** 17. 2, 10 **10** 18. 5, 12 **60** 19. 4, 15 **60**

Graph each function and decide whether it is linear or quadratic. *[Lesson 10-3]*

20. $y = x^2 + 1$ 21. $y = 4x$ 22. $y = -x^2$ 23. $y = (-x)^2$

PROBLEM SOLVING

Name _____

Guided Problem Solving 11-3

GPS PROBLEM 11, STUDENT PAGE 578

A surveyor at this native-plant preservation area concludes that the fences on the right and left sides of the land are the same length. State the rule used to determine this.

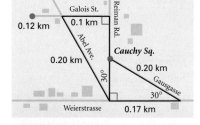

380 yd   380 yd
50°   50°
475 yd   475 yd

— **Understand** —

1. What are the measures of the sides and the angles in each triangle?

	Sides	Angles
a. Triangle on the left	380 yd and 475 yd	50°
b. Triangle on the right	380 yd and 475 yd	50°

2. How can showing that the sides are congruent prove that the fences have equal length? Corresponding sides of congruent figures are congruent.

— **Plan** —

3. Are the angles congruent? Explain. Yes, they have the same measure.

4. Are the given sides congruent? Explain. Yes, have same length.

5. What are the positions of any congruent sides and angles? Congruent angle is between two congruent sides.

— **Solve** —

6. What rule tells you that the triangles are congruent? SAS

— **Look Back** —

7. How could the surveyor check his answer? Measure the two fences.

SOLVE ANOTHER PROBLEM

A student concluded that the base of the triangle on the right and the base of the triangle on the left are the same length. State the rule used to determine this.

50°   50°
75 m   75 m
85°   85°

ASA.

ENRICHMENT

Name _____

Extend Your Thinking 11-3

Critical Thinking

1. The following figure consists of four lines. $\overline{AB} \parallel \overline{CD}$. Name two similar triangles. Explain why these triangles are similar.

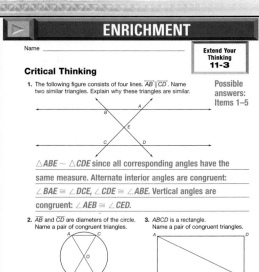

Possible answers: Items 1–5

△*ABE* ~ △*CDE* since all corresponding angles have the same measure. Alternate interior angles are congruent: ∠*BAE* ≅ ∠*DCE*, ∠*CDE* ≅ ∠*ABE*. Vertical angles are congruent: ∠*AEB* ≅ ∠*CED*.

2. $\overline{AB}$ and $\overline{CD}$ are diameters of the circle. Name a pair of congruent triangles.

△*AOC* ≅ △*BOD*

3. *ABCD* is a rectangle. Name a pair of congruent triangles.

△*ABC* ≅ △*CDA*

4. △*ABC* ≅ △*BAC*. What kind of triangle is △*ABC*? Explain.
$\overline{BC} ≅ \overline{AC}$. They are corresponding sides of congruent triangles. △*ABC* is isosceles. Since measure of ∠*BCA* is not known, triangle is not necessarily equilateral.

5. Explain why any two congruent triangles are similar.
Since corresponding angles of congruent triangles are congruent and the similarity ratio is 1 for corresponding sides, congruent triangles are also similar.

Trigonometry

► **Lesson Link** You've seen various ways of finding missing side lengths of triangles. Now you'll learn another way. ◄

The longest side of a right triangle is the hypotenuse. You can refer to the two other sides in relationship to an acute angle.

The side next to ∠1 is the **adjacent leg** . The side across from ∠1 is the **opposite leg** .

11-4

You'll Learn ...
■ to use ratios in order to find missing side lengths of a right triangle

... How It's Used
Navigators continuously calculate to determine the distance between their ship and their destination.

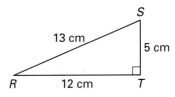

Vocabulary
adjacent leg

opposite leg

trigonometric ratios

sine

cosine

tangent

Explore   Trigonometric Ratios

Finding the Right Ratio

Materials: Dynamic geometry software, $8\frac{1}{2}$ in. by 11 in. paper

1. With the software, draw three similar right triangles. In each triangle, label one acute angle 1, 2, and 3.

2. On a sheet of paper, make a table with six columns labeled "angle," "opposite," "adjacent," "hypotenuse," "$\frac{opposite}{hypotenuse}$," and "$\frac{adjacent}{hypotenuse}$."

3. Record the measures of ∠1, ∠2, and ∠3 in the "angle" column.

4. Use the measure tool to find the length of each side of all three triangles and record your measurements in the table.

5. Use the measurements from Steps 3 and 4 to calculate and record the ratios for the remaining columns. Do you notice a pattern? Explain.

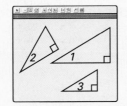

Learn   Trigonometry

As you have already learned, when triangles have two pairs of congruent angles and a corresponding pair of congruent sides, the triangles are congruent.

Now you will learn how to find the other sides of right triangles.

MEETING INDIVIDUAL NEEDS

Resources

11-4 Practice

11-4 Reteaching

11-4 Problem Solving

11-4 Enrichment

11-4 Daily Transparency
   Problem of the Day
   Review
   Quick Quiz

Teaching Tool Transparencies 2, 3, 22

Technology Master 61

Chapter 11 Project Master

 Interactive CD-ROM Lesson

 Wide World of Mathematics Geometry: Leaning Tower of Pisa

Learning Modalities

Logical In **Explore**, students draw and measure right triangles to discover a pattern between the ratios of the side lengths.

Visual Have students make a colorful poster showing the trigonometric ratios.

Individual Have students reflect on how trigonometric ratios might be used to find measurements in real-life situations.

English Language Development

Encourage students to use correct vocabulary when discussing problems. Consistent use will reinforce vocabulary and enhance understanding of problems. Further, encourage students to use correct mathematical vocabulary when referring to situations outside the textbook. This enhances transferability of geometric terms to everyday vocabulary.

Lesson Organizer

Objective
■ Use ratios in order to find missing side lengths of a right triangle.

Vocabulary
■ Adjacent leg, opposite leg, trigonometric ratios, sine, cosine, tangent

Materials
■ Explore: Dynamic geometry software, $8\frac{1}{2}$ in. by 11 in. paper

NCTM Standards
■ 1–4, 12

► Review
Find the side dimensions of this triangle if it is dilated by a scale factor of 3.

1. $\overline{RS}$ 39 cm
2. $\overline{ST}$ 15 cm
3. $\overline{RT}$ 36 cm

Available on Daily Transparency 11-4

1 Introduce

Explore

The Point
Students draw and measure right triangles to discover a pattern between the ratios of the side lengths.

Ongoing Assessment
For Step 1, check that all students have drawn three similar right triangles.

Draw another right triangle using the geometry utility. Measure one of the acute angles. Then measure the hypotenuse and the sides opposite and adjacent to the angle. Calculate the same ratios as you did in **Explore**. What do you notice?

Follow Up
Have students discuss the pattern they noticed in Step 5. How were they able to explain the pattern?

Answers for Explore
1–4. Answers may vary.

5. As the angle measure increases, $\frac{\text{opposite}}{\text{hypotenuse}}$ increases and $\frac{\text{adjacent}}{\text{hypotenuse}}$ decreases.

2 Teach

Learn

You may wish to use Teaching Tool Transparency 22: Scientific Calculator with this lesson.

Review the Angle-Side-Angle rule and the Side-Angle-Angle rule of congruence with students.

Alternate Examples

1. Use the right triangle shown to answer the following.

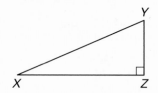

   a. Name the hypotenuse. $\overline{XY}$

   b. Name the leg opposite ∠YXZ. $\overline{YZ}$

   c. Name the leg adjacent to ∠YXZ. $\overline{XZ}$

2. Evaluate the trigonometric ratios for ∠TSU.

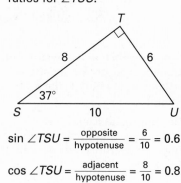

   $\sin \angle TSU = \frac{\text{opposite}}{\text{hypotenuse}} = \frac{6}{10} = 0.6$

   $\cos \angle TSU = \frac{\text{adjacent}}{\text{hypotenuse}} = \frac{8}{10} = 0.8$

   $\tan \angle TSU = \frac{\text{opposite}}{\text{adjacent}} = \frac{6}{8} = 0.75$

   $\sin \angle TSU = 0.6$; $\cos \angle TSU = 0.8$; $\tan \angle TSU = 0.75$

Example 1

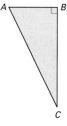

Use the right triangle shown to answer each.

a. Name the hypotenuse. Answer: $\overline{AC}$

b. Name the leg opposite ∠CAB. Answer: $\overline{BC}$

c. Name the leg adjacent to ∠CAB. Answer: $\overline{AB}$

Study TIP

The opposite leg gets its name because it is opposite a specific angle.

Try It

a. Name the hypotenuse. $\overline{KM}$

b. Name the leg opposite ∠MKL. $\overline{ML}$

c. Name the leg adjacent to ∠MKL. $\overline{KL}$

For any right triangle, the lengths of the hypotenuse, an adjacent leg, and an opposite leg may be compared by using three common **trigonometric ratios** .

TRIGONOMETRIC RATIOS

Sine	Cosine	Tangent
The sine of x is	The cosine of x is	The tangent of x is
$\sin(x) = \frac{\text{opposite}}{\text{hypotenuse}}$	$\cos(x) = \frac{\text{adjacent}}{\text{hypotenuse}}$	$\tan(x) = \frac{\text{opposite}}{\text{adjacent}}$

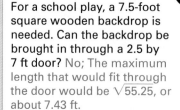

Example 2

For the triangle shown, evaluate the trigonometric ratios for ∠CAB.

$\sin \angle CAB = \frac{\text{opposite}}{\text{hypotenuse}} = \frac{3}{5} = 0.6$

$\cos \angle CAB = \frac{\text{adjacent}}{\text{hypotenuse}} = \frac{4}{5} = 0.8$

$\tan \angle CAB = \frac{\text{opposite}}{\text{adjacent}} = \frac{3}{4} = 0.75$

$\sin \angle CAB = 0.6$ $\cos \angle CAB = 0.8$ $\tan \angle CAB = 0.75$

Try It

Use the triangle in Example 2 to answer each question.

a. What is the sine ratio of ∠ACB? $\frac{4}{5}$

b. What is the tangent ratio of ∠ACB? $\frac{4}{3}$

580   *Chapter 11 • Similarity, Congruence, and Transformations*

MATH EVERY DAY

▶ Problem of the Day

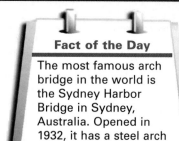

For a school play, a 7.5-foot square wooden backdrop is needed. Can the backdrop be brought in through a 2.5 by 7 ft door? No; The maximum length that would fit through the door would be $\sqrt{55.25}$, or about 7.43 ft.

Available on Daily Transparency 11-4

An Extension is provided in the transparency package.

Fact of the Day

The most famous arch bridge in the world is the Sydney Harbor Bridge in Sydney, Australia. Opened in 1932, it has a steel arch that is 1650 feet long.

Estimation

Estimate.

1. 50% of 257 130

2. 5% of 103 5

3. 20% of 247 50

Example 3

Use a calculator to find the cosine of $\angle BAC$.

Be sure that your calculator is set on degrees.

Enter 37 [cos].

The display reads *0.79863551*.

$\cos 37° \approx 0.8$

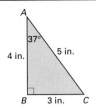

Using trigonometric ratios, we can find the unknown side lengths of a right triangle using one acute angle and one known side length.

Example 4

How high above ground level is the end of this drawbridge?

You're looking for the opposite leg and you know the hypotenuse, so use the sine ratio.

$\sin 45° = \dfrac{l}{150}$ Use a calculator.

$0.7071 \approx \dfrac{l}{150}$ Solve.

$106.066 \approx l$

The end of the drawbridge is about 106 ft high.

Water/moat

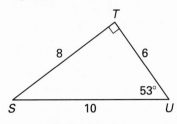

▶ History Link

In medieval times, a moat was dug around a castle and a lowered drawbridge was the only way into the castle.

Try It

a. Find the length of y on the right triangle.

≈ 11.78 m

b. Find the length of the hypotenuse.

≈ 12.79 m

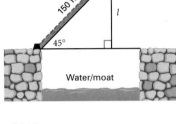

Check   Your Understanding

1. If you know the sine of one angle in a right triangle, what two sides do you know the ratio for? Explain.

2. What happens when you use your calculator to find the sine, cosine, and tangent of 90°?

3. How can the sine ratio for a given angle be the same no matter how big the triangle?

MEETING MIDDLE SCHOOL CLASSROOM NEEDS

Tips from Middle School Teachers

When I teach trigonometric functions, the class and I create a poster to display in the classroom. I begin by drawing a right triangle on a large poster board. One student labels the triangle. Then I list the terms *sine*, *cosine*, and *tangent* in a table and ask students to fill in the table with the appropriate definition. Finally, various students apply the definitions to the angles of the triangle to complete the table.

Team Teaching

Make sure that the science teacher on your team knows that students are familiar with the basic concepts of trigonometry so they can make references to it. The science teacher may want to point out that one of the most important modern applications of trigonometry is in the study of crystals, known as crystallography.

Cultural Connection

Trigonometry is based on the study of right-angled triangles. Theorems on the ratios of the sides of these triangles had been used by the Egyptians and Babylonians, but the sine ratios that we use today were first set out in about 150 B.C. by the ancient Greek astronomer Hipparchus of Nicea. He arranged the ratios in tables to help him in his astronomical studies. He recorded the locations of over 1080 fixed stars, and worked out the motion of the Moon relative to the Earth. Hipparchus' work was rewritten by Ptolemy. It was later used by Arab scholars such as Albuzjani (A.D. 940–998), who wrote another set of ratios known today as tangents.

Alternate Examples

3. Use a calculator to find the cosine of $\angle TUS$. Be sure that your calculator is set on degrees.

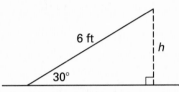

Enter 53 [cos].

The display reads *0.601815*.

$\cos 53° \approx 0.6$

4. Aki is building a structure with 6-foot boards and a 30° pitch. How high above ground level is the highest end of the structure?

Use the sine ratio:

$\sin 30° = \dfrac{h}{6}$ Use a calculator.

$0.5 = \dfrac{h}{6}$ Solve.

$3 = h$

The high end is 3 ft high.

3 Practice and Assess

Check

You may want to discuss what happens to the sine as the angle goes from 0 to 90. What happens to the cosine? Sine increases from 0 to 1; Cosine decreases from 1 to 0.

Answers for Check Your Understanding

1. Opposite and hypotenuse, since $\sin(a) = \dfrac{\text{opposite}}{\text{hypotenuse}}$ by definition.

2. 1; 0; Error.

3. If two right triangles are similar then the sine ratios will be the same.

Assignment Guide

- **Basic**
  1, 3, 6, 9, 10, 11–23 odds

- **Average**
  2, 4, 5, 7–9, 10–22 evens

- **Enriched**
  3, 6–14, 18, 21

Exercise Notes

■ **Exercise 5**

Extension In real-life situations like this one, the angle in question is called the angle of elevation. An angle of elevation is formed by the horizontal line of sight (or ground level) and the line of sight to the top of some object (or to some object above the horizon).

Exercise Answers

2. $\sin D = \frac{12}{13}$, $\cos D = \frac{5}{13}$, $\tan D = \frac{12}{5}$

3. $\sin E = \frac{1}{\sqrt{2}}$, $\cos E = \frac{1}{\sqrt{2}}$, $\tan E = 1$

4. $\cos G = \frac{9}{10.4}$, $\sin G = \frac{5.2}{10.4}$,
   $\tan G = \frac{5.2}{9}$

Reteaching

Activity

Materials: Red, green, and blue colored markers

- Work in groups of three.

- Draw a right triangle *ABC*, with angle *C* as the right angle.

- Have one person trace over the hypotenuse with red marker.

- Have another person trace over the leg opposite ∠*A* with green marker.

- Another person can trace over the leg adjacent to ∠*A* with blue marker.

- Now work together to find the trigonometric ratios for both ∠*A* and ∠*B* using color words to represent the side lengths. $\tan \angle A = \frac{green}{blue}$;

$\sin \angle A = \frac{green}{red}$; $\cos \angle A =$
$\frac{blue}{red}$; $\tan \angle B = \frac{blue}{green}$;

$\sin \angle B = \frac{blue}{red}$; $\cos \angle B = \frac{green}{red}$

Practice and Apply

1. **Getting Started** Find the length of side $\overline{PQ}$ on the triangle shown.
   a. Is $\overline{QR}$ opposite or adjacent to ∠*QPR*? **Opposite**
   b. Is $\overline{PQ}$ opposite or adjacent to ∠*QPR*? **Adjacent**
   c. Which ratio, sine, cosine, or tangent, compares the side opposite to the side adjacent? **Tangent**
   d. Use the ratio from 1c above to find the length of $\overline{PQ}$. ≈ **38.87 in.**

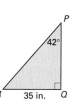

Use the lengths of the sides to write and evaluate the sine, cosine, and tangent ratios for each of the labeled angles.

2.

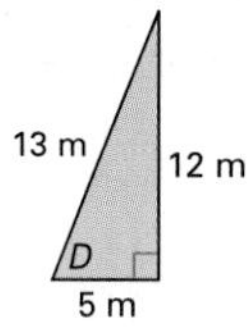

3.

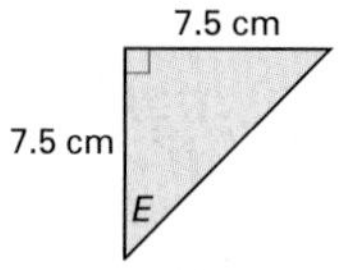

4.

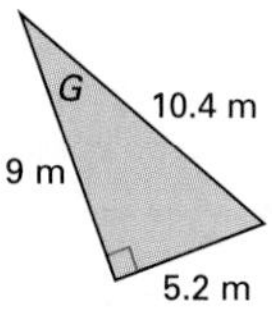

5. The top of a building forms a 68° angle with a point 250 m away from the building's base, as shown. How high is the building? ≈ **618.8 m**

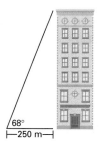

6. The head of this origami dinosaur forms a right triangle. For this triangle, what is the ratio of the length of the leg adjacent to the 35° angle and the length of the hypotenuse?

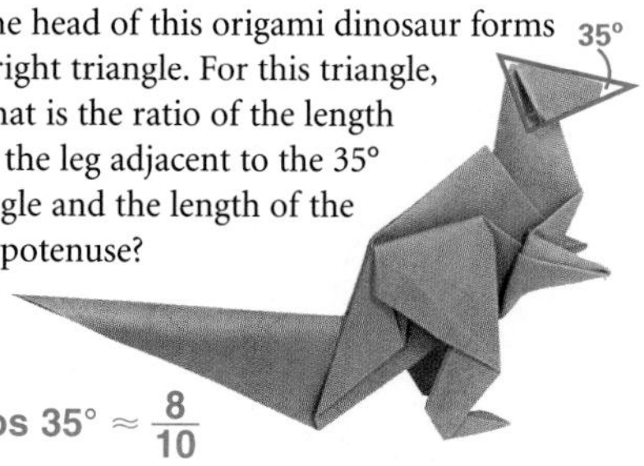

   $\cos 35° \approx \frac{8}{10}$

7. Find the length represented by *x*. ≈ **10.4 ft**

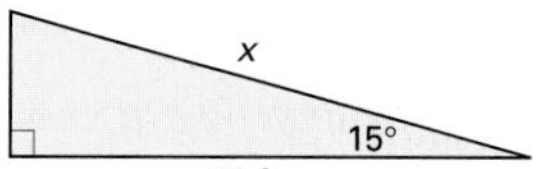

8. Find the length represented by *k*. ≈ **6.8 m**

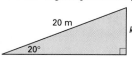

9. **Test Prep** Which represents the cosine of an angle in a right triangle? **B**

   Ⓐ $\frac{\text{opposite}}{\text{adjacent}}$ Ⓑ $\frac{\text{adjacent}}{\text{hypotenuse}}$ Ⓒ $\frac{\text{hypotenuse}}{\text{opposite}}$ Ⓓ None of these

---

PRACTICE

Name _____

Practice 11-4

Trigonometry

Use the lengths of the sides to evaluate the sine, cosine, and tangent ratios for each of the labeled angles.

1. $\sin \angle A = \frac{4}{5} = 0.8$
   $\cos \angle A = \frac{3}{5} = 0.6$
   $\tan \angle A = \frac{4}{3} \approx 1.333$

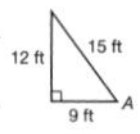

2. $\sin \angle B = \frac{12}{13} \approx 0.923$
   $\cos \angle B = \frac{5}{13} \approx 0.385$
   $\tan \angle B = \frac{12}{5} = 2.4$

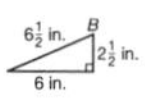

3. $\sin \angle C \approx 0.707$
   $\cos \angle C \approx 0.707$
   $\tan \angle C = 1$

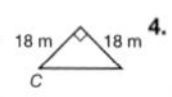

4. $\sin \angle D \approx 0.849$
   $\cos \angle D \approx 0.528$
   $\tan \angle D \approx 1.607$

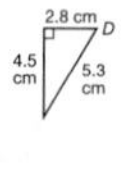

5. $\sin \angle E = \frac{36}{85} \approx 0.424$
   $\cos \angle E = \frac{77}{85} \approx 0.906$
   $\tan \angle E = \frac{36}{77} \approx 0.468$

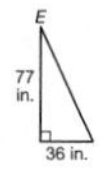

6. $\sin \angle F \approx 0.883$
   $\cos \angle F \approx 0.469$
   $\tan \angle F \approx 1.881$

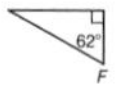

7. $\sin \angle G = \frac{48}{73} \approx 0.658$
   $\cos \angle G = \frac{55}{73} \approx 0.753$
   $\tan \angle G = \frac{48}{55} \approx 0.873$

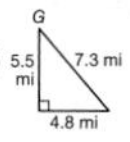

8. $\sin \angle H = \frac{56}{65} \approx 0.862$
   $\cos \angle H = \frac{33}{65} \approx 0.508$
   $\tan \angle H = \frac{56}{33} \approx 1.697$

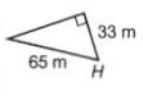

Find the length represented by x.

9. $x \approx 2.463$

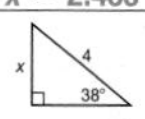

10. $x \approx 19.178$

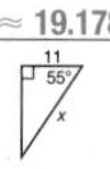

11. The top of the Landmark Tower in Yokohama, Japan, forms a 72° angle with a point $315\frac{1}{2}$ ft away from the tower's base, as shown. How tall is the Landmark Tower?

   About 971 ft

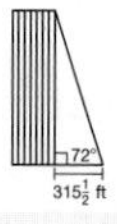

RETEACHING

Name _____

Alternative Lesson 11-4

Trigonometry

The side opposite the right angle in a right triangle is the **hypotenuse**. Think of each of the other two sides, or legs, as being *adjacent* to one of the acute angles and *opposite* the other acute angle.

In △*ABC*, the hypotenuse is $\overline{AC}$.

Side $\overline{AB}$ is the **adjacent leg** to ∠*A*.
Side $\overline{AB}$ is the **opposite leg** to ∠*C*.
Side $\overline{BC}$ is the **adjacent leg** to ∠*C*.
Side $\overline{BC}$ is the **opposite leg** to ∠*A*.

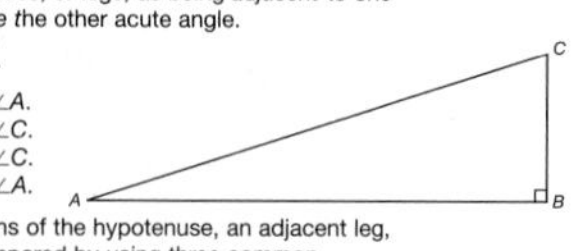

For any right triangles, the lengths of the hypotenuse, an adjacent leg, and an opposite leg may be compared by using three common **trigonometric ratios**.

Sine	Cosine	Tangent
The sine of *x* is	The cosine of *x* is	The tangent of *x* is
$\sin(x) = \frac{\text{opposite}}{\text{hypotenuse}}$	$\cos(x) = \frac{\text{adjacent}}{\text{hypotenuse}}$	$\tan(x) = \frac{\text{opposite}}{\text{adjacent}}$

— Example —

Evaluate the trigonometric ratios for ∠*EDF* in the triangle at the right to the nearest hundredth.

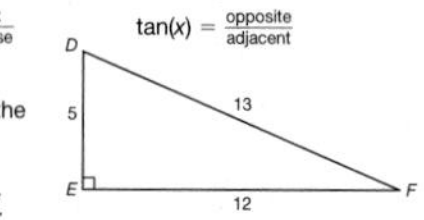

Identify the sides: The hypotenuse is $\overline{DF}$. The opposite leg is $\overline{EF}$. The adjacent leg is $\overline{DE}$.

Find the trigonometric ratios:

$\cos \angle EDF = \frac{\text{adjacent}}{\text{hypotenuse}} = \frac{5}{13} = 0.38$ $\tan \angle EDF = \frac{\text{opposite}}{\text{adjacent}} = \frac{12}{5} = 2.4$

Try It Evaluate the trigonometric ratios for ∠*HFG* in the triangle at the right to the nearest hundredth.

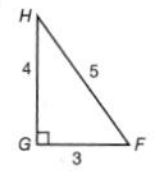

a. Name the hypotenuse. $\overline{HF}$

b. Name the opposite leg to ∠*HFG*. $\overline{GH}$

c. Name the adjacent leg to ∠*HFG*. $\overline{GF}$ d. $\sin \angle HFG = \frac{\text{opposite}}{\text{hypotenuse}}$ **0.80**

e. $\cos \angle HFG = \frac{\text{adjacent}}{\text{hypotenuse}}$ **0.60**   f. $\tan \angle HFG = \frac{\text{opposite}}{\text{adjacent}}$ **1.33**

Evaluate the trigonometric ratios for ∠*XYZ* in the triangle at the right to the nearest hundredth.

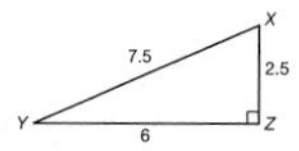

g. Hypotenuse $\overline{XY}$

h. Adjacent leg $\overline{YZ}$ i. Opposite leg $\overline{XZ}$

j. $\sin \angle XYZ =$ **0.33**   k. $\cos \angle XYZ =$ **0.80**   l. $\tan \angle XYZ =$ **0.42**

10. Science A model rocket travels straight up from its launch pad. At a point, there is a 55° angle. Determine the distance between the nose of the rocket and the launch pad. ≈ **142.8 ft**

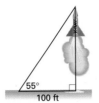
55°
100 ft

Problem Solving and Reasoning

11. Critical Thinking The New River Gorge Bridge in West Virginia has the world's longest single steel span, arching 876 ft above the river. The bridge forms a 30° angle with the side of the gorge. How long is the bridge? ≈ **3035 ft**

30°
876 ft

12. Communicate Suppose two right triangles have a pair of congruent acute angles. Are the triangles similar? Are they congruent? Explain.

13. Geometry Construct a right triangle with a 60° angle. Then measure all three sides. Use your calculator to find the sine, cosine, and tangent of 60°.

14. Choose a Strategy A right triangle has a 15° angle and the adjacent side is 6 ft. A classmate calculates that the length of the opposite leg is 1.6 ft and the hypotenuse is 7 ft. Check your classmate's calculations and make corrections if necessary.

Problem Solving STRATEGIES
- Look for a Pattern
- Make an Organized List
- Make a Table
- Guess and Check
- Work Backward
- Use Logical Reasoning
- Draw a Diagram
- Solve a Simpler Problem

Mixed Review

Write each as a fraction or mixed number in lowest terms. *[Lesson 7-4]*

15. 2.02 $2\frac{1}{50}$ **16.** 0.05 $\frac{1}{20}$ **17.** 4.24 $4\frac{6}{25}$ **18.** 1.33 $1\frac{33}{100}$ **19.** 9.9 $9\frac{9}{10}$

Identify each function as linear, quadratic, exponential, or step. *[Lesson 10-4]*

20. $y = 0.5x^2$ **21.** $y = 0.5^x$ **22.** $y = 5$ **23.** $y = 5x$

Project Progress

Stand the 3 in. by 5 in. card on the 3 in. side. Cut a slit the width of one ruler above the bottom of the card. Fold the longer flap vertically so it makes a right angle. Along the crease of the flap, mark $\frac{1}{2}$ in. lengths. Tape the ruler-width part of the card onto a ruler.

Problem Solving
Understand
Plan
Solve
Look Back

Exercise Notes

■ Exercise 11

History The Romans were the first people to build large-arch bridges. Their arch bridges were an important part of the large road system that connected the cities of the Roman Empire.

■ Exercise 14

Problem-Solving Tip You may wish to use Teaching Tool Transparencies 2 and 3: Guided Problem Solving, pages 1–2.

Project Progress

You may want to have students use Chapter 11 Project Master.

Exercise Answers

12. Similar; Not necessarily congruent; Since two pairs of angles are congruent, all pairs of angles are congruent, but the triangles might be different sizes.

13. sin(60°) ≈ 0.866, cos(60°) = 0.5, tan(60°) ≈ 1.732

14. $1.6^2 + 6.0^2 \neq 7.0^2$; The hypotenuse measures 6.2 ft.

20. Quadratic

21. Exponential

22. Linear

23. Linear

Alternate Assessment

Self Assessment Give students the opportunity to evaluate what they have learned in the lesson. Did they find their introduction to trigonometry difficult? What did they find helpful?

PROBLEM SOLVING

Name _____

Guided Problem Solving 11-4

GPS PROBLEM 10, STUDENT PAGE 583

A model rocket travels straight up from its launch pad. At a point, there is a 55° angle. Determine the distance between the nose of the rocket and the launch pad.

55°
100 ft

— Understand —

1. What kind of triangle is formed by the point, the nose of the rocket, and the launch pad? **Right triangle.**

2. What is the distance from the launch pad to the point? **100 ft**

— Plan —

3. Is the side showing the distance the rocket travels opposite or adjacent to the 55° angle? **Opposite.**

4. Which ratio will you use to find the distance traveled? **c**

   a. $\sin 55° = \frac{opposite}{hypotenuse}$ **b.** $\cos 55° = \frac{adjacent}{hypotenuse}$ **c.** $\tan 55° = \frac{opposite}{adjacent}$

5. Use your calculator or a table to find the decimal value to the nearest thousandth of the ratio you chose in Item 4. **1.428**

— Solve —

6. Substitute known values in the equation you chose in Item 4. $1.428 = \frac{h}{100}$

7. Solve your equation. What is the distance between the nose of the rocket and the launch pad? **142.8 ft**

— Look Back —

8. How could you use another ratio to find the distance between the nose of the rocket and the launch pad? **Subtract the sum of 90° and 55° from 180° to find the measure of the other acute angle. Then use tan 35° to solve.**

SOLVE ANOTHER PROBLEM

A model rocket travels straight up from its launch pad. At a point, there is a 50° angle. Determine the distance between the nose of the rocket and the launch pad.

238.4 ft

50°
200 ft

ENRICHMENT

Name _____

Extend Your Thinking 11-4

Decision Making

Arturo and Tasha are forming a band. Arturo plays the drums and Tasha plays the keyboards. They would prefer to concentrate on composing and playing their instruments rather than on singing.

Possible answers: Items 1–5

1. How many other band members will they need if they want to perform at student dances? What will be the other members' responsibilities?
   Three members for lead guitar, bass, and as a lead singer.
   They may also want a manager to book performances, keep
   track of equipment, and money.

2. How can Tasha and Arturo find the other members to form the band?
   Advertise in a local paper; talk to their friends; get referrals
   from other bands.

3. How can they fund the band until they start making a profit?
   Each member can maintain their own equipment. They could
   all contribute an equal amount to pay for transporting
   equipment and promoting the band.

4. How should they divide any profits from performances?
   Divide seven equal ways—each member gets a share and
   one share is for future band expenses.

5. After considering the financial aspects, would you still advise Arturo and Tasha to have the same number of members in the band as you did in Question 1? Explain.
   Yes, they need all instruments to be competitive. They could
   find a singer who also plays an instrument or act as own
   manager, but savings would not be that great.

▶ Quick Quiz

Identify the following for ∠A.

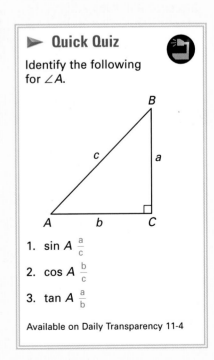

1. sin A $\frac{a}{c}$

2. cos A $\frac{b}{c}$

3. tan A $\frac{a}{b}$

Available on Daily Transparency 11-4

Lesson 11-4 **583**

- **Apply your knowledge of geometry and trigonometric ratios.**

- **Explore: Dynamic geometry software**

- **1–5, 9, 12**

> **Review**

Find the value of *n* in each of the proportions.

1. $\frac{4}{5} = \frac{8}{n}$ 10

2. $\frac{2}{3} = \frac{18}{n}$ 27

3. $\frac{11}{20} = \frac{n}{8.5}$ 4.675

4. $\frac{21}{24} = \frac{n}{11}$ 9.625

Available on Daily Transparency 11-5

---

1 Introduce

Explore

You may wish to use Teaching Tool Transparency 22: Scientific Calculator with **Explore**.

The Point
Students use geometry software to draw two parallel lines and two transversals that are perpendicular to each other. Then they calculate all of the measurements they can.

Ongoing Assessment
In Step 1, check to see that all students are able to create the initial drawing properly.

For Groups That Finish Early
Draw another transversal to the two parallel lines. Calculate all angle measurements associated with the new line.

Follow Up
Have the students discuss Step 8. Then ask if any of the groups were able to find all six side measurements and all twenty angle measures.

11-5 Indirect Measurement

You'll Learn ...

■ to apply your knowledge of geometry and trigonometric ratios

... How It's Used

Paleontologists use indirect measurement to figure out what the size of a living dinosaur was based on bone measurements.

▶ **Lesson Link** You've seen how to find the side lengths of right triangles using trigonometric ratios. Now you'll apply these ratios to real-world situations. ◀

Explore | **Indirect Measurement**

It's Not What You Know, It's Where You Know It

Materials: Dynamic geometry software, $8\frac{1}{2}$ in. by 11 in. paper

1. Draw two parallel lines. Draw two transversals that are perpendicular to each other.

2. Label all intersection points.

3. On paper, make a table with three columns. Label the columns "part," "measurement," and "reason."

4. In the first column of your table, list all sides and all angles of both triangles that appear in your drawing.

5. Measure all angles and all side lengths of these two triangles. Enter the results in the second column of your table.

6. Find as many other side and angle measurements as you can and enter them in your table's second column. For each measurement, use the third column of your table to briefly state how you got the measurement.

7. Discuss the results with your group. How many angle measurements could you find? How many side measurements?

8. What was listed most frequently in the third column of your table?

Learn | **Indirect Measurement**

Sometimes a length can't be measured with a ruler. Often you can find the measurement indirectly.

When solving a problem with similar triangles, you can use the similarity ratio.

584 Chapter 11 • Similarity, Congruence, and Transformations

▶ | **MEETING INDIVIDUAL NEEDS**

Resources
11-5 Practice
11-5 Reteaching
11-5 Problem Solving
11-5 Enrichment
11-5 Daily Transparency
Problem of the Day
Review
Quick Quiz
Teaching Tool Transparency 22
Lesson Enhancement Transparency 61
Interactive CD-ROM Geometry Tool

Learning Modalities

Logical In **Explore**, students use geometry software to draw two parallel lines and two transversals that are perpendicular to each other. Then they calculate all of the measurements they can.

Visual As students do the exercises they might find it helpful to color code the triangles to emphasize corresponding parts of the trigonometric ratios.

Individual Several exercises in the lesson provide opportunities for students to reflect on the lesson concepts in order to write an explanation.

Challenge

See how many triangles you can count in the large square. Look carefully at each square, counting the triangles, then add them together. There are 12 triangles in all.

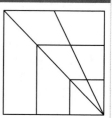

Example 1

Part of a bridge roadway is 150 m long. On its scale model, the corresponding length is 2 m. On the same model, a cable from the roadway to the top of a tower is almost 2.17 m. How long is the actual cable?

The triangles on the bridge and model are similar.

$\frac{150}{2} = 75$ Use a ratio to find the scale factor.

$75 \cdot 2.17 = 162.75$ m

The cable is almost 163 m long.

Example 2

Megan, who is 5 ft tall, stands in the shadow of a redwood tree. Megan is 388 ft from the tree and her shadow is 7 ft long. If the tip of Megan's shadow and the tree's shadow are at the same point on the ground, how tall is the tree?

The diagram shows the similar triangles.

$7 + 388 = 395$ ft   Find the length of the tree's shadow.

$\frac{x}{395} = \frac{5}{7}$ Set up a proportion and solve.

$x \approx 282$

The tree is approximately 282 ft tall.

Try It

Find the length of the base of the larger triangle. The triangles are similar. **7 cm**

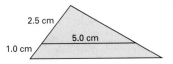

▶ **Literature Link**

Author John Steinbeck referred to redwood trees as "ambassadors from another time."

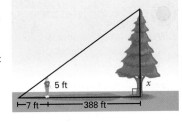

11-5 • Indirect Measurement **585**

▶ Problem of the Day

Brenda purchased six party hats for her little sister's birthday party. Each hat was a different color. She put one hat at each place at the table. In how many different ways could she arrange the hats?
720 ways

Available on Daily Transparency 11-5

An Extension is provided in the transparency package.

Fact of the Day

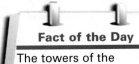

The towers of the Verrazzano-Narrows Bridge across New York Harbor are so far apart, 4260 feet, that the Earth's curvature was considered in their construction.

Mental Math

Do these mentally.

1. 50% of 650 325

2. 5% of 200 10

3. 15% of 800 120

Answers for Explore

1–6, 8. See students' work.

7. Answers may vary. You can get all six side measurements and all twenty angle measurements.

2 Teach

Learn

You may wish to use Lesson Enhancement Transparency 61 with Example 2.

Alternate Examples

1. Marc is making a model of his sailboat. Dimensions of the actual sail and the scale model are shown. How long is the vertical side on the actual sail?

   Similar triangles are formed by the actual sail and model.

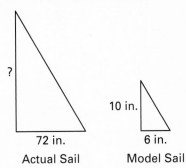

   Actual Sail   Model Sail

   $\frac{72}{6} = 12$ Use a ratio to find the scale factor.

   $12 \cdot 10 = 120$ in.

   The vertical side on the actual sail is 120 in., or 10 ft.

2. Peter, who is $4\frac{1}{2}$ ft tall, stands in the shadow of a flagpole. Peter is 10 ft from the flagpole and his shadow is 6 ft long. If the tip of Peter's shadow and the flagpole's shadow are at the same point on the ground, how tall is the flagpole?

   The diagram shows the similar triangles.

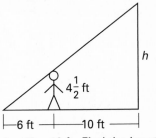

   $6 + 10 = 16$ ft Find the length of the flagpole's shadow.

   $\frac{4.5}{6} = \frac{h}{16}$ Set up a proportion and solve.

   $h = 12$

   The flagpole is 12 ft tall.

Lesson 11-5   **585**

Alternate Examples

3. $\triangle ABC \sim \triangle EDC$. Find the length of $\overline{EC}$.

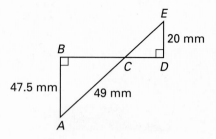

Identify the corresponding sides.
$\overline{AB}$ corresponds to $\overline{ED}$.
$\overline{AC}$ corresponds to $\overline{EC}$.

$\frac{x}{49} = \frac{20}{47.5}$ Set up a proportion and solve.

$x = 20.63$

The length of $\overline{EC}$ is 20.63 mm.

4. A bird-watcher sees a bird's nest up in a tree 30° above horizontal. The person is 1000 feet from the tree. How far is the bird's nest from the person?

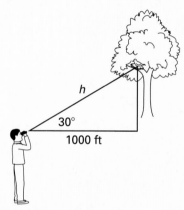

The person's line of vision forms a hypotenuse.
The adjacent side of the 30° angle is 1000 ft.

$\cos 30° = \frac{1000}{h}$ Use the cosine to set up a proportion.

$0.866 \approx \frac{1000}{h}$ Use a calculator to find cos 30°.

$0.866 \cdot h \approx 1000$ Solve.

$h \approx 1154.7$

The distance is about 1155 ft.

DID YOU KNOW?

When you talk about similar or congruent figures, list the points in corresponding order. For example, you should say "$\triangle TSR \sim \triangle TUV$" and not "$\triangle TSR \sim \triangle TVU$."

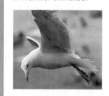

Example 3

$\triangle TSR \sim \triangle TUV$. Find the length of $\overline{RT}$.

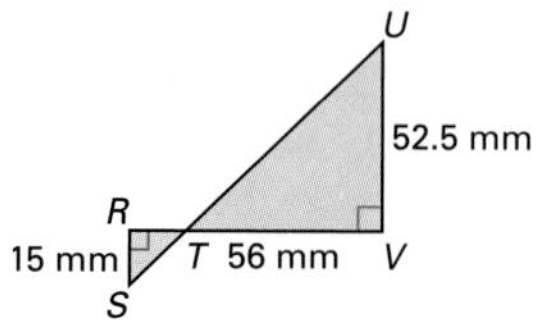

Identify the corresponding sides.

$\overline{UV}$ corresponds to $\overline{SR}$.

$\overline{VT}$ corresponds to $\overline{RT}$.

$\frac{x}{56} = \frac{15}{52.5}$ Set up a proportion and solve.

$x = 16$

The length of $\overline{RT}$ is 16 mm.

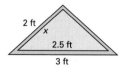

Try It

In the figure, the triangles are similar.

Find x. $\frac{5}{3}$ ft

When you solve a problem with right triangles, you can use trigonometric ratios.

▶ Science Link

Adult gulls usually have gray plumage above and white below. Gulls are whiter in colder climates and browner in warmer climates.

Example 4

A person on a boat sees a seagull perched on a bridge 22° above the horizon. The boat is 800 ft from the bridge. How far is the seagull from the passenger?

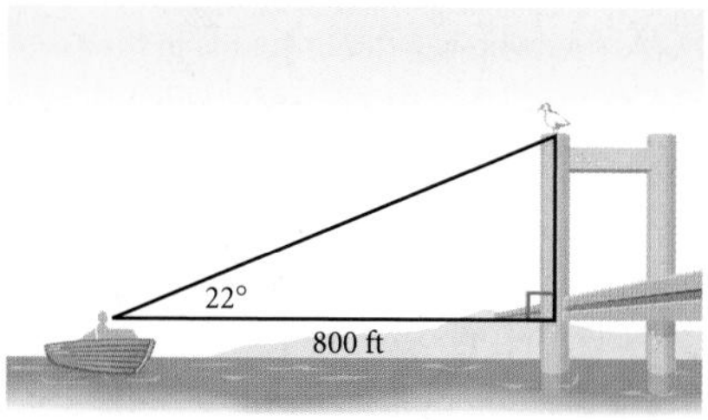

The passenger's line of vision forms a hypotenuse.

The adjacent side is 800 ft with respect to the 22° angle.

$\cos 22° = \frac{800}{h}$ Use the cosine to set up a proportion.

$0.927 \approx \frac{800}{h}$ Use a calculator to find cos 22°.

$0.927 \cdot h \approx 800$ Solve.

$h \approx 863$

The distance is about 863 ft.

MEETING MIDDLE SCHOOL CLASSROOM NEEDS

History Connection

Suspension bridges made from ropes and planks have been used since the Stone Age, but rope is not strong enough and does not last long enough to build long suspension bridges—that had to wait until iron became available. The first successful long suspension bridge was built in 1826 in Wales. The Menai Strait Bridge was 580 feet long, with its roadway suspended on chains made of iron bars bolted together.

Team Teaching

Make sure that the science teacher on your team is aware that students are familiar with indirect measurement and trigonometric ratios. The science teacher may encourage students to put their knowledge to use when doing real-life measurement.

Cooperative Learning

Have students work in small groups and choose some distance that is impractical to measure directly. The group should develop a plan for measuring the distance indirectly. Have them collect the necessary data, construct a diagram to represent the situation, and solve the problem. Some distances that could be calculated are heights of tall buildings, distances across bodies of water, and so on.

Find the height of the larger triangle.

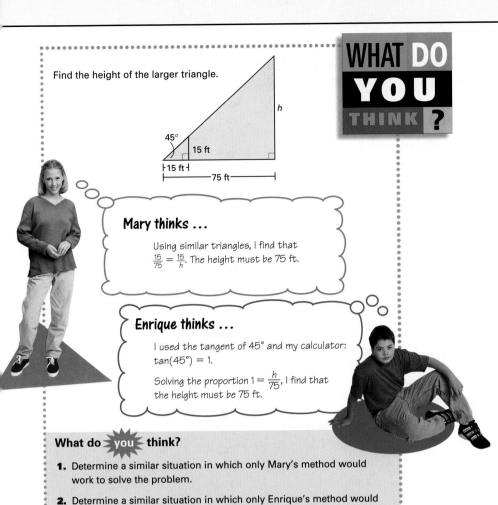

Mary thinks ...

Using similar triangles, I find that $\frac{15}{75} = \frac{15}{h}$. The height must be 75 ft.

Enrique thinks ...

I used the tangent of 45° and my calculator: $\tan(45°) = 1$.

Solving the proportion $1 = \frac{h}{75}$, I find that the height must be 75 ft.

What do think?

1. Determine a similar situation in which only Mary's method would work to solve the problem.

2. Determine a similar situation in which only Enrique's method would work to solve the problem.

3. Is there another way to find the answer? Explain.

Check | Your Understanding

1. Suppose a real-world problem requires the height of some object that can't be measured directly. Which method is easier to use, similarity ratios or trigonometry? Explain.

2. What do we mean by indirect measurement?

Students are presented with two correct methods for finding the length of one side of a triangle. One method uses a proportion based on similar triangles, the other method uses the tangent ratio. Students can decide which method they prefer.

Answers for What Do You Think?

1. If the 45° measurement was not given.

2. If one or both of the 15 ft measurements were not given.

3. Possible answer: The large triangle is an isosceles right triangle, so the height and the base are the same.

3 Practice and Assess

Check

For Question 2, you might have students first explain what we mean by direct measurement.

Answers for Check Your Understanding

1–2. Answers may vary.

11-5 Exercises and Applications

Practice and Apply

1. **Getting Started** Find the length of $\overline{EG}$.

a. Determine the length of $\overline{GF}$. **16 cm**

b. Set up and solve a proportion using the given lengths of the similar triangles.
$mEG = 14.4$ cm

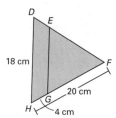

2. Find the length of side $\overline{BC}$.
$\approx$ **12.87 cm**

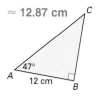

3. Find the length of side $\overline{UV}$. $\approx$ **11.58 in.**

4. Find the length of side $\overline{LM}$. $\approx$ **18.67 yd**

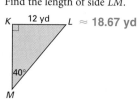

5. **Test Prep** On the two triangles shown, $\triangle CBD \sim \triangle CAE$. If $\overline{CD}$
GPS measures 5 cm, what does $\overline{CE}$ measure? **D**

Ⓐ 7.6 cm   Ⓑ 7.3 cm   Ⓒ 7.1 cm   Ⓓ 7.9 cm

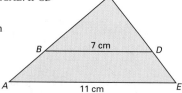

6. **Marine Navigation** A ship near shore measures the compass heading to a lighthouse as 50° east of north. It also measures the compass heading to an oil refinery as 90° east of north. The refinery is known to be 4 mi directly south of the lighthouse. How far is the ship from the lighthouse? From the refinery? (Start by applying your knowledge of parallel lines and alternate interior angles.)

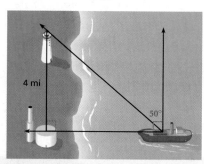

PRACTICE

Name _____

Practice 11-5

Indirect Measurement

1. Find the length of side $\overline{YZ}$.

$\approx$ **3.30 cm**

2. The two triangles are similar. If $\overline{UW}$ measures 6.3 m, find $m\overline{UV}$.

4.05 m

3. **Fine Arts** Giorgione's 1508 painting, *The Tempest*, is about 82 cm tall. A 16-cm-tall reproduction of this painting in a book features a bridge that is about 5.3 cm long. How long is the bridge on the actual painting?

About 27.2 cm

4. Eve is 55 in. tall. Find the length of her shadow if the sun makes an angle of 38° as shown.

About 70.4 in.

5. Larry wants to know the distance between two trees, A and B, on the opposite side of a river. He knows the river is 25 m wide. He marks off and measures a right triangle as shown. The two triangles are similar. How far apart are the trees?

40 m

6. **Geography** Santa Fe, New Mexico, is about 480 mi from Fort Worth, Texas. Find the distance from Fort Worth to Oklahoma City, Oklahoma, if the three cities form a right triangle as shown.

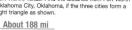

About 188 mi

7. Harold is 4 ft tall. When he stands 9 ft away from the base of a streetlight, his shadow is 3 ft long. How tall is the streetlight? (Start by finding the length of the base of the larger triangle.)

16 ft

RETEACHING

Name _____

Alternative Lesson 11-5

Indirect Measurement

Sometimes you are not able to measure the length of a side of a triangle. However, if you know that the triangle is similar to another triangle which can be measured, then you can find the unknown length using the similarity ratio.

— Example —

$\triangle ABC \sim \triangle FGC$. Find the length of $\overline{FG}$.

Find the corresponding sides.
$\overline{AB}$ corresponds to $\overline{FG}$. $\overline{BC}$ corresponds to $\overline{GC}$.

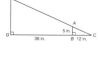

Find the length of each side. $\overline{AB} = 5$ in.
$\overline{BC} = 12$ in. $\overline{GC} = 36 + 12 = 48$, or 48 in.

Write and solve a proportion.
Let $x = \overline{FG}$.
$\frac{x}{5} = \frac{48}{12}$
$x = 20$

The length of $\overline{FG}$ is 20 in.

Try It $\triangle JKL \sim \triangle NML$. Find the length of $\overline{JK}$.

a. Which side corresponds to $\overline{JK}$? ___ $\overline{NM}$

b. What is another pair of corresponding sides whose side lengths are given?
___ $\overline{LM}, \overline{LK}$

c. What are the given lengths? ___ $\overline{NM} = 8$ m, $\overline{LM} = 20$ m, $\overline{LK} = 90$ m

d. Write and solve a proportion. $\frac{x}{8} = \frac{90}{20}$; $x = 36$

e. What is the length of $\overline{JK}$? ___ 36 m

$\triangle PQR \sim \triangle WXY$. Find the length of $\overline{PR}$.

f. Which side corresponds to $\overline{PR}$? ___ $\overline{WY}$

g. What is another pair of corresponding sides whose side lengths are given?
___ $\overline{QR}, \overline{XY}$

h. What are the given lengths? ___ $\overline{WY} = 26$ ft, $\overline{XY} = 25$ ft, $\overline{QR} = 50$ ft

i. Write and solve a proportion. $\frac{x}{26} = \frac{50}{25}$; $x = 52$

j. What is the length of $\overline{PR}$? ___ 52 ft

Problem Solving and Reasoning

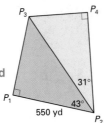
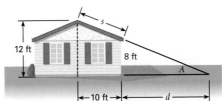

7. **Algebra** A surveying team plots two points, P_1 and P_2, 550 yd apart. It then plots two more points, P_3 and P_4, and measures four angles, as shown. How far apart are P_3 and P_4? **≈ 387.32 yd**

8. **Patterns** The points $A(1, 1)$; $B(4, 1)$; and $C(4, 5)$ form a triangle when connected. Compare the slope of $\overline{AC}$ to the tangent of $\angle CAB$.

Communicate Use the diagram of the house to answer these questions.

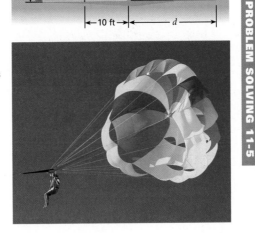

9. Suppose you know that $\angle A$ measures 22°. How can you find s?

10. Suppose instead of $m\angle A$, you know that $d = 20$ ft. Explain how you could find s.

11. How many similar triangles are identified? Describe where they are.

12. **Estimation** The rope between a parasailer and the boat is 600 ft long and forms a 30° angle with the water. About how far above the water is the parasailer? **300 ft**

13. **Number Sense** Suppose you use a trigonometric ratio to find a length measurement on a bridge. Why will your measurement be only an approximation?

14. **Math Reasoning** Draw a right triangle with a 45° angle. Find the cos 45° and sin 45° and use your drawing to explain their relationship.

Mixed Review

Add or subtract. Write each answer in lowest terms. *[Lesson 7-5]*

15. $0.219 - 0.043$
    0.176
16. $128.6 + 204.7$
    333.3
17. $\frac{5}{8} - \frac{3}{16}$ $\frac{7}{16}$
18. $3\frac{7}{8} + 4\frac{6}{8}$ $8\frac{5}{8}$

Write each polynomial expression in descending order and find its degree.
[Lesson 10-5]

19. $2x + 5 - 3x^2$
    $-3x^2 + 2x + 5; 2$
20. $x^4 + 4x - 2x^2$
    $x^4 - 2x^2 + 4x; 4$
21. $3x - x^2 - x^3 - 3$
    $-x^3 - x^2 + 3x - 3; 3$
22. $x^5 + x^{10}$
    $x^{10} + x^5; 10$

---

8. They are equal.

9. Possible answer: Since $\angle A$ is congruent to the corresponding angle of the triangle for which s is the hypotenuse and 10 ft is the length of the adjacent side of that angle, solve the equation $\frac{10}{s} = \cos(22°)$.

10. Possible answer: Use similar triangles and solve $\frac{20}{20 + 10} = \frac{\sqrt{8^2 + 20^2}}{s + \sqrt{8^2 + 20^2}}$.

11. 4; Two in the roof, each with hypotenuse s long. Third has a leg length of $d + 10$. Fourth has legs 8 ft and d.

13. Because most trigonometric ratios are irrational numbers, results from using them are approximate rather than exact.

14. Illustration should have two 45° angles and one 90° angle. cos 45° ≈ 0.71 and sine 45° ≈ 0.71. The sin and cos are equal because the leg lengths are equal.

Alternate Assessment

You may want to use the *Interactive CD-ROM Journal* with this assessment.

Journal Have the students look back at **What Do You Think?** on page 587 and write about which of the two methods they prefer and why.

▶ Quick Quiz

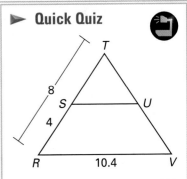

1. Determine the length of $\overline{ST}$.
   4

2. Find the length of $\overline{SU}$. 5.2

Available on Daily Transparency 11-5

▶ PROBLEM SOLVING

Name _____

| Guided Problem Solving 11-5 |

GPS PROBLEM 5, STUDENT PAGE 588

On the two triangles shown, $\triangle CBD \sim \triangle CAE$. If $\overline{CD}$ measures 5 cm, what does $\overline{CE}$ measure?

(A) 7.6 cm   (B) 7.3 cm
(C) 7.1 cm   (D) 7.9 cm

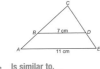

— Understand —
1. What does the symbol ~ mean? **Is similar to.**
2. What is the length of $\overline{CD}$? **5 cm**
3. What are you asked to find? **Length of $\overline{CE}$.**

— Plan —
4. Identify the corresponding side to each side below.
   a. $\overline{AE}$ **$\overline{BD}$**   b. $\overline{CE}$ **$\overline{CD}$**
5. Write a ratio for the corresponding sides. **$\frac{11}{7}$**
6. Set up a proportion using the given values for the lengths of the sides. Let x represent the unknown side. **$\frac{x}{5} = \frac{11}{7}$**

— Solve —
7. Solve the proportion. **$x = 7.857$**
8. Which answer choice is the correct one? **Choice D.**

— Look Back —
9. Why aren't the correct answer choice and your answer to Item 7 the same?
   Answer choice is rounded to the nearest tenth.

| SOLVE ANOTHER PROBLEM |

On the two triangles shown, $\triangle ABC \sim \triangle ADE$. If $\overline{AC}$ measures 4 m, what does $\overline{AE}$ measure?

7.2 m

▶ ENRICHMENT

Name _____

| Extend Your Thinking 11-5 |

Critical Thinking

For any two points on a coordinate plane, there are three possibilities for the line segment connecting these points.

The segment is parallel to the y-axis.
The segment is parallel to the x-axis.
The segment is not parallel to either axis, and there is another point that forms a right angle with the two points.

If $A(x_1, y_1)$ and $B(x_2, y_2)$ form a line segment that is not parallel to either axis, then there is a point $C(x_2, y_1)$ that forms the right triangle $\triangle ABC$. Using the Pythagorean theorem, you can find the length of the hypotenuse of $\triangle ABC$.

The subscripts (dropped numerals) are used to identify the point. It identifies the coordinate so that you can readily tell which point the x- and y-coordinates refer to.

$(AB)^2 = (AC)^2 + (BC)^2$
$(AB)^2 = (x_2 - x_1)^2 + (y_2 - y_1)^2$
$AB = \sqrt{(x_2 - x_1)^2 + (y_2 - y_1)^2}$

This is the **distance formula** on a plane. You can use this formula to find the distance between two points on a coordinate plane.

Find the length of the line segment with the given endpoints. Round your answer to the nearest hundredth if necessary.

1. $A(4, -2)$ and $B(4, 7)$ **9 units.**
2. $A(-1, -3)$ and $B(2, 0)$ **4.24 units.**
3. $A(1, 2)$ and $B(4, 6)$ **5 units.**
4. $A(0, 3)$ and $B(4, 1)$ **4.47 units.**
5. $A(-2, -2)$ and $B(6, -8)$ **10 units.**
6. On the coordinate plane, draw a right triangle $\triangle ABC$ so that the segment AB is not parallel to either axis and $\angle ACB$ is the right angle. Find the length of $\overline{AB}$.
   Possible answer: 5 units.

Technology

Using a Search Engine • Searching the World Wide Web

The Point
Students use a search engine to find information using the World Wide Web.

Materials
Access to the World Wide Web

About the Page

- It may be helpful to write the method of restricting a search ("music NOT opera" versus "music - opera") on the board.

- Make sure students are comfortable with selecting key words when using a search engine. You may want to lead students in selecting key words for two or three hypothetical searches.

Ask ...
- Why would you want to use a search engine instead of just looking randomly through the World Wide Web? A search engine will save much time when searching for a subject as well as find more information.

- Why do you think search engines use words such as *or*, *and*, or *not* in searches? These words allow you to restrict your search to information you can really use.

Answers for Try It
a. Possible answer: boats NOT sails.

b. Possible answer: mammals NOT whales.

Answers for On Your Own
- *Not* eliminates search results that are not relevant. Eliminating things is like subtracting, so the number decreases.

- Answers may vary.

TECHNOLOGY

Using a Search Engine • Searching the World Wide Web

Problem: Search for documents related to music, then search for documents about music and not opera. What is the difference between the number of documents found in each search?

Search engines have different ways to search. For example, typing "music NOT opera" or "music–opera" are just two possible ways to search for music except for opera. Learn how your favorite search engine works so you can answer the question.

1 After you've learned what you need to know about a search engine, search for music. Record the number of matching documents found.

Search! found **1362470** documents about: **music**.
Documents **1–10** sorted by **confidence**

65% **Music**   Sort by Site

2 Search for music except for opera using the appropriate keystrokes. Record the number of matching documents.

Search! found **1277440** documents about: **music NOT opera**.
Documents **1–10** sorted by **confidence**

57% **Music NOT Opera**   Sort by Site

Solution: The music except for opera search had 85,030 less documents than the music search.

TRY IT

a. What would you type if you're looking for information about boats that don't have sails?

b. If you wanted information about all mammals except for whales, what would you type in your search?

ON YOUR OWN

▶ Describe how *not* affects a search. Why does the number of matching documents decrease?

▶ Search engines usually use commands that act like the words *or*, *and*, and *not*. Give three examples of a search each using one of these words.

590

590

Section 11A Connect

At the beginning of Section 11A, you saw that geometry is used in the design and construction of bridges. Now you'll construct a model of your own bridge design using what you know about geometry.

Un-a-bridged

Materials: Toothpicks, Scissors, Tape, Ruler

Before bridges are built in the real world, scale models are made using proportions. You can build a model bridge out of toothpicks.

Your group is a team of people hired to design and build a bridge.

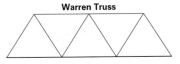
Warren Truss

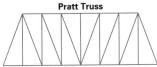
Pratt Truss

1. Decide on a bridge design that includes congruent and similar triangles. Choose from the two designs shown, or make your own.

2. Determine the toothpick measurements for the model bridge. Use your ruler, scissors, and tape to construct the necessary lengths.

3. When you are finished constructing your model bridge, count the pairs of similar triangles. How many pairs can you find? How do you know that these are similar pairs? Do the same for congruent triangles.

4. How many pairs of congruent triangles can you find? How do you know that they are congruent?

5. How many right triangles are used in your bridge? Are they all congruent to each other? How do you know?

6. Push gently on your bridge. Can it support a load? Would the result have been different if you had based your bridge on parallelograms instead of triangles? Explain.

7. Is there a place on your bridge where both sides are mirror images of each other? If so, where is it and what would your bridge be like without this feature?

591

Un-a-bridged

The Point
In *Un-a-bridged* on page 563, students were introduced to the use of congruent triangles, similar triangles, and symmetry in bridges. Now they apply these concepts to building a model bridge out of toothpicks.

Materials
Toothpicks, scissors, tape, ruler

About the Page
- Make sure students understand that they are not limited to the two bridge designs shown.

- Guide students to notice that in the Pratt Truss design several successive sloping cross members are parallel, while in the Warren Truss design the slopes of successive cross members are alternately positive and negative.

- Point out to students that they should draw a plan for the bridge before they start constructing it.

Ongoing Assessment
Check students' drawings and monitor their progress in building the bridge. At each stage ensure that students are using symmetry and congruent and similar triangles.

Extension
The class might want to hold a competition to see whose bridge can support the most weight. Each bridge, in turn, should be supported at its ends by, perhaps, placing it on two tables or chairs. A string should be tied to the center of the bridge, and a container such as a small paper bag or cardboard box should be tied to the other end. Weights of some kind (coins or small rocks or marbles) should gradually be added to the container. A recorder should keep track of the total weight required to collapse each bridge.

Answers for Connect
1–2. Check students' work.

3–7. Answers may vary.

Review Correlation

Item(s)	Lesson(s)
1	11-1
2	11-2
3–5	11-3
6	11-4
7, 8	11-5

Test Prep

Test-Taking Tip

Tell students that if they are taking a multiple-choice test, they should make sure they understand what type it is. Is there only one correct choice for each item, or may there be more than one?

Answers for Review

6. Possible answer: Subtract the sum of the two known angles from 180° to obtain the third angle measure.

REVIEW 11A

Section 11A Review

1. The trapezoids are similar. Find the length represented by x. **6 in.**

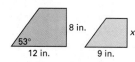

8 in.

53°
12 in.   9 in.   x

2. Measure to determine if the two pentagons are congruent. **Yes**

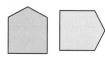

State whether each pair is congruent and the rule that justifies your answer.

3. 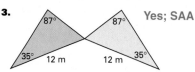 **Yes; SAA**

87°   87°
35° 12 m   12 m 35°

4. **No**

51° 51°
7.5 cm   7.5 cm

5. A lens casts a 3 in. image of a tree onto a sheet of paper. The image is 5 in. from the lens, and the lens is 10 ft from the tree. Find the object's size. **6 ft**

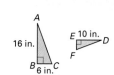

10 ft   3 in.
5 in.

6. **Journal** Suppose you're given the hypotenuse length of a right triangle and the measure of one of the acute angles. How would you use this information to prove congruence to another triangle by the Angle-Side-Angle method?

7. A tornado watcher spots the top of a funnel cloud 14° above the horizon as the funnel crosses a lake 2.5 mi away. How high is the top of the funnel to the nearest 10 ft? **3290 ft**

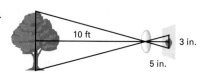

Test Prep

On a multiple choice test, be careful not to confuse similar figures and congruent figures. Also, when finding a missing part of similar triangles, check to make sure the proportion is set up correctly.

8. △ABC ~ △DEF. What is the length of $\overline{EF}$? **A**
   Ⓐ 3.75 in.   Ⓑ 1 in.
   Ⓒ 4.4 in.   Ⓓ 5.4 in.

A
16 in.   E 10 in. D
F
B 6 in. C

592 *Chapter 11 • Similarity, Congruence, and Transformations*

Resources

Practice Masters
   Section 11A Review

Assessment Sourcebook
   Quiz 11A

 TestWorks
   Test and Practice Software

PRACTICE

Name _____

Practice

Section 11A Review

1. The pentagons are similar. Find the length represented by x.   **20 cm**

24 cm   x   18 cm   15 cm

2. Measure to determine if the two quadrilaterals are congruent.   **Congruent**

State whether each pair of triangles has congruence; if it does, give the rule that justifies your answer.

3. **No**

3.2 cm
35° 80°   80°   35°
3.2 cm

4. **Yes; Side-Angle-Side**

32 ft
32 ft   56°   56°   27 ft
56°
27 ft

5. A small table is supported by diagonal legs as shown. If △ABC ~ △EDC, find the width $m\overline{AB}$ of the table.   **14.4 in.**

A   B
18 in.
C
15 in.
D 12 in. E

6. Kelly is flying a kite. If the kite string is 24 m long and makes an angle of 55° with the ground, how high is the kite?   **About 19.66 m**

7. A cone-shaped container for a crushed ice drink is 5 in. tall and has a $3\frac{1}{2}$-in. diameter. How many cubic inches of crushed ice can the container hold? *[Lesson 9-5]*   **About 16.0 in³**

8. A ball is thrown upwards at a speed of 96 ft/sec. Its height, in feet, after t seconds is given by $h = 96t - 16t^2$. *[Lesson 10-3]*

   a. Graph the function $h = 96t - 16t^2$.

   b. Estimate when the ball has height 108 ft.
   At t = 1.5 sec and t = 4.5 sec

   c. When does the ball hit the ground?
   At t = 6 sec

Visit **www.teacher.mathsurf.com** for links to lesson plans from teachers and other professionals, NCTM information, and other sites.

LESSON PLANNING GUIDE

► **Student Edition**　　　　　► **Ancillaries**

LESSON	MATERIALS	VOCABULARY	DAILY	OTHER
Section 11B Opener				
11-6 Transformations and Congruence	Dynamic geometry software	transformation, reflection, rotation, center of rotation, angle of rotation, translation	11-6	Teaching Tool Trans. 8, 16 Lesson Enhancement Transparencies 62–67 Technology Masters 62, 63 *CD-ROM Geometry Tool* *WW Math*—Geometry
11-7 Transformations and Similarity	graph paper, ruler		11-7	Teaching Tool Trans. 7, 8, 15 Technology Master 64 Ch. 11 Project Master
11-8 Symmetry	8-1/2 in. by 11 in. paper, protractor, scissors	symmetry, line symmetry, line of symmetry, rotational symmetry, point symmetry	11-8	Teaching Tool Trans. 2, 3, 16
11-9 Covering the Plane	graph paper, power polygons	tessellation	11-9	Teaching Tool Trans. 7, 18, 19 *WW Math*—Geometry
Connect				Interdisc. Team Teaching 11B
Review				Practice 11B; Quiz 11B; *TestWorks*
Chapter 11 Summary and Review				
Chapter 11 Assessment				Ch. 11 Tests Forms A–F *TestWorks;* Ch. 11 Letter Home
Cumulative Review, Chapters 1–11				Cumulative Review Ch. 1–11

SKILLS TRACE

LESSON	SKILL	FIRST INTRODUCED			DEVELOP	PRACTICE/ APPLY	REVIEW
		GR. 6	GR. 7	GR. 8			
11-6	Transforming figures.	✗			pp. 594–597	pp. 598–599	pp. 616, 619, 667
11-7	Dilating figures.		✗		pp. 600–602	pp. 603–604	pp. 616, 619, 620
11-8	Identifying line, point, and rotational symmetries.		✗		pp. 605–607	pp. 608–609	pp. 616, 619, 675
11-9	Tessellating the plane.	✗			pp. 610–612	pp. 613–614	pp. 619, 620

CONNECTED MATHEMATICS

The unit *Kaleisocopes, Hubcaps, and Mirrors (Symmetry and Transformations),* from the **Connected Mathematics** series, can be used with Section 11B.

Math and Art

(Worksheet pages 45–46: Teacher pages T45–T46)

In this lesson, students use knowledge of polygons and tessellations to explore patterns in art.

Name _____   *Math and Art*

Patterns · in · Native · American · Art

Use knowledge of polygons and tessellations to explore patterns in art.

When Europeans and Africans first came to North America centuries ago, they found a continent populated by hundreds of tribes of Native Americans, each with its own unique culture. The method of making everyday objects like clothing, blankets, pottery, and jewelry varied from tribe to tribe.

The Navajo are a desert tribe in the U.S. Southwest. They are known as master weavers. According to legend, the Navajo were taught to weave in ancient times by Spider Woman, who used a loom made of sun rays and lightning bolts. Actually, the Navajo learned weaving from their Pueblo neighbors sometime during the second half of the seventeenth century.

In the Pueblo tribe most weavers were men, but most Navajo weavers were women. Women owned the sheep herds, sheared the sheep, and dyed the wool needed to weave cloth. Before the mid-1800s, Navajo women used undyed wool to create cloth with gray, brown, and white stripes. Later, some weavers created pale colors for their blankets with dyes made from sagebrush, juniper berries, or indigo. Eventually, weavers used brighter colors such as red, which they got by unraveling colored cloth they received in trades with Europeans.

Navajo weaving is known for its use of geometric patterns, which have become bolder over time. Weavers create patterns using stripes, zigzag bands, and interlocking diamonds.

The Navajo used their weaving to create everyday items for their own use, such as blankets.

quality of Navajo weaving, the objects began to be in demand outside the tribe. Today, Navajo woven objects are prized as works of art.

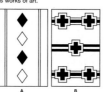

A   B

Use the illustrations of Navajo blanket patterns above to help you answer the questions below.

1. What might influence the blanket weaver's choice of pattern?

   Answers will vary. Because this is an opinion, accept all reasonable answers. They might include natural colors and objects around the weaver, religious and other cultural symbols, or patterns on other objects with which the weaver is familiar.

Name _____   *Math and Art*

2. Look at the diamond pattern in "A". What type of transformation has created it? Explain.

   A translation. All of the diamonds are congruent. The top figure has been repeated by sliding it farther and farther down.

3. a. Examine the pattern in "B" above. If the cross-like figures were rotated 45° about their center, would the pattern stay the same? Explain.

   No. A 45° rotation would turn the crosses slightly so their edges would no longer be parallel to the edges of the blanket.

   b. How about if they were rotated 90°?

   Yes. A 90° rotation would not change the pattern.

4. Are either of the Navajo blanket patterns tessellations? Explain your answer.

   No. A tessellation pattern would repeat the basic design or figure without gaps and would run all the way to the edge of the blanket.

5. Consider the regular polygons below. Which of them could you use to create a tessellation? Which could not be used? Cut out similar figures and try fitting them together to test your ideas.

Triangle Square Pentagon Hexagon

   Only the triangle, square, and hexagon will tessellate by themselves. That is, without other shapes inserted between them. (See below.)

6. Create a tessellation using an octagon. Will the octagon tessellate by itself or must another type of polygon be used with it? Draw the resulting tessellation.

   The octagon will not tessellate by itself. A tessellation can be made using octagons and squares that fit in the gaps between them. (See below.)

7. Design a pattern for a blanket. It should be a tessellation that involves at least two of the regular polygons in item 5 above. The polygons can be of any size and color. Share your designs with your classmates.

   See below.

Answers

5.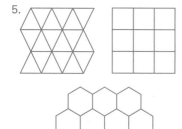

Triangles, squares, and hexagons tessellate

Pentagons will not tesselate

Tesselated octagons and squares

6.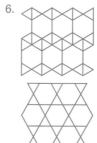

Tesselations using triangles and hexagons

7. Many designs are possible. Accept any that are true tessellations and involve the use of at least two of the polygons shown.

BIBLIOGRAPHY

FOR TEACHERS

Del Grande, John and Lorna Morrow. *Geometry and Spatial Sense (Addenda Series)*. Reston, VA: NCTM, 1993.

Geddes, Dorothy, et al. *Geometry in the Middle Grades (Addenda Series)*. Reston, VA: NCTM, 1992.

Overstreet, Charles W. *Plains Indian and Mountain Men Arts and Crafts*. Liberty, UT: Eagle's View, 1993.

Petroski, Henry. *Engineers of Dreams: Great Bridge Builders and the Spanning of America*. New York, NY: Alfred Knopf, 1995.

Underhill, Ruth Murray. *Pueblo Crafts*. Washington, DC: Bureau of Indian Affairs, U.S. Dept. of Interior, 1994.

FOR STUDENTS

Center for Occupational Research and Development. *Applied Mathematics, Unit 7: Working with Shapes in Two Dimensions*. Waco, TX: CORD, 1993.

Osinski, Alice. *The Tlingit*. Chicago, IL: Children's Press, 1990.

Sonneborn, Liz. *Arts and Crafts*. Vero Beach, FL: Rourke Publications, 1994.

Doing What Comes Naturally

"He's a born comedian." "She was born to be in the Olympics." When people say things like that, they mean that you were born with certain abilities.

The use of geometric shapes and patterns in centuries-old Native American art is an example of talents with which the artisan seemed to be born. We can be fairly certain he or she never studied geometry as you are doing.

Native American artisans have found that a repeating pattern is especially fitting when the work already involves repetition. The repetition involved in the work includes adding rows of colored threads to a woven blanket or sewing rows of beads to a decorative vest. A repeating design usually consists of repetitions of the same basic shape. The differences between shapes—their location and orientation—are related to transformations of the shapes.

1 What shapes do you see in this Native American design?

2 Choose a shape of your own and draw a design by repeating your shape.

593

Where are we now?

In Section 11A students explored congruent and similar figures and trigonometric ratios. They learned how to

- identify and draw similar and congruent figures.

- use similar figures and trigonometric ratios to make indirect measurements.

- apply their knowledge of geometry and trigonometric ratios to solve problems.

Where are we going?

In Section 11B students will

- reflect, rotate, and translate figures in the coordinate plane to obtain congruent figures.

- dilate figures in the coordinate plane to obtain similar figures.

- recognize whether a figure has line, rotational, or point symmetry.

- use transformations to tessellate the plane.

Theme: Native American Arts and Crafts

World Wide Web

If your class has access to the World Wide Web, you might want to use the information found at the Web site address given. The interdisciplinary links relate to topics discussed in this section.

About the Page

This page introduces the theme of the section, Native American arts and crafts, and discusses how the designs used by Native American artisans are related to geometry.

Ask …

- Do you have any art or craft objects made by Native American artisans? If so, describe one or two of them.

- How do you think Native American artisans learned the geometric concepts they use in their work? Possible answer: The knowledge was passed from one generation to the next through hands-on experience.

Extensions

The following activities do not require access to the World Wide Web.

Fine Arts
Geometric shapes are found repeatedly in Native American art. Have students research and report on what the various shapes symbolize.

History
Have students investigate how and when people first arrived on the North American continent and show their migration on a map.

Answers for Questions
1. Pentagons and rectangles.

2. Answers may vary.

Connect

On page 615, students will use their knowledge of symmetry, geometric transformations, and tessellations to design a pattern suitable for use on a Native American object.

Objective

- Move all the points of a figure and still have a congruent shape.

Vocabulary

- Transformation, reflection, rotation, center of rotation, angle of rotation, translation

Materials

- Explore: Dynamic geometry software

NCTM Standards

- 1–4, 9, 12

▶ **Review**

Plot these points on a coordinate grid.

1. A(–3, 4) 2. B(0, 3)
3. C(–1, –3) 4. D(1, 0)

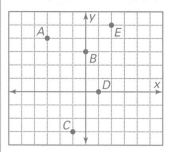

Available on Daily Transparency 11-6

1 Introduce

Explore

You may wish to use Teaching Tool Transparency 8: Coordinate Grids with this lesson.

The Point
Students use geometry software to reflect figures with respect to each axis, and try to find a pattern between the coordinates of the original and the reflected figures.

Ongoing Assessment
In Steps 2 and 5, check that students are reflecting the figure with respect to the correct axis.

11-6 Transformations and Congruence

You'll Learn ...

■ to move all the points of a figure and still have a congruent shape

... How It's Used

Transformations are the basis for patterns in art and architectural design.

Vocabulary

transformation
reflection
rotation
center of rotation
angle of rotation
translation

▶ **Lesson Link** You've seen many types of polygons. Now you will explore what happens when polygons are flipped or moved. ◀

A **transformation** is an operation that affects all points of a figure, such as a slide, flip, or turn.

You've seen your reflection in a mirror or in water. In math, a **reflection** is a transformation that flips a figure over a line.

A reflection is congruent to the original figure.

Reflection

Explore | **Reflections**

Time to Reflect

Materials: Dynamic geometry software

1. Display the x- and y-axes and draw a rectangle in the first quadrant.

2. Use the reflection tool to reflect the rectangle with respect to the y-axis.

3. Find the coordinates of each vertex of both rectangles. Identify corresponding vertices.

4. Is there a pattern between the x-coordinates of the corresponding corners? The y-coordinates?

5. Draw a polygon, reflect it with respect to the x-axis, and find the pattern between the coordinates of corresponding vertices. What can you conclude about reflections with respect to the y-axis? The x-axis?

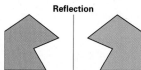

Learn | **Transformations and Congruence**

A **rotation** is a transformation that turns a figure about a point called a **center of rotation**. The **angle of rotation** is the angle of the turn. A rotated image of a figure is congruent to the original figure.

The transformation of a figure is labeled using prime notation for the corresponding vertices. For example, A corresponds to A'.

594 *Chapter 11 • Similarity, Congruence, and Transformations*

▶ **MEETING INDIVIDUAL NEEDS**

Resources
11-6 Practice
11-6 Reteaching
11-6 Problem Solving
11-6 Enrichment
11-6 Daily Transparency
Problem of the Day
Review
Quick Quiz
Teaching Tool Transparencies 8,16
Lesson Enhancement Transparencies 62–67
Technology Masters 62, 63

 Interactive CD-ROM Geometry Tool

 Wide World of Mathematics Geometry: Miniature Golf

Learning Modalities

Logical In **Explore**, students try to identify a pattern between the x-coordinates and the y-coordinates of the original figures and the reflected figures.

Kinesthetic Students might physically move a traced figure around on a coordinate grid as they experiment with transformations.

Social Students who have examples of woven materials that incorporate reflections, rotations, and translations can bring them from home and explain the patterns to the class.

English Language Development

For students who have difficulty understanding the words *translation*, *reflection*, and *rotation*, use the terms *slide*, *flip*, and *turn* along with the correct mathematical terms.

Example 1

The origin is the center of rotation. Rotate trapezoid *ABCD* clockwise 90° and 270° and give the vertex coordinates for each.

Use $\overline{CD}$ as a guide to rotate the trapezoid. $D(0, 0)$ is the center of rotation.

$A'B'C'D'$ is the result of the 90° rotation.

$A'(2, -1)$ $B'(2, -3)$ $C'(0, -4)$ $D'(0, 0)$

$A''B''C''D''$ is the result of the 270° rotation.

$A''(-2, 1)$ $B''(-2, 3)$ $C''(0, 4)$ $D''(0, 0)$

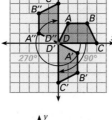

Try It

This pattern is from the Native American baskets of British Columbia. Rotate the figure clockwise 180° and 360°. Use the origin as the center of rotation and find the vertex coordinates.

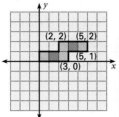

Try It:
(−2, −2), (−5, −2),
(−5, −1), (−3, 0);
(2, 2), (5, 2),
(5, 1), (3, 0)

A transformation that slides all points of a figure the same distance in the same direction is called a **translation**. All *x*- and *y*-coordinates of a translated figure change by adding or subtracting. A translated image of a figure is congruent to its original figure.

Example 2

The vertices of a triangle are *A*(2, 5), *B*(4, 2), and *C*(0, 2).

Give the vertices of △*ABC* translated to the <u>right 4</u> units and <u>up 2</u>.

On the *x*-axis, "right" is a positive direction, so **add 4** to each *x*-coordinate.

On the *y*-axis, "up" is a positive direction, so **add 2** to each *y*-coordinate.

Locate points *A*, *B*, *C* and draw △*ABC*.

△*ABC*	$(x + 4, y + 2)$	△*A'B'C'*
↓	↓	↓
$A(2, 5) \rightarrow$	$(2 + 4, 5 + 2) \rightarrow$	$A'(6, 7)$
$B(4, 2) \rightarrow$	$(4 + 4, 2 + 2) \rightarrow$	$B'(8, 4)$
$C(0, 2) \rightarrow$	$(0 + 4, 2 + 2) \rightarrow$	$C'(4, 4)$

Label corresponding vertices A', B', and C'.

The coordinates of △*A'B'C'* are *A'*(6, 7), *B'*(8, 4), and *C'*(4, 4).

11-6 • Transformations and Congruence **595**

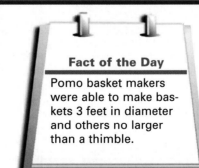

MATH EVERY DAY

---

2 Teach

Learn

You may wish to use Teaching Tool Transparency 16: Protractor and Lesson Enhancement Transparencies 62–67 with Examples 1–3.

Alternate Examples

1. The origin is the center of rotation. Rotate △*RST* clockwise 180° and 270° and give the coordinates for each vertex.

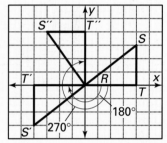

$R(0, 0)$ is the center of rotation.
△*R'S'T'* is the 180° rotation.
$R'(0, 0)$; $S'(-4, -3)$; $T'(-4, 0)$
△*R''S''T''* is the 270° rotation.
$R''(0, 0)$; $S''(-3, 4)$; $T''(0, 4)$

2. The vertices of a triangle are *D*(1, 1); *E*(5, 3); and *F*(5, 1). Give the vertex coordinates of △*DEF* translated to the left 2 units and down 3.

Draw △*DEF*.

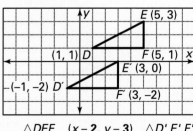

△*DEF*	$(x - 2, y - 3)$	△*D' E' F'*
↓	↓	↓

$D(1, 1) \rightarrow (1 - 2, 1 - 3) \rightarrow D'(-1, -2)$

$E(5, 3) \rightarrow (5 - 2, 3 - 3) \rightarrow E'(3, 0)$

$F(5, 1) \rightarrow (5 - 2, 1 - 3) \rightarrow F'(3, -2)$

Label corresponding vertices *D'*, *E'*, and *F'*. The coordinates of △*D' E' F'* are *D'*(−1, −2); *E'*(3, 0); *F'*(3, −2).

Alternate Examples

3. The coordinates of Figure *ABCD* are *A*(–3, 5), *B*(–3, 2), *C*(–5, 1), and *D*(–5, 4). Reflect Figure *ABCD* across the *y*-axis and determine the coordinates of *A'B'C'D'*.

Each *x*-coordinate changes because the reflection is across the *y*-axis.
Plot the vertices of *A'B'C'D'* and draw the sides.
Figure *ABCD* *x*-coordinates are negative. So *A'B'C'D'* *x*-coordinates are positive.

ABCD	(–*x*, *y*)	*A'B'C'D'*
↓	↓	↓

$A(-3, 5) \rightarrow (3, 5) \rightarrow A'(3, 5)$

$B(-3, 2) \rightarrow (3, 2) \rightarrow B'(3, 2)$

$C(-5, 1) \rightarrow (5, 1) \rightarrow C'(5, 1)$

$D(-5, 4) \rightarrow (5, 4) \rightarrow D'(5, 4)$

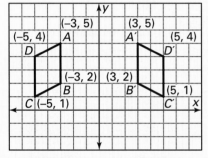

4. △*DEF* has coordinates *D*(4, 4); *E*(10, 3); and *F*(4, 1). Reflect △*DEF* across the *x*-axis and determine the coordinates of △*D'E'F'*.

The sign of each *y*-coordinate changes because the reflection is across the *x*-axis.
Plot and draw △*D'E'F'*.
△*D'E'F'* *y*-coordinates are negative.

D(4, 4)	→	*D'*(4, –4)
E(10, 3)	→	*E'*(10, –3)
F(4, 1)	→	*F'*(4, –1)

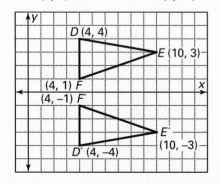

A reflection across the *x*-axis changes the sign of each *y*-coordinate.

A reflection across the *y*-axis changes the sign of each *x*-coordinate.

Example 3

△*ABC* has coordinates *A*(3, 5), *B*(6, 1), and *C*(1, 2). Reflect △*ABC* across the *x*-axis and determine the coordinates of △*A'B'C'*.

Each *y*-coordinate changes because the reflection is across the *x*-axis.

Plot the vertices of △*A'B'C'* and draw the triangle.

△*ABC* *y*-coordinates are positive.

So △*A'B'C'* *y*-coordinates are negative.

△*ABC*	(*x*, –*y*)	△*A'B'C'*
↓	↓	↓
A(3, 5) →	(3, –5) →	*A'*(3, –5)
B(6, 1) →	(6, –1) →	*B'*(6, –1)
C(1, 2) →	(1, –2) →	*C'*(1, –2)

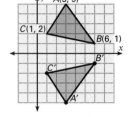

Example 4

Reflect Figure *STUV* across the *y*-axis and determine the coordinates of *S'T'U'V'*. The sign of each *x*-coordinate changes because the reflection is across the *y*-axis.

Plot and draw *S'T'U'V'*.

S'T'U'V' *x*-coordinates are positive.

$S(-2, 4) \rightarrow S'(2, 4)$

$T(-1, 2) \rightarrow T'(1, 2)$

$U(-3, 0) \rightarrow U'(3, 0)$

$V(-4, 2) \rightarrow V'(4, 2)$

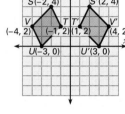

a. (–3, 1); (–1, 1); (–3, 4); (–1, 4)

b. (–1, –2); (–4, –2); (–1, –3); (–2, –3); (–2, –5); (–4, –4)

Try It

This pattern can be found in ancient Pueblo pottery. Determine the vertex coordinates of *A* and *B* after each reflection.

a. Reflect Figure *A* across the *x*-axis.

b. Reflect Figure *B* across the *y*-axis.

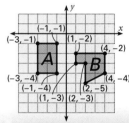

596 *Chapter 11 • Similarity, Congruence, and Transformations*

MEETING MIDDLE SCHOOL CLASSROOM NEEDS

Tips from Middle School Teachers

In lessons dealing with geometry, I like to take the opportunity to display as many examples of the uses of beautiful geometric shapes as possible. Many students who are not attracted to numerical aspects of mathematics will be interested in the spatial and aesthetic aspects of geometry. I want them to feel that their abilities and interests are just as important as those of students who are whizzes at calculation.

Cooperative Learning

Have students work in small groups and compose lists of things that clearly show translations, reflections, and rotations of patterns. Their lists will probably include things like designs on wallpaper or printed fabrics for translations and reflections, and pinwheels or helicopter blades for rotations.

Geography Connection

The Pueblos have lived in the same location in New Mexico and Arizona longer than any other people in the United States or Canada. Most Pueblos live in New Mexico, along the Rio Grande River, between Taos and Albuquerque. Others live in west-central New Mexico in the desert or mesa areas of Laguna or Acoma. There are 19 Pueblo villages in all. The Pueblos are known for their expert pottery making as mentioned in the **Try It** on page 596. Students might locate these areas on a map.

Rotate the figure clockwise 180° using the vertex of the right angle as the center of rotation.

Shauna thinks ...

I'll use the vertical side as a reference. If that line swings around 180°, the fan will look like this.

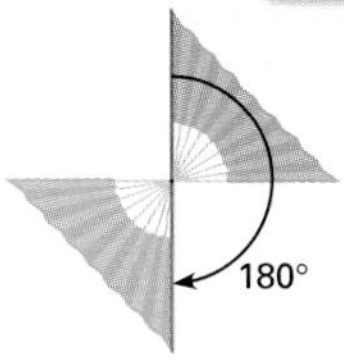

180°

Julio thinks ...

Let's see. I can use either the horizontal or vertical side as a reference.

I'll use the horizontal side. After rotating 180°, that side will be oriented horizontally.

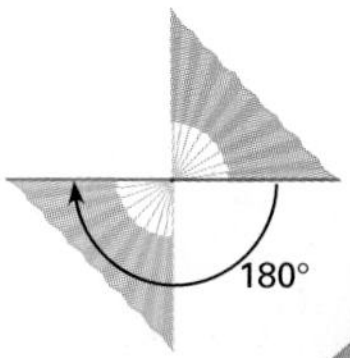

180°

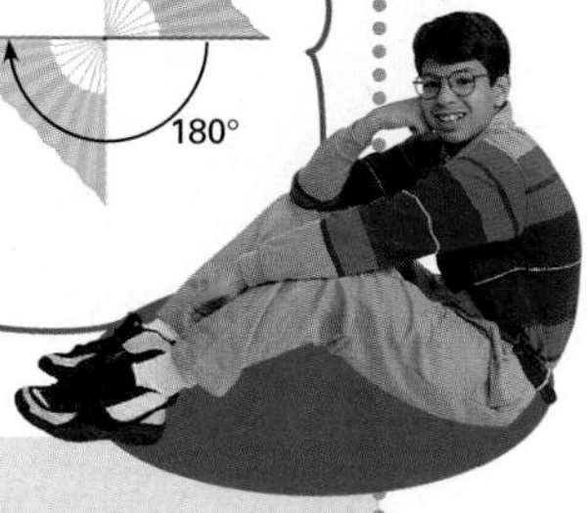

What do you think?

1. Explain why Julio said he could use either the horizontal or vertical side as a reference for his rotation.

2. Explain why Shauna and Julio got the same result.

Check Your Understanding

1. Describe how a figure's coordinates change after the figure is translated to the left on a coordinate grid.

2. Describe how a figure's coordinates change after the figure is reflected across the *y*-axis.

Students are presented with two methods for rotating a figure. Each method uses a different side of the figure as a reference.

Answers for What Do You Think?
1. He recognizes that either of the two perpendicular sides are good references for a rotation.

2. No matter what the reference, a 180° rotation will be the same.

3 Practice and Assess

Check

To answer the questions, students can translate and reflect a test point, and note how its coordinates change.

Answers for Check Your Understanding
1. The *x*-coordinates decrease while the *y*-coordinates remain unchanged.

2. The *x*-coordinates change signs while the *y*-coordinates remain unchanged.

Assignment Guide

■ **Basic**
1, 2, 4–11, 15–23 odds

■ **Average**
3–12, 16–24 evens

■ **Enriched**
3, 5–14, 18–24 evens

Exercise Answers

1. a–b.

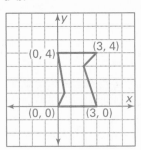

Reteaching

Activity

Materials: Graph paper, rulers, tracing paper, scissors

• Work with a partner.

• Draw *x*- and *y*-axes. Label each axis from –10 to 10.

• Draw a figure with vertices *A*(–5, 5), *B*(–2, 5), *C*(–5, 2), and *D*(–3, 2).

• Trace the figure on another piece of paper, cut it out, place it on top of the figure on the graph paper, and slide it 5 units to the right. Copy the figure at the new location and name the figure *A'B'C'D'*. What are the coordinates of the new figure's vertices? What happened to the coordinates of the vertices when you moved right? *A'*(0, 5); *B'*(3, 5); *C'*(0, 2); *D'*(2, 2); The *x*-coordinates increased by 5.

• Use *ABCD* again. What happens to the coordinates of the vertices when you move left? When you move up? When you move down? The *x*-coordinates decrease; The *y*-coordinates increase; The *y*-coordinates decrease.

598   Chapter 11

11-6 Exercises and Applications

Practice and Apply

PRACTICE 11-6

1. **Getting Started** Rotate the blue image clockwise 90°. What are the new coordinates? Use the origin as the center of rotation.

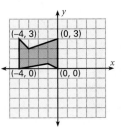

   a. Turn the figure to the right so the vertex on the origin stays there.

   b. Plot the new vertex coordinates.

   c. Identify the new vertex coordinates. **(0, 0), (0, 4), (3, 4), (3, 0)**

2. What transformation of the blue T-shirt gives the yellow T-shirt? **Translation**

3. What transformation of the pink shoe gives the yellow shoe? **Rotation**

4. **Geometry** Find the coordinates of points *A* and *B* on the trapezoid that has been translated 1.5 units left and 4.5 units up. *A*(1, 3.5), *B*(5.5, 1.5)

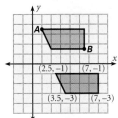

5. Across which axis was the figure reflected? **The *y*-axis**

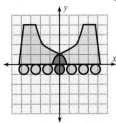

6. **Social Studies** The Yurok people of northern California wove intricate baskets using plants such as sourgrass. On the basket, what transformations do the parallelograms and triangles exhibit? **Translations, reflections**

598   *Chapter 11 • Similarity, Congruence, and Transformations*

PRACTICE

Name _____

Practice 11-6

Transformations and Congruence

Tell what transformation of the lightly shaded figure produced the dark one.

1. **Reflection**   2. **Rotation**   3. **Translation**

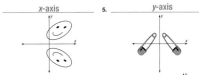

Across which axis was each figure reflected?

4. ____ *x*-axis   5. ____ *y*-axis

6. Find the coordinates of points *P* and *Q* on the triangle that has been translated 4 units to the right and 2.5 units up.

   P ___(1, −0.5)___   *Q* ___(3, 2.5)___

7. Find the coordinates of points *R* and *S* on the trapezoid that has been rotated 90° clockwise about the origin.

   R ___(2, 5)___   *S* ___(5, −1)___

8. a. Name each polygon, if any, that is a translation of 1.

   ___3___

   b. Name each polygon, if any, that is a reflection of 4.

   ___None___

   c. Name each polygon, if any, that is a rotation of 6.

   ___1, 2, 3, 5___

RETEACHING

Name _____

Alternative Lesson 11-6

Transformations and Congruence

A **transformation** is an operation that affects all points of a figure, such as a slide, flip, or turn.

A **reflection** is a transformation that flips a figure over a line. A **rotation** is a transformation that turns a figure about a point. A **translation** slides all points of a figure the same distance in the same direction.

A transformation is labeled using prime notation for the corresponding vertices. The transformation is congruent to the original figure.

━━ Example ━━

The coordinates of the vertices of △*ABC* are *A*(1, 5), *B*(2, 2), and *C*(5, 4). Give the vertices of △*ABC* translated to the right 3 units and down 2 units. Then plot △*A'B'C'* on the coordinate plane.

On the *x*-axis, "right" is a positive direction so, **add** 3 to each *x*-coordinate.
On the *y*-axis, "down" is a negative direction so, **subtract** 2 from each *y*-coordinate.

△*ABC*	(*x* + 3, *y* − 2)	△*A'B'C'*
↓	↓	↓
A(1, 5) →	(1 + 3, 5 − 2) →	*A'*(4, 3)
B(2, 2) →	(2 + 3, 2 − 2) →	*B'*(5, 0)
C(5, 4) →	(5 + 3, 4 − 2) →	*C'*(8, 2)

The coordinates of △*A'B'C'* are *A'*(4, 3), *B'*(5, 0), and *C'*(8, 2).

Try It The coordinates of the vertices of △*JKL* are *J*(1, 2), *K*(2, 1), and *L*(5, 4). Give the vertices of △*JKL* translated to the right 2 units and down 3 units. Then plot △*J'K'L'* on the coordinate plane.

a. Will you add or subtract 2 from the *x*-coordinate? ___Add 2.___

b. Will you add or subtract 3 from the *y*-coordinate? ___Subtract 3.___

c. Give the *x*-coordinates of each point.

   J' ___3___   *K'* ___4___   *L'* ___7___

d. Give the *y*-coordinates of each point.

   J' ___−1___   *K'* ___−2___   *L'* ___1___

e. Give the coordinates of each point.

   J' ___(3, −1)___   *K'* ___(4, −2)___   *L'* ___(7, 1)___

f. Plot the points and draw the figure.

7. [Test Prep] Some of these happy faces are transformations of each other. Which two are translations of each other? **C**

Ⓐ 2 and 3   Ⓑ 3 and 7   Ⓒ 2 and 7   Ⓓ 4 and 6

Problem Solving and Reasoning

8. Algebra The blue rhombus has been reflected across the *y*-axis. Give a general rule for changing coordinates (*x*, *y*) of the blue rhombus into corresponding coordinates on the green one.

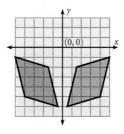

Critical Thinking What transformations, if any, will turn each collection of shapes into a math word you've recently learned? (Turning the book and using a mirror may help you decide.)

[GPS] **9.** ROTATE   **10.** REFLECT   **11.** TRANSLATE

9. A reflection

10. A 180° rotation

12. [Journal] Describe how two different transformations can result in the same image and provide an example.

13. Math Reasoning Is there a transformation that changes a parallelogram into a trapezoid? Explain.

14. Communicate Explain the difference between reflections and rotations. Provide a sketch as an example.

Mixed Review

Multiply or divide. Write each answer in lowest terms. *[Lesson 7-6]*

15. 26.9 × 14.2   **16.** 0.081 × −0.9   **17.** $\frac{4}{7} \times \frac{4}{9}$ $\frac{16}{63}$ **18.** 12 × $\frac{5}{6}$ 10
381.98   **−0.0729**

19. 2.04 ÷ 3 **0.68**   **20.** 44 ÷ $\frac{1}{4}$ **176**   **21.** $9\frac{1}{3} ÷ \frac{3}{28}$ **22.** −4.5 ÷ −2.25 **2**
                                                    $87\frac{1}{9}$

Add. Simplify if possible. *[Lesson 10-6]*

23. $(2x^2 + 4x + 5) + (x^3 + 5x^2 − 4x − 7)$ **24.** $(8p^5 − p^2) + (2p^5 + 4p^3 + 11)$
        $x^3 + 7x^2 − 2$ $10p^5 + 4p^3 − p^2 + 11$

Exercise Notes

■ **Exercise 8**

Problem-Solving Tip If students have trouble writing a general rule, suggest that they first consider specific cases and then try to generalize from them.

Exercise Answers

8. Change signs on the *x*-coordinates and leave the *y*-coordinates unchanged.

11. No transformations of the word "TRANSLATE" as a whole will work. Each letter must be reflected and rotated separately.

12. Rotating a rectangle 180° about its center gives the same result as a reflection across a line of symmetry.

13. No; A parallelogram and a trapezoid are not congruent.

14. Possible answer: Reflections require an axis or a line to reflect across. Rotations require a center of rotation and an angle measurement.

Alternate Assessment

Performance Have students create a figure on a coordinate grid and give a rule for translating it. Then have them exchange papers and perform the translation.

▶ **Quick Quiz**

The reflection of △*RST* about the *y*-axis is △*R'S'T'*.

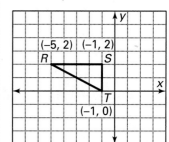

Find each of the following.

1. Coordinates of *R'*. (5, 2)

2. Coordinates of *S'*. (1, 2)

3. Coordinates of *T'*. (1, 0)

Available on Daily Transparency 11-6

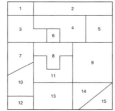 

Objective

- Transform a figure and have a shape that is similar to but not congruent to the original.

Materials

- Explore: Graph paper, ruler

NCTM Standards

- 1–4, 12, 13

▶ **Review**

Calculate the lengths of the sides of this triangle if it is dilated by a scale factor of 2.5.

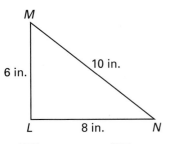

6 in. — 10 in.

L — 8 in. — N

M

1. $\overline{LM}$ 15 in.   2. $\overline{MN}$ 25 in.

3. $\overline{LN}$ 20 in.

Available on Daily Transparency 11-7

1 Introduce

Explore

You may wish to use Teaching Tool Transparencies 7: $\frac{1}{4}$-inch Graph Paper and 15: Rulers with **Explore**.

The Point
Students dilate a design and compare the result to the original.

Ongoing Assessment
For Step 1, check that all students have the original figure copied. In Step 2, check that students used graph paper with squares that are 2 units by 2 units.

For Groups That Finish Early
Create your own design and dilate it by a scale factor of 2.

Answers for Explore on page C5.

11-7 Transformations and Similarity

You'll Learn …

- to transform a figure and have a shape that is similar to but not congruent to the original

… How It's Used

Photo developers create similar figures when creating enlargements.

▶ **Lesson Link**   You've seen how transformations result in congruent figures. Now you'll use a transformation that results in a figure that is similar to but not congruent to the original. ◀

Explore | Dilations

This Is Getting Expansive

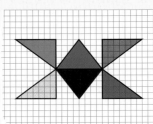

Materials: Graph paper, Ruler

This design is adapted from Sioux art. It represents six directions: east (red), west (yellow), north (blue), south (black), up, and down.

1. Copy this figure onto graph paper.

2. On another piece of graph paper, draw a scale drawing of this design using a scale factor of 2.

3. Is each of the six triangles of the dilated design congruent to its corresponding triangle of the original design? Is it similar? Explain.

Learn | Transformations and Similarity

The coordinates of a dilation on the coordinate plane can be determined by multiplying every coordinate by the scale factor.

Example 1

Use a scale factor of 2 to dilate △ABC. Give the vertex coordinates of the dilation.

$$\triangle ABC \qquad (2 \cdot x, 2 \cdot y) \qquad \triangle A'B'C'$$
$$\downarrow \qquad\qquad \downarrow \qquad\qquad \downarrow$$
$$A(2, 1) \rightarrow (2 \cdot 2, 2 \cdot 1) \rightarrow A'(4, 2)$$
$$B(2, 4) \rightarrow (2 \cdot 2, 2 \cdot 4) \rightarrow B'(4, 8)$$
$$C(4, 3) \rightarrow (2 \cdot 4, 2 \cdot 3) \rightarrow C'(8, 6)$$

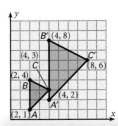

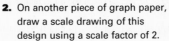

MEETING INDIVIDUAL NEEDS

Resources

- 11-7 Practice
- 11-7 Reteaching
- 11-7 Problem Solving
- 11-7 Enrichment
- 11-7 Daily Transparency
    - Problem of the Day
    - Review
    - Quick Quiz
- Teaching Tool Transparencies 7, 8, 15
- Technology Master 64
- Chapter 11 Project Master

Learning Modalities

Visual In **Explore**, students copy a design on graph paper and then dilate the design to see if the resulting design and the original are congruent or similar figures.

Social Have small groups of students create their own designs by using dilations and other transformations.

Logical In **Check Your Understanding** students identify a dilation as an enlargement or a reduction before drawing it.

Inclusion

Students who have limited perception may have a difficult time discerning the original figure from the dilated figure on a coordinate grid. You might suggest that they use different colored pencils for drawing each figure and labeling each figure's vertices.

A scale factor greater than 1 causes an enlargement, whereas a positive nonzero scale factor less than 1 causes a reduction.

Example 2

Use a scale factor of $\frac{1}{3}$ to dilate Figure *KLMN*. Give the coordinates of the vertices that correspond to *KLMN*.

Find the new vertex coordinates, then plot the dilated figure.

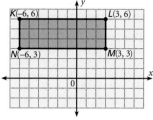

$$KLMN \quad \left(\frac{1}{3} \cdot x, \frac{1}{3} \cdot y\right) \quad K'L'M'N'$$

$$\downarrow \qquad\qquad \downarrow \qquad\qquad \downarrow$$

$$K(-6, 6) \rightarrow \left(\frac{1}{3} \cdot -6, \frac{1}{3} \cdot 6\right) \rightarrow K'(-2, 2)$$

$$L(3, 6) \quad \rightarrow \left(\frac{1}{3} \cdot 3, \frac{1}{3} \cdot 6\right) \quad \rightarrow L'(1, 2)$$

$$M(3, 3) \quad \rightarrow \left(\frac{1}{3} \cdot 3, \frac{1}{3} \cdot 3\right) \quad \rightarrow M'(1, 1)$$

$$N(-6, 3) \rightarrow \left(\frac{1}{3} \cdot -6, \frac{1}{3} \cdot 3\right) \rightarrow N'(-2, 1)$$

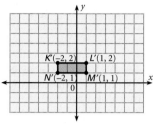

Language Link

The prefix *non-* means "not."

So "*x* is a nonzero number" means $x \neq 0$.

Try It

Find the new vertex coordinates after each dilation.

a. Use a scale factor of 2.5.

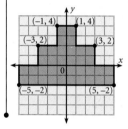

b. Use a scale factor of $\frac{2}{3}$.

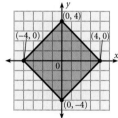

Example 3

The point $A'(4, 12)$ is on a polygon that has been dilated by a scale factor of 4. What are the coordinates of the corresponding point A?

$(4 \div 4, 12 \div 4) \rightarrow A(1, 3)$ Divide A' coordinates by 4.

11-7 • Transformations and Similarity **601**

MATH EVERY DAY

▶ Problem of the Day

The art of Japanese flower arranging is called *Ikebana*. Some Japanese flower arrangements are made with a flower, a leaf, and a branch. How many possible arrangements are there if you use one of each of the following:

flowers: tulip, iris, rose, lily
leaves: ivy, hosta
branches: oak, pine, maple
24 possible arrangements

Available on Daily Transparency 11-7

An Extension is provided in the transparency package.

Fact of the Day

The tallest totem pole, at 173 feet tall, stands at Alert Bay, British Columbia, Canada. It tells the story of the Kwakiutl tribe.

Mental Math

Do these mentally.

1. $3 \cdot 4 \cdot 5$ 60

2. $5 \cdot 5 \cdot 6$ 150

3. $2 \cdot 4 \cdot 8$ 64

Learn

You may wish to use Teaching Tool Transparency 8: Coordinate Grids with this lesson.

Alternate Examples

1. Use a scale factor of 3 to dilate $\triangle RST$. Give the coordinates of the dilated triangle.

$$\triangle RST \quad (3 \cdot x, 3 \cdot y) \quad \triangle R'S'T'$$

$$\downarrow \qquad\qquad \downarrow \qquad\qquad \downarrow$$

$$R(1, 1) \rightarrow (3 \cdot 1, 3 \cdot 1) \rightarrow R'(3, 3)$$

$$S(4, 1) \rightarrow (3 \cdot 4, 3 \cdot 1) \rightarrow S'(12, 3)$$

$$T(1, 3) \rightarrow (3 \cdot 1, 3 \cdot 3) \rightarrow T'(3, 9)$$

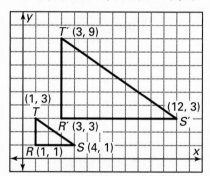

2. Use a scale factor of 0.5 to dilate Figure *ABCD*. Give the coordinates of the vertices that correspond to $A'B'C'D'$

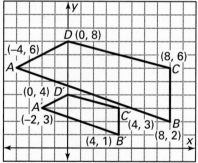

Find the new vertex coordinates, then plot the dilated figure.

$$A(-4, 6) \rightarrow (\tfrac{1}{2} \cdot -4, \tfrac{1}{2} \cdot 6) \rightarrow A'(-2, 3)$$

$$B(8, 2) \rightarrow (\tfrac{1}{2} \cdot 8, \tfrac{1}{2} \cdot 2) \rightarrow B'(4, 1)$$

$$C(8, 6) \rightarrow (\tfrac{1}{2} \cdot 8, \tfrac{1}{2} \cdot 6) \rightarrow C'(4, 3)$$

$$D(0, 8) \rightarrow (\tfrac{1}{2} \cdot 0, \tfrac{1}{2} \cdot 8) \rightarrow D'(0, 4)$$

Answers for Try It on page C5.

3. The point $M'(4, -2)$ is on a triangle that has been dilated by a scale factor of $\frac{1}{3}$. What are the coordinates of the corresponding point M?

Multiply M' coordinates by 3: $M'(4 \times 3, -2 \times 3) \rightarrow M(12, -6)$

Lesson 11-7 **601**

4. This is another design used by the Northwest American tribes. Find the scale factor of the dilation by comparing corresponding vertices.

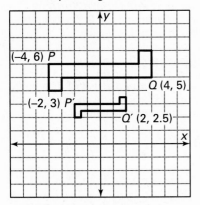

Compare the x- or y-coordinates of P(–4, 6) and P'(–2, 3).

$$\frac{\text{coordinate after dilation}}{\text{coordinate before dilation}} = \frac{3}{6} = \frac{1}{2}$$

The scale factor of the dilation is $\frac{1}{2}$.

3 Practice and Assess

Check

For Question 1, it should be noted that if the scale factor is greater than 1, the dilation is an enlargement and if the scale factor is less than 1, the dilation is a reduction.

Answers for Check Your Understanding

1. Enlargements have a scale factor greater than 1; Reductions have a scale factor less than 1.

2. Yes; Possible explanation: Suppose Figure Y is dilated by a factor of a to produce Figure X. Someone could see the figures and think that X was dilated by a factor of $\frac{1}{a}$ to produce Figure Y.

3. The coordinates stay the same.

If you have a figure and its dilation and you know the coordinates of corresponding vertices, then you can find the scale factor of the dilation.

▶ **Geography Link**

Native American tribes of the Northwest are known for using animal designs in wood carvings. They also used animal names for geometric designs, such as "snake track" or "grasshopper."

Example 4

The design shown here is one of many from Northwest American tribes that are based on diagonal lines.

Find the scale factor of the dilation by comparing corresponding vertices.

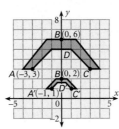

Compare the x- or y-coordinates of A(–3, 3) and A'(–1, 1).

$$\frac{\text{coordinate after dilation}}{\text{coordinate before dilation}} = \frac{-1}{-3} = \frac{1}{3}$$

The scale factor of the dilation is $\frac{1}{3}$.

Try It

a. Find the scale factor of the dilation of Figure A to Figure B. $\frac{1}{5}$

b. Find the scale factor of the dilation of Figure B to Figure A. 5

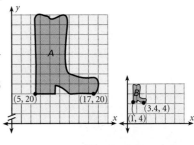

Check | Your Understanding

1. Before drawing a dilation, how can you tell whether it will be an enlargement or a reduction?

2. If Figure X is a dilation of Figure Y, can Y also be a dilation of X? Explain.

3. What happens to the coordinates of a figure after a dilation of a scale factor of 1?

▷ ## MEETING MIDDLE SCHOOL CLASSROOM NEEDS

Team Teaching

Work with an art teacher to have students create their own Native American-style posters. Have reference books on hand that students can peruse for ideas. Tell them to use both congruent figures and dilated similar figures in their artwork.

Cultural Connection

The interesting carvings on the totem poles of the Pacific Northwest tribes are actually family, clan, or tribe emblems. The clan totem may be a bird, fish, animal, or plant. Some clans may have rulings against killing or eating the species to which the totem belongs. Some also believe the totem to be holy.

Fine Arts Connection

In the early 1800s, white traders introduced the Plains Indians to the glass beads that we usually associate with Indian art. Previous to that time, the Indians used porcupine quills, which had to be dyed. The beads were easier to work with than the quills and they came already brightly colored. There were three kinds of beads that were bartered by the traders. Pony beads were introduced around 1800. They were large and usually blue or white. Around 1840, seed beads were introduced. They were smaller and had a much wider range of colors. After 1870, translucent beads in still richer colors and more varied shapes became popular.

11-7 Exercises and Applications

Practice and Apply

1. **Getting Started** Which two figures are dilations of each other? **2 and 3**

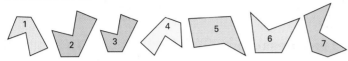

2. Trapezoid 2 is a dilation of trapezoid 1. Classify the dilation as a reduction or an enlargement, and find the scale factor.

Enlargement, 2

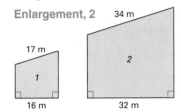

34 m
17 m
2
1
16 m   32 m

3. The smaller hand is a dilation of the larger hand. Classify the dilation as a reduction or an enlargement, and find the scale factor.

Reduction, $\frac{2}{3}$

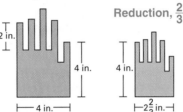

2 in.
4 in.   4 in.
├— 4 in.—┤   ├—2$\frac{2}{3}$ in.—┤

4. a. Use a scale factor of $\frac{1}{3}$ to dilate pentagon *ABCDE*. Find the coordinates of the vertices of the dilation.

b. Graph pentagon *A'B'C'D'E'*.

5. **Test Prep** Which of the following properties does *not* remain the same after a dilation? **B**

Ⓐ Angle measure   Ⓑ Side length

Ⓒ Orientation   Ⓓ Shape

6. Complete the sentence: Two figures with the same shape but different sizes are _____ but not _____. **Similar; Congruent**

7. An image on a photo can be considered a dilation of the figure on a negative. A typical negative is $1\frac{1}{4}$ in. by $\frac{7}{8}$ in. What is the scale factor if the photo is 6 in. by 4.2 in? **≈ 4.8**

8. A figure on a coordinate grid includes the points $K(-3, 5)$; $L(2, 0)$; and $M(4, 2)$. What are the coordinates of the corresponding points after a dilation of:

a. 3   **b.** 0.6   **c.** $\frac{1}{4}$ **d.** 2.5

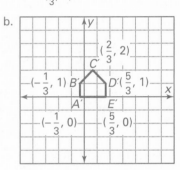

11-7 • Transformations and Similarity **603**

Assignment Guide

■ **Basic**
1–10, 13, 14, 16–22 evens

■ **Average**
3–6, 8–14, 15–23 odds

■ **Enriched**
2–5, 7–14, 15–21 odds

Exercise Notes

■ **Exercise 1**

Error Prevention Some students may not realize that dilations preserve orientation.

Exercise Answers

4. a. $A' = (-\frac{1}{3}, 0)$, $B' = (-\frac{1}{3}, 1)$,
   $C' = (\frac{2}{3}, 2)$, $D' = (\frac{5}{3}, 1)$,
   $E' = (\frac{5}{3}, 0)$

   b.

8. a. $K' = (-9, 15)$; $L' = (6, 0)$;
   $M' = (12, 6)$
   b. $K' = (-1.8, 3)$; $L' = (1.2, 0)$;
   $M' = (2.4, 1.2)$
   c. $K' = (-\frac{3}{4}, 1\frac{1}{4})$; $L' = (\frac{1}{2}, 0)$;
   $M' = (1, \frac{1}{2})$
   d. $K' = (-7.5, 12.5)$; $L' = (5, 0)$;
   $M' = (10, 5)$

PRACTICE

Name _____

Practice 11-7

Transformations and Similarity

1. Hexagon 2 is a dilation of hexagon 1. Classify the dilation as a reduction or enlargement, and find the scale factor.

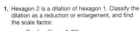

Reduction; 0.75

2. The larger dinosaur is a dilation of the smaller one. Classify the dilation as a reduction or enlargement, and find the scale factor.

Enlargement; 1.6

3. a. Use a scale factor of 1.5 to dilate trapezoid *ABCD*. Find the coordinates of the vertices of the dilation.

A' _(0, 4.5)_   B' _(3, 1.5)_
C' _(1.5, −1.5)_   D' _(−4.5, −4.5)_

b. Graph trapezoid *A'B'C'D'*.

4. Complete the sentence: The scale factor of a(n) _reduction_ is less than 1.

5. Draw a reduction of this envelope. Use a scale factor of $\frac{1}{3}$.

    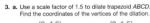

6. Draw an enlargement of this paper clip. Use a scale factor of 1.75.

7. An APS camera uses a 1.6-cm by 2.8-cm negative to produce a photograph measuring 10.16 cm by 17.78 cm. Think of the photograph as a dilation of the negative. What is the scale factor? _6.35_

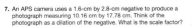

RETEACHING

Name _____

Alternative Lesson 11-7

Transformations and Similarity

The coordinates of a dilation on the coordinate plane can be determined by multiplying every coordinate by the scale factor. A scale factor greater than 1 causes an enlargement. A positive nonzero scale factor less than 1 causes a reduction. The original figure and the dilated figure are similar.

— Example —

Use a scale factor of 3 to dilate △*XYZ*. Find the coordinates of the vertices of the dilation. Then plot both triangles.

Multiply each coordinate by the scale factor.

△*XYZ*   (3 · x, 3 · y)   △*X'Y'Z'*
↓   ↓   ↓
X(1, 1) → (3 · 1, 3 · 1) → X'(3, 3)
Y(2, 3) → (3 · 2, 3 · 3) → Y'(6, 9)
Z(4, 2) → (3 · 4, 3 · 2) → Z'(12, 6)

Try It Use a scale factor of 2 to dilate △*LMN*. Find the coordinates of the vertices of the dilation. Then draw the dilation.

a. Complete the table.

△*LMN*   (2 · x, 2 · y)   △*L'M'N'*
L(_1_, _1_) → (2 · _1_, 2 · _1_) → L'(_2, 2_)
M(_5_, _2_) → (2 · _5_, 2 · _2_) → M'(_10, 4_)
N(_2_, _3_) → (2 · _2_, 2 · _3_) → N'(_4, 6_)

b. Plot the points. Draw the dilation.

Try It Use a scale factor of $\frac{1}{3}$ to dilate △*DEF*. Find the coordinates of the vertices of the dilation. Then draw the dilation.

c. Complete the table.

△*DEF*   ($\frac{1}{3}$ · x, $\frac{1}{3}$ · y)   △*D'E'F'*
D(_3, 6_) → ($\frac{1}{3}$ · _3_, $\frac{1}{3}$ · _6_) → D'(_1, 2_)
E(_6, 3_) → ($\frac{1}{3}$ · _6_, $\frac{1}{3}$ · _3_) → E'(_2, 1_)
F(_9, 6_) → ($\frac{1}{3}$ · _9_, $\frac{1}{3}$ · _6_) → F'(_3, 2_)

d. Plot the points. Draw the dilation.

Reteaching

Activity

Materials: Graph paper, ruler

• Work with a partner.

• Draw *x*- and *y*-axes on graph paper. Create your own design on the grid.

• Mark the coordinates of the vertices of your design.

• Now specify the scale factor by which you want your design to be dilated. Trade designs with your partner and do the dilation.

Lesson 11-7   **603**

Project Progress

You may want to have students use Chapter 11 Project Master.

Exercise Answers

9. The result will be a lizard 11.75 cm long and 6.25 cm wide.

10. The result will consist of small squares that all have a side length of approximately 0.5 cm.

12. $A'(-12, -3)$

13. a. The quotient is 2 in every case.
    b. Answers may vary.

14. $E' = (4, 0)$, $F' = (5, 3)$, $G' = (2.5, 4)$, $H' = (0, 3)$, $I' = (1, 0)$

15. $E'' = (8, 0)$, $F'' = (10, 6)$, $G'' = (8, 0)$, $H'' = (0, 6)$, $I'' = (2, 0)$

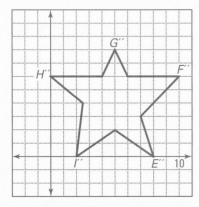

Alternate Assessment

Self Assessment Give students the opportunity to evaluate what they learned in the lesson. Did they find anything particularly difficult about the lesson? What did they find helpful?

▶ Quick Quiz

Use a scale factor of $\frac{1}{2}$ to dilate $\triangle JKL$. Find the coordinates of the vertices of the dilation.

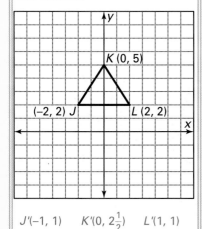

$J'(-1, 1)$ $K'(0, 2\frac{1}{2})$ $L'(1, 1)$

Available on Daily Transparency 11-7

---

9. Draw an enlargement of this Native American symbol for "lizard" with a scale factor of $2\frac{1}{2}$.

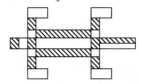

10. Draw a reduction of this figure using a scale factor of 0.5.

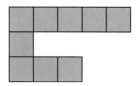

Problem Solving and Reasoning

Measurement Reduce $\triangle ABC$ by a scale factor of $\frac{3}{4}$.

11. How long is side $\overline{A'B'}$? 12

12. What are the coordinates of vertex A'?

13. a. **Technology** Using geometry software with x- and y-axes showing, draw a polygon that crosses at least one axis. Dilate the figure by a scale factor of 2 and use $(0, 0)$ as the center. Display all vertex coordinates and divide the corresponding x-coordinates. What do you find?

   b. **Communicate** Is this ratio what you would have expected? Explain.

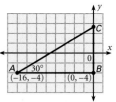

Critical Thinking Use the figure to answer Exercises 14 and 15.

[GPS] 14. Reflect the figure across the y-axis and give the new coordinates.

15. Use a scale factor of 2 to enlarge the reflection. What are the new vertex coordinates? Graph the enlargement.

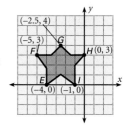

Mixed Review

Determine each square root and write in lowest terms. *[Lesson 7-7]*

16. $\sqrt{\frac{36}{49}}$ $\frac{6}{7}$ 17. $\sqrt{\frac{4}{9}}$ $\frac{2}{3}$ 18. $\sqrt{\frac{121}{16}}$ $2\frac{3}{4}$ 19. $\sqrt{\frac{64}{81}}$ $\frac{8}{9}$ 20. $\sqrt{\frac{169}{144}}$ $1\frac{1}{12}$

Write the additive inverse of each polynomial. *[Lesson 10-7]*

21. $-2x^3 + 4x^2 - 2x + 5$
    $2x^3 - 4x^2 + 2x - 5$

22. $4x^4 - (x^2 + 8)$
    $-4x^4 + x^2 + 8$

23. $x^2 - (-5x - 2)$
    $-x^2 - 5x - 2$

Project Progress

What object will you measure and how far away from it will you be?

Problem Solving
Understand
Plan
Solve
Look Back

604 Chapter 11 • Similarity, Congruence, and Transformations

▶ PROBLEM SOLVING

Name _____

Guided Problem Solving 11-7

[GPS] **PROBLEM 14, STUDENT PAGE 604**

Reflect the figure across the y-axis and give the new coordinates.

— Understand —

1. What shape is the figure?
   Star.

2. Across which axis will you reflect the figure?
   y-axis.

3. What else are you asked for?
   New coordinates.

— Plan —

4. Name the coordinates of the figure above.
   E _(−4, 0)_ F _(−5, 3)_ G _(−2.5, 4)_ H _(0, 3)_ I _(−1, 0)_

5. Will the distance from the y-axis change or stay the same? **Stay same.**

6. How will the coordinates change when reflected across the y-axis? **Signs of** x-coordinates change, y-coordinates stay the same.

— Solve —

7. Graph the reflection. What are the new coordinates?
   E' _(4, 0)_ F' _(5, 3)_ G' _(2.5, 4)_ H' _(0, 3)_ I' _(1, 0)_

— Look Back —

8. Why does one point not change when the figure is reflected?
   The point $(0, 3)$ is on the y-axis.

SOLVE ANOTHER PROBLEM

Reflect the figure in the grid above across the x-axis and give the new coordinates.

E'' _(−4, 0)_ F'' _(−5, −3)_ G'' _(−2.5, −4)_ H'' _(0, −3)_ I'' _(−1, 0)_

▶ ENRICHMENT

Name _____

Extend Your Thinking 11-7

Patterns in Geometry

When you draw a diagonal within a square, the result is two isosceles right triangles. Another name for an isosceles right triangle is a 45-45-90 triangle.

1. Use the Pythagorean Theorem to find the missing side of each triangle. Round your answer to the nearest tenth if necessary.

Leg a	Leg b	Hypotenuse
1	1	1.4
2	2	2.8
3	3	4.2
4	4	5.7
5	5	7.1
6	6	8.5

2. What pattern do you notice in the columns of the table above?
   Possible answer: Relatively steady increases; Column 1 and Column 2 by 1 unit, Column 3 by ≈ 1.4 units.

3. What pattern do you notice in the rows of the table above?
   Possible answer: Column 1 = Column 2, and Column 3 is ≈ 1.4 times Column 1.

4. The lengths of the sides of any 45-45-90 triangles are x, x, and $x\sqrt{2}$. See how that compares to your answers to Questions 2 and 3. Then draw a triangle and label the sides using x, x, and $x\sqrt{2}$.

5. Graph these ordered pairs: $(1, 6)$, $(1, 1)$, and $(6, 1)$. What kind of triangle did you graph?
   Isosceles right; 45-45-90.

6. What is the length of each leg? **5 units.**

7. What is the length of the hypotenuse? **7.1 units.**

Symmetry

▶ **Lesson Link** You've seen how transformations affect figures. Now you'll see how transformations can show whether a figure has symmetry. ◀

A figure has **symmetry** if it coincides with itself after a transformation.

A figure has **line symmetry** if there is a **line of symmetry** that divides the figure into two identical halves. Line symmetry is based on the reflection.

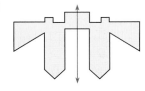

You'll Learn ...

■ to recognize several types of symmetry

... How It's Used

Luthiers, people who make and repair string instruments, use concepts of symmetry to craft instruments that allow the strings to vibrate properly.

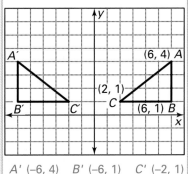

Vocabulary

symmetry

line symmetry

line of symmetry

rotational symmetry

point symmetry

Explore Line Symmetry

The Splittin' Image

Materials: $8\frac{1}{2}$ in. by 11 in. paper, Scissors

1. Fold a sheet of paper in half. At a point on one side of the fold, draw a curved line that starts and finishes on the fold.

2. With the paper folded, cut along the line you drew. Compare each side of the fold and describe what happened after you cut the shape. What is the line of symmetry?

3. Fold a fresh sheet of paper in half, then fold it in half again. Draw a curved line that begins on one fold and ends on the other. Cut along the line. How many lines of symmetry does it have?

Learn Symmetry

Example 1

Which line is a line of symmetry?

$\overleftrightarrow{AR}$, because it separates mirror images.

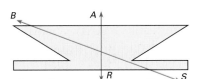

Objective

■ **Recognize several types of symmetry.**

Vocabulary

■ **Symmetry, line symmetry, line of symmetry, rotational symmetry, point symmetry**

Materials

■ **Explore: $8\frac{1}{2}$ in. by 11 in. paper, scissors**

NCTM Standards

■ **1–4, 12**

▶ Review

$\triangle ABC$ has been reflected across the y-axis to produce $\triangle A'B'C'$. Give the coordinates of A', B', and C'.

A' (–6, 4) B' (–6, 1) C' (–2, 1)

Available on Daily Transparency 11-8

---

1 Introduce

Explore

You may wish to use Teaching Tool Transparency 16: Protractor with **Explore**.

The Point

Students fold a sheet of paper, draw a shape on it that starts and ends at the fold, and cut the shape out to find the line of symmetry.

Ongoing Assessment

For Step 3, check that students draw their line starting at one fold line and ending at the other, without crossing a fold line.

MEETING INDIVIDUAL NEEDS

Resources

11-8 Practice
11-8 Reteaching
11-8 Problem Solving
11-8 Enrichment
11-8 Daily Transparency
  Problem of
  the Day
  Review
  Quick Quiz
Teaching Tool
Transparencies 2, 3, 16

Learning Modalities

Visual In **Explore**, students draw a shape on a folded piece of paper and then cut the shape out to find the line of symmetry.

Kinesthetic Students can experiment with folding and cutting paper to create their own symmetrical figures.

Individual For Exercise 16 on page 609, students are asked to write a Journal entry comparing point symmetry to a reflection across a point instead of a line.

Inclusion

Students who have limited perception may need as many hands-on experiences as possible. As often as practical in this lesson, allow these students to trace the figures, cut the figures out, and physically fold them to find the lines of symmetry.

2 Teach

Learn

Alternate Examples

1. Which line is a line of symmetry?

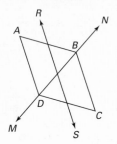

$\overleftrightarrow{MN}$, because it separates mirror images.

2. How many lines of symmetry does the figure have?

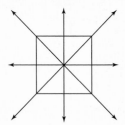

The square has four lines of symmetry.

3. Does the figure have rotational symmetry? If so, after how many degrees of rotation does the pattern rotate onto itself?

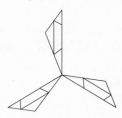

The figure has rotational symmetry because the pattern coincides after a 120° rotation and also after a 240° rotation.

Example 2

How many lines of symmetry does the figure have?

Find every line that produces a mirror image.

The figure has three lines of symmetry.

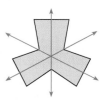

A figure has **rotational symmetry** if it can be rotated onto itself after a rotation of less than 360°.

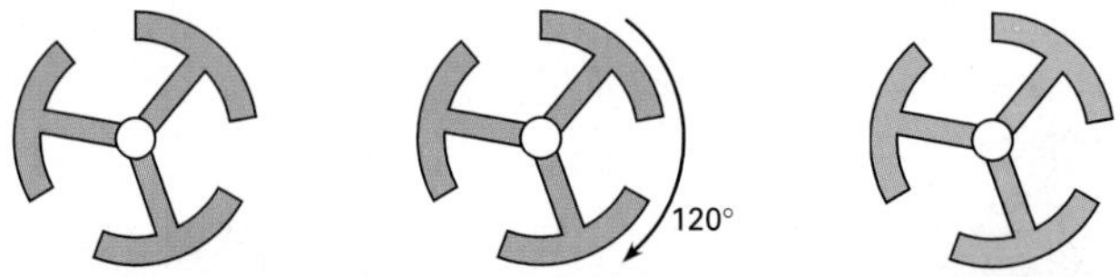

120°

Example 3

Does the painted design of an ancient Pueblo bowl have rotational symmetry? If so, after how many degrees of rotation does the pattern rotate onto itself?

Rotate the design to see if the pattern coincides.

Try 90° clockwise.

A 90° rotation works!

The Pueblo design has rotational symmetry because the pattern coincides after a 90° rotation.

The design also coincides after a 180° or 270° rotation.

90°

Try It

a. How many lines of symmetry does the figure have? **Four**

b. Does the figure have rotational symmetry? If so, after how many degrees of rotation does it rotate onto itself? **Yes; 90°**

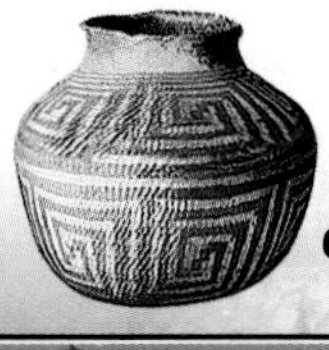

MATH EVERY DAY

▶ **Problem of the Day**

Karli can read 5 books in the same time as it takes Xenia to read 4 books. If they start reading at the same time, how many books will each girl have read when Karli has read twice as many books as Xenia? At the stated rate, Karli cannot read twice as many books as Xenia. Xenia will always have read 80% as many books as Karli.

Available on Daily Transparency 11-8

An Extension is provided in the transparency package.

Fact of the Day

The world's largest quilt measures 85 feet by 134 feet. It was made by 7000 people for the 1989 centennial of North Dakota.

Mental Math

Find these sums mentally.

1. 35.75 + 20.25 56
2. 55.5 + 5.5 61
3. 22.25 + 28.25 50.5

A figure has **point symmetry**, a specific type of rotational symmetry, when it rotates onto itself after a rotation of exactly 180°.

Example 4

Does this central piece of a Navajo sand painting have point symmetry?

Rotate the figure 180°.

Yes, the sand painting design has point symmetry.

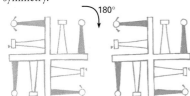

Example 5

What kinds of symmetry does the figure have?

It has two lines of symmetry.
Check for line symmetry.

It has rotational symmetry for 180°.
Check for rotational symmetry.

It has point symmetry also.

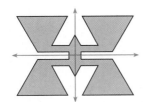

Try It

What kinds of symmetry does this hurricane symbol have?
Rotational and point symmetries

▶ **Science Link**

According to the Beaufort scale of wind effects, a hurricane is in action when the wind speed is 73 mi/hr or more. The Beaufort number for a hurricane is 12.

Check | Your Understanding

1. Describe the relationship between a figure with a line of symmetry and a reflection.

2. How many lines of symmetry does a circle have? Explain.

3. If a figure has rotational symmetry, is it guaranteed to have point symmetry? Explain.

11-8 • Symmetry **607**

Alternate Examples

4. Does this figure have rotational symmetry when rotated about the point *V*?

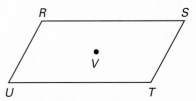

Rotate the figure 180°.
Yes, the parallelogram *RSTU* has rotational symmetry.

5. What kinds of symmetry does the figure have?

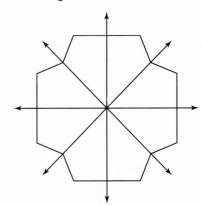

Check for line symmetry:
It has four lines of symmetry.

Check for rotational symmetry:
It has rotational symmetry for 90°, 180°, and 270°.

It has point symmetry also.

3 Practice and Assess

Check

If students are having trouble answering Exercise 3, have them trace the figure in Example 2 and experiment with doing a 180° rotation to check for point symmetry.

Answers for Check Your Understanding

1. A line of symmetry is a line across which the figure can be reflected and appear unchanged.

2. Infinitely many; Every line through the circle's center is a line of symmetry.

3. No; See Example 2.

MEETING MIDDLE SCHOOL CLASSROOM NEEDS

Tips from Middle School Teachers

I begin this lesson by having students list things in the real world that are symmetric. As the list becomes longer and longer, I impress on students that mathematics is all around us—not just in math class.

History Connection	Cultural Connection
The Winnebago Indians lived in Wisconsin and had an eastern woodlands culture. They hunted buffalo, fished, and did some farming. Winnebago chiefs, which included both men and women, inherited their rank. The Winnebago were known for observing many elaborate tribal ceremonies such as the buffalo dance and the winter feast.	Exercise 2 on page 608 deals with the culture of the mound building Indians. The mound builders were not a single group of people. Many Indians practiced mound building, but the activity was concentrated in a large area extending from the Appalachian Mountains west to the eastern edge of the prairies and from the Great Lakes area to the Gulf of Mexico. Mounds were built from about 1000 B.C. to after A.D. 1500. The mounds were built as burial places, as platforms to hold important buildings, and as ceremonial grounds. Mounds were often built in the shape of animals or geometric shapes.

11-8 Exercises and Applications

Assignment Guide

- **Basic**
  1–7, 12–14, 18–26 evens

- **Average**
  3–5, 6–12 evens, 13–15,
  17–25 odds

- **Enriched**
  3–5, 7–13 odds, 14–16,
  17–25 odds

Exercise Notes

■ **Exercise 3**

Test Prep If some students have difficulty with this question, you might want to review the concept of degree measure with them. Some students may also need the terms *clockwise* and *counterclockwise* clarified.

Exercise Answers

2. Line and point symmetry; The lines of symmetry run from the upper left to lower right and from the lower left to the upper right. The symmetry point is in the middle.

Reteaching

Activity

Materials: $8\frac{1}{2}$ in. by 11 in. paper, compass, scissors

- Work with a partner.

- Use your compass to draw a circle with a 4-inch diameter.

- Cut the circle out.

- Fold the circle in half three successive times.

- Cut two triangular notches in each straight side and one at the point of the folded paper.

- Unfold the paper to see the symmetrical figure you have created. How many lines of symmetry does your figure have? Four lines of symmetry.

Practice and Apply

1. **Getting Started** In each of the following, which lines are *not* lines of symmetry?

   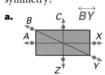 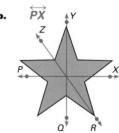 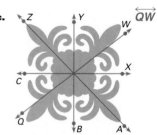

2. **History** Mound builders built large monuments made of earth between 1000 B.C. and A.D. 700. Artifacts of their life and culture have been found within these mounds. What kinds of symmetry are in this prehistoric plate pattern found in Tennessee? Sketch the plate and identify any lines of symmetry and rotation points.

   Ohio Serpent Mound, Adena culture

3. **Test Prep** Which rotation will give the same result as a rotation 90° clockwise? **C**

   Ⓐ 90° counterclockwise   Ⓑ 180° counterclockwise

   Ⓒ 270° counterclockwise   Ⓓ 360° counterclockwise

4. 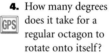 How many degrees does it take for a regular octagon to rotate onto itself?

   45°, 90°, 135°, 180°, 225°, 270°, 315°, 360°

5. How many degrees does it take for an equilateral triangle to rotate onto itself?

   120°, 240°, 360°

608 Chapter 11 • Similarity, Congruence, and Transformations

▷ **PRACTICE**

Name _____

Practice 11-8

Symmetry

1. **a.** What kinds of symmetry does this figure have?
   __Line, rotational, point__
   b. Identify any lines of symmetry and rotation points.

   Rotation point

2. **a.** What kinds of symmetry does this figure have?
   __Rotational, point__
   b. Identify any lines of symmetry and rotation points.

   Rotation point

3. **a.** How many degrees can this figure be turned and end up unchanged? __60°__
   b. Does the figure have rotational symmetry? __Yes__

4. **a.** How many degrees can this figure be turned and end up unchanged? __360°__
   b. Does the figure have rotational symmetry? __No__

5. How many lines of symmetry does the flower pattern have? __8__

For each letter shown, draw any and all lines of symmetry.

6. U   7. H   8. L   9. D

10. **Language Arts** The word BED has a horizontal line of symmetry. Find at least three other words that have a horizontal lines of symmetry.
    __Possible answer: BOX, CODE, CHECK, DOCK__

11. An adapter like the one shown can be used to make a 45-rpm record ("single") play on a standard record player.
    a. Draw all lines of symmetry, if any.
    b. How many degrees can this figure be turned and end up unchanged? __120°__

▷ **RETEACHING**

Name _____

Alternative Lesson 11-8

Symmetry

A figure has **line symmetry** if there is a **line of symmetry** that divides the figure into two identical halves. The two halves are mirror images of each other.

A figure has **rotational symmetry** if can be rotated onto itself after a rotation of less than 360°.

— Example 1 —

How many lines of symmetry does the figure have?

Find every line that produces a mirror image.

The figure has three lines of symmetry.

Try It How many lines of symmetry does each figure have? Draw the lines.

a. __1 line.__   b. __6 lines.__   c. __4 lines.__

Does this figure have rotational symmetry? If so, after how many degrees of rotation does the pattern rotate onto itself?

Rotate the figure to see if the pattern coincides.

The figure coincides after a 180° rotation, so the figure has rotational symmetry.

Try It Does each figure have rotational symmetry? If so, after how many degrees of rotation does the pattern rotate onto itself?

d. __No.__   e. __Yes. 90°__   f. __Yes. 72°__

6. a. How many degrees could you rotate this Alaskan star pattern around its center to produce an identical figure? **180°, 360°**
b. Does the pattern have rotational symmetry? **Yes**

7. Science There are 400 species of the passion flower, some of which bear fruit. How many lines of symmetry does this passion flower have? **Ten**

Copy each letter and draw any and all lines of symmetry.

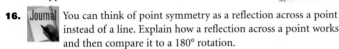

8. A   **9. E**   **10. W**   **11. Z**

12. The word "TOOT" has a vertical line of symmetry. Find at least three other words that have a vertical line of symmetry.

Problem Solving and Reasoning

This deer pattern appears on a woven bag used by the Winnebago tribe for storing dried food.

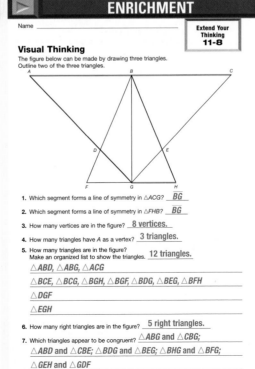

13. Patterns Are there similar figures? Congruent figures? Explain.

14. Communicate What kind of symmetry, if any, does the overall pattern have? Explain.

15. Math Reasoning How could you transform a deer in the upper row to create one in the bottom row?

16. [Journal] You can think of point symmetry as a reflection across a point instead of a line. Explain how a reflection across a point works and then compare it to a 180° rotation.

17. Choose a Strategy Draw a figure with four lines of symmetry.

Problem Solving
STRATEGIES
- Look for a Pattern
- Make an Organized List
- Make a Table
- Guess and Check
- Work Backward
- Use Logical Reasoning
- Draw a Diagram
- Solve a Simpler Problem

Mixed Review

Identify each of these numbers as rational or irrational. *[Lesson 7-8]*

18. $\sqrt{5}$ **19.** $\sqrt{22}$ **20.** $0.\overline{45}$ **21.** $\dfrac{\sqrt{36}}{6}$ **22.** 0.343443444

Find each product. Write your answers in scientific notation. *[Lesson 10-8]*

23. $(8.6 \times 10^4) \cdot (6.7 \times 10^9)$ **24.** $(3.0 \times 10^6) \cdot (2.9 \times 10^3)$
$\quad\quad 5.762 \times 10^{14}$ $\quad\quad\quad\quad 8.7 \times 10^9$
25. $(1.1 \times 10^2) \cdot (4.9 \times 10^5)$ **26.** $(3.2 \times 10^5) \cdot (1.3 \times 10^2)$
$\quad\quad 5.39 \times 10^7$ $\quad\quad\quad\quad 4.16 \times 10^7$

Exercise Notes
■ **Exercise 17**
Problem-Solving Tip You may wish to use Teaching Tool Transparencies 2 and 3: Guided Problem Solving, pages 1–2.

Exercise Answers
8. Vertical line through A.
9. Horizontal line through E.
10. Vertical line through W.
11. No lines of symmetry.
12. Possible answers: WOW, MUM, HAH.
13. Yes; Yes; The animal shapes in each row are congruent.
14. None of the kinds learned so far; A combination of reflection and translation is needed.
15. You can't because the deer in each row are looking in different directions.
16. Each point on the figure is moved to a new location directly across the symmetry point, and the same distance from it. This produces the same result as a 180° rotation.
17. Answers may vary.
18. Irrational   19. Irrational
20. Rational   21. Rational
22. Rational

Alternate Assessment
Ongoing Check that students can distinguish between a line of symmetry and any line that divides a figure in two. Verify that they can identify a line of symmetry as a mirror line with each half of the figure a reflection of the other.

> **PROBLEM SOLVING**

Name _____

Guided Problem Solving 11-8

GPS PROBLEM 4, STUDENT PAGE 608

How many degrees does it take for a regular octagon to rotate onto itself?

STOP

— Understand —
1. What is a regular octagon? An 8-sided figure with all sides and all angles congruent.

2. Why will you ignore the word STOP in the center of the sign?
Question concerns octagon's shape, not design inside this particular octagon.

— Plan —
3. How can you tell if the octagon rotates onto itself? Possible answer: All sides and angles coincide.

4. How many times can an octagon rotate onto itself? Count the final turn to return to the original position. 8 times.

5. How many degrees are in a complete rotation? 360°

6. How can you find the number of degrees in each turn? Divide 360° by 8.

— Solve —
7. List the degrees of the rotations.
45°, 90°, 135°, 180°, 225°, 270°, 315°, 360°

— Look Back —
8. How can you check your answer? Possible answer: Trace figure on another paper. Turn it on drawing to count rotations.

SOLVE ANOTHER PROBLEM

How many degrees does it take for a regular hexagon to rotate onto itself?
60°, 120°, 180°, 240°, 300°, 360°

> **ENRICHMENT**

Name _____

Extend Your Thinking 11-8

Visual Thinking
The figure below can be made by drawing three triangles. Outline two of the three triangles.

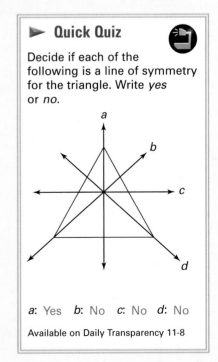

1. Which segment forms a line of symmetry in △ACG? $\overline{BG}$
2. Which segment forms a line of symmetry in △FHB? $\overline{BG}$
3. How many vertices are in the figure? 8 vertices.
4. How many triangles have A as a vertex? 3 triangles.
5. How many triangles are in the figure? Make an organized list to show the triangles. 12 triangles.
△ABD, △ABG, △ACG
△BCE, △BCG, △BGH, △BGF, △BDG, △BEG, △BFH
△DGF
△EGH
6. How many right triangles are in the figure? 5 right triangles.
7. Which triangles appear to be congruent? △ABG and △CBG; △ABD and △CBE; △BDG and △BEG; △BHG and △BFG; △GEH and △GDF

> **Quick Quiz**

Decide if each of the following is a line of symmetry for the triangle. Write *yes* or *no*.

a: Yes   *b*: No   *c*: No   *d*: No

Available on Daily Transparency 11-8

Lesson 11-8 **609**

Lesson Organizer

Objective

- **Create endless patterns using transformations.**

Vocabulary

- **Tessellation**

Materials

- **Explore: Graph paper, power polygons**

NCTM Standards

- **1, 2, 4, 12**

▶ **Review**

1. A movement of points that changes a figure is called a ___ . transformation

2. A ___ is a transformation that flips a figure over a line. reflection

3. A ___ is a transformation that slides all points of a figure the same distance in the same direction. translation

4. A transformation that turns a figure about a point is called a ___ . rotation

Available on Daily Transparency 11-9

▶ **Lesson Link**

Now, students will look at figures that form designs that cover entire areas, leaving no gaps or overlaps.

1 Introduce

Explore

You may wish to use Teaching Tool Transparencies 7: $\frac{1}{4}$-inch Graph Paper and 18: Power Polygons with **Explore**.

The Point

Students create tessellations and describe properties of shapes that tessellate.

Ongoing Assessment

In Step 1, check that students are not leaving gaps in or overlapping their pattern.

11-9 Covering the Plane

▶ **Lesson Link**   You'll use what you know about transformations that produce congruent figures to cover flat surfaces in interesting and attractive patterns. ◀

You'll Learn ...

■ to create endless patterns using transformations

... How It's Used

Fabric designers make one pattern that, when translated, creates a continuous pattern that can be printed on many yards of fabric.

Vocabulary

tessellation

Explore | **Tessellations**

Seeing Double, Triple, Quadruple ...

Materials: Graph paper, Power polygons

1. Trace the outline of one shape onto graph paper. Trace more outlines of that shape to make a pattern without gaps or overlaps.

2. Use another polygon to make another pattern without gaps or overlaps.

3. When did you use translations? Rotations?

4. Describe how the properties of each shape affected your use of translations or rotations.

5. Use both shapes together to draw another pattern without gaps or overlaps.

Learn | **Covering the Plane**

A **tessellation** is a repeating pattern of figures that covers a plane (flat surface) without gaps or overlaps.

Example 1

Is the woven thunderbird design from the Winnebago tribe a tessellation?

No, because there are gaps between the thunderbird shapes.

MEETING INDIVIDUAL NEEDS

Resources

11-9 Practice
11-9 Reteaching
11-9 Problem Solving
11-9 Enrichment
11-9 Daily Transparency
   Problem of the Day
   Review
   Quick Quiz

Teaching Tool Transparencies 7, 18, 19

 Wide World of Mathematics Geometry: Textile Works

Learning Modalities

Social   In **Explore**, students work in small groups as they trace shapes from the pattern block and experiment with tessellations. They then share their finished designs with the class.

Logical   In **Check Your Understanding** students explain when two different shapes will form a tessellation.

Visual   For Exercise 2 on page 613, students are given a figure and need to use 8 translations to produce a tessellation of it.

Challenge

Allow students to experiment with combining shapes to produce interesting and artistic tessellations. Suggest that they cut the shapes from colored construction paper and glue them in place on poster board. Challenge students to create their own shapes.

Example 2

Is the design made by M. C. Escher, the artist, a tessellation?

Yes, because there are no gaps or overlaps.

Many tessellations are made by rotating, reflecting, or translating one shape again and again.

► **Fine Arts Link**

It could take M. C. Escher months to develop a new idea. He is famous for his "intellectual" period, after 1936, when he repeatedly used transformations to create designs.

Example 3

What transformation is used to make this tessellation of an octagon?

Translations are used.

Some tessellations use more than one transformation.

Example 4

Does this tessellation display any of the transformations?

a. Translations   **b.** Rotations   **c.** Reflections

Check for each transformation.

Translations are shown.   Rotations are shown.   Reflections are shown.

Try It

Does this tessellation display any of the transformations?

a. Translations **Yes**

b. Rotations **Yes**

c. Reflections **No**

Drawing by Ryan Evans from *Tessellation Winners: Original Student Art*, The Second Contest (Palo Alto, CA: Dale Seymour Publications, 1994). Copyright © 1994 by Dale Seymour Publications.

11-9 • *Covering the Plane*   **611**

MATH EVERY DAY

► Problem of the Day

Alexi works on Monday, Wednesday, and Friday. Dexter works every other day. Felicia works on Friday, Saturday, and Sunday. They all worked on Friday, April 4. When will they all work together again? Friday, April 18

Available on Daily Transparency 11-9

An Extension is provided in the transparency package.

► Fact of the Day

A soccer ball is actually a 3-D tessellation of a sphere made up of a combination of regular spherical pentagons and regular spherical hexagons.

Estimation

Estimate each product.
Possible answers

1. 500 • 10.5   5,000

2. 305 • 106   30,000

3. 7,000 • 98   700,000

For Groups That Finish Early

Find another shape that you can fit together to make a pattern without gaps or overlaps. Then find a shape that will not work.

Answers for Explore

1–5. Answers may vary.

2 Teach

Learn

You may wish to use Teaching Tool Transparency 19: Tangram with this lesson.

Alternate Examples

1. Is the pattern of pentagons a tessellation?

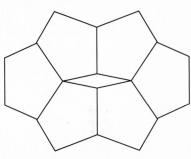

No, because there are gaps between the pentagons.

2. Is the pattern of hexagons a tessellation?

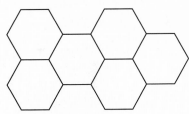

Yes, because there are no gaps or overlaps.

3. What transformation is used to make this tessellation?

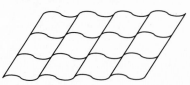

Translations are used.

4. Does this tessellation display any of the transformations?
   a. Translations
   b. Rotations
   c. Reflections

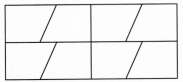

Check for each transformation.
Translations are shown.
Rotations are shown.
Reflections are not shown.

Lesson 11-9   611

5. Part of a kitchen wall is 6 ft × 3 ft = 18 ft². The decorative tiles to cover the space are squares with $\frac{1}{3}$-ft side lengths. How many tiles are needed to cover this part of the kitchen wall?

$(\frac{1}{3})^2 = \frac{1}{9}$ ft²   Find the area of one tile.

$18 \div \frac{1}{9} = x$ Divide by $\frac{1}{9}$.

$18 \cdot 9 = 162$ Multiply by the reciprocal of $\frac{1}{9}$.

About 162 tiles are needed to cover this part of the kitchen wall.

3 Practice and Assess

Check

Help students discover that in order for a shape to tessellate, the corners where adjacent shapes meet must form angles whose measures equal 360°.

Answers for Check Your Understanding

1. No; Possible explanation: A randomly chosen animal shape is not likely to tessellate.

2. Yes; Possible explanation: To find the area of the tessellation, you multiply the area of the tessellated shape by the number used.

3. Answers may vary.

4. Yes; Possible explanation: A tessellation like the one shown in Example 4 could use three transformations.

Triangles and quadrilaterals tessellate, but many shapes don't. To find out whether a shape tessellates, you have to experiment. For example,

Some irregular pentagons do; Regular pentagons don't.

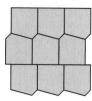

When a shape is tessellated, you can find the total area of the tessellation by multiplying the area of a single shape by the number of shapes used.

Remember

Dividing by a fraction requires you to multiply by the fraction's reciprocal. **[Page 357]**

Example 5

A kitchen floor is 6 ft by 10 ft = 60 ft². The tiles used to cover the floor are squares with $\frac{1}{2}$ ft side lengths. How many tiles are needed to cover the floor?

$\left(\frac{1}{2}\right)^2 = \frac{1}{4}$ Find the area of one tile.

$60 \div \frac{1}{4} = x$ Divide by $\frac{1}{4}$.

$60 \cdot 4 = 240$ Multiply by the reciprocal of $\frac{1}{4}$.

About 240 tiles are needed to cover the kitchen floor.

Try It

A 24 inch by 60 inch counter will be covered by square tiles with 4-inch side lengths. How many tiles are needed? Tiles can be cut to fit if necessary. **90**

Check Your Understanding

1. Can any shape create a tessellation? Explain.

2. If you know the area of a shape used to tessellate a surface and the number of shapes used, can you always calculate the area of the tessellation? Explain.

3. If someone gives you two different shapes and asks whether or not they can form a tessellation, describe what steps you would take to answer their question.

4. Can you use more than one transformation to create a tessellation? Explain and provide an example.

MEETING MIDDLE SCHOOL CLASSROOM NEEDS

Team Teaching

Working with an art teacher, display as many of the works of Dutch graphic artist M.C. Escher as possible. Several of his pieces are used as examples in this lesson. Most of his works consisted of tessellations arranged so as to create strange optical effects. His work was sometimes called "mathematical art."

Science Connection

Scientists study possible tessellations in their analysis of crystal structures. Minerals are often identified solely by their crystal system, which is the mathematical arrangement of their crystals.

Cultural Connection

Exercise 5 on page 613 uses the Alhambra in Spain as an example of how skilled the Islamic artists were in their use of tessellations. The Alhambra was built by the Moors, between 1248 and 1354, for Muslim sultans. The beauty of the palace lies in the elaborate decorations of the inner courts and halls where all seventeen possible tessellating patterns have been found on the tiles.

Practice and Apply

1. **Getting Started** State whether each pattern will tessellate.

a.

No

b.

Yes

c. No

2. Use eight translations of the figure to produce a tessellation.

3. a. Which regular polygons tessellate?

b. Explain why regular pentagons do not tessellate.

4. **Test Prep** Which transformation would have to be used for the tessellation shown? **B**

Ⓐ Translation   Ⓑ Rotation

Ⓒ Reflection   Ⓓ Dilation

5. History Tiles on floors or ceilings often form tessellations. The Alhambra in Spain, built around 1300, is an elaborate example of Islamic architecture. How many square tiles with 6 in. sides would it take to cover a wall with an area of 1000 ft²? **4000**

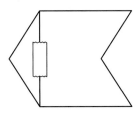

6. a. Name and draw a polygon that will tessellate.

b. Name and draw a polygon that will not tessellate.

c. Name and draw two polygons that can tessellate together.

7. Name the figures used in each tessellation.

a. 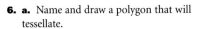   **b.**   **c.**

Assignment Guide

■ **Basic**
1, 2, 4–9, 11, 13, 14–20 evens

■ **Average**
2, 4–12, 15–19 odds

■ **Enriched**
2–9, 11, 12, 14, 17, 20

Exercise Answers

2.

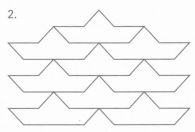

3, 6–7. See page C5.

Reteaching

Activity

Materials: $8\frac{1}{2}$ in. by 11 in. paper, scissors, index card, tape

• Work in groups of three.

• Draw a 1 in. square on the index card.

• Change one side of the square slightly by cutting a V-shape or half-circle shape out of it.

• Tape the shape you cut out to the opposite side of the square like this:

• Cut the new shape out of the index card. This is your template.

• Use the template to try to produce a tessellation. Does your shape tessellate? The shape should tessellate.

• Trade templates with other group members to experiment with making different tessellations.

Exercise Notes

■ **Exercise 11**

Extension Interested students may enjoy designing floors for the classroom or a room in their home. Have them create a tessellating tile design similar to the one in the photograph. Then have them use the pattern and floor area to decide how many tiles of each type/color they will need.

Exercise Answers

10. Yes; Possible explanation: You can use translations to copy the rhombuses and half of the parallelograms, and a reflection followed by translations to copy the other parallelograms.

11. No; 175 ($\frac{1}{4}$ ft^2) < 150 ft^2

12. Answers may vary.

13. Possible answers: T, I, E, F, H, L, and V.

Alternate Assessment

Portfolio Students will undoubtedly enjoy choosing some of their explorations with tessellating to include in their portfolios for future reference.

▶ Quick Quiz

1. A ____ is a repeating pattern of figures that covers a plane without gaps or overlaps. tessellation

2. The ____ used to create tessellations are translation, rotation, and/or reflection. transformations

3. Regular pentagons (do, do not) tessellate. do not

4. Triangles (always, sometimes, never) tessellate. always

Available on Daily Transparency 11-9

Social Studies A tribe from British Columbia called these designs the mouth and the fish net.

8. What polygons are used? Rectangles and hexagons

9. Can the patterns be produced using
   a. Only translations? Yes b. Only rotations? Yes
   c. Only reflections? No d. A combination? Yes

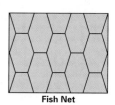

Mouth   Fish Net

Problem Solving and Reasoning

10. **Journal** This pattern is created using a rhombus and a parallelogram. Can this tessellation be created using only reflections and translations? Explain.

11. **Communicate** A flooring contractor **GPS** has 175 tiles that are 6 in. by 6 in. for covering a kitchen floor that is 15 ft by 10 ft. Does he have enough tiles? Explain.

12. **Patterns** You can tessellate any triangle or quadrilateral using 180° rotations around the midpoints of the sides. This pattern starts with an obtuse triangle. Do the same thing with an acute triangle and a trapezoid and sketch the result for each.

13. **Math Reasoning** Find five letters of the alphabet that tessellate. (*Hint:* You can draw the letters.)

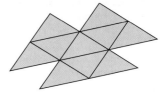

Mixed Review

Find the missing side length for each right triangle. [Lesson 7-9]

14. ≈ 10.3 ft

15. ≈ 15.9 in.

16. 8 m

Solve each proportion. [Lesson 5-4]

17. $\frac{4}{5} = \frac{x}{100}$ $x = 80$

18. $\frac{2.5}{20} = \frac{7.5}{x}$ $x = 60$

19. $\frac{6}{7} = \frac{21}{x}$ $x = 24.5$

20. $\frac{4.3}{8.6} = \frac{x}{50}$ $x = 25$

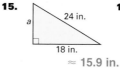

614 *Chapter 11 • Similarity, Congruence, and Transformations*

PROBLEM SOLVING 11-9

PROBLEM SOLVING

Name _____

Guided Problem Solving 11-9

GPS PROBLEM 11, STUDENT PAGE 614

A flooring contractor has 175 tiles that are 6 in. by 6 in. for covering a kitchen floor that is 15 ft by 10 ft. Does he have enough tiles? Explain.

Possible answer: Item 10

— Understand —
1. How many tiles does the contractor have? __175 tiles.__
2. What are the dimensions of each tile? __6 in. by 6 in.__
3. What are the dimensions of the floor? __15 ft by 10 ft.__

— Plan —
4. Use decimals to write the dimensions of the tiles in feet. __0.5 ft by 0.5 ft.__
5. What is the area of each tile in square feet? __0.25 ft²__
6. What is the area of the kitchen floor? __150 ft²__
7. How can you find the number of tiles needed to cover the floor? __Divide 150 by 0.25.__

— Solve —
8. How many tiles are needed to cover the floor? __600 tiles.__
9. Does he have enough tiles? Explain. __No, he needs 600 tiles but only has 175 tiles.__

— Look Back —
10. How could you find the answer in another way? __Convert measures to inches and compute: 21,600 ÷ 36 = 600.__

SOLVE ANOTHER PROBLEM

A section of a kitchen wall is 4 ft by 7 ft. It will be covered with tiles that are 3 in. by 3 in. The contractor has 450 tiles. Does she have enough tiles? Explain.

Yes, she needs 448 tiles and has 450 tiles on hand.

ENRICHMENT

Name _____

Extend Your Thinking 11-9

Decision Making

Lester has three different plans for college.

The first plan is to attend a community college for two years and then transfer to a four-year college to finish his degree. He estimates the cost for tuition, fees, and books at the community college to be $2,000 per year. He will live at home, so he does not need to consider room and board costs.

The second plan is to attend an in-state public four-year college. He estimates the cost to be $9,000 per year. This includes living on campus.

The third is to attend a private four-year college with an estimated cost of $20,000 per year. This includes living on campus.

1. How much would it cost for Lester to attend the in-state college for four years if the cost remains the same each year? __$36,000__

2. How much would it cost for Lester to attend the private college for four years if the cost remains the same each year? __$80,000__

3. How much would it cost for Lester to attend the community college for two years and then transfer to the public college if the cost remains the same each year? How much if he transfers to the private college?
Public college: $22,000; private college: $44,000.

4. Lester's parents want him to investigate ways to finance his education. What are some of the ways he can prepare to fund his education?
Possible answer: Work part-time and during summers through high school; work part-time while in college, apply for student loans, scholarships.

5. Suppose these are the same costs you would incur to attend each college. Which college would you choose? How would you pay for it?
Check students' answers.

---

614   Chapter 11

Section 11B Connect

At the beginning of Section 11B, you saw how Native American arts and crafts repeat shapes to make patterns. You'll design your own pattern by using various transformations.

Doing What Comes Naturally

The Pueblo people of the American Southwest are known for their pottery. Pottery made by the Zuni, Laguna, and Acoma tribes display many patterns, including geometric designs and natural shapes such as birds and lizards.

Symmetry and transformations are frequently used in the paintings on their pottery.

1. Look at the photo and notice the symmetry. Discuss the types of symmetry you see. Is there a type of symmetry that every piece has?

2. Now discuss the types of transformations you see and how often they appear. Point out tessellations if you see any.

3. With your group, design a pattern to put on a traditional Native American object (pottery, tepee, rug, mask, beadwork, jewelry, blanket). Start by dividing the object into four equal areas.

4. Each of the four areas will have a unique shape.

   Area 1: Shape with exactly one line of symmetry.

   Area 2: Shape with exactly three lines of symmetry.

   Area 3: Shape with point symmetry.

   Area 4: Shape with any symmetry you like.

5. Apply a different transformation to each of the four shapes. Rotate, translate, reflect, and dilate.

6. If any of the shapes make a tessellation, that area of your piece will be filled with that tessellation. Do you think a dilation will tessellate?

7. Sketch some plans for your design.

615

Doing What Comes Naturally

The Point

In *Doing What Comes Naturally* on page 593, students learned about the use of geometric shapes and patterns in Native American art. Now they apply their knowledge of symmetry, geometric transformations, and tessellations to design similar patterns.

About the Page

- Steps 1 and 2 are the planning stages. Encourage all students in each group to contribute their ideas at this time.

- Steps 3–7 are the execution stages. Here students can share the work, each taking responsibility for a different part of the design.

Ongoing Assessment

Check that the students have divided the object into four equal areas in Step 3 and that they are including the various requirements specified in Steps 4–6.

Extension

After students complete their design, they may want to color it, using paints, crayons, or colored markers. You might provide a display area for finished designs.

Answers for Connect
1–7. Answers may vary.

11B Review

Section 11B Review

Review Correlation

Item(s)	Lesson(s)
1–3	11-6
4	11-7
5	11-6, 11-7
6, 7	11-8

Test Prep

Test-Taking Tip
Tell students that if they are taking a test with a large group (200 or more students), it is best to sit near the front of the room. They will be able to hear instructions, as well as questions and answers about procedures, better.

Answers for Review

2. (2, 3), (3, 2), (2, 1), (4, 2)

3. For each point (x, y) the reflected point is (–x, y).

4. (16, 24), (–28, 8), (12, –12)

5. Possible answer: Give up translation, which can be replaced by two successive rotations with different axes of rotation. Or, give up rotation, which can be replaced by two successive reflections using intersecting reflection lines.

6. c. Four

REVIEW 11B

---

1. What transformation is used in each pair of figures?

a.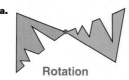
Rotation

b.
Translation

c.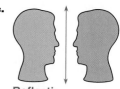
Reflection

The crescent shape is reflected across the _y_-axis.

2. List the corresponding vertex coordinates of the reflected figure.

3. What is the general rule for reflecting points across the _y_-axis?

4. A triangle with vertices at coordinates (4, 6), (−7, 2), and (3, −3) is dilated with respect to the origin by a factor of 4. What are the vertex coordinates of the dilation?

5. Suppose you had to give up one of the transformations but still wanted to be able to do all the same things with shapes that you could do before. Which one would you give up: Translation? Rotation? Reflection? Dilation? Explain your choice.

6. a. How many degrees can this design be rotated until it is rotated onto itself? **90°, 180°, 270°, 360°**
   b. What kind(s) of symmetry does it have? **Rotational symmetry, point symmetry, line symmetry**
   c. How many lines of symmetry does the figure have?

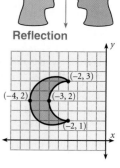

Test Prep

When you work with line symmetry, try to imagine folding the figure along the line of symmetry. The two halves should match exactly.

7. Which of the figures has a line of symmetry? **B**

Ⓐ Ⓑ Ⓒ Ⓓ

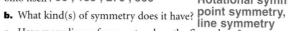

PRACTICE

Resources

Practice Masters
   Section 11B Review

Assessment Sourcebook
   Quiz 11B

  TestWorks
  Test and Practice Software

Name _____

Practice

Section 11B Review

1. What transformation is used in each of the two pairs of figures?

a. **Dilation**
b. **Reflection**

2. The shape is reflected across the x-axis. What are the corresponding vertex coordinates of the reflected figure?

W′ **(3, −3)**   X′ **(5, 1)**
Y′ **(2, 0)**   Z′ **(1, −1)**

3. What is the general rule for reflecting point (x, y) across the x-axis?
Possible answer: Change to (x, −y).

4. A parallelogram with vertices P(3, 3), Q(0, −3), R(−4, −2), and S(−1, 4) is dilated with respect to the origin, by a factor of 4/5. What are the new coordinates of the vertices?

P′ **(2.4, 2.4)**   Q′ **(0, −2.4)**   R′ **(−3.2, −1.6)**   S′ **(−0.8, 3.2)**

5. a. How many degrees can this figure be turned and look just as it did before? **90°**
   b. What kind or kinds of symmetry does it have?
   Line, rotational, point

6. **Geography** What is the absolute position of Mexico City using latitude and longitude? *[Lesson 8-3]*
   About 19.4° N, 99.2° W

7. **Science** The heaviest door in the world is designed to protect people from radiation at the Natural Institute for Fusion Science in Japan. It is 11.7 m high, 11.4 m wide, and 2.0 m thick. Find the volume of the door. *[Lesson 9-6]*
   266.76 m³

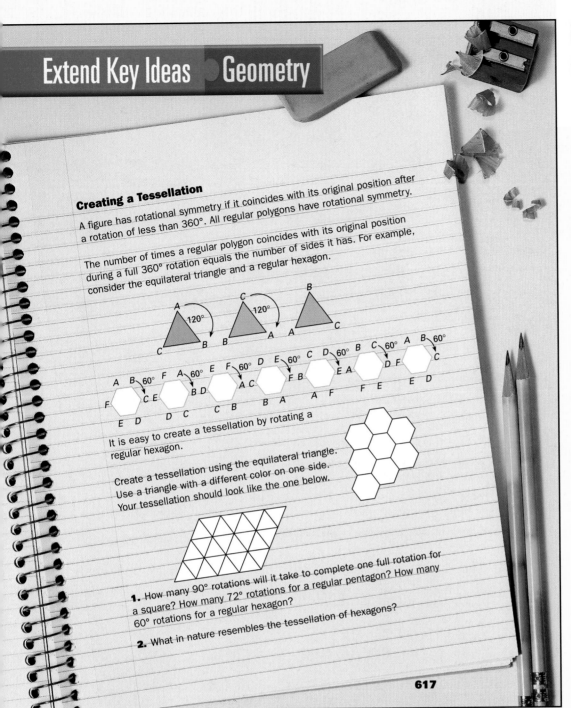

Creating a Tessellation

A figure has rotational symmetry if it coincides with its original position after a rotation of less than 360°. All regular polygons have rotational symmetry.

The number of times a regular polygon coincides with its original position during a full 360° rotation equals the number of sides it has. For example, consider the equilateral triangle and a regular hexagon.

It is easy to create a tessellation by rotating a regular hexagon.

Create a tessellation using the equilateral triangle. Use a triangle with a different color on one side. Your tessellation should look like the one below.

1. How many 90° rotations will it take to complete one full rotation for a square? How many 72° rotations for a regular pentagon? How many 60° rotations for a regular hexagon?

2. What in nature resembles the tessellation of hexagons?

617

Geometry

The Point
Students explore rotational symmetry of regular polygons.

About the Page

• Make sure students understand that the number of rotations needed to bring a regular polygon back to its original position, with all vertices back where they started, is equal to the number of sides of the polygon.

• Students also should understand that the magnitude of each rotation is 360° divided by the number of sides in the polygon.

Ask …
• How many rotations will it take to complete one full turn of 360° for an equilateral triangle? A regular hexagon? 3; 6

• How many degrees are there in each rotation for an equilateral triangle? A regular hexagon? 120°; 60°

Extension

Have students consider the following questions: As the number of sides of a regular polygon increases, what happens to the number of rotations needed to bring the polygon back to its original position? What happens to the number of degrees in each rotation? It increases; It decreases.

Answers for Questions
1. 4; 5; 6

2. Honeycomb

Review Correlation

Item(s)	Lesson(s)
1	11-1
2	11-3
3	11-2
4, 5	11-4
6	11-5
7	11-8
8, 9	11-9
10	11-8
11	11-9

For additional review, see page 686.

Answers for Review

1. $x = 18$ in.; $m\angle 1 = 135°$

2. Congruent by SAA.

3. Not congruent.

4. a. ≈ 0.87
   b. ≈ 0.87
   c. 1

5. $\sin \angle A = \dfrac{1.75}{6.25} = 0.28$;

   $\cos \angle A = \dfrac{6.0}{6.25} = 0.96$;

   $\angle A = \dfrac{1.75}{6.0} \approx 0.29$

6. 15 cm

7. a. $K'(0, 0)$; $L'(3, -1)$; $M'(2, -4)$; and $N'(0, -5)$
   b. $K'(0, 0)$; $L'(-3, 1)$; $M'(-2, 4)$; and $N'(0, 5)$
   c. $K'(0, 0)$; $L'(-1, 3)$; $M'(-4, 2)$; and $N'(-5, 0)$

8. $A'(1, -1)$; $B'(1, -2)$; $C'(3, -2)$

9. Dilation; Yes; No

10. $\overleftrightarrow{MW}$; $\overrightarrow{YP}$

11. Yes.

618

Chapter 11 Summary and Review

Graphic Organizer

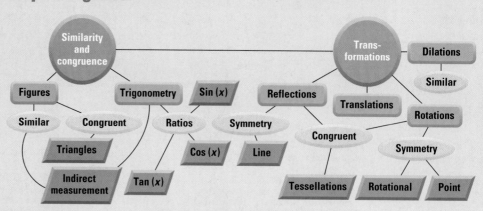

Section 11A   Similarity and Congruence

Summary

- Two figures are **congruent** ($\cong$) if they have the same shape and size. Two figures are **similar** ($\sim$) if they have the same shape but not necessarily the same size. Corresponding angles and corresponding sides appear in both congruent and similar figures.

- You can use the **Side-Side-Side, Side-Angle-Side, Angle-Side-Angle,** and **Side-Angle-Angle** rules to determine congruence of two triangles.

- For an acute angle in a right triangle, the **adjacent leg** is the leg next to the angle and the **opposite leg** is opposite the angle.

- The **trigonometric ratios sine, cosine,** and **tangent** can be used for **indirect measurement** of triangles.

Review

1. The two pentagons are similar. Find the length x and the measure of $\angle 1$.

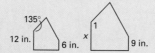

2. State whether the triangles are congruent; if they are, give the rule that justifies your answer.

618   *Chapter 11 • Similarity, Congruence, and Transformations*

Resources

Practice Masters
   Cumulative Review
   Chapters 1–11

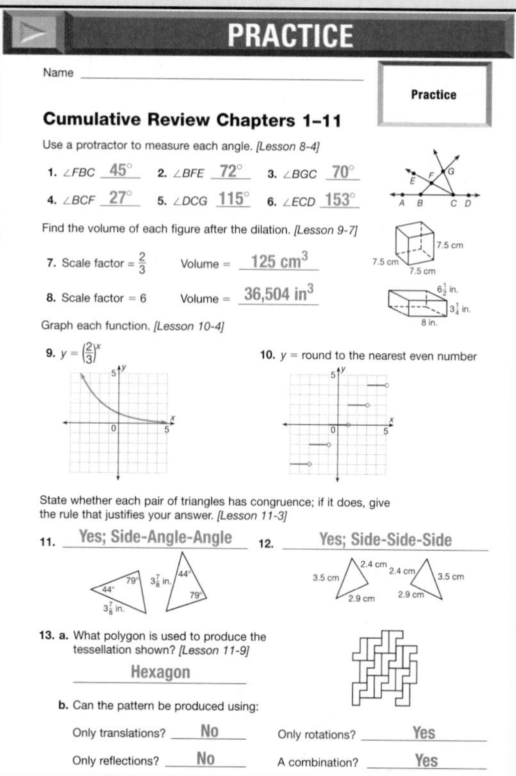

Name _____

Practice

Cumulative Review Chapters 1–11

Use a protractor to measure each angle. *[Lesson 8-4]*

1. $\angle FBC$ **45°** 2. $\angle BFE$ **72°** 3. $\angle BGC$ **70°**

4. $\angle BCF$ **27°** 5. $\angle DCG$ **115°** 6. $\angle ECD$ **153°**

Find the volume of each figure after the dilation. *[Lesson 9-7]*

7. Scale factor = $\frac{2}{3}$ Volume = **125 cm³**

8. Scale factor = 6   Volume = **36,504 in³**

Graph each function. *[Lesson 10-4]*

9. $y = \left(\frac{2}{3}\right)^x$

10. $y =$ round to the nearest even number

State whether each pair of triangles has congruence; if it does, give the rule that justifies your answer. *[Lesson 11-3]*

11. **Yes; Side-Angle-Angle**

12. **Yes; Side-Side-Side**

13. a. What polygon is used to produce the tessellation shown? *[Lesson 11-9]*

   Hexagon

b. Can the pattern be produced using:

Only translations?   **No**   Only rotations?   **Yes**

Only reflections?   **No**   A combination?   **Yes**

Section 11A Similarity and Congruence *continued*

3. Are the figures congruent?

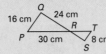

4. Calculate each trigonometric ratio.

   a. sin 60°   **b.** cos 30°   **c.** tan 45°

5. Use the lengths of the sides to write and evaluate the sine, cosine, and tangent ratios for the labeled angle.

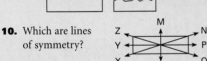

6. In the figure, △PQR is similar to △TSR. Find the length of $\overline{RT}$.

Section 11B Transformations

Summary

■ A **transformation** is a change in a figure that could be a **reflection, translation, rotation,** or **dilation.**

■ A figure has **symmetry** if it coincides with itself after a transformation. Three types of symmetry are: **line symmetry, rotational symmetry,** and **point symmetry.**

■ A **tessellation** is a repeating pattern of figures that covers a plane without gaps or overlaps.

Review

7. A figure has vertex coordinates K(0, 0); L(3, 1); M(2, 4); and N(0, 5). Find the coordinates of K′, L′, M′, and N′ after each transformation.

   a. Reflection across the x-axis

   b. Reflection across the y-axis

   c. Rotation 90° counterclockwise

8. △ABC is translated 4 units right and 1 unit down. Find the coordinates of A′, B′, and C′.

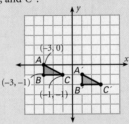

9. Which transformation has occurred? Are the figures similar? Congruent?

10. Which are lines of symmetry?

11. Can this tessellation be made using only rotations of a single triangle?

Chapter 11 Assessment

Assessment Correlation

Item(s)	Lesson(s)
1	11-1
2	11-2
3	11-3
4	11-4
5	11-5
6	11-6
7	11-7
8	11-9
9	11-4
10	11-6

Answers for Assessment

1. Yes.

2. $x = 7$; $y = 13$

3. Yes; by SAS.

4. About 43.86 ft (or about 43 ft 10 in.)

5. 7.5 cm

6. a. $A'(-2, 7)$
   b. $B'(0, 1)$
   c. $C'(-3, 4)$

7. 1.5

8. Pentagon, parallelogram.

9. a. ≈ 0.41
   b. ≈ -0.91
   c. ≈ 28.6

10. a. $W'(0, 0)$; $V'(0, -4)$; and $X'(2, -3)$

    b. $W'(0, 0)$; $V'(0, -4)$; and $X'(-2, -3)$

Performance Task

Possible answer:

Chapter 11 Assessment

1. Are the figures similar?

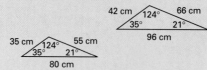

2. **Algebra** In the figure, the rectangles are congruent. Find the values of x and y.

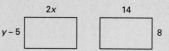

3. Are the triangles congruent? If so, state the rule that justifies your answer.

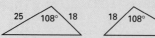

4. The top of a flagpole forms a 31° angle with a tourist who is 73 ft away from the base of the flagpole. How tall is the flagpole?

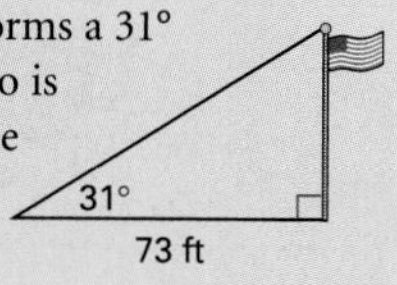

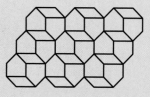

5. In the figure, $\triangle ACE$ is similar to $\triangle BCD$. If $\overline{CE}$ has a length of 18 cm, find the length of $\overline{CD}$.

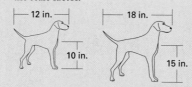

6. $\triangle ABC$ with vertex coordinates of $A(2, 7)$; $B(0, 1)$; and $C(3, 4)$ has been reflected across the y-axis to produce $\triangle A'B'C'$. Give the coordinates of

   a. A'

   b. B'

   c. C'

7. The dog shape on the left was enlarged. Find the scale factor.

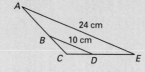

8. What polygons is the tessellation based on?

9. Calculate each trigonometric ratio.

   a. sin 24°

   b. cos 156°

   c. tan 88°

10. A figure has vertex coordinates $W(0, 0)$; $V(0, 4)$; and $X(2, 3)$. Find the coordinates of W', V', and X' after each transformation.

    a. Reflection across the x-axis

    b. Rotation 180° counterclockwise

Performance Task

Show how to make a tessellation using a concave quadrilateral such as the one shown. It may be helpful to cut five or ten identical shapes to see how they fit together.

Performance Assessment Key

See key on page 561.

Resources
Assessment Sourcebook
Chapter 11 Tests
Forms A and B (free response)
Form C (multiple choice)
Form D (performance assessment)
Form E (mixed response)
Form F (cumulative chapter test)
TestWorks
Test and Practice Software
Home and Community Connections
Letter Home for Chapter 11
in English and Spanish

Suggested Scoring Rubric

4 • Provides a neat drawing of a valid tessellation using a concave quadrilateral.

3 • Provides a fair drawing of a nearly valid tessellation using a concave quadrilateral.

2 • Attempts, but does not provide a valid tessellation using a concave quadrilateral.

1 • Does not attempt to provide a valid tessellation.

Performance Assessment

Choose one problem.

A Triangle That's Not Quite Right

There is no Side-Side-Angle rule to show congruent triangles. Can you create one obtuse triangle and one acute triangle that would be "congruent" if such a rule existed? Explain your reasoning.

Palindrommytry

"Madam I'm Adam," "mom," "1881." These are all palindromes: phrases, words, or numbers that are the same when written backward or forward. What kind of symmetry do palindromes have? Give a few of your own examples of palindromes. Can you create a palindrome with two lines of symmetry?

A PUZZLING TESSELLATION

Jigsaw puzzles have entertained us all. Create a jigsaw puzzle piece that will tessellate. Repetitions of the piece should interlock with the others. Draw a picture to show your tessellation. Describe how you created the puzzle piece that tessellates.

The Task of a Mask

A mask is a sculpted face used for ornamentation or disguise. Masks, like most all faces, have one line of symmetry. List some features (for example, a nose) on a face and identify the type of symmetry each exhibits. Then, for a mask, draw a face with three lines of symmetry.

Cumulative Review Chapters 1–11 **621**

About Performance Assessment

The Performance Assessment options ...

- provide teachers with an alternate means of assessing students.
- address different learning modalities.
- allow students to choose one problem.

Teachers may encourage students to choose the most challenging problem.

Learning Modalities
A Triangle That's Not Quite Right **Logical** Students find a counter-example for Side-Side-Angle.
Palindrommytry **Verbal** Students create palindromes.
A Puzzling Tessellation **Visual** Students create a jigsaw puzzle piece that tessellates.
The Task of a Mask **Visual** Students draw a mask that has three lines of symmetry.

Suggested Scoring Rubrics

See key on page 561.

A Triangle That's Not Quite Right

- 4 • Draws a neat counterexample for Side-Side-Angle and gives a clear explanation.

- 3 • Draws a fair counterexample for Side-Side-Angle and gives a fair explanation.

- 2 • Draws a poor counterexample for Side-Side-Angle and gives a poor explanation.

- 1 • Draws a poor counterexample, or none at all, for Side-Side-Angle and gives no explanation.

Rubric for **The Task of a Mask** is on page C5.

Palindrommytry

- 4 • Recognizes that many palindromes have symmetry with respect to a vertical line.
  • Creates several palindromes, including one that is also symmetric over a horizontal line.

- 3 • Recognizes that many palindromes have symmetry with respect to a vertical line.
  • Creates a few palindromes, including one that is also symmetric over a horizontal line.

- 2 • Recognizes that many palindromes have symmetry with respect to a vertical line.
  • Creates at least one palindrome.

- 1 • Does not recognize that many palindromes have symmetry with respect to a vertical line.
  • Creates an invalid palindrome.

A Puzzling Tessellation

- 4 • Creates a jigsaw puzzle piece that interlocks on all four sides and tessellates.
  • Draws a neat picture of the tessellation and gives a clear explanation of how the puzzle piece was created.

- 3 • Creates a jigsaw puzzle piece that interlocks on two or three sides and tessellates.
  • Draws a fair picture of the tessellation and gives a fair explanation of how the puzzle piece was created.

- 2 • Creates a jigsaw puzzle piece that interlocks on only one side and does not really tessellate.
  • Draws an inadequate picture of the tessellation and gives a poor explanation.

- 1 • Creates a jigsaw puzzle piece that does not interlock or tessellate.
  • Provides no picture or explanation.

Chapter

12

▶ OVERVIEW

Counting

and

Probability

Section 12A

Counting: Students explore the counting principle and ways to arrange or group objects.

12-1
Tree Diagrams and the Counting Principle

12-2
Permutations and Arrangements

12-3
Combinations and Groups

Section 12B

Chance and Probability: Students investigate various aspects of probability, including experimental and theoretical probability as well as geometrical and conditional probability. They also find probabilities of dependent and independent events.

12-4
Probability

12-5
Experimental and Geometric Probability

12-6
Conditional Probability

12-7
Dependent and Independent Events

Curriculum Standards

S T A N D A R D S

			pages
1	**Problem Solving**	Skills and Strategies	624, 627, 636, 642, 658
		Applications	629, 635, 641, 649, 655, 661, 666
		Exploration	623, 626, 631, 637, 642, 646, 651, 657, 663, 667
2	**Communication**	Oral	622, 623, 625, 628, 630, 634, 636, 640, 645, 648, 650, 654, 660, 665
		Written	*624*, 630, 636, *642*, 644, 650, 656, 662, 670
		Cooperative Learning	*628*, 629, 631, 632, *633*, 635, 637, *641*, 646, *649*, 651, *655*, 657, *661*, 663, *666*, *667*
3	**Reasoning**	Critical Thinking	636, 642, 650, 656, 662, 667
4	**Connections**	Mathematical	See Standards 5, 11, 12 below.
		Interdisciplinary	Career 635, 659, 661; Consumer 630, *633*, 641, 644, *645*, 662; Fine Arts *622*, 623; Geography 630, 636, *639;* Health *656;* History *625*, *628*, 641, *648*, 649, 654, *659*, *665*; Industry 666; Literature 641; Science *622*, 623, 636, 641, 649, *662*; Social Science 622, *625*, 644, *645*, 647
		Technology	*622*, *631*, 668
		Cultural	*622*, 623, *625*, *639*, *648*, *649*, *653*, 665
5	**Number and Number Relationships**		650
8	**Patterns and Functions**		630, *667*
10	**Statistics**		661
11	**Probability**		635, 638–639, 642, 645–670
12	**Geometry**		655, 662

Italic type indicates Teacher Edition reference.

TECHNOLOGY

For the Teacher

- **Teacher Resource Planner CD-ROM**
  Use the teacher planning CD-ROM to view resources available for Chapter 12. You can prepare custom lesson plans or use the default lesson plans provided.

- **World Wide Web**
  Visit **www.teacher.mathsurf.com** for links to lesson plans from teachers and other professionals, NCTM information, and other sites.

- **TestWorks**
  TestWorks provides ready-made tests and can create custom tests and practice worksheets.

For the Parent

- **World Wide Web**
  Parents can use the Web site at **www.parent.mathsurf.com**.

For the Student

- **Interactive CD-ROM**
  Lesson 12-5 has an *Interactive CD-ROM Lesson*. The *Interactive CD-ROM Journal* and *Interactive CD-ROM Spreadsheet/Grapher Tool* are also used in Chapter 12.

- **Wide World of Mathematics**
  Lesson 12-1 Geometry: One Long Detour
  Lesson 12-2 Geometry: DNA
  Lesson 12-5 Middle School: Hurricane Prediction
  Lesson 12-7 Middle School: Two-Sport Athlete

- **World Wide Web**
  Use with Chapter and Section Openers;
  Students can go online to the Scott Foresman-Addison Wesley Web site at **www.mathsurf.com/8/ch12** to collect information about chapter themes.

- **Jasper Woodbury Videodisc**
  Lesson 12-1: Get Out the Voice
  Lesson 12-2: Journey to Cedar Creek
  Lesson 12-3: Rescue at Boone's Meadow

SECTION 12A	LESSON	OBJECTIVE	ITBS Form M	CTBS 4th Ed.	CAT 5th Ed.	SAT 9th Ed.	MAT 7th Ed.	Your Form
	12-1	• Use tree diagrams and develop counting methods.			✗	✗	✗	
	12-2	• Develop ways of counting in situations for which the order of items is important.			✗	✗		
	12-3	• Recognize unordered selections as combinations and develop ways of counting in situations for which the order of items is not important.				✗	✗	

SECTION 12B	LESSON	OBJECTIVE	ITBS Form M	CTBS 4th Ed.	CAT 5th Ed.	SAT 9th Ed.	MAT 7th Ed.	Your Form
	12-4	• Compute probability.	✗	✗	✗	✗	✗	
	12-5	• Use experiments to find probabilities.	✗	✗	✗	✗	✗	
	12-6	• Understand what affects the probability of an event.						
	12-7	• Recognize an independent event.						

Key: ITBS - Iowa Test of Basic Skills; CTBS - Comprehensive Test of Basic Skills; CAT - California Achievement Test; SAT - Stanford Achievement Test; MAT - Metropolitan Achievement Test

ASSESSMENT PROGRAM

▶ **Traditional Assessment**

QUICK QUIZZES	SECTION REVIEW	CHAPTER REVIEW	CHAPTER ASSESSMENT FREE RESPONSE	CHAPTER ASSESSMENT MULTIPLE CHOICE	CUMULATIVE REVIEW
TE: pp. 630, 636, 642, 650, 656, 662, 667	SE: pp. 644, 670 *Quiz 12A, 12B	SE: pp. 672–673	SE: p. 674 *Ch. 12 Tests Forms A, B, E	*Ch. 12 Tests Forms C, E	SE: p. 675 *Ch. 12 Test Form F; Quarterly Test Ch. 1–12

▶ **Alternate Assessment**

INTERVIEW	JOURNAL	ONGOING	PERFORMANCE	PORTFOLIO	PROJECT	SELF
TE: pp. 642, 667	SE: pp. 630, 644, 650, 656, 670 TE: p. 630	TE: pp. 626, 631, 637, 643, 646, 651, 656, 657, 663, 669	SE: p. 674 *Ch. 12 Tests Forms D, E	TE: p. 636	SE: pp. 623, 642, 667 TE: p. 623	TE: p. 650

*Tests and quizzes are in *Assessment Sourcebook.* Test Form E is a mixed response test. Forms for Alternate Assessment are also available in *Assessment Sourcebook.*

 TestWorks: Test and Practice Software

► REGULAR PACING

Day	5 classes per week
1	Chapter 12 Opener; Problem Solving Focus
2	Section **12A** Opener; Lesson **12-1**
3	Lesson **12-2**
4	Lesson **12-3**
5	**12A** Connect; **12A** Review
6	Section **12B** Opener; Lesson **12-4**
7	Lesson **12-5**
8	Lesson **12-6**
9	Lesson **12-7**
10	Technology
11	**12B** Connect; **12B** Review; Extend Key Ideas
12	Chapter 12 Summary and Review
13	Chapter 12 Assessment
14	Cumulative Review, Chapters 1–12

► BLOCK SCHEDULING OPTIONS

Block Scheduling for Complete Course

Chapter 12 may be presented in

- nine 90-minute blocks
- twelve 75-minute blocks

Each block consists of a combination of

- Chapter and Section Openers
- Explores
- Lesson Development
- Problem Solving Focus
- Technology
- Extend Key Ideas
- Connect
- Review
- Assessment

For details, see *Block Scheduling Handbook.*

Block Scheduling for Lab-Based Course

In each block, 30–40 minutes is devoted to lab activities including

- Explores in the Student Edition
- Connect pages in the Student Edition
- Technology options in the Student Edition
- Reteaching Activities in the Teacher Edition

For details, see *Block Scheduling Handbook.*

Block Scheduling for Interdisciplinary Course

Each block integrates math with another subject area.

In Chapter 12, interdisciplinary topics include

- Olympics
- Birthdays

Themes for Interdisciplinary Team Teaching 12A and 12B are

- Olympics
- Probabilities in Monopoly®

For details, see *Block Scheduling Handbook.*

Block Scheduling for Course with *Connected Mathematics*

In each block, investigations from **Connected Mathematics** replace or enhance the lessons in Chapter 12.

Connected Mathematics topics for Chapter 12 can be found in

- *Clever Counting*
- *Samples and Populations*

For details, see *Block Scheduling Handbook.*

Set Up

Divide the bulletin board into three sections. In each section, place pictures that reflect an area of interest to your students. Label the section with an appropriate theme. Also, place a large envelope labeled *Counting Principle,* another labeled *Permutations or Combinations,* and another labeled *Probability* on the bulletin board.

Procedure

Organize students into three groups, and assign a theme to each group. Have each group write one question which applies the counting principle to their theme. One person should place the question in the *Counting Principle* envelope and choose another group's question from the envelope. Repeat this procedure for *Permutations or Combinations* and for *Probability.* Have students work in their group to answer the questions.

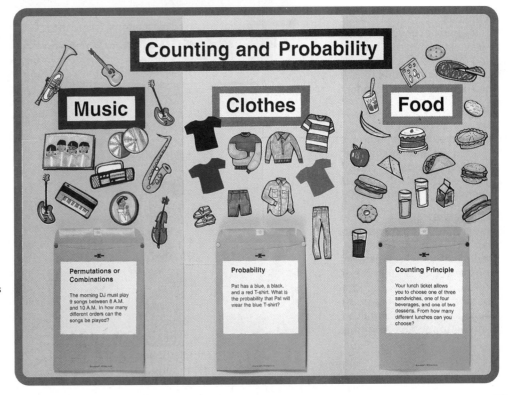

The information on these pages shows how counting and probability are used in real-life situations.

World Wide Web

If your class has access to the World Wide Web, you might want to use the information found at the Web site addresses given.

Extensions

The following activities do not require access to the World Wide Web.

People of the World

Many other African-American women have made significant contributions to various causes. Interested students may wish to do some research to identify such women. Or, they may choose to further investigate the accomplishments of Shirley Chisholm. Have students present their findings to the class.

Entertainment

Suggest that students learn more about the rules of the African stone game Mancala and duplicate the game for the class to play. Ask students to identify the strategies needed to win the game.

Social Studies

Many cultures have wedding customs. Have students research the wedding customs of a culture of their choice. Ask students to identify any tradition that is popular today.

Science

Siamese is the most popular short-haired cat and Persian is the most popular long-haired cat. Have interested students trace the development of the Himalayan cat.

Arts & Literature

Ask students to bring in a picture of a flag from a country of their choice that contains interesting symbolism, and to explain the symbolism to the class. Then have the class write and solve a problem related to the mathematics integrated into the design of the flag.

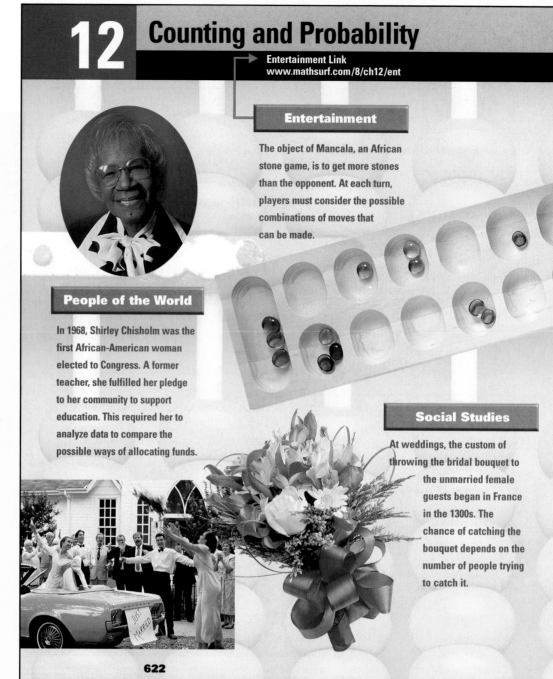

12 Counting and Probability

Entertainment Link
www.mathsurf.com/8/ch12/ent

Entertainment

The object of Mancala, an African stone game, is to get more stones than the opponent. At each turn, players must consider the possible combinations of moves that can be made.

People of the World

In 1968, Shirley Chisholm was the first African-American woman elected to Congress. A former teacher, she fulfilled her pledge to her community to support education. This required her to analyze data to compare the possible ways of allocating funds.

Social Studies

At weddings, the custom of throwing the bridal bouquet to the unmarried female guests began in France in the 1300s. The chance of catching the bouquet depends on the number of people trying to catch it.

622

TEACHER TALK

Meet Kent Novak

Wickford Middle School
North Kingston, Rhode Island

To stimulate students' interest, a few days before the lesson on probability, I put a jar filled with two pounds of M & M's® on my desk. Students generally ask why I have the candies, and when I tell them, they eagerly await the activity. To begin the activity, I distribute small packages of M & M's to each student. They count and record the number of pieces of each color in their package and find the probability of each color occurring. Then we combine all of the individual results. Using this data, students estimate the total number of M & M's in the jar as well as the number of each color. Finally students check their estimates by counting the M & M's. We end the activity with a candy treat.

Science

Following much experimentation with various combinations of Siamese and Persian cats, breeders developed a new breed of long-haired cat—the much-sought-after Himalayan.

Arts & Literature

Three-line symbols called *trigrams*, commonly found in Asian art, are made of combinations of solid and broken lines. The ones on this flag symbolize heaven, earth, fire, and water. The Counting Principle can be used to determine how many ways these three-line symbols can be made.

KEY MATH IDEAS

You can count the number of ways a series of events can occur by using a tree diagram or the Counting Principle.

A permutation, or arrangement, is an ordered selection of objects. A combination is a selection of objects without regard to order.

The probability, or theoretical probability, of an event is the likelihood that the event occurs.

Experimental probability is the number of times the event occurs divided by the number of trials. Geometric probability is calculated by comparing areas, lengths, or other measures.

Conditional probability is the probability that event *B* will occur, given that event *A* has already occurred. The events may be independent events or dependent events.

CHAPTER PROJECT

Problem Solving
Understand
Plan
Solve
Look Back

Create a game that involves permutations and/or combinations. Use your knowledge of probability to make the game interesting. You may want to use cards, coins, spinners, number cubes, or just select numbers or objects from a hat. You might want the game to involve several players, or it could be a game of solitaire.

623

Chapter Project

Students create a game that involves permutations and/or combinations.

Resources

Chapter 12 Project Master

Introduce the Project
- Discuss with students commercially made games that they have played that involve permutations and/or combinations.

Project Progress
Section A, page 642 Students think about whether they want their game to involve permutations, combinations, or both.

Section B, page 667 Students think about the probabilities they want for their game and how permutations or combinations could be used to design the game.

Community Project

A community project for Chapter 12 is available in *Home and Community Connections*.

Cooperative Learning

You may want to use Teaching Tool Transparency 1: Cooperative Learning Checklist with **Explore** and other group activities in this chapter.

PROJECT ASSESSMENT

You may choose to use this project as a performance assessment for the chapter.

Performance Assessment Key

Level 4 Full Accomplishment

Level 3 Substantial Accomplishment

Level 2 Partial Accomplishment

Level 1 Little Accomplishment

Suggested Scoring Rubric

4
- Idea for game indicates a complete understanding of permutations and/or combinations.
- Finished game is interesting, challenging, and playable.

3
- Idea for game indicates some understanding of permutations and/or combinations.
- Finished game is interesting and playable.

2
- Idea for game indicates a very elementary understanding of permutations and/or combinations.
- Finished game, if playable, is not interesting.

1
- Idea and finished game indicate little, if any, understanding of the purpose of the project.

Problem Solving Focus

Checking for a Reasonable Answer

The Point
Students focus on deciding if a given answer is reasonable for the situation.

Resources
Teaching Tool Transparency 17: Problem-Solving Guidelines

 Interactive CD-ROM Journal

About the Page

Using the Problem-Solving Process
Discuss the following steps for deciding if an answer is reasonable:

- Read the problem carefully to determine exactly what it is asking you to find.

- Estimate the answer.

- Check whether the answer is appropriate based on your estimate.

Ask ...
- Did you estimate the answer?

- Does the answer seem reasonable based on your estimate?

Answers for Problems
1. Too high; 660^2 is 435,600, whereas 200^2 is 40,000, so 200 is a much better estimate.

2. Too low; The radius is 6 ft, $\pi(6)^2$ is just over 100, 100(150) is 15,000, $\frac{4}{5}$ of that is $\approx$ 12,000 ft³.

3. Close enough; There are 60(24)(30), or 43,200, minutes in 30 days, and 100 times this number is 4,320,000.

4. Too high; 100% postconsumer would cost $7.80 for 3000 sheets, 20% postconsumer would cost $6.40 for 3000 sheets. 100% postconsumer is $1.40 more for 3000, which is about $0.50 for 1000, $0.05 for 100, $0.005 for 10, or $0.0005 for 1 sheet.

Journal

Have students write one or two paragraphs describing how they decide whether or not an answer to a problem is reasonable.

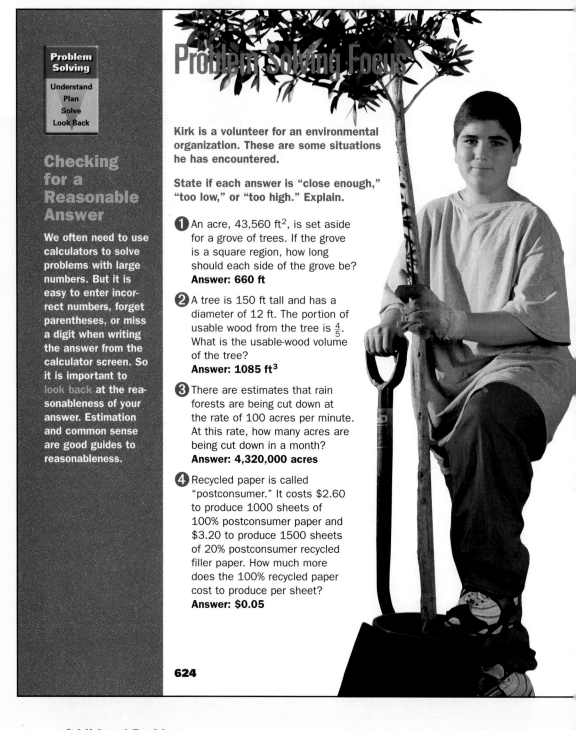

Checking for a Reasonable Answer

We often need to use calculators to solve problems with large numbers. But it is easy to enter incorrect numbers, forget parentheses, or miss a digit when writing the answer from the calculator screen. So it is important to look back at the reasonableness of your answer. Estimation and common sense are good guides to reasonableness.

Kirk is a volunteer for an environmental organization. These are some situations he has encountered.

State if each answer is "close enough," "too low," or "too high." Explain.

1 An acre, 43,560 ft², is set aside for a grove of trees. If the grove is a square region, how long should each side of the grove be?
Answer: 660 ft

2 A tree is 150 ft tall and has a diameter of 12 ft. The portion of usable wood from the tree is $\frac{4}{5}$. What is the usable-wood volume of the tree?
Answer: 1085 ft³

3 There are estimates that rain forests are being cut down at the rate of 100 acres per minute. At this rate, how many acres are being cut down in a month?
Answer: 4,320,000 acres

4 Recycled paper is called "postconsumer." It costs $2.60 to produce 1000 sheets of 100% postconsumer paper and $3.20 to produce 1500 sheets of 20% postconsumer recycled filler paper. How much more does the 100% recycled paper cost to produce per sheet?
Answer: $0.05

624

Additional Problem

State if the answer is "close enough," "too low," or "too high." Explain.

Kirk and some of the other volunteers were collecting wildflower seeds from the prairie. They were able to collect about 1 lb of seeds from every square yard area of ground. How many pounds of seeds should they be able to collect in an area 16 ft by 20 ft?
Answer: ≈ **320 lbs**

Too high; 16 ft = 5.33 yd and 20 ft = 6.66 yd, so the area of the rectangle would be about 5 yd × 7 yd, or 35 yd². They should be able to collect about 35 lbs of seeds.

Visit **www.teacher.mathsurf.com** for links to lesson plans from teachers and other professionals, NCTM information, and other sites.

LESSON PLANNING GUIDE

▶ **Student Edition**

▶ **Ancillaries***

LESSON	MATERIALS	VOCABULARY	DAILY	OTHER
Chapter 12 Opener				Ch. 12 Project Master Ch. 12 Community Project Teaching Tool Trans. 1
Problem Solving Focus				Teaching Tool Trans. 17 *Interactive CD-ROM Journal*
Section 12A Opener				
12-1 Tree Diagrams and the Counting Principle		tree diagram, counting principle	12-1	*WW Math—Geometry*
12-2 Permutations and Arrangements	4 cards marked A, B, C, and D for each group	arrangement, permutation, factorial	12-2	Teaching Tool Trans. 2, 3, 22 Lesson Enhancement Trans. 68 *WW Math—Geometry*
12-3 Combinations and Groups		combination	12-3	Teaching Tool Trans. 2, 3, 22 Technology Master 65 Ch. 12 Project Master
12A Connect				Interdisc. Team Teaching 12A
12A Review				Practice 12A; Quiz 12A; *TestWorks*

* Daily Ancillaries include Practice, Reteaching, Problem Solving, Enrichment, and Daily Transparency. Teaching Tool Transparencies are in *Teacher's Toolkits*. Lesson Enhancement Transparencies are in *Overhead Transparency Package*.

SKILLS TRACE

LESSON	SKILL	FIRST INTRODUCED			DEVELOP	PRACTICE/ APPLY	REVIEW
		GR. 6	GR. 7	GR. 8			
12-1	Using tree diagrams and the counting principle.	✗			pp. 626–628	pp. 629–630	pp. 644, 672, 674, 675
12-2	Calculating the number of permutations.		✗		pp. 631–634	pp. 635–636	pp. 644, 672, 674
12-3	Calculating the number of combinations.		✗		pp. 637–640	pp. 641–642	pp. 644, 672, 674, 675

CONNECTED MATHEMATICS

The unit *Clever Counting (Combinations),* from the **Connected Mathematics** series, can be used with Section 12A.

Math and Social Studies
(Worksheet pages 47–48: Teacher pages T47–T48)

In this lesson, students use tree diagrams, the counting principle, and permutations to answer questions about planning for events related to the Olympics.

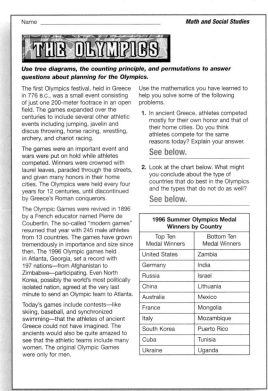

Name _____ *Math and Social Studies*

THE OLYMPICS

Use tree diagrams, the counting principle, and permutations to answer questions about planning for the Olympics.

The first Olympics festival, held in Greece in 776 B.C., was a small event consisting of just one 200-meter footrace in an open field. The games expanded over the centuries to include several other athletic events including jumping, javelin and discus throwing, horse racing, wrestling, archery, and chariot racing.

The games were an important event and wars were put on hold while athletes competed. Winners were crowned with laurel leaves, paraded through the streets, and given many honors in their home cities. The Olympics were held every four years for 12 centuries, until discontinued by Greece's Roman conquerors.

The Olympic Games were revived in 1896 by a French educator named Pierre de Coubertin. The so-called "modern games" resumed that year with 245 male athletes from 13 countries. The games have grown tremendously in importance and size since then. The 1996 Olympic games held in Atlanta, Georgia, set a record with 197 nations—from Afghanistan to Zimbabwe—participating. Even North Korea, possibly the world's most politically isolated nation, agreed at the very last minute to send an Olympic team to Atlanta.

Today's games include contests—like skiing, baseball, and synchronized swimming—that the athletes of ancient Greece could not have imagined. The ancients would also be quite amazed to see that the athletic teams include many women. The original Olympic Games were only for men.

Use the mathematics you have learned to help you solve some of the following problems.

1. In ancient Greece, athletes competed mostly for their own honor and that of their home cities. Do you think athletes compete for the same reasons today? Explain your answer.

See below.

2. Look at the chart below. What might you conclude about the type of countries that do best in the Olympics and the types that do not do as well?

See below.

1996 Summer Olympics Medal Winners by Country	
Top Ten Medal Winners	Bottom Ten Medal Winners
United States	Zambia
Germany	India
Russia	Israel
China	Lithuania
Australia	Mexico
France	Mongolia
Italy	Mozambique
South Korea	Puerto Rico
Cuba	Tunisia
Ukraine	Uganda

Name _____ *Math and Social Studies*

3. During the Olympic medal-awarding ceremony, the flags of the gold, silver, and bronze medal winners are displayed. Complete the tree diagram below to show the number of possible arrangements for any three flags. How many possible arrangements are there?

There are six possible arrangements.

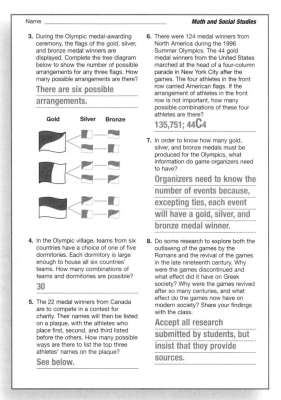

Gold   Silver   Bronze

4. In the Olympic village, teams from six countries have a choice of one of five dormitories. Each dormitory is large enough to house all six countries' teams. How many combinations of teams and dormitories are possible?

30

5. The 22 medal winners from Canada are to compete in a contest for charity. Their names will then be listed on a plaque, with the athletes who place first, second, and third listed before the others. How many possible ways are there to list the top three athletes' names on the plaque?

See below.

6. There were 124 medal winners from North America during the 1996 Summer Olympics. The 44 gold medal winners from the United States marched at the head of a four-column parade in New York City after the games. The four athletes in the front row carried American flags. If the arrangement of athletes in the front row is not important, how many possible combinations of these four athletes are there?

135,751; 44C4

7. In order to know how many gold, silver, and bronze medals must be produced for the Olympics, what information do game organizers need to have?

Organizers need to know the number of events because, excepting ties, each event will have a gold, silver, and bronze medal winner.

8. Do some research to explore both the outlawing of the games by the Romans and the revival of the games in the late nineteenth century. Why were the games discontinued and what effect did it have on Greek society? Why were the games revived after so many centuries, and what effect do the games now have on modern society? Share your findings with the class.

Accept all research submitted by students, but insist that they provide sources.

Answers

1. Accept any reasonable answer. Some students will agree that athletes train hard and often compete for love of the sport and the chance to represent their country. Others might think that the huge amounts of money that can be made by top Olympic athletes in the most popular sports are a major motivating factor.

2. The countries in the top ten tend to be developed countries where the citizens have the income to spend on training or where the country has placed a lot of emphasis on building facilities and supporting young people who are good athletes. With some exceptions, the countries that did less well are those that are less developed or that do not place a large emphasis on training athletes for Olympic competition.

5. There are 9,240 ways to list the top three winners. (See p.T47.)

BIBLIOGRAPHY

FOR TEACHERS

Anton, Glenn. *Who Shares Your Birthday? Famous Birthdays Listed for Each Day of the Year.* Downers Grove, IL: Kingsley Press, 1994.

Goldschneider, Gary. *The Secret Language of Birthdays: Personology Profiles for Each Day of the Year.* New York, NY: Viking Studio Books, 1994.

Isaac, Richard. *The Pleasures of Probability.* New York, NY: Springer-Verlag, 1995.

Wallechinsky, David. *The Complete Book of the Olympics, 1992 Edition.* Boston, MA: Little, Brown and Co., 1991.

FOR STUDENTS

Anderson, Dave. *The Story of the Olympics.* New York, NY: William Morrow and Co., 1996.

Center for Occupational Research and Development. *Applied Mathematics, Unit 20: Working with Probabilities.* Waco, TX: CORD, 1992.

Siddons, Larry, and the Associated Press. *The Olympics at 100: A Celebration in Pictures.* New York, NY: Macmillan, 1995.

Counting

▶ Social Studies Link ▶ History Link ▶ http://www.mathsurf.com/8/ch12/olympics

SWIFTER, HIGHER, STRONGER

Thousands of people in the stadium, and millions more around the world, are cheering you on. The starter gun sounds, every muscle in your body strains, your lungs search desperately for air, and before you know it, you cross the finish line victorious. You're an Olympic champion, and the national anthem sounds as you accept the accolades of your country and the world. In the future, what do you think will be remembered about the Olympic Games held in Atlanta? The American gymnast who vaulted with an injured ankle and enabled her team to win the gold? The decathlon winner who, four years earlier, though favored to win, hadn't even qualified? Or the gold-medal swimmer who, because of exercise-induced asthma, sometimes passed out during vigorous workouts? Perhaps the individuals themselves won't be remembered. Maybe what will be remembered is their dedication and courage to perform their very best and never give up.

1 The number of women athletes in the 1992 Barcelona Games was 2708. In the Atlanta Games four years later, the number rose to 3779. What percent of increase is this?

2 In the Atlanta Games, Turkey's 141-pound Naim Suleymanoglu lifted 413 pounds. How many times his weight did he lift?

625

Where are we now?

In Grades 6 and 7 students explored probability, geometric models of probability, tree diagrams, independent events, and fairness and unfairness. They also investigated counting methods, arrangements, and experimental and theoretical probability.

They learned how to

- understand geometric models of probability.

- make tree diagrams.

- identify independent and dependent events.

- distinguish between fairness and unfairness.

- use different arrangements.

- choose a group.

Where are we going?

In Grade 8, Section 12A, students will

- use tree diagrams and develop counting methods.

- develop ways of counting in situations where the order of arrangement is important.

- recognize unordered selections as combinations and develop ways of counting in situations where the order of arrangement is not important.

Theme: Olympics

World Wide Web

If your class has access to the World Wide Web, you might want to use the information found at the Web site address given. The interdisciplinary links relate to topics discussed in this section.

About the Page

This page introduces the theme of the section, the Olympics, and discusses the importance of dedication and courage to the Olympic athlete.

Ask ...

- Did you ever hear of any of the Olympic athletes whose situations are mentioned?

Extensions

The following activities do not require access to the World Wide Web.

Social Studies

The modern Olympic Games were first held in Athens in 1896, and except on three occasions, were held every four years until 1992. Now they are held every two years, alternating between winter games (1994, 1998, 2002, etc.) and summer games (1996, 2000, 2004, etc.). Have students find out why the Olympics were canceled on the three occasions, and why at various times certain countries boycotted the Olympics.

History

The first of the ancient Olympic Games was held in 776 B.C. in Greece. These games were held for 1000 years, ending in 394 A.D. Have interested students research the ancient Olympic Games—who played in them, what games were played, and what was the significance of the games.

Answers for Questions
1. ≈ 39.5%   2. ≈ 2.9

Connect

On page 643, students apply combinations and permutations to computations associated with the Olympic Games.

■ **Use tree diagrams and develop counting methods.**

Vocabulary

■ **Tree diagram, counting principle**

NCTM Standards

■ **1, 2, 4**

► **Review**

Evaluate each expression for *n* = 2, 5, and 10.

1. *n*(*n* – 1)   2, 20, 90

2. (*n* + 3)*n*   10, 40, 130

3. (*n* + 4)(*n* – 2)   0, 27, 112

Available on Daily Transparency 12-1

► **Lesson Link**

Have students discuss some of the choices they make in the mornings, such as what to wear and what to have for breakfast. From how many different outfits can they choose (for example, three pairs of pants, four matching shirts)? How many breakfast choices do they have (for example, two kinds of toast, three different jellies, two kinds of juice)?

---

1 **Introduce**

Explore

The Point
Students list modes of transportation for getting to and from school, and count the number of different ways to make the round trip.

Ongoing Assessment
Check students' results after Step 4. This organized list or drawing could be set up as a tree diagram.

12-1 Tree Diagrams and the Counting Principle

► **Lesson Link**   In some situations, counting can be difficult. You know how to use multiplication to count square units in rectangles. A similar method can be used when counting choices. ◄

You'll Learn …

■ to use tree diagrams and to develop counting methods

… How It's Used

Car dealers use counting methods to determine the kinds and numbers of models to keep on their lots.

Vocabulary

tree diagram

counting principle

Explore   Tree Diagrams

The Way to School

1. What different modes of transportation could you take to and from school?

2. Assuming you can take only one of these modes to school each day, how many different ways could you get to school?

3. Assuming you can take only one of these modes home from school each day, how many ways could you get home from school?

4. Make an organized list or drawing of all the modes you can use to get to school and back again (ignore whether you actually have your bike at school, for example). How many modes are there?

Learn   Tree Diagrams and the Counting Principle

To get to the 1996 Olympic Games in Atlanta, Jose could not get a direct flight from Shreveport, Louisiana. He had choices of connecting cities—Dallas, New Orleans, and Houston—and choices of airlines—Skies and Airway. You can show his options by making a table.

	Airline	
Connecting City	**Skies**	**Airway**
Houston	X	X
New Orleans	X	X
Dallas	X	X

From the list, you can count 6 choices. There are other ways to find this information. One way is to use a **tree diagram**. A tree diagram shows branches for each point where a choice is made. Each branch of a tree lists a possible outcome.

626   *Chapter 12 • Counting and Probability*

MEETING INDIVIDUAL NEEDS

Resources
12-1 Practice
12-1 Reteaching
12-1 Problem Solving
12-1 Enrichment
12-1 Daily Transparency
Problem of the Day
Review
Quiz
Wide World of Mathematics Geometry: One Long Detour

Learning Modalities
Visual   Tree diagrams are used to demonstrate the Counting Principle.
Kinesthetic   Have students use a concrete object, such as a sandwich-shop menu that offers the customer a choice of various combinations, as an example of possible choices. Then have students display the choices in a tree diagram.
Verbal   Ask students to compare using a tree diagram with using the counting principle to find possible choices. Is one method always more efficient than the other? Which method do they consider more efficient in Exercise 4 on page 629?

Inclusion
Students with impaired vision may have difficulty making the tree diagrams. Pair such students with a partner who can assist them.

Example 1

Make a tree diagram to show all possible choices for the 3 connecting cities: Dallas, New Orleans, Houston, and the 2 airlines: Skies and Airway.

Connecting City	Airline	Choice
Dallas	Skies	Through Dallas on Skies
	Airway	Through Dallas on Airway
New Orleans	Skies	Through New Orleans on Skies
	Airway	Through New Orleans on Airway
Houston	Skies	Through Houston on Skies
	Airway	Through Houston on Airway

Try It

Jay has a choice of 4 flights from Newark to St. Louis and a choice of 3 return flights. Make a tree diagram. How many different pairs of flights can he take?

12 pairs

You don't need to make an organized list or a tree diagram. You may have noticed in Example 1 that:

$$\underset{\text{Connecting cities}}{3} \quad \times \quad \underset{\text{Airlines}}{2} \quad = \quad 6 \text{ choices}$$

COUNTING PRINCIPLE

If a situation can occur in m ways, and a second situation can occur in n ways, then these things can occur together in $m \times n$ ways.

Problem Solving TIP

Use the Counting Principle first. Then see if it makes sense to make a list or tree diagram to see the individual choices.

The Counting Principle also works for more than two situations.

Example 2

A computer-designed birthday card can be designed with 4 different messages, 7 different colors, and 5 different borders. How many different choices of cards do you have?

Using the Counting Principle, you have $4 \times 7 \times 5$ or 140 card choices.

Try It

Gifties has 10 types of wrapping paper, 12 colors of ribbons, and 3 different kinds of bows. How many gift-packaging options do you have? **360**

12-1 • Tree Diagrams and the Counting Principle **627**

MATH EVERY DAY

▶ Problem of the Day

Markus cut a board in half. Then he cut one half into three equal pieces. Finally, he cut one of those three pieces into four equal pieces. The four equal pieces were each 8 in. long. How many feet long was the original board?

16 ft

Available on Daily Transparency 12-1

An Extension is provided in the transparency package.

Fact of the Day

It is believed that the first Olympiad in 776 B.C. consisted of one event, a 200-yard foot race. The race was held near Olympia, Greece.

Mental Math

Find each product mentally.

1. $4 \cdot 5 \cdot 3 \cdot 6$ 360
2. $8 \cdot 4 \cdot 2 \cdot 5$ 320
3. $9 \cdot 3 \cdot 5 \cdot 0 \cdot 4 \cdot 1$ 0

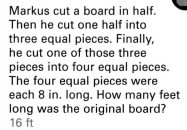

For Groups That Finish Early

Include one more mode of transportation you can use to get to school and back again. Now how many options are there for getting to and from school?

Follow Up

Discuss students' lists or drawings in Step 4. Point out how the different options are displayed visually. Ask students if there might be an easier way to determine the number of options than counting each one from the diagram. Multiply the number of options for going to school by the number of options for getting back home.

Answers for Explore

1. Possible answers: Car, bus, bike, skates, walk.

2–4. Answers may vary.

2 Teach

Learn

The tree diagram could also be constructed with the 2 airlines first, with 3 branches from each airline, one for each of the connecting cities. Note that there are still 6 choices.

Alternate Examples

1. Make a tree diagram showing all possible sandwich choices (1 bread and 1 meat) with 2 breads: rye and wheat, and 3 meats: bologna, salami, and turkey.

Bread	Meat	Choice
rye	bologna	rye, bologna
	salami	rye, salami
	turkey	rye, turkey
wheat	bologna	wheat, bologna
	salami	wheat, salami
	turkey	wheat, turkey

2. A sweatshirt comes in 8 colors, with 6 different designs, and in 4 sizes. How many different sweatshirts are available?

Using the Counting Principle, there are $8 \times 6 \times 4$ or 192 different sweatshirts available.

3. A movie theater has 10 door-ways for exits, but only 2 of these are used for entrances. How many ways are there to enter and exit the movie theater?

Using the Counting Principle, there are 2 × 10 = 20 ways to enter and exit the theater.

3 Practice and Assess

Check

For Question 2, students might be tempted to multiply 4 by 1, since one-topping pizzas are being made. Ask how many pizzas could be made if there were 3 toppings available. To count the number of pizzas, multiply 4 by the number of toppings available, *t*, not by the number of toppings to be placed on the pizza.

Answers for Check Your Understanding
1. Possible answers: Can be used to count combinations of shirts and shoes selected from a wardrobe; Cannot be used to count combinations of shirts and shoes purchased with a fixed amount of money (since the cost of the shoes affects the number of shirts that can be purchased or vice versa).

3. The total possibilities are the same; Possible example: Visiting one of four historic sites and then dining at one of two restaurants.

Be sure that you understand the problem before using the Counting Principle.

Example 3

An Olympic stadium has 83,100 seats. Your ticket states, "Enter through the north gates." Gates A through E are on the north side and gates F through K are on the south side. How many ways can a ticketholder enter through a north gate and exit through any gate?

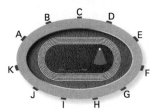

There are 5 north gates and 6 south gates. There are 5 ways to enter the stadium. To exit, there are 5 + 6 = 11 possible gates.

Using the Counting Principle, there are 5 × 11 = 55 ways to enter through a north gate and exit through any gate.

Try It

Animal researchers put identification tags on animals to study their habits. How many tag codes are possible? **3600**

May be any of 26 letters or 10 numbers (0–9) May be any of 100 numbers (00–99)

Check | Your Understanding

1. Give an example of a situation in which the Counting Principle can be used, and one in which it cannot.

2. Suppose that there are 4 types of pizza sauce and *t* types of toppings. How many different 1-topping pizzas could be made? **4*t***

3. How does a situation with 4 choices followed by 2 choices compare with the choices switched—2 choices followed by 4 choices? Give an example.

628 Chapter 12 • Counting and Probability

MEETING MIDDLE SCHOOL CLASSROOM NEEDS

Tips from Middle School Teachers

When discussing the counting principle, I use situations right in our own building. For example, there are four stairways from the first floor to the second, and three stairways from the second floor to the third floor. How many stairway routes are possible from the first to the third floor?

Cooperative Learning	History Connection
Have small groups of students collaborate on making posters that illustrate the Counting Principle.	Have students research the Olympic Games, especially the role of the French educator Baron Pierre de Coubertin, who was instrumental in starting the modern games.

12-1 Exercises and Applications

Practice and Apply

1. [Getting Started] At the Olympics, a deli ran a special on sandwiches. Here are the choices.

a. Copy and complete the diagram, showing all possible sandwiches.

b. How many different sandwiches are there?

Filling	Cheese	Bread
BBQ pork	Swiss	Wheat
Roast beef	American	Rye
	Jack	

Filling	Cheese	Bread	Sandwich
	Swiss	Wheat	Pork and Swiss on Wheat
		Rye	Pork and Swiss on Rye
BBQ pork	American	Rye	Pork and American on Rye
	Jack		
Roast beef			

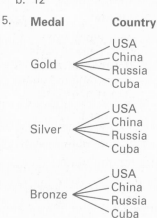

2. Beatrice took a red, a white, and a blue shirt and a red, a white, and a blue pair of shorts to the Olympic Games.

a. How many choices of shirts are there? How many choices of shorts? **3; 3**

b. Use the Counting Principle to find the number of different choices in outfits. You may want to check it by drawing a tree diagram. **9**

4. Sports In major league baseball, there are 14 teams in the National League and 14 in the American League. How many different World Series match-ups (one team from each league) are possible? **196**

3. How many different choices do you have in each situation?

a. 4 types of yogurt, 10 types of toppings (only 1 topping allowed) **40**

b. 3 types of pizza crust, 2 types of sauces, 3 types of cheeses **18**

c. 5 types of toast, 4 types of jams **20**

5. Make a tree diagram to show the possible results of spinning both spinners.

12-1 • Tree Diagrams and the Counting Principle **629**

PRACTICE 12-1

Assignment Guide

- **Basic**
  1–11, 13–19

- **Average**
  2–13, 15–19

- **Enriched**
  3–19

Exercise Notes

■ **Exercise 4**

Sports In 1998, the Arizona Diamondbacks (Phoenix) and the Tampa Bay Devil Rays are scheduled to begin Major League play. Then each league will have 15 teams.

Exercise Answers

1. a. See page C5.

   b. 12

5.

Medal	Country
Gold	USA / China / Russia / Cuba
Silver	USA / China / Russia / Cuba
Bronze	USA / China / Russia / Cuba

PRACTICE

Name _____

Practice 12-1

Tree Diagrams and the Counting Principle

1. A restaurant offers a choice of apple pie or pecan pie. Each slice of pie can be ordered with whipped cream, ice cream, or fresh fruit.

a. How many choices of pie are there? **2**

How many choices of garnish or topping are there? **3**

b. Use the Counting Principle to find the number of different ways to order a slice of pie with topping or garnish. You may want to check it by drawing a tree diagram. **6**

2. Make a tree diagram to show the possible results of spinning both spinners.

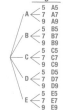

```
    5  A5
A < 7  A7
    9  A9
    5  B5
B < 7  B7
    9  B9
    5  C5
C < 7  C7
    9  C9
    5  D5
D < 7  D7
    9  D9
    5  E5
E < 7  E7
    9  E9
```

3. How many choices do you have in each situation?

a. 4 types of muffin, 3 types of spread **12**

b. 5 t-shirt color choices, 4 sizes **20**

c. 12 ice cream flavors, cone or cup, with or without sprinkles **48**

The early bird special from the Mighty Cafe is shown. Use it to answer Exercises 4 and 5.

Early Bird Special $6.49
- Soup or Salad
- Quiche, Casserole, or Pasta
- Potatoes, Peas, Broccoli, or Carrots
- Milk, Juice, or Soda

4. How many different early bird specials can be ordered? **72**

5. If the Mighty Café runs out of soup and pasta, how many different early bird specials can be ordered? **24**

6. Geography Rich is trying to get from San Francisco to San Jose, California. He needs to stop in San Bruno on the way. There are 3 major roads or freeways from San Francisco to San Bruno, and 3 major roads or freeways from San Bruno to San Jose. How many routes can Rich take? **9**

RETEACHING

Name _____

Alternative Lesson 12-1

Tree Diagrams and the Counting Principle

A **tree diagram** lists possible choices you can make in a given situation. It shows branches for each possible outcome.

The **Counting Principle** can be used to find the total number of ways choices can occur. If a situation can occur in m ways, and a second situation can occur in n ways, then these things can occur together in $m \times n$ ways.

— Example 1 —

Suppose you want to make a sandwich for your lunch. You have the following sliced meats: turkey, beef, and ham, and you have white and whole wheat bread. Make a tree diagram showing all possible sandwich choices.

Meat	Bread	Choice
Turkey	White	Turkey on white
	Whole wheat	Turkey on whole wheat
Beef	White	Beef on white
	Whole wheat	Beef on whole wheat
Ham	White	Ham on white
	Whole wheat	Ham on whole wheat

Try It

a. Make a tree diagram showing all possible outcomes for available pizza by the slice: thin or thick crust, cheese, sausage, or pepperoni topping.

Pizza Crust	Pizza topping	Choice
Thin	Cheese	Thin cheese
	Sausage	Thin sausage
	Pepperoni	Thin pepperoni
Thick	Cheese	Thick cheese
	Sausage	Thick sausage
	Pepperoni	Thick pepperoni

— Example 2 —

Chris has four sweatshirts that can be worn with three different pairs of pants. How many different outfits does Chris have with these sweatshirts and pants?

Using the counting principle, Chris has 4×3, or 12 possible outfits.

Try It

b. A school binder is available in five colors and has four different designs. How many different choices of binders are available? **20 choices.**

Reteaching

[Activity]

Materials: Coin, number cube

- Work with a partner.

- Flip the coin, and then toss the cube. Do this a few times and notice the results.

- Make a tree diagram to show all possible results of flipping the coin followed by tossing the number cube.

- How do the results from flipping the coin and tossing the cube compare to the results shown in the tree diagram? The results should approximate the tree diagram, with each result occurring about once in every twelve trials.

■ Exercise 10

Test Prep Students answering A may have simply subtracted 1, since one item was removed. Point out that each item is part of more than one combination. Using the counting principle, the factor of 3 for the vegetable should be changed to 2, to exclude the peas.

Exercise Answers

12. 512; You can have 10 heads, 10 faces, 10 chins.

Alternate Assessment

You may want to use the *Interactive CD-ROM Journal* with this assessment.

Journal Have students write about a situation in their own lives to which the counting principle can be applied.

► Quick Quiz

1. George can pick from 8 shirts, 3 pairs of jeans, and 2 pairs of sneakers. How many different outfits can George make? 48

There are 4 roads that lead from Town A to Town B, and 3 roads that go from Town B to Town C.

2. How many ways are there to get from Town A to Town C? 12

3. Suppose one of the roads from Town A to Town B is closed for construction. Now how many ways are there to get from Town A to Town C? 9

4. Suppose that road is reopened, but that one of the roads from Town B to Town C is closed for construction. Now how many ways are there to get from Town A to Town C? 8

Available on Daily Transparency 12–1

---

6. The Atlanta Committee for the Olympic Games provided Olympic athletes with 540 cases of tennis balls, each containing 24 cans, and each can containing 3 tennis balls. How many tennis balls were provided? **38,880**

7. **Geography** Katrina is trying to get from Dallas to Abilene, through Fort Worth. There are 4 major highways from Dallas to Fort Worth and 2 from Fort Worth to Abilene. How many routes can she take? **8**

8. Suppose your school has voted to wear uniforms. There are 3 colors of shirts and 3 colors of pants. Girls may also choose from 3 colors of skirts. How many uniform choices are there for boys? For girls? **9; 18**

The lunch menu from Rambo's Restaurant is shown. Use it to answer Exercises 9 and 10.

9. How many different lunch specials can be ordered? **36**

10. **Test Prep** If Rambo's runs out of peas, how many different lunch specials could be ordered? **B**

 Ⓐ 35   Ⓑ 24   Ⓒ 16   Ⓓ 8

Problem Solving and Reasoning

11. **Language Arts** One word is to be chosen from each list.
GPS How many sentences can be made? **240**

article	adjective	noun	verb	adverb
The	quick	dog	ran	quickly.
A	smelly	robot	slipped	badly.
	purple	king	cooked	
	scraggly		scratched	
			waited	

12. **Communicate** How many different people can be made with the flip book? How would you change it if you wanted to say "It makes 1000 different people"?

13. **Journal** Describe a situation in which using an organized list or a tree diagram is more useful than using the Counting Principle. **Answers may vary**

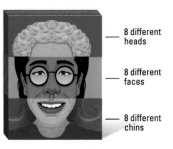
— 8 different heads
— 8 different faces
— 8 different chins

Mixed Review

Solve. *[Lesson 3-7]*

14. $x - 10 < 12$ $x < 22$
15. $x + 4 > 6$ $x > 2$
16. $5x \geq 35$ $x \geq 7$
17. $4x - 2 \leq 14$ $x \leq 4$
18. $\frac{1}{2}x + 1 < 9$ $x < 16$

19. Find the area of the paper used to make a snow cone that has a diameter of 3 in. and a height of 5 in. (use $A = \frac{1}{2} \cdot C \cdot s$). *[Lesson 9-5]*
$\frac{3}{4}\pi\sqrt{109}$ in$^2 \approx 24.6$ in^2

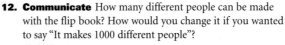

► PROBLEM SOLVING

Name _____

Guided Problem Solving 12-1

GPS PROBLEM 11, STUDENT PAGE 630

One word is to be chosen from each list. How many sentences can be made?

article	adjective	noun	verb	adverb
The	quick	dog	ran	quickly
A	smelly	robot	slipped	badly
	purple	king	cooked	
	scraggly		scratched	
			waited	

— **Understand** — Possible answer: Items 4 and 7
1. How many words are in each list?
 a. Article **2 words.**   b. Adjective **4 words.**   c. Noun **3 words.**
 d. Verb **5 words.**   e. Adverb **2 words.**

2. How many words will be chosen from each list? **One word.**

3. Do you need to be concerned with how well the sentences read? **No.**

— **Plan** —
4. How can you use the Counting Principle to find the number of sentences?
 Multiply the number of words in each list.

5. Write an expression to find the number of sentences. $2 \times 4 \times 3 \times 5 \times 2$

— **Solve** —
6. Simplify your expression in Item 5. How many sentences can be made. **240 sentences.**

— **Look Back** —
7. What is a different way to find the answer? Which way is easier? Explain. **Tree diagram; Counting Principle is easier because there are a lot of choices.**

SOLVE ANOTHER PROBLEM

School shirts can be ordered through the Student Council. How many different shirts are possible?

color	sleeve	size	style	design
blue	short	small	tee	name only
gold	long	medium	sweat	name and logo
		large	jersey	
		x-large		

96 shirts.

► ENRICHMENT

Name _____

Extend Your Thinking 12-1

Patterns in Numbers

1. Study the triangle of numbers and describe the numbers in the pattern.
 The numbers are consecutive odd numbers.

2. Continue the triangle by writing the numbers in the next four rows.

```
                1
             3     5
          7    9    11
       13   15   17   19
    21   23   25   27   29
 31   33   35   37   39   41
 43  45  47  49  51  53  55
57  59  61  63  65  67  69  71
73  75  77  79  81  83  85  87  89
91  93  95  97  99  101  103  105  107  109
```

3. Find the sum of the numbers in each row. Describe these numbers.
 1, 8, 27, 64, 125, 216, 343, 512, 729, and 1000; They are cubes. 1^3, 2^3, 3^3, and so on.

4. Find the mean (average) of the numbers in each row. Describe these numbers.
 1, 4, 9, 16, 25, 36, 49, 64, 81, and 100; They are squares: 1^2, 2^2, 3^2, and so on.

5. Look for the following diagonals in the triangle. List the next three numbers in each sequence.
 a. 11, 17, 25, 35, **47**, **61**, **77**, **95**, **115**
 b. 21, 33, **47**, **63**, **81**, **101**, **123**
 c. Describe the pattern. **Each number in the sequence increases by two more than the preceding number increased.**

6. Does this pattern hold true for the other diagonals in the triangle? **Yes.**

Permutations and Arrangements

12-2

▶ Lesson Link You have learned about tree diagrams and the Counting Principle. You will now extend these concepts to counting situations in which order is important. ◀

Explore | Permutations

Get in Line

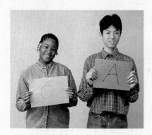

Materials: 4 cards marked A, B, C, and D for each group

Each person in your group should take one card marked A, B, C, or D.

1. If the student with card A lines up alone, how many ways can this student line up? 1
2. If the students with card A and card B line up, how many ways can these 2 students line up? 2
3. Add the student with card C. Where can you slot this third student in line when the first 2 students are in order AB? When they are in order BA? How many ways are there for 3 students to line up? How does this relate to the number of ways to line up 2 students?
4. Add the student with card D. Where can you slot this fourth student in line when the first 3 students are in order ABC? When they are in the other orders? How many ways are there for 4 students to line up? How does this relate to the number of ways to line up 3 students?
5. Predict how many ways 5 students could line up.

Learn | Permutations and Arrangements

When looking at options or choices, you often look at the **arrangement**, or order, of people, letters, numbers, or other things. A **permutation** is an arrangement in which order is important. The permutation ABC is different from the permutation CBA. The Counting Principle can help you determine the number of choices or permutations.

You'll Learn ...

- to develop ways of counting in situations for which the order of items is important

... How It's Used

When determining the competition order of a team, the coach must be aware of the possible arrangements that could be made.

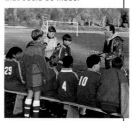

Vocabulary

arrangement

permutation

factorial

12-2 Lesson Organizer

Objective

- Develop ways of counting in situations for which the order of items is important.

Vocabulary

- Arrangement, permutation, factorial

Materials

- Explore: 4 cards marked A, B, C, and D for each group

NCTM Standards

- 1–4, 11

▶ Review

Find each product.

1. $1 \cdot 2 \cdot 3$ 6
2. $1 \cdot 2 \cdot 3 \cdot 4 \cdot 5$ 120
3. $1 \cdot 2 \cdot 3 \cdot 4 \cdot 5 \cdot 6 \cdot 7$ 5040

Available on Daily Transparency 12-2

▶ Lesson Link

Have students discuss situations in which order is important (such as putting on your socks and shoes) and situations in which it is not important (such as combing your hair and brushing your teeth). The focus at this time should just be on recognizing whether or not order is important.

1 Introduce

Explore

The Point
Students physically arrange themselves in different ways, and discover how to use the counting principle to count all the possible ways.

Ongoing Assessment
Check students' results after Step 3 to make sure they have considered all possible arrangements.

MEETING INDIVIDUAL NEEDS

Resources

- 12-2 Practice
- 12-2 Reteaching
- 12-2 Problem Solving
- 12-2 Enrichment
- 12-2 Daily Transparency
  - Problem of the Day
  - Review
  - Quick Quiz
- Teaching Tool Transparencies 2, 3, 22
- Lesson Enhancement Transparency 68
- *Wide World of Mathematics* Geometry: DNA

Learning Modalities

Kinesthetic In **Explore,** students can actually line up to form the various arrangements, or they can form the arrangements by using the lettered cards.

Logical For students with graphing calculators, you might want to show them the *nPr* feature, which calculates the number of permutations of *r* objects chosen from *n* objects. Some non-graphing calculators also have *nPr* and *nCr* keys.

Individual Have students reflect on their ability to distinguish situations in which order is important and when it is not important. Have them give an example of each.

Inclusion

For students with perceptual disabilities, use concrete objects to physically demonstrate permutations.

For Groups That Finish Early
Predict the number of ways 6 and 7 students can line up. 720; 5040

Follow Up
Discuss how the Counting Principle may be applied in this **Explore** activity.

Answers for Explore

3. ABC, ACB, CAB; BAC, BCA, CBA; 6; 3 × 2

4. DABC, ADBC, ABDC, ABCD; 1st, 2nd, 3rd, or 4th in line each time; 24; 4 times the number of ways you can line up 3 students.

5. 5 × 24 = 120 ways

2 Teach

Learn

You may wish to use Lesson Enhancement Transparency 68 with Example 1. Teaching Tool Transparency 22: Scientific Calculator can be used with Example 3.

When working with permutations, it is not uncommon to have an expression such as $\frac{4!}{0!} = 24$. For example, the number of ways that four objects can be selected and arranged from a group of four objects is $\frac{4!}{(4-4)!} = \frac{4!}{0!}$. In order to obtain 24 as the result, it is necessary to define $0! = 1$.

Alternate Examples

1. There are 8 lanes for the swimming events. If the top 3 swimmers are assigned lanes 3, 4, and 5, in how many ways can the other 5 swimmers be assigned their lanes?

   For the first of the remaining 5 swimmers there are 5 possible lane assignments. Once a selection is made for the first swimmer, there are only 4 lanes left from which to assign the second swimmer. After the second swimmer is assigned to a lane, there are only 3 lanes left from which to assign the third swimmer, and so on.

   By the Counting Principle, the total choices are 5 • 4 • 3 • 2 • 1 = 120.

   The are 120 possible ways to assign the remaining 5 swimmers their lanes.

Example 1

In the women's 4 × 100 m relay, the U.S. team was made up of Chryste Gaines, Gail Devers, Inger Miller, and Gwen Torrence. The coach decided that Gwen Torrence would run the anchor leg. In how many different orders could the coach have Gaines, Devers, and Miller run the first 3 legs?

DID YOU KNOW?

In the 200 m butterfly final at Barcelona in 1992, the race was so fast that the first 7 finishers set personal records.

Chryste Gaines | Gail Devers | Inger Miller | Gwen Torrence

For the first runner, there are 3 possibilities. Once a selection is made for the first runner, there are only 2 runners left from which to choose for the second leg. After that person is chosen, there is only 1 choice for the third leg.

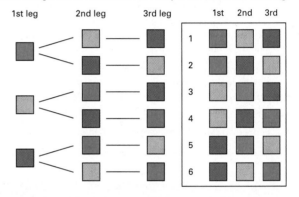

By the Counting Principle, the total choices are 3 • 2 • 1 = 6 ways.

There are 6 possible ways that the coach could order the 3 runners.

Try It

There were 8 lanes in which swimmers could compete in the 200 m butterfly races. How many different ways could the swimmers be arranged in the lanes? 40,320

MATH EVERY DAY

▶ Problem of the Day

An artist has two pieces of glass shaped like equilateral triangles. How can she make a single cut in one triangle and rearrange the pieces to make a rectangle?

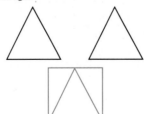

Available on Daily Transparency 12-2

An Extension is provided in the transparency package.

Fact of the Day

The Olympic motto is *"Citius, Altius, Portius"*— "Swifter, Higher, Stronger."

Mental Math

Calculate each factorial expression mentally.

1. 6! ÷ 4! 30

2. 10! ÷ 9! 10

3. 8! ÷ 5! ÷ 3! 56

Exponential notation is used to write a product when all of the factors are the same: $3 \cdot 3 \cdot 3 \cdot 3 = 3^4$. **Factorial** notation is used to write a product when the factors are consecutive whole numbers.

4 factorial is written as 4!, meaning $4 \cdot 3 \cdot 2 \cdot 1$.   0! is defined to be 1.

Example 2

Eight people were selected to carry the Olympic torch through downtown.

a. How many ways could the torchbearers be arranged in order?

Select all 8 torchbearers and see how many ways they can be arranged.

$8! = 8 \times 7 \times 6 \times 5 \times 4 \times 3 \times 2 \times 1 = 40,320$

There are 40,320 different ways to arrange the torchbearers.

b. How many ways could 3 of them be selected and arranged to carry the torch past three V.I.P. reviewing stands?

The ways to order 8 torchbearers are $8 \times 7 \times 6 \times 5 \times 4 \times 3 \times 2 \times 1$.

You only want to select and order 3 of the 8. The other 5 don't need to be arranged. Divide by the number of ways to arrange torchbearers who won't be passing the reviewing stands.

$$\frac{8!}{5!} = \frac{8 \times 7 \times 6 \times 5 \times 4 \times 3 \times 2 \times 1}{5 \times 4 \times 3 \times 2 \times 1} \quad \text{Remove all common factors.}$$

$$= 8 \times 7 \times 6$$

$$= 336$$

There are 336 ways to select and arrange the 3 torchbearers.

This makes sense because there are 8 people who can carry the torch past the first reviewing stand, then 7 who can carry it past the next one, and finally 6 who can carry it past the last one.

Try It

a. Evaluate 4! **24**   **b.** Evaluate $(7 - 3)!$ **24**

c. A radio station has a contest. They name the top 10 songs, and listeners must tell the correct order of the top 5 songs to win. How many ways could a listener select and order 5 songs from a list of 10? **30,240**

MEETING MIDDLE SCHOOL CLASSROOM NEEDS

Tips from Middle School Teachers

Some students are actually intimidated by the word *permutations*. They say "that sounds hard!" I start out by using the word *arrangements*, and I emphasize that in arrangements order *is* important. Later, when we study combinations, I call them *selections* or *groups*, and I point out that in selections or groups order is *not* important.

Cooperative Learning

Have students work in groups to determine ways to use their graphing calculators to calculate permutations. Each group should share its discoveries with the class. Then the class can agree on some general guidelines.

Consumer Connection

Because of consumer demand due to number of users, multiple lines, cellular telephones, pagers, faxes, and modems, many area codes ran out of combinations of 7-digit telephone numbers. Therefore, new area codes had to be created for regions of the country. Because of the demand for new area codes, the way area codes were numbered had to be changed. Originally, area codes were restricted to having a 0 or 1 as the second digit. Also, prefixes (the first 3 numbers of a 7-digit telephone number) could *not* have a 0 or 1 as the second digit. Today, any 3-digit combination for both area codes and prefixes is possible. Of course, some combinations, such as 800 and 911, are reserved for special uses.

3. From the 9 players in the batting order, in how many ways can a baseball manager choose and order

a. The first 3 batters?
b. The first 4 batters?
c. The first 5 batters?

a. For 3 batters, 6 are not chosen.

9 ! ÷ 6 ! = 504

There are 504 ways to choose and order 3 batters.

b. For 4 batters, 5 are not chosen.

9 ! ÷ 5 ! = 3024

There are 3024 ways to choose and order 4 batters.

c. For 5 batters, 4 are not chosen.

9 ! ÷ 4 ! = 15,120

There are 15,120 ways to choose and order 5 batters.

3 Practice and Assess

Check

For Question 3, students might find it helpful to start with smaller numbers, such as ordering 3 people from 6 or 4 people from 8.

Answers for Check Your Understanding

2. Exponential; For larger numbers it is increasing very rapidly.

3. The difference is $\frac{40!}{20!}$ compared to 40!.

Example 3

Suppose you had to select and order parade vehicles and floats out of a group of 10. How many arrangements can you make if you select

a. 4 vehicles?
b. 5 vehicles?
c. 7 vehicles?

Scientific calculators have a factorial key, ! .

a. For 4 vehicles, 6 vehicles are not selected.

10 ! ÷ 6 ! = 5,040

There are 5040 ways to select and arrange 4 vehicles.

b. For 5 vehicles, 5 vehicles are not selected.

10 ! ÷ 5 ! = 30,240

There are 30,240 ways to select and arrange 5 vehicles.

c. For 7 vehicles, 3 vehicles are not selected.

10 ! ÷ 3 ! = 604,800

There are 604,800 ways to select and arrange 7 vehicles.

MATH NUM HYP PRB
1: rand
2: nPr
3: ncr
4:!

Graphing utilities usually have factorial as a math menu item.

Try It

a. How many ways are there to select and order 7 students to be hall monitors from a group of 9 student aides? **181,440**

b. If you press 3 different buttons in the correct order, the door will open. How many ways are there to do this? **60**

c. Suppose you had to select and order 3 students out of a group of 5 and assign them specific tasks for a class project. How many arrangements can you make? What if you could select 4 students? 5 students? **60; 120; 120**

Check Your Understanding

1. Explain what 5! means. **5 · 4 · 3 · 2 · 1**

2. Of the functions you have studied—linear, quadratic, exponential, and so on—which does the factorial resemble? Why?

3. How does the number of ways to select and order 20 people out of 40 differ from the number of ways to order 40 people?

Exercise Answers, Page 635

1. a.

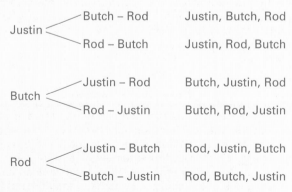

Justin
— Butch – Rod   Justin, Butch, Rod
— Rod – Butch   Justin, Rod, Butch

Butch
— Justin – Rod   Butch, Justin, Rod
— Rod – Justin   Butch, Rod, Justin

Rod
— Justin – Butch   Rod, Justin, Butch
— Butch – Justin   Rod, Butch, Justin

12-2 Exercises and Applications

Practice and Apply

1. **Getting Started** The members of the gold-medal-winning U.S. archery team were Justin Huish, Butch Johnson, and Rod White. How many different ways could the coach have arranged the members' competition order?

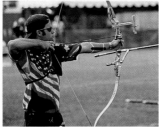

Justin Huish

Justin < Butch —— ——
Justin < Rod —— ——

Butch < —— —— ——
Butch < Rod Justin Butch, Rod, Justin

—— < —— —— ——
—— < —— Justin ——

a. Complete the tree diagram to show the possible arrangements.

b. How many arrangements are possible?

c. What factorial could be used to count the arrangements?

2. Show all arrangements of the letters A, B, C, and D.

Evaluate.

3. 6! 720 **4.** (2!)(3!) 12 **5.** 10! 3,628,800 **6.** (10 − 5)! 120

7. $\frac{10!}{5!}$ 30,240 **8.** 6(5!) 720 **9.** $\frac{7!}{6!}$ 7 **10.** $\frac{7!}{(7-3)!}$ 210

11. **Career** Dusty, a disc jockey, has picked 5 songs to be played before the next commercial. How many ways can she order these songs? 120

How many ways can the letters in each of these words be arranged? (No letter is used twice.) The letters do not have to form a word.

12. GOLD 24 **13.** TRACK 120 **14.** MEDALS 720 **15.** GYMNAST 5040

16. **Test Prep** Which formula would give the number of ways that r objects can be selected and arranged from a group of n objects? C

Ⓐ $\frac{n!}{r!}$ Ⓑ $\frac{r!}{n!}$ Ⓒ $\frac{n!}{(n-r)!}$ Ⓓ $\frac{n!}{(r-n)!}$

17. **Chance** In the women's single-slalom kayak race, racers from the Czech Republic, France, and the U.S. won medals. If you didn't know which team won the gold, silver, and bronze, what are your chances of guessing the correct order? 1 in 6

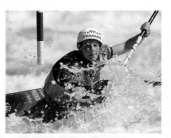

12-2 Exercises and Applications

Assignment Guide

- **Basic**
  1–16, 22–30
- **Average**
  2–11, 16–20, 22–30
- **Enriched**
  2, 8–30

Exercise Answers

1. a. Answer on page 634.
   b. 6
   c. 3!
2. ABCD, ABDC, ACBD, ACDB, ADBC, ADCB, BACD, BADC, BCAD, BCDA, BDAC, BDCA, CABD, CADB, CBAD, CBDA, CDAB, CDBA, DABC, DACB, DBAC, DBCA, DCAB, DCBA

Reteaching

Activity

Materials: Five counters of five different colors

- Work with a partner.
- Choose any two counters and place them in positions 1 and 2 in a row. Now arrange the remaining three counters in the row in as many ways as possible. Record each arrangement. How many are possible? 6
- Next, choose every possible group of two of the five counters and arrange them in a row in as many ways as possible. Record each arrangement. How many are possible? 20
- Using factorial notation, show how to find the result by computing.
  $\frac{5!}{3!} = \frac{5 \cdot 4 \cdot 3 \cdot 2 \cdot 1}{3 \cdot 2 \cdot 1} = 20$

PRACTICE

Name ______________________

Practice 12-2

Permutations and Arrangements

1. Show all arrangements of the letters R, E, A, and D.
ADER, ADRE, AEDR, AERD, ARDE, ARED, DAER, DARE, DEAR, DERA, DRAE, DREA, EADR, EARD, EDAR, EDRA, ERAD, ERDA, RADE, RAED, RDAE, RDEA, READ, REDA

Evaluate.

2. 4! 24 **3.** (5!)(3!) 720 **4.** (8 − 5)! 6 **5.** $\frac{6!}{3!}$ 120

6. 7(6!) 5,040 **7.** 7! 5,040 **8.** $\frac{12!}{9!}$ 1,320 **9.** (11 − 6)! 120

10. (6 − 2)! 24 **11.** $\frac{7!}{2!}$ 2,520 **12.** (4!)(6!) 17,280 **13.** $\frac{8!}{(8-2)!}$ 56

How many ways can the letters of each of these words be arranged? (No letter is used twice.) The letters do not have to form a word.

14. WORDS 120 **15.** THE 6 **16.** EQUATION 40,320

17. SALE 24 **18.** SWITZERLAND 39,916,800 **19.** NATURE 720

20. A librarian has 7 books to arrange on a shelf. How many ways can he order them? 5,040

21. Five runners are competing in the 100-yard dash. In how many orders can the runners finish? Assume there are no ties. 120

22. Jill bought 4 new CD singles. In how many orders can she play them? 24

23. An 18-member club is choosing its president, vice president, secretary, and treasurer. In how many ways can these four officers be chosen? 73,440

24. **Geography** On vacation in Hawaii, Kevin wants to visit the islands of Maui, Kauai, Hawaii, Molokai, and Oahu. He only has time to visit 3 islands. In how many ways can he select and order the islands he will visit? 60

RETEACHING

Name ______________________

Alternative Lesson 12-2

Permutations and Arrangements

A **permutation** is an arrangement in which order is important. **Factorial** notation is used to write a product when the factors are consecutive whole numbers. The product 5 × 4 × 3 × 2 × 1 is written **5!** and called **5 factorial.**

— Example 1 —

In how many different ways can four students A, B, C, and D, be seated in chairs for the Student Council assembly?

There are four students who could sit in the first chair. Whoever sits in that chair cannot sit in any other chair, so there are three students who could sit in the second chair. There are only two students left who could sit in the third chair, and one student left to sit in the fourth chair.

First chair	Second chair	Third chair	Fourth chair
4	3	2	1

Using the Counting Principle, there are 4 × 3 × 2 × 1 or 24 ways for these students to be seated for the assembly.

Try It

a. How many different numbers can you make using the digits 1, 3, 5, 7, 9? 120 different numbers.

— Example 2 —

Suppose you have seven different magazines and want to display four of them. In how many ways can they be selected and arranged?

Step 1: Find all possible ways seven magazines can be arranged. $7 \times 6 \times 5 \times 4 \times 3 \times 2 \times 1$

Step 2: Since you only need to select and order 4 of the 7 magazines, divide by the number of ways to arrange the *three* magazines that were not chosen. $\frac{7 \times 6 \times 5 \times 4 \times \cancel{3} \times \cancel{2} \times \cancel{1}}{\cancel{3} \times \cancel{2} \times \cancel{1}}$

Step 3: Simplify. $7 \times 6 \times 5 \times 4 = 840$

There are 840 different ways to select and arrange 4 of the 7 magazines for the display.

Try It

b. How many different numbers can you make using only three of the five digits 1, 3, 5, 7, 9? 60 different numbers.

c. In how many different ways can a debate team of 5 students be chosen from a group of 7 students? 2520 different ways.

■ **Exercise 23**

Problem-Solving Tip You may wish to use Teaching Tool Transparencies 2 and 3: Guided Problem Solving, 1–2.

Exercise Answers

18. 6 orders; Butter, flour, milk is best.

20. 5! is 120 arrangements.

23. LULL has repeated letters; SALT has 4! = 24 arrangements, and PEPPER has 60. (For PEPPER: Write the P's down. The E's can go between the P's in 10 different ways, and the R can go between the P's and E's in 6 different ways. 10 × 6 = 60)

24. 2; 6; 24; 120; 720; 5040; 40,320; Possible answer: The growth is faster than for a geometric series, because the ratio between terms is increasing.

25. No; Order is not important.

Alternate Assessment

Portfolio Check students' responses to Exercises 2, 10, 16, and 25. Then have students put their responses in their Portfolios. These exercises highlight the important concepts: listing all possible arrangements, understanding factorial notation, finding the number of ways to select and arrange *r* objects out of *n* objects, and determining whether order is important.

▶ Quick Quiz

1. Write all the possible three-digit numbers using the digits 4, 7, and 9. 479, 497, 749, 794, 947, 974

2. Evaluate $\frac{8!}{5!}$ 336

3. There are 9 candidates for student government. There are 4 different positions. In how many ways can the student government be chosen? 3024

Available on Daily Transparency 12–2

PROBLEM SOLVING 12-2

18. **Cooking** A white sauce can be made by slowly combining milk, flour, and melted butter in the correct order. How many orders are there? Guess the correct order. You may want to try it out!

20. **Geography** Fran wanted to visit New Zealand, Fiji, Australia, Bali, and New Guinea, but she was having trouble deciding the order. She tried to list all the orders. Why was she having trouble?

22. **GPS** Mr. Lehr has 8 groups in his math class. Tomorrow, 3 of the groups will give their group-project reports. How many different ways can he select and order the groups? 336

Problem Solving and Reasoning

23. **Choose a Strategy** Why are there fewer possible arrangements for the letters in the word LULL than the word LUGE? Which would you say has more possible arrangements, SALT or PEPPER? Why?

24. **Critical Thinking** Calculate the factorials 2! through 8!. Why do you think there is such rapid growth?

25. **Communicate** Nila picked 4 batteries out of 6 to use in her boombox. Does this situation describe a permutation? Explain.

Mixed Review

Check each pair of ratios to see if a proportion is formed. *[Lesson 5-2]*

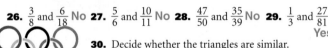

26. $\frac{3}{8}$ and $\frac{6}{18}$ No   27. $\frac{5}{6}$ and $\frac{10}{11}$ No   28. $\frac{47}{50}$ and $\frac{35}{39}$ No   29. $\frac{1}{3}$ and $\frac{27}{81}$ Yes

30. Decide whether the triangles are similar. *[Lesson 11-1]* Yes

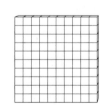

---

19. **Biochemistry** To make an enzyme solution, Jay must pour the stabilizer, add the enzyme, and then add the reactant. He doesn't know which is which. What is the chance that he will mix them correctly? $\frac{1}{6}$

21. **Olympics** There are 10 decathlon events: the 100 m run, long jump, shot put, high jump, and 400 m run on the first day; the 110 m hurdles, discus throw, pole vault, javelin throw, and 1500 m run on the second day.

   a. In how many ways could the 10 events have been ordered? 14,400

   b. In how many ways could the events on either day have been ordered? 120

Problem Solving STRATEGIES

- Look for a Pattern
- Make an Organized List
- Make a Table
- Guess and Check
- Work Backward
- Use Logical Reasoning
- Draw a Diagram
- Solve a Simpler Problem

▶ PROBLEM SOLVING

Name _____

Guided Problem Solving 12-2

GPS PROBLEM 22, STUDENT PAGE 636

Mr. Lehr has 8 groups in his math class. Tomorrow, 3 of the groups will give their group-project reports. How many different ways can he select and order the groups?

— Understand —

1. How many groups are in the class? **8 groups.**

2. How many groups will give reports tomorrow? **3 groups.**

3. What are you asked to find? **How many different ways Mr. Lehr can choose to order groups reporting on their products.**

— Plan —

4. How many groups will *not* give reports tomorrow? **5 groups.**

5. Use factorial notation to write the number of ways to select

   a. all the groups. **8!**   b. the groups not selected. **5!**

6. Use factorial notation to write an expression to show how many different ways Mr. Lehr can select and order the groups. $\frac{8!}{5!}$

— Solve —

7. How many different ways can Mr. Lehr select and order the groups? **336 ways.**

8. Write a sentence to give the final answer. **Mr. Lehr can select and order the groups in 336 ways.**

— Look Back —

9. Rewrite the expression in Item 6 using factors instead of factorial notation.

$$\frac{8 \times 7 \times 6 \times 5 \times 4 \times 3 \times 2 \times 1}{5 \times 4 \times 3 \times 2 \times 1}$$

SOLVE ANOTHER PROBLEM

Mrs. Lenzi has 7 groups in her math class. Next Monday, 4 of the groups will give their group-project reports. How many different ways can she select and order the groups? **840 ways.**

▶ ENRICHMENT

Name _____

Extend Your Thinking 12-2

Visual Thinking

Rosa's little sister, Maria, made a solid figure by stacking her play cubes. After all the cubes have been stacked, Rosa painted the outside of each figure Maria made.

1. Complete the table to find how many cubes in the figure below will have the given number of painted faces.

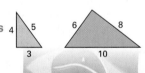

Number of painted faces	Number of cubes with given number of painted faces
6	0
5	0
4	4
3	32
2	64
1	0
0	0

2. Complete the table to find how many cubes in the figure below will have the given number of painted faces.

Number of painted faces	Number of cubes with given number of painted faces
6	0
5	0
4	0
3	8
2	96
1	384
0	512

Combinations and Groups

▶ **Lesson Link** You have learned about selections in which order was important. Now you will learn that in many situations order is not important. ◀

Explore | Combinations

What Difference Does It Make?

The U.S. team of LaMont Smith, Alvin Harrison, Derek Mills, and Arthuan Maybank won the gold medal in the men's 4 × 400 meter relay in the 1996 Summer Olympics.

1. In how many ways could the lead runner and the anchor runner have been selected?

2. List the different arrangements of lead and anchor runner. Is order important in these selections?

3. A television station requested that any 2 of the runners appear together for an interview. How many different selections of 2 members of the team could be made? List the members.

4. How is the selection of 2 team members for an interview different from the selection of a lead runner and an anchor runner?

Learn | Combinations and Groups

Suppose your school holds an election for student council. Four students—Julie, Maria, Leroy, and Stephan—are running. The student with the most votes becomes president and the student with the second most becomes vice president. These are the possible outcomes of the election.

In this situation, order is important, so there are 4 · 3 = 12 possible outcomes.

12-3 • Combinations and Groups **637**

You'll Learn ...

■ to recognize unordered selections as combinations and to develop ways of counting in situations for which the order of items is not important

... How It's Used

Selecting Senate committee members involves combinations.

Vocabulary
combination

12-3

Lesson Organizer

Objective

■ **Recognize unordered selections as combinations and develop ways of counting in situations for which the order of items is not important.**

Vocabulary

■ **Combination**

NCTM Standards

■ 1–4

▶ **Review**

Find the value of each.

1. 6! 720
2. 4! × 3! 144
3. $\frac{5 \times 4 \times 3}{3!}$ 10
4. $\frac{8 \times 7 \times 6 \times 5}{4!}$ 70
5. $\frac{10!}{7!}$ 720

Available on Daily Transparency 12-3

▶ **Lesson Link**

Tell students that they will build upon their knowledge of permutations, in which order mattered, to learn about selections in which order does not matter.

1 Introduce

Explore

The Point
Students work with partners to create two lists—one in which the arrangement of team members matters, and the other in which the arrangement does not matter.

Ongoing Assessment
Some students may be confused by the term *anchor runner*. Explain that an anchor runner is usually the strongest member of a relay team who performs the last stage of a relay race. In Step 1, check that students are making an organized list as they analyze the choices and arrangements for lead runner and anchor runner.

MEETING INDIVIDUAL NEEDS

Resources

12-3 Practice
12-3 Reteaching
12-3 Problem Solving
12-3 Enrichment
12-3 Daily Transparency
    Problem of
    the Day
    Review
    Quick Quiz
Teaching Tool
Transparencies 2, 3, 22
Technology Master 65
Chapter 12 Project
Master

Learning Modalities

Kinesthetic Have three students come to the front of the class. Ask the three students to form as many different *pairs* as they can. Have another student write on the chalkboard the names of the two students who form each different pair. After all possible pairs have been formed, ask students to explain how and why the final result is different from the number of permutations that could have been formed.

Verbal Have students discuss why there will always be fewer combinations of two or more items than permutations of the same items. The number of permutations includes all combinations and arrangements.

English Language Development

Students with limited English proficiency may have difficulty distinguishing between a permutation problem and a combination problem. Having students read and interpret several problems aloud in class or in small groups may be helpful.

For Groups That Finish Early

Think of another example, similar to this one, where in a certain situation the order would matter and where in another situation the order would not matter.

Follow Up

Have the students discuss their conclusions from Step 4. Then allow groups to share their examples with the rest of the class.

Answers for Explore

1. 12

2. Smith, Harrison; Smith, Mills; Smith, Maybank; Harrison, Smith; Harrison, Mills; Harrison, Maybank; Mills, Smith; Mills, Harrison; Mills, Maybank; Maybank, Smith; Maybank, Harrison; Maybank, Mills; Yes, order matters.

3. 6 ways; Smith, Harrison; Smith, Mills; Smith, Maybank; Harrison, Mills; Harrison, Maybank; Mills, Maybank.

4. The order is not important.

2 Teach

Learn

You may wish to use Teaching Tool Transparency 22: Scientific Calculator with this lesson. Stress the difference between permutations and combinations.

Alternate Examples

1. Dana, Erica, Jamie, and Michelle are trying out for the volleyball team. There are slots for only 3 players. What are the different combinations of 3 players that could be chosen for the team?

   Make an organized list.

   Dana/Erica/Jamie
   Dana/Erica/Michelle
   Dana/Jamie/Michelle
   Erica/Jamie/Michelle

   There are 4 possible combinations of 3 players chosen from a group of 4 players.

Answers for Try It

Abby/Bonita/Chantall
Abby/Bonita/Dani
Abby/Bonita/Eleni
Abby/Chantall/Dani
Abby/Chantall/Eleni
Abby/Dani/Eleni
Bonita/Chantall/Dani
Bonita/Chantall/Eleni
Bonita/Dani/Eleni
Chantall/Dani/Eleni
10 combinations

But suppose the students with the top 2 votes simply become members of the council. It does not matter who of the 2 got the most votes; both become members. How does this change the number of outcomes?

President	Vice Pres
Julie	Maria
Julie	Leroy
Julie	Stephan
Maria	Julie
Maria	Leroy
Maria	Stephan
Leroy	Julie
Leroy	Maria
Leroy	Stephan
Stephan	Julie
Stephan	Maria
Stephan	Leroy

Council Members	
Julie	Maria
Julie	Leroy
Julie	Stephan
~~Maria~~	~~Julie~~
Maria	Leroy
Maria	Stephan
~~Leroy~~	~~Julie~~
~~Leroy~~	~~Maria~~
Leroy	Stephan
~~Stephan~~	~~Julie~~
~~Stephan~~	~~Maria~~
~~Stephan~~	~~Leroy~~

The outcome Maria/Julie is the same as Julie/Maria, so it can be eliminated. Leroy/Julie is the same as Julie/Leroy, so it is eliminated, and so on.

The number of outcomes drops from 12 to 6.

When the order is not important, the number of outcomes is reduced. A selection of a number of objects that forms a set of objects, without regard to order, is called a **combination** of the objects.

Example 1

Problem Solving TIP

Whenever possible, use alphabetical order as an organization tool.

Five students, Abby, Bonita, Chantall, Dani, and Eleni, are trying out for the dance team. There are slots for only 2 students. What are the different combinations of 2 students who could place on the dance team?

Make an organized list.

Abby/Bonita	Bonita/Chantall	Chantall/Dani	Dani/Eleni
Abby/Chantall	Bonita/Dani	Chantall/Eleni	
Abby/Dani	Bonita/Eleni		
Abby/Eleni			

There are 10 possible combinations of 2 students chosen from a group of 5.

Try It

A third slot opened up for the dance team. What are the possible combinations of students now? How many combinations are there?

638 Chapter 12 • Counting and Probability

MATH EVERY DAY

▶ Problem of the Day

Three more than twice the sum of two consecutive odd numbers is 659. What are the two numbers? 163, 165
$[3 + 2(x + x + 2) = 659;$
$4x + 7 = 659; x = 163;$
$x + 2 = 165]$

Available on Daily Transparency 12-3

An Extension is provided in the transparency package.

Fact of the Day

The Olympic "gold" medal that each first-place finisher receives is actually made of silver, and it has a gold coating.

Estimation

Estimate each product.

1. 76×1010 76,000

2. $0.51 \times 20,315$ 10,000

3. $9.12 \times 100,500$ 912,000

638 Chapter 12

Often the number of combinations will be too large for an organized list or a tree diagram. You can use the ideas that you learned about permutations to find the number of combinations.

On page 633, you found that to *select and arrange* 3 torchbearers from a group of 8, you didn't need to arrange the 5 unselected torchbearers. In this situation, you would divide 8! by 5! to find the number of permutations.

To find the number of ways to merely *select* 3 torchbearers from 8 torchbearers, you don't need to arrange the 3 selected torchbearers either. Divide 8! by the number of ways to arrange the *selected* torchbearers as well.

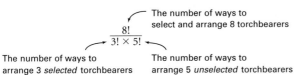

The number of ways to select and arrange 8 torchbearers

$$\frac{8!}{3! \times 5!}$$

The number of ways to arrange 3 *selected* torchbearers

The number of ways to arrange 5 *unselected* torchbearers

Example 2

There are 20 paintings in a collection. How many ways can the following groups be selected? Write the answers in factorial notation.

a. 3 paintings

There are $\frac{20!}{3! \times 17!}$ ways to select 3 paintings.

b. 17 paintings

There are $\frac{20!}{17! \times 3!}$ ways to select 17 paintings.

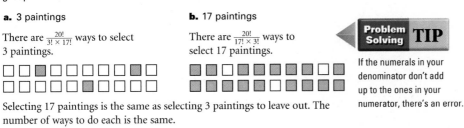

> **Problem Solving TIP**
>
> If the numerals in your denominator don't add up to the ones in your numerator, there's an error.

Selecting 17 paintings is the same as selecting 3 paintings to leave out. The number of ways to do each is the same.

Example 3

For the all-around teams at the 1996 Olympics, 3 gymnasts were selected from each nation. The U.S. women's team had 6 gymnasts. How many different all-around teams could have been chosen?

Order is not important in the selection, so you are looking for a combination.

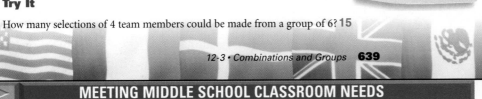

$\frac{6!}{3! \times 3!} = 6$ [!] [÷] [(] 3 [!] [×] 3 [!] [)] [=] *20*

There are 20 ways to select a group of 3 team members from the 6 gymnasts.

> **MENTAL MATH**
>
> If you realize that this is $6 \times 5 \times 4$ divided by $3 \times 2 \times 1$, and that the 6 cancels with the denominator, all that's left is 5×4.

Try It

How many selections of 4 team members could be made from a group of 6? **15**

2. How many ways can the following groups be selected? Write the answers in factorial notation.

   a. 47 books from a collection of 100 books

      There are $\frac{100!}{47! \times 53!}$ ways to select 47 books from 100.

   b. 53 books from the same collection

      There are $\frac{100!}{53! \times 47!}$ ways to select 53 books from 100.

      Selecting 53 books out of 100 is the same as selecting 47 books out of 100.

3. For the All-Star softball team, 4 players were chosen from the eligible players on each team. The Dewhurst Denizens had 10 eligible players. How many different All-Star team selections could have been chosen?

   Order is not important in the selection, so you are looking for a combination.

   $\frac{10!}{4! \times 6!} =$

   10 [!] [÷] [(] 4 [!] [×] 6 [!] [)]
   [=] 210

   There are 210 ways to select a group of 4 All-Star team members from the 10 eligible players.

Tips from Middle School Teachers

To emphasize the difference between permutations and combinations, I have students use 4 different colored counters (red, blue, green, yellow). First I have them show and list all the ways they can select 3 of the 4 counters if order is not important. There are 4 combinations: RBG, RBY, RGY, and BGY. Then I have them show and list all the ways if order is important. We consider the combination RBG, and notice that if order is important, GRB GBR must be considered as different. Continuing in this way we find 24 permutations.

Cultural Connection

The Olympic symbol is five interlocking circles, colored blue, yellow, black, green, and red, on a white background. The circles represent the five continents. At least one of the colors appears in the national flag of every country on Earth.

Geography Connection

Olympia, Greece, the site of the original Olympic Games, is a valley about 11 miles from Pirgos, Greece. All of the buildings in Olympia were for worship or for games. The religious buildings were clustered in the Altis (sacred grove), which lies where the Cladeus River flows into the Alpheus River. Olympia was destroyed by earthquakes and floods. From 1829–1879 French, and then German, expeditions unearthed many important artifacts at the Olympia site, including the entire Altis and surrounding buildings.

Students are presented with two different methods for calculating the number of ways to select a group of 4 students from 9—one method uses a calculator, the other lists the factors.

Answers for What Do You Think?
Yes. Either 4! or 5! can divide out of 9!

3 Practice and Assess

Check

For Question 1, as long as the group has two or more elements there will always be fewer combinations than permutations.

Answers for Check Your Understanding

1. Order matters for permutations but not for combinations; since order matters for permutations, different permutations are considered to be the same combination.

2. The number of combinations is the same, because $\frac{7!}{2! \times 5!}$ is the same as $\frac{7!}{5! \times 2!}$.

Four of 9 students will be selected to attend the MathCounts competition. How many different teams could be selected?

Ashley thinks ...

Order is not important. I am looking for the number of ways to select a group of 4 students from 9. I'll use my calculator.

$$\frac{9!}{4!(9-4)!} = 9\ [!] \div ([4][!] [\times] 5 [!]) [=] 126$$

There are 126 different teams.

Seung thinks ...

I'll list the factors. I can divide out 5! right away.

$$\frac{9!}{4! \times 5!} = \frac{9 \times 8 \times 7 \times 6 \times 5 \times 4 \times 3 \times 2 \times 1}{(4 \times 3 \times 2 \times 1)(5 \times 4 \times 3 \times 2 \times 1)}$$

$$= \frac{9 \times 8 \times 7 \times 6 \times \cancel{5 \times 4 \times 3 \times 2 \times 1}}{(4 \times 3 \times 2 \times 1)(\cancel{5 \times 4 \times 3 \times 2 \times 1})}$$

There are other common factors.

$$\frac{\overset{3}{\cancel{9}} \times \cancel{8} \times 7 \times 6}{\cancel{4} \times \cancel{3} \times \cancel{2} \times 1} = 3 \times 7 \times 6 = 126$$

There are 126 different teams.

What do think?

Will one of the factorials always divide out?

Check Your Understanding

1. How are combinations different from permutations? Why are there fewer combinations than permutations when selecting from a group?

2. How is choosing 2 from 7 related to choosing 5 from 7? Why?

Practice and Apply

Getting Started In which of these situations is order important?

1. Gold, silver, and bronze medals will be given to 3 of 8 competitors. **Yes**

2. Certificates of merit will be given to 5 of 10 entrants. **No**

3. Four of 10 students will be selected to each swim one stroke: butterfly, backstroke, breaststroke, or freestyle in the swim meet relay. **Yes**

4. Four of 10 students will attend the Olympics in Sydney, Australia. **No**

5. **Biology** In how many ways can 24 seedlings be selected from a group of 96 seedlings to test a growth enhancer? Write in factorial notation. $\dfrac{96!}{24! \times 72!}$

Evaluate.

6. $\dfrac{12!}{9! \times 3!}$ **220**

7. $\dfrac{10!}{5! \times 5!}$ **252**

8. $\dfrac{12!}{8!(12-8)!}$ **495**

9. $\dfrac{5!}{2!(5-2)!}$ **10**

10. In how many ways can 2 pizza toppings be selected from a group of 6 toppings? **15**

11. **Consumer** How many ways could you select 3 possible components for a sound system from a tape deck, CD player, laser disc, equalizer, and surround-sound stereo? **10**

12. After the class picnic, 10 of the 30 students are needed to clean up. How many different ways could they be selected? **30,045,015**

13. There were 12 players on the 1996 U.S. Olympic basketball team. In how many ways could 5 starters be chosen? (Don't worry about player positions.) **792**

14. **History** Henry VIII had 6 wives. How many ways could 2 of them be selected for portrayal in a documentary film? **15**

15. A class is told that it should do only 8 out of 10 questions on the test. Is this the same as being told that it should omit 2 of the 10 questions? **Yes**

16. **Literature** The most common type of poetry is lyric poetry which includes haikus, odes, elegies, sonnets, limericks, rondels, triolets, and villanelles. If you were assigned to write an essay describing 3 of these types of lyric poetry, how many ways could you select them? **56**

PRACTICE 12-3

12-3 Exercises and Applications

Assignment Guide

■ **Basic**
1–7, 11–13, 17–27 odds

■ **Average**
1–6, 9–19 odds, 20–26 evens

■ **Enriched**
2–8 evens, 9–12, 14–16, 18, 19, 20–26 evens

Exercise Notes

■ **Exercise 5**

Biology The group of hormones that regulate plant growth are called gibberellins. They occur naturally in green plants and fungi or can be produced from green plants and fungi in a laboratory. There are more than 60 types of gibberellins, gibberellic acid being the most well known. When sprayed on a plant, gibberellins cause the stem of the plant to grow faster and taller than it normally would and may also speed up sprouting.

■ **Exercise 14**

History Henry VIII's private life greatly influenced England's political history. In his insistence to try to divorce his first wife, he denied that the pope had authority over England. He then insisted, in 1534, that Parliament pass two acts that made the break with the Roman Catholic Church complete. These two acts began the separation of the Church of England from the Roman Catholic Church and established the Reformation in England.

PRACTICE

Name _____

Practice 12-3

Combinations and Groups

Evaluate.

1. $\dfrac{8!}{3! \times 5!}$ **56**

2. $\dfrac{5!}{4! \times 1!}$ **5**

3. $\dfrac{7!}{5! \times 2!}$ **21**

4. $\dfrac{11!}{8! \times 3!}$ **165**

5. $\dfrac{6!}{5!(6-5)!}$ **6**

6. $\dfrac{4!}{2!(4-2)!}$ **6**

7. $\dfrac{9!}{6!(9-6)!}$ **84**

8. $\dfrac{5!}{3!(5-3)!}$ **10**

9. In how many ways can 9 Senators be selected from among 100 Senators to serve on a committee? Write in factorial notation. $\dfrac{100!}{9! \times 91!}$

10. In how many ways can a used car lot manager choose 12 of his 45 cars to feature in a newspaper advertisement? Write in factorial notation. $\dfrac{45!}{12! \times 33!}$

11. Becky wants to buy 12 of the posters at a poster shop, but she only has enough money for 3 posters. How many ways can she select 3 out of 12 posters? **220**

12. A test instructs you to "answer 2 of the next 5 questions." How many ways can you choose 2 questions to answer? **10**

13. A teacher wants 5 of her 25 students to write solutions on the board. How many ways can she select a group of 5 students? **53,130**

14. **Social Science** In 1995, President Clinton had 20 men and women on his cabinet. How many ways could he select 4 cabinet members to consult regarding a particular issue? **4,845**

15. Patrick read 10 short stories for his English class. He needs to write an essay describing 3 of the stories. How many ways can he choose 3 stories to write about? **120**

16. A pancake restaurant has 8 different syrups, jams, and honeys. Tammy wants to put a different topping on each of her 4 pancakes. How many ways can she choose 4 toppings? **70**

17. Chih is joining a music club. He needs to choose 4 out of 65 compact discs for his first shipment. How many ways can he choose? Write in factorial notation. $\dfrac{65!}{4! \times 61!}$

18. A computer drawing program has 256 colors available, but you can only use 16 colors at a time. How many ways can you choose 16 out of 256 colors? Write in factorial notation. $\dfrac{256!}{16! \times 240!}$

RETEACHING

Name _____

Alternative Lesson 12-3

Combinations and Groups

A selection of a number of objects, that forms a set of objects, without regard to order is called a **combination** of the objects. Since order is not important, the arrangements of ABC, ACB, BCA, BAC, CAB, and CBA contain the same three letters in different orders but are only one combination of the letters ABC.

— **Example** —

There are 7 magazines in a collection. How many ways can 4 magazines be selected? Write your answers in factorial notation.

Step 1: Find the number of ways to select all magazines without arranging them in order. $7 \times 6 \times 5 \times 4 \times 3 \times 2 \times 1$

Step 2: Since the order of the selected (4!) and the unselected (3!) magazines does not matter, divide by 4! × 3! $\dfrac{7 \times 6 \times 5 \times 4 \times 3 \times 2 \times 1}{4 \times 3 \times 2 \times 1 \times 3 \times 2 \times 1}$

Step 3: Simplify. $\dfrac{7 \times 6 \times 5 \times 4 \times 3 \times 2 \times 1}{4 \times 3 \times 2 \times 1 \times 3 \times 2 \times 1} = 35$

There are 35 different ways of choosing 4 magazines from 7 magazines.

Try It

a. In how many ways can you choose to buy three CDs from eight available CDs?

Number of ways to select and arrange the 8 CDs: **8!**

Number of ways to arrange the 3 selected CDs: **3!**

Number of ways to arrange the 5 CDs not selected: **5!**

Number of ways to choose to buy 3 CDs from 8 available CDs: **56 ways.**

b. In how many ways can a committee of three be selected from a group of five people? **10 ways.**

c. There are 4 books on a shelf. In how many different ways can 2 books be selected? **6 ways.**

d. There are 7 students on the student council. In how many different ways can a committee of 2 be selected? **21 ways.**

e. There are 10 girls on a basketball team. In how many different ways can a 5-member team be selected? **252 ways.**

f. There are 21 players on a baseball team. In how many different ways can a 9-member team be selected? **293,930 ways.**

Reteaching

Activity

Materials: Red, white, blue, and green chips

• Work with a partner.

• First work with a red, a white, and a blue chip. How many different color combinations of two chips can you make? Name them. **3; RW, RB, WB**

• Now work with a red, a white, a blue, and a green chip. Now how many different color combinations of two chips can you make? Name them. **6; RW, RB, RG, WB, WG, BG**

■ Exercise 18

Sports There are two types of diving competition in the Olympics: springboard diving and platform diving. In springboard diving, the board is flexible, and the diver bounces to give added height. In platform diving, the platform is rigid.

■ Exercise 22

Problem-Solving Tip You may wish to use Teaching Tool Transparencies 2 and 3: Guided Problem Solving, 1–2.

Project Progress

You may want to have students use Chapter 12 Project Master.

Exercise Answers

17. The chances of winning are 1 in $\frac{53!}{6! \times 47!}$, or 1 in 22,957,480.

21. 5 people, since the value of $\frac{10!}{r!(10-r)!}$ peaks when r is half of 10.

Alternate Assessment

Interview Ask students to list all of the 3-letter permutations of the letters A, P, and T. APT; PTA; TAP; ATP; PAT; TPA

Ask students if these permutations are also combinations of the letters A, P, and T. How many combinations? Yes; One—they are all the same three letters.

► Quick Quiz

Choose the correct word.

1. A selection in which order does not matter is called a (combination/permutation). Combination

2. For 2 or more objects, the number of permutations is always (greater/less) than the number of combinations. Greater

3. A selection in which order does matter is called a (combination/permutation). Permutation

4. To find the number of (combinations, permutations) eliminate any additional arrangements with the same elements. Combinations

Available on Daily Transparency 12-3

17. **Chance** To win a game, you must guess 6 numbers from the numbers 1–53. They must match 6 randomly selected numbers. Why is this game virtually impossible to win?

18. In Olympic diving, 7 judges award a score for each dive. The high and low scores are removed. In how many ways can 2 judges' scores be removed? 21

19. **Test Prep** A flower shop carries 12 types of flowers and sells a special Crazy 8 birthday bouquet using your choice of 8 different flowers. How many different ways can 8 flowers be selected? B
Ⓐ 96 　 Ⓑ 495 　 Ⓒ 12^8 　 Ⓓ 40,320

Problem Solving and Reasoning

20. **Critical Thinking** How many ways can you give 10 swim-team members a snack if you have 12 snacks and each swimmer is to receive 1? 66

21. **Communicate** Suppose you select a group from 10 people. What size group has the most ways of being selected? Explain.

22. **Choose a Strategy** How many ways can groups of from 0 to 12 items be chosen from 12 items? 4096

23. **Math Reasoning** How many different ways can you select 3 players from 10 for one basketball team, and then 3 from the remaining 7 for another team? 4200

Problem Solving
STRATEGIES
- Look for a Pattern
- Make an Organized List
- Make a Table
- Guess and Check
- Work Backward
- Use Logical Reasoning
- Draw a Diagram
- Solve a Simpler Problem

Mixed Review

Is the table an equal ratio table? If so, find the value of k, where $\frac{y}{x} = k$. *[Lesson 5-3]*

24.
x	3	6	9	12
y	4	7	10	13

No

25.
x	2	4	6	8
y	3	6	9	12

Yes; $k = \frac{3}{2}$

Determine whether each pair of figures is congruent. *[Lesson 11-2]*

26. 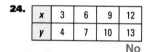 Yes

27.   No

Project Progress

Think about whether you want your game to involve permutations, combinations, or both. Which would make the game more difficult?

Problem Solving
Understand
Plan
Solve
Look Back

642 *Chapter 12 • Counting and Probability*

PROBLEM SOLVING 12-3

PROBLEM SOLVING

Name _____

Guided Problem Solving 12-3

GPS PROBLEM 11, STUDENT PAGE 641

How many ways could you select 3 possible components for a sound system from a tape-deck, CD player, laser disk, equalizer, and surround-sound stereo?

— Understand

1. Circle the number of components that will be in the sound system.

2. Underline the possible components to include in the system.

3. Are you asked for how the system can be assembled or the number of ways it can be assembled?   Number of ways.

— Plan

4. Write each in factorial notation.
   a. number of ways to select and arrange all components 5!
   b. number of ways to arrange the selected components 3!
   c. number of ways to arrange the components that are *not* selected 2!

5. Which shows the number of ways to assemble the sound system? b
   a. $\frac{5!}{3!}$ 　 b. $\frac{5!}{3! \times 2!}$
   c. $\frac{3! \times 2!}{5!}$ 　 d. $\frac{3!}{2!}$

— Solve

6. How many ways could you select 3 components for the sound-system? 10 ways.

— Look Back

7. Check your answer by making a list of the possible sound-system components. Use T, C, L, E, and S to represent the components.
   TCL; TCE; TCS; TLE; TLS; TES; CLE; CLS; CES; LES

SOLVE ANOTHER PROBLEM

How many ways could you make a hamburger with 4 toppings if the available toppings are tomato, cheese, onion, pickle, lettuce, bacon, and relish? 35 ways.

ENRICHMENT

Name _____

Extend Your Thinking 12-3

Visual Thinking

Circle the letter of the fraction that represents the shaded part of each figure.

1.
$\frac{1}{2}$ a. 　 $\frac{2}{5}$ b. 　 $\frac{1}{4}$ c. 　 $\frac{1}{3}$ d.

2.
$\frac{3}{5}$ a. 　 $\frac{3}{5}$ b. 　 $\frac{1}{2}$ c. 　 $\frac{5}{8}$ d.

3.
$\frac{1}{2}$ a. 　 $\frac{1}{3}$ b. 　 $\frac{2}{5}$ c. 　 $\frac{1}{4}$ d.

4.
$\frac{1}{4}$ a. 　 $\frac{1}{8}$ b. 　 $\frac{1}{3}$ c. 　 $\frac{2}{3}$ d.

5.
$\frac{5}{6}$ a. 　 $\frac{1}{2}$ b. 　 $\frac{1}{4}$ c. 　 $\frac{5}{6}$ d.

6.
$\frac{1}{24}$ a. 　 $\frac{1}{8}$ b. 　 $\frac{1}{4}$ c. 　 $\frac{1}{16}$ d.

7. Which of the figures above would you rather use as a target if you were playing darts and got 5 points for each dart that landed in the shaded area? Explain.

Figure 4 because a greater portion of the figure is shaded increasing chances of hitting the shaded area.

You have seen many examples of counting situations. In this Connect, you will compute the combinations and permutations associated with the Olympic Games.

Swifter, Higher, Stronger

The interlocked rings of the Olympic symbol represent Africa, the Americas, Asia, Australia, and Europe.

1. In how many ways could the colors of the Olympic symbol have been arranged among the rings?

2. Let each group in the room be a "nation" in the Olympics. In how many orders can the groups march in the opening ceremonies?

3. In how many ways can the teams win gold, silver, and bronze in the first event? (Assume that each team can win no more than 1 medal.)

4. If only the top 3 teams can compete in the all-around competition, how many ways can they be arranged?

5. If the rules are changed and the top 4 teams can compete in the all-around competition, how many ways can they now be arranged?

6. In how many ways can the gold medal be awarded if each team competes in the first 5 events?

7. If 10 events are to be held, in how many different ways can the events be ordered?

8. Use one of the situations explored here. Show that choosing a group (combination), then ordering the group (permutation) is the same as selecting and ordering a group (permutation).

643

Swifter, Higher, Stronger

The Point
In *Swifter, Higher, Stronger* on page 625, students are reminded of the dedication and courage displayed by the athletes who participate in the Olympic Games. Now students will have an opportunity to compute combinations and permutations associated with the Olympic Games.

About the Page

- Tell students to read each question carefully so they understand what is being asked.

- Remind students to use organized lists or tree diagrams to help them organize the information for their problems.

Ongoing Assessment
You might want to check students' progress at Questions 4 and 6 because each is followed by a similar question.

Extension

The colors of the Olympic rings were chosen because the flag of every nation has at least one of these colors. Ask students to add another ring with a sixth color. Now how many ways can the colors of the Olympic symbol be arranged? 720

Answers for Connect
1. 120 ways

2–6. Answers may vary.

7. 3,628,800

8. Answers may vary.

Review Correlation

Item(s)	Lesson(s)
1–8	12-2
9, 10	12-3
11, 12	12-1
13–17	12-2
18	12-3
19	12-2
20	12-2, 12-3
21	12-3

Test Prep

Test-Taking Tip

Tell students that when taking a multiple-choice test for which answers are recorded on a separate answer sheet, they should be very careful to record each answer on the correct line. Sometimes, skipping an answer can cause all answers thereafter to be recorded on the wrong line.

Answers for Review

11. HHH, HHT, HTH, HTT, THH, THT, TTH, TTT

12.

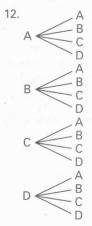

20. Possible answer: Selecting 3 from 7 as a permutation means $\frac{7!}{4!} = 210$. Selecting the 3 as a group means $\frac{210}{3!} = 35$. The 3 selections do not need to be arranged.

Evaluate.

1. 40,320
2. 479,001,600
3. 5040

1. 8!
2. 12!
3. (10 − 3)!
4. (3!)(3!) 36
5. $\frac{10!}{2!}$ 1,814,400

6. 4(3!) 24
7. $\frac{8!}{6!}$ 56
8. $\frac{7!}{(7-4)!}$ 840
9. $\frac{8!}{3! \times 5!}$ 56
10. $\frac{6!}{2!(6-4)!}$ 180

11. Make an organized list or tree diagram showing the possible outcomes of tossing 3 coins.

12. Make a tree diagram to show the possible outcomes of spinning the spinner twice.

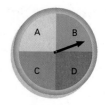

How many ways can the letters in each of these words be arranged if no letter is used twice? The letters do not have to form a word.

13. SILVER 720
14. MEDALIST 40,320
15. WRESTLING 362,880

16. **Consumer** On his vacation, Fred wanted to take 6 tours, but he was having trouble deciding in what order to take them. How many different ways could he go on the tours? 720

17. **Olympics** In the heptathlon, there are 7 events—hurdles, high jump, shot put, 200 m dash, javelin throw, long jump, and 800 m run. These events are held in a certain order. How many different ways could these 7 events be ordered? 5040

18. **Civics** A candidate will visit 9 of the 50 states the week before the election. How many ways can this be done? Write in factorial notation. $\frac{50!}{9! \times 41!}$

19. **Olympics** Mark Spitz won 7 gold medals in swimming at the 1972 Olympic Games in Munich. If he wanted to display the medals in a row on his wall, how many different ways could he arrange them? 5040

20. **Journal** Compare selecting 3 items from 7 if the selection is a permutation to selecting 3 items from 7 if the selection is a group.

Test Prep

Think about whether order is important.

21. For an international flight, how many different ways can 5 flight attendants be selected from 10 flight attendants? **D**

Ⓐ 10 × 5   Ⓑ 10!   Ⓒ $\frac{10!}{5!}$ Ⓓ $\frac{10!}{5! \times 5!}$

REVIEW 12A

Resources

Practice Masters
    Section 12A Review

Assessment Sourcebook
    Quiz 12A

TestWorks
Test and Practice Software

PRACTICE

Name _____

Practice

Section 12A Review

Evaluate.

1. 9! **362,880**
2. 11! **39,916,800**
3. (15 − 8)! **5,040**
4. 8(7!) **40,320**
5. $\frac{12!}{7!}$ **95,040**
6. $\frac{14!}{4!(14-4)!}$ **1,001**

7. A bag contains many blue, green, and red marbles. Make an organized list showing the possible outcomes of removing two marbles, one after the other.

    Blue-blue, blue-green, blue-red, green-blue, green-green, green-red, red-blue, red-green, red-red

8. Suppose you remove one marble from the bag in Exercise 7, then flip a coin twice. Make a tree diagram to show the possible outcomes.

How many ways can the letters of each of these words be arranged if no letter is used twice? The letters do not have to form a word.

9. SQUARE **720**
10. IOWA **24**
11. SURVEY **720**

12. At an amusement park, Faye and Gary have chosen 5 rides they want to go on. In how many different orders can they go on the rides? **120**

13. A group of friends plan to share 6 of the 36 dishes on the menu at a Chinese restaurant. How many ways can they choose what dishes to order? Write in factorial notation. $\frac{36!}{6! \times 30!}$

14. **Science** A ball is thrown upward at a speed of 48 ft/sec from a height of 12 ft. After t seconds, the height (in feet) is given by the sum of $-16t^2$ and $48t + 12$. What is the height of the ball after 2.5 sec? [Lesson 10-6] **32 ft**

15. The Renaissance Tower in Dallas, Texas, is 216 m tall. A scale model of it is 54 cm tall. What is the scale factor of the model? [Lesson 11-1] $\frac{1}{400}$

Section 12B

Chance and Probability

Visit www.teacher.mathsurf.com for links to lesson plans from teachers and other professionals, NCTM information, and other sites.

LESSON PLANNING GUIDE

▶ **Student Edition**

▶ **Ancillaries**

LESSON	MATERIALS	VOCABULARY	DAILY	OTHER
Section 12B Opener				
12-4 Probability		experiment, outcomes, sample space, event, probability	12-4	
12-5 Experimental and Geometric Probability	shiny new nickels	theoretical probability, experimental probability, trial, geometric probability	12-5	Lesson Enhancement Trans. 69 *Interactive CD-ROM Lesson WW Math*—Middle School
12-6 Conditional Probability		conditional probability	12-6	Lesson Enhancement Trans. 70 *WW Math*—Geometry
12-7 Dependent and Independent Events	paper bag, 3 algebra tiles, tape or dry marker	compound events, independent events, dependent events, multiplication property	12-7	Teaching Tool Trans. 13, 14 Lesson Enhancement Trans. 71 Ch. 12 Project Master *WW Math*—Middle School
Technology	graphing calculator			Teaching Tool Trans. 23 *Interactive CD-ROM Spreadsheet/Grapher Tool*
Connect				Interdisc: Team Teaching 12B
Review				Practice 12B; Quiz 12B; *TestWorks*
Extend Key Ideas				
Chapter 12 Summary and Review				
Chapter 12 Assessment				Ch. 12 Tests Forms A–F *TestWorks;* Ch. 12 Letter Home
Cumulative Review, Chapters 1–12				Cumulative Review Ch. 1–12 Quarterly Test Ch. 1–12

SKILLS TRACE

LESSON	SKILL	FIRST INTRODUCED			DEVELOP	PRACTICE/ APPLY	REVIEW
		GR. 6	GR. 7	GR. 8			
12-4	Computing probabilities.	✗			pp. 646–648	pp. 649–650	pp. 670, 673, 674
12-5	Finding experimental probabilities.		✗		pp. 651–654	pp. 655–656	pp. 673, 674, 675
12-6	Finding conditional probabilities.			✗ p. 657	pp. 657–660	pp. 661–662	pp. 670, 673, 674
12-7	Finding probabilities of dependent and independent events.		✗		pp. 663–665	pp. 666–667	pp. 670, 673, 674, 675

CONNECTED MATHEMATICS

The units *Clever Counting (Combinations)* and *Samples and Populations (Data and Probability),* from the **Connected Mathematics** series, can be used with Section 12B.

Math and Social Studies

(Worksheet pages 49–50: Teacher pages T49–T50)

In this lesson, students compute probabilities in the Monopoly® game.

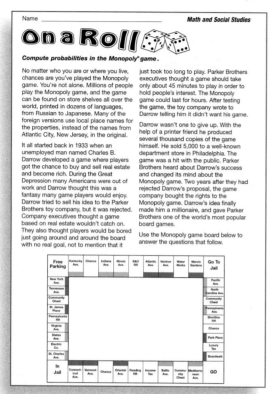

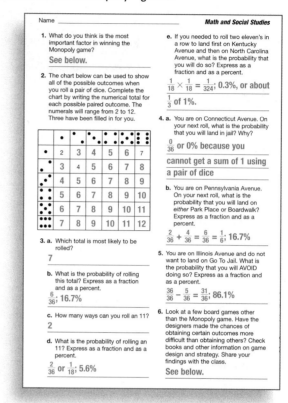

Answers

1. Answers may vary. Some possible answers: Having enough money to buy properties and build houses and hotels; not landing on another player's property; luck; making wise decisions about buying or not buying properties.

6. Answers may vary depending on the games examined. The answers should primarily be descriptive, such as, "You have to roll an exact number to enter the center area and have a chance to win in Trivial Pursuit," or, "In chess, some pieces are more limited in their movements than others. It is harder for such pieces to capture an opponent's pieces." Accept all reasonable research and answers.

BIBLIOGRAPHY

▷ FOR TEACHERS

Anton, Glenn. *Who Shares Your Birthday? Famous Birthdays Listed for Each Day of the Year.* Downers Grove, IL: Kingsley Press, 1994.

Goldschneider, Gary. *The Secret Language of Birthdays: Personology Profiles for Each Day of the Year.* New York, NY: Viking Studio Books, 1994.

Isaac, Richard. *The Pleasures of Probability.* New York, NY: Springer-Verlag, 1995.

Wallechinsky, David. *The Complete Book of the Olympics, 1992 Edition.* Boston, MA: Little, Brown and Co., 1991.

▷ FOR STUDENTS

Center for Occupational Research and Development. *Applied Mathematics, Unit 20: Working with Probabilities.* Waco, TX: CORD, 1992.

Feldman, Eve B. *Birthdays! Celebrating Life Around the World.* Mahwah, NJ: BridgeWater Books, 1996.

West, Robin. *My Very Own Birthday: A Book of Cooking and Crafts.* Minneapolis, MN: The Lerner Group, 1996.

Chance and Probability

▶ Consumer Link   ▶ Social Studies Link   ▶ http://www.mathsurf.com/8/ch12/birthday

HAPPY BIRTHDAY, BABY

How many birthdays has the average person had? Actually, just one. All the other days you celebrate as birthdays are the anniversaries of that day. But "Happy Anniversary to You" is too difficult to sing, so we call them all birthdays.

You undoubtedly share this day with someone famous. Born February 17? Michael Jordan shares your birthday. Born May 16? So were Janet Jackson, Pierce Brosnan, and Tori Spelling.

We celebrate the birthdays of people important to our country, such as George Washington and Martin Luther King, Jr., with national holidays.

The day on which different people celebrate their birthdays is sometimes filled with coincidences. Five presidents were either born on, or died on, July 4.

Were you born alone or along with a brother or sister? When you were born, you had …

– 1 chance in 80 of being a twin,
– 1 chance in 6400 of being a triplet,
– 1 chance in 512,000 of being a quadruplet,
– 1 chance in 40,960,000 of being a quintuplet.

1 Of 250 million Americans, about how many were born on April 15?

2 Martin Luther King, Jr.'s birthday is celebrated on the third Monday in January. Does this always fall on his birthday? Why do you think this is done?

3 Which has the greater chance of occurring, being born a twin or a quintuplet?

645

Where are we now?

In Section 12A students explored methods of counting. They learned how to

- use tree diagrams and develop counting methods.

- develop ways of counting in situations where the order of arrangement is important.

- recognize unordered selections as combinations and develop ways of counting in situations where the order of arrangement is not important.

Where are we going?

In Section 12B students will

- compute probability.

- use experiments to find probabilities.

- understand what affects the probability of an event.

- recognize an independent event.

Objective

- **Compute probability.**

Vocabulary

- **Experiment, outcomes, sample space, event, probability**

NCTM Standards

- **1, 2, 4, 5, 11**

► Review

Write each fraction in lowest terms.

1. $\frac{24}{30}$ $\frac{4}{5}$

2. $\frac{18}{54}$ $\frac{1}{3}$

3. $\frac{100}{450}$ $\frac{2}{9}$

4. $\frac{24}{72}$ $\frac{1}{3}$

5. $\frac{57}{190}$ $\frac{3}{10}$

Available on Daily Transparency 12-4

► Lesson Link

Ask students to explain what they think the phrase "the chance that an outcome will happen" means. If necessary, explain that it means how likely it is that something will occur.

1 Introduce

Explore

The Point
Students decide on the probability of five different events occurring and then discuss their decisions with the rest of their group. They then make a list of examples of events that they think are either impossible or a sure thing.

Ongoing Assessment
As you move around the classroom, observe students to make sure they are following directions. Have they made their number lines correctly? Do they understand that they are to indicate on the number line what *they think* the probability of each event is?

12-4   Probability

► Lesson Link   You have worked with methods for counting possible outcomes. Now you will learn to compute the chance that an outcome will happen. ◄

Explore   Probability

It's a Sure Thing

1. Draw a number line similar to this one.

| 0 | 0.1 | 0.2 | 0.3 | 0.4 | 0.5 | 0.6 | 0.7 | 0.8 | 0.9 | 1 |

If 0 indicates that something is impossible and 1 indicates that something is a sure thing, label points along this line that would show the chance of the following events occurring.

a. Rolling a 6 in a single roll of a number cube

b. Getting heads on a single flip of a coin

c. Selecting a pair of matching socks from a drawer, without looking, if there are two pairs of socks in the drawer

d. Drawing a card containing a vowel from a set of 10 cards containing the first 10 letters of the alphabet

e. Rolling a number other than 6 in a single roll of a number cube

2. Provide a rationale for each of your selections of position. Does each person in your group have the points in the same order?

3. Describe events you could place at 0 and at 1.

Learn   Probability

Suppose you toss a coin as an **experiment** . The coin can land on heads or tails, so there are two equally likely results or **outcomes** possible.

The set of all possible outcomes of an experiment is the **sample space** . Usually we are interested in the chance of a particular **event** occurring. This is called the **probability** of the event.

646   *Chapter 12 • Counting and Probability*

You'll Learn ...

■ to compute probability

... How It's Used

Probability is used to predict the place a hurricane will occur.

Vocabulary

experiment

outcomes

sample space

event

probability

MEETING INDIVIDUAL NEEDS

Resources
12-4 Practice
12-4 Reteaching
12-4 Problem Solving
12-4 Enrichment
12-4 Daily Transparency
Problem of the Day
Review
Quick Quiz

Learning Modalities

Social   In **Explore**, students decide on the probability of five different events occurring and share their decisions with their group.

Kinesthetic   You might have students use the actual objects mentioned in **Explore** to demonstrate the various outcomes.

Challenge

Have students collect promotional contest or sweepstakes materials received in the mail or in the media. Have them work in groups to find and make a list of the odds of winning sweepstakes and other promotional contests. (This information is required to be presented with the contest literature.) Then students should research the probability of such things as a person: having a car accident, being struck by lightning, and being elected president. Students can present to the class the comparisons of the probabilities of these events with the probabilities of winning the contests.

Probability can be expressed as a decimal, fraction, ratio, or percent.

$$P(\text{event}) = \frac{\text{number of outcomes in the event}}{\text{number of outcomes in the sample space}}$$

Examples

1 Jason and Alexander are playing a game with a number cube. If Jason rolls a *3 or more* on his next roll, he wins the game.

What are the outcomes in the sample space? Outcomes satisfying the event *3 or more*?

What is the probability of the event *3 or more*?

Sample space: 6 outcomes → 1, 2, 3, 4, 5, 6

Event *3 or more*:   4 outcomes →   3, 4, 5, 6

The probability of Jason rolling a *3 or more* on his next roll is $\frac{4}{6}$, or $\frac{2}{3}$.

2 Nicole likes to try to guess a person's birthday. What is the probability that she can guess the correct month of Jessica's birthday on the first try? Assume that it is equally likely for a person to have been born in any month.

There are 12 months in the year, so the number of outcomes in the sample space is 12. Jessica's birthday could only be during 1 month, so the number of outcomes in the event is 1.

$$P(\text{guessing correct month}) = \frac{1}{12}$$

Try It

For each situation, what are the outcomes in the sample space? What is the probability of the event?

a. If Alexander rolls a *5 or more* on his next roll of a number cube, he wins the game. 1, 2, 3, 4, 5, 6; $\frac{1}{3}$

b. Will the next large Pacific earthquake occur *on a weekend*? (Assume that it is equally likely to occur on any day of the week.)
Sun, Mon, Tues, Wed, Thur, Fri, Sat; $\frac{2}{7}$

> **► Science Link**
>
> The Ring of Fire surrounds the entire Pacific Ocean with earthquake activity. It is the most active earthquake zone in the world.

12-4 • Probability **647**

MATH EVERY DAY

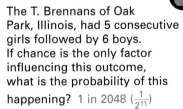

► Problem of the Day

The T. Brennans of Oak Park, Illinois, had 5 consecutive girls followed by 6 boys. If chance is the only factor influencing this outcome, what is the probability of this happening? 1 in 2048 $\left(\frac{1}{2^{11}}\right)$

Available on Daily Transparency 12-4

An Extension is provided in the transparency package.

Fact of the Day

More U.S. presidents (6) celebrated their birthday in October than in any other month. The months with the fewest presidential births are June and September (1 each).

Mental Math

Find these sums mentally.

1. $3 + 4 + 3 + 9$ 19

2. $2 + 9 + 4 + 3$ 18

3. $4 + 8 + 4 + 1$ 17

Follow Up
Have students discuss their answers to Steps 2 and 3. Make a master list of all of the suggestions the class made for Step 3.

Answers for Explore

1. See page C5.

2. Answers may vary.

3. Possible answers: 0—the sun not rising tomorrow; 1—getting an H or T on one toss of a coin.

2 Teach

Learn

Explain that a probability such as "one in four" can be written as 0.25, $\frac{1}{4}$, 1:4, or 25%. Students should be aware that *P* in the formula stands for probability.

Alternate Examples

1. Kari and Susie are playing a game with three colored markers—green, red, and blue. On her next turn, if Susie chooses a marker at random *and it is green*, she wins the game.

   What are the outcomes in the sample space? Outcomes satisfying the event *of choosing a green marker*?

   What is the probability of the event *of choosing a green marker*?

   Sample space:
   3 outcomes → green, red, blue

   Event *of choosing a green marker*:
   1 outcome → green

   The probability of Susie *choosing a green marker* on her next turn is $\frac{1}{3}$.

2. Nicole found out that Jessica was born in May. What is the probability that she can guess the correct date of Jessica's birthday on the first try?

   There are 31 days in May, so the number of outcomes in the sample is 31. Jessica could only be born on one day, so the number of outcomes is 1.

   $P(\text{guessing correct date}) = \frac{1}{31}$

Alternate Examples

3. Melody has six jelly beans in her pocket—2 are black, 2 are pink, and 2 are green. What is the probability that the next jelly bean she takes out of her pocket at random will be
   a. Black?
   b. Black, pink, or green?
   c. Yellow?
   d. *Not* black?

   a. $P(\text{black}) = \frac{2}{6} = \frac{1}{3}$

   b. $P(\text{black, pink, or green})$
   $= \frac{6}{6} = 1$ (certain)

   c. $P(\text{yellow}) = 0$ (impossible)

   d. $P(\textit{not} \text{ black}) = \frac{4}{6} = \frac{2}{3}$

3 Practice and Assess

Check

Remind students who are having difficulty with Question 3 that the sum of the probabilities of an event occurring and the event not occurring is 1.

Answers for Check Your Understanding

1. An event sometimes covers several outcomes (example: "roll a 5 or a 6"); An outcome can be an event.

2. 25% < 0.4; 25% = $\frac{1}{4}$

3. $P(B) = 1 - P(A)$; Because $P(A) + P(B) = 1$.

The probability of an event occurring is always written as a number from 0 to 1.

When it is impossible for an event to occur, the probability is 0. When an event is certain to occur, the probability is 1.

Impossible   Certain

0          $\frac{1}{4}$ $\frac{1}{2}$ $\frac{3}{4}$ 1

Example 3

Suppose you get one spin on the spinner at the right. What is the probability that the spinner will land on ...

a. Red   **b.** Red or blue   **c.** Green   **d.** *Not* red

a. $P(\text{red}) = \frac{2}{5}$

b. $P(\text{red or blue}) = 1$ (certain)

c. $P(\text{green}) = 0$ (impossible)

d. $P(\textit{not} \text{ red}) = \frac{3}{5}$

You can see that the probability of red plus the probability of *not* red is 1. The sum of the probability of an event occurring and the event *not* occurring is 1.

> **Remember**
>
> A **prime number** is an integer larger than 1 that is only divisible by itself and 1. **[Page 324]**

Try It

Find the probability that one roll of a number cube results in a

a. Prime number $\frac{1}{2}$

b. Composite number $\frac{1}{3}$

c. Number > 5 $\frac{1}{6}$

d. Number < 7 1

e. Fraction between 1 and 2 **0**

Check Your Understanding

1. Explain the difference between an outcome and an event. Can an outcome be an event?

2. How does a probability of 25% compare with a probability of 0.4? With a probability of $\frac{1}{4}$?

3. If events *A* and *B* account for all of the possibilities in the sample space, what do you know about $P(B)$? Why?

▷ MEETING MIDDLE SCHOOL CLASSROOM NEEDS

Tips from Middle School Teachers

I like to have students brainstorm uses of probability in various areas. I start them off with the following:

Social Studies: voting predictions; traffic patterns/urban planning
Science: meteorology and weather forecasts; success rates with medicines
Language Arts: identifying unknown authors; analyzing coded messages

History Connection	Cultural Connection
Many of the people who helped to develop the theory of probability were gamblers or their patrons were gamblers. They hoped that an understanding of probability would help them in winning games.	The French mathematician Blaise Pascal (1623–1662), together with Pierre de Fermat, developed mathematical theories of probability and discussed some of their applications to gambling. Pascal devised a pattern, now called Pascal's triangle, which could be used to calculate probabilities. Although the theories concerned frequently occurring events, Pascal, a deeply religious man, was also interested in the probability of unusual events occurring—in particular, events classed as miracles.

12-4 Exercises and Applications

Practice and Apply

1. **Getting Started** Find the probability of rolling a 2 on a number cube.

   a. List all of the outcomes in the sample space. **1, 2, 3, 4, 5, 6**

   b. How many outcomes are in the sample space? **6**

   c. How many outcomes of rolling a 2 are in the sample space? **1**

   d. Write a ratio using answers from **b** and **c** to find the probability. $\frac{1}{6}$

   e. Express the probability as a fraction, decimal, and percent.

   1e. $\frac{1}{6}$; 0.1666...; $16\frac{2}{3}$%

2. **History** Two U.S. Presidents, James Polk and Warren Harding, were both born on November 2. What is the probability of 2 people with November birthdays sharing the same birthday? (November has 30 days.) $\frac{1}{30}$

List all outcomes in each sample space.

3. Rolling a number cube **1, 2, 3, 4, 5, 6**

4. Drawing a marble from a bag with 3 red, 2 green, and 3 blue marbles

Express the probability as a fraction, decimal, and percent.

5. Rolling an even number on a single roll of a number cube $\frac{1}{2}$, 0.5, 50%

6. Drawing a red sock out of a drawer that contains only red socks **1, 1, 100%**

7. Going to math class on New Year's Day **0, 0, 0%**

8. That a person's birthday is not on the fourth of July $\frac{364}{365}$, 0.997, 99.7%

9. **Test Prep** Which has the greatest probability of occurring? **B**

   Ⓐ Tossing heads on a coin toss

   Ⓑ Tossing heads or tails on a coin toss

   Ⓒ Tossing a 6 on a number cube

   Ⓓ Not tossing a 6 on a number cube

10. On Jim's birthday, he chose a pet from a litter of dalmations. They were so cute, he just closed his eyes and picked one. If there were 3 males and 2 females, what are the chances that Jim's puppy is female? $\frac{2}{5}$

11. **Science** Chromosomes determine whether a child is male or female. The probability of having 13 children that are all male is $\frac{1}{8192}$. What is the probability of having 13 children that are **not** all male? $\frac{8191}{8192}$

PRACTICE 12-4

Assignment Guide

■ **Basic**
1–11 odds, 12–14, 16, 17, 18–26 evens

■ **Average**
2–8 evens, 9, 11–15, 18, 19–25 odds

■ **Enriched**
2–8 evens, 9, 10, 14, 15, 18, 19, 21, 23–26

Exercise Notes

■ **Exercise 11**

Science All of the chromosomes in the human body come in matching pairs except for those that determine if a person is to be male or female. In humans, these chromosomes are labeled X and Y. Females have two X chromosomes; males have one X chromosome and one Y chromosome.

Exercise Answers

4. Red, red, red, green, green, blue, blue, blue.

Reteaching

Activity

Materials: Blank paper, scissors, paper bag

• Work with a partner.

• Pretend that you are picking a group leader at random. Write five names on slips of paper and put them into a paper bag. Now use the bag to help you model the answers to these questions.

• What probability does each person have of becoming group leader? $\frac{1}{5}$

• Assuming that a person cannot serve as group leader again, what chance does someone else have in a second random drawing? Third random drawing? Fourth random drawing? Fifth random drawing?
$\frac{1}{4}$, $\frac{1}{3}$, $\frac{1}{2}$, 1 (certain)

• Assuming that a person *can* serve again, what chance does someone else have in a second random drawing? Third random drawing? Fourth random drawing? Fifth random drawing?
$\frac{1}{5}$, $\frac{1}{5}$, $\frac{1}{5}$, $\frac{1}{5}$

PRACTICE

Name _____

Practice 12-4

Probability

List all outcomes in each sample space.

1. Tossing a coin — **Heads, tails**

2. Choosing one of 7 cards labeled with the days of the week — **Sun., Mon., Tue., Wed., Thu., Fri., Sat.**

3. Asking a student at your school what grade he or she is in — **Answers will vary.**

Express the probability as a fraction, decimal, and percent.

4. Tossing a coin that lands heads — $\frac{1}{2}$; 0.5; 50%

5. Having 60 minutes in the next hour — 1; 1.0; 100%

6. Having a birthday that is *not* in January (assuming that all months are equally likely) — $\frac{11}{12}$; ≈0.917; ≈91.7%

7. Drawing a white marble out of a bag that contains 3 white and 7 black marbles — $\frac{3}{10}$; 0.3; 30%

The blue, gold, and white sectors of the spinner are each $\frac{1}{5}$ of the spinner area.

8. Which color or colors have the same probability as gold? — **Blue, white**

9. What is the probability of spinning black? — $\frac{2}{5}$

10. What is the probability of spinning blue? — $\frac{1}{5}$

11. What is the probability of *not* spinning black? — $\frac{3}{5}$

12. Suppose you choose someone at random from your school. What is the probability that he or she was born on the same day of the week as you? — $\frac{1}{7}$

13. In the game of Monopoly™, the probability of going to jail in any one turn is about 4.5%. What is the probability of *not* going to jail? — **About 95.5%**

RETEACHING

Name _____

Alternative Lesson 12-4

Probability

If you spin the spinner, there are eight equally likely results, or **outcomes** possible. The chance of landing on any one space is equally likely. The set of all possible outcomes is the **sample space**. The chance of a particular **event** occurring is the **probability** of the event.

$P(\text{event}) = \dfrac{\text{number of outcomes in the event}}{\text{number of outcomes possible}}$

■ **Example**

Lisa uses the spinner while playing a game. She needs to spin an *A* to win the game. What is the probability of spinning *A*?

Outcomes satisfying sample space 8 outcomes → A, B, C, D, A, A, B, C
Outcomes satisfying event *A*   3 outcomes → A, A, A

$P(\text{spinning } A) = \frac{3}{8}$

The probability of Lisa spinning an *A* is $\frac{3}{8}$.

Try It Carmen spun the spinner above. She wants to spin a *B*.

a. How many outcomes satisfy the sample space? **8 outcomes.**

b. How many outcomes satisfy the event *B*? **2 outcomes.**

c. $P(\text{spinning } B) = \frac{2}{8}$ or $\frac{1}{4}$

Liz rolls a six-sided number cube. She wants to roll an even number.

d. Which outcomes make up the sample space? How many are there?
1, 2, 3, 4, 5, and 6; 6 outcomes.

e. Which outcomes satisfy the event? How many are there?
2, 4, 6; 3 outcomes.

f. $P(\text{rolling an even number}) = \frac{3}{6}$ or $\frac{1}{2}$

Find each probability.

g. Jose rolls a six-sided number cube. What is the probability he will roll a number less than 5?
$P(\text{rolling a number less than 5}) = \frac{4}{6}$ or $\frac{2}{3}$

h. Carleen spins the spinner above. What is the probability she will spin X? $P(\text{spinning } X) = 0$

Exercise Answers

17. First in top row and the third in bottom row; 1 in 36

20. A possible event *could* happen, whereas a probable event *is likely* to happen.

21. The number of favorable outcomes cannot be more than the total number of outcomes; Possible example: Rolling less than 7 with a number cube.

22.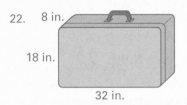

Volume: 4608 in³ = $2\frac{2}{3}$ ft³

23.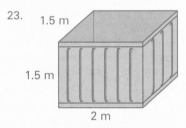

Volume: 4.5 m³

24.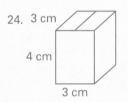

Volume: 36 cm³

Alternate Assessment

Self Assessment Have students evaluate their understanding of probability, sample spaces, outcomes, and events. Is something still causing them difficulties?

The yellow and green sectors of the spinner are each $\frac{1}{4}$ of the spinner area.

12. What is the probability of spinning red? $\frac{1}{2}$

13. Which two colors have equal probability? **Yellow, green**

GPS 14. What is the probability of not spinning green? $\frac{3}{4}$

15. **Number Sense** Suppose you randomly select answers on a test. What is the probability of selecting the correct answer in each situation?

   a. Multiple choice question with 4 choices $\frac{1}{4}$

   b. True-false question $\frac{1}{2}$

16. **Chance** The *odds* of an event happening is the ratio of the ways it can happen to the ways it *cannot* happen. What are the odds of rolling a 3 with one number cube? **1:5**

Problem Solving and Reasoning

17. **Math Reasoning** Two of these cakes are identical. Which are they? Suppose you had chosen two of them randomly. What is the probability that you would have chosen the two identical cakes?

Critical Thinking Answer "always," "sometimes," or "never."

18. An event that is certain _____ has a probability of 1. **Always**

19. An impossible event _____ has a probability of 1. **Never**

20. **Communicate** Explain the difference between *possible* and *probable*.

21. **Journal** Explain why the probability of an event can never be greater than 1. Give an example of an event that has a probability of 1.

Mixed Review

Sketch each figure and find its volume. *[Lesson 9-6]*

22. A suitcase measuring 18 in. by 32 in. by 8 in.

23. A dumpster measuring 2 m by 1.5 m by 1.5 m

24. A box that is 3 cm by 4 cm by 3 cm

Are the triangles congruent? If so, state the rule that justifies your answer. *[Lesson 11-3]*

25.  **Yes; SAS**

26. **Yes; ASA**

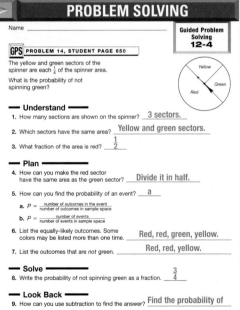

650 *Chapter 12 • Counting and Probability*

PROBLEM SOLVING

Name _____

Guided Problem Solving 12-4

GPS PROBLEM 14, STUDENT PAGE 650

The yellow and green sectors of the spinner are each $\frac{1}{4}$ of the spinner area.

What is the probability of not spinning green?

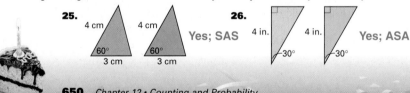

— **Understand** —

1. How many sections are shown on the spinner? **3 sectors.**

2. Which sectors have the same area? **Yellow and green sectors.**

3. What fraction of the area is red? $\frac{1}{2}$

— **Plan** —

4. How can you make the red sector have the same area as the green sector? **Divide it in half.**

5. How can you find the probability of an event? **a**

   a. $P = \frac{\text{number of outcomes in the event}}{\text{number of outcomes in sample space}}$

   b. $P = \frac{\text{number of events}}{\text{number of events in sample space}}$

6. List the equally-likely outcomes. Some colors may be listed more than one time. **Red, red, green, yellow.**

7. List the outcomes that are *not* green. **Red, red, yellow.**

— **Solve** —

8. Write the probability of not spinning green as a fraction. $\frac{3}{4}$

— **Look Back** —

9. How can you use subtraction to find the answer? **Find the probability of spinning green and subtract from 1.**

SOLVE ANOTHER PROBLEM

The white and black sectors of the spinner are each $\frac{1}{5}$ of the spinner area. What is the probability of not spinning black?

$\frac{4}{5}$

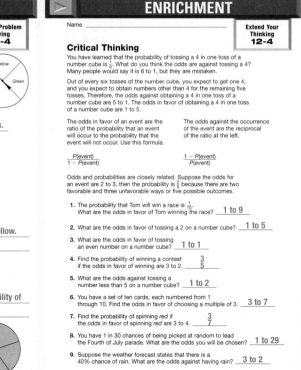

ENRICHMENT

Name _____

Extend Your Thinking 12-4

Critical Thinking

You have learned that the probability of tossing a 4 in one toss of a number cube is $\frac{1}{6}$. What do you think the odds are against tossing a 4? Many people would say it is 6 to 1, but they are mistaken.

Out of every six tosses of the number cube, you expect to get one 4, and you expect to obtain numbers other than 4 for the remaining five tosses. Therefore, the odds against obtaining a 4 in one toss of a number cube are 5 to 1. The odds in favor of obtaining a 4 in one toss of a number cube are 1 to 5.

The odds in favor of an event are the ratio of the probability that an event will occur to the probability that the event will not occur. Use this formula.

The odds against the occurrence of the event are the reciprocal of the ratio at the left.

$\frac{P(\text{event})}{1 - P(\text{event})}$

$\frac{1 - P(\text{event})}{P(\text{event})}$

Odds and probabilities are closely related. Suppose the odds for an event are 2 to 3, then the probability is $\frac{2}{5}$ because there are two favorable and three unfavorable ways or five possible outcomes.

1. The probability that Tom will win a race is $\frac{1}{10}$. What are the odds in favor of Tom winning the race? **1 to 9**

2. What are the odds in favor of tossing a 2 on a number cube? **1 to 5**

3. What are the odds in favor of tossing an even number on a number cube? **1 to 1**

4. Find the probability of winning a contest if the odds in favor of winning are 3 to 2. $\frac{3}{5}$

5. What are the odds against tossing a number less than 5 on a number cube? **1 to 2**

6. You have a set of ten cards, each numbered from 1 through 10. Find the odds in favor of choosing a multiple of 3. **3 to 7**

7. Find the probability of spinning *red* if the odds in favor of spinning red are 3 to 4. $\frac{3}{7}$

8. You have 1 in 30 chances of being picked at random to lead the Fourth of July parade. What are the odds you will be chosen? **1 to 29**

9. Suppose the weather forecast states that there is a 40% chance of rain. What are the odds against having rain? **3 to 2**

Experimental and Geometric Probability

▶ **Lesson Link**   You have learned how to compute probabilities. Now you will see if what is likely to happen *does* happen. ◀

Explore   Experimental Probability

Materials: Shiny new nickels

Putting a Spin on It

1. Working in your groups, determine whose birthday is the latest in his or her birth month (for example, in a group in which students were born on the 12th, 3rd, 24th, and 19th, the 24th is the latest). Call this number *n*.

2. You will be spinning a nickel *n* times (24 times for the above). Write down how many times you expect to get heads. $\frac{n}{2}$

3. Spin the nickel *n* times. Record the number of times you get heads. Is this the number you expected? **3–5. Answers may vary**

4. Divide the number of heads by the number of spins. Round to the nearest hundredth and write this as your probability.

5. What is the highest group probability? The lowest?

6. Tally the class results (total heads, total spins), and divide to find the class probability. Is this closer to what you expected?

You'll Learn ...

■ to use experiments to find probabilities

... How It's Used

Food manufacturers use market testing and probability to determine whether a recipe will be successful.

Vocabulary

theoretical probability

experimental probability

trial

geometric probability

Learn   Experimental and Geometric Probability

Sometimes it is easy to calculate the actual, or **theoretical probability**, of an event. When you roll a number cube, it is clear that each side has a $\frac{1}{6}$ probability of coming up. But for other situations, you may need to estimate the probability from survey or experimental data. The probability calculated by this method is called **experimental probability**.

The best way to understand experimental probability is to use it in a situation in which we know the theoretical probability and then compare the two.

12-5 • Experimental and Geometric Probability   **651**

MEETING INDIVIDUAL NEEDS

Resources

12-5 Practice

12-5 Reteaching

12-5 Problem Solving

12-5 Enrichment

12-5 Daily Transparency

    Problem of the Day

    Review

    Quick Quiz

Lesson Enhancement Transparency 69

 Interactive CD-ROM Lesson

 Wide World of Mathematics Middle School: Hurricane Prediction

Learning Modalities

Logical   Throughout the examples, students use numbers and create logical patterns to aid them in their understanding of probability.

Visual   Students use diagrams as they investigate geometric probability.

Challenge

Hermits 1, 2, 3, 4, 5, and 6 are the only occupants of an island. Today, Hermit 1 has an illness that can be passed on to anyone who is not immune. The illness lasts one day, after which the person is immune. Hermits 2–6 have never had the illness.

Roll a number cube to simulate which person the sick hermit visits for help. (Ignore the sick hermit's number if it comes up.) The next day, the visited hermit will be ill and will visit someone for help. Roll the number cube again to determine whom. Continue this experiment until a sick hermit visits an immune one and the illness dies out. Repeat the experiment 5 times, and find the average number of hermits who get the illness before it dies out.

Objective

■ **Use experiments to find probabilities.**

Vocabulary

■ **Theoretical probability, experimental probability, trial, geometric probability**

Materials

■ **Explore: Shiny new nickels**

NCTM Standards

■ **1–4, 11, 12**

▶ **Review**

Using a calculator, compute the percents.

1. $\frac{4}{129} \approx 3.1\%$

2. $\frac{7}{233} \approx 3\%$

3. $\frac{9}{123} \approx 7.3\%$

4. $\frac{8}{217} \approx 3.7\%$

5. $\frac{12}{487} \approx 2.5\%$

Available on Daily Transparency 12-5

▶ **Lesson Link**

Tell students that this lesson will highlight situations similar to testing a weather forecaster's predictions over time.

1 Introduce

Explore

The Point
Students spin nickels to see how close their expectation of getting heads is to the number of times they actually get heads.

Ongoing Assessment
In Step 3, check that students are keeping accurate records by assigning one person the task of keeping track of the number of spins and another person the task of keeping track of the number of times the nickel turns up heads.

For Groups That Finish Early

Repeat the experiment using another person's birthday number.

Follow Up

Was the class probability closer to the expected results than the individual group probabilities? Why?

The class probability should be close to $\frac{n}{2}$; In general, an experimental probability is closer to the expected (theoretical) probability for a larger sample size (but this is not necessarily the case).

Answers for Explore

6. Due to the weight and beveling of a nickel, the average should be greater than $\frac{1}{2}$.

2 Teach

Learn

You may wish to use Lesson Enhancement Transparency 69 with Example 1.

Theoretical probability can also be described by saying that it tells what *should* happen in an experiment.

Alternate Examples

1. a. What is the theoretical probability of rolling an even sum when rolling a pair of number cubes? An odd sum?

    Using the Counting Principle, there are $6 \times 6 = 36$ possible outcomes. Use the diagram and table from Example 1 to calculate the percent of probability of rolling an even sum. P(even sum) = 2.8% + 8.3% + 13.9% + 13.9% + 8.3% + 2.8% = 50%

    Do the same for an odd sum. P(odd sum) = 5.6% + 11.1% + 16.7% + 11.1% + 5.6% = 50%

   b. Compare the experimental results to the theoretical percents for even and odd sums that you calculated.

    The percents of the experimental and theoretical probabilities are close. In general, they would be closer if the student had used a large number of trials.

Each time you perform an experiment, it is called a **trial**.

Example 1

a. What is the theoretical probability of rolling each possible sum when rolling a pair of number cubes?

Using the Counting Principle, there are $6 \times 6 = 36$ possible outcomes. You can draw a diagram or make an organized list to see all possible sums.

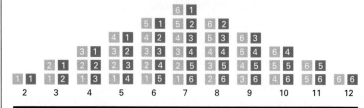

Theoretical Probabilities											
Sum	2	3	4	5	6	7	8	9	10	11	12
Outcomes	1	2	3	4	5	6	5	4	3	2	1
Percent	2.8	5.6	8.3	11.1	13.9	16.7	13.9	11.1	8.3	5.6	2.8

b. To find the experimental probabilities, roll a pair of number cubes 50 times and keep track of the sums that appear.

One student obtained these results:

Experimental Probabilities											
Sum	2	3	4	5	6	7	8	9	10	11	12
Outcomes	2	4	3	5	7	8	9	5	4	3	0
Percent	4	8	6	10	14	16	18	10	8	6	0

c. Compare these experimental results to the theoretical percents for sums from 2 through 12.

The percents of the experimental and theoretical probabilities are close. They would be much closer if the student had used a large number of trials.

Try It

a. What is the theoretical probability of tossing 2 heads, 1 head, and 0 heads when tossing a pair of coins?

b. To find the experimental probability, toss a pair of coins 50 times. Keep track of the number of times each result occurs.

c. Compare your experimental results to the theoretical percents.

652　Chapter 12 • Counting and Probability

DID YOU KNOW?

The chance that a randomly selected person was born on leap day—February 29—is about 1 in 1461.

MATH EVERY DAY

▶ Problem of the Day

During the 1994 baseball strike, the media liked to remind sports fans that the average salary of a player was $1.2 million. In fact, the median salary was $500,000. Which is true:
a. Half of the baseball players in 1994 made $1.2 million.
b. Half of the baseball players in 1994 made under $500,000. b

Available on Daily Transparency 12-5

An Extension is provided in the transparency package.

Fact of the Day

The song "Happy Birthday to You" was released in 1893 by a kindergarten teacher, Mildred Hill. Lyrics for the song were written by her sister, Patty.

Mental Math

Find these sums mentally.

1. $3\frac{1}{2} + 4\frac{1}{4} + 1\frac{1}{4}$ 9

2. $2\frac{1}{8} + 4\frac{2}{8} + 3\frac{1}{8}$ $9\frac{1}{2}$

3. $8\frac{1}{3} + 4\frac{2}{3} + 1\frac{2}{3}$ $14\frac{2}{3}$

In many situations, it may be difficult or impossible to find the theoretical probability, so experimental methods are necessary.

Example 2

At many birthday parties, it is traditional to fill a piñata with treats and hang it from a tree. After being blindfolded and spun around a few times, guests are given 2 chances to break the piñata open with a bat or stick. When it breaks, there is a free-for-all for the treats.

▶ **Language Link**

In Spanish, *piñata* means "pot." Originally, a clay pot was used to hold the treats, but now piñatas are made from wire, cardboard, and papier-maché.

El Burro manufactures piñatas. It would like the probability that a solid hit with the bat breaks the piñata to be about 8%. The company brings in children to test piñatas.

Complete the table to find the probability that a hit breaks each type of piñata. Which piñatas are ready to sell?

Piñata Type	Number of Hits	Piñatas Broken	P(Hit Breaks Piñata)
Dragon	107	18	?
Bull	216	8	?
Burro	254	19	?

Dragon $P = \frac{18}{107} \approx 16.8\%$; bull $P = \frac{8}{216} \approx 3.7\%$; burro $P = \frac{19}{254} \approx 7.5\%$.

The burro piñatas are ready to sell.

Try It

Quality control is important in many businesses. BrightLights makes candles. BrightLights will tolerate a 0.5% defective rate for each package of candles (missing wicks, chips, and so on). Tests were run in different factories.

Complete the table to find the probability that a box contains defective candles. Which factories passed the inspection?

Factory	Number with Defects	Number of Packages Checked	P(Box Contains Defective Candles)
San Antonio	20	4534	?
Tulsa	27	5324	?
Uvalde	10	1095	?

If the number of packages produced at the San Antonio factory were 10,000 a day, how many would you predict would contain defective candles?

MEETING MIDDLE SCHOOL CLASSROOM NEEDS

Tips from Middle School Teachers

I discuss with my class an interesting fact about probability: The more times an experiment is repeated, two seemingly contradictory things tend to happen. The average of the results corresponds more to the theoretical average, and the chance is greater for a very extreme result to happen as well. For example, if there is a one in a million chance that a person will coincidentally dream about something that actually happens later, more than 200 Americans are likely to have such a dream.

Team Teaching

Work with a science teacher to introduce the concept of probability found in experiments and nature. For example, students can observe patterns in nature, such as right-handedness, and determine the probability that a randomly selected person will be right-handed.

Cultural Connection

Piñatas are the subject matter of Example 2. Invite students who have piñatas at home, or pictures of piñatas that they had at parties, to bring them in to share with the class. Explain to students that piñatas are traditionally used in certain Latin American countries as a part of birthday or holiday celebrations. The piñatas are filled with candy and toys, suspended from a height, and broken open by blindfolded children using a stick.

Alternate Examples

1. (continued)

   c. To find the experimental probabilities, roll a pair of number cubes 50 times and keep track of the even and odd sums that appear.

   Rolling the pair of number cubes 50 times, you may have gotten results similar to these:

Experimental Probabilities		
Sums	Even	Odd
Frequency	27	23
Percent	54%	46%

Answers for Try It

a. 2 heads: $\frac{1}{4}$; 1 head: $\frac{1}{2}$;

   0 heads: $\frac{1}{4}$

b. Answers may vary.

c. There should be approximately 25% of 2 heads, 50% of 1 head, and 25% of 0 heads.

2. L & M Spring Company has a quality control policy that does not allow them to release any new types of springs that do not pass at least 375 tests with a 1.5% or less failure rate. Complete the table to find the probability of failure for each new spring type. Which spring type is able to be released?

Spring Type	Number of Tests	Failed Springs	P(Spring Failure)
E2010	375	7	?
E2015	412	8	?
E2025	378	5	?

E2010 $P = \frac{7}{375} \approx 1.9\%$

E2015 $P = \frac{8}{412} \approx 1.9\%$

E2025 $P = \frac{5}{378} \approx 1.3\%$

The E2025 is ready to be released.

Answers for Try It

San Antonio is the only one that passed; You would expect to find defective candles in ≈ 44 boxes out of 10,000.

San Antonio $P = \frac{20}{4534} \approx .44\%$

Tulsa $P = \frac{27}{5324} \approx .51\%$

Uvalde $P = \frac{10}{1095} \approx .91\%$

3. Mayme has been swimming in a pool. When she gets out of the water, she notices that her ring is missing. It can be anywhere on the bottom of the pool with equal likelihood. What is the probability that her ring is in the shallower end of the pool?

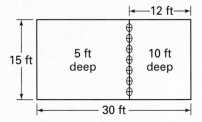

The area of the entire rectangular pool is 15 ft × 30 ft = 450 ft². The deep end is 12 ft × 15 ft, or 180 ft², so the shallower area is 450 − 180 = 270 ft².

The probability that the ring is in the shallower end is $\frac{270}{450}$.

270 ÷ 450 = 60%

3 Practice and Assess

Check

If students are having a difficult time answering Question 2, remind them that the 1 stands for an event certain to occur.

Answers for Check Your Understanding

1. Possible answer: Theoretical probability is based on assumptions about a situation, while experimental probability is based on how similar situations have turned out in the past; Doctor's probabilities are usually experimental; Geometric probability is theoretical.

▶ **History Link**

In 1582, Pope Gregory XIII corrected the calendar, adjusting leap year to occur every 4 years—except for years divisible by 100, unless it is also divisible by 400.

Another way to determine probability is by using geometric models and comparing areas, lengths, or other measures. This is called **geometric probability** .

Example 3

A small prize is placed randomly in the birthday cake. It can be anywhere in the cake with equal likelihood. What is the probability that the prize is under one of the **iced edges**?

The area of the entire rectangle is 36 in. × 24 in. = 864 in². The center area is 30 in. × 18 in., or 540 in², so the area under the icing is 864 − 540 = 324 in².

The probability that the prize is in an edge piece is $\frac{324}{864}$.

324 ÷ 864 = *0.375*, or 37.5%.

Try It

A small prize is placed randomly in the birthday cake. It can be anywhere in the cake with equal likelihood. What is the probability that the prize is under one of the flowers? $\frac{4}{27}$

Check | Your Understanding

1. Explain the difference between theoretical and experimental probability. Are probabilities quoted by doctors theoretical or experimental? Is geometric probability theoretical or experimental?

2. Carinna says that an experimental probability can exceed 1. Is this true? If so, give an example. **No**

3. Suppose a quality-control tester at BrightLights tested 20 boxes, found defective candles in 1, and said the factory failed the test. Is this fair? **No, because the test involves too few boxes to be reliable.**

12-5 Exercises and Applications

Practice and Apply

Getting Started Decide whether each probability is theoretical or experimental.

1. The probability that a bowler makes a strike is 30%. **Experimental**

2. The probability that a number cube lands on 6 is $\frac{1}{6}$. **Theoretical**

3. Two coins are tossed 100 times. Two heads come up 23 times. **Experimental**

4. For his grandmother's 100th birthday celebration, Jeremy's mother asked him to find out what flavor cake each guest would prefer so she could begin cutting the 4 delicious cakes.

Flavor of Cake	No. of Requests
Chocolate	62
White	28
Carrot	22
Lemon	14

   a. What is the probability that a guest selected chocolate? $\frac{31}{63}$

   b. What is the probability that a guest would choose lemon? $\frac{1}{9}$

   c. What is the probability that the next guest would request a flavor other than carrot cake? $\frac{52}{63}$

5. Geometry A player throws a marker onto the game board. It lands in a random location.

   a. What is the probability of its landing in the triangle? $\frac{7}{30}$

   b. What is the probability of its landing outside the triangle? $\frac{23}{30}$

Toss 3 coins 50 times and make a table to record your results. Use the data to find the experimental probability of each event.

6. Tossing 3 heads and no tails   **7.** Tossing 2 heads and 1 tail **About $\frac{3}{8}$.**

                                      6. About $\frac{1}{8}$.

8. Compare the experimental probability of tossing 3 heads and no tails with the theoretical probability. **The two should be roughly equal.**

9. Geometry A particle travels around the perimeter of the hexagon and stops at a random location. What is the probability that it lands on the shortest side? $\frac{2}{27}$

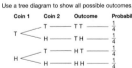

10. The day before her birthday, Shirin begged her mother to let her open one of her 7 gifts. With her mother's permission, she picked one to open, hoping it would be the radio she knew her father had bought her. Two of the packages were too small to be a radio. What is the probability that Shirin picked the radio? **20%**

PRACTICE 12-5

Assignment Guide

■ **Basic**
1–8, 10–12, 14, 17–20

■ **Average**
1–8, 10–13, 16, 18–20

■ **Enriched**
1–12, 15, 18–20

Exercise Notes

■ **Exercise 5**

Computer simulations of this kind of marker (or dart) throwing are actually used to estimate irregularly shaped areas.

■ **Exercise 10**

Remind students that in real-life situations they can often reduce the sample space when finding probabilities by using logic, such as Shirin does in this exercise.

Reteaching

Activity

Materials: Red, white, and blue chips; paper bag

• Work in groups of three.

• Prepare a chart with the following headings: Chip color, Theoretical probability, Tally, Frequency, Experimental probability.

• Put 5 red, 3 white, and 2 blue chips in the bag. Compute the theoretical probability of drawing each color chip from the bag and write it on the chart. Red: $\frac{5}{10}$ or $\frac{1}{2}$; White: $\frac{3}{10}$; Blue: $\frac{2}{10}$ or $\frac{1}{5}$.

• Now, draw a chip from the bag, tally the color, and return the chip to the bag. Continue doing this a total of 50 times.

• When finished, compute the experimental probability for drawing each color. Answers may vary.

• How do the theoretical and experimental probabilities compare? Answers may vary.

• How do you think the comparison might change if you conducted the experiment 100 times? Possible answer: It might be closer.

PRACTICE

Name _____

Practice 12-5

Experimental and Geometric Probability

1. Toss 4 coins 40 times and complete the table to record your results. Use the data to find the experimental probability of each event. Give each probability as a percent. **Answers will vary.**

Outcome	4 heads	3 heads 1 tails	2 heads 2 tails	1 heads 3 tails	4 tails
Frequency					
Experimental Probability					

2. Compare the experimental probability of tossing 4 tails and no heads with the theoretical probability.
Answers will vary. (Theoretical probability is 6.25%.)

3. Helen works in an ice cream shop. For the last three hours, she has recorded what flavor each customer purchased. Her data is shown.

Outcome	Customers
Vanilla	27
Chocolate	14
Strawberry	16
Other	13

  a. What is the probability that a customer purchased chocolate? **20%**

  b. What is the probability that a customer purchased vanilla or strawberry? **About 61.4%**

  c. What is the probability that the next customer will *not* purchase strawberry? **About 77.1%**

4. A player tosses a coin onto the game board.

  a. What is the probability that the coin lands in the circle? **About 24.7%**

  b. What is the probability that the coin lands outside the circle? **About 75.3%**

5. Social Science The stem-and-leaf diagram shows the ages of U.S. Presidents at inauguration.

```
stem | leaf
  4  | 2366899
  5  | 00111122444455556677778
  6  | 0111244589
```

  a. What is the probability that a President was 57? **About 9.8%**

  b. What is the probability that a President was over 59? **About 24.4%**

RETEACHING

Name _____

Alternative Lesson 12-5

Experimental and Geometric Probability

If you toss a coin, you can calculate the actual, or **theoretical** probability, of tossing heads and tossing tails. The probability of either outcome occurring is $\frac{1}{2}$. But if you actually toss a coin and keep track of the results after each toss, your results are the **experimental probability** of the experiment.

— Example 1 —

What is the theoretical probability of tossing only one tail when you toss two coins? Use a tree diagram to show all possible outcomes.

Coin 1	Coin 2	Outcome	Probability
T	T	T T	$\frac{1}{4}$
	H	T H	$\frac{1}{4}$
H	T	H T	$\frac{1}{4}$
	H	H H	$\frac{1}{4}$

There are two events that result in tossing only one tail, so the theoretical probability of tossing one tail with two coins is $\frac{1}{2}$.

Try It

  a. Suppose you toss two coins. What is the theoretical probability that *at least* one coin will be heads? $\frac{3}{4}$

— Example 2 —

Tim tossed two coins twenty times to find the experimental probability of tossing only one tail. How did his results compare with the theoretical probability of tossing one tail that you found in Example 1?

Coin 1	Coin 2	Outcome	Frequency	Percent
T	T	T T	4	20%
	H	T H	6	30%
H	T	H T	5	25%
	H	H H	5	25%

The experimental probability is 55%, which is close to the theoretical probability of $\frac{1}{2}$.

Try It

  b. Find the experimental probability of tossing two heads when you toss one coin 25 times. How does this compare with the theoretical probability?
Check students' work. The two probabilities will usually be similar.

Exercise Notes

■ Exercise 13

Health Placebos contain no medicine, but many patients show medical improvement when given a placebo, perhaps because the placebo reinforces the patient's expectation to get well. This result is known as the placebo effect.

Exercise Answers

13. Yes; 50% were helped by the medicine, while only 12.5% reported improvement with the placebo.

14. Theoretical: $\frac{7}{24} \approx 29\%$;

    Experimental: $\frac{5}{12} \approx 42\%$.

15. Yes. Possible example: In a million tosses, a coin might land on edge once or twice, and the experimental probability of getting heads or tails would be a little less than 1.

16. 50%; By definition, half of all cakes are more expensive than the median and half are less expensive.

Alternate Assessment

Ongoing When students are recording events, as in **Try It** on page 652, take note that they are recording their results accurately. Then check that experimental probabilities are calculated by dividing the number of successes for an outcome by the total number of trials in the experiment.

► Quick Quiz

Tell whether each probability is theoretical or experimental.

1. A paper cup tossed in the air will fall on its side 73% of the time. Experimental

2. The probability that a flipped coin will turn up heads is $\frac{1}{2}$. Theoretical

3. The probability that a batter hits a home run is 5%. Experimental

Available on Daily Transparency 12-5

---

11. **Problem Solving** Cliff surveyed his class to find the day of the month each person was born and organized his data in a stem-and-leaf diagram.

    a. What is the probability that a student was born on the 17th?

    b. What is the probability that a student was born after the 29th?

    c. What is the probability that a student was not born on the 4th?

Stem	Leaf
0	1 3 5 7 7 8 8 9
1	1 1 3 5 6 7 7 7 8 9
2	0 0 1 2 2 3 4 6 6 7 8 9
3	0 0 1

11.a. $\frac{1}{11}$

b. $\frac{1}{11}$

c. 1

12. **Test Prep** Estimate the probability that a person was born in May. **A**

Ⓐ 8.5% Ⓑ 12% Ⓒ $\frac{11}{12}$ Ⓓ 60.1%

Problem Solving and Reasoning

13. **Communicate** Of 1000 patients, 600 were given a new medicine, and the rest were given a placebo (which has no effect). Of those given the medicine, 300 said their condition had improved, compared to 50 who received the placebo. Would you say the medicine is effective? Why?

14. **Journal** 7 candles from a box of 24 regular candles were switched with "magic" candles that don't blow out. When Perry tried to blow out his 12 birthday candles, 5 of them remained lit. Compare the theoretical probability to the experimental probability that a candle would not blow out.

15. **Critical Thinking** If the theoretical probability of an event is 1, can the experimental probability be less than 1?

16. **Math Reasoning** What is the probability that the price of a birthday cake exceeds the median price for all birthday cakes? Explain.

Mixed Review

Find the volume of each prism after a dilation with a scale factor of 2. *[Lesson 9-7]*

17.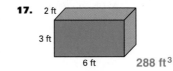
2 ft, 3 ft, 6 ft
288 ft³

18.
2 m, 2 m, 2 m
64 m³

19.
8 in., 5 in., 5 in.
1600 in³

20. Evaluate the trigonometric ratios for ∠BAC. *[Lesson 11-4]*

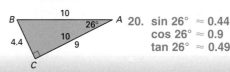

20. sin 26° ≈ 0.44
cos 26° ≈ 0.9
tan 26° ≈ 0.49

PROBLEM SOLVING

Name _____

Guided Problem Solving 12-5

GPS PROBLEM 11, STUDENT PAGE 656

Cliff surveyed his class to find the day of the month each person was born and organized his data in a stem and leaf diagram.

a. What is the probability that a student was born on the 17th?

b. What is the probability that a student was born after the 29th?

c. What is the probability that a student was not born on the 4th?

Stem	Leaf
0	1 3 5 7 7 8 8 9
1	1 1 3 5 6 7 7 7 8 9
2	0 0 1 2 2 3 4 6 6 7 8 9 9
3	0 0 1

— Understand —

1. What does each response represent? __Birthdate of one student.__

— Plan —

2. How many outcomes are in the sample space? __33 outcomes.__

3. Write the number of students that were born each date.

a. 17th __3 students.__ b. 30th or 31st __3 students.__ c. 4th __0 students.__

4. How many students were *not* born on the 4th? __33 students.__

— Solve —

5. Write the probability that a student was born on each given date.

a. 17th __$\frac{3}{33}$ or $\frac{1}{11}$__ b. after the 29th __$\frac{3}{33}$ or $\frac{1}{11}$__ c. not on 4th __1__

— Look Back —

6. Write each probability in Item 5 as a percent.

a. 17th __9.09%__ b. after the 29th __9.09%__ c. not on 4th __100%__

SOLVE ANOTHER PROBLEM

Add two more birthdates, the ninth and the twenty-ninth to Cliff's stem and leaf diagram above. Then answer the questions below.

a. What is the probability that a student was born on the 25th? __0__

b. What is the probability that a student was born after the 16th? __$\frac{21}{35} = \frac{3}{5}$__

c. What is the probability that a student was not born on the 10th? __1__

ENRICHMENT

Name _____

Extend Your Thinking 12-5

Critical Thinking

A random number table consists of many rows of digits selected at random. Each digit has an equal probability of being selected. You can use the table of random numbers below to simulate an experiment instead of actually performing the experiment.

32927	63790	80972	33410	65456
18173	00234	84378	04983	91020
74362	39890	42822	19514	71085
26604	31433	63805	15113	39975
38291	27493	78239	34028	21105

1. Simulate the experiment of tossing a coin 100 times. The first 100 digits can represent the 100 trials. Assign even numbers and zero to heads and odd numbers to tails. The first twenty have been completed for you.

3 2 9 2 7	6 3 7 9 0	8 0 9 7 2	3 3 4 1 0
T H T H T	H T T T H	H H T T H	T T H T H

a. How many heads did you get? What is the probability?

There are 48 even numbers and zeros, so 48 heads are represented in the experiment. $P(\text{heads}) = \frac{48}{100}$.

b. How does this result compare with the theoretical probability of tossing a coin?

The theoretical probability is $\frac{1}{2}$ or $\frac{50}{100}$; The simulated probability of $\frac{48}{100}$ is close to $\frac{50}{100}$.

2. To simulate tossing a number cube using the random number table, you must first decide how to assign the digits in the table. Choose any six digits in the table to represent the numbers on the number cube. The other digits in the table are not used in the simulation.

a. What are the results when you simulate tossing a number cube 50 times? Give the probability.

$P(1) = 8; \frac{4}{25}$ $P(2) = 10; \frac{2}{5}$ $P(3) = 12; \frac{12}{25}$

$P(4) = 10; \frac{2}{5}$ $P(5) = 4; \frac{4}{25}$ $P(6) = 6; \frac{6}{25}$

b. How do these results compare with the theoretical probability?

Possible answer: Theoretical probability of rolling any digit is $\frac{1}{6}$. Results are close but somewhat skewed.

Conditional Probability

▶ **Lesson Link** You have learned to compute probabilities of single events. Now you will learn how additional information and conditions affect probabilities. ◀

Explore | Conditional Probability

Food for Thought

Suppose that you have the following information about meal orders at a class function. You are working in the kitchen handing out meals on plates.

	Chicken	Vegetarian
Boys	73	11
Girls	52	29
Teachers	4	3

1. What is the probability that a person ordered a vegetarian meal? What is the probability that any meal is for a teacher? $\frac{1}{4}$, $\frac{7}{172}$

2. Is a vegetarian meal more likely to be for a boy, a girl, or a teacher? Is a chicken meal more likely to be for a boy, a girl, or a teacher?

3. Suppose a girl needs a meal. Is she more likely to have ordered chicken or vegetarian? Would you have been more sure or less sure of the meal selection if the person had been a boy? Why?

4. Suppose the first three teachers order a vegetarian meal. How sure would you be of the choice for the next teacher's meal?

You'll Learn …

■ to understand what affects the probability of an event

… How It's Used

Planning a large event requires considering many "what-ifs"—conditions and probabilities—so that risk is minimized.

Vocabulary

conditional probability

Learn | Conditional Probability

In many real-world situations, knowledge of one event affects your decisions about a second event. This is true in probability situations also. Often additional information leads to a more accurate ability to find the theoretical probability of an event.

12-6 • Conditional Probability **657**

Objective

■ Understand what affects the probability of an event.

Vocabulary

■ Conditional probability

NCTM Standards

■ 1, 2, 4, 11, 12

▶ **Review**

Write the decimal equivalent for each fraction.

1. $\frac{1}{4}$ 0.25

2. $\frac{1}{8}$ 0.125

3. $\frac{7}{8}$ 0.875

4. $\frac{3}{5}$ 0.6

5. $\frac{2}{10}$ 0.2

Available on Daily Transparency 12-6

▶ **Lesson Link**

Have students think of situations where the more information they had about something, the easier it was for them to make a decision. Allow them to share their examples.

1 Introduce

Explore

The Point
Students use a chart to answer questions about meals ordered at a class function.

Ongoing Assessment
Check that students begin answering the questions correctly. Their first calculation should be to find the total number of meals.

For Groups That Finish Early
What is the probability that a person ordered a chicken meal? What is the probability that any meal is for a boy? What is the probability that any meal is for a girl? $\frac{129}{172} \approx$

0.75; $\frac{84}{172} = \frac{21}{43} \approx 0.49$; $\frac{81}{172} \approx 0.47$

MEETING INDIVIDUAL NEEDS

Resources	**Learning Modalities**
12-6 Practice	**Kinesthetic** Students could flip coins or roll number cubes to help them model the situations in Example 1.
12-6 Reteaching	
12-6 Problem Solving	
12-6 Enrichment	**Social** In **Explore**, students work with a partner to answer questions about probability.
12-6 Daily Transparency	
Problem of the Day	**Visual** Students should draw appropriate pictures, such as tree diagrams, to determine the number of outcomes of an event.
Review	
Quick Quiz	

Lesson Enhancement
Transparency 70

Wide World of Mathematics
Geometry: DNA

Inclusion

Students with impaired vision might benefit from using a jar filled with marbles or other objects of distinctly different sizes and shapes to perform probability experiments. The objects, however, should not be so large or so small that they will interfere with each other or produce nonrandom results.

Lesson 12-6 **657**

Discuss with students how the information for the other categories in the chart helped them to answer the questions.

Answers for Explore

2. Vegetarian is probably for a girl; Chicken probably for a boy.

3. Chicken; You would be even more sure if the person had been a boy; A boy is more likely to order chicken than a girl ($\frac{73}{73 + 11}$ is more than $\frac{52}{52 + 29}$).

4. You can be certain that it will be chicken.

2 Teach

Learn

You may want to use Lesson Enhancement Transparency 70 with this lesson.

Ask students to suppose that about half of the jerseys sold in a sports store chain are from state college teams and that the other half are for professional teams. They are going to survey a store within one mile of a major state college. Do they think the ratio of jerseys sold will be about 1:1 in that store?

Alternate Examples

1. Suppose that you have three cards face down on the table: one has a circle on it, one has a square, and one has a triangle. You turn over one card and it is a triangle.

   a. What is the probability that the next card will have a circle? If you did not know anything about the first card, the probability of a circle would be $\frac{1}{3}$. Because you know that the first card is a triangle, then the sample space is reduced. There are now only 2 possible outcomes in the sample space. The probability of a circle, given that the first card came up a triangle, is $\frac{1}{2}$.

   b. What is the probability that the next card will have a triangle?

   Because the first card came up a triangle, and there is only one triangle card, the probability of a triangle is 0.

Example 1

Suppose that you toss 2 coins. The first coin comes up heads.

a. What is the probability that you will toss 2 heads?

If you did not know anything about the first coin, the probability of 2 heads would be $\frac{1}{4}$. Because you know that the first coin is heads, then the sample space is reduced. There are now only 2 possible outcomes in the sample space. The probability of 2 heads, given that the first coin came up heads, is $\frac{1}{2}$.

1st coin   2nd coin   Outcomes

b. What is the probability that you will toss 2 tails?

Because the first coin came up heads, the probability that you will toss 2 tails is 0.

Try It

Suppose you roll two number cubes. The first cube comes up 1.

a. What is the probability that the sum of the two number cubes is 6? $\frac{1}{6}$

b. What is the probability that the sum of the two number cubes is 8? 0

Problem Solving TIP

Rather than making an organized list, you may find it easier to draw a tree diagram to find the theoretical probability.

Conditional probability is the probability that, given that event A has already occurred, event B will occur. The fact that event A has already occurred reduces the sample space for calculating the conditional probability of B.

Example 2

Vanessa Mae, youngest person to record the Tchaikovsky and Beethoven Violin Concertos, shares a birthday with the legendary violinist Nicolò Paganini. Paganini was born in October of 1782.

a. What is the probability that you could guess her birthday randomly?

Since you know her birthday is in October, a month with 31 days, the probability is $\frac{1}{31}$.

b. What is the probability that she was born in a month that has exactly 30 days?

Because October has 31 days, the probability that she was born in a month with 30 days is 0.

658   *Chapter 12 • Counting and Probability*

MATH EVERY DAY

▶ Problem of the Day

Here is a stack of standard number cubes. What is the total of the dots on the hidden faces, assuming you can walk around the table and see all exposed faces?

19 [The opposite sides on a standard number cube have a sum of 7. So the sum of the hidden faces equals 7 times the number of cubes minus the number showing on top of the top cube.]

Available on Daily Transparency 12-6

An Extension is provided in the transparency package.

Fact of the Day

The first successful parachute descent from a great height was made in 1797 by the French aeronaut Jacques Garnerin, who dropped 3,000 feet from a balloon.

Estimation

Estimate each quotient.

1. 789 ÷ 42   20

2. 6095 ÷ 97   61

3. 80 ÷ 410   0.2

Example 3

Movie reviewers Gene Siskel (born January 26) and Roger Ebert (born June 18) give each film they review "thumbs up" or "thumbs down." The table shows their ratings of 213 movies they reviewed between September 9, 1995, and July 27, 1996.

a. What is the probability that Roger would give a movie thumbs up? That Gene would give a movie thumbs up?

	Roger 👍	Roger 👎	Total
Gene 👍	80	20	100
Gene 👎	36	77	113
Total	116	97	213

Roger gave 116 of 213 movies thumbs up, so the probability is $\frac{116}{213} \approx 54\%$ that Roger would give a movie thumbs up. Gene gave 100 of 213 movies thumbs up, so the probability is $\frac{100}{213} \approx 47\%$ that Gene would give a movie thumbs up.

b. If Gene gives a movie thumbs up, what is the probability that Roger would too?

If **Gene** gives a movie thumbs up, the sample space is reduced. The probability is $\frac{80}{100}$, or 80%, that Roger would give it thumbs up too.

c. If Gene gives a movie thumbs down, what is the probability that Roger would give it thumbs up?

If **Gene** gives a movie thumbs down, the probability is $\frac{36}{113} \approx 32\%$ that Roger would give it thumbs up.

▶ **Career Link**

To become a movie critic, you can study film criticism at a university.

Try It

The results of a student survey are shown. First find the totals.

	Like Math	Don't Like Math
Calculators used in class	56	34
Calculators not used in class	35	25

a. What is the probability that a student selected at random would like math?

b. If you know that a student uses calculators in class, what is the probability that the student would like math?

a. $\frac{91}{150} \approx 60.7\%$

b. $\frac{28}{45} \approx 62.2\%$

12-6 • Conditional Probability **659**

MEETING MIDDLE SCHOOL CLASSROOM NEEDS

Tips from Middle School Teachers

I like to impress students with the predictive power of probability. I prepare small boxes (like individual cereal boxes) filled with 10 marbles of different colors (for example, some red, some green, and some white). The box has only a small opening, large enough for a marble to fit. I instruct students as follows: "Mix the marbles thoroughly, pick one from the box, then replace it. Do this 60 times, and record the results in a table. Then (a) find the experimental probability of each color, (b) predict how many marbles of the 10 in the box are of each color, and (c) compare your prediction to the marbles in the box."

Career Connection

An emergency medical technician (EMT) is a person trained to appraise and initiate emergency medical care for victims of trauma or acute illness. EMTs must be extremely aware of all of the conditions that affect an emergency situation and be able to base their decisions on these conditions.

History Connection

Motion pictures date back only to the late 1800s, so they have a relatively brief history compared to such art forms as music and painting. A company owned by Thomas Edison displayed the first commercial motion-picture machine at the World's Columbian Exposition in Chicago in 1893. Edison's machine, called a kinetoscope, allowed a person to watch through a peephole as the 35-millimeter black-and-white film moved on spools within a cabinet. The films ran about 90 seconds. Kinetoscopes were soon replaced by projection machines that projected images on a screen.

Alternate Examples

2. What is the probability that Alex was born in the spring if:

   a. The month in which he was born begins with the letter A?

   There are two months that begin with the letter A, April and August. April is a spring month so the probability is $\frac{1}{2}$.

   b. The month in which he was born begins with the letter S?

   There is one month that begins with the letter S. September is not a spring month so the probability is 0.

3. A total of 342 eighth-graders were surveyed to see if the students like or do not like classical music. Each student was also asked if they did or did not play an instrument. Results are shown in the table.

	Like Classical	Don't Like Classical
Play	98	11
Don't Play	101	132

   a. What is the probability that a student chosen at random would like classical music?

   $\frac{199}{342} \approx 58.2\%$

   There is a 58.2% probability that a student chosen at random would like classical music.

   b. What is the probability that a student who does not play an instrument would like classical music?

   $\frac{101}{233} \approx 43.3\%$

   There is a 43.3% probability that a student who does not play an instrument would like classical music.

   c. What is the probability that a student who plays an instrument would like classical music?

   $\frac{98}{109} \approx 89.9\%$

   There is an 89.9% probability that a student who plays an instrument would like classical music.

4. Given that a point is inside the rectangle *PQRS*, what is the probability that it is inside square *XYRS*?

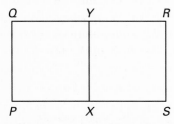

Since you know that the point is in rectangle *PQRS*, then it could possibly be in the square *XYRS*. This square is about $\frac{1}{2}$ of the area of rectangle *PQRS*, so the probability that the point is in *XYRS* is about $\frac{1}{2}$, or about 0.50.

3 Practice and Assess

Check

For Question 2, encourage students to think of real-world examples. Allow them to share their examples.

Answers for Check Your Understanding

1. No; Possible example: The probability of getting heads on a coin flip, given that you got heads on the last flip.

2. Possible answer: The probability of making the basketball team increases, if you are over 6 feet tall; The probability of being stopped by a police officer decreases, if you are obeying the speed limit.

3. 0; The second number would have to be a 7, which is not on the number cube.

You use geometric probability when you play a game like Battleship™, where you use information to locate ships.

Conditional probability can be shown geometrically. You know that a specific happening occurred in one region and you want to know the probability that it would occur in a smaller or intersecting region.

In the figure, the probability of a point being in square *B* is $\frac{1}{16}$. But if we know that the point is somewhere within square *A*, then the probability that the point is in square *B* is now $\frac{1}{4}$.

Example 4

Given that a point is inside the rectangle *RSTU,* what is the probability that it is inside square *ABCD*?

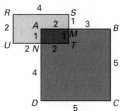

Because you know that the point is in rectangle *RSTU*, then it could possibly be in the rectangle *AMTN*. This rectangle is $\frac{1}{4}$ of the area of *RSTU*, so the probability that the point is in *ABCD* is $\frac{1}{4}$, or 0.25.

Try It

a. Given that a point lies in square *ABCD* above, what is the probability that it is inside rectangle *RSTU*? $\frac{2}{25}$

b. What is the probability that a point within the large circle is also within the shaded region? Given that the point is within the small circle, what is the probability that it is within the shaded region? $\frac{1}{18}$, $\frac{1}{2}$

Study TIP

Before studying for a test, make a list of important facts you need to know. Ask your teacher to help you make the list.

Check | Your Understanding

1. Do new conditions always change the probability of an event? Explain.

2. Give an example of probability that increases given some condition. Give an example of probability that decreases given some condition.

3. Two number cubes are thrown. The first number cube shows a 2. What is the probability that the sum of the two number cubes is 9? Why?

12-6 Exercises and Applications

Practice and Apply

1. **Getting Started** Suppose you spin the spinner twice.

   a. Make a tree diagram or an organized list to show the possible outcomes.

   b. How many possible outcomes are there? **16**

   c. If the first spin lands on red, now how many possible outcomes are there? **4**

   d. What is the probability that both spins will land on red? $\frac{1}{16}$

2. Suppose you spin the spinner 3 times. What is the probability that it lands on green all 3 times? $\frac{1}{64}$

Suppose that a fly lands on a checkerboard square. What is the probability that it lands...

3. On a red square? $\frac{1}{2}$

4. On a square in the third row? $\frac{1}{8}$

5. On a red square in the third row? $\frac{1}{16}$

6. If you know that the fly landed on a black square, what is the probability that it landed on the bottom right corner square? $\frac{1}{32}$

7. You roll a pair of number cubes in a board game. If the first cube comes up a 6, find the probability that the sum of the two number cubes is

   GPS

   a. 6 **0**   b. 7 $\frac{1}{6}$ c. Greater than 10 $\frac{1}{3}$ d. Greater than 6 **1**

The graph shows the percent of people who have lost a job for various reasons.

8. **Career** Two employees are let go from an electronics company. What is the probability that both are let go due to negative attitudes? **1%**

- 16% — Incompetence
- 12% — Can't get along with others
- 10% — Dishonesty
- 7% — Negative attitude
- 10% — No motivation
- 45% — Other

9. **Math Reasoning** This graph represents 5000 people. About how many people were let go because they could not get along with others? **≈ 800 people**

10. February 29 is sometimes referred to as Sadie Hawkins Day. Sadie was a character in Al Capp's comic strip *Li'l Abner*. Suppose one small spot on the comics page misprinted. If *Li'l Abner* was $\frac{1}{3}$ page and the Sadie Hawkins panel was $\frac{1}{6}$ of the comic strip, what is the probability that the misprint was on the Sadie Hawkins panel? $\frac{1}{18}$

12-6 • Conditional Probability   **661**

PRACTICE 12-6

12-6 Exercises and Applications

Assignment Guide

- **Basic**
  1–4, 7–17

- **Average**
  1–13, 15, 17

- **Enriched**
  1–9, 11–16

Exercise Notes

■ **Exercise 1**

Error Prevention Some students may be confused about how many tree diagram columns to use to solve a problem. Explain that in a tree diagram each decision requires a column. The rows for each column indicate the number of choices for each decision. The last column lists all possible choices.

Exercise Answers

1. a. red, red; red, blue; red, yellow; red, green

   blue, blue; blue, red; blue, yellow; blue, green

   yellow, yellow; yellow, red; yellow, blue; yellow, green

   green, green; green, red; green, blue; green, yellow

Reteaching

Activity

Materials: 2 red chips, 1 blue chip

- Work with a partner.

- A bag contains 2 red chips and 1 blue chip. What is the probability of drawing 2 red chips if you draw a chip and do not replace it for the second drawing?

- Use the chips to model the possibilities. How many possibilities are there? What are they? 6; BR_1, BR_2, R_1B, R_2B, R_1R_2, R_2R_1

- What is the probability of drawing 2 red chips? $\frac{2}{6} = \frac{1}{3}$

Lesson 12-6   661

Science Parachutes are designed to slow the descent of a falling body by creating drag as it passes through the air. The rate of descent for a parachute carrying a human is about 18 feet per second.

Exercise Answers

14. $\dfrac{\text{safe area}}{\text{safe area + fountain}}$

$= \dfrac{40 \cdot 50 - 12^2\pi - 6^2\pi}{40 \cdot 50 - 12^2\pi} \approx 93\%.$

The fountain covers $\frac{1}{4}$ as much area as the trees.

Alternate Assessment

You may want to use the *Interactive CD-ROM Journal* with this assessment.

Performance Ask students to write about a situation in their life that could be concerned with conditional probability. For example, their favorite musical group is coming to town. What circumstances determine the probability that they are able to attend the concert? There are several conditions that need to be met: whether they have enough money to go, whether they have permission to go, whether they are able to get tickets, and so on.

► Quick Quiz

Suppose you roll two number cubes. If the first one comes up 2:

1. What is the probability that the sum of the two number cubes is 4? $\frac{1}{6}$

2. What is the probability that the sum of the two number cubes is 5? $\frac{1}{6}$

3. What is the probability that the sum of the two number cubes is 9? 0

Available on Daily Transparency 12-6

---

11. **Consumer** You are planning a pizza party and need a pizza parlor to provide the food. The results of the research on customer satisfaction of various pizza delivery services in your area are shown below.

	Satisfied	Not Satisfied	Total
Jay & Dee	12	6	18
The Coloseum	32	10	42
Peet-sa!	15	20	35
Total	59	36	95

What is the probability that if you choose a delivery service randomly from the ones shown …

a. You will be satisfied? $\frac{59}{95} \approx 62.1\%$

b. You will be satisfied if you choose The Coloseum? $\frac{32}{42} \approx 76.2\%$

c. What is the probability that a person who was surveyed rated the Coloseum? $\frac{42}{95} \approx 44.2\%$

Problem Solving and Reasoning

12. **Geometry** If the inner circle has a radius of 2 in. and each ring has a width of 2 in., what is the probability of hitting a bull's-eye if a person's dart has hit in one of the black areas? $\frac{1}{6} \approx 16.7\%$

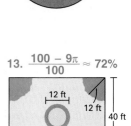

Critical Thinking Suppose a parachutist lands in the rectangular region shown.

13. $\dfrac{100 - 9\pi}{100} \approx 72\%$

13. What is the probability that the parachutist will land in a safe (light green) area, away from the corner trees and central fountain?

14. **Communicate** If she misses the trees, what is the probability that she will land in the safe area? Explain your strategy. What is the relationship between the sections of trees and the fountain?

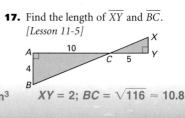

Mixed Review

Find the volume of each solid. Use 3.14 for π. *[Lesson 9-8]*

15. 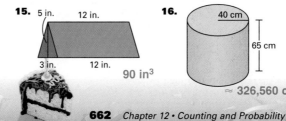 $90\ \text{in}^3$

16. 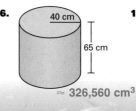 $\approx 326,560\ \text{cm}^3$

17. Find the length of $\overline{XY}$ and $\overline{BC}$. *[Lesson 11-5]*

$XY = 2; BC = \sqrt{116} \approx 10.8$

PROBLEM SOLVING 12-6

► PROBLEM SOLVING

Name _____

Guided Problem Solving 12-6

GPS PROBLEM 7, STUDENT PAGE 661

You roll a pair of number cubes in a board game. If the first cube comes up a ⑥, find the probability that the sum of the two number cubes is:

a. 6 b. 7 c. greater than 10 d. greater than 6

— **Understand** —

1. How many number cubes will you roll? __2 number cubes.__

2. Circle the number that came up when the first cube was rolled.

— **Plan** —

3. What are the possible outcomes for the second number cube? __1, 2, 3, 4, 5, 6__

4. List the possible outcomes for the two rolls.

a. 6 + __1__ = __7__ b. 6 + __2__ = __8__ c. 6 + __3__ = __9__

d. 6 + __4__ = __10__ e. 6 + __5__ = __11__ f. 6 + __6__ = __12__

5. Which sums are greater than 10? __11, 12__ Greater than 6? __7–12__

— **Solve** —

6. Use the data in Item 4 to find each probability.

a. P(sum is 6) = __0__   b. P(sum is 7) = __$\frac{1}{6}$__

c. P(sum > 10) = __$\frac{2}{6} = \frac{1}{3}$__   d. P(sum is > 6) = __1__

— **Look Back** —

7. Which probability can you determine without listing the possible outcomes in Item 4? Explain. __Possible answer:__

__P(sum is 6), since any roll of second cube gives a sum > 6,__

__so probability is 0.__

SOLVE ANOTHER PROBLEM

You roll a pair of number cubes in a board game. If the first cube comes up a 4, find the probability that the sum of the two number cubes is:

a. 6 b. 11 c. less than 8 d. greater than 5

__$\frac{1}{6}$__   __0__   __$\frac{1}{2}$__   __$\frac{5}{6}$__

► ENRICHMENT

Name _____

Extend Your Thinking 12-6

Decision Making

Suppose you set up the booth shown below at your school fair.

To play a game, blindfolded players will choose a marble from the designated bucket. If the player chooses a white marble, he will win a prize for that category. You need to decide what to charge for each turn in each category in order to make a reasonable profit for your class.

1. What is the probability of picking a white marble from each bucket?

P(A) = __$\frac{3}{8}$__   P(B) = __$\frac{2}{5}$__   P(C) = __$\frac{1}{4}$__   P(D) = __$\frac{3}{20}$__

The value of the prizes are:
Bucket A, $12; Bucket B, $10, Bucket C, $30; and Bucket D, $80.
You want to make a profit of $5 or more for each prize you give away.

2. How many prizes do you expect to give away in 8 tries for Bucket A? How much will they cost?

__3 prizes in 8 tries; $36.__

3. How much will you need to charge for each ticket you sell for Bucket A in order to make a profit of $5 or more on each prize? Explain.

__You must charge at least $6.38 ($36 + $15 = $51;__

__51 ÷ 8 = 6.375) but can charge more.__

4. How much will you need to charge for each ticket to make a profit of $5 or more on each prize for these buckets?

Bucket B: __$6__   Bucket C: __$8.75__   Bucket D: __$12.75__

Dependent and Independent Events

▶ Lesson Link You have learned about how one event can change the probability of another event. Now you will learn about whether one event can depend on another. ◀

Explore | Probability and Dependency

Point of No Return

Materials: Paper bag
3 Algebra tiles
Tape or dry marker

Mark the red side of two tiles and the yellow side of the third tile with tape or dry marker.

1. Without looking, take 1 tile out of the bag and record whether the red or yellow side is marked. Return the tile to the bag.

2. Take a second tile out of the bag and record whether the red or yellow side is marked.

3. As a class, make a table of the experimental outcomes.

	Second Tile	
First Tile	Red	Yellow
Red		
Yellow		

4. Repeat the experiment, but this time do not replace the tile.

5. Describe the effect of the first draw on the second draw in each case.

Learn | Dependent and Independent Events

Events that contain more than one outcome are called **compound events**. Sometimes the occurrence of one event affects the probability of a second event; sometimes it has no effect. If there is no effect, we say that the events are **independent events**.

If the events are not independent, the second event is a **dependent event**. You have considered several such situations in dealing with conditional probability earlier.

12-7 • Dependent and Independent Events **663**

You'll Learn ...
■ to recognize an independent event

... How It's Used
Electricians need to know when flows of electricity are independent from each other before they begin work.

Vocabulary
compound events
independent events
dependent events
multiplication property

Objective
■ Recognize an independent event.

Vocabulary
■ Compound events, independent events, dependent events, multiplication property

Materials
■ Explore: Paper bag, 3 Algebra tiles, tape or dry marker

NCTM Standards
■ 1–4, 11

▶ Review

Multiply these fractions.

1. $\frac{2}{7} \times \frac{5}{6}$ $\frac{5}{21}$

2. $\frac{7}{9} \times \frac{3}{8}$ $\frac{7}{24}$

3. $\frac{3}{45} \times \frac{3}{44}$ $\frac{1}{220}$

4. $\frac{6}{8} \times \frac{3}{7}$ $\frac{9}{28}$

5. $\frac{1}{9} \times \frac{5}{8}$ $\frac{5}{72}$

Available on Daily Transparency 12-7

MEETING INDIVIDUAL NEEDS

Resources
12-7 Practice
12-7 Reteaching
12-7 Problem Solving
12-7 Enrichment
12-7 Daily Transparency
   Problem of the Day
   Review
   Quick Quiz
Teaching Tool Transparencies 13, 14
Lesson Enhancement Transparency 71
Chapter 12 Project Master

 Wide World of Mathematics Middle School: Two-Sport Athlete

Learning Modalities

Kinesthetic In **Explore**, students conduct two hands-on probability experiments using different colored tiles.

Verbal Have students give an example of a probability-related concept, such as equally likely events, and explain their choice.

Visual Students should draw tree diagrams to help solve some of the exercises.

Challenge

In the game of Monopoly®, two dice are rolled for each turn. The probability of rolling "doubles" is $\frac{1}{6}$. If a player rolls doubles three times in a row, the player goes to "jail." What is the probability of rolling doubles three times in a row?

$\frac{1}{6} \cdot \frac{1}{6} \cdot \frac{1}{6} = \frac{1}{216}$

---

1 Introduce

Explore

The Point
Students conduct two experiments involving drawing tiles. In the first experiment they replace the tile before drawing again. In the second experiment they do not replace the tile. Then, in each case, they describe the effect of the first draw on the second draw.

Ongoing Assessment
In Step 4, make sure that students do not replace the first tile after it has been drawn.

For Groups That Finish Early
Draw tree diagrams that demonstrate the results of each of the experiments.

Have students discuss the conclusions they came to in Step 5.

Answers for Explore

1–4. See students' results.

5. With replacement, the outcome of the first draw does not affect the outcome of the second. With no replacement, a red first tile means a 50% chance of a red second tile, and a yellow first tile means a 100% chance of a red second tile.

2 Teach

Learn

You may wish to use Lesson Enhancement Transparency 71 with this lesson.

Alternate Examples

1. Are these events independent or dependent?

   a. Two cards are drawn at random, one after the other, from a deck. The first card drawn is not replaced.

      The card drawn first was not replaced, so there are fewer choices remaining. The second event is dependent on the first.

   b. Nick got an A on his social studies test so he will get an A on his math test.

      Just because Nick got an A on one test does not mean that he will get an A on the other. The events are independent.

   c. Tossing heads on the first flip of a coin and tossing heads on the second flip of the same coin.

      The result of the second flip does not depend on the result of the first flip. The events are independent.

2. A game you are playing has a spinner divided into sixths that are numbered 1 through 6. What is the probability that you will get a 1 on the first spin and then get an even number on the second spin?

   The result of the first spin does not influence the result of the second spin. The probability of spinning a 1 and then spinning an even number is $P(1 \text{ and even}) = \frac{1}{6} \times \frac{3}{6} = \frac{3}{36} = \frac{1}{12}$, or 8.3%.

Example 1

Are these events independent?

a. The first roll of a number cube is 5, and the sum of the first two rolls is 4.

The second event is dependent on the first since the probability of rolling a sum of 4 changes to 0.

b. It is sunny and a movie theater changes its movies.

The fact that the sky is sunny has no effect on a theater changing its movies. The events are independent.

c. One person was born on May 27th and another was born on May 27th.

The birthday of the second person does not depend on the birthday of the first person. The events are independent.

Try It

Are these events independent?

a. It is raining and the parade is canceled. **Dependent**

b. You wear a Yankee cap, and the Yankees win. **Independent**

If events A and B are independent events, then the probability of both A and B occurring is given by $P(A \text{ and } B) = P(A) \times P(B)$. This property for independent events is known as the **multiplication property**.

You could show the situation geometrically. If the probability of event A is $\frac{2}{5}$ and the probability of event B is $\frac{3}{4}$, then the probability of both event A and event B is $\frac{2}{5} \times \frac{3}{4} = \frac{6}{20}$, or $\frac{3}{10}$.

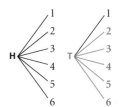

$A = \frac{2}{5}$

$B = \frac{3}{4}$

Example 2

Find the probability of flipping a coin and getting tails and then tossing a number cube and getting a number greater than 1.

The result of the coin flip does not influence the result of tossing the number cube. The probability of getting tails and tossing a number greater than 1 is $P(\text{tails, and roll} > 1) = \frac{1}{2} \times \frac{5}{6} = \frac{5}{12}$, or about 42%.

This can be shown by a tree diagram as well.

There are 12 possible outcomes; 5 satisfy the conditions, so the probability is $\frac{5}{12}$.

MATH EVERY DAY

▶ Problem of the Day

The Igbo people of southern Nigeria, Africa, play *Igba-ita*, which means "pitch and toss." Four cowrie shells are tossed. To score a point, all four shells must land up or all four shells must land down. If there is an equal chance of a shell landing up or down, what is the probability of scoring a point in one toss? $\frac{2}{16}$ or $\frac{1}{8}\left[\left(\frac{1}{2}\right)^3\right]$

Available on Daily Transparency 12-7

An Extension is provided in the transparency package.

Fact of the Day

Over 90% of people are right-handed since the brain's left motor cortex directs the right hand and is dominant over the right motor cortex, which directs the left hand.

Estimation

Estimate these dollar amounts.

1. $19.95 × 4 $80.00

2. $2.79 × 3 $9.00

3. $11.15 × 6 $66.00

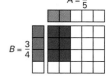

DID YOU KNOW?

Identical twins must be the same gender, but fraternal twins can be of both genders.

Example 3

Suppose you select a student at random. The probability that the student is either sex is 0.5 and the probability that the student is left-handed is 0.06. What is the probability that the student is a left-handed male?

P(male and left-handed) $= 0.5 \times 0.06 = 0.03$. The probability of selecting a left-handed male is 3%.

Try It

At Artistes, 80% of the customers are female, and 43% make a purchase. What is the probability that a customer is a woman who makes a purchase?

34.4%

When drawing a card from a deck, whether or not you replace each card affects the probability.

Example 4

a. A card is drawn and replaced. A second card is drawn. What is the probability that the first card is red and the second is blue?

b. Two cards are drawn (the first card is not replaced). What is the probability that the first card is red and the second is blue?

a. First card: $P(R) = \frac{4}{7}$ Second card: $P(B) = \frac{1}{7}$
P(red and blue) $= \frac{4}{7} \times \frac{1}{7} = \frac{4}{49}$ ($\approx$ 8.2%)

b. First card: $P(R) = \frac{4}{7}$ Second card: $P(B) = \frac{1}{6}$
P(red and blue) $= \frac{4}{7} \times \frac{1}{6} = \frac{4}{42}$ ($\approx$ 9.5%)

Try It

Two cards are drawn. What is the probability that both will be green if the first card is replaced? If it is not replaced? $\frac{4}{49}, \frac{2}{42}$

Check | Your Understanding

1. How is the independence of events important to a person using probability?

2. Why can you use the multiplication property to find the probability associated with a pair of independent events?

3. For event A, the probability is $\frac{1}{2}$; for B it is $\frac{1}{3}$; and for A and B, $\frac{1}{5}$. Would you say A and B are independent events? Explain? **No;** $\frac{1}{2} \cdot \frac{1}{3} \neq \frac{1}{5}$

MEETING MIDDLE SCHOOL CLASSROOM NEEDS

Tips from Middle School Teachers

Students, like many adults, tend to believe that long runs of an event make other independent events more likely. For example, several heads in a row make tails more likely or several female births in a row make a male birth more likely. I like to help students realize that such conclusions are the results of a nonexistent "law of averages." I point out that in the long run such events do tend to split 50-50, but still in any one case, either result is just as likely as the other.

Cultural Connection	History Connection
In the U.S., "Happy Birthday to You" is the traditional birthday song. Students who have lived in other countries might explain what song, if any, is traditional on birthdays in those countries. For example, *Sto Lat* (meaning "One Hundred Years" and containing the refrain "May you live one hundred years") is traditional in Poland.	The theory of probability, as first developed by Blaise Pascal in the 1600s, was further advanced in the early 1800s by Marquis de Laplace. A French astronomer and mathematician, Laplace lived from 1749–1827. He became famous for his theory regarding the origin of the solar system—called the nebular hypothesis—which was accepted for a long time, but has now been replaced by other theories.

Alternate Examples

3. Suppose you select a student at random. The probability of either gender is 0.5. Suppose the probability of blond hair is 0.25. What is the probability that the student is a blond female?

P(female and blond) $= 0.5 \times 0.25 = 0.125$. The probability of selecting a blond-haired female is 12.5%.

4.

a. A card is drawn and replaced. A second card is drawn. What is the probability that the first card is a star and the second card is stripes?

b. Two cards are drawn (the first card is not replaced). What is the probability that the first card is a star and the second card is stripes?

a. 1st card: P(star) $= \frac{3}{5}$

2nd card: P(stripes) $= \frac{2}{5}$

P(star and stripes) $= \frac{3}{5} \times \frac{2}{5}$

$= \frac{6}{25}$ ($= 24\%$)

b. 1st card: P(star) $= \frac{3}{5}$

2nd card: P(stripes) $= \frac{2}{4}$

P(star and stripes) $= \frac{3}{5} \times \frac{2}{4}$

$= \frac{6}{20} = \frac{3}{10}$ ($= 30\%$)

3 Practice and Assess

Check

If students are having difficulty with Question 1, suggest that they think of what they can do with independent events that they cannot do when events are dependent.

Answers for Check Your Understanding

1. Possible answer: It allows you to use the multiplication property.

2. Possible answer: When events are independent, the condition of the first outcome does not change the probability of the other.

Assignment Guide

■ **Basic**
1–5, 6–10, 14–17, 21, 23

■ **Average**
2–5, 7–11 odds, 12, 14–18, 20, 22, 23

■ **Enriched**
2, 4, 7–11 odds, 12–20, 22, 23

Reteaching

Activity

Materials: Blank paper, scissors

• Work with a partner.

• Suppose you are playing a word game where each person takes turns choosing two letters. The rules of the game state that once a letter is chosen, it is not replaced. You have the following letters to work with.
A K E E L J X O M U
Cut the paper into squares and write each of the letters on a square.

• Model this situation: What is the probability of first drawing a K and then drawing a vowel?

• First, write the equation for this situation. Then use the paper squares and perform 50 trials, replacing the chosen squares after each trial.
$P(\text{K, then vowel}) = \frac{1}{10} \times \frac{4}{9} = \frac{4}{90} = \frac{2}{45}$; Answers should approximate this probability.

• Now model the situation: What is the probability of first drawing a vowel and then a K?

• First, write the equation for this situation. Then use the paper squares and perform 50 trials, replacing the chosen squares after each trial.
$P(\text{vowel, then K}) = \frac{5}{10} \times \frac{1}{9} = \frac{5}{90} = \frac{1}{18}$; Answers should approximate this probability.

• Does order seem to matter?
Yes, order does matter.

666   Chapter 12

Practice and Apply

1. **Getting Started** A number cube is tossed two times. Find $P(\text{even number}, 6)$.
   a. Find the probability of rolling an even number. $\frac{1}{2}$
   b. Find the probability of rolling a 6. $\frac{1}{6}$
   c. Multiply the two probabilities and express your answer as a percent. $\approx 8.3\%$

State whether each pair of events is independent or dependent.

2. A number cube is rolled twice. **Independent**

3. Choose a marble, replace it, and choose a second marble. **Independent**

4. Two children are born into a family—a girl, then a boy. **Independent**

5. Your birthday is today and you have a birthday party. **Dependent**

Suppose that two marbles are drawn from the bag. The first marble is replaced before the second is drawn. Find each probability.

6. $P(\text{blue, yellow})$ $\frac{1}{12}$ 7. $P(\text{blue, blue})$ $\frac{1}{4}$ 8. $P(\text{green, not green})$ $\frac{2}{9}$

Suppose that two marbles are drawn from the bag. The first marble is *not* replaced before the second is drawn. Find each probability.

9. $P(\text{blue, yellow})$ $\frac{1}{10}$ 10. $P(\text{blue, blue})$ $\frac{1}{5}$ 11. $P(\text{green, not green})$ $\frac{4}{15}$

In the maze, a mouse picks his paths at random and continues toward the rooms marked A and B.

12. If the mouse reaches **2**, what is the probability that he ends in room A? $\frac{1}{2}$

13. If the mouse reaches **3**, what is the probability that he ends in room B? 1

14. What is the probability that the mouse shown ends in room A? In room B? $\frac{1}{2}, \frac{1}{2}$

15. **Industry** Suppose a security system and its backup each have a 97% chance of functioning correctly. If the systems are independent, what is the probability that they both fail? **0.09%**

Name _____

Practice 12-7

Dependent and Independent Events

State whether each pair of events is independent or dependent.

1. You roll a 6 on a number cube and then flip a coin that comes up heads. **Independent**

2. A person was born in winter and born in February. **Dependent**

3. You get an A in science and an A in math. **Independent**

4. A man is 42 years old and his phone number begins with the digits 4 and 2. **Independent**

5. You draw a red marble from a bag, and then another red marble (without replacing the first marble). **Dependent**

Suppose that two tiles are drawn from the collection shown at the right. The first tile is replaced before the second is drawn. Find each probability.

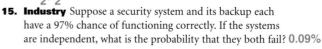

6. $P(A, A)$ $\frac{4}{225}$ 7. $P(R, C)$ $\frac{2}{25}$ 8. $P(E, \text{not } E)$ $\frac{44}{225}$

9. $P(\text{vowel, vowel})$ $\frac{4}{25}$ 10. $P(\text{vowel, not } R)$ $\frac{6}{25}$ 11. $P(\text{consonant, vowel})$ $\frac{6}{25}$

Suppose that two tiles are drawn from the collection shown above. The first tile is *not* replaced before the second is drawn. Find each probability.

12. $P(A, A)$ $\frac{1}{105}$ 13. $P(R, C)$ $\frac{3}{35}$ 14. $P(E, \text{not } E)$ $\frac{22}{105}$

15. $P(\text{vowel, vowel})$ $\frac{1}{7}$ 16. $P(\text{vowel, not } R)$ $\frac{8}{35}$ 17. $P(\text{consonant, vowel})$ $\frac{9}{35}$

Suppose you're new in town and you do not know your way around, so you choose your path randomly. Assume that you always travel in a northbound direction.

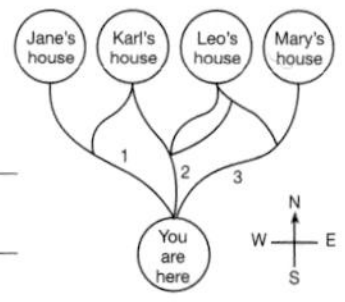

18. If you take path 1, what is the probability that you end up at Karl's house? $\frac{1}{2}$

19. If you take path 2, what is the probability that you end up at Leo's house? $\frac{2}{3}$

20. Find the probability that you end up at:
Jane's house $\frac{1}{6}$ Karl's house $\frac{5}{18}$ Leo's house $\frac{7}{18}$ Mary's house $\frac{1}{6}$

Name _____

Alternative Lesson 12-7

Dependent and Independent Events

A **compound event** contains more than one outcome. The events are **independent events** if the probability of each event has no effect on the other. If the events are not independent, the second event is a **dependent event**. To find the probability of two events occurring, multiply the probability for both events.

— **Example 1** —

Suppose you spin the same color on a spinner two times in a row. Are the pairs of events dependent or independent?

Each spin is independent of the other spins because the outcome of the first spin does not have any effect on the outcome of the second spin.

Try It You draw a card at random and then draw another card without replacing the first card.

a. Does the outcome of the first event affect the outcome of the second? **Yes.**

b. Are the pairs of events dependent or independent? **Dependent.**

Are the pairs of events dependent or independent?

c. You toss a coin showing heads two times in a row. **Independent.**

d. You draw one card at random showing B, do not replace the card, and then draw another card showing B. **Dependent.**

— **Example 2** —

Find the probability of getting 3 heads when tossing a penny, a nickel, and a dime at the same time.

The probability of getting heads when tossing any coin is $\frac{1}{2}$. Multiply the probability for each event: $\frac{1}{2} \times \frac{1}{2} \times \frac{1}{2} = \frac{1}{8}$.

The probability of getting 3 heads when tossing a penny, a nickel, and a dime at the same time is $\frac{1}{8}$.

Try It Find the probability of rolling two 4s when tossing two number cubes at the same time.

e. What is the probability of rolling 4 when tossing a number cube? $\frac{1}{6}$

f. How many number cubes will be rolled? **2 cubes.**

g. Multiply to find $P(\text{two 4s})$. $\frac{1}{6} \times \frac{1}{6} = \frac{1}{36}$

h. Find the probability of getting 3 tails when tossing three different coins at the same time. $\frac{1}{2} \times \frac{1}{2} \times \frac{1}{2} = \frac{1}{8}$

16. **Test Prep** You buy a box of 50 birthday candles that has 10% red, 30% blue, 30% green, 20% yellow, and 10% white candles. If you pull 2 candles from the box, what is the probability that they are both blue? **A**

Ⓐ 8.6% Ⓑ 9% Ⓒ 15% Ⓓ 60%

17. You won a prize on your birthday.

 a. If the prizes are chosen at random, what is your chance of winning the concert tickets? **1 in 5**

b. If the first-place winner chose the graphing calculator, what are your chances of winning the concert tickets now? **1 in 4**

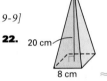

PRIZES!
★ Concert Tickets
★ Graphing Calculator
★ Computer Game
★ 3 Music CDs
★ Dinner for 2

Problem Solving and Reasoning

18. Critical Thinking Two different letters are selected from the word BIRTHDAY. The first letter is not replaced.

a. What is the probability that at least one letter is a vowel? $\frac{13}{28}$

b. If the first letter selected is R, what is the probability that at least one letter is a vowel? $\frac{2}{7}$

c. If the first letter selected is A, what is the probability that at least one letter is a vowel? **1**

19. Communicate Explain how you could use the Counting Principle to find the probability of a compound event.

20. Chance You toss a coin three times and each time it comes up heads. What is the probability that it will come up heads on the fourth toss? $\frac{1}{2}$

Mixed Review

Find the volume of each solid. Use 3.14 for π. [Lesson 9-9]

21.
11 in.
2.5 in.
≈ **71.96 in³**

22.
20 cm
8 cm
≈ **426.67 cm³**

23. What are the coordinates of the point $(-1, -2)$ after being translated 2 units right and 4 units up? *[Lesson 11-6]* **(1, 2)**

Project Progress

Think about the probabilities you would want for your game. Can you use permutations or combinations to help you design your game?

Problem Solving
Understand
Plan
Solve
Look Back

12-7 • Dependent and Independent Events **667**

PROBLEM SOLVING 12-7

Exercise Notes

■ **Exercise 16**

Test Prep Students need only consider the number of blue candles—30% of 50 = 15. The probability of both blue is $\frac{15}{50} \cdot \frac{14}{49}$, or ≈ 8.6%.

Project Progress

You may want to have students use Chapter 12 Project Master.

Exercise Answers

19. Possible answer: Modify the principle to say that if a situation occurs m times in p trials, and a second situation occurs n times in q trials, then these things will occur together $m \times n$ times in $p \times q$ trials.

Alternate Assessment

Interview Have students interview one another by asking this question: How can you tell if two events are dependent or independent? You may wish to tape record the interviews. A dependent event is affected by the event that takes place before it does; independent events do not affect each other.

► Quick Quiz

A spinner in a game is divided into tenths and numbered 1 through 10. What is the probability of spinning:

1. An even number? $\frac{1}{2}$

2. An even number followed by an odd number? $\frac{1}{4}$

3. A 3 and then 7? $\frac{1}{100}$

4. A 1 and then an even number? $\frac{1}{20}$

Available on Daily Transparency 12-7

▷ PROBLEM SOLVING

Name _____

Guided Problem Solving 12-7

GPS PROBLEM 17, STUDENT PAGE 667

You enter a contest on your birthday. Suppose you win a prize in the contest.

PRIZES!
Concert Tickets
Graphing Calculator
Computer Game
3 music CDs
Dinner for 2

a. If the prizes are chosen at random, what is your chance of winning the concert tickets?

b. If the first place winner chose the graphing calculator, what are your chances of winning the concert tickets now?

— Understand —

1. How many different prizes are possible? **5 prizes.**

2. How are the prizes awarded? **Randomly.**

3. Is the prize awarded to subsequent winners dependent or independent of the prizes awarded to prior winners? **Dependent.**

— Plan —

4. How many outcomes (prizes) are available to the first winner? **5 prizes.**

5. How many outcomes are available to the second winner? **4 prizes.**

6. How many outcomes (prizes) can you win? **1 prize.**

— Solve —

7. What is your chance of getting the concert tickets if you are the first winner? **1 in 5.**

8. If you are the second winner, what are your chances of winning concert tickets if the calculator has already been awarded? **1 in 4.**

— Look Back —

9. As other prizes are awarded to other winners, are you more or less likely to win the concert tickets? Explain. **More likely, since sample space is smaller.**

SOLVE ANOTHER PROBLEM

Prizes at a raffle are $100, $75, $25, $25, $25, and $25.

a. If the prizes are chosen at random, what is your chance of winning $75? **1 in 6.**

b. If the $100 prize has already been won, what are your chances of winning $75? **1 in 5.**

▷ ENRICHMENT

Name _____

Extend Your Thinking 12-7

Patterns in Numbers

Pascal, a French mathematician and scientist, was quite interested in the study of probability and invented the triangle below as a shortcut for finding the chance of getting any special combination when tossing coins.

1. Study Pascal's triangle and extend it five more rows. Each line represents the outcomes for tossing coins. For line 1 (tossing a single coin), there are 2 possible outcomes. For line 2 (tossing two coins), there are 4 possible outcomes, and so on. The first number in each line represents tossing all heads. The second number represents tossing one less head, and so on.

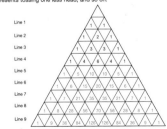
Line 1
Line 2
Line 3
Line 4
Line 5
Line 6
Line 7
Line 8
Line 9

2. Describe any patterns you can find in the triangle.

Possible answer: Any number under a pair of numbers is the sum of the pair. The numbers at the beginning and end of each line are ones.

3. Suppose you toss four coins. Use Pascal's triangle to find the probability of tossing two heads and two tails. Explain.

Possible answer: 6 (3rd number since the first number represents 4 heads, the second represents 3 heads, and so on) out of 16 (1 + 4 + 6 + 4 + 1) possible outcomes: P (tossing 2 heads and 2 tails) = $\frac{6}{16}$, or $\frac{3}{8}$.

Using a Graphing Calculator • Simulation

The Point
Students generate random probabilities with a graphing calculator to simulate how often people arrive at a checkout counter.

Materials
Graphing calculator (or scientific calculator)

Resources
Teaching Tool Transparency 23

Interactive CD-ROM Spreadsheet/Grapher Tool

About the Page
If students have not used a graphing calculator before:

- Identify how to start with the home screen and access the calculator's random probability generation.

- Note that for some calculators you may only need to press ENTER once.

Ask ...
- What numbers did you use to complete the chart? 0.88 to 0.95; 0.95 to 1

- If the random number is between 0.5 and 0.75, what does it represent? It represents 1 customer arriving.

- How many people arrived during each of the first five "minutes"? 1, 1, 0, 0, 0

- What would the calculator have to read to show that 2 people showed up within the same minute? 0.75 to 0.88

- Did 2 or more people show up within the same minute during the first 5-minute period? No.

- Did 2 or more people show up within the same minute during any other 5-minute periods you tested? Answers may vary.

Try It
Assuming the free throws are independent events, the probability that the player makes all three is (0.710)(0.710)(0.710) ≈ 35.8%.

On Your Own
Assuming the 11 spinner sectors are congruent, the probability of landing on a sector is $\frac{1}{11} \approx 0.09$.

TECHNOLOGY

Using a Graphing Calculator • Simulation

Problem: Simulate how often people arrive at a checkout counter. Estimate the probability that at least 2 people will show up at the same time within a 5-minute period.

You can use a graphing or scientific calculator to do this.

Suppose that the number of people arriving at a checkout counter each minute is given by the probabilities shown in the table.

Generate a random probability with your calculator. Find out how many people this represents using the last column of the table.

1 Complete the table (look for a pattern).

Number Arriving	Probability	Use
0	0.5	0 to 0.5
1	0.25	0.5 to 0.75
2	0.13	0.75 to 0.88
3	0.07	0.88–0.95
4	0.05	0.95–1

Solution: Generate several more 5-minute periods and record whether 2 or more people show up. To estimate the probability, divide the total number of times 2 or more people show up by the total number of 5-minute periods.

2 Press MATH, then choose **PRB** and **rand**. When you press ENTER twice, you get a random number between 0 and 1. Because this number is between 0.5 and 0.75, it represents 1 customer arriving.

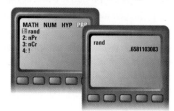

3 Pressing ENTER 4 more times gives you 5 "minutes." For the numbers shown, 1, 1, 0, 0, and 0 customers arrived at the register. Two or more people did **not** show up within the same minute.

TRY IT

Suppose the probability that a basketball player makes a free throw is 0.710. Use a simulation to estimate the probability that she makes 3 out of 3 free throws.
≈ **35.8%**

ON YOUR OWN

▶ Try to simulate spins of a spinner numbered from 0 to 10.

668

Answers for On Your Own
Possible answer:

You can simulate spins by using round (11 ***rand**–0.5, 0).

In the Connect, you will apply your knowledge of probability to a famous birthday problem.

Happy Birthday, Baby

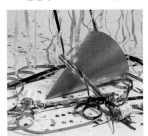

Your mission: Get through the room without finding two people with the same birthday. It should be easy, true? After all, there are 366 possible birthdays and only 20 to 30 of you.

Don't ask birthdays yet!

1. You will be the first student. Begin with one other student. What is the probability that you two share a birthday? Is this experimental or theoretical probability?

2. Assuming that you two do not share a birthday, how many birthdays remain that are open (not one of your birthdays)?

3. Add a third person. Does the birthday match either of your birthdays?

4. Continue adding a person at a time. What's happening to the probability of any pair sharing a birthday? Is the chance of each new person sharing a birthday with the others independent of the number of people already there?

5. Did you succeed in your mission? If there was a match, how many people did it take? How many matches were there in your class? Are you surprised?

6. If there were 370 people in the room, would there have to be a pair that share a birthday? Why?

669

Happy Birthday, Baby

The Point
In *Happy Birthday, Baby* on page 645, matching birthdays were discussed. Now, students apply their knowledge of probability to a famous birthday problem that has to do with having the same birthday as someone else.

About the Page
- For Step 5, are students surprised at the results of their birthday experiment?

- Tell students to make sure that they use common sense for the last question.

Ongoing Assessment
You might want to check students' progress at Steps 3 and 4 to make sure they understand what they are to do since all of the succeeding steps build on one another.

Extension

The numbers 7 and 11 are "lucky numbers" for many people. What is the probability that a person selected at random would have his or her birthday on the 7th or the 11th of any month? $\frac{24}{365}$, or about $6\frac{1}{2}\%$

Answers for Connect

1. $\frac{1}{365.25}$; Theoretical (based on $365\frac{1}{4}$ days per year)

2. 364

3. Answers may vary.

4. Going up; No.

5. Answers may vary.

6. Yes; There aren't enough different birthdays to go around.

Review Correlation

Item(s)	Lesson(s)
1–3	12-4
4	12-7
5, 6	12-4
7–10	12-7
11	12-6

Test Prep

Test-Taking Tip

Tell students that it is especially important on tests with probability problems to organize yourself as you work through an exercise— make organized lists or tree diagrams. Organization helps you think more clearly.

Answers for Review

1. Sample space: 1, 2, 3, 4, 5, 6

   a. 1 outcome; Probability $\frac{1}{6}$

   b. 3 outcomes; Probability $\frac{1}{2}$

   c. 0 outcomes; Probability 0

2. Sample space: red, red, red, red, green, green, blue, blue, blue

   a. 4 outcomes; Probability $\frac{4}{9}$

   b. 6 outcomes; Probability $\frac{2}{3}$

4. a. $\frac{3}{32}$; $\frac{3}{28}$

   b. $\frac{9}{64}$; $\frac{3}{28}$

   c. $\frac{15}{64}$; $\frac{15}{56}$

9. Yes; There is one less person left to pick from.

10. With independent events, the outcome of one doesn't affect the probabilities of the other. With dependent events, the first outcome does have an effect.

Section 12B Review

Identify the sample space for each experiment, find the number of outcomes satisfying each event, and find the probability of each event.

1. Rolling a number cube with faces numbered 1 through 6. Events:

   a. Rolling a 5   b. Rolling a multiple of 2   c. Rolling a 7

2. Drawing a marble from a bag of 4 red, 2 green, and 3 blue marbles. Events:

   a. Drawing a red marble   b. Not drawing a blue marble

3. If you toss two number cubes, what are the following probabilities?

   a. P(sum of 2) $\frac{1}{36}$ b. P(sum > 9) $\frac{1}{6}$ c. P(sum of 6, 7, or 8) $\frac{4}{9}$

4. You draw two marbles from a bag of 3 red, 2 green, and 3 blue marbles. Find the probability if the first marble is replaced. Then find the probability if it is not replaced.

   a. P(red, then green)   b. P(red, then red)   c. P(red, then **not** red)

5. What is the probability of spinning yellow? $\frac{1}{4}$

6. What is the probability of **not** spinning red? $\frac{1}{2}$

7. If you spin the spinner twice, what is the probability of spinning red, then yellow? $\frac{1}{8}$

8. If the first spin lands on red, what is the probability that both spins will land on red? $\frac{1}{2}$

9. If one person is selected from a group to serve on a committee, does that affect the probability of the next selection? Why or why not?

10. Compare and contrast independent and dependent events.

Test Prep

Be sure to read the question carefully before you choose an answer.

11. What is the probability of a fly landing in square A if you know that it landed somewhere in square B? **D**

   Ⓐ $\frac{1}{6}$ Ⓑ $\frac{1}{4}$ Ⓒ $\frac{1}{3}$ Ⓓ 1

REVIEW 12B

Resources

Practice Masters
   Section 12B Review

Assessment Sourcebook
   Quiz 12B

 TestWorks
   Test and Practice Software

PRACTICE

Name _____

Practice

Section 12B Review

1. Identify the sample space for the experiment of randomly choosing a letter from the word C O M P U T E R. Find the number of outcomes in each event, and find the probability of each event.

   Sample space: _____ C, O, M, P, U, T, E, R

   Events: a. Choosing *R*   b. Choosing a vowel   c. Not choosing *P*

   Number of outcomes: 1   3   7

   Probability: $\frac{1}{8}$ $\frac{3}{8}$ $\frac{7}{8}$

2. If you toss two number cubes, what are the following probabilities?

   a. P(sum of 10) $\frac{1}{12}$ b. P(sum < 7) $\frac{5}{12}$ c. P(sum of 8, 9, or 12) $\frac{5}{18}$

3. You draw two chips from a bag containing 2 white, 3 red, and 5 blue chips. Find each probability if the first chip is replaced. Then find each probability if it is not replaced.

	a. P(blue then blue)	b. P(white then red)	c. P(red then *not* red)
If replaced:	$\frac{1}{4}$	$\frac{3}{50}$	$\frac{21}{100}$
If not replaced:	$\frac{2}{9}$	$\frac{1}{15}$	$\frac{7}{30}$

4. What is the probability of spinning orange? $\frac{1}{3}$

5. If you don't spin pink, what is the probability of spinning brown? $\frac{3}{5}$

6. If you spin the spinner twice, what is the probability of spinning orange then brown? $\frac{1}{6}$

7. If the first spin lands on brown, what is the probability that both spins land on brown? $\frac{1}{2}$

8. A living room on a floor plan is 4 in. by $5\frac{1}{2}$ in. If the scale factor is 36, what are the perimeter and area of the living room? *[Lesson 9-2]*

   Perimeter: _____ 684 in.   Area: _____ 28,512 in^2

9. The top of the Commerzbank Tower in Frankfurt, Germany, forms a 71° angle with a point 89.2 m from the tower's base. How tall is the Commerzbank Tower? *[Lesson 11-4]*   _____ About 259 m

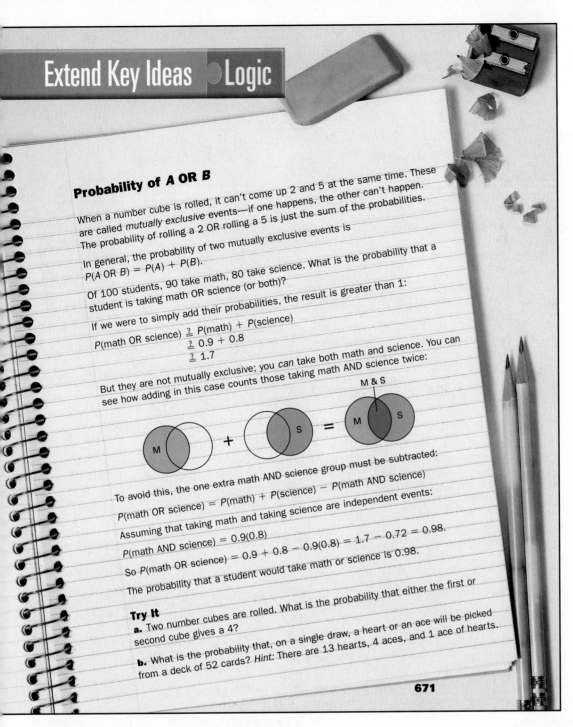

Probability of *A* OR *B*

When a number cube is rolled, it can't come up 2 and 5 at the same time. These are called *mutually exclusive* events—if one happens, the other can't happen. The probability of rolling a 2 OR rolling a 5 is just the sum of the probabilities.

In general, the probability of two mutually exclusive events is
$P(A \text{ OR } B) = P(A) + P(B)$.

Of 100 students, 90 take math, 80 take science. What is the probability that a student is taking math OR science (or both)?

If we were to simply add their probabilities, the result is greater than 1:

$P(\text{math OR science}) \overset{?}{=} P(\text{math}) + P(\text{science})$
$\overset{?}{=} 0.9 + 0.8$
$\overset{?}{=} 1.7$

But they are not mutually exclusive; you *can* take both math and science. You can see how adding in this case counts those taking math AND science twice:

To avoid this, the one extra math AND science group must be subtracted:
$P(\text{math OR science}) = P(\text{math}) + P(\text{science}) - P(\text{math AND science})$
Assuming that taking math and taking science are independent events:
$P(\text{math AND science}) = 0.9(0.8)$
So $P(\text{math OR science}) = 0.9 + 0.8 - 0.9(0.8) = 1.7 - 0.72 = 0.98$.
The probability that a student would take math or science is 0.98.

Try It
a. Two number cubes are rolled. What is the probability that either the first or second cube gives a 4?

b. What is the probability that, on a single draw, a heart or an ace will be picked from a deck of 52 cards? *Hint:* There are 13 hearts, 4 aces, and 1 ace of hearts.

671

Extend Key Ideas

Probability of *A* OR *B*

The Point
Students find the probability of mutually exclusive events.

About the Page

Students may need to be reminded that the multiplication property holds for independent events; that is why $P(\text{math AND science}) = 0.9(0.8)$.

Ask …
- How can you explain mutually exclusive events? If one event happens, the other event cannot happen.

- What is the formula for finding the probability of mutually exclusive events? $P(A \text{ OR } B) = P(A) + P(B)$

- What is wrong with getting a probability greater than 1? Probabilities must be between 0 and 1.

- Why must the math AND science group be subtracted? If this group were not subtracted when finding $P(\text{math OR science})$, students taking both math AND science would be counted twice.

Extension

Assume that the 366 possible birthdays are each written on a slip of paper and put in a paper bag. What is the probability of picking one slip of paper and getting a birthday in June or December?

$P(\text{June OR December}) = P(\text{June}) + P(\text{December}) =$
$\frac{30}{366} + \frac{31}{366} = \frac{61}{366}$

Answers for Try It
a. $\frac{1}{6} + \frac{1}{6} - \frac{1}{36} = \frac{11}{36}$

b. $\frac{13}{52} + \frac{4}{52} - \frac{1}{52} = \frac{4}{13}$

Chapter 12 Summary and Review

Review Correlation

Item(s)	Lesson(s)
1, 2	12-1
3–6	12-2, 12-3
7–9	12-4
10	12-5
11–13	12-4
14	12-6
15, 16	12-7

For additional review, see page 687.

Answers for Review

1.

Chapter 12 Summary and Review

Graphic Organizer

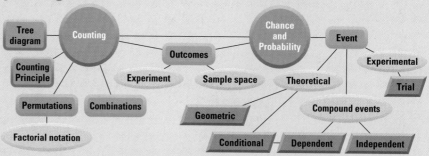

Section 12A   Counting

Summary

■ The **Counting Principle** states that if a situation can occur in m ways, and a second situation can occur in n ways, then these things can occur together in $m \times n$ ways. You can also use a table or **tree diagram** to count.

■ **Factorial** notation is used to write a product of consecutive whole numbers. 4! is 4 factorial, meaning $4 \times 3 \times 2 \times 1$. 0! is defined to be 1.

■ A **permutation**, or **arrangement**, is an ordered selection of objects. You can use the Counting Principle or factorials to count permutations.

■ A **combination** is a selection of objects without regard to order. The number of combinations is the number of permutations divided by the number of ways to arrange or order the *selected* objects.

Review

1. Make a tree diagram to show the possible results of spinning both spinners.

2. There are 5 roads from Morgantown to Shelbyville and 3 roads from Shelbyville to Tekton. How many routes are there from Morgantown through Shelbyville to Tekton? **15**

3. Evaluate each expression.

   a. 5! **120** **b.** $(6 - 2)!$ **24** **c.** $\dfrac{7!}{3! \times 4!}$ **35**

4. How many ways can the letters in PENCIL be arranged? **720**

5. A club has 8 members. How many ways can a president, vice president, and secretary be chosen? **336**

6. A Szechwan Chinese restaurant offers 10 entrees. How many ways can a family select 4 dishes to share? **210**

672 *Chapter 12 • Counting and Probability*

Resources

Practice Masters
  Cumulative Review
  Chapters 1–12

Assessment Sourcebook
  Quarterly Test Chapters 1-12

PRACTICE

Name _____

Practice

Cumulative Review Chapters 1–12

Find the surface area of each figure. *[Lesson 9-4]*

1. ____ **1734 in²**

2. ____ **209.88 cm²**

3. ____ **1347 ft²**

Multiply. *[Lesson 10-8]*

4. $(3x^2)(4x^5)$ **12x⁷**

5. $2p(p^2 - 3p + 5)$ **2p³ − 6p² + 10p**

6. $-t^3(t^3 - 8t)$ **−t⁶ + 8t⁴**

7. $3u^2(u^4 - 5u^2 + 7)$ **3u⁶ − 15u⁴ + 21u²**

8. $\frac{2}{3}c(12c^2 - 18)$ **8c³ − 12c**

9. $8d(3d^2 - 4d - 11)$ **24d³ − 32d² − 88d**

Tell what transformation of the left figure in each pair produces the right one. *[Lesson 11-6]*

10. ____ **Rotation**

11. ____ **Translation**

12. ____ **Reflection**

How many ways can the letters of each of these words be arranged? (No letter is used twice.) The letters do not have to form a word. *[Lesson 12-2]*

13. MYOPIA ____ **720** 14. BARN ____ **24** 15. MONKEYS ____ **5,040**

16. FORMALITY **362,880** 17. DINOSAUR **40,320** 18. POWER ____ **120**

Express the probability as a fraction, decimal, and percent. *[Lesson 12-4]*

19. Rolling a 3 or 5 on a single roll of a number cube $\frac{1}{3}$; ≈0.333; ≈33.3%

20. Drawing a rectangle that is also a pentagon 0; 0.0; 0%

21. Selecting a purple marble from a bag that contains 8 purple and 22 red marbles $\frac{4}{15}$; ≈0.267; ≈26.7%

22. A randomly chosen person being born on a Saturday or Sunday $\frac{2}{7}$; ≈0.286; ≈28.6%

Section 12B Chance and Probability

Summary

- A **sample space** is the set of all possible **outcomes,** or results, of an **experiment.** An **event** is an outcome or a collection of outcomes.

- The **probability,** or **theoretical probability,** of an event is

  $$P(\text{event}) = \frac{\text{number of equally likely outcomes in the event}}{\text{number of outcomes in the sample space}}.$$

- The sum of the probability of an event occurring and the probability of the event *not* occurring is 1.

- **Experimental probability** is calculated using data from surveys or experiments. It is the number of times the event occurs divided by the number of **trials.**

- **Geometric probability** is calculated by using geometric models and comparing areas, lengths, or other measures. **Conditional probability** is the probability that event B will occur, given that event A has already occurred.

- If the occurrence of one event does not affect the probability of a second event, the events are **independent events.**

- The **multiplication property** states that, for independent events A and B, $P(A \text{ and } B) = P(A) \times P(B)$.

Review

7. What is the probability of rolling a 5 or more on one toss of a number cube? $\frac{1}{3}$

8. What is the probability that a card chosen from a 52-card deck is one of the 4 jacks? $\frac{1}{13}$

9. A radio station announces that there is an 80% probability of rain today. What is the probability that it will **not** rain today? **20%**

10. Roll a number cube 30 times. Record your results and calculate the experimental probability of rolling a 4. **Answers may vary**

11. A fly lands on the tablecloth shown. What is the probability that the fly lands on a green square? $\frac{13}{25}$

12. The game of Scrabble® uses 100 letter tiles. There are 42 vowel tiles, of which 12 are E's. What is the probability that a tile chosen at random is an E, given that it is a vowel? $\frac{2}{7}$

13. There is a hole in a green square of the tablecloth shown above. Find the probability that the hole is in the center square. $\frac{1}{13}$

14. You roll a pair of number cubes and the first one comes up 3. What is the probability that the sum of the two number cubes is 9? $\frac{1}{6}$

15. A bag contains 3 blue, 4 red, and 5 yellow marbles. Two marbles are chosen in order. Find $P(\text{yellow AND yellow})$ if

  a. The first marble is replaced before choosing the second. $\frac{25}{144}$

  b. The first marble is **not** replaced. $\frac{5}{33}$

16. A number cube is rolled twice. Find the probability that an odd number is rolled both times. Are these independent or dependent events? $\frac{1}{4}$, **Independent**

Chapter 12 Summary and Review **673**

Chapter 12 Assessment

Assessment Correlation

Item(s)	Lesson(s)
1, 2	12-1
3	12-2, 12-3
4, 5	12-2
6	12-3
7, 8	12-4
9	12-5
10	12-4
11, 12	12-6
13, 14	12-7

Answers for Assessment

8. R, R, R, R, R, R, R, B, B, B, G, G, G, G; $\frac{2}{7}$

Answers for Performance Task

4-letter combinations from the word SAMPLE:

$\frac{6!}{4!2!}$ = 15; SAMP, SAML, SAME, SAPL, SAPE, SALE, SMPL, SMPE, SMLE, SPLE, AMPL, AMPE, AMLE, APLE, MPLE

---

1. Carmen's is having an outfit special. Buyers can choose one of 3 shirts, pants in one of 5 colors, and shoes in one of 2 styles. How many different outfits can a buyer choose? **30**

2. The lunch special at Earl's Eatery includes soup or salad, and a choice of pasta, quiche, or sandwich. How many different lunch specials can be ordered? **6**

3. Evaluate each expression.
   a. $7!$ **5040** b. $\frac{8!}{5!}$ **336** c. $\frac{6!}{2!(6-2)!}$ **15**

4. How many ways can the letters of the word PHONE be arranged? **120**

5. A disc jockey has chosen 6 songs he wants to play, but there is only enough time for 3 of them before the news. How many different ways can he select and order the 3 songs? **120**

6. The debate club has 11 members.
   a. Find the number of ways to choose a committee of 3 members. **165**
   b. Find the number of ways to choose 8 members to go on a trip. **165**

7. What is the probability that a student chosen at random was born in March? Give your answer as a fraction, decimal, and percent. *Hint:* March has 31 days. $\frac{31}{365}$; ≈ 0.085; ≈ 8.5%

8. A pencil is chosen at random from 7 red, 3 blue, and 4 green pencils. List the possible outcomes in the sample space. What is the probability that the chosen pencil is green?

9. Cecilia rolled a number cube 60 times. Her results are shown. Give the experimental probability of rolling a 2. $\frac{3}{20}$

Result	1	2	3	4	5	6
Number of Rolls	12	9	10	11	8	10

10. A wire is bent to make a trapezoid, as shown at the right. Find the probability that an ant crawling along the wire is on the 5 cm side. $\frac{5}{16}$

11. Find the probability that the ant in Exercise 10 is on the 6-cm side, given that it is on one of the two parallel sides. $\frac{3}{4}$

12. Julio was born on the 30th day of the month. Find the probability that he was born in October. *Hint:* All months except February have at least 30 days. $\frac{1}{11}$

13. A card is drawn at random from a deck of 52 cards containing 13 diamonds. It is replaced and the cards are shuffled, and then a second card is drawn. Find the probability that both cards are diamonds. Are these *independent* or *dependent* events? $\frac{1}{16}$; Independent events

14. What would your answers be in Exercise 13 if the first card is **not** replaced? $\frac{1}{17}$; Dependent events

Performance Task

Show several ways to find the number of 4-letter combinations from the word SAMPLE. Then write down all of the combinations in an organized list.

Performance Assessment Key

See key on page 623.

Resources

Assessment Sourcebook
Chapter 12 Tests
    Forms A and B (free response)
    Form C (multiple choice)
    Form D (performance assessment)
    Form E (mixed response)
    Form F (cumulative chapter test)
 TestWorks
Test and Practice Software
Home and Community Connections
    Letter Home for Chapter 12
    in English and Spanish

Suggested Scoring Rubric

4
- Shows several ways to find the number of 4-letter combinations from SAMPLE.
- Writes all 15 of the combinations in an organized list.

3
- Shows a few ways to find the number of 4-letter combinations from SAMPLE.
- Writes most of the combinations in an organized list.

2
- Shows one way to find the number of 4-letter combinations from SAMPLE.
- Writes some of the combinations in an organized list.

1
- Shows little understanding of how to find 4-letter combinations.

Multiple Choice

Choose the best answer.

1. If the value of k in $\frac{y}{x} = k$ is 8 and $x = 4$, what is the value of y? *[Lesson 5-3]* **C**

    Ⓐ 2   Ⓑ 16   Ⓒ 32   Ⓓ 64

2. Holly's Appliance Depot buys an oven for $600 and sells it for $750. What is the percent increase? *[Lesson 6-4]* **B**

    Ⓐ 20%   Ⓑ 25%

    Ⓒ 80%   Ⓓ 125%

3. Which number is divisible by 9? *[Lesson 7-1]* **B**

    Ⓐ 6,829,269   Ⓑ 4,286,484

    Ⓒ 9,238,832   Ⓓ 5,757,365

4. Find the angle supplementary to 73°. *[Lesson 8-4]* **B**

    Ⓐ 27°   Ⓑ 107°   Ⓒ 117°   Ⓓ 163°

5. Find the area of a circle with a diameter of 12 cm. Use 3.14 for π. *[Lesson 9-3]* **C**

    Ⓐ 37.68 cm^2 Ⓑ 75.36 cm^2

    Ⓒ 113.04 cm^2 Ⓓ 452.16 cm^2

6. Subtract the polynomials. *[Lesson 10-7]* **A**

    $(2x^2 - 4) - (5x^2 + 3x + 4)$

    Ⓐ $-3x^2 - 3x - 8$ Ⓑ $-3x^2 - 3x$

    Ⓒ $-3x^2 + 3x - 8$ Ⓓ $-3x^2 + 3x$

7. What rule shows that the triangles are congruent? *[Lesson 11-3]* **D**

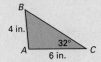

    Ⓐ Angle-Side-Angle   Ⓑ Side-Angle-Side

    Ⓒ Side-Angle-Angle   Ⓓ None of these

8. $\triangle PQR$ is similar to $\triangle TSR$. Find the length of $\overline{TR}$. *[Lesson 11-5]* **D**

    Ⓐ 28.8 cm

    Ⓑ 31.5 cm

    Ⓒ 41.14 cm

    Ⓓ 45 cm

9. What kinds of symmetry are in this figure? *[Lesson 11-8]* **D**

    Ⓐ Line symmetry

    Ⓑ 90° rotational symmetry

    Ⓒ Point symmetry

    Ⓓ A and C

    Ⓔ A, B, and C

10. A pizza parlor offers 3 sizes and 8 toppings. How many different 1-topping pizzas can be ordered? *[Lesson 12-1]* **B**

    Ⓐ 8   Ⓑ 24   Ⓒ 56   Ⓓ 336

11. A test requires students to choose 3 of the 5 essay questions. How many ways can the 3 questions be chosen? *[Lesson 12-3]* **A**

    Ⓐ 10   Ⓑ 15   Ⓒ 20   Ⓓ 60

12. Arlene flipped a coin 100 times and got 48 heads and 52 tails. What is the experimental probability of flipping tails? *[Lesson 12-5]* **C**

    Ⓐ $\frac{12}{25}$ Ⓑ $\frac{12}{13}$ Ⓒ $\frac{13}{25}$ Ⓓ $\frac{1}{2}$

13. You roll a number cube twice. What is the probability that you get a 4 on the first roll and an odd number on the second roll? *[Lesson 12-7]* **B**

    Ⓐ $\frac{1}{36}$ Ⓑ $\frac{1}{12}$ Ⓒ $\frac{1}{4}$ Ⓓ $\frac{2}{3}$

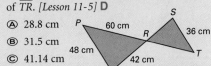

About Multiple-Choice Tests

The Cumulative Review found at the end of Chapters 2, 4, 6, 8, 10, and 12 can be used to prepare students for standardized tests.

Students sometimes do not perform as well on standardized tests as they do on other tests. There may be several reasons for this related to the format and content of the test.

• Format

Students may have limited experience with multiple-choice tests. For some questions, such tests are harder because having options may confuse the student.

• Content

A standardized test may cover a broader range of content than normally covered on a test, and the relative emphasis given to various strands may be different than given in class. Also, some questions may assess general aptitude or thinking skills and not include specific pieces of mathematical content.

It is important not to let the differences between standardized tests and other tests shake your students' confidence.

CONTENTS

1.

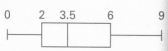

2.

Stem	Leaf
1	4 5 9 9
2	6 6 8 9
3	5

3. Mean: 47.3
   Median: 46.05
   Mode: 41.2

4.

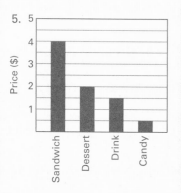

5.

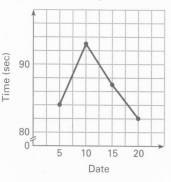

6. Possible answer: Have each customer write his or her name on a card. Shuffle the cards and then choose some of the cards with your eyes closed.

7.

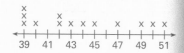

8. No. Possible explanation: This sample omits the vast majority of movie-goers, who do not necessarily view premieres.

9. About 300 rap items, 250 alternative items, 250 top 40 items, 150 jazz items, and 100 country items

10. About 400 in 1987, 1000 in 1988, 1200 in 1989, 800 in 1990, 1700 in 1991, and 1200 in 1992

Chapter Review

Chapter 1 Review

CHAPTER REVIEW

1. Construct a line plot for the data set 43, 39, 51, 45, 40, 39, 49, 47, 42, 50, 39, 42, 44.

2. Make a stem-and-leaf diagram for the data set 28, 14, 29, 26, 35, 26, 19, 15, 19.

3. Find the mean, median, and mode of the data values 50.3, 41.2, 59.0, 46.7, 41.2, and 45.4.

4. Construct a box-and-whisker plot for the data set 3, 7, 2, 9, 4, 5, 2, 1, 0, 6.

5. Make a bar graph to show that a sandwich costs $4.00, a dessert $2.00, a drink $1.50, and a candy bar $0.50.

6. Describe a method for taking a random sample of customers in a bookstore.

7. Make a line graph for the following running times (in sec): 84 on September 5, 93 on September 10, 87 on September 15, and 82 on September 20.

8. Would a random selection of 200 people watching a movie premiere be a random sample of the population of moviegoers? Explain.

9. Read the bar graph to determine the number of each item in the music store.

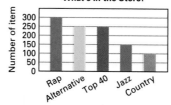

10. Read the line graph to determine the number of alternative CDs purchased by the music store each year.

11. Create a frequency table for the data set 4, 2, 5, 3, 2, 6, 5, 4, 5, 6, 2, 6, 4, 2.

12. Create a frequency table for the data set 1.5, 1.1, 0.8, 1.4, 0.9, 1.1, 1.5, 1.0, 1.3, 0.9, 1.5, 1.0, 1.3, 1.2.

13. Make a frequency table showing four occurrences each of 9.3 and 5.7, two of 1.5, and one each of 6.4 and 7.7.

14. Create a scatterplot and draw a trend line for the data set (1982, 10.3), (1984, 8.4), (1986, 11.4), (1988, 10.0), (1990, 13.5), and (1992, 14.2).

15. The U.S. government collected individual income taxes totaling $240 billion in 1980, $330 billion in 1985, $470 billion in 1990, and $590 billion in 1995 (estimated). Create a scatterplot and draw a trend line if possible.

16. One day in July, the temperature during the day was 89°F at 1:00 P.M., 92°F at 2:00 P.M., 94°F at 3:00 P.M., 96°F at 4:00 P.M., and 95°F at 5:00 P.M. Create a scatterplot for the data.

11.

Value	Frequency
2	4
3	1
4	3
5	3
6	3

12.

Value	Frequency
0.8	1
0.9	2
1.0	2
1.1	2
1.2	1
1.3	2
1.4	1
1.5	3

13.

Value	Frequency
1.5	2
5.7	4
6.4	1
7.7	1
9.3	4

14.

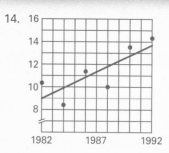

15 and 16.   See page 677.

Chapter 2 Review

1. Find the absolute value of -93.

2. Find $|15| + |-23|$.

Compute.

3. $-37 + (-29)$ **4.** $73 + (-41)$ **5.** $-63 - 22$

6. $-38 - (-84)$ **7.** -12×8 **8.** $-54(-19)$

9. $84 \div (-7)$ **10.** $-273 \div (-13)$ **11.** 7×-6

12. $-4(12 - 19)$ **13.** $4 \times 11 - 56 \div (-8)$ **14.** $5 - \dfrac{4(14 - 9)}{2}$

15. The temperature was $-18°F$ and it went down $7°$. What was the new temperature?

Give the coordinates of each point.

16. A **17.** B

18. C **19.** D

20. E **21.** F

22. Write 8^4 in expanded form.

23. Write 12^5 in expanded form.

24. Write $9 \times 9 \times 9 \times 9 \times 9 \times 9$ in exponential form.

25. Write $2 \times 2 \times 2 \times 2$ in exponential form.

Evaluate.

26. $(-5)^3$ **27.** -4^0 **28.** -8^2 **29.** 1^8

Write each number in scientific notation.

30. Forty-two million   **31.** Seven thousandths   **32.** 835,000   **33.** 0.00000091

34. Write 6.31×10^6 in standard notation.   **35.** Write 2.97×10^{-4} in standard notation.

36. A microgram is 0.000001 g. Express this weight in scientific notation.   **37.** Venus is 67,200,200 mi from the sun. Express this distance in scientific notation.

38. The population of New Orleans, Louisiana, was 1,240,000 in 1990. Write this number in scientific notation.   **39.** A milligram in the metric system equals 0.0000022 lb. Write this number in scientific notation.

Chapter 2 Review **677**

Chapter 2 Review

Answers

1. 93
2. 38
3. -66
4. 32
5. -85
6. 46
7. -96
8. 1026
9. -12
10. 21
11. -42
12. 28
13. 51
14. -5
15. $-25°F$
16. $(-3, 4)$
17. $(-5, -4)$
18. $(4, 0)$
19. $(2, 3)$
20. $(-2, -1)$
21. $(1, -3)$
22. $8 \times 8 \times 8 \times 8$
23. $12 \times 12 \times 12 \times 12 \times 12$
24. 9^6
25. 2^4
26. -125
27. -1
28. -64
29. 1
30. 4.2×10^7
31. 7×10^{-3}
32. 8.35×10^5
33. 9.1×10^{-7}
34. 6,310,000
35. 0.000297
36. 1×10^{-6} g
37. 6.72×10^7 mi or 6.72002×10^7
38. 1.24×10^6
39. 2.2×10^{-6} lb

Answers for Review, page 676

15.

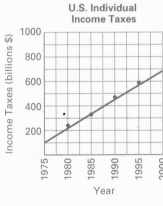

16.

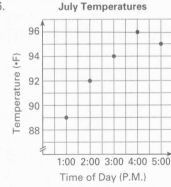

Chapter 3 Review

Answers

1. $w = \frac{d}{7}$
2. 28.16 m²
3. $12.50x + 2.00$
4. $6b - 18$
5. -2
6. -28
7. -13
8. 36
9. 13
10. 7
11. 3 sandwiches
12. No. Possible explanation: If $x = 0$, then $x - 2 = -2$ and $4x = 0$.
13. 87
14. 47
15. 0.55
16. 15
17. 0.15
18. 294
19. 4
20. 12
21. 20 ft
22. $y < 28$
23. $b \le 19.75$
24. $x > 46$
25. $y \ge 24$
26. $w \ge 34.5$
27. $k < 8.28$
28. $h \le 62$
29. $f < 26$
30. $x \le -3$

31. $y \ge 3$

32. $x > 14$

33. $x > 1\frac{1}{3}$

34. $x < 12$

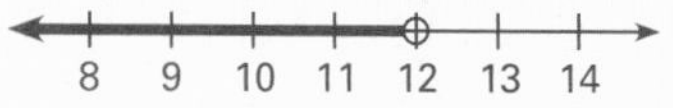

35. $x \le 3$

36. $x > 1$

37. $y < -2$

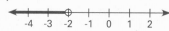

Chapter 3 Review

1. Using w for weeks and d for days, write a formula for the number of weeks in d days.

2. Find the area of a triangle with base 6.4 m and height 8.8 m. Use the formula $A = \frac{1}{2}bh$, where b is the base and h is the height.

3. Write an algebraic expression for "$12.50 each, plus $2.00 shipping and handling."

4. Simplify the expression $6(b - 3)$.

5. Evaluate the expression $5x + 2y$ for $x = -2$ and $y = 4$.

6. Evaluate the expression $-6x + 5y$ for $x = 3$ and $y = -2$.

Solve each equation.

7. $23 = m + 36$
8. $\frac{x}{3} = 12$
9. $z - 9 = 4$
10. $4y = 28$

11. The Pizza-n-More restaurant sells submarine sandwiches for $6 each and charges $2 for delivery. With $20, how many subs can you buy?

12. Are $x - 2$ and $4x$ equivalent expressions? Justify your answer.

Solve each equation.

13. $n - 40 = 47$
14. $x + 31 = 78$
15. $y \times 6 = 3.3$
16. $10 = \frac{2x}{3}$

17. $2.4 = 16z$
18. $7 = \frac{h}{42}$
19. $4x + 18 = 34$
20. $2x - 12 = 12$

21. The maximum height h (in ft) of an object thrown straight up from an initial height of a (in ft) with velocity v (in ft/sec) is given by the formula $h = a + \frac{v^2}{64}$. Find the initial height when $h = 36$ ft and $v = 32$ ft per sec.

Solve each inequality.

22. $y + 21 < 49$
23. $7.9 \ge \frac{2b}{5}$
24. $x - 14 > 32$
25. $12 \le \frac{1}{2}y$

26. $w + (-2) \ge 32.5$
27. $\frac{k}{3} < 2.76$
28. $67 \ge h + 5$
29. $13 > \frac{3f}{6}$

Solve each inequality, then graph the solution.

30. $10 + 2x \le 4$
31. $2y - 8 \ge -2$
32. $7 < \frac{x}{2}$
33. $3x - 1 > 3$

34. $\frac{x}{3} < 4$
35. $4x - 7 \le 5$
36. $17 + 3x > 20$
37. $y + 14 < 12$

Chapter 4 Review

1. Find the value of y when $x = -2$ in the equation $y = -3x$.

2. Make a table of values for the equation $y = x - 9$. Use 0, 1, 2, 3, 4, and 5 for x.

3. Find the rule that relates x and y in the table. Then find y when $x = 28$.

x	1	2	3	4	5
y	4	8	12	16	20

4. Determine whether each ordered pair is a solution of $y = \frac{3}{2}x - 2$.

   a. $(2, 5)$ b. $\left(3, \frac{5}{2}\right)$ c. $(6, 9)$ d. $(8, 10)$

5. Give two solutions for the equation $y = 4x + 1$.

6. Graph the equation $y = 2x - 3$. Use 0, 1, 2, and 3 as x values.

7. A towing company charges a fee of $50 plus $2 per mile to tow a car. Graph the price charged. Use x for the number of miles towed.

8. Draw a line through the origin with the given slope.

   a. -2 b. $\frac{3}{4}$ c. $-\frac{1}{2}$

9. Graph the equation $y = -\frac{1}{4}x + 1$. Find the slope, the x-intercept, and the y-intercept.

10. For each line, find the slope, the x-intercept, and the y-intercept.

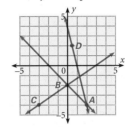

   a. Line through A and B
   b. Line through B and C
   c. Line through A and D

11. For each line, find the slope, x-intercept, and y-intercept.

   a. $y = 5x - 2$
   b. $y = -x + 1$
   c. $y = x - \frac{1}{2}$

Solve each system of equations by graphing.

12. $y = 2x + 3$ $y = -\frac{1}{2}x - 2$

13. $y = x + 2$ $y = 2x + 1$

14. Econo Taxi charges $2 per trip plus $2 per mi. Super Taxi charges $5 per trip plus $1 per mi. For what number of mi is each cost the same?

Graph each inequality.

15. $y \geq 3x - 2$ 16. $y < -\frac{1}{2}x - 1$ 17. $y \leq x + 2$ 18. $y > 2x - 1$

Chapter 4 Review **679**

CHAPTER REVIEW

Chapter 4 Review

Answers

1. $y = 6$

2.

x	0	1	2	3	4	5
y	-9	-8	-7	-6	-5	-4

3. $y = 4x$; $y = 112$

4. a. No   b. Yes
   c. No   d. Yes

5. Possible answer: $(0, 1)$, $(1, 5)$

6.

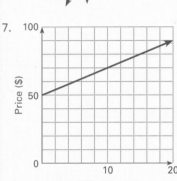

7.

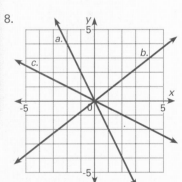

8.

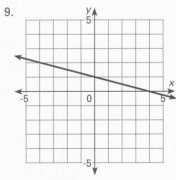

9.

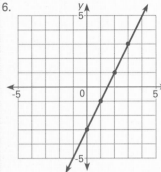

Slope: $-\frac{1}{4}$; x-intercept: 4; y-intercept: 1

CHAPTER REVIEW

10. a. Slope: -1; x-intercept: -2; y-intercept: -2

   b. Slope: $\frac{2}{3}$; x-intercept: 3; y-intercept: -2

   c. Slope: -4; x-intercept: 1; y-intercept: 4

11. a. Slope: 5; x-intercept: $\frac{2}{5}$; y-intercept: -2

   b. Slope: -1; x-intercept: 1; y-intercept: 1

   c. Slope: 1; x-intercept: $\frac{1}{2}$; y-intercept: $-\frac{1}{2}$

12. $(-2, -1)$

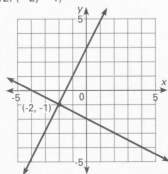

Answers for Ex. 13–16, page 680

Chapter 5 Review

Answers

1. $\frac{5}{6}$

2. Possible answer: 4 circles and 3 squares, or 8 circles and 6 squares, or 12 circles and 9 squares, and so on.

3. Green to total: $\frac{4}{9}$;

   total to green: $\frac{9}{4}$;

   yellow to total: $\frac{5}{9}$;

   total to yellow: $\frac{9}{5}$;

   green to yellow: $\frac{4}{5}$;

   yellow to green: $\frac{5}{4}$

4. $248 \times 7 \neq 392 \times 4$; Not equal

5. Yes; $k = \frac{5}{6}$

6.

5	10	15	20	25	30
8	16	24	32	40	48

7. $y = 300$

8. $x = 4$

9. $m = 36$

10. $x = 144$

11. $x = 54$

12. $x = 68$

13. $\frac{\$220}{1 \text{ week}}$; Possible formula: $P = 220t$

14. About 940 words

15. About 48 jackets

16. 28 teachers

17. 12 ft tall and 52 ft across

18. $x = 3$; $y = 12$

19. a. \$0.40 per candy bar
    b. \$0.005 (or 0.5¢) per clip
    c. 60 mi/hr

Chapter 5 Review

1. Write the ratio 5 to 6 as a fraction.

2. Draw a picture to show a ratio 4:3 of circles to squares.

3. Write all the ratios that can be made using the figure at the right.

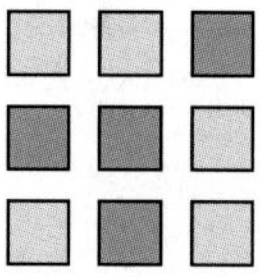

4. Jean drives 248 mi in 4 hr and Paul drives 392 mi in 7 hr. Use cross products to determine whether these rates are equal.

5. Is the table an equal ratio table? If so, find the value of k.

x	6	12	18	24	30
y	5	10	15	20	25

6. Complete the table to create ratios equal to the given ratio.

5			20		30
8	16	24		40	

7. If the value of k in $\frac{y}{x} = k$ is 12 and $x = 25$, what is the value of y?

8. If the value of k in $\frac{y}{x} = k$ is 3 and $y = 12$, what is the value of x?

Solve each proportion.

9. $\frac{84}{48} = \frac{63}{m}$

10. $\frac{36}{81} = \frac{x}{324}$

11. $\frac{x}{102} = \frac{72}{136}$

12. $\frac{17}{x} = \frac{8}{32}$

13. Find the unit rate and create a rate formula for a rate of \$1540 in 7 weeks.

14. Julie types 251 words in 4 min. Estimate how many words she would type in 15 min.

15. The ratio of jackets to shirts sold by Carla's Clothing Store is 6:17. In a two-week period, the store sold 136 shirts. About how many jackets were sold?

16. Last year, Central School had 420 students and 24 teachers. This year, there are 490 students. If the student-teacher ratio remained the same, how many teachers are there this year?

17. A scale drawing of a house is 3 in. tall and 13 in. across. If the scale is 1 in. = 4 ft, what are the dimensions of the actual house?

18. Find the missing measures in the pair of similar figures.

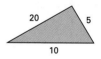

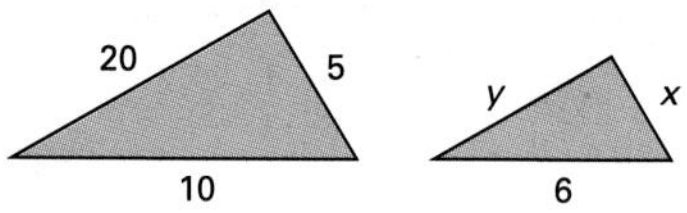

19. Find the unit rate for each situation.
    a. \$7.20 buys 18 candy bars
    b. \$0.50 for 100 paper clips
    c. Traveled 120 miles in 2 hours

Answers for Review, page 679

13. (1, 3)

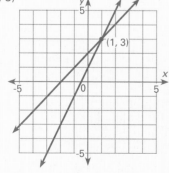

14. 3 mi

15.

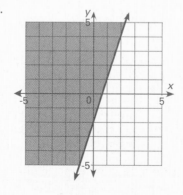

16.

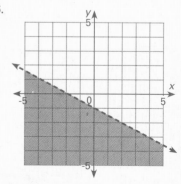

Chapter 6 Review

1. Use the information in the circle graph.

a. What percent of the students watch 1 hr of television or less per day?

b. What percent of the students watch 2 to 3 hr of television per day?

c. What percent of the students watch 3 or more hr of television per day?

Hours Spent Watching Television per Day

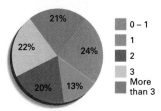

- 0 – 1
- 1
- 2
- 3
- More than 3

2. Write the fraction, decimal, and percent that describe how much of the figure is shaded.

3. Estimate the percent of the shaded region.

4. What number is 65% of 280?

5. Estimate 55% of 342.

6. Of the people at a concert, 12% bought a T-shirt after the show. If 156 people bought T-shirts, how many people were at the concert all together?

7. Find the total cost of a $110 stereo when its price is increased by 12%.

8. Estimate 37% of 248.

9. 15 is 24% of what number?

10. Pete's Boutique buys a sweatshirt for $24.95 and sells it for $39.95. What is the percent of increase?

11. A video normally sells for $29.95. Find its price during a 20%-off sale.

12. Abdul bought a book priced at $22.95. What was the tax rate if he had to pay $24.67 with tax?

13. Sharon earned $260 in simple interest on an investment in 5 yr. If the interest rate was 8%, what was her principal?

14. The price of a plane ticket can vary depending on the time of travel. Find the percent decrease for a ticket with a price of $210 in June and $145 in September.

15. Sal receives a discount on all purchases at the store where he works. He buys a radio for which the store originally paid $49.60. The store marked the price up 25% for retail, but Sal's price is $49.60. What percent discount did he receive?

16. Gina has a car valued at $4500. She sells it at an auction at an increase of 19%, but the auctioneer took 5% of the selling price. What amount did Gina receive when she sold her car?

Chapter 6 Review **681**

Chapter 6 Review

Answers

1. a. 37%
   b. 42%
   c. 43%
2. $\frac{1}{2}$; 0.5; 50%
3. Possible answer: About 50%
4. 182
5. Possible answer: 190
6. 1300 people
7. $123.20
8. Possible answer: 80
9. 62.5
10. About 60%
11. $23.96
12. 7.5%
13. $650
14. About 30.95%
15. 20%
16. $5087.25

CHAPTER REVIEW

CHAPTER REVIEW

Answers for Review, page 679

17.

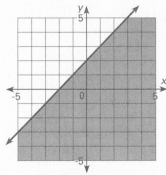

18.

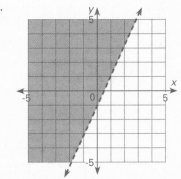

Answers

1. Divisible by 2, 4, and 8
2. $504 = 2^3 \times 3^2 \times 7$;
   Possible factor tree:

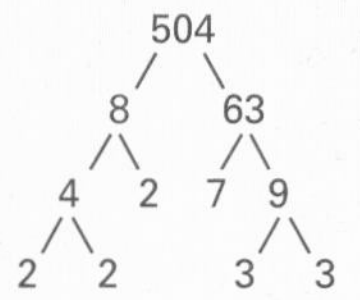

3. $21 = 3 \times 7$
4. $68 = 2^2 \times 17$
5. $117 = 3^2 \times 13$
6. $136 = 2^3 \times 17$
7. 6
8. $60 = 2^2 \times 3 \times 5$
   $294 = 2 \times 3 \times 7^2$
   GCF (60, 294) = 6
9. $\frac{9}{13}$
10. 120
11. $\frac{4}{21}$
12. In 12 days
13. $0.\overline{42}$; Repeating
14. $10.9119 < 10.912$
15. $\frac{31}{50}$
16. 73.889
17. $16\frac{1}{8}$
18. $\frac{114}{155}$
19. $\frac{14}{25}$
20. $\frac{19223}{250}$, or $76\frac{233}{250}$
21. $\frac{1}{3}$
22. $\frac{163}{99}$, or $1\frac{64}{99}$
23. $35 = 5 \times 7$
    $84 = 2^2 \times 3 \times 7$
    LCM (35, 84) = 420
24. $26 = 2 \times 13$
    $78 = 2 \times 3 \times 13$
    GCF (26, 78) = 26
25. 9
26. −11
27. ±12
28. −25
29. Yes, it is a perfect square.
30. $\frac{2}{5}$
31. 9 and 10
32. About 6.93 ft
33. ±19
34. 48

Chapter 7 Review

1. Determine whether 184 is divisible by 2, 3, 4, 5, 6, 7, 8, 9, or 10.

2. Use a factor tree to determine the prime factorization of 504.

Determine the prime factorization of each number.

3. 21

4. 68

5. 117

6. 136

7. Find the GCF of 48 and 66.

8. Use prime factorization to find the GCF of 60 and 294.

9. Write the fraction $\frac{72}{104}$ in lowest terms.

10. Find the LCM of 24 and 30.

11. In one classroom, $\frac{4}{7}$ of the students are wearing T-shirts and $\frac{1}{3}$ of the students with T-shirts are wearing jeans. What fraction of the students are wearing both a T-shirt and jeans?

12. Rebecca does aerobics every three days and weight training every four days. Today she did both. In how many days will Rebecca again do both aerobics and weight training on the same day?

13. Write $\frac{14}{33}$ as a decimal and determine whether it is repeating or terminating.

14. Replace $\square$ with $>$, $<$, or $=$ to compare 10.9119 $\square$ 10.912.

15. Write 0.62 as a fraction in lowest terms.

16. Subtract $98.24 - 24.351$.

17. Add $4\frac{5}{8} + 11\frac{1}{2}$.

18. Divide $3\frac{4}{5} \div 5\frac{1}{6}$.

Write each decimal as a fraction in lowest terms.

19. 0.56

20. 76.892

21. $0.\overline{33}$

22. $1.\overline{64}$

23. Use prime factorization to find the LCM of 35 and 84.

24. Use prime factorization to find the GCF of 26 and 78.

Determine each square root.

25. $\sqrt{81}$

26. $-\sqrt{121}$

27. $\pm\sqrt{144}$

28. $-\sqrt{625}$

29. State whether 169 is a perfect square.

30. Find the square root of $\frac{36}{225}$.

31. Find the two consecutive integers that $\sqrt{89}$ is between.

32. What is the side length of a square with area 48 ft^2?

33. Find $\pm\sqrt{361}$.

34. Find the missing side length for the right triangle.

Chapter 8 Review

1. Convert 16 pt to qt.

2. Convert 6.2 m to cm.

3. What metric unit would you use for the mass of a bicycle?

4. Determine which measurement is more precise, 6 m or 605 cm.

5. Calculate 12.34 ft × 3.194 ft with the correct number of significant digits.

6. Find the complementary and supplementary angle measures for a 73° angle.

7. What are the latitude and longitude of Munich?

8. What is the position of Berlin relative to Frankfurt?

9. Classify 60° as a right, straight, obtuse, or acute angle.

10. In the figure shown,
    a. Which lines are parallel?
    b. Which lines are perpendicular?
    c. Which angle is a supplement to ∠A?

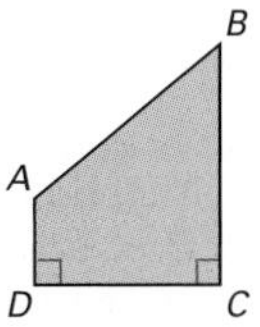

11. In the figure shown,
    a. Which angle is obtuse?
    b. Which angle is acute?
    c. Which angle is 90°?

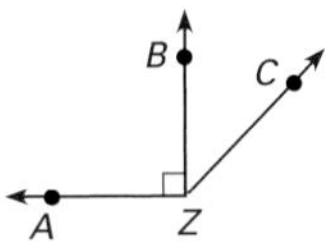

12. Draw the top view for the cube tower.

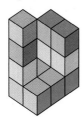

13. Classify the shape of this polygon by the number of sides. Then find the sum of the angle measures. [Hint: 180°(k − 2)]

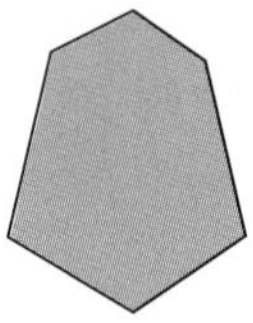

Chapter 8 Review **683**

Answers

1. 8 qt
2. 620 cm
3. Possible answer: Kilogram
4. 605 cm
5. 39.41 ft²
6. Complementary angle: 17°; Supplementary angle: 107°
7. 48°N, 11.5°E
8. About 3°N, 5°E
9. Acute
10. a. $\overline{AD}$ and $\overline{BC}$
    b. $\overline{AD}$ and $\overline{DC}$
       $\overline{BC}$ and $\overline{CD}$
    c. ∠B
11. a. ∠AZC
    b. ∠BZC
    c. ∠AZB
12.

4	1	3
1	1	3

13. Hexagon; 720°

CHAPTER REVIEW

683

Chapter 9 Review

Answers

1. a. Perimeter: 68 in.;
   Area: 270 in.^{2}
   b. Perimeter: 92 cm;
   Area: 360 cm^2

2. a. Perimeter: 102 in.;
   Area: 607.5 in^2
   b. Perimeter: 69 cm;
   Area: 202.5 cm^2

3. Circumference:
   About 70.96 m;
   Area: About 400.95 m^2

4. About 0.75 in.

5. a. About 43.96 cm^2

   b. 808 ft^2

6. a. Slant height: 17 in.;
   Surface area: about 628 in^2

   b. Slant height: $\approx$ 15.59 ft;
   Surface area: 864 ft^2

7. a. 504 m^3
   b. About 65.94 in^3

8. a. 31.5 m^3

   b. 1780.38 in^3

9.

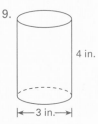

   Volume: About 28.26 in^3

10.

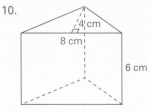

   Volume: 96 cm^3

11. a. 5500 cm^3

    b. About 12.167 ft^3

12. a. 12 in^3

    b. 48 in^3

684

Chapter 9 Review

1. Find the perimeter and area of each polygon.

   a.
   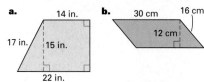

   b.

2. Find the perimeter and area of

   a. the polygon in Exercise 1a after a dilation by a scale factor of $\frac{3}{2}$.

   b. the polygon in Exercise 1b after a dilation by a scale factor of $\frac{3}{4}$.

3. For the circle shown, find the circumference and the area.

   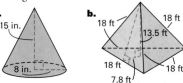

4. Katie wears a ring that has a circumference of 2.36 in. Find the diameter of the ring.

5. Find the surface area of each figure.

   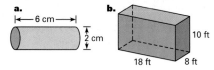

6. Find the slant height and the surface area of each figure.

   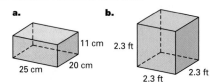

7. Find the volume of each solid.

   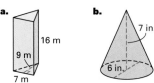

8. a. Find the volume of the solid in Exercise 7a after scaling two dimensions by a scale factor of $\frac{1}{4}$.

   b. Find the surface area and volume of the solid in Exercise 7b after a dilation by a scale factor of 3.

9. Sketch a cylinder with a diameter of 3 in. and a height of 4 in. Then find its volume.

10. Sketch a triangular prism 6 cm in height. The triangular faces each have a base of 8 cm and a height of 4 cm. Then find its volume.

11. Find the volume of each solid.

    a. b.

12. A circular cone has a base area of 12 in^2. Find the volume of the cone if it's height is:

    a. 3 in.

    b. 12 in.

Chapter 10 Review

1. For the function machine shown,

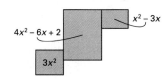

| Input | Multiply by 3 | Output |

   a. Find the output value for an input of 4;

   b. Find the input value for an output of -15.

2. What is a possible rule for the input and output shown in the table?

Input	3	5	7	9	10
Output	5	9	13	17	19

3. For the function rule $y = -4x - 1$, complete the table of values.

x	−1	0	1	2	3
y					

4. A ball is dropped from a height of 240 ft. Its height after t sec is given by $h = -16t^2 + 240$. Graph the function. When did the ball hit the ground?

5. Graph the functions $y = x^2$ and $y = x^2 - 2$ and explain their differences.

6. Graph the equation $y = 2x + 4$. Does the equation describe a linear function?

7. A car rental company charges $35 for each day or portion thereof. Graph this function.

8. Write the polynomial expression $4x^2 - 7x^4 + 2x - 1 + x^3$ in descending order. Find the degree of the polynomial.

Evaluate each expression for the given value of the variable.

9. $g^2 - 4g$ for $g = 2$ **10.** $2x^2 + 5x - 7$ for $x = -4$ **11.** $x^3 - x^2 + 6x - 2$ for $x = -3$

Simplify each expression. Write the resulting polynomial in descending order.

12. $3 - 6x + x^2 + x - 12 + 4x^3$ **13.** $2x - 9 + 4x^2 - x + 17$

Add or subtract each polynomial. Write each answer in simplest form.

14. $(y^2 - 7y + 4) + (3y^2 - y - 9)$

15. $(x^2 + 8x - 11) + (2x^2 + 3x - 1)$

16. $(-y^2 + 5y) - (2y^2 - 3y + 8)$

17. $(x^3 + 2x^2 - x + 4) - (x^3 - 2x^2 - 2x + 10)$

18. Find the total area of the region.

$x^2 - 3x$

$4x^2 - 6x + 2$

$3x^2$

19. The perimeter is $3x^2 - 4x + 9$. Find the missing side length.

$x^2 + 4$

$2x + 7$

$x^2 + 5x - 9$

20. Find the area of a rectangle with a width of $3x + 4$ and a length of $2x^2$. Write the answer in lowest terms.

21. Multiply $-\frac{1}{3}t^2(3 - 12t)$.

Chapter 10 Review **685**

8. $-7x^4 + x^3 + 4x^2 + 2x - 1$; Degree: 4

9. -4

10. 5

11. -56

12. $4x^3 + x^2 - 5x - 9$

13. $4x^2 + x + 8$

14. $4y^2 - 8y - 5$

15. $3x^2 + 11x - 12$

16. $-3y^2 + 8y - 8$

17. $4x^2 + x - 6$

18. $8x^2 - 9x + 2$

19. $x^2 - 11x + 7$

20. $6x^3 + 8x^2$

21. $4t^3 - t^2$

Answers

1. a. 12

  b. -5

2. Possible answer: Multiply by 2 and then subtract 1.

3.

x	−1	0	1	2	3
y	3	−1	−5	−9	−13

4.

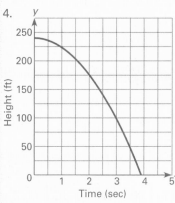

After about 3.9 sec

5.

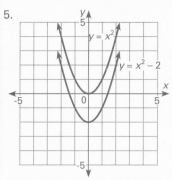

Possible answer: The graphs have the same shape, but the graph of $y = x^2 - 2$ is shifted downward.

6.

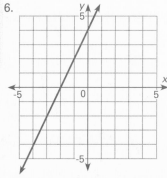

Yes, it is a linear function.

7.

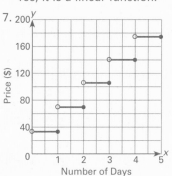

685

Chapter 11 Review

Answers

1. $x = 8.4$ m; m$\angle A = 110$

2. Not congruent

3. Yes; Side-Angle-Side

4. $\sin 30.5° = \dfrac{33}{65}$

   $\cos 30.5° = \dfrac{56}{65}$

   $\tan 30.5° = \dfrac{33}{56}$

5. 8.25 cm

6. $\overline{AB}$, $\overline{HG}$, $\overline{FE}$

7. Dilation; Similar but not congruent

8. $A(-5, 1)$; $B(-3, 6)$

9. Yes

Chapter 11 Review

1. The two trapezoids are similar. Find the length x and the measure of $\angle A$.

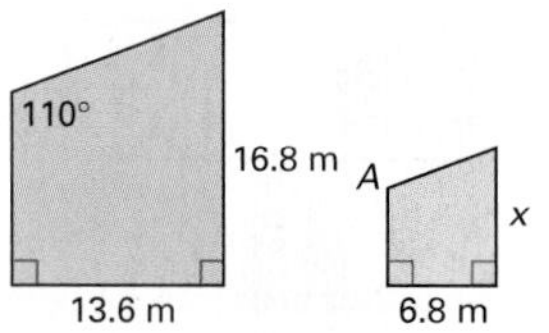

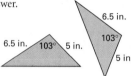

2. Are the figures congruent?

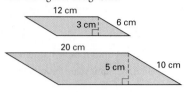

3. State whether the triangles are congruent; if they are, give the rule that justifies your answer.

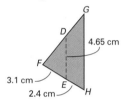

4. Use the lengths of the sides to write and evaluate the sine, cosine, and tangent ratios for the labeled angle.

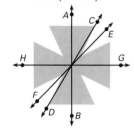

5. In the figure, $\triangle DEF$ is similar to $\triangle GHF$. Find the length of $\overline{GH}$.

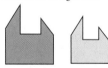

6. Which are lines of symmetry?

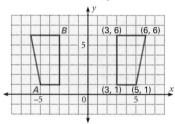

7. Which transformation has occurred? Are the figures similar? Congruent?

8. The trapezoid was reflected across the y-axis. Find the coordinates of points A and B.

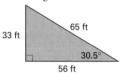

9. Can this tessellation be made using only rotations of a single polygon?

CHAPTER REVIEW

1. Make a tree diagram to show the possible results of spinning both spinners.

3. Evaluate.

   a. $(4!)(2!)$ **b.** $(8 - 5)!$ **c.** $\dfrac{9!}{3!(9 - 3)!}$

5. Ten people are running in a race. How many ways can runners place first, second, and third?

7. An office has 200 employees. How many ways can 15 employees be chosen to attend a conference? Use factorial notation for your answer.

9. What is the probability that a card chosen from a 52-card deck is one of the 13 hearts?

11. Roll a pair of number cubes 25 times. Record the sums that appear and calculate the experimental probability of rolling sums greater than 9.

13. What is the probability that a card chosen from a 52-card deck is an ace, given that it is a diamond?

15. A drawer contains 6 black socks, 5 white socks, and 2 brown socks. Two socks are chosen in order. Find P(black, brown) if

   a. the first sock is replaced before choosing the second.

   b. the first sock is not replaced.

17. State whether Exercise 15 involves *independent* or *dependent* events.

2. There are 6 different types of sandwiches and 5 different drinks. How many choices are there if only one sandwich and one drink are allowed?

4. How many ways can the letters of the word CAPTION be arranged?

6. A pizza parlor offers 12 different toppings for its pizzas. How many ways can a customer select 5 toppings for a pizza?

8. What is the probability of rolling an odd number on one toss of a number cube?

10. The probability that a tennis player will win a match is 60%. What is the probability that the player will lose the match?

12. A dart is thrown at the target shown. What is the probability that the dart lands in a red area?

14. You roll a pair of number cubes and the first one comes up 5. What is the probability that the sum of the two number cubes is less than 8?

16. A gumball machine contains 16 blue, 22 white, 12 yellow, and 25 green gumballs. Find the probability of

   a. getting one white followed by one blue gumball.

   b. getting two yellow gumballs.

18. A number cube is rolled twice. Find the probability that 4 is rolled both times.

Chapter 12 Review

Answers

1. Possible results:

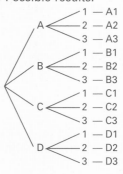

2. 30 choices

3. a. 48
   b. 6
   c. 84

4. 5040 ways

5. 720 ways

6. 792 ways

7. $\dfrac{200!}{15! \cdot 185!}$

8. $\dfrac{1}{2}$

9. $\dfrac{1}{4}$

10. 40%

11. Answers may vary. Experimental probability should be about $\dfrac{1}{6}$.

12. $\dfrac{3}{8}$

13. $\dfrac{1}{13}$

14. $\dfrac{1}{3}$

15. a. $\dfrac{12}{169} \approx 7.1\%$

    b. $\dfrac{1}{13} \approx 7.7\%$

16. a. $\dfrac{176}{2775} \approx 6.3\%$

    b. $\dfrac{22}{925} \approx 2.4\%$

17. 15a: Independent
    15b: Dependent

18. $\dfrac{1}{36}$

CHAPTER REVIEW

Geometric Formulas

Rectangle
Area: $A = lw$
Perimeter: $p = 2l + 2w$

Square
Area: $A = s^2$
Perimeter: $p = 4s$

Parallelogram
Area: $A = bh$

Triangle
Area: $A = \frac{1}{2}bh$
$m\angle A + m\angle B + m\angle C = 180°$

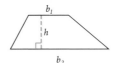

Trapezoid
Area: $A = \frac{1}{2}h(b_1 + b_2)$

Polygon
Sum of angle measures for
n-sided polygon: $S = (n - 2)180°$
Perimeter: sum of measures of
all sides

Circle
Area: $A = \pi r^2$
Circumference: $C = \pi d = 2\pi r$

Prism
Volume: $V = Bh$
Surface Area: $SA = ph + 2B$

Cylinder
Volume: $V = \pi r^2 h$
Surface Area: $SA = 2\pi rh + 2\pi r^2$

Measurement Conversion Factors

Metric Measures of Length

1000 meters (m) = 1 kilometer (km)

100 centimeters (cm) = 1 m

10 decimeters (dm) = 1 m

1000 millimeters (mm) = 1 m

10 cm = 1 decimeter (dm)

10 mm = 1 cm

Area

100 square millimeters = 1 square centimeter

(mm^2) (cm^2)

10,000 cm^2 = 1 square meter (m^2)

10,000 m^2 = 1 hectare (ha)

Volume

1000 cubic millimeters = 1 cubic centimeter

(mm^3) (cm^3)

1000 cm^3 = 1 cubic decimeter (dm^3)

1,000,000 cm^3 = 1 cubic meter (m^3)

Capacity

1000 milliliters (mL) = 1 liter (L)

1000 L = 1 kiloliter (kL)

Mass

1000 kilograms (kg) = 1 metric ton (t)

1000 grams (g) = 1 kg

1000 milligrams (mg) = 1 g

Temperatures in Degrees Celsius (°C)

0°C = freezing point of water

37°C = normal body temperature

100°C = boiling point of water

Time

60 seconds (sec) = 1 minute (min)

60 min = 1 hour (hr)

24 hr = 1 day

Customary Measures of Length

12 inches (in.) = 1 foot (ft)

3 ft = 1 yard (yd)

36 in. = 1 yd

5280 ft = 1 mile (mi)

1760 yd = 1 mi

6076 ft = 1 nautical mile

Area

144 square inches = 1 square foot

(in^2) (ft^2)

9 ft^2 = 1 square yard (yd^2)

43,560 sq ft^2 = 1 acre (A)

Volume

1728 cubic inches = 1 cubic foot

(cu in.) (cu ft)

27 cu ft = 1 cubic yard (cu yard)

Capacity

8 fluid ounces (fl oz) = 1 cup (c)

2 c = 1 pint (pt)

2 pt = 1 quart (qt)

4 qt = 1 gallon (gal)

Weight

16 ounces (oz) = 1 pound (lb)

2000 lb = 1 ton (T)

Temperatures in Degrees Fahrenheit (°F)

32°F = freezing point of water

98.6°F = normal body temperature

212°F = boiling point of water

TABLES

TABLES

Symbols

$+$	plus or positive	$\llcorner$	right angle
$-$	minus or negative	$\perp$	is perpendicular to
$\cdot$	times	$\parallel$	is parallel to
$\times$	times	AB	length of $\overline{AB}$; distance between A and B
$\div$	divided by		
$\pm$	positive or negative	$\triangle ABC$	triangle with vertices A, B, and C
$=$	is equal to	$\angle ABC$	angle with sides $\overrightarrow{BA}$ and $\overrightarrow{BC}$
$\neq$	is not equal to	$\angle B$	angle with vertex B
$<$	is less than	$m\angle ABC$	measure of angle ABC
$>$	is greater than	$'$	prime
$\leq$	is less than or equal to	a^n	the nth power of a
$\geq$	is greater than or equal to	$|x|$	absolute value of x
$\approx$	is approximately equal to	$\sqrt{x}$	principal square root of x
$\%$	percent	π	pi (approximately 3.1416)
$a{:}b$	the ratio of a to b, or $\frac{a}{b}$	(a, b)	ordered pair with x-coordinate a and y-coordinate b
$\cong$	is congruent to		
$\sim$	is similar to	$P(A)$	the probability of event A
$^\circ$	degree(s)	$n!$	n factorial
$\overleftrightarrow{AB}$	line containing points A and B		
$\overline{AB}$	line segment with endpoints A and B		
$\overrightarrow{AB}$	ray with endpoint A and containing B		

Squares and Square Roots

N	N^2	$\sqrt{N}$		N	N^2	$\sqrt{N}$
1	1	1		51	2,601	7.141
2	4	1.414		52	2,704	7.211
3	9	1.732		53	2,809	7.280
4	16	2		54	2,916	7.348
5	25	2.236		55	3,025	7.416
6	36	2.449		56	3,136	7.483
7	49	2.646		57	3,249	7.550
8	64	2.828		58	3,364	7.616
9	81	3		59	3,481	7.681
10	100	3.162		60	3,600	7.746
11	121	3.317		61	3,721	7.810
12	144	3.464		62	3,844	7.874
13	169	3.606		63	3,969	7.937
14	196	3.742		64	4,096	8
15	225	3.873		65	4,225	8.062
16	256	4		66	4,356	8.124
17	289	4.123		67	4,489	8.185
18	324	4.243		68	4,624	8.246
19	361	4.359		69	4,761	8.307
20	400	4.472		70	4,900	8.367
21	441	4.583		71	5,041	8.426
22	484	4.690		72	5,184	8.485
23	529	4.796		73	5,329	8.544
24	576	4.899		74	5,476	8.602
25	625	5		75	5,625	8.660
26	676	5.099		76	5,776	8.718
27	729	5.196		77	5,929	8.775
28	784	5.292		78	6,084	8.832
29	841	5.385		79	6,241	8.888
30	900	5.477		80	6,400	8.944
31	961	5.568		81	6,561	9
32	1,024	5.657		82	6,724	9.055
33	1,089	5.745		83	6,889	9.110
34	1,156	5.831		84	7,056	9.165
35	1,225	5.916		85	7,225	9.220
36	1,296	6		86	7,396	9.274
37	1,369	6.083		87	7,569	9.327
38	1,444	6.164		88	7,744	9.381
39	1,521	6.245		89	7,921	9.434
40	1,600	6.325		90	8,100	9.487
41	1,681	6.403		91	8,281	9.539
42	1,764	6.481		92	8,464	9.592
43	1,849	6.557		93	8,649	9.644
44	1,936	6.633		94	8,836	9.695
45	2,025	6.708		95	9,025	9.747
46	2,116	6.782		96	9,216	9.798
47	2,209	6.856		97	9,409	9.849
48	2,304	6.928		98	9,604	9.899
49	2,401	7		99	9,801	9.950
50	2,500	7.071		100	10,000	10

Trigonometric Ratios

Degrees	Sin	Cos	Tan	Degrees	Sin	Cos	Tan
0°	0.0000	1.0000	0.0000	46°	0.7193	0.6947	1.0355
1°	0.0175	0.9998	0.0175	47°	0.7314	0.6820	1.0724
2°	0.0349	0.9994	0.0349	48°	0.7431	0.6691	1.1106
3°	0.0523	0.9986	0.0524	49°	0.7547	0.6561	1.1504
4°	0.0698	0.9976	0.0699	50°	0.7660	0.6428	1.1918
5°	0.0872	0.9962	0.0875				
6°	0.1045	0.9945	0.1051	51°	0.7771	0.6293	1.2349
7°	0.1219	0.9925	0.1228	52°	0.7880	0.6157	1.2799
8°	0.1392	0.9903	0.1405	53°	0.7986	0.6018	1.3270
9°	0.1564	0.9877	0.1584	54°	0.8090	0.5878	1.3764
10°	0.1736	0.9848	0.1763	55°	0.8192	0.5736	1.4281
11°	0.1908	0.9816	0.1944	56°	0.8290	0.5592	1.4826
12°	0.2079	0.9781	0.2126	57°	0.8387	0.5446	1.5399
13°	0.2250	0.9744	0.2309	58°	0.8480	0.5299	1.6003
14°	0.2419	0.9703	0.2493	59°	0.8572	0.5150	1.6643
15°	0.2588	0.9659	0.2679	60°	0.8660	0.5000	1.7321
16°	0.2756	0.9613	0.2867	61°	0.8746	0.4848	1.8040
17°	0.2924	0.9563	0.3057	62°	0.8829	0.4695	1.8807
18°	0.3090	0.9511	0.3249	63°	0.8910	0.4540	1.9626
19°	0.3256	0.9455	0.3443	64°	0.8988	0.4384	2.0503
20°	0.3420	0.9397	0.3640	65°	0.9063	0.4226	2.1445
21°	0.3584	0.9336	0.3839	66°	0.9135	0.4067	2.2460
22°	0.3746	0.9272	0.4040	67°	0.9205	0.3907	2.3559
23°	0.3907	0.9205	0.4245	68°	0.9272	0.3746	2.4751
24°	0.4067	0.9135	0.4452	69°	0.9336	0.3584	2.6051
25°	0.4226	0.9063	0.4663	70°	0.9397	0.3420	2.7475
26°	0.4384	0.8988	0.4877	71°	0.9455	0.3256	2.9042
27°	0.4540	0.8910	0.5095	72°	0.9511	0.3090	3.0777
28°	0.4695	0.8829	0.5317	73°	0.9563	0.2924	3.2709
29°	0.4848	0.8746	0.5543	74°	0.9613	0.2756	3.4874
30°	0.5000	0.8660	0.5774	75°	0.9659	0.2588	3.7321
31°	0.5150	0.8572	0.6009	76°	0.9703	0.2419	4.0108
32°	0.5299	0.8480	0.6249	77°	0.9744	0.2250	4.3315
33°	0.5446	0.8387	0.6494	78°	0.9781	0.2079	4.7046
34°	0.5592	0.8290	0.6745	79°	0.9816	0.1908	5.1446
35°	0.5736	0.8192	0.7002	80°	0.9848	0.1736	5.6713
36°	0.5878	0.8090	0.7265	81°	0.9877	0.1564	6.3138
37°	0.6018	0.7986	0.7536	82°	0.9903	0.1392	7.1154
38°	0.6157	0.7880	0.7813	83°	0.9925	0.1219	8.1443
39°	0.6293	0.7771	0.8098	84°	0.9945	0.1045	9.5144
40°	0.6428	0.7660	0.8391	85°	0.9962	0.0872	11.4301
41°	0.6561	0.7547	0.8693	86°	0.9976	0.0698	14.3007
42°	0.6691	0.7431	0.9004	87°	0.9986	0.0523	19.0811
43°	0.6820	0.7314	0.9325	88°	0.9994	0.0349	28.6363
44°	0.6947	0.7193	0.9657	89°	0.9998	0.0175	57.2900
45°	0.7071	0.7071	1.0000	90°	1.0000	0.0000	

Glossary

absolute position   Location given as coordinates. [p. 402]

absolute value   A number's distance from zero, represented by $|\ |$. Example: $|-8| = 8$. [p. 63]

acute angle   An angle measuring less than 90°. [p. 412]

Addition Property of Equality   If $a = b$, then $a + c = b + c$. [p. 141]

additive inverse   A number's opposite. The sum of additive inverses is zero. Example: 5 and -5 are additive inverses of each other. [p. 67]

adjacent leg   For an acute angle on a right triangle, the leg lying on one of the angle's sides. [p. 579]

algebraic expression   An expression involving variables, numbers, and operation symbols. Example: $2x + 17$. [p. 128]

alternate angles   Two angles formed by a transversal and each of the lines it crosses, on opposite sides of the transversal, either both interior or both exterior. [p. 417]

angle   A figure formed by two lines meeting at one point. [p. 410]

angle bisector   A line, segment, or ray that divides an angle into two congruent angles. [p. 413]

angle of rotation   The angle through which a figure turns during a rotation. [p. 594]

Angle-Side-Angle (ASA)   A rule used to determine whether triangles are congruent by comparing corresponding parts. [p. 575]

area   The number of square units contained in a figure. [p. 446]

arrangement   The order in which people, letters, numbers, or other things appear. [p. 631]

Associative Property (of Addition)   The fact that grouping does not affect the sum of two or more numbers. Example: $(a + b) + c = a + (b + c)$. [p. 69]

Associative Property (of Multiplication)   The fact that grouping does not affect the product of two or more numbers. Example: $(ab)c = a(bc)$.

bar graph   A graph using bars to represent the values of a data set. [p. 23]

base   On a three-dimensional figure, the top or bottom. [p. 462]

binomial   A two-term polynomial. [p. 533]

boundary line   On a graph of a linear inequality, the line separating points that are solutions from points that are not. [p. 207]

box-and-whisker plot   A visual way of showing median values for a data set. [p. 17]

center   The point that is the same distance from all points on a circle. [p. 456]

center of rotation   The point about which a rotation turns a figure. [p. 594]

circle   A plane figure whose points are all the same distance from its center. [p. 457]

circle graph   A graph in the form of a circle cut into wedges, also called a pie chart. [p. 274]

circular cone   A three-dimensional figure with a circular base and one vertex. [p. 469]

circumference   The distance around a circle. [p. 456]

circumscribed   A polygon with exactly one point of each side on the circumference of a circle. [p. 458]

coefficient   A constant by which a variable is multiplied. Example: in $12y$, 12 is the coefficient. [p. 146]

combination   A selection of objects from a set, without regard to order. [p. 638]

common denominator   A denominator that is the same for two or more fractions. [p. 345]

common factor   A factor shared by two numbers. Example: 7 is a common factor of 28 and 42. [p. 330]

common multiple   A multiple shared by two numbers. Example: 12 is a common multiple of 2 and 3. [p. 335]

Commutative Property (of Addition)   The fact that order does not affect the sum of two or more numbers. Example: $a + b = b + a$. [p. 69]

Commutative Property (of Multiplication)   The fact that order does not affect the product of two or more numbers. Example: $ab = ba$.

complementary   Two angles whose measures add up to 90°. [p. 412]

693

composite number An integer larger than 1 that is not prime. [p. 324]

compound event Event containing more than one outcome. Example: rolling first a 3 and then an even number with a number cube. [p. 663]

compound interest Interest based on both principal and previous interest. [p. 308]

compound statement A logical statement formed by joining two or more statements. [p. 163]

concave polygon A polygon with one or more diagonals lying outside the figure. [p. 424]

conditional probability The probability that an event B will occur, given that event A has already occurred. [p. 658]

cone A solid with one circular base. [p. 469]

congruent Two figures with the same shape and size. [p. 413]

conic projection A map projection that uses a cone shape to represent a spherical surface. [p. 499]

conjunction A logical set of statements joined by the word *AND*. [p. 163]

constant A number that does not vary. [p. 123]

constant of proportionality The quantity $\frac{y}{x}$ for two variables x and y whose ratio is constant. [p. 235]

convex polygon A polygon with all diagonals lying inside the figure. [p. 424]

coordinate system A set of intersecting number lines used to locate points. [p. 91]

coordinates A pair of numbers used to locate a point on the coordinate plane. [p. 235]

corresponding angles Matching angles on similar figures. The angles on the same side of a transversal that intersects two or more lines. [p. 417]

corresponding sides Matching sides on figures. [p. 565]

cosine For an acute angle x on a right triangle, the cosine of x is $\cos(x) = \frac{\text{adjacent leg}}{\text{hypotenuse}}$. [p. 580]

Counting Principle If a situation can occur in m ways, and a second situation can occur in n ways, then these things can occur together in $m \times n$ ways. [p. 627]

cross multiplication Multiplying opposite numerators and denominators of two ratios. [p. 243]

cross product The product of a numerator of one ratio with the denominator of another. [p. 229]

cube A 6-sided prism whose faces are congruent squares. [p. 479]

cylinder A three-dimensional figure with two parallel, congruent circles for bases. [p. 463]

cylindrical projection A map projection that uses a cylinder shape to represent a spherical surface. [p. 499]

degree For a polynomial, the value of the largest exponent of a variable. Example: the degree of $7x - x^3$ is 3. [p. 533]

dependent events Events for which the occurrence of one affects the probability of the other. [p. 663]

dependent variable The output variable for a function. [p. 513]

diagonal On a polygon, a segment connecting two vertices that do not share a side. [p. 423]

diameter The length of the segment that passes through the center of a circle and has both endpoints on the circle. [p. 457]

dilation A proportional reduction or enlargement of a figure. [p. 450]

direct variation When two variables are related by a constant ratio. [p. 555]

disjunction A logical set of statements joined by the word OR. [p. 163]

Distributive Property The fact that $a(b + c) = ab + ac$. [p. 83]

divisible Can be divided by another integer without remainder. [p. 324]

double bar graph A combination of two bar graphs, comparing two related data sets. [p. 24]

double line graph A combination of two line graphs, comparing two related data sets. [p. 25]

double stem-and-leaf diagram A stem-and-leaf comparison of two sets of data in a single diagram. [p. 7]

edge A segment where two faces of a polyhedron meet. [p. 461]

endpoint A point at the end of a line segment or ray. [p. 411]

equal ratios Ratios naming the same amount. Example: $\frac{6}{2}$ and $\frac{3}{1}$. [p. 227]

equation A statement that two numerical or variable expressions are equal. [p. 128]

equilateral triangle A triangle with three congruent sides. [p. 422]

equivalent equations Equations that are true for exactly the same variable replacements. [p. 141]

equivalent expressions Two expressions that always have the same value for the same substitutions. [p. 164]

evaluate To substitute values for variables in an expression and then simplify by applying the order of operations. [p. 128]

event A set of outcomes. Example: when a number cube is rolled, an event may be an even number turns up. [p. 646].

experiment In probability, any activity involving chance, like a coin flip. [p. 646]

experimental probability An estimated probability based on data from experiments or surveys. [p. 651]

exponent A raised number showing repeated multiplication. Example: $5^3 = 5 \cdot 5 \cdot 5$, where 3 is the exponent. [p. 96]

exponential function A nonlinear function in which an exponent is a variable. [p. 524]

exterior angles Angles formed by a transversal and the lines it crosses, outside of those lines. [p. 417]

face One of the polygon surfaces composing a polyhedron. [p. 461]

factor An integer that divides another integer without remainder. Example: 6 is a factor of 42. [p. 324]

factor tree A diagram showing how a whole number breaks into its prime factors. [p. 326]

factorial The product of all positive integers less than or equal to a number. Example: 6 factorial $= 6! = 6 \cdot 5 \cdot 4 \cdot 3 \cdot 2 \cdot 1$. [p. 633]

formula A statement of a relationship among unknown quantities. Example: $P = 2(b + h)$. [p. 123]

frequency The number of times something occurs in a survey. [p. 38]

frequency table A table showing classes of things, a tally, and the frequency with which things occur. [p. 38]

function An input-output relationship giving only one output for each input. [p. 508]

Fundamental Theorem of Arithmetic All integers greater than 1 can be written as an unique product of prime numbers. [p. 325]

geometric probability A probability based on comparing measurements of geometric figures. [p. 654]

golden rectangle Rectangle with a length to width ratio of approximately 1.618. [p. 265]

greatest common factor (GCF) The largest number that is a common factor. Example: 15 is the GCF of 45 and 60. [p. 330]

height On a pyramid, the perpendicular distance from the base to the (opposite) vertex. [p. 466]

heptagon A seven-sided polygon. [p. 421]

hexagon A six-sided polygon. [p. 421]

histogram A type of bar graph where the categories are numeric. [p. 38]

hypotenuse The side opposite the right angle in a right triangle. [p. 374]

identity For any operation, the number that keeps another number the same. 0 is the additive identity, since $a + 0 = a$, 1 is the multiplicative identity since $a \times 1 = a$. [p. 141]

independent events Events for which the occurrence of one has no effect on the probability of the other. [p. 663]

independent variable The input variable for a function. [p. 513]

inequality A mathematical sentence involving $<$, $>$, $\leq$, or $\geq$. [p. 156]

inscribed A polygon with all its vertices on the circumference of a circle. [p. 458]

integers Whole numbers and their opposites: ... $-3, -2, -1, 0, 1, 2, 3, \ldots$. [p. 63]

interest Money paid for the use of money. [p. 308]

interior angles Angles formed by a transversal and the lines it crosses, between those lines. [p. 417]

inverse variation When two variables are related by a constant product. [p. 555]

irrational number A number, such as $\sqrt{2}$, that cannot be expressed as a repeating or terminating decimal. [p. 370]

isosceles triangle A triangle with at least two congruent sides. [p. 422]

latitude A measurement in degrees east or west from the prime meridian. [p. 90]

least common multiple (LCM) The smallest number that is a common multiple. Example: 48 is the LCM of 12 and 16. [p. 335]

like terms Terms in which the same variable is raised to the same exponent. Example: $3x^2$ and $9x^2$ are like terms. [p. 537]

line A one-dimensional figure extending forever in both directions. [p. 411]

line graph A line drawn through pairs of associated numbers on a grid, usually to show changes in data over time. [p. 24]

695

line of symmetry The line that divides a figure with line symmetry into two identical halves. [p. 605]

line plot A display of data that uses stacked X's to show how many times each data value occurs. [p. 7]

line segment Part of a straight line, with two endpoints. [p. 411]

line symmetry A figure has line symmetry if one half is the mirror image of the other. [p. 605]

linear equation An equation for which the graph is a straight line. [p. 182]

linear function A function whose graph is a straight line. [p. 514]

linear inequality A mathematical sentence involving $<$, $>$, $\leq$, or $\geq$ whose graph is a region with a straight-line boundary. [p. 207]

longitude A measurement in degrees north or south from the equator. [p. 90]

lower quartile The median of the lower half of a data set. [p. 18]

mean The sum of a set of data values, divided by the number of values. [p. 11]

measure of central tendency A single value summarizing a set of numerical data. [p. 11]

median The middle value of a data set, when the values are arranged in numerical order. [p. 12]

metric system A system of measurement based on the meter, the gram, and the liter. [p. 390]

mode The most common value in a data set. [p. 13]

monomial A one-term polynomial. [p. 533]

multiple A product of a given integer and some other integer. Example: 35 is a multiple of 5, since $5 \cdot 7 = 35$. [p. 324]

multiplication property If A and B are independent events, then the probability of both occurring is given by $P(A$ and $B) = P(A) \cdot P(B)$. [p. 664]

Multiplication Property of Equality If $a = b$, then $ac = bc$. [p. 146]

multiplicative inverse If the product of two numbers is 1, each number is the multiplicative inverse of the other. Example: 6 and $\frac{1}{6}$ are multiplicative inverses. [p. 78]

mutually exclusive If either event A or B occurs, then the other cannot occur. [p. 671]

negative number A number less than zero. [p. 63]

negative slope The slope of a line slanting downward. [p. 191]

negative square root The opposite of the principal square root of a number. [p. 369]

net A pattern that could be folded to create a three-dimensional figure such as a prism. [p. 462]

nonlinear equation An equation whose graph is a curve rather than a line. [p. 213]

nonlinear function A function for which equal changes in x do not result in equal changes in y. [p. 518]

obtuse angle An angle measuring more than 90° but less than 180°. [p. 412]

octagon An eight-sided polygon. [p. 421]

opposite leg For an acute angle on a right triangle, the leg lying across from the angle. [p. 579]

opposites Two numbers on opposite sides from zero and the same distance from zero, such as 3 and -3. [p. 62]

Order of Operations The rules telling what order to do operations in: Do any operations inside grouping symbols, exponents, multiplications and divisions and additions and subtractions. [pp. 83, 97]

ordered pair A pair of numbers, such as $(-2, 8)$, used to describe a point in a coordinate system. [p. 91]

origin The point $(0, 0)$ in a coordinate system, where the x-axis and y-axis intersect. [p. 91]

outcome One of the possible equally likely results of an experiment. [p. 646]

outlier An extreme value in a data set, separated from most of the other values. [p. 12]

parabola A U-shaped or upside-down U-shaped curve, the graph of a quadratic function. [p. 518]

parallel lines Lines in a plane that never intersect. On a graph, lines with the same slope. [p. 197]

parallelogram A quadrilateral with two pairs of congruent sides. [p. 423]

pentagon A five-sided polygon. [p. 421]

percent A ratio comparing a number to 100. Example: 63% means $\frac{63}{100}$. [p. 274]

percent decrease The decrease in an amount expressed as a percent of the original amount. [p. 300]

percent increase The increase in an amount expressed as a percent of the original amount. [p. 294]

perfect square A number with an integer square root. [p. 364]

perimeter The distance around a figure. [p. 444]

permutation An arrangement in which order is important. [p. 631]

perpendicular Lines forming a right angle. [p. 416]

perpendicular bisector A line, segment, or ray that is perpendicular to a line segment and divides the line segment into two congruent parts. [p. 416]

pi (π) The ratio of a circle's circumference to its diameter: 3.14159265... . [p. 457]

point symmetry Point symmetry is a kind of rotational symmetry. A figure has point symmetry if it rotates onto itself after a rotation of 180°. [p. 607]

polygon A figure formed by three or more points joined by line segments. [p. 421]

polyhedron A three-dimensional figure composed of polygons. [p. 461]

polynomial An algebraic expression that is the sum of one or more terms. [p. 532]

population The collection of all things to be studied in a survey. [p. 32]

positive number A number greater than zero. [p. 63]

positive slope The slope of a line slanting upward. [p. 191]

power A number that can be written as a product of equal factors (or, in other words, as an integer with an integer exponent). Example: $32 = 2^5$. [p. 96]

precision The exactness of a measurement, determined by the unit of measure. [p. 396]

prime factor A prime number that divides another integer without remainder. [p. 325]

prime factorization A number written as a product of prime factors. Example: $120 = 2^3 \cdot 3 \cdot 5$. [p. 326]

prime number An integer larger than 1 divisible only by itself and one. The primes start with 2, 3, 5, 7, 11, ... [p. 324]

principal An amount of money deposited or borrowed, on which interest is paid. [p. 308]

principal square root The positive square root of a number. [p. 369]

prism A polyhedron with vertical sides whose bases are congruent and parallel. [p. 462]

probability The chance that a particular event can occur. [p. 646]

proportion An equation stating that two ratios are equal. [p. 229]

pyramid A polyhedron with one base, on which all other faces are triangles meeting at a single point. [p. 466]

Pythagorean Theorem For every right triangle, the sum of the squares of each leg equals the square of the hypotenuse. [p. 374]

quadrant One of the four regions into which the x- and y-axes divide the coordinate grid. [p. 91]

quadratic function A function where the value of x is squared. The graph of a quadratic function is a parabola. [p. 518]

quadrilateral A four-sided polygon. [p. 421]

quartile One of the numbers dividing a data set into equal fourths. [p. 17]

radical sign $\sqrt{}$, the symbol for the square root of a number. [p. 364]

radius The distance from the center of a circle to any point on the circle. [p. 456]

random sample A sample chosen in such a way that every member of the population has an equal chance of being included. [p. 33]

range The difference between the highest and lowest values in a data set. [p. 6]

rate A ratio in which two quantities using different units of measure are compared. Example: 76 dollars per 8 hours. [p. 224]

ratio A comparison of two quantities by division. [p. 222]

rational number A number that can be written as a ratio of two integers, such as $\frac{2}{3}$. [p. 344]

ray Part of a straight line, with just one endpoint. [p. 411]

real numbers All rational and irrational numbers. [p. 370]

reciprocal One divided by a number. The number and its reciprocal are multiplicative inverses. [pp. 78, 357]

rectangle A quadrilateral with four right angles. [p. 423]

reflection A transformation that flips a figure over a line. [p. 594]

regular polygon A polygon with all sides and all angles congruent. [p. 424]

relative position Location given in relationship to another place. [p. 402]

repeating decimal A decimal with a repeating digit or group of digits on the right, like 5.787878... . [p. 345]

rhombus A parallelogram with four sides of equal length. [p. 423]

right angle   An angle measuring 90°. [p. 412]

right triangle   A triangle with one right angle. [p. 374]

rise   For a line on a graph, the vertical change for a given horizontal change, or run. [p. 191]

rotation   A transformation that turns a figure about a point. [p. 594]

rotational symmetry   A figure has rotational symmetry if it rotates onto itself after a rotation of less than 360°. [p. 606]

run   For a line on a graph, the horizontal change used to find the vertical change, or rise. [p. 191]

sample   The part of the population examined in a survey. [p. 32]

sample space   The set of all possible outcomes of an experiment. [p. 646]

scale   The ratio of measurements in a scale drawing to the measurements of the actual object. [p. 256]

scale drawing   A drawing showing the shape of an object exactly, but not the actual size. [p. 256]

scale factor   The ratio of new dimensions to old dimensions after a dilation. [p. 450]

scalene triangle   A triangle with no congruent sides. [p. 422]

scatterplot   A graph showing a set of points based on two data sets. [p. 43]

scientific notation   Writing a number as a power of 10 times a number whose absolute value is less than 10 but greater than or equal to 1. Example: $0.097 = 9.7 \times 10^{-2}$. [p. 102]

sequence   A patterned arrangement of numbers. [p. 113]

Side-Angle-Angle (SAA)   A rule used to determine whether triangles are congruent by comparing corresponding parts. [p. 575]

Side-Angle-Side (SAS)   A rule used to determine whether triangles are congruent by comparing corresponding parts. [p. 575]

Side-Side-Side (SSS)   A rule used to determine whether triangles are congruent by comparing corresponding parts. [p. 575]

significant digits   In a measured quantity, the digits representing the actual measurement. [p. 397]

similar   Having the same shape but not necessarily the same size. [p. 259]

similarity ratio   The ratio between corresponding side lengths on similar figures. [p. 565]

simple interest   Interest based on principal alone. [p. 308]

simplified   A polynomial containing no like terms. [p. 538]

simplify   To reduce the complexity of an expression by applying the order of operations. [p. 128]

simulation   An experimental model used to find probability. [p. 668]

sine   For an acute angle x on a right triangle, the sine of x is $\sin(x) = \frac{\text{opposite leg}}{\text{hypotenuse}}$. [p. 580]

slant height   On a pyramid, the perpendicular distance from one edge of the base to the vertex. [p. 466]

slope   For a line on a graph, the rise divided by the run. [p. 191]

solution   The variable replacement making an equation true. [p. 128]

solution of a system   The variable replacements making all equations in a system true. [p. 202]

solve   To find the variable replacement that makes an equation true. [p. 128]

sphere   A solid whose points are all the same distance from its center. [p. 479]

square   A rectangle with four sides of equal length. [p. 423]

square root   The square root of N is the number that when multiplied by itself gives N. Example: 9 is the square root of 81. [p. 364]

stem-and-leaf diagram   A display of data that uses the digits of the data numbers to show the shape and distribution of the data set. [p. 7]

step function   A function in which different rules are applied to different input values. The graph of a step function is made up of unconnected pieces. [p. 525]

straight angle   An angle measuring 180°. [p. 412]

substitute   To replace a variable with a specific value. [p. 123]

supplementary   Two angles whose measures add up to 180°. [p. 412]

surface area   On a polyhedron, the sum of the areas of the faces. [p. 461]

survey   A study that requires collecting and analyzing information. [p. 32]

symmetry   A figure has symmetry if it coincides with itself after some transformation. [p. 605]

system of linear equations   Two or more linear equations considered together. [p. 202]

tally   A quick record of a count taken during a survey. [p. 38]

tangent   For an acute angle x on a right triangle, the tangent of x is $\tan(x) = \frac{\text{opposite leg}}{\text{adjacent leg}}$. [p. 580]

term   A number in a sequence. [p. 113]

terminating decimal   A number with a fixed number of digits. [p. 345]

terms   A part of a polynomial containing a variable with a whole-number exponent and coefficient. [p. 532]

tessellation   A repeating pattern of figures that covers a plane without gaps or overlaps. [p. 610]

theoretical probability   The actual probability of an event. The ratio of the number of equally likely outcomes in the event to the number in the sample space. [p. 651]

transformation   A movement of points that affects all points of a figure. [p. 594]

translation   A transformation that slides all points of a figure the same distance in the same direction. [p. 595]

transversal   A line crossing two or more other lines. [p. 417]

trapezoid   A quadrilateral with exactly one pair of parallel sides. [p. 423]

tree diagram   A tree-like diagram on which each branch shows a possible outcome of a situation. [p. 626]

trend   A pattern formed by points on a scatterplot. [p. 43]

trend line   A line that approximately "fits" points forming a trend in a scatterplot. [p. 43]

trial   One experiment. [p. 652]

triangle   A three-sided polygon. [p. 421]

trigonometric ratios   Ratios of the side lengths of a right triangle, related to the measures of the triangle's acute angles. [p. 580]

trinomial   A three-term polynomial. [p. 533]

unit rate   A rate in which the second number in the comparison is one unit. Example: 300 million meters per second. [p. 224]

U.S. customary units   A system of measurement units, including the inch, the pound, and the gallon, widely used in the United States. [p. 390]

upper quartile   The median of the upper half of a data set. [p. 18]

variable   A symbol, such as x, that represents an unknown quantity. [p. 123]

Venn diagram   A visual aid that shows relationships by grouping things into sets. [p. 422]

vertex   On an angle or a polygon, the point where the two sides intersect. On a polyhedron, the intersection point of three or more faces. [pp. 410, 421, 461]

vertical angles   Angles on opposite sides of the intersection of two lines. [p. 418]

volume   The number of cubic units in a solid. [p. 476]

x-axis   The horizontal number line in a coordinate system. [p. 91]

x-coordinate   The first number in an ordered pair used to locate a point in a coordinate system. [p. 91]

x-intercept   The x-coordinate of the point where a graph crosses the x-axis. [p. 196]

y-axis   The vertical number line in a coordinate system. [p. 91]

y-coordinate   The second number in an ordered pair used to locate a point in a coordinate system. [p. 91]

y-intercept   The y-coordinate of the point where a graph crosses the y-axis. [p. 196]

Zero Property of Addition   The sum of an integer and its additive inverse is 0. [p. 67]

Chapter 1

1-1 Try It

Leaf	Stem	Leaf
	0	9
	1	2 4 7
9 8 6 3 2	2	1 1
6	3	

1-1 Exercises & Applications

1. a. 5 **b.** 3 or 12–15 **c.** 13; 15
3. Range: $2 to $7

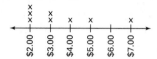

5. Range: 8 to 33

Stem	Leaf
0	8
1	2 6 8
2	2 3
3	3

7.

Leaf	Stem	Leaf
2	12	
	13	
5	14	
0	15	
5	16	0
	17	
5 5 5	18	0 0 0
	19	
5	20	0
	21	5
	22	0
	23	
	24	3

9.

Stem	Leaf
5	0 3 7
6	6
7	5 5 6
8	1
10	1
11	7

13. 437 **15.** 50,000
17. 7,030,000 **19.** 725 **21.** 8803
23. 6109 **25.** 10,500

1-2 Try It

Mean: $9; Median: $7.50

1-2 Exercises & Applications

1. a. 774 **b.** 9 **c.** 86 **3.** Mean:
180; Median: 174; Mode: None
5. Outlier: 31; Revised mean:
≈ 11.4; Revised median: 10.5
7. Mean: 91 million people **9.** C
11. Mean: $5.80 **13.** Eight hun-
dred fifty-six **15.** Four thousand
eight hundred twenty-six
17. Forty-five thousand six hundred
19. Three million seven hundred
forty-six thousand seven hundred
21. 726 **23.** 398 **25.** 3854
27. 4848

1-3 Try It (Example 1)

a. 20 or 0–20 **b.** Median: 4
c. Lower quartile: 2; Upper quartile:
10 **d.** One-quarter of the 12- to 15-
year-olds have been to a music store
between 10 and 20 times.

1-3 Try It (Example 2)

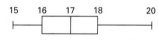

Between 16 and 18

1-3 Exercises & Applications

1. a. 100; 90 **b.** 95 **c.** 93 **d.** 99
e.

90   93 95   99 100

3. Between 20 and 24.5

16   20   22.5 24.5 25

5.

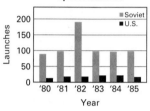

Possible answer: The middle half of
the data has a range of 1524 to
2515. **7.** With outliers **11.** 18,486
13. 19,886 **15.** 558,448
17. 274,752 **19.** 43,640
21. 37,000 **23.** 46,400

1-4 Try It (Example 1)

a. 1990 **b.** 1994

1-4 Try It (Example 4)

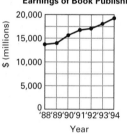

1-4 Exercises & Applications

1.

Earnings of Book Publishing

3.

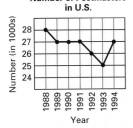

Number of Postmasters in U.S.

Probably stayed the same. **5.** D
7. Yes; all the data would still be shown. **9.** 26 **11.** 36 **13.** 7 R11
15. 578, 735, 2378, 4321 **17.** 4257, 4527, 4725 **19.** 642, 654, 664, 684

Section 1A Review

1. Mean: 3.8; Median: 5; Mode: 5

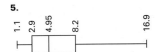

3. 140,400 km²; 6.47 million

5.

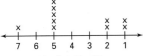

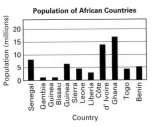

Population of African Countries

7. (44 × 6595 + 7462) ÷ 45 = (about) 6614 fans

1-5 Try It

a. 679 **b.** No: a person who is on-line had a better chance of being surveyed than a person who is not.

1-5 Exercises & Applications

1. City households; 2301 **3.** U.S. state governors; Random
5. Country music fans; Not random
7. No; Sample is too small.
9. a. Women **b.** 7244 **11.** No; Possible answers: Only people who respond to surveys responded.
13. Possible answer: Advertisers want to influence buyers, not users.
15. 56,460 **17.** 974,352

1-6 Try It (Example 1)

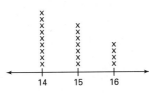

1-6 Try It (Example 2)

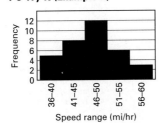

Speed range (mi/hr)

1-6 Exercises & Applications

1. a.

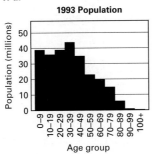

1993 Population

Age group

b. No, the frequency table gives intervals instead of exact ages.
c. A histogram

5.

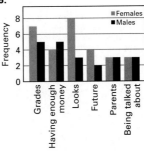

Number one worry

7. 2,066,592 **9.** 5,975,692
11. 1,758,591 **13.** 1,367,888
15. Mean: ≈ 55.44; Median: 64
17. Mean: 75.5; Median: 75.5

1-7 Try It (Example 1)

As the total waste increases, the amount recycled increases.

1-7 Try It (Example 2)

a. No **b.** No relationship

1-7 Exercises & Applications

1. a. No trend **b.** Yes, positive
c. Yes, negative
3.

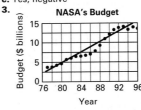

NASA's Budget

Year

$17 billion **5.** D **9.** Yes
11. 891,488 **13.** 15,251,067,288
15. 77,732,551,971

701

1-8 Try It

a. How many hours do you spend on homework each week?
b. Possible answer: Pick names randomly.   **c.** Possible answer: A box-and-whisker plot.

1-8 Exercises & Applications

1. a. U.S. teenagers   **b.** To get U.S. teenagers to buy more of the company's shoes.   **c.** No, since New Yorkers might have different music tastes than the rest of the country.
3. Possible answer: What sports do you participate in?   **5.** Possible answer: How many TVs are in your home?   **7.** B   **11.** 32,768
13. 161,051   **15.** 7,311,616

Section 1B Review

1. a. Not random; Every 1st through 49th car.   **b.** Not random; Students who aren't the student's friends.
3.

Wait time (sec)	Frequency
0–60	4
61–120	6
121–180	3
181–240	1
241 +	1

Yes; The average wait time is about 112 seconds.   **5.** D

Chapter 1 Summary & Review

1.

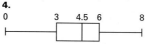

2.

Stem	Leaf
0	67
1	334
2	1227

3. 16; 15.7; 14.9
4.

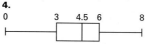

5.

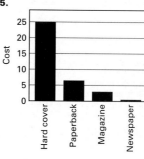

6.

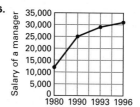

7. Answers may vary.   **8.** No, not all American adults read *TV Guide*.
9. Fiction: 1400; Non-Fiction: 1600; Reference: 1200; Multimedia: 500; Periodicals: 200   **10.** 1985: 200 books; 1986: 250 books; 1987: 300 books; 1988: 400 books; 1989: 300 books; 1990: 200 books

11.

0	1
1	1
2	3
4	1
5	3
6	2
7	2

12.

1	1
2	1
3	3
5	2
6	1
7	3
9	2

13.

1.57	2
2.45	1
2.74	1
5.35	3
7.39	1

14.

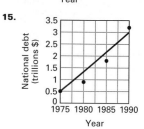

15.

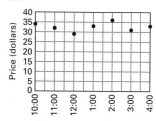

16.

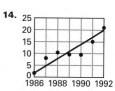

Chapter 2

2-1 Try It (Example 1)

a. 3   **b.** −$3   **c.** 0

2-1 Try It (Example 2)

17, −17

2-1 Try It (Example 3)

Belgium, Denmark, France

2-1 Exercises & Applications

1. a.

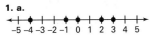

-5 -4 -3 -2 -1 0 1 2 3 4 5

b. −4 **c.** −4, −1, 0, 2, 3 **3.** 42
5. 0 **7.** Possible answer:
Temperature on a winter day is 25°
below zero. **9.** Possible answer:
Owe $60. **11.** Possible answer:
Deducted 75 points. **13.** D **15.** =
17. < **19.** > **21.** > **23.** 18
25. 2 **27.** 19,340 ft **29.** C
31. Possible answer: −$0.08
33. Random

2-2 Try It (Example 1)

a. 8 **b.** 2 **c.** −2 **d.** −8

2-2 Try It (Example 4)

a. 11 **b.** −22

2-2 Exercises & Applications

1. a. −2 + 2 + (−4) + (−3) + 5
b. (−2 + 2) + [(−4) + (−3)] + 5
c. 0 + (−7) + 5 **d.** −2 **3.** 3 + −5 =
−2 **5.** −62 **7.** −6 **9.** −142
11. −48 **13.** −125 **15.** A
17. Never **19.** Always **21.** 327
gold bars **25.** It will be on the 29th
floor. (Maybe the 30th floor because
many buildings do not have a 13th
floor.)
27. No trend

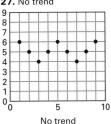

No trend

29. Women **31.** People who live in
warm climates.

2-3 Try It (Example 2)

a. −12 **b.** −12 **c.** 12 **d.** 12

2-3 Try It (Example 3)

a. −31 **b.** Rose 25 ft

2-3 Exercises & Applications

1. a. −2 **b.** 9 **c.** −10 **3. a.** 12 +
−24 = −12 **b.** −24 + −12 = −36
c. 24 + 12 = 36 **d.** −12 + 24 = 12
5. −148 **7.** −110 **9.** 967 **11.** −2
13. −48 **15.** 420 **17.** No
19. 1165°F **21.** D **23. a.** >; 5 is
added on the left. **b.** <; 5 is added
on the right.

25.

Stem	Leaf
3	2 4 8
4	1 2 2 6
5	3 8

2-4 Try It (Example 1)

−$10.00

2-4 Try It (Example 3)

a. $\frac{1}{-8}$ **b.** $\frac{5}{2}$ **c.** $\frac{3}{-8}$

2-4 Exercises & Applications

1. a. 78 **b.** −78 **3.** 48 **5.** −48
7. −12 **9.** −12 **11.** −14 **13.** 2
15. 0 **17.** −140 **19.** 0 **21.** −9
23. 0 **25.** 14 **27.** 28 **29.** C
31. $61 loss per month **33.** 100
35. Commutative **37.** −14°F
39. a. Positive **b.** Negative
41. $47\frac{2}{3}$; 47

2-5 Try It (Example 1)

10

2-5 Try It (Example 2)

a. −24 **b.** −792

2-5 Exercises & Applications

1. a. Multiplication **b.** Addition
c. Division **d.** Addition **3.** 22, 22
5. −12, −12 **7.** −9, −1 **9.** 90
11. −81 **13.** $36.44 **15.** 20
17. 1 **19.** 2° **21.** 100 + 24 ÷
(3 + 1) = 106 **23.** −5 × (3 + 3 × 6) =
−105 **25.** 1.8 in. **27.** Possible
answers: 3 ÷ 3 = 1; $\frac{3+3}{3+3}$ = 1; 3 − 3 +
3 ÷ 3 = 1 **29. a.** 36(100 + 1)
b. 50(100 − 1) **c.** (50 − 1)13
d. (100 − 2)42
31.

78 85.5 92 97.5   115

33.

Length (in.)	Frequency
1–8	6
9–16	4
17–24	8
25–32	3
33–40	5

Section 2A Review

1. a. 10°, 20°, 30°, 40°, 50° **b.** −10°,
−20°, −30°, −40° **c.** 10°, −10°; 20°,
−20°; 30°, −30°; 40°, −40° **d.** 50°
e. −40° **3.** −612 **5.** −1,326 **7.** 3
9. −9 **11.** 100 **13.** 10 **15.** 0
17. −500 **19.** −3 **21.** 5 **23.** −1
25. 682,650 **27.** C

2-6 Try It (Example 1)

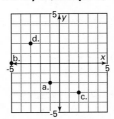

2-6 Try It (Example 2)

A is (2, 4); The low tide was 2, the
high tide was 4.

B is (−4, −1); The low tide was −4,
the high tide was −1.

C is (−7, −1); The low tide was −7,
the high tide was −1.

D is (0, 3); The low tide was 0, the
high tide was 3.

2-6 Exercises & Applications

1. a. *x* **b.** Left; −2 is negative.
c. *x* **d.** Down; −4 is negative.
2–5.

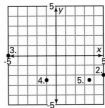

7. (1, 3) **9.** (−2, −3) **11.** (6, 0)
13. G **15.** K **17.** 24° S, 46° W
19. 19° N, 73° E
21.

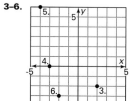

23. (−1, 2), (1, 4), (1, 0), (3, 0), (3, 4),
(5, 2); Hexagon **25. a.** II **b.** I
c. III **d.** IV **29.** 317 **31.** 22

2-7 Try It (Example 2)

a. 625 **b.** 759,375 **c.** −8

2-7 Try It (Example 3)

a. 4 **b.** 18 **c.** 255 characters

2-7 Exercises & Applications

1. a. 8 **b.** 4 **c.** 4 **d.** 4,096 **3.** 9
5. 64 **7.** 8 **9.** 125 **11.** 24,900 mi
and 9860 mi **13.** 49 **15.** 1
17. −1 **19.** 16 **21.** 1 **23.** 0
25. −20 **27.** 11 ft **29.** 8, −8
31. 3 **35.** Random **37.** 6
39. −38

2-8 Try It (Example 1)

a. 326,000,000; 3.26×10^8
b. 98,000,000; 9.8×10^7

2-8 Try It (Example 2)

$15 \times 1,000,000$; 1.5 ⊠ 10 ⌃ 7

2-8 Try It (Example 3)

a. 96,000,000,000
b. −3,800,000,000,000
c. 10,200,000,000,000

2-8 Exercises & Applications

1. a. 28,000,000 **b.** 7 **c.** 7
3. 9.36×10^8 **5.** 8.11×10^7
7. 1,200,000,000 **9.** 74,400,000
11. 9,140,000,000 **13.** 18,000,000
15. a. 3.4×10^5; $10^5 > 10^4$ **b.** 8.9×10^5; 8.9 > 3.95 **c.** 1.2×10^2; −4.6 is

negative **d.** 1.1×10^8; $10^8 > 10^7$
17. 130,200 km; 143,000 − 12,800
19. a. 10,536 hr **b.** 6.3216×10^5
min **27.** −12 **29.** −74

2-9 Try It (Example 2)

a. 1×10^{-6} **b.** 3×10^{-5}

2-9 Try It (Examples 3–4)

a. 0.000000003 or 3.0×10^{-9}
b. $8 \div 1,000,000 = 8$ ⊠ 10 ⌃ 6
+/−

2-9 Exercises & Applications

1. a. 0.00035 **b.** 4; right **c.** −4
3. C **5.** 4.55×10^{-3} **7.** 2.54×10^{-1} mm **9.** 7×10^{-5} m
11. 0.000000001 **13.** 3×10^{-4}
15. 0.00000004004 **17.** −0.00021
19. a. 4.4×10^2 **b.** 1.95×10^{-3}
c. 1.5×10^{-2} **d.** 9.8×10^{-7}
21. 0.000000000316 m **23.** b, a, c,
d **27.** −48 **29.** −60 **31.** −4
33. 6

Section 2B Review

1. 33° S, 71° W
3–6.

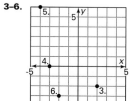

7. 16 units^2 **11.** 475,000
13. 4,140,000 **15.** 0.00019 **17.** d,
a, b, c

Chapter 2 Summary & Review

1. 43 **2.** 4 **3.** 57 **4.** 34 **5.** −144
6. 2,088 **7.** 8 **8.** −8 **9.** 15
10. −24°F **11. a.** (4, 1) **b.** (0, 0)
c. (−2, 3) **12.** A(−5, −5), B(−1, 0),
C(3, −2) **13.** $4 \times 4 \times 4 \times 4 \times 4 \times 4$
14. 7^4 **15.** 15 **16.** −27
17. 3.5×10^5 **18.** 2×10^{-4}
19. 0.0000725 **20.** 378,000
21. 7.76×10^7 **22.** 3.4×10^{-6}
23. 9×10^{-6} mm **24.** 9.5×10^5 gal

**Cumulative Review
Chapters 1–2**

1. D **2.** A **3.** C **4.** B **5.** C **6.** B
7. C **8.** C **9.** B **10.** A

Chapter 3

3-1 Try It (Example 3)

a. 2.5 hr; ≈ 1.4 hr; ≈ 0.65 hr
b. Yes; The temperature will be
−5°C, which is below freezing.

3-1 Exercises & Applications

1. $r = \frac{d}{t}$; 200 mi/hr **2.** $t = \frac{d}{r}$; 4 min
3. $d = rt$; 165 mi **4.** $r = \frac{d}{t}$;
4.55 m/min **5.** 3515 **7.** 3136
9. 68 **11.** $0.99 **13.** ≈ 107.8 mi/hr
17. C **19. a.** 4.72 hr; 5.26 hr;
5.68 hr **b.** No

3-2 Try It

a. 20 **b.** 8

3-2 Exercises & Applications

1. a. 16 **b.** 640 **c.** 890 **3.** 336
5. 102 **7.** 95 **9.** 2196 **11.** 7
13. 4 **15.** −20 **17.** −5 **19.** 66
games **21.** 12.5 times **23.** B
25. a. $A + 0.5Z$ **b.** Yes
27. Mean: 40.64; Median: 42.8
29. 0 **31.** 13 **33.** 2 **35.** 4

3-3 Try It (Examples 1–2)

a. If b is the weight of the hummingbird, then 100,000b is the weight of
the ostrich. **b.** C = 100 + 2s; $124,
$140, $196

3-3 Try It (Example 3)

4.5 + y; 0.05(4.5 + y) = 0.225 + 0.05y
miles

3-3 Exercises & Applications

1. c **2.** a **3.** e **4.** d **5.** b **6.** f
7. 3t **9.** $\frac{i}{36}$ **11.** 9n = 10n − n
13. m = (a + b + c) ÷ 3
17. a. About 670 mi/hr **b.** About
675 mi/hr **c.** Yes **21.** 7 **23.** 4
25. 0 **27.** −19

Section 3A Review

1. 50 **3.** 169 **5.** ≈ 52.6 mi/hr
7. 390 **9.** 105.6 **11.** 36 **13.** 12
15. −9 **17.** 120 + (5 − 2) • 85;
≈ 375 g **19.** C

3-4 Try It

a. 18 **b.** 21 **c.** 505 **d.** −145
e. −7 **f.** −12°F

3-4 Exercises & Applications

1. Take 3 blocks from each side.
2. Take 3 blocks from each side.
3. Add 5 to each side. **5.** Add 6 to
each side. **7.** 15 **9.** 15 **11.** 37
13. 6 **15.** −7 **17.** 37 **19.** $7\frac{1}{2}$
21. 32 **23.** 70 watts **25.** 139
27. a. 500 + x = 5500; 5000 watts
b. 100 + x = 3000; 2900 watts
31. 11 **33.** 6

3-5 Try It

a. 9 **b.** −180 **c.** 21

3-5 Exercises & Applications

1. Divide by 10. **2.** Multiply by 6.
3. Multiply by 4. **4.** Multiply by $\frac{3}{2}$.
5. 3 **7.** 9 **9.** 32 **11.** 6.8 **13.** $\frac{1}{2}$
15. 90 **17.** 1 **19.** 20 **21.** −15.5
23. 12.5 **25.** 0.05 **27.** A
29. ≈ $41\frac{2}{3}$ hr **31.** About 53 times
as efficient. **35.** People with telephones **37.** −54 **39.** −6

3-6 Try It (Examples 1–2)

a. 5 **b.** 6.5 **c.** 30 **d.** 30

3-6 Try It (Example 3)

$9x$ + 10 = 75; ≈ 7.22 months

3-6 Exercises & Applications

1. Add 5 **2.** Subtract 6 **3.** Add 3
4. Subtract 5 **5. a.** 5, 5 **b.** 24
c. 6 **7.** 7 **9.** −1 **11.** 6 **13.** 3
15. 20 **17.** 42 **19.** 9 **21.** 0
23. 180 kWh **25.** 127.5 hr **27.** C
31. 2 hours **33.** $42.05; $32.94
35. −17 **37.** −3 **39.** 16
41. 1331 **43.** −1

3-7 Try It

a.

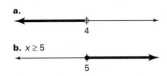

4

b. $x \geq 5$

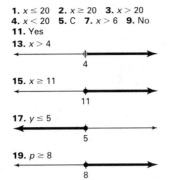

5

3-7 Exercises & Applications

1. $x \leq 20$ **2.** $x \geq 20$ **3.** $x > 20$
4. $x < 20$ **5.** C **7.** $x > 6$ **9.** No
11. Yes
13. $x > 4$

4

15. $x \geq 11$

11

17. $y \leq 5$

5

19. $p \geq 8$

8

21. $z \geq 5.25$

5.25

23. $n \leq 6\frac{2}{3}$

$6\frac{2}{3}$

25. $x \leq 0.5$ ft **27.** At least $120
33. 73,200,000 **35.** 9,373,400,000,000
37. 1.6384×10^4 **39.** 1.44×10^4

Section 3B Review

1. 25 **3.** 15 **5.** 60 **7.** 60
9. 188.9 kWh
11.

10

13.

2

15. 84 **17.** 108 **19.** Because the
two bears eat up to 105 lb/day.
21. B

Chapter 3 Summary & Review

1. $m = \frac{d}{f}$ **2.** $5.95x$ + 3.00

3. 15.625 cubic centimeters
4. $-5w$ + 35 **5.** −74 **6.** b = 516.6
7. p = 16 **8.** 440°F **9.** Only for
x = 3 **10.** b = 91 **11.** n = 34
12. w = 4.68 **13.** 0.0825 = x
14. 140 = k **15.** R = 14.4 ohms
16. x = 5 **17.** $v < 38$ **18.** 7.28 ≤ z
19. $h \geq 5$

5

Chapter 4

4-1 Try It (Examples 1–2)

d	A
0	0
1	50
2	100
3	150

4-1 Try It (Example 3)

$y = 30x$; y = 1500 when x = 50

4-1 Exercises & Applications

1. a. $y = 12x$ **b.** $y = 12 \times 5$
c. y = 60 **3.** 8 **5.** −5
7.

x	0	1	2	3	4	5
$y = -6x$	0	−6	−12	−18	−24	−30

9.

x	0	1	2	3	4	5
$y = x - 8$	−8	−7	−6	−5	−4	−3

11.

x	0	1	2	3	4	5
$y = -10x$	0	−10	−20	−30	−40	−50

13.

x	0	1	2	3	4	5
$y = x - 15$	−15	−14	−13	−12	−11	−10

15. $y = -7x$; −140
17. $y = x - 3$; 17
19.

x	1	2	3	4	5
y	3	4	5	6	7

23.

g	10	20	30	40
f	20	40	60	80

705

b. $f = 2g$, where g is the number of gallons and f is the maximum number of fish. **25.** 12 **27.** −419 **29.** 8^6

4-2 Try It (Examples 1–2)

a. No **b.** Possible answer: (4, 0), (6, −1)

4-2 Try It (Example 3)

a. $150 **b.** $1735

4-2 Exercises & Applications

1. a. Yes **b.** Yes **c.** No **3. a.** Yes **b.** No **c.** Yes **5. a.** No **b.** No **c.** Yes **7. a.** No **b.** Yes **c.** Yes **9. a.** No **b.** No **c.** Yes **11–17.** Possible answers given: **11.** (0, 2), (1, 3) **13.** (0, 3), (1, 5) **15.** (0, 2), (2, 12) **17.** (1, 8), (2, 7)

19.

Number of Toppings	Price
1	$ 8.25
2	$ 9.00
3	$ 9.75
4	$10.50

21. Possible answer: (20, 12), (30, 13), (40, 14) **23. a.** $y = \frac{1}{4}x$ **b.** 75 pounds **c.** 800 pounds **25.** They are all ordered pairs in which the x-coordinate and y-coordinate are equal. **27.** 46 **29.** 0 **31.** C

4-3 Try It (Example 1)

Possible points on line: (2, 5) and (4, 7)
For (2, 5), $5 = 2 + 3$
For (4, 7), $7 = 4 + 3$
Possible point not on line: (0, 5)
For (0, 5), $5 \neq 0 + 3$

4-3 Try It (Example 2)

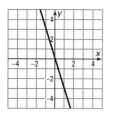

4-3 Exercises & Applications

1. 1; 2; Does

a.

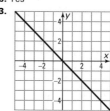

b. Yes

3.

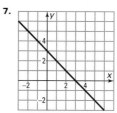

5.

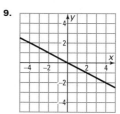

7.

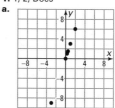

9.

11.

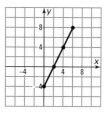

Graph is linear.

13.

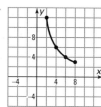

Graph is not linear.

15.

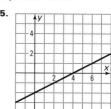

17. a.

x	1	2	3	4
y	22	24	26	28

b. Yes

c.

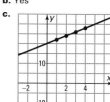

706

19. $c = 2p$, where c is cubic feet of space needed and p is pounds of scraps added per day.

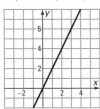

21. 360 **23.** −0.01 **25.** 4.107 × 10^5 **27.** 9.4 × 10^{-2}

Section 4A Review

1. 56 **3.** 3

5.
x	0	1	2	3	4
y	0	−3	−6	−9	−12

7.
x	0	1	2	3	4
y	0	2.5	5	7.5	10

9. a. No **b.** Yes **c.** No
11. $y = 4x$; 240
13.

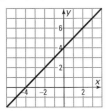

15. C

4-4 Try It (Example 1)

0.35; No

4-4 Try It (Example 2)

−2

4-4 Try It (Example 3)

a.

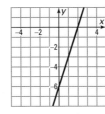

b.

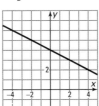

4-4 Exercises & Applications

1. Rise; Run **2.** 4, 2, 2 **3.** $\frac{1}{8}$
5. $-\frac{1}{5}$ **7.** $\frac{2}{5}$ **9.** $\frac{4}{3}$
11.

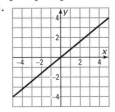

13.

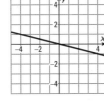

15. $\frac{1}{12}$ **17.** $\frac{rise}{run}$ is about 0.6

19. a. $\frac{1}{4}$; $\frac{1}{2}$; $\frac{2}{5}$; $\frac{1}{4}$ **b.** Diamond Peak and Bear Valley **21.** Horizontal: $\frac{rise}{run} = \frac{0}{run} = 0$; Vertical: $\frac{rise}{run} = \frac{rise}{0}$, and division by 0 is not defined.

23. −41 **25.** $A = 63$

4-5 Try It

a. 3; 2; −6

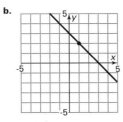

b. $-\frac{1}{2}$; 8; 4

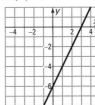

4-5 Exercises & Applications

1. 2; 4; $\frac{1}{2}$ **2.** −4 **3.** 2 **5.** 2; −1; 2
7. 1; 0; 0
9. 2; 3; −6

707

11. −1; 0; 0

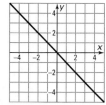

13. 5; $-\frac{2}{5}$; 2

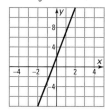

15. $\frac{1}{2}$; 4; −2

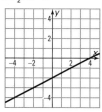

17. A
19.

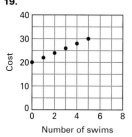

21. 1800 ft; 450 ft per hr   **25.** −46
27. 90   **29.** 40   **31.** 6

4-6 Try It

a. 2 rides   **b.** 10 rides

4-6 Exercises & Applications

1. a. Yes   **b.** Yes
3.

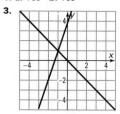

(−1, 1)

5.

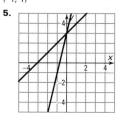

(0, 3)

7.

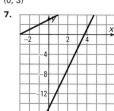

(6, 9)

9.

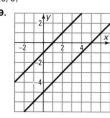

No solution

11.

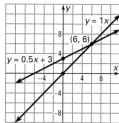

Each side has 6 oz on it.   **13.** For 5
times, the cost is the same either
way. For 6 times, the cost is $55 for
the first plan, but $60 for the second.
So she should take the first plan.
15. The cost is $48 in either case. It
doesn't matter.   **17.** −48   **19.** −8
21. $D + 4$ **23.** $2p + 17$

4-7 Try It (Examples 1–2)

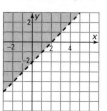

4-7 Try It (Example 3)

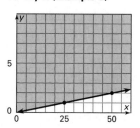

At least 11 teachers

4-7 Exercises & Applications

1. D   **2.** C   **3.** A   **4.** B   **5. a.** No
b. No   **c.** No

708

7.

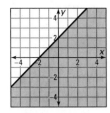

9.

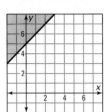

11.

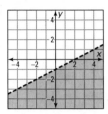

13.

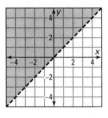

15. y = teachers, x = students
17. $n \geq 4x$, where n is the number of calories and x is the weight in grams.

19.

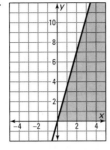

21. No
23.

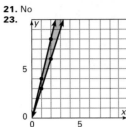

27. 8^2 **29.** 2^3 **31.** 32 **33.** 3
35. 0.06 **37.** $-\frac{1}{8}$

Section 4B Review

1. 2; 1; -2
3.

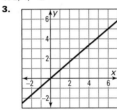

5.

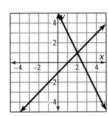

(2, 1)

7.

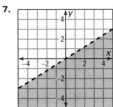

9. $y > 2x$

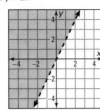

11. Substitute the coordinates for the ordered pair into the equation or inequality. If the resulting statement is true, the ordered pair is a solution.

Chapter 4 Summary & Review

1. $y = -15$
2.

x	0	1	2	3	4	5
y	4	5	6	7	8	9

3. $y = -7x$; $y = -161$ **4. a.** No
b. Yes **c.** No **5.** Possible answer: (0, 15), (5, 0)
6.

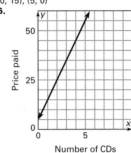

Number of CDs

709

7. a.

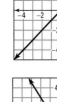

b.

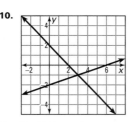

8. a. Slope $-\frac{1}{2}$; x-intercept -2; y-intercept -1 **b.** Slope $-\frac{3}{2}$; x-intercept 2; y-intercept 3 **c.** Slope 2; x-intercept $-\frac{3}{2}$; y-intercept 3

9. Slope $\frac{3}{5}$; x-intercept 5; y-intercept -3

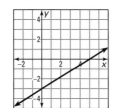

10.

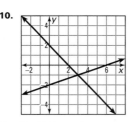

$(3, -1)$ **11.** 8 months

12. a.

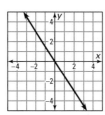

b.

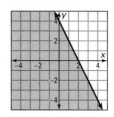

Cumulative Review
Chapters 1–4

1. B **2.** D **3.** D **4.** B **5.** C **6.** B
7. B **8.** C **9.** A **10.** C **11.** C
12. A **13.** B **14.** D **15.** B

Chapter 5

5-1 Try It (Examples 1-2)

a. 4 to 9; 5 to 9; 4 to 5; 5 to 4; 9 to 4; 9 to 5 **b.** 1:9

5-1 Try It (Example 3)

a. ≈ 0.82 **b.** $\approx 62{,}500{,}000$

5-1 Exercises & Applications

1. a. 3:4 **b.** 4:7 **c.** 7:4
3. a.

b.

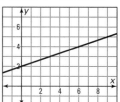

5. No **7. a.** 8:25 **b.** 21:7 or 3:1
c. 25 to 7; 7 to 25 **9.** 3:2 **11.** 2:5
13. 3:5 **15. a.** 4:5 **b.** 5:1 **c.** Yes;
When amount of stored memory
increases, available memory
decreases. **19.** 6.94×10^{-3}
21. 1×10^{-9} **23.** $x = 35$
25. $x = -6$

5-2 Try It (Examples 1-2)

a. 3; 5; 20; 150

b.

Tickets	20	40	60
Cost ($)	5	10	15

$\approx \$11$

5-2 Try It (Example 3)

a. No **b.** Yes

5-2 Exercises & Applications

1. a. $\frac{12}{36}$ **b.** $\frac{24}{72}$ **c.** $\frac{1}{3}$ **d.** $\frac{2}{6}$ **e.** $\frac{8}{24}$
3. 4; 6; 8; 10 **5.** C **7.** = **9.** $\neq$
11. $\neq$ **13.** $\neq$ **15.** No **17.** Yes,
$\frac{50}{14{,}400} = \frac{120}{34{,}560}$ **21. a.** Triangle
b. Painting **c.** Steam
d. Proportion **23.** $A = 121$
25. $F = 57.2$ **27.** $x = 54$

5-3 Try It (Example 1)

a. $\frac{4}{1}, \frac{8}{2}, \frac{12}{3}, \frac{16}{4}, \frac{20}{5}$ **b.** 40; 80
c. If $y =$ number of pages and
$x =$ time, $y = 4x$.

5-3 Try It (Example 2)

a. $k = 2$
x 5 10 15
y 10 20 30

b. 2; They are the same.

5-3 Try It (Example 3)

a. The graph does not show a
proportional relationship.

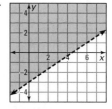

710

b. The graph shows a proportional relationship.

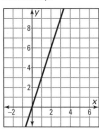

5-3 Exercises & Applications

1. a. $\frac{y}{x} = 3$ **b.** $\frac{y}{x} = 10$ **c.** $\frac{y}{x} = 0.5$
3. Yes, $k = 6$ **5.** Yes, $k = 11$ **7.** 5
9. 2; 2 cost $5.34 and 3 cost $8.01
11. a. 5 **b.** $k = 5$ **c.** $p = 5h$
d. $85.00
13.

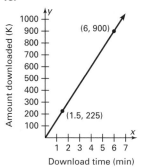

15. 69 **17.** 175 **19.** Yes **21.** Yes

Section 5A Review

1. 2:6 = 1:3 **3.** 1:5 **5.** $\neq$ **7.** $\neq$
9. 18, 27, 45, 54 **11. a.** 3:2
b. Word proc. to video games.
c. Educ. programs to homework.
13. C

5-4 Try It

5000 films

5-4 Exercises & Applications

1. a. 7×3 **b.** 21 **c.** 21 **d.** $5\frac{1}{4}$
3. $\frac{12}{x} = \frac{8}{2.50}$ **5.** 75 **7.** 12 **9.** B

---

11. D **13.** 8 **15.** 31 **17.** 20
19. 8 **21.** C **23.** No; $\frac{2}{22} \neq \frac{1}{7}$
25. $\approx$ 23 ft **27.** $x = 3$ **29.** $x = 3\frac{1}{3}$
31. 24 cm, 20 cm, 12 cm
33. 2.3884×10^5 **35.** -42 **37.** 5

5-5 Try It (Example 1)

$1,368

5-5 Try It (Example 2)

75 ounces for $8.99

5-5 Try It (Example 3)

a. 2880 frames; 25 seconds
b. $F = 30s$; 300 seconds (5 min)

5-5 Exercises & Applications

1. a. 30 **b.** $d = 30t$ **c.** $d = 30 \cdot 7$;
$d = 210$ mi **3.** 40 words per
minute; $W = 40m$ **5.** 55 miles per
hour; $M = 55h$ **7.** $40,000 per day;
$C = 40,000d$ **9. a.** $2.88 per lb
b. $3.59 per lb **11.** ≈ 10.5 **13.** A
6 oz box for $1.25 **15.** $\frac{1}{4}$ lb for $2.00
17. Yes; The average height of each
floor is about 12.2 ft **21. a.** about
400 **b.** Hire 35 more teachers
23. 0.0084 **25.** Possible answers:
(1, 6); (2, 7) **27.** Possible answers:
(1, –5); (2, –4)

5-6 Try It

120 frames; 30 fps

5-6 Exercises & Applications

1. a. 360 **b.** 5 **c.** 12 **3.** A and B
5. a. $\approx$ 95.3 million **b.** $\approx$ 953,000
7. $\frac{2}{4} = \frac{4}{8}, \frac{4}{8} = \frac{8}{16}, \frac{8}{16} = \frac{16}{32}, \frac{16}{32} = \frac{2}{4}, \frac{2}{4} = \frac{16}{32}, \frac{2}{8} = \frac{4}{16}, \frac{4}{16} = \frac{8}{32}, \frac{2}{16} = \frac{4}{32}, \frac{4}{32} = \frac{2}{16}, \frac{4}{32} = \frac{16}{32}$

and all reciprocals of these.
9. 236 in. **11.** 840 ft

5-7 Try It (Example 3)

Possible answer: 1 in. = 10 ft

5-7 Try It (Examples 4-5)

12.5

5-7 Exercises & Applications

1. a. Shape; Size **b.** Sizes; Shape
3. 1200 mi **5.** $\approx$ 2520 mi **7.** 30 cm
9. 13.425 cm **11.** $\frac{1}{32}$ in. **13.** 24 ft
15. 10.8 **17.** $b = 15$, $c = 9$, $a = 10$
21. About 24 in. **23.** $x = -16$
25. $r = 45$

Section 5B Review

1. $\frac{10 \text{ bottles}}{x} = \frac{6 \text{ bottles}}{1.99}$; $x = 3.32$
3. 80 **5.** 40 **7.** 560 **9.** Possible
answer: $P = 22.5n$ **11.** $a = 2.5$;
$b = 4$; $c = 2$ **13.** 5 ft

Chapter 5 Summary & Review

1. $\frac{3}{7}$

2.

3. Red area to total area: 2:5. Total
area to red area: 5:2. Blue area to
total area: 3:5. Total area to blue
area: 5:3. Red area to blue area: 2:3.
Blue area to red area: 3:2. **4.** Not
equal **5.** No

6.

4	8	12	16	20	24
5	10	15	20	25	30

7. $x = 60$ **8.** $u = 77$ **9.** 3 gallons
per hour; $g = 3h$, where g is the
number of gallons and h is the number of hours. **10.** About 350 mi.
11. 231 pairs of blue shoes.
12. 5166 comedy videos. **13.** 7.5 ft
tall and 17.5 ft across. **14.** $x = 12$;
$z = 22.5$

Chapter 6

6-1 Try It (Example 3)

a. 82% **b.** 12.5% **c.** 50%
d. 12.5% **e.** 0.6%

6-1 Try It (Example 4)

a. $\frac{12}{100} = \frac{3}{25}$; 0.12 **b.** $\frac{45}{1000} = \frac{9}{200}$;
0.045 **c.** $\frac{200}{100} = 2$; 2.00

711

6-1 Exercises & Applications

1. a. $\frac{74}{100} = \frac{37}{50}$ **b.** 0.74 **c.** 74%
2. a. $\frac{1}{4}$ **b.** 0.25 **c.** 25%
3. Possible Answer:

5. 80% **7.** 120% **9.** 0.35% **11.** $\frac{49}{50}$; 0.98 **13.** $\frac{3}{40}$; 0.075 **15.** $\frac{7}{5} = 1\frac{2}{5}$; 1.40 **17.** $\frac{3}{400}$; 0.0075 **19.** No; The risk is too high. **21.** 20% off; It is the largest reduction. **23.** 70%; 20%; 10% **25.** 90% of 50 = 45; The student answered 45 correctly. **27. a.** 50%; 25%, 50%, and 75%. **b.** You scored better than 9500 students.

6-2 Try It (Example 3)

1. a. 12.5% **b.** 36 **c.** 90

6-2 Try It (Example 4)

3200 oz = 200 lb

6-2 Exercises & Applications

1. $\frac{12}{x} = \frac{40}{100}$ **3.** 4 **5.** 22 **7.** $33\frac{1}{3}$% **9.** 200% **11.** 20 **13.** 1.25 **15.** 435 students **17. a.** 16 passengers **b.** 104 **c.** U.S. **19.** 1% **21.** Iron **23.** 30% **25.** $\frac{(a+b+c+d)}{4}$; Answers may vary.

6-3 Try It (Example 1)

a. 180 **b.** 60

6-3 Try It (Example 2)

About 80 or 90 mg

6-3 Try It (Example 3)

a. About $33\frac{1}{3}$% **b.** About 250 students

6-3 Try It (Example 4)

About 35–40%. The top part is about 25%. The bottom part is half of that or 13%. 25% + 13% = 38%.

6-3 Exercises & Applications

1. a. $\frac{1}{3}$ **b.** $\frac{1}{5}$ **c.** $\frac{1}{100}$ **d.** $\frac{1}{10}$ **3.** 25% **5.** 98% **7.** 14 **9.** 4 **11.** 30% **13.** 67% **15.** > **17.** < **19.** 0.3 g **21.** B **23.** It cannot be determined. About 75% of his serves are in bounds. **27.** $y = 19$ **29.** $p = -2$
31.

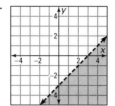

Section 6A Review

1. a. $\frac{4}{5}$; 0.8; 80% **3.** 67% **5.** 1450% **7.** 0.72; $\frac{18}{25}$ **9.** 0.1275, $\frac{51}{400}$ **11.** 0.56, $\frac{14}{25}$ **13.** 25% **15.** 12 **17.** 20% **19.** 12.5 **21.** About 60% **23.** D

6-4 Try It (Examples 1-2)

a. ≈ 50% **b.** $79.13

6-4 Try It (Example 3)

4593

6-4 Exercises & Applications

1. a. $1.20 **b.** $17.19 **c.** $17.19
3. 100% **5.** 17% **7.** 14%
9. $909.42 **11.** $21 **13.** ≈162 cm
15. January **17.** ≈ 596%
21. a. 1.2 oz **b.** 1.44 oz **c.** 12%
23. 3:5; 3:8; 5:3; 5:8; 8:3; 8:5

6-5 Try It (Example 1)

$12.23

6-5 Try It (Example 2)

20%

6-5 Try It (Example 3)

$279.75

6-5 Exercises & Applications

1. a. 78% **b.** 70% **c.** 80% **d.** 60%
3. 8% **5.** 18% **7.** 9% **9.** $1.91
11. 29 **13.** $31.25 **15.** C
19. a. $78.80; $80.38 **21.** = **23.** =

6-6 Try It (Example 2)

a. $81.72 **b. i.** $38.40 **ii.** $42.00

6-6 Try It (Example 3)

20%

6-6 Exercises & Applications

1. a. 150% **b.** $90 **c.** $90; $133\frac{1}{3}$%
d. $120 **3.** 25 **5.** 75 **7.** 100
9. 2 **11.** $49.94 **13.** $121.50
15. $100.31 **17.** 25% **19. a.** 1350
b. About 11% **21.** 12 notes
23. 37.5% **25.** $y = 19$ **27.** $a = -3$
29. $p = -\frac{1}{3}$ **31.** 17.4 **33.** 0.1

Section 6B Review

1. 25% decrease **3.** 0% (neither)
5. 33% increase **7.** $109.97 **9.** 8%
11. $44.10 **13.** $239.50 **15.** $600
17. No

Chapter 6 Summary & Review

1. $\frac{4}{5}$; 0.8; 80% **2. a.** 16% **b.** 24%
c. 60% **3.** 161 **4.** 75 **5.** 225
6. About 20% **7.** About 10%
8. About 40 **9.** About 37.2%
10. 6.5% **11.** $24.36 **12.** $221
13. About 75% **14.** $2400
15. $139,872 **16.** About 23.1%

Cumulative Review
Chapters 1–6

1. B **2.** A **3.** B **4.** D **5.** C **6.** B
7. B **8.** C **9.** A **10.** C **11.** C
12. D **13.** C **14.** B **15.** B **16.** A

Chapter 7

7-1 Try It (Example 1)

a. 2 only **b.** 2, 3, 4, 5, 6, 8, 10 **c.** 2, 4 **d.** 3, 5

7-1 Try It (Example 2-3)

a. $2 \times 3 \times 3 \times 3$ **b.** $2 \times 2 \times 3 \times 11$
c. $2 \times 2 \times 59$ **d.** $2 \times 3 \times 59$

7-1 Exercises & Applications

1. Prime **3.** Composite **5.** Prime
7. 3, 9 **9.** 2 **11.** 3, 9 **13.** 2
15. 2, 4, 8 **17.** 1, 2, 4, 8, 11, 22, 44,
88 **19.** 1, 2, 4, 5, 10, 20, 25, 50, 100
21. $2 \times 3 \times 3 \times 3$ or 2×3^3 **23.** 2^7
25. $2 \times 2 \times 5 \times 11$ or $2^2 \times 5 \times 11$
27. $3 \times 5 \times 5 \times 5$ or 3×5^3
29. 5×101 **31.** D **33.** $n = 81$
35. $w = 1250$ **37.** $2^3 \times 3^2 \times 5$
39. 34 **41.** Possible answers: $3 = 2^2 - 1$; $7 = 2^3 - 1$; $31 = 2^5 - 1$
43. Possible answers: 24, 36, 48, 600
45. B **50.** 37.5 hr or 37 hours and
30 minutes

7-2 Try It (Example 2)

a. 6 **b.** 7 **c.** 4

7-2 Try It (Examples 3-4)

a. 5 **b.** $\frac{3}{4}$

7-2 Exercises & Applications

1. a. 1, 3, 9, 27 **b.** 1, 3, 5, 9, 15, 45
c. 1, 3, 9 **d.** 9 **3.** 4 **5.** 7 **7.** 9
9. 30 **11.** 8 **13.** 4 **15.** 14 **17.** 5
19. 12 **21.** 2 **23.** $\frac{2}{5}$ **25.** $\frac{1}{4}$
27. $\frac{9}{10}$ **29.** $\frac{2}{3}$ **31.** $\frac{6}{11}$ **33.** 210,
512, 915, 972 **35.** $18 = 2 \times 3^2$
37. A **39.** Possible answers: 4 and
7; 15 and 16; 9 and 20. **41.** 1; Yes
43. Slope = 2; x-intercept = 2;
y-intercept = −4. **45.** Slope = −3;
x-intercept = $\frac{8}{3}$; y-intercept = 8.
47. Slope = −7; x-intercept = 0;
y-intercept = 0.

7-3 Try It (Example 2)

a. 30 **b.** 147 **c.** 9384

7-3 Try It (Example 4)

a. $\frac{6}{21}$ and $\frac{14}{21}$ **b.** $\frac{28}{48}$ and $\frac{15}{48}$

7-3 Exercises & Applications

1. a. 8, 16, 24, 32, 40, 48, 56, 64, 72,
80 **b.** 12, 24, 36, 48, 60, 72, 84, 96,
108, 120 **c.** 24, 48, 72 **d.** 24

3. 40 **5.** 60 **7.** 144 **9.** 60 **11.** 84
13. 88 **15.** 744 **17.** 60 **19.** 7000
21. 3432 **23.** $\frac{4}{6}$ and $\frac{1}{6}$ **25.** $\frac{3}{8}$ and $\frac{6}{8}$
27. $\frac{20}{36}$ and $\frac{15}{36}$ **29.** $\frac{45}{60}$, $\frac{40}{60}$, and $\frac{42}{60}$
31. $\frac{28}{252}$, $\frac{72}{252}$, and $\frac{105}{252}$ **33.** Every 90
days. **35.** A **37.** Multiply the two
numbers; their product is the LCM.
38. Possible answers: A 10 3 6 rectangle **41.** (−3, 8) **43.** (4, −1)
45. 176% **47.** 0.5% **49.** 320%
51. 0.3% **53.** 640% **55.** 275%
57. 0.2%

Section 7A Review

1. 2, 3, 6, 9 **3.** 2, 4, 5, 8, 10 **5.** 2, 4
7. $5^2 \times 19$ **9.** $2^4 \times 3^2$ **11.** GCF, 1;
LCM, 36 **13.** GCF, 3; LCM, 120
15. $\frac{3}{5}$ **17.** $\frac{3}{7}$ **19.** $\frac{2}{3}$ **21.** 12
23. 24 **27.** A

7-4 Try It (Example 3)

a. $0.8\overline{3}$; Repeating **b.** 0.125;
Terminating **c.** 0.75; Terminating

7-4 Try It (Example 4)

a. $\frac{15}{100}$ or $\frac{3}{20}$ **b.** $2\frac{6}{10}$ or $2\frac{3}{5}$ **c.** $\frac{46}{1000}$ or
$\frac{23}{500}$

7-4 Try It (Example 5)

a. $2\frac{13}{99}$ **b.** $\frac{8}{33}$

7-4 Try It (Example 6)

a. $-4\frac{1}{3} < -4.3$ **b.** $2.07 < 2\frac{1}{7}$

7-4 Exercises & Applications

1. a. 210 **b.** $-\frac{140}{210}$, $\frac{175}{210}$, $\frac{0}{210}$, $-\frac{120}{210}$,
$\frac{189}{210}$, $-\frac{42}{210}$, $\frac{35}{210}$ **c.** $-\frac{140}{210}$, $-\frac{120}{210}$, $-\frac{42}{210}$,
$\frac{0}{210}$, $\frac{35}{210}$, $\frac{175}{210}$, $\frac{189}{210}$ **3.** < **5.** < **7.** >
9. < **11.** 0.44; Terminating
13. $0.\overline{285714}$; Repeating **15.** $\frac{9}{20}$
17. $4\frac{14}{25}$ **19.** $2\frac{1}{3}$
21.

23. The sea cow **25.** Ana
27. 3.14084507; 3.14285714
29. $\frac{3}{8}$ **31.** Possible answer: $\frac{11}{50}$
33. Possible answer: $-\frac{62}{72}$ **35.** $12 + n$
37. $36k$ **39.** 150 **41.** 40

7-5 Try It (Example 1)

a. 111.63 **b.** 36.75 **c.** 527.05
d. 3.74

7-5 Try It (Example 3)

a. $2\frac{1}{2}$ **b.** $5\frac{5}{6}$

7-5 Try It (Example 4)

a. $-5\frac{1}{4}$ **b.** $14\frac{5}{24}$

7-5 Exercises & Applications

1. a. $\frac{24}{30}$, $\frac{25}{30}$ **b.** $\frac{49}{30}$ **c.** $1\frac{19}{30}$
3. −160.713 **5.** 164.14 **7.** $-\frac{1}{4}$
9. $-\frac{2}{15}$ **11.** $10\frac{2}{5}$ **13.** $4\frac{4}{7}$
15. $-14\frac{43}{60}$ **17.** $n = -1\frac{1}{2}$ **19.** $n = 11\frac{1}{4}$ **21.** 3.29 miles per second
23. $\frac{1}{20}$ **25.** B **29.** $x = \frac{3}{4} + \frac{3}{8} - 1\frac{1}{4} = -\frac{1}{8}$ **31.** $x = 17$ **33.** $k = -54$
35. $r = -4.9$ **37.** $n = -2.2$
39. 43%

7-6 Try It (Example 1)

a. −3.6 **b.** 56.1697

7-6 Try It (Example 2)

a. 2.24 **b.** $-68.\overline{18}$

7-6 Try It (Example 3)

a. $-3\frac{31}{48}$ **b.** 22

7-6 Try It (Example 4)

a. 4 **b.** $4\frac{1}{2}$

7-6 Exercises & Applications

1. a. $\frac{13}{4}$ **b.** $\frac{78}{4}$ **3.** 0.0072 **5.** 0.032
7. $\frac{1}{9}$ **9.** $-2\frac{1}{3}$ **11.** $\frac{1}{6}$ **13.** $1\frac{67}{115}$
15. $\frac{9}{14}$ **17.** $1\frac{2}{7}$ **19.** 150 **21.** $\frac{5}{114}$

23. ≈ 4,524,518 square miles
25. $\frac{1}{4}$ × 100 gallons **27.** A **29.** No
31. No; Possible answer: If both of the numbers are < 1, their product would have to be < 1. **33.** $x = 9$
35. $x = -44$ **37.** $x = -41$ **39.** $x = 21$ **41.** 33% **43.** 19%

Section 7B Review

1.

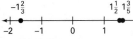

3.

$-1\frac{2}{3}$ ⋯ $1\frac{1}{2}$ $1\frac{3}{5}$

5. 0.75; Terminating
7. $11.\overline{714285}$; Repeating
9. 4.7; Terminating **11.** $3\frac{1}{200}$
13. $\frac{364}{999}$ **15.** 7.42 **17.** -0.1326
19. $\frac{1}{24}$ **21.** $1\frac{5}{8}$ **23.** $-\frac{1}{6}$ **25.** 15
27. $x = -\frac{2}{15}$ **29.** $x = \frac{3}{7}$ **31.** D

7-7 Try It (Example 1)

a. Yes **b.** No **c.** Yes **d.** No

7-7 Try It (Example 2)

a. 12 **b.** 21 **c.** 50 **d.** 91

7-7 Try It (Example 3)

a. 3 and 4; 3.2 **b.** 4 and 5; 4.6
c. 5 and 6; 5.5 **d.** 8 and 9; 8.9

Try It (Example 4)

a. $\frac{5}{8}$ **b.** $\frac{10}{25}$ **c.** $\frac{11}{18}$ **d.** $\frac{6}{15}$

7-7 Exercises & Applications

1. a. $\frac{\sqrt{9}}{\sqrt{144}}$ **b.** $\frac{3}{12}$ **c.** $\frac{1}{4}$ **3.** Yes
5. No **7.** 5 and 6 **9.** 8 and 9
11. 5 and 6 **13.** $1\frac{1}{2}$ **15.** $\frac{3}{5}$
17. ≈ 230.22 meters **19.** 9, 10
21. 12 in. **23.** 7.5 seconds
25. 8 feet **27.** Possible answers:
$(1 \cdot 2 \cdot 3 \cdot 4) + 1 = 25 = 5^2$; $(2 \cdot 3 \cdot 4 \cdot 5) + 1 = 121 = 11^2$; $(3 \cdot 4 \cdot 5 \cdot 6) + 1 = 361 = 19^2$; $(5 \cdot 6 \cdot 7 \cdot 8) + 1 =$

$1,681 = 41^2$; $(6 \cdot 7 \cdot 8 \cdot 9) + 1 = 3025 = 55^2$ **29.** Yes **37.** $\frac{11}{66}$ **39.** $\frac{3 \text{ ft}}{1 \text{ yd}}$

7-8 Try It

a. Irrational **b.** Rational; -30
c. Rational; ±74 **d.** Irrational

7-8 Exercises & Applications

1. a. 9.7467943 **b.** Irrational
3. Irrational **5.** Irrational
7. Irrational **9.** Irrational
11. Rational **13.** 3.873 **15.** 9.950
17. 15.875 **19.** 44.721 **21.** 21.354
23. ≈ 5.48 in. **25.** 6.5 m **27.** 22 ft × 22 ft **29.** A **31.** 1; 4: 1, 2, 4; 9: 1, 3, 9; 16: 1, 2, 4, 8, 16; 25: 1, 5, 25; 36: 1, 2, 3, 4, 6, 9, 12, 18, 36; 49: 1, 7, 49; 64: 1, 2, 4, 8, 16, 32, 64; 81: 1, 3, 9, 27, 81; 100: 1, 2, 4, 5, 10, 20, 25, 50, 100. Possible answers: They all have an odd number of factors.
33. 38.3 miles; No; They would see about 54.2 miles. **35.** $y = 39$
37. $y = 17$
39.

x	0	1	2	3	4	5
y	-3	-2	-1	0	1	2

41.

x	0	1	2	3	4	5
y	-4	-3	-2	-1	0	1

7-9 Try It (Example 1)

a. $c = 5$ in. **b.** $h \approx 17.69$ cm

7-9 Try It (Example 2)

a. $a \approx 9.16$ m **b.** $a \approx 10.39$ ft

7-9 Try It (Example 4)

a. $a \approx 5$ in. **b.** $c \approx 8.367$ m

7-9 Exercises & Applications

1. a. $12^2 + 16^2 = c^2$ **b.** $144 + 256 = c^2$; $400 = c^2$ **c.** $c = 20$ cm
3. $a \approx 21.07$ **5.** ≈ 7.2 ft **7.** 1600 ft
9. C **11.** Yes **13.** Yes **15. a.** 9 ft
b. ≈ 12.728 ft **17.** Possible answers: (2, 1); (6, 3) **19.** Possible answers: (10, 6); (15, 9)
21. $x = 66$ **23.** $x = 1$

Section 7C Review

1. No **3.** No **5.** Yes **7.** ≈ 8.25
9. $\frac{2}{5}$ **11.** -6 **13.** ±3.5 **15.** -3

17. Rational **19.** Rational
21. ≈ 5.66 in. **23.** 21 cm
25. ≈ 2.06 ft **27.** $m = 15$

Chapter 7 Summary & Review

1. Divisible by 2, 3, 6, and 9
2. $924 = 2^2 \times 3 \times 7 \times 11$ **3.** 3 **4.** $\frac{3}{4}$
5. 75 **6.** 60 **7.** 0.1875;
Terminating **8.** 3.806 > 3.8059
9. $\frac{3}{25}$ **10.** 18.478 **11.** $5\frac{1}{18}$ **12.** $\frac{57}{80}$
13. No **14.** $\frac{5}{6}$ **15.** 7 and 8
16. ≈ 5.657 cm **17.** ±23 **18.** -27

Chapter 8

8-1 Try It (Examples 1-2)

a. 32,000 m **b.** ≈ 1.96 mi

8-1 Try It (Example 3)

a–d. Possible answers: **a.** mL
b. min **c.** lb **d.** kg

8-1 Try It (Example 4)

a–d. Possible answers: **a.** m²
b. mm³ **c.** g **d.** mi

8-1 Exercises & Applications

1. a. $\frac{1 \text{ mi}}{5280 \text{ ft}}$ **b.** ≈ 5.5 mi **3.** mi
5. mL **7.** kg **9.** 2,500,000 mL
11. 4 lb **13.** 5 qt **15.** 15.66 g
17. A **21.** in² **23.** Composite
25. Prime **27.** Composite
29. Composite **31.** 14 **33.** 1
35. 3 **37.** 2

8-2 Try It (Example 2)

a. 2638 ft **b.** 197.5 cm **c.** 35.75 in.

8-2 Try It (Example 3)

a. 2 **b.** 6 **c.** 1 **d.** 5

8-2 Try It (Example 5)

a. 14.1 g; 3 **b.** 9.8 mL; 2 **c.** 47 in.; 2 **d.** 22 m; 2

8-2 Exercises & Applications

1. a. 3 **b.** 3 **c.** 6 **3.** 2 **5.** 5
7. 235 cm **9.** 0.25 L **11.** 3.30 hr

13. 44 mi   **15.** 49 m²   **17.** 13° C
19. 42,600 m   **23.** 21   **25.** 55
31.

33.

35. $2\frac{17}{100}$ **37.** $\frac{1}{2}$

8-3 Try It (Example 2)

a. 4 blocks east   **b.** $c - 17$

8-3 Try It (Examples 3-4)

a. Brazil   **b.** 30° N, 90° W

8-3 Exercises & Applications

1. 10C   **3.** Salt Lake City Municipal
Airport No. 2   **5.** Northeast   **7.** 4°
latitude; ≈ 1° longitude   **9.** Mt.
Everest   **11.** About 395 mi
13. About 200 mi   **15.** Answers
may vary   **17.** Possible answer:
Distance between longitude lines
decrease as you get closer to the
north and south poles because they
all intersect at the poles.   **19.** East
21. 55 mi/hr   **23.** $6 per hr
25. ≈ 2.3 children per home
27. 3.115   **29.** 140.256   **31.** $2\frac{2}{3}$

Section 8A Review

1. Liter   **3.** cm²   **5.** ≈ 4.08 hr
7. 2,500,000 mL   **9.** 28 oz   **11.** 1
13. 3   **15.** 1.89 L   **17.** 3499 in.
19. 13.6 g   **21.** 93 cm²   **23.** China
25. C

8-4 Try It (Example 1)

a. 145°   **b.** 52°

8-4 Try It (Example 2)

Acute

8-4 Try It (Examples 3-4)

a. 47.3°   **b.** 72°

8-4 Exercises & Applications

1. a. 53°; 53°   **b.** Yes   **3.** Acute
5. Acute   **7.** Acute   **9.** Straight
11. Obtuse   **13.** 68°   **15.** 80.9°
17. 60°   **19.** 90°   **21.** 120°
23. 135°   **25.** 162°   **27.** 105°
29.

31.

33. C   **35.** 157°   **37.** 60°   **41.** $x +$
$y = 180$; $y = 180 - x$; $y = 109°$
43. They are congruent. The same
two lines form the sides for both
angles.   **45.** 240   **47.** $8   **49.** 3
51. 27.51

8-5 Try It (Example 1)

$\angle DQK$ and $\angle GRL$; $\angle KQE$ and $\angle FRL$

8-5 Try It (Examples 2-3)

a. 146°   **b.** 146°   **c.** 34°

8-5 Exercises & Applications

1. a. 4; 6; 8   **b.** 1; 3; 5   **3.** 1 and 8; 2
and 7   **5.** Possible answers: 1 and 4;
2 and 3; 5 and 8; 6 and 7   **7.** 130°
9. 130°   **11.** 139°   **13.** Alternate
exterior angles   **15.** 47°   **17.** parallel   **19.** congruent   **23.** $m\angle 3 = 75°$;
$m\angle 4 = 55°$; $m\angle 5 = 50°$; $m\angle 6 = 125°$;
$m\angle 7 = 130°$ **25.** $x = 4$ **27.** $x = 5$
29. $\frac{63}{64}$ **31.** 1.78

8-6 Try It (Examples 1-2)

a. 5 in.   **b.** 5 in.   **c.** 60°, 60°, 60°

8-6 Try It (Examples 3-4)

a. 114°   **b.** 114°   **c.** $\overline{QS}$

8-6 Try It (Examples 5-6)

Regular convex hexagon

8-6 Exercises & Applications

1. a. 84°   **b.** 96°   **3.** Irregular convex hexagon   **5.** Irregular convex
octagon   **7.** False   **9.** True   **11.** 71°
13. 61°   **15.** 720°   **17.** 1080°

19. a. Triangles and rectangles
b. Pentagons and hexagons   **21.** n
23. A concave polygon must have at
least 4 sides.
25.

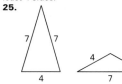

The length of the third side could be
4 in. or 7 in.; There are two possible
triangles.   **31.** 7   **33.** 13   **35.** 4
37. $\frac{3}{11}$

8-7 Try It

a. **b.**

c. **d.**

8-7 Exercises & Applications

1. a. **b.**

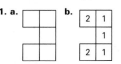

3.

5. Possible answer:

7.

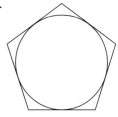

9. A **17.** Irrational **19.** Irrational
21. Rational

Section 8B Review

1. Acute **3.** Acute **5.** Right
7. 32.5° **9.** 130° **11.** 130°
13. d **15.** b **17.** Pentagon
19. Parallelogram **21.** Their
shapes are the same but the base
plan has the number of units
stacked up written on it.

Chapter 8 Summary & Review

1. Liter **2.** 192 oz **3.** 438 ft
4. 36.1 cm² **5.** 40° N; 83° W
6. About 235 mi south
7. Complement: 52°; Supplement:
142°
8.

3	4	3	4
1	2	3	4

9. a. $\overline{AB}$ and $\overline{CD}$ **b.** $\overline{AB}$ and $\overline{BC}$ or
$\overline{BC}$ and $\overline{CD}$ **c.** ∠D **10.** Obtuse
11. 540°

Cumulative Review, Chapters 1-8

1. C **2.** B **3.** A **4.** C **5.** B **6.** A
7. D **8.** A **9.** C **10.** C **11.** D
12. A **13.** C **14.** C **15.** D **16.** A

Chapter 9

9-1 Try It (Examples 2–3)

a. 2.12 in. **b.** 22 m

9-1 Try It (Example 5)

a. $10\frac{5}{6}$ yd² **b.** 34.4375 cm²

9-1 Try It (Example 7)

a. 105 mm² **b.** 390 in²

9-1 Exercises & Applications

1. a. $A = (\frac{1}{2})(5.5) \cdot 4$ **b.** $A = 11$ cm²
3. 25 cm; 39.0625 cm² **5.** 24 m;
24 m² **7.** ≈ 35.2 cm; ≈ 52 cm²
9. 64.4 m; 237.475 m² **11.** 15.75
cm; 11.8125 cm² **13.** $13\frac{1}{3}$ ft; $11\frac{1}{9}$ ft²
15. a. 80 ft **b.** 384 ft² **17.** 5; ≈ 6.4
19. ≈ 47.4 cm **21.** 37 ft **23. a.** 20
cm **b.** Find the area of the triangle
and multiply it by 5. **25. a.** 6 by 8,
4 by 12, 3 by 16, and 2 by 24
b. 6 m by 8 m; 2 by 24 **27.** 9%
29. 142% **31.** No **33.** Yes

9-2 Try It (Examples 1–2)

5

9-2 Try It (Example 4)

$p = 31\frac{1}{2}$ m and $A = 61\frac{1}{4}$ m²

9-2 Exercises & Applications

1. a. $b = 16.8$ cm; $h = 24$ cm
b. 201.6 cm² **3.** 57.6 ft; 138.24 ft²
5. 42 m; 81 m² **7.** 9 cm; 3.9 cm²
9. 250 m² **11.** A **13.** Enlargement
15. Perimeter increases slightly, but
the area doubles. **17.** 2 ft² **21.** 80
23. 400 **25.** 1.5 m **27.** $16\frac{1}{3}$ ft

9-3 Try It (Example 2)

a. 1.73 m **b.** ≈ 10.86 m

9-3 Try It (Example 4)

a. ≈ 50.24 cm² **b.** Yes

9-3 Exercises & Applications

1. a. 4 cm **b.** ≈ 50.24 cm²
3.

5. ≈ 28.26 m **7.** ≈ 31.4 mi
9. ≈ 33.17 ft² **11.** ≈ 7.5 km²

13. ≈ 39 in. **15.** ≈ 785,000 ft²
17. The circumference for a full
circle would be 188.4 ft, so for a
semicircle the perimeter would be
half of that plus 60 ft, or 154.2 ft;
The area of a full circle would be
2826 ft², so the area of a half-circle
would be 1413 ft². **21. a.** 15.6 cm²
b. 93.6 cm² **c.** ≈ 113.04 cm²
d. 19.4 cm² **23.** 70% **25.** 10%
27. 5 **29.** 3

9-4 Try It (Example 1)

22 in²

9-4 Try It (Example 2)

a. $A ≈ 50.2$ in² **b.** $A ≈ 150.7$ in²
c. $SA ≈ 251$ in²

9-4 Exercises & Applications

1. a.

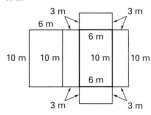

b. 3 × 6 = 18, 3 × 10 = 30, and
6 × 10 = 60 **c.** 216 m²
3. 201.5 in²

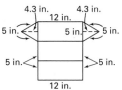

5. $37\frac{1}{2}$ ft²

7. $116\frac{3}{4}$ yd

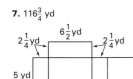

9. 8 in² **11.** 336 in² **13.** 324 cm²
15. 816 in² **17.** $2(bh + hw + bw)$
19. a. Cylinder B; It has the same area on its side as two cylinder As put together, and it has more area on the ends. **b.** Cylinder B; Two cylinder As could be put inside it with room to spare. **21.** 100%
23. Obtuse **25.** Right **27.** Acute

9-5 Try It (Example 1)

a. Square pyramid **b.** 8 cm
c. ≈ 8.5 cm **d.** ≈ 25.5 cm²
e. ≈ 138 cm²

9-5 Try It (Example 2)

a. 11 ft **b.** ≈ 2.6 ft **c.** ≈ 16.5 ft²
d. ≈ 53.4 ft²

9-5 Exercises & Applications

1. a. 4 **b.** 252 ft² **c.** 252 ft² each
d. 1008 ft² **3. a.** 11.2 in. **b.** 291.2 in² **5.** 384 ft² **7.** D **9.** ≈ 423.9 ft²
11. Possible answer: The height is like one of the legs of a right triangle and the slant height is like the hypotenuse. **13.** The pyramid
15. 7, 9; If the base of a pyramid has k sides, then the pyramid has $k + 1$ faces. **17.** 1, −3, 3 **19.** −2, 0, 0 **21.** 3, 0, 0 **23.** 4, $\frac{5}{4}$, −5
25. 2, 3, 4, 5

Section 9A Review

1. Perimeter **3.** Prism **7.** 34 in.;
$61\frac{3}{4}$ in. **9.** $13\frac{1}{2}$ ft; $7\frac{7}{8}$ ft² **11.** 59 ft;
192 ft² **13.** 6480 m² **15.** 2014 cm²

9-6 Try It (Example 2)

a. 205.8 cm³ **b.** $274\frac{5}{8}$ in³

9-6 Try It (Example 3)

246 ft³

9-6 Exercises & Applications

1. a. 12 **b.** 60 **3.** 663 m³
5. $99\frac{3}{4}$ yd³ **7.** $27\frac{13}{16}$ ft³
9. 6000 ft³

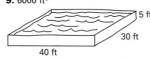

11. $\frac{4}{9}$ of a cent per in³
13. ≈ 113.04 cm³
15. 125 cm³; $V = s^3$

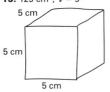

17–18.

L	W	H	V	A
1	1	36	36	146
1	2	18	36	112
1	3	12	36	102
1	4	9	36	98
1	6	6	36	96
2	2	9	36	80
2	3	6	36	72
3	3	4	36	66

19. The prism with dimensions 1 in. × 1 in. × 36 in. has the greatest surface area. The prism with dimensions 3 in. × 3 in. × 4 in. has the least. **21.** Both items have a volume of 648 in³. The book will not fit in the box because of its 9 in. length.
23. Yes **25.** No **27.** 1080°
29. 360°

9-7 Try It (Example 1)

a. 120 in³ **b.** 480 in³ **c.** 1920 in³

9-7 Try It (Example 2)

a. 5375 ft³ **b.** 5.375 ft³

9-7 Exercises & Applications

1. a. $\frac{1}{8}$ **b.** 45 ft³ **3.** 5184 in³
5. 6048 in³ **7.** 13.824 m³ **9.** D
11. 785,000 cm³; 0.785 cm³, $\frac{1}{1,000,000}$
13. a. Speedy Shipping **b.** No; E-Z Shipping would be cheaper for a 10 in. × 10 in. × 10 in. package, for example. **15. a.** Possible answer: $\frac{1}{30}$, which makes the model 18 in. long—a suitable size for a class project. **b.** 404 in² not including the floor **c.** 720 in³
17. a. Yes **b.** Yes **c.** Yes **19.** 13

9-8 Try It (Example 1)

a. $3\frac{1}{2}$ in. **b.** 7 in² **c.** 49 in³

9-8 Try It (Example 2)

a. ≈ 310.86 cm³ **b.** ≈ 2289.06 in³

9-8 Exercises & Applications

1. a.

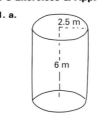

b. ≈ 19.625 m² **c.** ≈ 117.75 m³
3. ≈ 254.34 cm³ **5.** ≈ 565.2 cm³
7. ≈ 2893.824 cm³ **9.** 0.09 m³
11. ≈ 753.6 in³ **13. a.** 221,174 m³
b. 25,277 m² **15.** The tallest prism will have the greatest volume; The shortest will have the least; Since the volume of a prism is the base area times the height, the volume will be proportional to height.
17. (2, −3) **19.** (−5, 4)

9-9 Try It (Example 1)

$V ≈ 39.25$ m³

9-9 Try It (Example 3)

a. 50 m³ **b.** 126 in³

9-9 Exercises & Applications

1. a. $12\frac{1}{4}$ ft² **b.** $16\frac{1}{3}$ ft³ **3.** 36 cm³

5. 56 ft³ **7.** ≈ 94.2 cm³ **9.** ≈ 11.9 mm **11.** 680 cm³ (This is only an approximation, since part of the cone actually sticks into the cylinder.) **13.** The pyramid **15.** $h^2 + 81 = 225$ $h = 12$ in. **17.** 6280 cm³ **19.** 64 **21.** 64 **23. a.** Yes **b.** No **25. a.** Yes **b.** No

Section 9B Review

1. 561 in³ **3.** ≈ 48.2304 cm³ **5.** 1296 m³ **7.** 560 in³ **9.** ≈ 1515 cm³ **11.** 27 in³ **13.** 50.24 in³

Chapter 9 Summary & Review

1. a. $p = 26$ cm; $A = 28$ cm² **b.** $p = 16$ in.; $A = 14$ in² **2. a.** $p = 78$ cm; $A = 252$ cm² **b.** $p = 6.4$ in.; $A = 2.24$ in² **3.** $C \approx 52.1$ cm; $A \approx 216$ cm² **4.** ≈ 45 ft **5. a.** ≈ 149.2 ft² **b.** 1710 cm² **6. a.** $s = 13$ in.; $SA = 360$ in² **b.** $s = 25$ m; $SA \approx 1884$ m² **7. a.** $V = 125$ cm³ **b.** $V = 7350$ ft³ **8. a.** $V \approx 184$ in³ **b.** $V = 192.5$ cm³ **9. a.** $V = 120$ cm³

4 cm — 6 cm — 10 cm

b. $V \approx 83.7$ in³

5 in. — 8 in.

10. a. $V = 5$ cm³ **b.** SA = 114,562 ft²; $V = 2{,}521{,}050$ ft³ **11. a.** $V = 13.5$ m³ **b.** $V = 27$ m³ **12. a.** $V = 24$ ft³ **b.** $V = 6$ ft³

Chapter 10

10-1 Try It (Example 1)

$110; Yes; 10 hours

10-1 Try It (Example 2)

Yes; For any given number of Buddy Biscuits, there is only one price.

10-1 Try It (Example 3)

a. Yes; Input n yields output n^2
b. No; There are two output values for 1 and two output values for 2.

10-1 Exercises & Applications

1. a. 4 **b.** 8 **c.** Multiply by 3 and subtract 4 **d.** 14 **3.** −2.25 **5.** 1.75 **7.** 16 **9.** −16 **11.** Multiply by 2 and subtract 1 **13.** C
15. a. Calories burned = minutes × 13.5; 202.5; 270; 405; 607.5
b. About 22 min **c.** Yes; Yes; Each input value yields only one output. **17.** Yes; For any given time there is only one height **19.** Take the absolute value. **21.** 23% **23.** 30%

10-2 Try It (Example 2)

a. Yes; The graph is a straight line.
b. Money earned = $4 × number of shirts sold; 9 shirts; Yes; The number of shirts determines the amount of money earned.

10-2 Exercises & Applications

1. a. y **b.** x **c.** $y = -2$, $y = 3$, $y = 8$ **3.** 11, 10, 9, 8, 7 **5.** B
7. Yes **9.** No **11. a.** $d = 34.5t$
b. 69 mi, 207 mi, 345 mi **13.** No; Inputs −1 and −2 each have two output values. **15. a.** $c = 6.5n + 18$
c. Yes **19.** 12 in., $4\sqrt{3} \approx 6.9$ in²
21. Perimeter can't be determined, 230 cm²

10-3 Try It (Examples 1–2)

a.
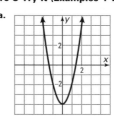

b.
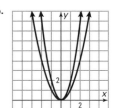

The graphs have the same general shape, but the $2x^2$ graph is skinnier.

10-3 Try It (Example 3)

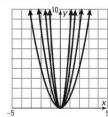

10-3 Exercises & Applications

1. Neither **3.** Linear
5.
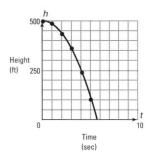

Same general shape, but varying widths.
7.
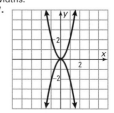

Same shape, but one opens up and one opens down.

9. F **11.** D **13.** B **15.** C
17. The canyon is 400 ft deep; The value is negative because the function represents height measured from the canyon's rim. **21.** 27 **23.** 66 cm

10-4 Try It (Examples 1–2)

a.

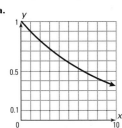

0.66, 2.12 **b.** About $7\frac{3}{4}$ hours

10-4 Try It (Example 3)

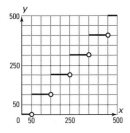

10-4 Exercises & Applications

1. B **3.** C

5.

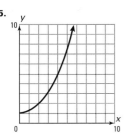

7.

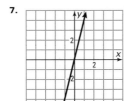

9. There will be $1000 \times 2^1 = 2000$ butterflies after 1 year, $1000 \times 2^2 = 4000$ butterflies after 2 years, $1000 \times 2^3 = 8000$ butterflies after 3 years, and $1000 \times 2^{10} = 1{,}024{,}000$ butterflies after 10 years. **11. b.** Step **13.** Quadratic **15.** Linear **17. a.** \$1402.55 **b.** 11 years **19. a.** Increase **b.** Decrease for $x < 0$, increase for $x > 0$ **c.** Increase **d.** Decrease **21.** Exponential, increasing **23.** $10 - 2n$ **25.** 12π m, 36π m^2 **27.** 5.8π m, 8.41π m^2

Section 10A Review

1. -10 **3.** 0 **5.** -2 **7.** C **13.** Yes; Each x value corresponds to only one y value.

15.

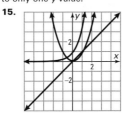

Similar: All three functions are increasing to the right of the origin. Different: $y = x$ is a straight line, $y = x^2$ curves up at both ends (and so is decreasing to the left of the origin), and $y = 4^x$ is nearly flat on the left and curves up on the right.

17. a.

Time (sec)	Height (ft)
0	0
1	-16
2	-64
3	-144
4	-256
5	-400
6	-576
7	-784
8	-1024

b. 256 ft; Height is measured from ground level.

10-5 Try It (Examples 1–2)

$-4x^2 + x + 22$

10-5 Try It (Examples 3–4)

a. 5, -34 **b. i.** ≈ 2.09 ft^3
ii. ≈ 134 ft^3 **iii.** ≈ 23.8 m^3

10-5 Exercises & Applications

1. a. 3 **b.** 1 **c.** 2 **3.** Trinomial
5. Binomial **7.** $2x + 4$; 1 **9.** $-x^4 - x^3 + x^2$; 4 **11.** -3 **13.** 51 **15.** 6; 910 **17.** 3; -5 **19.** 175.9 in^2
21. B **23. a.** 85,486 ft^2
b. 2,350,879 ft^3 **25.** $V = ns^3$ where s is the side length and n is the number of boxes. **27.** 0, 1, 5, 14, 30; The differences are the perfect squares 1, 4, 9, 16. **29.** 105
31. 180 **33.** 3584 cm^2

10-6 Try It (Examples 1–2)

a. $7x^2 + 7x + 1$ **b.** $-11n^2 - n - 9$
c. $3x^2 + 8x - 10$

10-6 Try It (Example 3)

$2x^2 + x - 11$; 199

10-6 Exercises & Applications

1. a. Descending **b.** Like terms
c. Distributive **3.** Already simplified **5.** $7m^2 - 3m$ **7.** $4a + 6$
9. $-2x^2 + 1$ **11.** $13x^2 + 4x - 7$
13. $4x^2 - x + 9$ **15.** A **17.** $x^3 + 5x^2 + 4x + 7x$; $x^3 + 9x^2 + 7x$; 582 ft^3 **19.** $2x^2 + 13x + 20$
21. $3x^2 + 13x + 11$ **23.** Possible answer: $4x - 3x + 2x - x$
25. No; Should be $7x$

719

27. a. Incorrect; Added exponents, forgot to add coefficients. **b.** Incorrect; Added exponents. **c.** Correct; Added coefficients but not exponents. **d.** Incorrect; Forgot to add coefficients. **29.** 36 **31.** 9 **33.** $\approx 30.8 \text{ cm}^2$

10-7 Try It (Examples 1–2)

a. $2x^3 - 1$ **b.** $2x^3 + 6x^2 + 6x - 5$

10-7 Try It (Example 3–4)

a. $-70p^2 + 1495p - 300$; $7650
b. $6x - 5$

10-7 Exercises & Applications

1. a. x^3 **b.** $-4x^2$ **c.** $-2x$ **d.** $7x^5$
e. -27 **3.** $-x^4 + 2$ **5.** $-3x^3 - 2x$
7. $x^5 - 2x - 9x^3 + 3$ **9.** $2x^2 + 4x - 1$ **11.** $-4m^2 + 4m - 1$
13. $2v^3 - 8v^2 + 6v - 1$ **15.** $a^3 - 6a^2 + 2a - 3$ **17.** $11x^2 - 2x + 1$
19. $12x^2 + 4x + 3$ **21.** $x^2 - 3x + 3$
23. $x^2 + 4$ **25.** $10t - 8$ **27.** No; She dropped the variable.
31. $2x^5 + 2x^4 + 3x^2 - 2x + 1$
33. $2 \cdot 3^2 \cdot 5$ **35.** $3 \cdot 29$ **37.** $3 \cdot 5^3$
39. 232.56 m^3

10-8 Try It (Example 2)

1. a. 5^6 **b.** 8^3 **c.** x^8 **d.** $-32x^6$

10-8 Try It (Example 3)

a. $-10x^6 - 12x^3$
b. $6x^4 + 10x^3 - 2x^2$

10-8 Try It (Examples 4–5)

a. 3.5×10^{11} **b.** 4.94×10^{12}

10-8 Exercises & Applications

1. a. $x \cdot x \cdot x \cdot x$ **b.** $x \cdot x \cdot x$ **c.** 7
d. x^7 **3.** 4^7 **5.** $6r^6$ **7.** $-24d^{10}$
9. $20f^{15}$ **11.** $3b^5$ **13.** $-6t + 6t^3$
15. $15g^7 - 10g^6 + 25g^5 + 40g^4$
17. $2m^2 + 4m$ **19.** 9.92×10^9
21. 8.16×10^6 **25. a.** 2.47×10^{11}
b. 5.89×10^{10} **c.** 8.55×10^9
d. 5.89×10^{11} **27.** $3^6 = 729$; a^6
29. a. Subtract exponents
b. $2^1 = \frac{8}{4} = 2$ **31.** 25 **33.** 3
35. 884.736 m^3

Section 10B Review

1. Binomial, two terms.
3. Monomial, one term. **5.** 1; $8x - 6$ **7.** 5; $-x^5 + x^2 - x$ **9.** 7; $x^7 - 3$
11. Already simplified **13.** $10x + 5$
15. $2x^2 + 4x - 1$ **17.** $p^2 - 2p - 9$
19. x^6 **21.** $-20x^{10}$ **23.** $y^2 + 3y$
25. $x^6 + 5x^4$ **27.** C

Chapter 10 Summary & Review

1. a. -18 **b.** 4 **2.** Multiply by 3 and add 1.

3. Yes

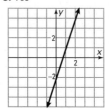

4. Answers may vary.

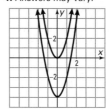

5. 64 ft

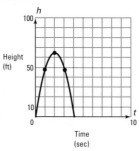

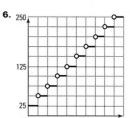

7. $-4x^3 - 7x^2 + 3x + 5$ **8. a.** 18
b. 12 **9.** $5x^3 - 5x^2 - 3x + 14$
10. $4p^2 - 1$ **11.** $4x^2 + 2x + 5$
12. $x^2 - x - 5$ **13.** $6x^3 - 9x^2 - 2x + 15$ **14.** $g^2 + 8g + 3$
15. $6x^3 - 15x^2$ **16.** 4.14×10^{14}
17. $-15u^5 + 21u^4 - 12u^3$

**Cumulative Review
Chapters 1–10**

1. D **2.** D **3.** C **4.** B **5.** D **6.** A
7. B **8.** C **9.** B **10.** C **11.** A
12. B **13.** D

Chapter 11

11-1 Try It (Example 2)

a. $\frac{8}{5}$ **b.** 118°

11-1 Try It (Example 4)

a. Yes **b.** No

11-1 Exercises & Applications

1. a. $\frac{1.5}{3.0} = \frac{1.8}{3.6}$ **b.** Yes, $(1.5)(3.6) = (3.0)(1.8) = 5.4$ **3.** Yes **5.** 1 in.:50 ft **7.** A **9.** $64x^2$ **11.** Each cable forms a different angle measurement where it intersects the road.
15. Factors: 1, 2, 3, 6, 11, 22, 33, 66; Prime factors: 2, 3, 11 **17.** Factors: 1, 2, 3, 4, 6, 8, 12, 16, 24, 48; Prime factors: 2, 3 **19.** 12 **21.** 5.01
23. -17

11-2 Try It (Example 2)

No

11-2 Try It (Example 4)

a. $\overline{HI}$ **b.** $\frac{5}{8}$ in. **c.** 120°

720

11-2 Exercises & Applications

1. a. The corresponding sides are not congruent.   **b.** The corresponding angles are congruent.   **3.** 6 mm
5. Yes   **7.** 8   **11.** They are congruent.   **15.** 8   **17.** 10
19. Yes   **21.** Yes

11-3 Try It (Example1)

No.

11-3 Try It (Example 3)

Yes; The SAS rule.

11-3 Exercises & Applications

1. a. $\overline{QS}$ **b.** $\overline{RS}$ **c.** $\angle Q$ **d.** $\angle R$
e. $\angle S$ **3.** Yes; The SSS rule.
5. Yes; The SAA rule.   **7.** Yes; The SAS rule   **9. a–c.** Answers may vary.   **11.** The SAS rule.   **13.** Not necessarily; The triangles are the same shape (i.e., similar) but not necessarily the same size.   **15.** 60
17. 10   **19.** 60

11-4 Try It (Example 1)

a. $\overline{KM}$ **b.** $\overline{ML}$ **c.** $\overline{KL}$

11-4 Try It (Example 2)

a. $\frac{4}{5}$ **b.** $\frac{4}{3}$

11-4 Try It (Example 4)

a. ≈ 11.78 m   **b.** ≈ 12.79 m

11-4 Exercises & Applications

1. a. Opposite   **b.** Adjacent
c. Tangent   **d.** ≈ 38.87 in.   **3.** $\sin = \frac{1}{\sqrt{2}}$, $\cos = \frac{1}{\sqrt{2}}$, $\tan = 1$ **5.** ≈ 618.8 m
7. ≈ 10.4 ft   **9.** B   **11.** ≈ 3035 ft
13. $\sin(60°) \approx 0.866$, $\cos(60°) = 0.5$, $\tan(60°) \approx 1.732$ **15.** $2\frac{1}{50}$ **17.** $4\frac{6}{25}$
19. $9\frac{9}{10}$ **21.** Exponential
23. Linear

11-5 Try It (Example 2)

7 cm

11-5 Try It (Example 3)

$1.\overline{66}$ ft

11-5 Exercises & Applications

1. a. 16 cm   **b.** $m\overline{EG} = 14.4$ cm
3. ≈ 11.58 in.   **5.** D   **7.** ≈ 387.32 yd
9. Possible answer: Since $\angle A$ is congruent to the corresponding angle of the triangle for which s is the hypotenuse and 10 ft is the length of the adjacent side of that angle, solve the equation $\frac{10}{s} = \cos(22°)$.   **11.** 4
13. Because most trigonometric ratios are irrational numbers, the results involving them are approximate rather than exact.   **15.** 0.176
17. $\frac{7}{16}$ **19.** $-3x^2 + 2x + 5$; 2
21. $-x^3 - x^2 + 3x - 3$; 3

Section 11A Review

1. 6 in.   **3.** Yes, SAA   **7.** 3290 ft

11-6 Try It (Example 1)

$(-2, -2)$, $(-5, -2)$, $(-5, -1)$, $(-3, 0)$; $(2, 2)$, $(5, 2)$, $(5, 1)$, $(3, 0)$

11-6 Try It (Examples 3-4)

a. $(-3, 1)$; $(-1, 1)$; $(-3, 4)$; $(-1, 4)$
b. $(-1, -2)$; $(-4, -2)$; $(-1, -3)$; $(-2, -3)$; $(-2, -5)$; $(-4, -4)$

11-6 Exercises & Applications

1. a.

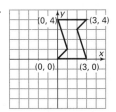

c. $(0, 0)$, $(0, 4)$, $(3, 4)$, $(3, 0)$
3. Rotation   **5.** The y-axis   **7.** C
9. A reflection   **11.** No transformations of the word "TRANSLATE" as a whole will work. Each letter must be reflected and rotated separately.
13. No; A parallelogram and a trapezoid are not congruent.
15. 381.98   **17.** $\frac{16}{63}$ **19.** 0.68
21. $87\frac{1}{9}$ **23.** $x^3 + 7x^2 - 2$

11-7 Try It (Example 2)

a. $(-12.5, -5)$; $(-7.5, 5)$; $(-2.5, 10)$; $(2.5, 10)$; $(7.5, 5)$; $(12.5, -5)$
b. $(-2\frac{2}{3}, 0)$; $(0, 2\frac{2}{3})$; $(2\frac{2}{3}, 0)$; $(0, -2\frac{2}{3})$

11-7 Try It (Example 4)

a. $\frac{1}{5}$ **b.** 5

11-7 Exercises & Applications

1. 2 and 3   **3.** Reduction, $\frac{2}{3}$ **5.** B
7. ≈ 4.8 **9.** The result will be a lizard 11.75 cm long and 6.25 cm wide.   **11.** 12   **13. a.** The quotient is 2 in every case.   **b.** Yes
15. $E'' = (8, 0)$, $F'' = (10, 6)$, $G'' = (5, 8)$, $H'' = (0, 6)$, $I'' = (2, 0)$ **17.** $\frac{2}{3}$
19. $\frac{8}{9}$ **21.** $2x^3 - 4x^2 + 2x - 5$
23. $-x^2 - 5x - 2$

11-8 Try It (Example 3)

a. Four   **b.** Yes; 90°

11-8 Try It (Example 5)

Rotational and point symmetries

11-8 Exercises & Applications

1. a. $\overleftrightarrow{BY}$ **b.** $\overleftrightarrow{PX}$ **c.** $\overleftrightarrow{QW}$ **3.** C
5. 120°, 240°, 360°   **7.** Ten
9. Horizontal line through E.
11. No lines of symmetry.   **13.** Yes; Yes; The deer in the top two rows are congruent.   **15.** You can't because the deer in each row are looking in different directions.   **19.** Irrational   **21.** Rational   **23.** 5.762 $\times 10^{14}$ **25.** 5.39×10^7

11-9 Try It (Example 4)

a. Yes   **b.** Yes   **c.** No

11-9 Try It (Example 5)

90

11-9 Exercises & Applications

1. a. No   **b.** Yes   **c.** No
3. a. Triangles, squares, hexagons.

b. Possible answer: They do not fit together to cover the plane without gaps or overlaps. **5.** 4000
7. a. Equilateral triangles
b. Trapezoids **c.** Regular hexagons
9. a. Yes **b.** Yes **c.** No **d.** Yes
15. ≈ 15.9 in. **17.** $x = 80$ **19.** 24.5

Section 11B Review

1. a. Rotation **b.** Translation
c. Reflection **3.** For each point (x, y) the reflected point is $(-x, y)$.
5. Possible answer: Give up translation, which can be replaced by two successive rotations with different axis points, or by two reflections with parallel reflection lines. The other option: Give up rotation, which can be replaced by two successive reflections using intersecting reflection lines. **7.** B

Chapter 11 Summary & Review

1. $x = 18$ in.; $m\angle 1 = 135°$
2. Congruent by SAA **3.** Not congruent **4. a.** ≈ 0.87 **b.** ≈ 0.87
c. 1 **5.** $\sin \angle A = \frac{1.75}{6.25}$; $\cos \angle A = \frac{6}{6.25}$; $\tan \angle A = \frac{1.75}{6}$ **6.** 15 cm
7. a. $K'(0, 0)$; $L'(3, -1)$; $M'(2, -4)$; and $N'(0, -5)$ **b.** $K'(0, 0)$; $L'(-3, 1)$; $M'(-2, 4)$; and $N'(0, 5)$ **c.** $K'(0, 0)$; $L'(-1, 3)$; $M'(-4, 2)$; and $N'(-5, 0)$
8. $A'(1, -1)$, $B'(1, -2)$, $C'(3, -2)$
9. Dilation; Yes; No **10.** $\overleftrightarrow{MW}, \overleftrightarrow{PY}$
11. Yes

Chapter 12

12-1 Try It (Example 1)

Possibilities are: Flight 1 return A, flight 1 return b, flight 1 return C, flight 2 return A, flight 2 return B, flight 2 return C, flight 3 return A, flight 3 return B, flight 3 return C, flight 4 return A, flight 4 return B, flight 4 return C.

12 pairs

12-1 Try It (Example 2)

360

12-1 Try It (Example 3)

3600

12-1 Exercises & Applications

1. a. Possibilities are: Pork and Swiss on wheat, pork and Swiss on rye, pork and American on wheat, pork and American on rye, pork and jack on wheat, pork and jack on rye, beef and Swiss on wheat, beef and Swiss on rye, beef and American on wheat, beef and American on rye, beef and jack on wheat, beef and jack on rye. **b.** 12 **3. a.** 40 **b.** 18 **c.** 20
5.

7. 8 **9.** 36 **11.** 240 **15.** $x > 2$
17. $x \le 4$ **19.** ≈ 24.6 in²

12-2 Try It (Example 1)

40,320

12-2 Try It (Example 2)

a. 24 **b.** 24 **c.** 30,240

12-2 Try It (Example 3)

a. 181,440 **b.** 60 **c.** 60; 120; 120

12-2 Exercises & Applications

1. a. Possibilities are: Justin, Butch, Rod; Justin, Rod, Butch; Butch, Justin, Rod; Butch, Rod, Justin; Rod, Justin, Butch; Rod, Butch, Justin
b. 6 **c.** 3! **3.** 720 **5.** 3,628,800

7. 30,240 **9.** 7 **11.** 120 **13.** 120
15. 5040 **17.** 1 in 6 **19.** $\frac{1}{6}$
21. a. 14,400 **b.** 120 **23.** LULL has repeated letters; SALT has 4! = 24 arrangements, and PEPPER has 3! = 6. **25.** No; Order is not important. **27.** No **29.** Yes

12-3 Try (Example 1)

Abby / Bonita / Chantall
Abby / Bonita / Dani
Abby / Bonita / Eleni
Abby / Chantall / Dani
Abby / Chantall / Eleni
Abby / Dani / Eleni
Bonita / Chantall / Dani
Bonita / Chantall / Eleni
Bonita / Dani / Eleni
Chantall / Dani / Eleni
10 combinations

12-3 Try It (Example 3)

15

12-3 Exercises & Applications

1. Yes **2.** No **3.** Yes **4.** No
5. $\frac{96!}{24! \times 72!}$ **7.** 252 **9.** 10 **11.** 10
13. 792 **15.** Yes **17.** The chances of winning are 1 in $\frac{53!}{6! \times 47!}$, or 1 in 22,957,480. **19.** B **21.** 5 people, since the value of $\frac{10!}{r!(10 - r)!}$ peaks when r is half of 10.
23. 4200 **25.** Yes; $k = \frac{3}{2}$ **27.** No

Section 12A Review

1. 40,320 **3.** 5040 **5.** 1,814,400
7. 56 **9.** 56 **11.** 3 heads, 2 heads and 1 tail, 2 tails and 1 head, 3 tails
13. 720 **15.** 362,880 **17.** 5040
19. 5040 **21.** D

12-4 Try It (Examples 1–2)

a. 1, 2, 3, 4, 5, 6; $\frac{1}{3}$ **b.** Sun, Mon, Tues, Wed, Thur, Fri, Sat; $\frac{2}{7}$

12-4 Try It (Example 3)

a. $\frac{1}{2}$ **b.** $\frac{1}{3}$ **c.** $\frac{1}{6}$ **d.** 1 **e.** 0

12-4 Exercises & Applications

1. a. 1, 2, 3, 4, 5, 6 **b.** 6 **c.** 1 **d.** $\frac{1}{6}$
e. $\frac{1}{6}$; 0.1666...; $16\frac{2}{3}$% **3.** 1, 2, 3, 4, 5,
6 **5.** $\frac{1}{2}$, 0.5, 50% **7.** 0, 0, 0%
9. B **11.** $\frac{8191}{8192}$ **13.** Yellow, green
15. $\frac{1}{4}$, $\frac{1}{2}$ **17.** First in top row, third
in bottom row; 1 in 36 **19.** Never
25. Yes

12-5 Try It (Example 1)

a. 2 heads: $\frac{1}{4}$; 1 head: $\frac{1}{2}$; 0 heads: $\frac{1}{4}$
b. Answers may vary. **c.** There
should be $\approx$ 25% of 2 heads, 50% of
1 head, and 25% of 0 heads.

12-5 Try It (Example 2)

San Antonio is the only one that
passed; You would expect to find
defective candles in $\approx$ 44 boxes out
of 10,000.

12-5 Try It (Example 3)

$\frac{4}{27}$

12-5 Exercises & Applications

1. Experimental **2.** Theoretical
3. Experimental **5. a.** $\frac{7}{30}$ **b.** $\frac{23}{30}$
7. About $\frac{3}{8}$ **9.** $\frac{2}{27}$ **11. a.** $\frac{1}{11} \approx$ 9%
b. $\frac{1}{11} \approx$ 9% **c.** 1 **13.** Yes **15.** Yes
17. 288 ft^3 **19.** 1600 in^3

12-6 Try It (Example 1)

a. $\frac{1}{6}$ **b.** 0

12-6 Try It (Example 3)

a. $\frac{91}{150} \approx$ 60.7% **b.** $\frac{28}{45} \approx$ 62.2%

12-6 Try It (Example 4)

a. $\frac{2}{25}$ **b.** $\frac{1}{18}$; $\frac{1}{2}$

12-6 Exercises & Applications

1. a. red, red blue, blue yellow,
yellow green, green red, blue
blue, red yellow, red green, red
red, yellow blue, yellow yellow,
blue green, blue red, green
blue, green yellow, green green,
yellow **b.** 16 **c.** 4 **d.** $\frac{1}{16}$ **3.** $\frac{1}{2}$
5. $\frac{1}{16}$ **7. a.** 0 **b.** $\frac{1}{6}$ **c.** $\frac{1}{3}$ **d.** 1
9. 800 people **11. a.** $\frac{59}{95} \approx$ 62.1%
b. $\frac{32}{42} \approx$ 76.2% **c.** $\frac{42}{95} \approx$ 44.2%
13. $100 - \frac{9\pi}{100} \approx$ 72% **15.** 90 in^3
17. $XY = 2$; $BC \approx 10.77$

12-7 Try It (Example 1)

a. Dependent **b.** Independent

12-7 Try It (Example 3)

34.4%

12-7 Try It (Example 4)

a. $\frac{4}{49}$ **b.** $\frac{2}{42}$

12-7 Exercises & Applications

1. a. $\frac{1}{2}$ **b.** $\frac{1}{6}$ **c.** $\approx$ 8.3%
3. Independent **5.** Dependent
7. $\frac{1}{4}$ **9.** $\frac{1}{10}$ **11.** $\frac{4}{15}$ **13.** 1
15. 0.09% **17. a.** 1 in 5 **b.** 1 in 4
21. 71.96 in^3 **23.** (1, 2)

Section 12B Review

1. Sample space: 1, 2, 3, 4, 5, 6
a. 1 outcome; Probability: $\frac{1}{6}$ **b.** 3
outcomes; Probability: $\frac{1}{2}$ **c.** 0 outcomes; Probability: 0 **3. a.** $\frac{1}{36}$ **b.** $\frac{1}{6}$
c. $\frac{4}{9}$ **5.** $\frac{1}{4}$ **7.** $\frac{1}{8}$ **9.** Yes; There is
one less person left to pick from.
11. D

Chapter 12 Summary & Review

1.

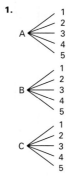

2. 15 **3. a.** 120 **b.** 24 **c.** 35
4. 720 **5.** 336 **6.** 210 **7.** $\frac{1}{3}$ **8.** $\frac{1}{13}$
9. 20% **11.** $\frac{13}{25}$ **12.** $\frac{2}{7}$ **13.** $\frac{1}{13}$
14. $\frac{1}{6}$ **15. a.** $\frac{25}{144}$ **b.** $\frac{5}{33}$ **16.** $\frac{1}{4}$;
Independent events

Cumulative Review
Chapters 1–12

1. C **2.** B **3.** B **4.** B **5.** C **6.** A
7. D **8.** D **9.** D **10.** B **11.** A
12. C **13.** B

723

Photographs

Cover/Spine   Don Mason

Front Matter   **iii** GHP Studio*
iii(background) John Banagan/The Image Bank
v–xviT GHP Studio*   **xviiiTL** Roy Morsch/The
Stock Market   **xviiiR** Peter Menzel/Stock, Boston
xviiiB Marc Chamberlain/Tony Stone Images
ixT Ken Karp*   **xixB** Ken Karp,* Dennis Geaney*
& Parker/Boon Productions and Dorey Sparre
Photography*   **xxii** Ken Karp*   **xxiii** Ken Karp*
xxv Ken Karp*   **xxvi** Michael Rosenfeld/Tony
Stone Images   **xxviiL** David Young Wolff/Tony
Stone Images   **xxviiCL** Hans Reinhard/Bruce
Coleman Inc.   **xxviiCCL** Frank Siteman/Stock,
Boston   **xxviiCCR** Robert Pearcy/Animals,
Animals   **xxviiCR** Peter Vandermark/Stock, Boston
xxviiR Fritz Prenzel/Animals, Animals

Chapter 1   **2–3(background)** Suzanne
Murphy/Tony Stone Images   **2L** Bruno De
Hogues/Tony Stone Images   **2TR** Culver Pictures
2B Ken Karp*   **3T** CNRI/SPL/Photo Researchers
3B Cheryl Fenton*   **4T** The Image Bank
4B Jenny Thomas*   **5** Cheryl Fenton*
6 Ken Karp*   **7T** Blair Seitz/Photo Researchers
7B John Scheiber/The Stock Market   **8** Ben Van
Hook/Duomo   **9** Gabe Palmer/The Stock Market
10 Greg Pease Photography   **11** Jim Pickerell/
Stock, Boston   **12T** SPL/Photo Researchers
12B Lyle Leduc/Liaison International   **13** Michael
Skott/The Image Bank   **14L** Ken Karp*
14R Dennis Geaney*   **15** Jenny Thomas*
16 Chuck Savage/The Stock Market   **17L** GHP
Studio*   **17R** Jose L. Pelaez/The Stock Market
18 John Elk III   **20** Ben Simmons/The Stock
Market   **21T** Mark Reinstein/Uniphoto Picture
Agency   **21B** SIU/Visuals Unlimited   **22** Randy
Duchaine/The Stock Market   **22L** Cheryl Fenton*
23 Cheryl Fenton*   **25** NASA/Stock, Boston
26 George Haling/Photo Researchers
27L Popperfoto/Archive Photos   **27R** Mitchell
Layton/Duomo   **31** Cheryl Fenton*   **32L** Bob
Daemmrich/Uniphoto Picture Agency
32C Cheryl Fenton*   **32R** Cheryl Fenton*
33 Ken Karp*   **35** Photo 20-20   **37L** Cheryl
Fenton*   **37R** Bodhan Hrynewych/Stock, Boston
39 David R. Frazier Photolibrary   **40T** George
East/Visuals Unlimited   **40B** Gene Gray/
Transparencies, Inc.   **41L** Dennis Geaney*
41R Ken Karp*   **42** Ed Lallo/Liaison International
43 Burrows/Liaison International   **45** Space
Telescope Science Institute/NASA/SPL/Photo
Researchers   **46** Bob Daemmrich/Tony Stone
Images   **47** Barros & Barros/The Image Bank
48 M. Antman/The Image Works   **49** Cheryl
Fenton*   **50** Ken Karp*   **52** NASA/Mark
Marten/Photo Researchers   **53** Geoffrey Nilsen
Photography*   **57T** Cheryl Fenton*   **57BL** Cheryl
Fenton*   **57BR** Romilly Lockyer/The Image Bank

Chapter 2   **58DL** Superstock, Inc.   **58DR**
Corrine Johns   **58–59(background)** Ralph A.
Clevenger/Westlight   **58TL** Tournament of Roses
58TR Tony Stone Images   **58B** Fred Bavendam/
Peter Arnold, Inc.   **59T** Jose Fuste Raga/The Stock
Market   **59BL** John Cancalosi/Peter Arnold, Inc.
59BR Larry Ulrich/Tony Stone Images   **60T** Zig
Leszczynski/Animals, Animals   **60B** Bruce
Hands/Tony Stone Images   **62L** Ed Bock/The Stock
Market   **62R** Bernard Boutrit/Woodfin Camp &
Associates   **64** Mark Harwood/Tony Stone Images
65 Phil Schofield/Tony Stone Images   **66** Cheryl
Fenton*   **67** David Madison/Duomo   **68** Ken
Karp*   **69** Kenneth Eward/BioGrafx/Photo
Researchers   **70** Robert E. Daemmrich/Tony Stone
Images   **71T** Western History Collections,
University of Oklahoma Libraries   **71B** Peter

Poulides/Tony Stone Images   **72L** Robert Frerck/
Woodfin Camp & Associates   **72R** Ken Karp
73 Jenny Thomas*   **74** Mitchell Layton/Duomo
75 J. L. Bulcao/Liaison International   **76TL**
Edmondson/Liaison International   **76TR**
NASA/Mark Marten/Photo Researchers   **76B** Jim
Cambon/Tony Stone Images   **77L** GHP Studio*
77R Richard Megna/Fundamental Photographs
78 James Wilson/Woodfin Camp & Associates
79 Frank White/Liaison International   **80** Jan
Halaake/Photo Researchers   **81** David Madison/
Tony Stone Images   **82L** David Madison/Duomo
82TR Harald Sund/The Image Bank   **82BR** Cheryl
Fenton*   **84L** Parker/Boon Productions and Dorey
Sparre Photography*   **84R** Ken Karp*   **85** R.
Rathe/FPG International   **88** H. R. Bramaz/Peter
Arnold, Inc.   **89TL** Douglas Faulkner/Photo
Researchers   **89TC** Alain Evrard/Photo Researchers
89TR Warren Morgan/Westlight   **89CL** Connie
Coleman/Tony Stone Images   **89C(background)**
Thomas Wiewandt/Masterfile   **89CR** Michael
Busselle/Tony Stone Images   **89BL** Anthony
Cassidy/Tony Stone Images   **89BC** Neil Gilchrist/
Panoramic Images   **89BR** Mark Joseph/Tony Stone
Images   **90L** Bob Daemmrich Photos, Inc.   **91** Yu
Trung Dung/Liaison International   **92** National
Geographic Image Collection   **94** Demetrio
Carrasco/Tony Stone Images   **96** Francois Gohier/
Photo Researchers   **96R** GHP Studio*   **97** Clyde
H. Smith/Peter Arnold, Inc.   **98** Dennis Geaney*
100 Paula Lerner/Woodfin Camp & Associates
101 Nancy Simmerman/Tony Stone Images
102 John Eastcott-Yva Momatiuk/Woodfin Camp &
Associates   **104** Piero Codato/Camera Photo/
Liaison International   **105** Sovfoto/Eastfoto
106L Andrew Syred/SPL/Photo Researchers
106R Terry Eiler/Stock, Boston   **107** Gunther F.
Bahr/AFIP/Tony Stone Images   **108T** Wernher
Krutein/Liaison International   **108B** Prof. P.
Motta/Dept. of Anatomy/University "La Sapienza,"
Rome/SPL/Photo Researchers   **109T** Robert
Brons/BPS/Tony Stone Images   **109B** Diane
Schiumo/Fundamental Photographs   **110** Dr.
Jeremy Burgess/SPL/Photo Researchers
111T Warren Morgan/Westlight   **111CL** Thomas
Wiewandt/Masterfile   **111CR** Michael Busselle/
Tony Stone Images   **111BC** Neil Gilchrist/
Panoramic Images   **111BR** Mark Joseph/Tony
Stone Images   **113** Geoffrey Nilsen Photography*
116 John Lund/Tony Stone Images   **117** S. Lowry/
Univ. Ulster/Tony Stone Images

Chapter 3   **118T** John Mitchell/Photo
Researchers   **118BR** Dallas & John Heaton/Stock,
Boston   **118BR** Steve Dunwell/The Image Bank
119T NASA   **119B** Peter Southwick/AP/Wide
World Photos   **120** Jenny Thomas*   **121** Brownie
Harris/The Stock Market   **121(inset)** Cheryl
Fenton*   **121(background)** W. Cody/Westlight
122L Mark Wagner/Tony Stone Images
122C Superstock   **122R** Jerry Wachter/Photo
Researchers   **123** Archive Photos   **124** Richard
Kaylin/Tony Stone Images   **125** Archive Photos
126L Kaoru Ishie/Nature Production   **126C** D.
Cavagnaro/DRK Photo   **126R** M. P. Kahl/Bruce
Coleman Inc.   **127** Cheryl Fenton*   **128** David R.
Frazier Photolibrary   **129** Ken Karp*
132 Broderbund Software, Inc.   **133** Richard
Megna/Fundamental Photographs   **134L** AP/Wide
World Photos   **134R** Ray Pfortner/Peter Arnold,
Inc.   **136L** AP/Wide World Photos   **136R** Ross
Harrison Koty/Tony Stone Images   **137** Brownie
Harris/The Stock Market   **137(inset)** Cheryl
Fenton*   **138** Frank Schneidermeyer/Oxford
Scientific Films   **139** Bob Shaw/The Stock Market
140 M. Rutherford/Superstock   **141** Michael
Dwyer/Stock, Boston   **142** Larry Mayer
145 Michael Dalton/Fundamental Photographs

146 Alain Eurard/Liaison International
147L Dennis Geaney*   **147R** Parker/Boon
Productions and Dorey Sparre Photography*
148 Dennis Geaney*   **149L** Ray Stott/The Image
Works   **149R** Tony Stone Images   **150** Isaac
Geib/Grant Heilman Photography   **151** Torin
Boyd/Liaison International   **152** Superstock
154 W. H. Black/Bruce Coleman Inc.   **155L** Ed
Wheeler/The Stock Market   **155R** Jenny Thomas*
157 Antman/The Image Works   **158** Larry Mayer
159 Jenny Thomas*   **161** Bob Shaw/The Stock
Market   **162** Keren Su/Tony Stone Images
167C Tony Stone Images   **167B** William R.
Sallaz/Duomo

Chapter 4   **168–169(background)** Joanne
Lotter/Tom Stack & Associates   **168TL** Paul
Chesley/Tony Stone Images   **168TR** Superstock
168BC M. Gadomski/Bruce Coleman Inc.
168BR M. Antman/The Image Works   **169T** Art
Wolfe/Tony Stone Images   **169C** U.S. Postal Service
169B Superstock   **170** Liza Loeffler*   **171** Jenny
Thomas*   **172** Roger Tully/Tony Stone Images
173T Jenny Thomas*   **173B** Ron Kimball
174 Herbert W. Booth III/Liaison International
175 Jean-Michel Labat/Jacana/Photo Researchers
176 Hans Reinhard/Bruce Coleman Inc.
177L Jenny Thomas*   **177C** Jenny Thomas*
177R Paul S. Howell/Liaison International
179 Leonard Lee Rue III/Animals, Animals
180 Tony Cordoza/Liaison International
181 Holt Studios International (Nigel Cattlin)/
Photo Researchers   **182L** Ken Karp*
182R Gerard Lacz/Animals, Animals   **184** Dennis
Geaney*   **185** Adolfo Previdere/Bruce Coleman
Inc.   **186** Ken Karp*   **187** Jenny Thomas*
188 J. Gerard Smith/Photo Researchers
189 William R. Sallaz/Duomo   **190L** Perquis-
Jerrican/Photo Researchers   **190R** Ken Karp*
191 David Madison/Bruce Coleman Inc.
192 J. C. Carton/Bruce Coleman Inc.   **193B** Bob
Daemmrich/Stock, Boston   **194** Lee Snider/The
Image Works   **195L** Bernard Boutrit/Woodfin
Camp & Associates   **195R** R. Crandall/The Image
Works   **196** Michael Weisbrot & Family/Stock,
Boston   **198** Alan Carey/The Image Works
199 William J. Sallaz/Duomo   **201L** Superstock
201R David R. Frazier Photolibrary   **202** Sylvain
Grandadam/Photo Researchers   **203** Chris
Speedie/Tony Stone Images   **204** Lori Adamski
Peek/Tony Stone Images   **205** C. C. Lockwood/
Bruce Coleman Inc.   **206L** Larry Lefever/Grant
Heilman Photography   **206R** Jock Montgomery/
Bruce Coleman Inc.   **208** David R. Frazier/Photo
Researchers Inc.   **209** Kolvoord/The Image Works
210T Robert E. Daemmrich/Tony Stone Images
210B Lee Snider/The Image Works   **211L** Bob
Winsett/Tom Stack & Associates   **211R** William R.
Sallaz/Duomo   **212** Jim Goodwin/Photo
Researchers   **213** Geoffrey Nilsen Photography*

Chapter 5   **218–219(background)**
Chromosohm/Sohm/The Stock Market
218T Duomo   **218BL** Jeff Greenberg/The Image
Works   **218BR** David Hiser/Tony Stone Images
219T Vic Thomasson/Tony Stone Images
219B Lawrence Migdale/Stock, Boston
220 Ken Karp*   **221** David Young Wolff/Tony
Stone Images   **222L** Bob Daemmrich/Stock,
Boston   **222TR** Stephen Frisch/Stock, Boston
222BR Larry Mulvehill/Rainbow   **224L** Superstock
224R Renee Lynn*   **225** GHP Studio*
226 Grantpix/Stock, Boston   **227L** Ken Karp*
227R Richard Hutchings/Photo Researchers
228T Parker/Boon Productions and Dorey Sparre
Photography*   **228B** Bob Daemmrich/The Image
Works   **229** Cheryl Fenton*   **230** Ken Karp*
231 Lee Snider/The Image Works   **232L** R. Lee/

CREDITS

725

Wark/Peter Arnold, Inc. **460B** Thor Bognar/The Stock Market **461** Superstock **465** Ken Karp* **466** Catherine Karnow/Woodfin Camp & Associates **467** Richard Open/Camerapress/Globe Photos **469** Michael Collier/Stock, Boston **470T** Bob Torrez/Tony Stone Images **470B** Photofest **471** Western History Collections, University of Oklahoma Libraries **473L** K. Harrison/The Image Works **473R** Michael Pole/Westlight **475** Ron Watts/Westlight **476** Ed Lallo/Liaison International **477** Peter Poulides/Tony Stone Images **478** Culver Pictures **480T** Frank Siteman/Stock, Boston **480C** Andy Sacks/Tony Stone Images **480B** Ken Karp* **481** Ken Karp* **482** GHP Studio* **483** Desmond Burdon/Tony Stone Images **484L** Dennis Geaney* **484R** Ken Karp* **485** Kevin Morris/Tony Stone Images **487** GHP Studio* **488** Cheryl Fenton* **489** Cheryl Fenton* **490** John Bradley/Positive Images **491T** Gary Moon/Tony Stone Images **491B** Shephard Sherbell/Stock, Boston **492** Naideau/The Stock Market **495** Hugh Sitton/Tony Stone Images **497** Ron Watts/Westlight **503T** Don Mason/The Stock Market **503BL** Cheryl Fenton* **503BR** Ken Karp*

Chapter 10 **504DL** Focus on Sports **504DCL** Eric Meola/Image Bank **504DCR** Tony Freeman/PhotoEdit **504DR** Travel Pix/FPG International **504–505(background)** Runk-Schoenberger/Grant Heilman Photography **504T** The Granger Collection, New York **504C** David M. Allen/New Pickle Circus **504B** Michael Dwyer/Stock, Boston **505T** Courtesy Harvard College Observatory **505B** Martin Barraud/Tony Stone Images **506** Jenny Thomas* **507** Tim Davis/Tony Stone Images **508L** Digital Art/Tony Stone Images **508R** Cheryl Fenton* **509** Blair Seitz/Photo Researchers **510** Photo Chiasson/Liaison International **511** Hank Morgan/Photo Researchers **512T** Camerique/The Picture Cube **512B** GHP Studio* **513** Uniphoto Picture Agency **514** Jose Carrillo/Stock, Boston **515** Dennis Geaney* **516** Francois Gohier/Photo Researchers **517** Alan & Linda Detrick/Photo Researchers **518** Sepp Dietrich/Tony Stone Images **519** Bob Daemmrich/Stock, Boston **520** Joyce Photographics/Photo Researchers **522** Ken Karp* **523** John Cancalosi/Stock, Boston **524** A. B. Dowsett/SPL/Photo Researchers **525** Alastair Black/Tony Stone Images **526** Ron Sanford/Tony Stone Images **529L** Roy Morsch/The Stock Market **529R** Tim Davis/Tony Stone Images **531** Peter Fisher/The Stock Market **531(background)** Stephen Frisch/Stock, Boston **532L** Alan Levenson/Tony Stone Images **532R** Runk-Schoenberger/Grant Heilman Photography **533** Frank Herholdt/Tony Stone Images **534** David Weintraub/Stock, Boston **536T** Cosmo Condina/Tony Stone Images **536B** Superstock **537** Andy Levin/Photo Researchers **539** Watson/The Image Works **540** S. Nielsen/DRK Photo **542** Peter Vandermark/Stock, Boston **544** Larry Lefever/Grant Heilman Photography **545L** Parker/Boon Productions and Dorey Sparre Photography* **545R** Dennis Geaney* **547** Robert A. Lubeck/Animals, Animals **548L** Royal Observatory, Edinburgh/SPL/Photo Researchers **548C** Andrew Syred/SPL/Photo Researchers **548R** S. J. Krasemann/Peter Arnold, Inc. **550** Sanford-Agliolo/The Stock Market **552** Gregory K. Scott/Photo Researchers **553** Peter Fisher/The Stock Market **553(background)** Stephen Frisch/Stock, Boston **555** Geoffrey Nilsen Photography*

Chapter 11 **560DTR** The Lowe Art Museum, University of Miami/Photo: Superstock, Inc. **560DBL** Phil Borden/PhotoEdit **560DBR** Superstock, Inc. **560–561(background)** Jerry Jacka Photography **560L** Henry Groskinsky/Peter Arnold, Inc. **560TR** ©1996 Cordon Art - Baarn - Holland. All rights reserved **560BR** Paul J. Sutton/Duomo **561T** Fred J. Maroon/Photo Researchers **561B** H. de Marcillac/GLMR/Liaison International **562T** Ted Horowitz/The Stock Market **562B** Stock, Boston **563** Simon Jauncey/Tony Stone Images **564** Granitsas/The Image Works **567** James Blank/Bruce Coleman Inc. **568** A. Autenzio/Explorer **569** Barry L. Runk/Grant Heilman Photography **571** Mulvehill/The Image Works **573** Oliver Benn/Tony Stone Images **574** Michael Furman/The Stock Market **575** Ron Schramm **576** Donald C. Johnson/The Stock Market **578T** Jeff Lepore/Photo Researchers **578B** Jim Corwin/Photo Researchers **579** David R. Austen/Australia/Stock, Boston **581** Topham/The Image Works **582** Frederic Reglain/Liaison International **583** Peter Menzel/Stock, Boston **584** M. Grecco/Stock, Boston **585T** Jay Syverson/Stock, Boston **585B** Greg Probst/Stock, Boston **586** Peter Vandermark/Stock, Boston **587L** Parker/Boon Productions and Dorey Sparre Photography* **587R** Dennis Geaney* **589** Michele & Tom Grimm/Tony Stone Images **591** Simon Jauncey/Tony Stone Images **592** Howard Bluestein/Photo Researchers **593** Bill Gillette/Liaison International **594** Jeff Greenberg/MRP/Photo Researchers **595** Royal British Columbia Museum **597L** Dennis Geaney* **597R** Ken Karp* **598TL** Ken Karp* **598TR** Ken Karp* **598B** The Heard Museum, Phoenix, AZ **600** Andy Sacks/Tony Stone Images **602** Lawrence Migdale/Stock, Boston **603** Farrell Grehan/Photo Researchers **605** Andy Sacks/Tony Stone Images **607** Frederick Ayer/Photo Researchers **608TR** Mark C. Burnett/Stock, Boston **608BC** Philip & Karen Smith/Tony Stone Images **608BR** Craig Newbauer/Peter Arnold, Inc. **609** Christi Carter/Grant Heilman Photography **610** Will & Deni McIntyre/Photo Researchers **611T** 1996 Cordon Art - Baarn - Holland. All rights reserved. **611B** Ryan Evans **612** Catherine Karnow/Woodfin Camp & Associates **613** Ed Bock/The Stock Market **614** Gary Chowanetz/The Stock Market **615L** Jerry Jacka Photography **615R** Bill Gillette/Liaison International **617** Geoffrey Nilsen Photography* **621T** Paul Chauncey/The Stock Market **621BL** Ken Karp* **621BR** Jerry Jacka Photography

Chapter 12 **622–623(background)** Ken Karp* **622TL** Paul Figura/Liaison International **622TR** Cheryl Fenton* **622BL** Chuck Savage/The Stock Market **622BR** Ken Karp* **623** Norvia Behling **624** Liza Loeffler* **625** Pete Saloutos/The Stock Market **626L** Bob Daemmrich/The Image Works **626R** Jenny Thomas* **627** Hartsfield Atlanta International Airport **628** Focus of Sports **629** Ken Karp* **630T** William R. Sallaz/Duomo **631L** Ken Karp* **631R** Amanda Merullo/Stock, Boston **632T** Steven E. Sutton/Duomo **632BL** David Madison/Duomo **632BLC** J.O. Atlanta 96/Liaison International **632BRC** J.O. Atlanta 96/Liaison International **632BR** David Madison/Duomo **633** Gehring/Liaison International **634** Smith/Stock, Boston **635T** J.O. Atlanta 96/Liaison International **635B** Robin Rudd/Unicorn Stock Photos **636** David Madison/Duomo **637L** David Madison/Duomo **637R** Richard Ellis/Sygma **640L** Ken Karp* **640R** Parker/Boon Productions and Dorey Sparre Photography* **641** J.O. Atlanta 96/Liaison International **642** Ben Van Hook/Duomo **643** Pete Saloutos/The Stock Market **645** Ken Karp* **646L** Gary Williams/Liaison International **646R** Geoffrey Nilsen Photography* **647** Peter Beck/The Stock Market **648** Geoffrey Nilsen Photography* **649TL** Culver Pictures **649TR** Culver Pictures **649B** Jerry Irwin/Photo Researchers **651** Ken Karp* **653L** Ken Karp* **653R** M. B. Duda/Photo Researchers **654** Gerard Smith/Photo Researchers **656** Jenny Thomas* **657L** Katsuyoshi Tanaka/Woodfin Camp & Associates **657R** Bob Daemmrich/The Image Works **658** Richard Open/Camera Press/Retna Ltd. **659** Jon Randolph/Tony Stone Images **661** Camerique/The Picture Cube **662** Andrew M. Levine/Photo Researchers **663L** Ken Karp* **663R** Larry Lawfer/The Picture Cube **664** Ed Birch/Unicorn Stock Photos **665** Ken Karp* **666** Ken Karp* **669R** Ken Karp* **669L** Cheryl Fenton* **671** Geoffrey Nilsen Photography*

*Photographs provided expressly for Scott Foresman-Addison Wesley.

Illustration

Christine Benjamin: **xxixa, 33c, 42a, 57b, 129e, 263c, 269d** Joe Heiner Studio: **all icons and borders** Paul Koziarz: **324a, 325a, 326a, 339a, 369a, 444c, 445a, 448n, 450b, 452c, 454h, 456c, 459b, 459j, 464h, 466b, 476b, 480b, 486b, 487a, 492a-d, 497a-c, 497g, 498a-c, 498f-i, 565b, 566b, 567f, 578a, 578b, 581b, 585c, 585d, 586c, 588f, 589b, 592e, 600a, 605b** Maryland Cartographics: **93b. 401a. 402a-c, 403a, 404a, 405a-c, 406a, 408a, 420a, 437d, 438a, 499a, 499b, 683a** Helene Moore: **344a, 378b** Andrew Muonio: **132a, 144a, 161c, 274b, 509b, 630a, 666b, 666c** William Pasini: **11a, 15b, 30a, 76c, 102a, 112a, 131a, 257b, 260a, 289e, 333a, 350a, 479h, 636a** Precision Graphics: **All illustrative technical artwork throughout; all generated electronically.** QYA Design: **41a-b, 465a, 620b, 676i, C4d** William Rieser: **368a, 373b, 375d, 377g, 379a-c, 395a, 396a, 398b, 420b, 426a, 451b, 463a, 508b** Rob Schuster: **xxviiia, 34a, 34b, 75b, 90a, 99i, 103a, 140a, 141a, 143a, 143b, 176a, 191e, 193b-d, 201a, 338a, 338b, 342a, 377e, 377f, 381a, 551b, 574a, 628b, 630b, 654a, 654c** Susan Todd: **599a, 606e-g, 607a-c, 608e, 609c, 610a, 616e, 621a** Joe VanDerBos: **167d** Tom Ward: **xxiva, 650d** Jil Weil: **5b, 17b, 19a, 31b, 44b, 48a**

Literature

320 Haiku by Basho (English translation) from *Benet's Reader's Encyclopedia*, 3rd edition by William Rose Benet. Copyright 1948, 1955, 1987 by Harper & Row, Publishers, Inc. Reprinted by permission of HarperCollins Publishers, Inc.

Chapter 7

Page 334

7-2 Exercise Answers

43.

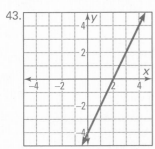

slope = 2; x-intercept = 2; y-intercept = –4.

44.

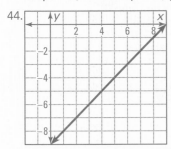

slope = 1; x-intercept = 9; y-intercept = –9.

45.

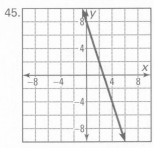

slope = –3; x-intercept = $\frac{8}{3}$; y-intercept = 8.

46.

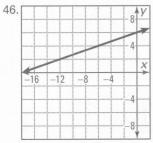

slope = $\frac{1}{3}$; x-intercept = –18; y-intercept = 6.

47.

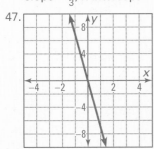

slope = –7; x-intercept = 0; y-intercept = 0.

Page 373

7-8 Exercise Answers

38.

x	0	1	2	3	4	5
y	5	6	7	8	9	10

39.

x	0	1	2	3	4	5
y	–3	–2	–1	0	1	2

40.

x	0	1	2	3	4	5
y	1	3	5	7	9	11

41.

x	0	1	2	3	4	5
y	–4	–3	–2	–1	0	1

Page 385

Suggested Scoring Rubric

An Alternative Spud Topper

4 •All three answers are computed correctly and rounded logically.

3 •Two answers are computed correctly and rounded logically

2 •One answer is computed correctly and rounded logically.

1 •No answers are computed correctly or one or two answers are computed correctly but are rounded illogically

Chapter 8

Page 426

8-6 Exercise Answers

28.

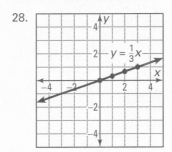

29.

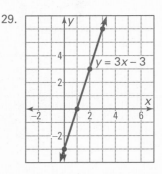

Chapter 9

Page 464

9-4 Exercise Answers

2.

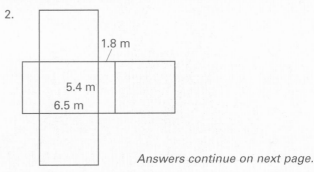

Answers continue on next page.

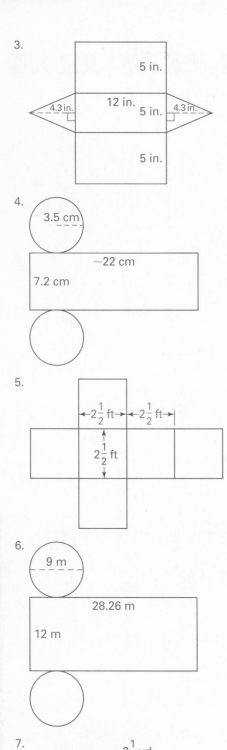

3.

4.

5.

6.

7.

Suggested Scoring Rubric

How Much Is Money?

4
- Easily finds the area of the circular base, the height, and the volume of each coin.
- Is able to make an accurate comparison of the ratios of coin value to coin volume.

3
- Finds the area of the circular base, the height, and the volume of each coin.
- Is able to make a passable comparison of the ratios of coin value to coin volume.

2
- Finds the area of the circular base, the height, and the volume of each coin with assistance.
- Is able to make a passable comparison of the ratios of coin value to coin volume with assistance.

1
- Shows only a remote understanding of how to find the area of the circular base, the height, and the volume of each coin. Is only able to make a comparison of the ratios of coin value to coin volume with assistance.

Chapter 10

Page 516

10-2 Exercise Answers

7.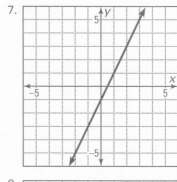

Yes

8.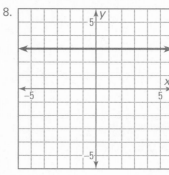

Yes

Answers continue on next page.

9.

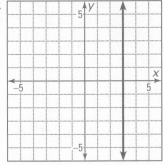

No

10. a. Possible answer:

x	y = 8 + 2x
1	10
2	12
4	16
5	18
8	24
10	28

b. Yes

c. Yes

Page 519

10-3 Answers for Explore

4. There are none; A number squared is always positive.

5.

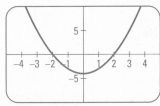

y is negative when x is between −2 and 2.

10-3 Answers for Try It

a.

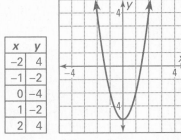

x	y
−2	4
−1	−2
0	−4
1	−2
2	4

b. $y = 2x^2$

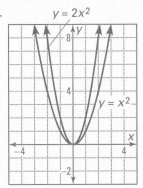

The graphs have the same general shape, but the $2x^2$ graph is stretched vertically.

Page 521

10-3 Exercise Answers

5.

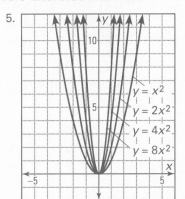

$y = x^2$
$y = 2x^2$
$y = 4x^2$
$y = 8x^2$

Same general shape, but varying widths.

6.

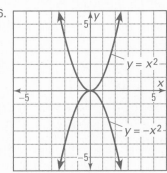

$y = x^2$

$y = -x^2$

Same shape, but one opens up and one opens down.

7.

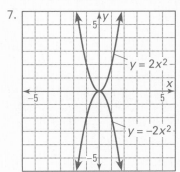

$y = 2x^2$

$y = -2x^2$

Same shape, but one opens up and one opens down.

Page 526

10-4 Exercise Answers

7.

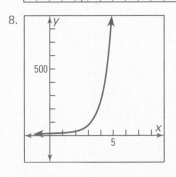

8.

Answers continue on next page.

ADDITIONAL ANSWERS

9. There will be $1000 \times 2^1 = 2000$ birds after 1 year, $1000 \times 2^2 = 4000$ birds after 2 years, $1000 \times 2^3 = 8000$ birds after 3 years, and $1000 \times 2^{10} = 1,024,000$ birds after 10 years.

10. a.

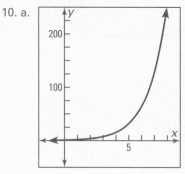

   b. Day 6
   c. Day 8

11. a.

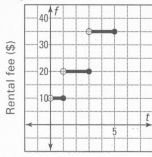

Rental time (days)

   b. Step

Page 530

Answers for 10A Review

11. Possible answer:

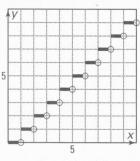

13. Yes; Each x value corresponds to only one y value.

14. No; For $x = -2$ and $x = -1$ there are two y values each.

15.

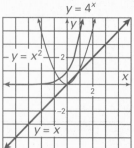

Similar: All three functions are increasing to the right of the origin. Different: $y = x$ is a straight line, $y = x^2$ curves up at both ends (and so is decreasing to the left of the origin), and $y = 4^x$ is nearly flat on the left and curves up on the right.

16. $d = 0.0005t$; 0.084 km

17. a.

h	1	2	3	4	5	6	7	8
t	−16	−64	−144	−256	−400	−576	−784	−1024

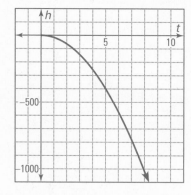

   b. 256 ft; Height is measured from ground level.

Chapter 11

Page 578

11-3 Exercise Answers

21.

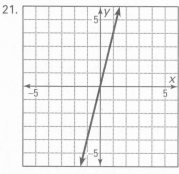

Linear

22.

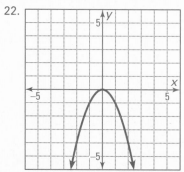

Quadratic

23.

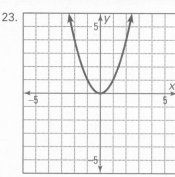

Quadratic

Page 596

11-6 Answers for Explore

1–2. See students' work

3. (−5, 4) corresponds to (5, 4), (−1, 4) corresponds to (1, 4), (−1, 2) corresponds to (1, 2), (−5, 2) corresponds to (5, 2).

Answers continue on next page.

4. The *x*-coordinates have changed signs and the *y*-coordinates are unchanged.

5. The *y*-axis reflection changes signs on the *x*-coordinates and leaves the *y*-coordinates unchanged; The *x*-axis reflection changes signs on the *y*-coordinates and leaves the *x*-coordinates unchanged.

Page 600

11-7 Answers for Explore

1–2. Answers may vary.

3. No; Yes; Pairs of triangles are similar but not congruent.

Page 601

11-7 Answers for Try It

a. $(-12.5, -5)$; $(-7.5, 5)$; $(-2.5, 10)$; $(2.5, 10)$; $(7.5, 5)$; $(12.5, -5)$

b. $(-2\frac{2}{3}, 0)$; $(0, 2\frac{2}{3})$; $(2\frac{2}{3}, 0)$; $(0, -2\frac{2}{3})$

Page 613

11-9 Exercise Answers

3. a. Triangles, squares, hexagons

   b. Possible answer: They do not fit together to cover the plane without gaps or overlaps.

6. a. Equilateral triangle
   b. Possible answer: Regular pentagon
   c. Answers may vary.

7. a. Equilateral triangles
   b. Trapezoids
   c. Regular hexagons

Page 621

Suggested Scoring Rubric

The Task of a Mask

4
- Lists two or more features on a face and correctly identifies all types of symmetry each exhibits.
- Draws a neat picture of a mask that has exactly three lines of symmetry.

3
- Lists two or more features on a face and correctly identifies most types of symmetry each exhibits.
- Draws a fair picture of a mask that has two lines of symmetry.

2
- Lists only one feature on a face or identifies a type of symmetry for only one feature.
- Draws a poor picture of a mask that has one line of symmetry.

1
- Does not list a feature on a face or does not identify any type of symmetry for any feature.
- Draws a very poor picture of a mask that has no lines of symmetry.

Chapter 12

Page 629

12-1 Exercise Answers

1. a.

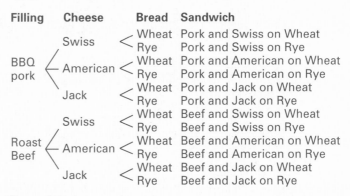

Page 647

12-4 Answers for Explore

1.

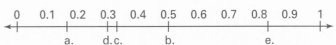

Archaeology, 324
Architecture, 233, 335, 367, 396, 415, 431, 594, 613
  bridges, 563
Area
  of circles, 368, *440A–440D, T442–T443*, 458–460, 463–465, 469–470, 474, 511, 527
  of parallelograms, 446–449, 474, 517
  of polygons, 440A, 440C–440D, T442–T443
  of rectangles, 446, 449, 451–455, 474, 517, 554, 654
  of squares, 99, 112, 367–368, 370, 372–373, 380, 446, 554, 612
  surface area of solids, 463–471, 474
  of triangles, 447–448, 454–455, 460, 472, 474, 517
Arrangement, 631–636
Art, 256, 390, 416, 427, 546, 594–596, 598–599, 602, 604, 606–611, 614–615
Arts and literature, 2, 58, 118, 168, 218, 270, 320, 386, 440, 504, 560, 623
Assessment Program, *2C, 58C, 118C, 168C, 218C, 270C, 320C, 386C, 440C, 504C, 560C, 622C*
  chapter review, 54–55, 114–115, 164–165, 214–215, 266–267, 316–317, 382–383, 436–437, 500–501, 556–557, 618–619, 672–673
  chapter test, 56, 116, 166, 216, 268, 318, 384, 438, 502, 558, 620, 674
  cumulative review, 57, 117, 167, 217, 269, 319, 385, 439, 503, 559, 621, 675
  curriculum standards, *2B, 58B, 118B, 168B, 218B, 270B, 320B, 386B, 440B, 504B, 560B, 622B*
  daily review. *See Review in the teaching notes for each lesson, for example, 6, 11, 13, 22, 32, 37.*
  interview, *71, 100, 285, 334, 395, 471, 552, 578, 642, 667*
  journal, *50, 66, 81, 86, 126, 149, 176, 194, 205, 238, 279, 349, 354, 415, 455, 465, 480, 496, 541, 547, 568, 589, 630, 662*
  ongoing, *27, 76, 110, 199, 299, 368, 406, 426, 512, 527, 609, 636, 656. See also Ongoing Assessment in the teaching notes for each lesson, for example, 6, 11, 13, 22, 32, 37.*
  performance, *16, 144, 210, 226, 251, 255, 290, 329, 373, 449, 599*
  performance rubric, *57, 116, 167, 216, 268, 318, 384, 438, 502, 558, 620, 674*
  portfolio, *10, 36, 46, 94, 131, 136, 154, 181, 246, 304, 360, 400, 431, 486, 536, 573, 614*
  project, *3, 59, 119, 169, 219, 271, 321, 378, 387, 441, 505, 561*
  quiz. *See Quick Quiz in the teaching notes for each lesson, for example, 10, 16, 21, 27, 36, 41.*
  section review. *See Section Review for each section, for example, 30, 52, 88, 112, 138, 162.*
  self-assessment, 21, 41, 105, 159, 186, 232, 261, 310, 339, 420, 460, 491, 517, 583, 604, 650

INDEX

INDEX

D7

INDEX